Microbiology—1977

Microbiology—1977

in

EDITED BY
DAVID SCHLESSINGER

American Society for Microbiology
Washington, D.C.
1977

Contents

III. Novel Aspects of Penicillin Action

IV. Bacterial Antigens and Host Response

Endotoxins and Other Cell Wall Components of Gram-Negative Bacteria and Their Biological Activities

Genetic and Cellular Aspects of Host Response to Endotoxin

Cell Wall Antigens of Gram-Positive Bacteria and Their Biological Activities

Modulation of the Immune Response by Bacteria

Adherence of Bacteria to Host Tissue

V. Persistent Viral Infections

Mechanisms of Establishment and Maintenance of Persistent Infections

Animal and Human Models of Persistent Viral Infections

Live Virus Vaccines for Use in Humans: Strategies and Problems

Persistent Viral Infections of Man

VI. The Endogenous Tumor Viruses

VII. Viruses and Plasmids in Fungi and Protozoa

Introductory Note

The pace of microbiology prevents us from filing away any topic as closed, for unanticipated results inevitably require substantial revisions within a short time. Included here are several of the most fascinating recent cases dealing with (i) the bacterial cell wall and its relation to cell integrity and pathogenicity and (ii) persistent and endogenous viruses.

Consider the mechanism of cell killing by antibiotics like penicillin. Pioneering studies demonstrated the blockage of cell wall synthesis; subsequent lysis was attributed to the "pressure" of newly formed protoplasm on a weakened wall. But recent extensions of the earlier work have expanded both the number of sites of action of the antibiotics and the understanding of the process of lysis (see "Novel Aspects of Penicillin Action" from a symposium at the 1976 Annual Meeting).

In determining the interaction of both host and antibiotics with pathogens, the differential roles of various bacterial envelope components are being clarified more and more, as emphasized in three recent ASM conferences. Many relevant features of envelope specification are included in partial proceedings of the conference on bacilli ("Cell Envelope and Cell Division in Bacilli"; other topical material from that conference has already appeared in *Microbiology—1976*). An extensive survey of "Bacterial Antigens and Host Response" is also provided, and there, as in the cases of the pathogenic "*Pseudomonas aeruginosa* and Related Species," the discussions turn repeatedly on cell surface components and their recognition by specific lymphocytes or other cell types. It seems likely that Professor Westphal's article and the related material, for example, will be a *locus classicus* for historical and prospective discussions of endotoxin and its effects.

Material from two symposia from the 1976 Annual Meeting, along with proceedings from the ASM conference on "Persistent Viral Infections," extends the coverage to special viral pathogens. Many of us have been steadily surprised by the unique variations encountered with each bacterial virus, and especially with lysogeny. But many additional phenomena are included for the viruses of eukaryotic cells studied here: the odd, semicryptic viruses of some simple eukaryotes (in "Viruses and Plasmids in Fungi and Protozoa") or the ominous "Endogenous Tumor Viruses." And even those readers comfortable with the notion of xenotropic viruses will likely find much to ponder in the reports on the establishment, maintenance, and control of "Persistent Viral Infections."

David Schlessinger

I. CELL ENVELOPE AND CELL DIVISION IN BACILLI

Cell Growth and Division: a Genetic Viewpoint

NEIL H. MENDELSON

*Department of Microbiology and Medical Technology, and Graduate Committee on Genetics,
University of Arizona, Tucson, Arizona 85721*

STRATEGY OF GROWTH AND DIVISION

The success of a living system is measured by its ability to perpetuate. Organisms in competition with one another must adequately cope with their physical and biological environments. In response to these pressures, marvelous adaptations have evolved which in one way or another define the limitations of species and individuals while assuring success at a given time and place. The environment is, however, a changing landscape, and genetic plasticity is therefore an essential for long-term survival. Key issues in keeping pace with the demands of selective pressure are mutation, genetic recombination, and the ability to separate the products of gene replication, thereby affording an opportunity for differential reproduction of favorable genes.

The process of DNA replication itself contains the rudiments of growth and division: the production of two new daughter strands represents a growth process, and the fact that both daughter molecules are separate individual entities rather than part of a single larger structure is analogous to division. Given these two properties, that is, the ability to replicate and separate, a system can evolve. It has in fact been demonstrated that selective pressure applied to an in vitro replicating nucleic acid system results in the evolution of particular nucleotide sequence optimal for rapid replication (64). The system operates as follows. Random errors arise during replication which result in new base sequences. Certain sequences are able to be replicated more rapidly than others and thus molecules with these "favorable" sequences rapidly outnumber others in the population. New errors continue to arise and the selection process continues until molecules with optimal sequences for rapid replication are produced. These molecules then become the predominant form in the population. The rate at which molecules can evolve in this system is dependent in part upon the rate at which accidental changes in nucleotide sequences that are "favorable" accumulate within the descendants of individual molecules. If a mechanism arose that enabled individual molecules to exchange parts of their nucleotide sequences with one another, then the rate of evolution in the system would be greatly accelerated for it would enable favorable subsequences to be rapidly brought together rather than necessitating each molecule to evolve its own total favorable sequence by the stepwise accumulation of changes within the descendants of the individual molecules. This is apparently the evolutionary advantage of genetic recombination and was recognized as such, although not at the level of nucleic acids, by the famous geneticist H. J. Muller in 1932 (70). Although advantageous, genetic exchange is not essential for evolution; separation of the products of gene replication is essential.

Within the cellular milieu, nucleotide sequences themselves are not directly subject to selective pressure but rather it is the complex phenotype resulting from gene function which interacts with the environment. The key to success here then is not to achieve a nucleotide sequence which is per se optimal for rapid replication, but rather to achieve a nucleotide sequence which governs the production of a cellular phenotype best suited for the particular environment in which the cell must operate. This objective is approached by the random production of nucleotide sequence change (mutations), the partitioning of the products of gene replication into individual cells, and the differential replication of cells with favorable phenotypes, hence favorable nucleotide sequences over those with less favorable endowment. Herein lies the evolutionary strategy of cell division: it is the mechanism by which individual genomes or multiples thereof become isolated, thereby providing an opportunity for selection to operate via differential replication.

There must be a strong evolutionary advantage in having individual genes connected to one another rather than on individual molecules, for in all organisms studied one finds the genetic material organized into chromosomes of one sort or another (19, 41, 87). One can think of two obvious advantages to this arrangement: first, by having fewer units to separate prior to cell division, there is less likelihood of gene loss during each division cycle, and, secondly, gene organization into chromosomes facilitates mechanisms of gene regulation such as the classical operons, which require physical continuity of regulatory and regulated elements (20, 43). In the better-studied bacterial model systems the genome is primarily organized into a single circular chromosome with the possibility also of additional smaller chromosomes, the episomes (11, 12, 88). In eucaryotic cells, chromosome numbers range from $n = 1$ to $n =$ hundreds (84), there currently being much interest in the relationship of chromosome numbers, DNA content, and the relatedness of organisms. Regardless of chromosome number or nuclear organization, the strategy of cell division remains the same: separate the copies of genes produced by chromosome replication, and compartmentalize them in separate daughter cells.

Within the framework developed above concerning cell division, cell growth may be viewed as providing the material necessary for compartmentalizing the genomes and to support them once division is completed. The relationship of growth to division must have been one of the earliest cellular processes to evolve, for despite the variations found in different organisms a fundamental theme prevails—there appears to be something equivalent to a unit amount of cell material associated with each genome (50, 66). This relationship is maintained by the coordination of growth, genome duplication, daughter genome separation, and cell division; not only is each of these processes itself under independent genetic regulation, but the coordination necessary to maintain an orderly cell cycle is also gene regulated (23, 34, 39, 45, 61). That being the case, it is understandable how variations in the cell cycle found in different biological systems must have arisen in response to selective pressures. In the initial stages of embryo development in the frog, for example, genome duplication and nuclear and cell division proceed in the absence of growth (3). As a result, the fertilized egg, which is a giant cell, is subdivided into numerous progeny cells of more normal size. At the same time the surface of the original fertilized egg is also partitioned into individual cells which eventually give rise to clones that follow diverse developmental sequences. In this system there is a temporal dissociation of growth and division which serves a particular developmental objective. Once this objective is satisfied, the basic theme of cell growth and division is reestablished. Similarly, the process of bacterial sporulation resembles a cell division modified for developmental purposes which proceeds in the absence of cell growth (40). After germination, however, the clone which emerges from a spore once again obeys the basic rule that each genome must have its domain of cytoplasm.

MECHANISM OF GROWTH AND DIVISION

Studies on the mechanism of growth and division in bacterial model systems have followed a curious scenario over the past 25 years. In the early 1950s a sharp controversy arose as to whether bacterial division was a true mitosis with stages equivalent to prophase, metaphase, anaphase, and telophase known in eucaryotic cells. The techniques available at the time included only light microscopy of stained material and the arguments centered on the interpretation of cytological data (21). There was at the time an adequate understanding of bacterial genetics to support the idea that mitosis or a genetically equivalent process must govern the passage of genetic material from parent to daughter cell during division even though the structure of the bacterial chromosome was far from understood (46). As a result, groping in the dark of the light microscope, some said mitosis and others said no. It took about 10 years and the electron microscope to clarify matters and to persuade the proponents of mitosis that a truly analogous cytological process is not present in bacterial cells (22). As a byproduct of the defeat of the bacterial-mitosis model, there seems to have developed a complete lack of interest on the part of those working on bacterial division to become informed of advances in the understanding of eucaryotic cell division. This I think is an unfortunate development, for I believe the genetic equivalence of both processes means that they have a great deal in common and there are things known about eucaryotic cell division which could help clarify as yet unresolved issues in the bacterial system. In this regard, let me briefly mention the centromere. In eucaryotic cells, chromosomes contain a specialized region known as the centromere, which can be mapped as any conventional gene locus, and which serves as the specific site to which the fibers responsible for separation of the chromosomes become attached (28, 35, 71). The centromere is therefore a gene essential for chromosome distribution which must be present on every chromosome. A chromosome without a centromere will not undergo the necessary movements during division, will not be included in the newly forming daughter nuclei, and is therefore lost (84). Do bacterial chromosomes contain a centromere or an analogous structure? If so, where is it located and what are its properties? Perhaps one of Schaechter's attachment sites is a candidate (39). Unfortunately we do not know. No one thinks about bacterial cell division in terms of eucaryotic mechanisms.

After the demise of the bacterial mitosis model, pertinent research branched in two directions. One line of research explored the kinetic aspects of macromolecular synthesis rates in bacterial populations (50). These studies led to the concept that cell division is dependent upon DNA synthesis. Cooper and Helmstetter assimilated this information and produced a model in which the time of DNA replication initiation within the cell cycle played a critical role in establishing the timing of cell division (17). A number of details of their model must now be modified to accommodate new information such as the fact that the DNA replication time is not always constant (92). The role of DNA replication initiation in regulating division is not universally accepted (A. Koch, personal communication). Recently, emphasis has shifted to the role of DNA replication completion, and events which occur during replication of genes near the chromosome terminus, in regulating cell division (44, 52, 82). Nevertheless, the Cooper-Helmstetter model still serves as a frame of reference for studies in which a kinetic approach is followed. A number of laboratories have determined the quantitative values of the Cooper-Helmstetter parameters in various organisms, both gram positive and gram negative. Although this work is still far from completed, there is already adequate information indicating that the interrelationships of cell cycle events are indeed similar if not identical in diverse bacterial systems. The rules which govern these interrelationships are still unknown, however.

During this same period another group of investigators focused upon the properties of the bacterial cell surface and on the manner in which new cell surface is synthesized and assembled. The initial direction in which this field has developed stems from the studies of R. M. Cole and his collaborators (13, 15). Using immunocytological methods, it was convincingly demonstrated that the assembly of new cell surface in streptococci occurs in discrete zones associated with the formation of division crosswalls. Cole's observations have been corroborated and extended by Shockman and his collaborators, who have progressed to the point where it now seems profitable to explore the regulation of autolysin activity as a means of understanding the mechanism of surface growth and division in streptococci (36, 37, 38). The fact that the streptococcal surface is assembled in a zone has had a marked impact on cell growth and division models regardless of the fact that evidence for similar zones in other bacterial systems is not at all well demonstrated. One of the key difficulties in locating the cell surface assembly areas has been the fact that the major cell surface components—peptidoglycan and teichoic acid or other negatively charged polymers in gram-positive cells, and peptidoglycan, proteins, and lipopolysaccharide in gram-negative cells—are not metabolically inert macromolecules but rather are involved in active turnover processes which may be independent of growth per se (9, 91). For this reason, isotope incorporation studies are difficult to interpret. For example, Ryter et al. reported that a pulse of isotope given to *Escherichia coli* initially appeared in a zone of the peptodiglycan but then when chased soon became randomized over the cell surface (81). Is this bacterial form of plate tectonics cell surface growth or metabolism or both? Additional criteria are needed to differentiate growth from metabolism. Even though a number of approaches have been brought to bear upon this problem, still no clearcut picture emerges. Some experiments, the flagella distribution experiment (80) and the direct visualization of growth regions in double mutants of *Bacillus subtilis* (62), as well as the direct observations of cell elongation and the penicillin-sensitive site in *E. coli* (24), support the concept of a discrete growth zone. Other experiments, however, such as the reappearance of normal-thickness wall after chloramphenicol inhibition and the teichuronic acid-teichoic acid nearest-neighbor analysis done on wall fragments of phosphate-starved bacilli (53), as well as studies on the distribution of labeled membrane lipids during growth (31, 49, 65) and even immunocytological studies in gram-negative organisms, seem to indicate a dispersive surface growth rather than discrete zones (14). In gram-negative cells the issue is further complicated by the fact that the outer surface consists of a membrane connected at various points through the peptidoglycan to the cell plasma membrane. Components of the outer membrane migrate through these adhesions from the inner membrane and then become dispersed by diffusion or other mechanisms that go on in the outer membrane (4, 67, 68). With this degree of complexity, it becomes almost a moot point to ponder the existence of zones. Why then the interest?

In 1963, Jacob et al. proposed that the replication of DNA in bacteria is under genetic regulation acting by control of the replication initiation process (42). They defined the term replicon as a unit of DNA capable of independent replication, that is, a unit containing all the necessary regulatory genes to permit replication. Their model visualized replicons as circular DNA molecules, each containing a specific pair of genes that only act in concert with one another, thereby assuring the individual nature of each replicon. The function ascribed to these replicon-specific genes was to control the initiation of DNA replication. In the same paper a mechanism to account for the spatial separation of daughter replicons after DNA replication was proposed. Replicons were visualized as being attached to some component of the interior of the cell surface. The segregation of daughter replicons was attributed to the zonal growth of cell surface in the region between two attachment points to which the daughter replicons were bound. The interest in zonal growth models is largely due to this proposal in which Cole's observations in streptococci have been offered as a possible mechanism to explain the manner in which DNA segregation takes place in all bacteria. Indeed, the regulation of DNA replication and the orderly segregation of daughter genomes into regions destined to be compartmentalized by division are so intimately related that some people consider the above segregation mechanism as part of the replicon model (39). In the ensuing 12 years, many aspects of the replicon model have been tested and found to be accurate. The attachment of DNA to cell membrane has been well documented in both *B. subtilis* and *E. coli* (47). The mechanism

of DNA segregation, however, has not been affirmed, and the meaning of DNA membrane attachment remains to be elucidated.

GENETIC REGULATION OF GROWTH AND DIVISION

The isolation and characterization of mutants defective in various aspects of growth and division have not only contributed to an understanding of the way in which these processes are controlled, but have also served to test hypotheses concerning the mechanisms of cell growth and division derived from other approaches. My own efforts have been applied to this direction using the *B. subtilis* model system. My associates and I have isolated and studied mutants that are DNA⁻ (54, 56, 61), cell division initiation negative (58), Rod⁻ (7, 8, 16), and minicell producing (19, 58, 76), and, recently, mutants that are capable of growth in an unusual helical or twisted morphology. In each instance we attempted to exploit the unique properties of the mutants and to learn something from them pertinent to cell growth and/or division. A brief review of the knowns, the unknowns, and possible further applications of each system will serve to measure the extent of our progress in this as-yet-unfinished business.

DNA Initiation Mutant

The prototype temperature-sensitive DNA initiation mutant in *B. subtilis*, *ts-134*, was isolated after exposure to 5-bromouracil. Kinetic analysis of DNA replication indicated that an amount of residual DNA synthesis adequate to account for completion of rounds of replication in progress occurred after transfer to restrictive temperature. At that time similar mutants had been reported in *E. coli* (45) but not in other bacteria, and a thorough study of the initiator class of mutants had not yet been published. In general, the properties of *ts-134* fit well those predicted by the replicon model for a mutant defective in the initiation of DNA replication. The mutant was then used to study the segregation of DNA during growth in the absence of DNA synthesis.

Two pertinent observations were made. First it was found that, when spores of the mutant were germinated at restrictive temperature in the presence of [³H]thymidine, isotope was incorporated into DNA. Autoradiographs indicated that, as growth continued, the DNA became segregated into two discrete grain clusters in each clone (54, 55). This finding was interpreted as indicating that the first round of DNA synthesis during outgrowth, but no further rounds, can occur at restrictive temperature. If so, perhaps the mutant defect has something to do with termination of a round of replication which must be completed before the following rounds can initiate. This seems an unlikely possibility now in view of the fact that bidirectional replication is known to occur (32, 33, 88), and therefore the origin and terminus are not spatially adjacent but rather 180° away from one another, plus the fact that multiple fork replication is known to occur in rapidly growing B. subtilis cells, indicating that initiations can begin prior to termination of the preceding round of replication (73). How, then, can one account for the observed incorporation of [³H]thymidine? Perhaps the first round of DNA synthesis during spore outgrowth is unique in that its initiation is determined prior to germination, and hence prior to the 45°C restrictive temperature. Or perhaps the use of thymidine to label DNA was restricted to repair-like rather than authentic semiconservative replication (89). The issue remains unsolved.

The second pertinent observation involves growth, DNA segregation, and cell division in the ts-134 and another presumed DNA initiation mutant, NV-75. By examining the relationship of the two grain clusters found in each clone to the growth of the clone, it was possible to deduce that cell growth must occur both in the region between the two clusters and in the regions between the clusters and outer poles of the clone (55). Zonal growth restricted to a single zone between the DNA grain clusters could not account for our observations. The very same autoradiographs also revealed that cell divisions were taking place in clones growing in the absence of DNA synthesis, thereby producing anucleate cells. This was strong evidence that the link between DNA replication and cell division could be disrupted by mutation and that DNA synthesis per se could not be an absolute requirement for continued cell division. In this regard, M. G. Sargent recently took up a detailed study of anucleate cell production by the ts-134 mutant and concluded that cells in which DNA synthesis has shut down still may be able to produce one division per generation for each DNA terminus in the cell (83). According to Sargent's model, events at the termination of DNA replication are critical in the initiation of cell division, particularly with respect to the physical location of the division which is visualized as arising at the site where the DNA terminus was attached to the cell surface prior to segregation. Donachie independently came to a similar conclusion in the E. coli system (44). In both models, the movement away from or detachment of a DNA terminus from its membrane site upon completion of replication triggers division initiation at that site. In light of these models it would seem important, therefore, to make sure that replication does actually go to completion in presumed DNA initiation mutants. To my knowledge, this has not been adequately done with the ts-134 mutant. A similar mutant isolated in Sueoka's laboratory (90) was exhaustively studied in this regard, and a third mutant found in the W23 strain in R. G. Wake's laboratory (85) was also examined by marker frequency analysis. Both of these appear to complete replication at least to the metB marker when incubated at restrictive temperature. On the new map, metB is found on the left arm several genes from the terminus (48).

Several years after the isolation of ts-134, I found another DNA⁻ mutant, ts-151, which is similar in many respects to ts-134 and is presumed to also belong to the DNA initiation class of mutants. ts-151 proved to be a suitable mutant for studies of DNA synthesis and segregation in cells returned to permissive temperature after growth at restrictive temperature in the absence of DNA synthesis (56). At the time of transfer back to permissive temperature, the cells consisted of long filaments with DNA restricted to a small region of the cell length. Measurements of autoradiographs revealed that, when DNA synthesis resumed, regions of cell length previously vacant became occupied by DNA, thus indicating that DNA can become distributed in cells independent of cell elongation. This conclusion is supported in the E. coli model system by films that Adler et al. produced of growing cells photographed in an environment which enables the nuclear regions to be visualized (2). If indeed DNA can shift positions along the cell length without regard to cell elongation, then the mechanism of genome segregation may be quite different from that proposed in the Jacob et al. model. Something functionally similar to a mitotic apparatus other than surface growth cannot be ruled out at present. If such exists, it not only may be responsible for the segregation of DNA in division but also might play some role in the conjugal transfer of DNA in E. coli where, thus far, only DNA replications in donor and recipients have been considered candidates for the force which drives this DNA movement (26). Recently Harmon and Tabor repeated the ts-151 experiments and found a particular membrane protein synthesized in large amounts after transfer from restrictive to permissive temperature (33a). It will be interesting to determine whether this protein is involved in the initiation of DNA synthesis or perhaps in the distribution of DNA.

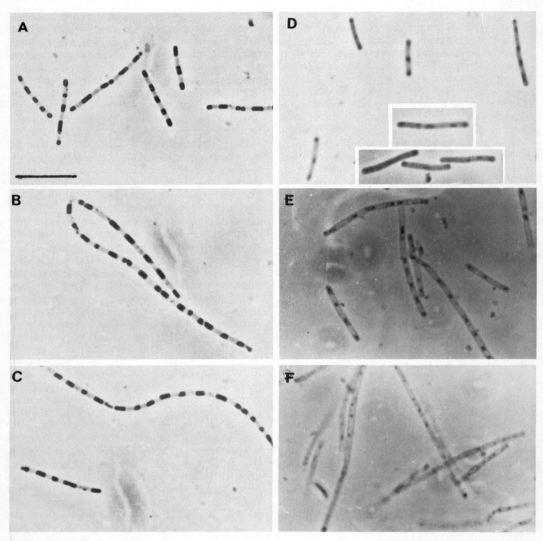

FIG. 1. *Effect of SDS treatment on cytoplasmic partitioning in* B. subtilis *divIV-B1. (A–C) Cells heated in a boiling water bath for 20 min in half-strength Trypticase soy broth plus 5% SDS, and then washed 8 to 10 times (until free of foaming) in 80°C Spizizen salt solution. (D) Sample of A digested with 1 mg of Pronase per ml in 0.1 M Tris-hydrochloride (pH 8.6) for 4 h at 37°C. (E) Sample of D digested with 100 μg of RNase per ml in same buffer for 3 h at 37°C. (F) Sample of E digested with 100 μg of DNase per ml in same buffer for 2 h at 37°C, resulting in mobilization of granules.*

Cell Division Initiation Mutants

Regulation of cell division per se was studied in a mutant (*ts-355*) blocked in the initiation of cell division, which in many respects bears the same relationship to cell division as the DNA initiation mutants do to DNA replication. When transferred to restrictive temperature, growth continued and cell divisions in progress went to completion. Long filaments were pro-duced which contained no compartmentalizations as revealed by electron micrographs of thin-sectioned cells. Each filament was therefore the equivalent of a clone of cells. The synthesis and segregation of DNA appeared normal during growth in the absence of cell division. This is a good example of the fact that growth processes are independent of cell division. It is as if the cell contents carry out their growth processes, including genome replication and segregation,

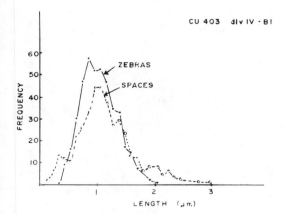

FIG. 2. *Size distribution of dark bands (zebras) and light bands (spaces) found in SDS-treated population of CU403 divIV-B1. Micrographs were projected onto a backscreen and measured with a Numonics Corp. graphics calculator.*

with no regard whatsoever to the fact that divisions are absent and daughter genomes reside in a common cytoplasm. Within the syncytium formed by growth in the absence of division, the domain of each genome became obscured. One might imagine that an amount of cytoplasm in the immediate vicinity of each genome equivalent to a unit cell may be regulated by the nearby genome, but an appropriate test of this hypothesis has not been devised thus far. We observed several properties of these filaments which could be interpreted as indicating that some type of unit cell organization still persisted even though compartmentalization could not be visualized by electron microscopy. For example, if the walls were removed from filaments with lysozyme, instead of the production of a single large protoplast, each filament yielded a string of what appeared to be approximately normal-sized protoplasts attached to each other by delicate membrane strands. Similar "strings of beads" have also been observed in other systems (27). In addition, we recently discovered that the detergent sodium dodecyl sulfate (SDS) produces an unusual partitioning of the cytoplasm in *B. subtilis* (Fig. 1A). When filaments were heated in the detergent, the cytoplasm partitioned into units approximately the size of normal cells. The size distribution of dark bands (termed zebras) and light bands (termed spaces) found in filaments of the CU403 *divIV-B1* minicell-producing mutant are shown in Fig. 2. The uniformity of zebra and space sizes is shown also by the correlation of zebra numbers and filament length (Fig. 3). These observations suggest that cytoplasmic organization may exist in the absence of actual physical compartmentaliza-

tion. This concept is supported by the fact that there is an orderly progression of zebra numbers found in outgrowing spore populations starting with one zebra in the newly emerged cells and increasing as a function of cell elongation. In addition, it is interesting to note that Ingle and Boyer (41a) observed similar cytoplasmic partitioning in untreated cultures grown for industrial fermentation purposes. The relationship of the zebra-like structures found in Ingle's cultures to those produced by SDS in our system remains to be elucidated. It is possible that an early stage of autolysis also reveals some internal cellular organization independent of physical compartmentalization.

We attempted to determine the role of DNA in zebra formation by examining autoradiographs of cells grown in [^{3}H]thymine prior to SDS treatment. Although grain clusters were difficult to locate in SDS-treated cells, we found them primarily located at the interface of zebras and spaces. In a DNA-defective mutant which can be manipulated so as to produce long filaments containing only a few genomes, the number of zebras was compared with the number of genomes, using similar autoradiographic procedures. These data indicate an excess of zebras over genomes by a factor of about 2.3.

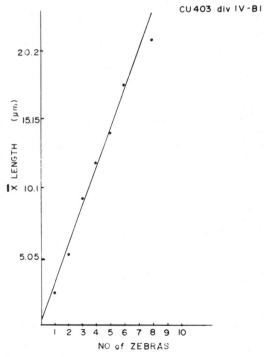

FIG. 3. *Relationship of average cell length found in cells with various numbers of dark bands (zebras).*

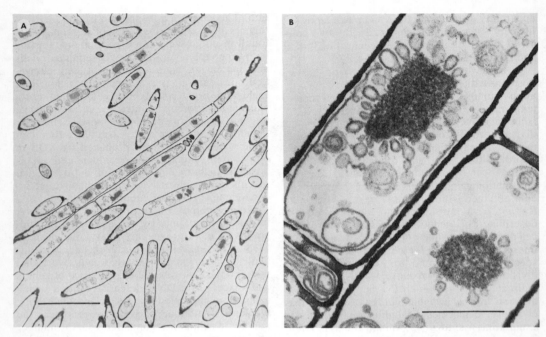

FIG. 4. Electron micrographs of ultrathin sections of B. subtilis CU403 divIV-B1 treated to produce granules as described in the text and Fig. 1. Embedding, sectioning, and microscopy by R. M. Cole. Bars represent 5 μm (A) and 0.5 μm (B).

We are currently attempting to examine other mutants with greater DNA deficiencies in terms of genomes per cell length to confirm this observation. If taken as valid, these findings indicate an organization independent of genome presence. Perhaps the production of normal size anucleate cells found in several DNA⁻ mutants is governed in this manner.

Several additional facts are known about the SDS zebras. First, we discovered that zebras are sensitive to digestion by Pronase and RNase. The resulting structures, termed granules, are shown in Fig. 1C and 4. Electron micrographs revealed that granules are comprised of a crystalline-like structure, often surrounded by or associated with membrane vesicle structures which presumably form during the washing after SDS exposure and subsequent enzyme digestions. In the phase-contrast microscope we observed that granules are fixed in place along the length of the cells. We were surprised to find that incubation with DNase mobilized the granules, which were then free to move about by Brownian motion within the cell walls. The structure of the granules did not appear to be altered by this digestion. The nature of the DNase-sensitive link which plays a role in anchoring the granules to the cell surface, as well as the component(s) of the granule to which the presumed DNA link is attached, is currently being explored.

When filaments of a temperature-sensitive cell division initiation mutant were returned to permissive temperature, cell divisions reappeared but not if protein synthesis inhibitors such as chloramphenicol or puromycin were present. A short incubation at permissive temperature followed by the addition of these inhibitors resulted in the appearance of some divisions, suggesting that new protein(s) must be synthesized to initiate division but not during the division process itself. Division resumption had little if any effect on growth with the exception that occasionally anucleate cells were generated in portions of the filaments and these, once formed, no longer grew. We studied the structural process by which both anucleate and normal cells were formed. The anucleate cells appeared to arise by the formation of a split division primordium which separated due to growth of lateral wall between the two primordia. By measuring the dimensions of length and width of these anucleate cells, it was possible to estimate that the rate of lateral wall growth was about equal to the rate of cross-wall formation during division. It was possible to do this because the two primordia which end up as the poles of the anucleate cell originated apparently at the same time and place along the filament's length. In normal cells, the two poles arise from divisions one generation apart and therefore have different ages.

In terms of structure and function, the cell divisions which appeared when cell division initiation mutants were returned to permissive temperature were apparently normal. The system is an ideal one, therefore, in which to study the division process because it is simple to experimentally manipulate the start of division in an entire culture. We and others (10, 51) have exploited this opportunity. I have used the information gained in this manner, in addition to data obtained from the study of other pertinent *B. subtilis* mutants, to create seven categories describing the genetic regulation of bacterial cell division. In so doing, I had hoped to stimulate interest in the search for additional cell division-specific mutations and to focus attention on division per se rather than upon the numerous indirect processes which eventually affect cell division in one way or another. A summation of these categories including representative examples is shown in Table 1 and Fig. 5. Some of the categories are well represented. Others, such as genes regulating cross-membrane or cross-wall synthesis, are still only hypothetical. In this instance it is possible that the two processes are obligately interdependent and therefore belong only to a single genetic category. Dependent upon the biochemical complexity of each process, the categories listed in Table 1 may each contain a number of different genes. Furthermore, some genes may belong to two or more categories because a single biochemical target may ultimately affect more than a single phenotypic aspect of cell division.

Rod Mutants

The importance of cell morphology in regulation of growth and division is aptly demonstrated by the properties of Rod⁻ mutants. Rogers and co-workers first discovered a salt-conditional Rod⁻ mutant that exhibited abnormal surface ultrastructure, morphology, and division when grown under restrictive conditions (77). Boylan and I then found a similar temperature-sensitive mutant (*tag-1*) (7). The properties of our mutant were studied in collaboration with R. M. Cole and F. E. Young (8, 16). Rather than review all of our published findings in detail, I would like to emphasize a few observations that bear upon growth and division in this mutant. First, it is clear that the genetic background influences the expression of the *tag-1* allele in terms of growth and division properties (75). Not only is cell shape determined by the particular genetic background in which *tag-1* is

TABLE 1. *Genetic regulation of cell division in* Bacillus subtilis

Mutation category	Phenotype	Examples	References
divI	Cell division initiation	*ts-355*	59
		tms-12	10, 18
		ts 33-6	51
		ts-76 ⎫	
		ts-12 ⎬	72
		ts-1 ⎭	
		divD	86
divII	Membrane partition synthesis		
divIII	Wall partition synthesis		
divIV	Division site location (some produce minicells)	*divIV-A1* ⎫	
		divIV-B1 ⎭	19, 76
		divA ⎫	
		divB ⎭	86
divV	Division plane orientation	*tag-1* (Rod A)	7, 8, 16
		Rod B ⎫	
		Rod C ⎭	79
		divIV-A1	58, 76
		divB	86
divVI	Daughter cell separation	BAO	25
		divB	86
divVII	Division clock (relationship of growth to division)	*dnaB*	57

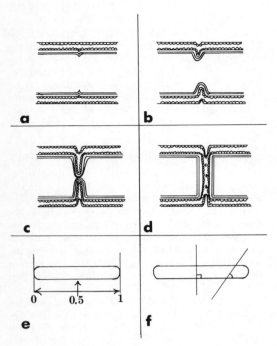

FIG. 5. *Illustrations of cell division mutation categories. (a–d) Three-layered wall and cell membrane. (a) div1 mutants blocked prior to first morphological sign of division. (a–d) divII and divIII presumed to block cross-membrane and cross-wall production. (e) divIV, division site location regulation concept. (f) divV, orientation of division plane shown. (d) divVI, regulation of cell separation and pole maturation blocked at stage shown. Not shown: divVII, division clock category regulating relationship of growth to division.*

expressed, but the ability to continue division at restrictive temperature is also determined in this manner. In a genetic background which permits continued division when growing in the sphere form, it is obvious that the cells retain a cylindrical orientation of growth and division similar to that found in streptococci (Fig. 6). In the case of the *tag-1* mutant, this growth constraint is a ramification of the genetic basis of rod structure in *B. subtilis*. In the case of streptococci, it is a moot point to argue whether the growth restraint is an evolutionary precursor to rod morphology or indicative of an evolutionary rodlike ancestor. The fact is that these spherical cells grow in a cylindrical orientation which reveals a fixed orientation of components within the sphere.

During our initial studies of the *tag-1* mutation, we noted that mutant spores germinated and grown at restrictive temperature develop into a cluster of irregular spheres. Electron

micrographs of thin sections revealed that the cell mass was being compartmentalized by divisions at distorted angles, some of which appeared to originate from other incomplete divisions (Fig. 7). This was a puzzling observation for, in normal cells, divisions mature to poles which do not play a role in the succeeding divisions. It would appear, therefore, that sites on the original septum remained active in the *tag-1* mutant grown at restrictive temperature. The unusual misoriented divisions which originated from preexisting septa seemed to form a similar pattern in different clones which may reveal something about the mechanism of the growth defect responsible for this condition. As shown in Fig. 8, if a normal rod was bent upon itself into a hairpin configuration, the second generation divisions would occur at right angles to the initial division. A cellular growth pattern in which primarily or only one surface of a cylinder can expand will generate a sphere in which the second round of divisions are obliquely oriented with respect to the initial division plane. This is a reasonable first approximation of the pattern found in the *tag-1* mutant. The distorted spherical growth observed when the *tag-1* allele was in several genetic backgrounds, as well as the division plane misorientation, may therefore be accounted for by the assumption that a portion of the cell surface is unable to expand properly and thereby fails to separate the second-round division site at one point but enables them to separate on the surface which does expand. In support of this suggestion is the fact that clusters of distorted spheres returned to permissive temperature grew back into a rod morphology by initial formation of a bent rod structure. The focus of the *tag-1* defect apropos growth and division may be a point on the cylindrical surface (Fig. 8, part 6) in contrast to the biochemical effects of the *tag-1* defect on cell surface ultrastructure which appears all over the cell surface. Growth and division phenotypes are not a single reflection, therefore, of cell surface ultrastructure in this system. We have been forced to this conclusion by repeated observations involving the *tag-1* allele in which the mutant growth process in strains carrying *tag-1* plus other mutations occurs independent of the cell surface ultrastructure changes associated with the *tag-1* allele (61a).

Even though the precise biochemical lesion of the *tag-1* allele has not yet been identified, we and others (63, 78, 79) have found the mutation useful in probing the mechanism of cell surface assembly and structural regulation. In the first instance, we studied the combination of *tag-1* plus the *divIV-A1* minicell-producing

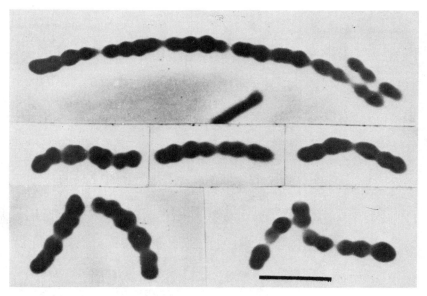

Fig. 6. *Chains of CU403* tag-1 *grown at 45°C which illustrate the linear orientation of spherical growth and division. Bar = 10 μm.*

mutation in which cell division is highly suppressed. In this hybrid strain, cell growth could be visualized directly by the appearance of a bulged region when the cells were transferred and grown at restrictive temperature. We studied the location of these zones as well as the sequential appearance of new zones at later stages of growth. Our observations suggested that discrete growth zones may arise at points distant from an initial growth zone, thereby precluding in this system any model of growth in which new zones arise by partition of old ones (61a). The distinction between growth and cell surface metabolism was clearly seen in those cells which exhibited the *tag-1* mutant wall ultrastructure phenotype all over the cell surface but grew only in restricted regions along the cell length.

Aspects of the cell surface chemistry in *tag-1* cells are currently being pursued by Rogers and co-workers (79) and therefore will not be detailed here. Suffice it to say that we originally found an excess of peptidoglycan and a deficiency of the glycerol teichoic acid in *tag-1* spheres. We were not aware of other negatively charged polymers in the walls of our strains at the time. We observed in our electron microscope studies a great increase in wall thickness in the spheres and the disappearance of inner and outer wall layers. Rogers et al. have now shown that peptidoglycan synthesis is immediately accelerated upon transfer of *tag-1* cells to high temperature. When returned to permissive temperature the derepressed rate of synthesis gradually returns to the normal slower rate. We earlier observed that, during this transition, the thick abnormal wall is transected by the appearance of a characteristic outer wall layer formed within the thick wall at the proper distance from the cell membrane. Eventually, material exterior to this layer is sloughed into the environment and a normal wall structure is regained. It is clear from these findings that the *tag-1* allele plays an important role in the regulation of wall structure.

Minicell-Producing Mutants

In *B. subtilis* we found two loci responsible for the production of minicells—*divIV-A* and *divIV-B* (76)—which are located at nearly symmetrical positions (about 4 and 8 o'clock) on the new genetic map. We used these mutants to study both the regulation of division responsible for the production of minicells as well as the minicells themselves (19, 63, 74). The latter is covered elsewhere by J. Reeve (73a). I will focus here on the division aspects of the system. As in the *E. coli* system (2, 29), *B. subtilis* minicells are produced by a structurally normal division which functions to separate two very unequal daughter cells. It is the division site location along the cell length which is abnormal in these mutants. The minicells produced by abnormal division are unable to grow, presumably because they lack DNA. To

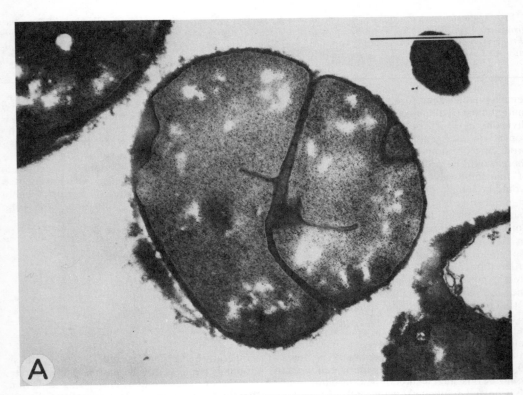

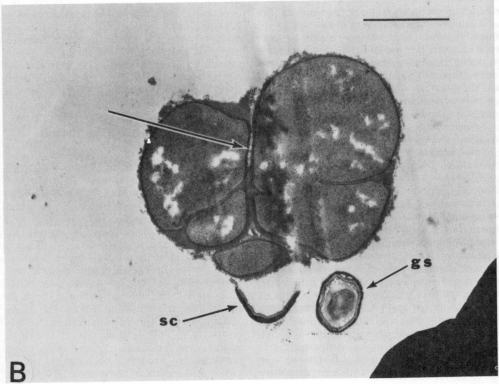

FIG. 7. *Electron micrographs of thin-sectioned* B. subtilis tag-1 *(in original 168* try C2⁻ thy⁻ *background) grown from spores at 45°C. Note the secondary divisions at apparent right angles to the initial division plane. (From reference 16 by permission of the publishers.) Bars = 1 μm. Abbreviations: Sc, Spore coat; gs, germinating spore. Arrow in B indicates autolysis of apparent initial cross wall.*

remain viable, therefore, a minicell-producing mutant must be able to carry out some "normal" divisions in which both daughter cells receive copies of the genome, as well as minicell-producing divisions. If this were not the case, there would be no way to increase the number of minicell-producing cells and the mutation would be lethal. Therefore, the division system in minicell-producing mutants is complex because each cell has the option of producing normal or abnormal divisions or perhaps both. In view of this, we devised methods of studying clone growth after spore germination in order to explore the division patterns generated by minicell-producing mutants. Our experience has indicated the following.

(i) The ratio of abnormal to normal divisions is allele specific. We have used the term P to indicate the probability of an abnormal or minicell-producing division. We have found P values in the range of 0.3 to 0.4 in our mutants. (ii) The location of the first division in outgrowing clones is random. That is, it may be a "normal" division or a minicell-producing division at either the distal or proximal pole relative to the spore coat which in the *divIV-B1* mutant remains attached to one pole. (iii) We frequently observed clustering of minicells at particular locations along clone length and found that pole age in generations is related to the clustering as follows: the older a pole is, the more cells it has been part of, and thus the chance of finding a minicell at a particular pole increases with pole age. Since a single "normal" division produces two sister poles which have the same age, the chance of minicells being produced from either of the sister poles is equal, and as the poles become older in generations the likelihood of having minicells produced at both increases. Minicell clusters containing more than two minicells, as well as clusters which arise at the outer poles of the clone, require additional explanation and will be discussed below. (iv) A quantitative study of the *divIV-A1* minicell-producing mutant revealed that the overall division ability of the mutant is sharply reduced (58). In comparison with wild-type clones, *divIV-A1* clones of comparable length produce only about 25% as many total divisions. In this system, division suppression is the primary cause of excessive cell lengths observed during growth of minicell-producing cells. Similar, although less severe, suppression is also found in the *divIV-B1*

system (60) and may in fact be a general feature of all minicell-producing bacterial systems. It has frequently been reported that minicell-producing cells in other systems are filaments longer than normal cell length (29).

Any attempt at understanding the mechanism of functioning of the minicell-producing mutation must take into consideration the multiple phenotypic ramifications of the mutation: (i) division

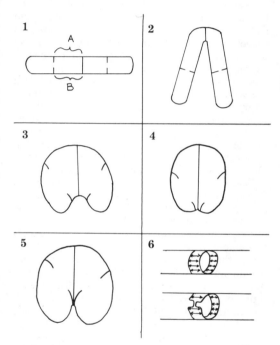

FIG. 8. *Diagram illustrating a growth-defect mechanism that approximates the observed* tag-1 *phenotype. (1) Wild-type rod growth indicating the equal extension on the A and B surfaces of the cylinder (A/B = 1). (2) Rod with hairpin bend indicating the orientation of first and second division planes to one another. The pattern may be produced by a bias in A/B ratio (A/B = 1.55). (3) A/B = 4.44. (4) A/B = 17.41. (5) A/B = ∞, an example of complete failure to extend the B surface. (6) Grown zones depicted as a ring. (6, top) Wild-type growth zone where ring is uniform dimensions throughout (arrows of equal length representing vectors of uniform growth). (6, bottom) A defective growth ring in which a portion at a fixed point on the cylinder circumference is unable to carry out new assembly at a rate equivalent to the remainder of the ring. A defect of this nature would lead to the B surface in frames 2, 3, and 4.*

TABLE 2. *Cell division ability of* Bacillus subtilis *mutants*

Strain	No. of clones	Temp (°C)	No. of divisions observed	No. of divisions expected[a]	% DE expressed vs. WT, 30°C	No. of divisions expected[b]	% DE expressed vs. tms-12, 30°C	No. of divisions expected[c]	% DE vs. WT, 30°C
CU403 *tms-12*	14	30	250	1,215.41	20.56	256.17	97.59		
	73	45	2	3,113.65	0.06	1,165.13	0.17	1,401.96	0.14
CU403 *tms-12*	10	30	52	1,746.88	2.97	857.45	6.06		
divIV-A1	61	45	0	2,085.27	0	694.10	0	943.69	0

[a] Based on division equivalents (DE) of WT, 30°C = $(\mu m - 15.27)/7.39$.
[b] Based on DE of *tms-12*, 30°C = $(\mu m - 71.2)/11.5$.
[c] Based on DE of WT, 45°C = $(\mu m - 9.41)/17.09$.

site location, (ii) the P value relating to the choice between normal and abnormal divisions, (iii) the fact that total division ability is suppressed, and (iv) the fact that minicells are anucleate. In searching for some unifying factor in these diverse properties, W. P. Segel and I recently examined macromolecular synthesis rates and DNA segregation patterns in minicell-producing the wild-type populations. (The details of these findings will be published elsewhere.) Suffice it to say that we found no significant variations in the rates of DNA, RNA, and protein syntheses indicative of minicell production. On the other hand, the location and segregation of DNA observed by autoradiography clearly indicated abnormalities. Regions of cell length free of DNA could sometimes be detected prior to the production of minicells. These vacant areas were often equivalent to several minicells in length and appeared to be precursors to minicell production. It would appear, therefore, that the primary defect in minicell-producing mutants may be one of DNA segregation. A reasonable explanation of the phenotypic properties listed above can be offered: the attachment of DNA to the cell surface somehow serves to suppress cell division. Abnormal DNA segregation generates regions free of DNA that are larger than the normal DNA-free region between genomes in wild-type cells. These large DNA-free regions are located in unusual positions along the cell length. The first cell division occurring in a long DNA-free region produces two daughter cells, both of which contain genomes and can grow. This division would be scored a "normal" division in our analyses. Subsequent divisions also arise in the DNA-free region which result in anucleate minicell clusters. If, as others have suggested, the movement of the DNA terminus away from its attachment site to the membrane is the stimulus for division initiation and also defines the location of division, then it is necessary to assume that the abnormal segregation re-sponsible for minicell cluster production involves some kind of stutter of the DNA along the membrane, thereby generating the multiple minicell division sites.

As an approach to further clarifying this situation, we constructed strains which carry the minicell-producing mutation in conjunction with either a *divI* (cell division initiation) mutation or a *dnaB* (DNA initiation) mutation. The former was constructed by J. C. Poos in my laboratory using *divIV-A1* and *tms-12*, a *divI* mutant originally isolated by Copeland and Marmur (18) and studied by Breakfield and Landman (10). As a control, *tms-12* was also transferred from its original background into the isogenic CU403 genetic background. Clone growth and division were examined after spore outgrowth at permissive and restrictive temperatures. In Table 2 a comparison is made of the division ability of strains carrying *tms-12* and *tms-12* plus *divIV-A1* mutations. Both 30 and 45°C data are included. Division equivalents were calculated as previously described, using division ability of CU403 wild-type cells grown at 30 and 45°C and of CU403 *tms-12* cells grown at 30°C (58). The data indicate that the hybrid strain is highly suppressed in division ability even when grown at permissive temperature (2.97% as many divisions as wild type). The *tms-12* mutation itself in the CU403 genetic background reduced division ability to only 20% of that found in wild-type clones. The block to division at restrictive temperature caused by the *tms-12* mutation also served to prevent minicell-producing divisions resulting from the *divIV-A1* mutation. Thus, at least one gene in the normal cell division pathway also regulated minicell division, further indicating the "normal" nature of abnormally located division in minicell-producing mutants. Similar experiments have been reported in the *E. coli* system.

S. Travis and I set out to determine the effect of DNA synthesis cessation on minicell production by construction of a *divIV-B1*—*ts-134*

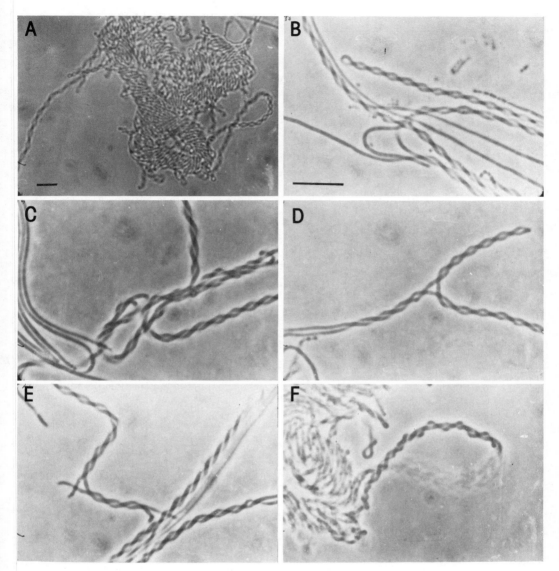

FIG. 9. *Helical growth in cultures of* B. subtilis *B1S, a derivative of strain M11, divIV-B1. (A–E) Examples of the regular and irregular helices found in cultures grown in complex medium.*

(a mutation that maps in the *dnaB* region responsible for the regulation of DNA synthesis initiation) hybrid strain, but the properties of the double mutant precluded our obtaining a clearcut answer (S. Travis and N. Mendelson, Abstr. Annu. Meet. Am. Soc. Microbiol. 1975, I34, p. 122). We could find no differential effects of DNA cessation on any of the minicell-phenotypic properties. However, the system breaks down due to the early lysis of clones produced by spores germinated and grown directly at restrictive temperature. We did find that the *ts-134* mutation increases division suppression in the double mutant grown at permissive temperature, that the amount of residual DNA synthesized after transfer to high temperature is increased over that found in strains carrying only the *ts-134* lesion, and also that it is possible to produce cells containing isolated genomes separated from one another in filaments by long DNA-free regions. We are currently attempting to utilize this system for the study of

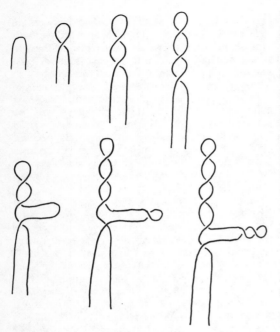

The sister filament was forced into a new hairpin upon itself and then generated a new double helix. Other asymmetries were also possible. In addition, we observed that one and the same clone could give rise to both "normal" straight sections of growth as well as helical regions. Recently we perfected a method of fluid culture in which helical clones arose after spore outgrowth. These studies indicated that helical forms arise only in young clones when both poles emerging from the spore remain bound to the spore coat. It appears therefore that helical structures are tension bound. Model building revealed that new cell elongation in this system probably occurs by insertion of material in a helical pattern around the cell surface. If so, the normal rod cells may twist during elonga-

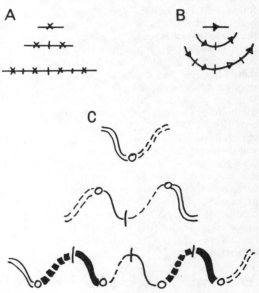

FIG. 10. *Diagram representing the production of helical growth and straight regions in cultures of BIS. The branch is generated by cessation of growth at a specific region in one of the strands which comprise the helix. The strand which continues to grow is forced into a new branch helix.*

division resumption relative to genome location and for determining the role of DNA in the production of SDS partitioning of cytoplasm.

Twisted Growth Mutants

We recently found an unusual strain which carries, in addition to a minicell-producing mutation, one or more mutations affecting growth in a spectacular manner. As shown in Fig. 9, growth consisted of a helical pattern in which frequently a hairpin bend proceeded to produce a double helix of very uniform pattern. Division suppression was required to enable the superstructure to hold together and generate the helical pattern. An initial hairpin bend had to occur to produce the two side-by-side filaments that formed the helix. The helix itself resulted from the symmetrical and complementary helical growth of each filament (Fig. 10). To maintain the structure, the growth rates and symmetries had to be closely maintained (Fig. 11). Examples of the consequences of one filament behaving differently from the other are shown in Fig. 9 and 10. In the extreme case, a portion of one filament ceased to grow altogether.

FIG. 11. *Simplified growth models pertinent to helical growth. (A) Wild-type model in which a symmetrical growth zone centrally located decays to form a septum when two new zones arise in the center of the daughter cells. (B) Ramifications of an asymmetrical growth zone which perpetuates itself as in wild-type cells. (C) A helical model of growth assuming a distorted zone is present in the initial cell. Dashed lines indicate curvature in the plane below the paper surface; solid lines represent curvature above the paper surface. The initial cell surface is shown as a double line. Newly synthesized surface in the first generation is shown as a thin single line. Newly synthesized surface in the second generation is shown as a heavy single line. By following the initial surface, it is obvious that growth forces the surfaces to alternate between above and below the paper surface. In other words, growth produces a screwlike turning of the entire structure.*

tion, causing the poles to rotate away from one another. When bound by the spore coat, an equal and opposite force will cause the structure to assume a helical morphology. By calculating the torque required to generate a tension-held helix as a result of growth rotation, it should be possible to determine the helix angle at which new surface is inserted. Such calculations are currently in progress and a full report of the new growth model appears elsewhere (58a).

Mutants that grow in an unusual twisted manner have also been found in other laboratories (25, 86), and C. L. Saxe, a student in my laboratory, has recently isolated another using DNA obtained from a stable L-form as a source of transforming DNA (5, 6). Some years ago, Fan and Beckman reported that it was possible to correct twisted growth with autolysin or low levels of lysozyme (25). We have found that the twisted growth responsible for helix formation is also phenotypically suppressible by the addition of culture filtrates from wild-type as well as mutant strains. The active factor in our system is heat labile and nondialyzable, and we naturally suspect that it may be an autolytic enzyme or similar protein. We are currently attempting to develop a methodology in which the correction of twisted growth serves as an assay for activity found in materials stripped from purified walls by a high salt concentration. Our ultimate objective in this case is to use growth and division defects that are correctable as bioassays in the search for regulatory molecules concerned with these processes. At present there are no pertinent biochemical assays available; consequently, our knowledge of the role of autolysins and other regulators of cell growth and division is superficial.

LIMITATIONS OF A GENETIC STRATEGY FOR THE ANALYSIS OF BACTERIAL GROWTH AND DIVISION

In the early days of genetics it was recognized that the more one knew about living systems in general, the more insight one had which could be brought to bear upon the issue of genetic mechanisms. Thus, H. J. Muller wrote in 1921 "must we geneticists become bacteriologists, physiological chemists and physicists simultaneously with being zoologists and botanists? Let us hope so" (69). In that era the dream was to apply these skills and knowledge to learning about the composition and functioning of genetic material. Today we have seen those objectives largely met although many of the details are still rather shaky. Nevertheless, at last we have the outlines to the answers of yesterday's questions. To move forward we must frame inquiries anew; a new set of questions to challenge a new generation of investigators must be developed. There are many directions to choose from: neurobiology, developmental biology, cell biology, environmental biology, and so on. Each of these problems may be attacked through a genetic approach. In a period of 55 years the situation has become inverted. Whereas initially other disciplines served to define and enlighten us about genetic mechanisms, now genetics can serve in turn to enlighten us about other disciplines.

I have attempted to apply a genetic approach to the analysis of cellular growth and division in bacteria. By studying the properties of mutants, I have attempted to deduce the ways in which things must work in wild-type "normal" cells. I think we have made a reasonable start in this direction and I am optimistic that continued effort in a similar vein will be fruitful. I do not want to leave the impression, however, that the genetic approach is without limitations or pitfalls. For example, the kinds of things one learns by studying mutants are ultimately defined by the properties of the particular mutants that one isolates and studies. Because of this, a clearcut objective can easily become thwarted midway along a project. Furthermore, the vital nature of both growth and division processes means that disrupting them will often be lethal. Conditional mutations must therefore be studied. Virtually all conditional-lethal bacterial mutants cease growth and division when incubated under restrictive conditions regardless of how distant the biochemical lesion is from an actual growth or division process. Thus, additional criteria must be applied to ascertain the precise target of the mutational defect. Present tools may prove inadequate in this regard. The biochemist's favorite environment, inside a clean test tube, may be no place to search for answers to higher-order phenomena such as growth and cell division. There is a need, therefore, to develop new analytical approaches that will enable us to explore the mechanisms of cellular events which take place in cells. Must we microbial geneticists become bacteriologists, biochemists, and physiologists simultaneously with being biophysicists and cell biologists? Apparently so.

ACKNOWLEDGMENTS

It has been a pleasure for me to benefit from association with the following individuals: S. Blough, R. J. Boylan, D. Brooks, R. M. Cole, J. B. Cornett, S. I. Coyne, J. D. Gross, L. L. Hallock, D. Karamata, S. Keener, J. C. Poos,

T. J. Popkin, J. N. Reeve, C. L. Saxe, W. P. Segel, S. Travis, and F. E. Young, all of whom have contributed to the research on bacillus mutants emphasized in this review. I am grateful for the support of both the National Science Foundation and the National Institutes of Health. I am currently supported by a Public Health Service research grant (GM 18735) and Research Career Development award (GM 70555) from the National Institute of General Medical Sciences.

LITERATURE CITED

1. **Adler, H. I., W. D. Fisher, A. Cohen, and A. A. Hardigree.** 1967. Miniature *Escherichia coli* cells deficient in DNA. Proc. Natl. Acad. Sci. U.S.A. **57:** 321–326.
2. **Adler, H. I., W. D. Fisher, and A. A. Hardigree.** 1970. Cell division in *Escherichia coli*. Trans. N.Y. Acad. Sci. **31:** 1059–1070.
3. **Alston, R. E.** 1967. Cellular continuity and development, p. 161–167. Scott Foresman and Co., Glenview, Ill.
4. **Bayer, M. E.** 1968. Adsorption of bacteriophage to adhesions between wall and membrane of *Escherichia coli*. J. Virol. **2:** 346–356.
5. **Bettinger, G. E., and F. E. Young.** 1975. Transformation of *Bacillus subtilis*: transforming ability of deoxyribonucleic acid in lysates of L-forms or protoplasts. J. Bacteriol. **122:** 987–993.
6. **Bettinger, G. W., and F. E. Young.** 1973. Transformation of *Bacillus subtilis* using gently lysed L-forms, a new mapping technique. Biochem. Biophys. Res. Commun. **55:** 1105–1111.
7. **Boylan, R. J., and N. H. Mendelson.** 1969. Initial characterization of a temperature-sensitive Rod⁻ mutant of *Bacillus subtilis*. J. Bacteriol. **100:** 1316–1321.
8. **Boylan, R. J., N. H. Mendelson, D. Brooks, and F. E. Young.** 1972. Regulation of the bacterial cell wall: analysis of a mutant of *Bacillus subtilis* defective in biosynthesis of teichoic acid. J. Bacteriol. **110:** 281–290.
9. **Braun, V., and K. Hantke.** 1974. Biochemistry of bacterial cell envelopes. Annu. Rev. Biochem. **43:** 89–121.
10. **Breakfield, X. O., and O. E. Landman.** 1973. Temperature-sensitive divisionless mutant of *Bacillus subtilis* defective in the initiation of septation. J. Bacteriol. **113:** 985–998.
11. **Cairns, J.** 1963. The chromosome of *Escherichia coli*. Cold Spring Harbor Symp. Quant. Biol. **28:** 43–46.
12. **Clowes, R. C.** 1972. Molecular structure of bacterial plasmids. Bacteriol. Rev. **36:** 361–405.
13. **Cole, R. M.** 1965. Bacterial cell wall replication followed by immunofluorescence. Bacteriol. Rev. **29:** 326–344.
14. **Cole, R. M.** 1964. Cell wall replication in *Salmonella typhosa*. Science **143:** 820–822.
15. **Cole, R. M., and J. J. Hahn.** 1962. Cell wall replication in *Streptococcus pyogenes*. Science **135:** 722–723.
16. **Cole, R. M., T. J. Popkin, R. J. Boylan, and N. H. Mendelson.** 1970. Ultrastructure of a temperature-sensitive Rod⁻ mutant of *Bacillus subtilis*. J. Bacteriol. **103:** 793–810.
17. **Cooper, S., and C. E. Helmstetter.** 1968. Chromosome replication and the division cycle of *Escherichia coli*. J. Mol. Biol. **31:** 519–540.
18. **Copeland, J. C., and J. Marmur.** 1968. Identification of conserved genetic functions in *Bacillus* by use of temperature-sensitive mutants. Bacteriol. Rev. **32:** 302–312.
19. **Coyne, S. I., and N. H. Mendelson.** 1974. Clonal analysis of cell division in the *Bacillus subtilis div IV-B1* minicell-producing mutant. J. Bacteriol. **118:** 15–20.
20. **Crawford, I. P.** 1975. Gene rearrangements in the evolution of the tryptophan synthetic pathway. Bacteriol. Rev. **39:** 87–120.
21. **DeLamater, E. D.** 1951. A new cytological basis for bacterial genetics. Cold Spring Harbor Symp. Quant. Biol. **16:** 381–412.
22. **DeLamater, E. D.** 1962. Withdrawal of the concept of the occurrence of classical mitosis in bacteria. Nature (London) **195:** 309–310.
23. **Donachie, W. D.** 1973. Regulation of cell division in bacteria. Br. Med. Bull. **29:** 203–207.
24. **Donachie, W. D., and K. J. Begg.** 1970. Growth of the bacterial cell. Nature (London) **227:** 1220–1224.
25. **Fan, D. P., and M. M. Beckman.** 1971. Mutant of *Bacillus subtilis* demonstrating the requirement of lysis for growth. J. Bacteriol. **105:** 629–636.
26. **Fisher, K. W., and M. B. Fisher.** 1968. Nalidixic acid inhibition of DNA transfer in *Escherichia coli* K12. Cold Spring Harbor Symp. Quant. Biol. **33:** 629–633.
27. **Fleck, J., J. P. Martin, and M. Mock.** 1974. Action of lysozyme on penicillin-induced filaments of *Proteus vulgaris*. J. Bacteriol. **120:** 929–933.
28. **Forer, A.** 1974. Possible roles of microtubules and actin-like filaments during cell-division, p. 319–336. *In* G. M. Padilla, F. L. Cameron, and A. Zimmerman (ed.), Cell cycle controls. Academic Press Inc., New York.
29. **Fraser, A. C., and R. Curtiss III.** 1974. Production, properties and utility of bacterial minicells. Curr. Top. Microbiol. Immunol. **69:** 1–84.
30. **Frehel, C., A. Beaufils, and A. Ryter.** 1971. Etude au microscope electronique de la croissance de la paroi chez *Bacillus subtilis* et *Bacillus megaterium*. Ann. Inst. Pasteur Paris **121:** 139–148.
31. **Green, E. W., and M. Schaechter.** 1972. The mode of segregation of the bacterial cell membrane. Proc. Natl. Acad. Sci. U.S.A. **69:** 2312–2316.
32. **Gyurastis, F. B., and R. G. Wake.** 1973. Bidirectional chromosome replication in *Bacillus subtilis*. J. Mol. Biol. **73:** 55–63.
33. **Harford, N.** 1975. Bidirectional chromosome replication in *Bacillus subtilis* 168. J. Bacteriol. **121:** 835–847.
33a. **Harmon, J. M., and H. W. Taber.** 1976. Relationship of membrane proteins to chromosomal replication of *Bacillus subtilis*, p. 105–115. *In* D. Schlessinger (ed.), Microbiology–1976. American Society for Microbiology, Washington, D.C.
34. **Hartwell, L. H.** 1974. *Saccharomyces cerevisiae* cell cycle. Bacteriol. Rev. **38:** 164–198.
35. **Heath, I. B.** 1974. Genome separation mechanism in procaryotes, algae and fungi, p. 487–515. *In* H. Busch (ed.), The cell nucleus, vol. 2. Academic Press Inc., New York.
36. **Higgins, M. L., L. Daneo-Moore, D. Boothby, and G. D. Shockman.** 1974. Effect of inhibition of deoxyribonucleic acid and protein synthesis on the direction of cell wall growth in *Streptococcus faecalis*. J. Bacteriol. **118:** 681–692.
37. **Higgins, M. L., and G. D. Shockman.** 1970. Model for cell wall growth of *Streptococcus faecalis*. J. Bacteriol. **101:** 645–648.
38. **Higgins, M. L., and G. D. Shockman.** 1971. Procaryotic cell division with respect to wall and membranes. Crit. Rev. Microbiol. **1:** 29–72.
39. **Hirota, Y., A. Ryter, and F. Jacob.** 1968. Thermosensitive mutants of *E. coli* affected in the processes of DNA synthesis and cellular division. Cold Spring Harbor Symp. Quant. Biol. **33:** 677–693.
40. **Hitchins, A., and R. A. Slepecky.** 1969. Bacterial sporulation as a modified procaryotic cell division. Nature (London) **223:** 804–807.
41. **Hsu, T. C., and K. Benirschke.** 1967. An atlas of mammalian chromosomes. Springer Verlag, New York.
41a. **Ingle, M. B., and E. W. Boyer.** 1976. Production of in-

dustrial enzymes by *Bacillus* species, p. 420–426. *In* D. Schlessinger (ed.), Microbiology—1976. American Society for Microbiology, Washington, D.C.

42. **Jacob, F., S. Brenner, and F. Cuzin.** 1963. On the regulation of DNA replication in Bacteria. Cold Spring Harbor Symp. Quant. Biol. **28:**329–347.

43. **Jacob, F., and J. Monod.** 1961. Genetic regulatory mechanisms in the synthesis of proteins. J. Mol. Biol. **3:**318–356.

44. **Jones, N. C., and W. D. Donachie.** 1974. Protein synthesis and the release of the replicated chromosome from the cell membrane. Nature (London) **251:**252–253.

45. **Kohimaya, M., D. Cousins, A. Ryter, and F. Jacob.** 1966. Mutants thermosensibles d' *Escherichia coli* K12.1. Isolement et characterisation rapide. Ann. Inst. Pasteur Paris **110:**465–486.

46. **Lederberg, J., E. M. Lederberg, N. D. Zinder, and E. R. Lively.** 1951. Recombination analysis of bacterial heredity. Cold Spring Harbor Symp. Quant. Biol. **16:** 413–441.

47. **Leibowitz, P. J., and M. Schaechter.** 1975. The attachment of the bacterial chromosome to the cell membrane. Int. Rev. Cytol. **41:**1–28.

48. **Lepesant-Kejzlarova, J., J. A. Lepesant, J. Walle, A. Billault, and R. Dedonder.** 1975. Revision of the linkage map of *Bacillus subtilis* 168: indications for circularity of the chromosome. J. Bacteriol. **121:** 823–834.

49. **Lin, E. C. C., Y. Hirota, and F. Jacob.** 1971. On the process of cellular division in *Escherichia coli.* J. Bacteriol. **108:**375–385.

50. **Maaloe, O., and N. O. Kjeldgaard.** 1966. Control of macromolecular synthesis. W. A. Benjamin, Inc., New York.

51. **Mach, F., and H. Englebrecht.** 1970. Isolation und erste Charakterisierung einer temperatursensitiven filamentesen Mutante von *Bacillus subtilis* SB 19. Z. Allg. Mikrobiol. **10:**383–395.

52. **Marunouchi, T., and W. Messer.** 1973. Replication of a specific terminal chromosome segment in *Escherichia coli* which is required for cell division. J. Mol. Biol. **78:**221–228.

53. **Mauck, J., and L. Glaser.** 1972. On the mode of *in vivo* assembly of the cell wall of *Bacillus subtilis.* J. Biol. Chem. **247:**1180–1187.

54. **Mendelson, N. H.** 1968. Can defective segregation prevent initiation? Cold Spring Harbor Symp. Quant. Biol. **33:**313–316.

55. **Mendelson, N. H.** 1968. Nuclear segregation without DNA replication in *Bacillus subtilis.* Biochim. Biophys. Acta **190:**132–138.

56. **Mendelson, N. H.** 1972. Deoxyribonucleic acid distribution in *Bacillus subtilis* independent of cell elongation. J. Bacteriol. **111:**156–162.

57. **Mendelson, N. H.** 1972. Division site regulation in a temperature-sensitive mutant of *Bacillus subtilis.* J. Bacteriol. **111:**298–300.

58. **Mendelson, N. H.** 1975. Cell division suppression in the *Bacillus subtilis* div *IV*-A1 minicell producing mutant. J. Bacteriol. **121:**1166–1172.

58a. **Mendelson, N. H.** 1976. Helical growth of *Bacillus subtilis*: a new model of cell growth. Proc. Natl. Acad. Sci. U.S.A. **73:**1740–1744.

59. **Mendelson, N. H., and R. M. Cole.** 1972. Genetic regulation of cell division initiation in *Bacillus subtilis.* J. Bacteriol. **112:**994–1003.

60. **Mendelson, N. H., and S. I. Coyne.** 1975. Minicell yield and cell division suppression in *Bacillus subtilis* mutants. J. Bacteriol. **121:**1200–1202.

61. **Mendelson, N. H., and J. D. Gross.** 1967. Characterization of a temperature-sensitive mutant of *Bacillus subtilis* defective in deoxyribonucleic acid replication. J. Bacteriol. **94:**1603–1608.

61a. **Mendelson, N. H., S. Keener, and R. M. Cole.** 1975. Growth of minicell-Rod⁻ double mutants of *Bacillus subtilis.* Microbios **13:**175–183.

62. **Mendelson, N. H., and J. N. Reeve.** 1973. Growth of the *Bacillus subtilis* cell surface. Nature (London) New Biol. **243:**62–64.

63. **Mendelson, N. H., J. N. Reeve, and R. M. Cole.** 1974. Physiological studies of *Bacillus subtilis* minicells. J. Bacteriol. **117:**1312–1319.

64. **Mills, D. R., R. L. Peterson, and S. Spiegelman.** 1967. An extracellular Darwinian experiment with a self-duplicating nucleic acid molecule. Proc. Natl. Acad. Sci. U.S.A. **58:**217–224.

65. **Mindich, L., and S. Dales.** 1972. Membrane synthesis in *Bacillus subtilis.* III. The morphological localization of the sites of membrane synthesis. J. Cell Biol. **55:** 32–41.

66. **Mitchison, J. M.** 1971. The biology of the cell cycle. Cambridge University Press, London.

67. **Muhlradt, P. F., J. Menzel, J. R. Golecki, and V. Speth.** 1973. Outer membrane of *Salmonella*: site of export of newly synthesized lipopolysaccharide on the bacterial surface. Eur. J. Biochem. **35:**471–481.

68. **Muhlradt, P. F., J. Menzel, J. R. Golecki, and V. Speht.** 1974. Lateral mobility and surface density of lipopolysaccharide in the outer membrane of *Salmonella typhimurium.* Eur. J. Biochem. **43:**533–539.

69. **Muller, H. J.** 1922. Variation due to change in the individual gene. Am. Nat. **56:**32–50.

70. **Muller, H. J.** 1932. Some genetic aspects of sex. Am. Nat. **64:**118–138.

71. **Nicklas, R. B.** 1974. Chromosome segregation mechanisms. Genetics **78:**205–213.

72. **Nukushina, J. I., and Y. Ikeda.** 1969. Genetic analysis of the developmental processes during germination and outgrowth of *Bacillus subtilis* spore with temperature-sensitive mutants. Genetics **63:**63–74.

73. **Oishi, M., H. Yoshikawa, and N. Sueoka.** 1964. Synchronous and dichotomous replication of the *Bacillus subtilis* chromosome during spore germination. Nature (London) **204:**1069–1073.

73a. **Reeve, J. N.** 1976. Macromolecular synthesis in bacteriophage-infected minicells of *Bacillus subtilis*, p. 332–339. *In* D. Schlessinger (ed.), Microbiology—1976. American Society for Microbiology, Washington, D.C.

74. **Reeve, J. N., and N. H. Mendelson.** 1974. Minicells of *Bacillus subtilis*: a unique system for transport studies. Biochim. Biophys. Acta **352:**298–306.

75. **Reeve, J. N., N. H. Mendelson, and R. M. Cole.** 1972. Cell morphology of *Bacillus subtilis*: the effect of genetic background on the expression of a Rod⁻ gene. Mol. Gen. Genet. **119:**11–26.

76. **Reeve, J. N., N. H. Mendelson, S. I. Coyne, L. L. Hallock, and R. M. Cole.** 1973. Minicells of *Bacillus subtilis.* J. Bacteriol. **114:**870–873.

77. **Rogers, H. J., M. M. McConnell, and I. D. J. Burdett.** 1968. Cell wall or membrane mutants of *Bacillus subtilis* and *Bacillus licheniformis* with grossly deformed morphology. Nature (London) **219:**285–288.

78. **Rogers, H. J., H. M. Pooley, P. F. Thurman, and C. Taylor.** 1974. Wall and membrane growth in bacilli and their mutants. Ann. Microbiol. (Inst. Pasteur) **125B:** 135–147.

79. **Rogers, H. J., P. F. Thurman, C. Taylor, and J. N. Reeve.** 1974. Mucopeptide synthesis by *rod* mutants of Bacillus subtilis. J. Gen. Micribiol. **85:**335–350.

80. **Ryter, A.** 1971. Etude de la croissance de la membrane chez *Bacillus subtilis* au moyen de la distribution des flagelles. Ann. Inst. Pasteur Paris **121:**271–288.

81. **Ryter, A., Y. Hirota, and U. Schwarz.** 1973. Process of cellular division in *Escherichia coli.* Growth pattern of *E. coli* murein. J. Mol. Biol. **78:**185–195.

82. **Sargent, M. G.** 1975. Control of cell length in *Bacillus subtilis*. J. Bacteriol. **123**:7–19.

83. **Sargent, M. G.** 1975. Anucleate cell production and surface extension in a temperature-sensitive chromosome initiation mutant of *Bacillus subtilis*. J. Bacteriol. **123**:1218–1234.

84. **Swanson, C. P., T. Merz, and W. J. Young.** 1967. Cytogenetics. Prentice Hall, Inc., Englewood Cliffs, New Jersey.

85. **Upcroft, P., H. J. Dyson, and R. G. Wake.** 1975. Characteristics of a *Bacillus subtilis* W 23 mutant temperature sensitive for initiation of chromosome replication. J. Bacteriol. **121**:121–127.

86. **Van Alstyne, D., and M. I. Simon.** 1971. Division mutants of *Bacillus subtilis*: isolation and PBSI transduction of division-specific markers. J. Bacteriol. **108**:1366–1379.

87. **Voeller, B. R.** (ed.). 1968. The chromosome theory of inheritance. Appleton-Century Crofts, New York.

88. **Wake, R. G.** 1973. Circularity of the *Bacillus subtilis* chromosome and further studies on its bidirectional replication. J. Mol. Biol. **77**:569–575.

89. **Werner, R.** 1971. Mechanism of DNA replication. Nature (London) **230**:570–572.

90. **White, K., and N. Sueoka.** 1973. Temperature-sensitive DNA synthesis mutants of *Bacillus subtilis*. Genetics **73**:185–214.

91. **Wong, W., F. E. Young, and A. N. Chatterjee.** 1974. Regulation of bacterial cell walls: turnover of cell walls in *Staphylococcus aureus*. J. Bacteriol. **120**:837–843.

92. **Zaritski, A., and R. H. Pritchard.** 1971. Replication time of the chromosome in thymineless mutants of *E. coli*. J. Mol. Biol. **60**:65–74.

Envelope Growth and Synthesis in *rod* Mutants and Protoplasts of Bacilli

HOWARD J. ROGERS

National Institute for Medical Research, Mill Hill, London NW7 1AA, England

INTRODUCTION

The general outlines of the chemical structure and the biosynthesis of bacterial wall polymers are by now reasonably well understood. Likewise, our knowledge of the membranes carrying several of the necessary biosynthetic enzymes is also rather advanced. However, this knowledge has not yet helped very much to explain in molecular terms the processes of the division and orderly growth of bacteria. This is in no way surprising and to express disappointment is like deprecating our first knowledge of amino acid sequences in proteins and of protein biosynthesis because the mechanisms of enzyme action and regulation could not be explained immediately, mechanisms which are infinitely simpler functions on the face of it. We should not retire in gloom because the blunt tools we presently possess fail to explain what is amiss in mutants disturbed in division and morphology. Rather, the mutants should be studied intently. In the process maybe the tools will be sharpened. This paper will concern itself firstly with the conditional and nonconditional mutants of *Bacillus subtilis* that can grow as grossly deformed spheres instead of rods. Secondly, some consideration will be given to the biosynthesis of wall polymers by reverting protoplasts, because on their way back to rods these also pass through a stage reminiscent of the *rod* mutants when growing as spheres.

rod MUTANTS OF BACILLI

rod mutants were first isolated from *B. subtilis* 168 *trpC* and from *B. licheniformis* 6346 as organisms growing somewhat better in media containing 0.8 M NaCl (20, 21). In such media they grew as normal-looking rods, but in the absence of the extra sodium chloride only deformed cocci with walls of uneven thickness and septa running in many directions were seen (Fig. 1). It was subsequently shown (19) that the morphology of some of these was corrected by the presence of sodium-L-glutamate or glutamine in the medium instead of the high concentration of salt. A temperature-sensitive *rod* mutant of *B. subtilis* was then described and studied (2, 4). Since that time, rod-type mutants have been isolated from a rather wide variety of species (24). By hindsight, it would also seem likely that other earlier candidates existed such as some so-called L-forms of *Proteus vulgaris* which have chemically normal, but spherically shaped, mucopeptide layers (16). From transformation and transduction work on the strains of *B. subtilis* (3, 12), it would seem very improbable that the grossly deformed phenotype is due to multiple mutations unless these are very closely linked. It is clear, however, that single mutations in different parts of the chromosome can produce the same morphology when expressed in the same strain but that each has a distinguishable chemical and physiological phenotype; for example, two

25

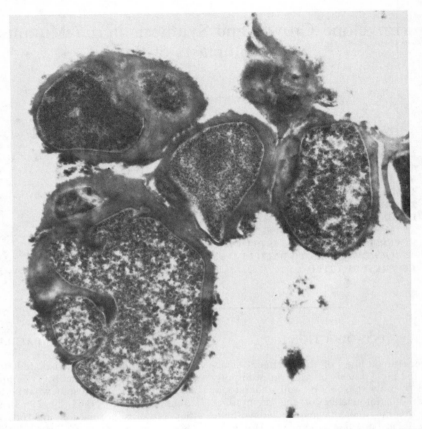

FIG. 1. *Section of a* rod *mutant growing under restrictive conditions as a deformed sphere.*

groups of *rod* mutants, A and C (12), are known that seem to be disturbed in the proportions of negative polymers attached to the mucopeptide in their walls and to have morphologies dependent, respectively, on growth temperature and the ionic strength of the medium. The third group, *rod* B, is different in having almost normal proportions of negative polymers in the walls and being nutritionally corrected by the presence in the growth medium of L-glutamic acid or its metabolic neighbors. The present paper will show that these two apparently different mutations possibly possess a common requirement. A fourth type of nonconditional *rod* mutant (*rod* D) has also been found that is deficient in CDP-glycerol pyrophosphorylase and is, therefore, unable to make teichoic acids (R. F. Rosenberger, unpublished work).

The hope, of course, in examining these grossly disturbed morphological mutants, as well as mutants that have superficially more simple lesions such as in septation and cell separation, is that, in unravelling any abnormalities of their metabolism, the importance of the particular missing steps will help in understanding division and growth of normally growing bacteria. It is very unlikely, however, that a linear series of steps will be revealed as, for example, in the biosynthesis of an amino acid. In morphological studies including cell division, we are involved with integrated biosynthesis of polymers which when put together form recognizable macrostructures. In such a process the following considerations are likely to be involved: (i) the biosynthesis of the particular polymers in their correct conformations; (ii) small additions to or subtractions from the polymers that may have profound affects on conformations and hence on the availability of these and other neighboring polymers to enzymes; (iii) the exact location on the surface of the cell at which the polymer is biosynthesized; (iv) if the biosynthetic enzymes are membrane bound, the possible effect of a pre-formed polymer, still attached at another place, on the lateral translation of the enzymes. Enzyme migration may also be affected by apparently irrelevant considerations such as the concentration of divalent cations in the membrane that can alter the movement of lipids, hence the viscosity of the bilayer and therefore the movement; (v) the time in the cell cycle in which new polymer chains are formed; (vi) the regulation of the relative rates of extension of the polymers, their linkage together, and the insertion of new biosynthetic enzymes at different times in the cell cycle.

ROLE OF NEGATIVELY CHARGED WALL POLYMERS

The first observation which indicated that the proportion of teichoic acids in bacterial walls might be important to normal division and cell growth was that *rod* A mutants growing under restrictive conditions were deficient in these macroanions (3, 4). Subsequent work showed that these mutants are regulatory ones in which mucopeptide synthesis is increased more than teichoic acid synthesis is decreased (24). Other situations have since been found, however, in which the biosynthesis of all wall macroanions is grossly reduced. In these, the morphology of the cells is very similar to that of the *rod* A or C mutants growing under restrictive conditions. One example is provided by mutants of *B. licheniformis* deficient in phosphoglucomutase which cannot make glucose-1-phosphate. In the absence of this intermediate, UDP-glucose and hence UDP-glucuronic acid synthesis is blocked. The bacteria cannot, therefore, make teichuronic acid, which is an alternative wall macroanion to the teichoic acids. As is now well known, when the growth of bacilli and other organisms is limited by phosphate, teichoic acids cease to be made. They are then ejected by turnover of the wall and are replaced by teichuronic acid (8, 9). In a phosphoglucomutase-deficient mutant this cannot happen, and coccal-shaped organisms with walls containing only mucopeptide and traces of other materials result (10). Transfer of the phosphoglucomutase gene to other strains of *B. licheniformis* results in similar behavior (C. W. Forsberg and H. J. Rogers, unpublished work). Growth of the mutants in a medium containing glycerol and galactose partially circumvents the lesion and allows the synthesis of negative wall polymers in phosphate-limited growth. The morphology is then corrected (10). Similar results have been obtained with the known

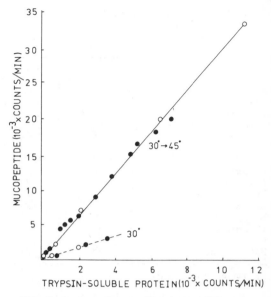

FIG. 2. *Increased rate of mucopeptide synthesis compared to protein synthesis when the temperature of growth of a* rod *A mutant is shifted at time 0 from 30 to 45°C. The solid line is for the shifted culture, the dotted line for the culture kept at 30°C. Symbols:* ●, ○, *Results from two experiments.*

(32, 33) phosphoglucomutase mutants of *B. subtilis*. These mutants are resistant to some phages because the teichoic acid in the walls is not glycosylated. R. F. Rosenberger of this department, arguing that if this is true then phage-resistant mutants should also exist that do not make the polyglycerophosphate backbone of teichoic acid because they lack the enzymes necessary for teichoic acid synthesis, has now isolated a CDP-glycerol pyrophosphorylase-deficient mutant. This organism has negligible amounts of teichoic acid in its walls and grows as a coccus. Hence we have three quite different mutations with different enzymatic deficiencies, all of which lead to a reduction in the proportion of negative polymers in the walls and to coccal instead of bacillary morphology. One further example of a lesion which under phosphate starvation can lead to walls deficient in macroanions is that in *B. licheniformis* 6346, which causes a lack of UDP-glucose pyrophosphorylase (Forsberg and Rogers, manuscript in preparation). This organism and appropriate transformants again showed the same morphological behavior as the phosphoglucomutase mutants. Teichoic and teichuronic acids are again absent under phosphate limitation as would be expected since, like

TABLE 1. *Analysis of* rod A *mutant of*
B. subtilis *grown at 30 and 45°C*

Component	nmol/mg of wall	
	30°C[a]	45°C[a]
Muramic acid	272	580
Glucosamine	359	676
Glutamate	344	851
m-Diaminopimelic acid	408	835
Alanine (L + D)	618	1346
Galactosamine	118	<10
Phosphorus	1032	192
Glycerol	998	
Glucose	851	49.7
Ester D-alanine[b]	112	40.5
Muramic acid	52[c]	179[c]
Wall phosphorus	220[c]	56.6[c]
Glycerol	194[c]	50.6[c]
Glucose	173[c]	16.5[c]
Ester alanine	15[c]	9.0[c]

[a] Temperature at which cells were grown.
[b] Estimated after incorporation of D-[14C]alanine.
[c] Nanomoles per milligram (dry weight) of cells.

them, these mutants cannot manufacture the UDP-glucose necessary for teichuronic acid synthesis. All of these mutants that lack macroanions, or that can be grown so that they lack macroanions, also have some degree of disturbance of their autolytic activity. The phosphoglucomutase and the UDP-glucose pyrophosphorylase are grossly deficient in *N*-acetylmuramyl-L-alanine amidase. The *rod* A mutants presumably produce autolytic enzymes, since the walls turn over under restrictive conditions (H. J. Rogers and H. M. Pooley, unpublished data) and the amidase is necessary for this to happen (23); but neither the cells nor the walls, when isolated from them after growth at 45°C, autolyze, whereas those of the wild type do. Presumably the walls of the *rod* A mutant bearing a low proportion of teichoic acid may not successfully absorb the lytic amidase. It is clear that a deficiency of autolytic activity does not of itself cause the morphological lesion whether or not the organisms are subjected to phosphate limitation. For example, a mutant of *B. subtilis* that produces only 4 to 5% of the amidase of the wild type, but normal levels of the relevant enzymes concerned with glucose metabolism, does not grow as spheres under phosphate limitation, but does grow as very long chains of unseparated bacilli (J. F. Fein and H. J. Rogers, unpublished work). Likewise, the polyglycerophosphate UDP-glucose transferase-deficient mutant isolated by Young et al. (33) produces only 25% of the amidase formed by the wild type but does not form cocci under phosphate limitation, whereas the

rod B mutants (see below) autolyze normally (21) but have the same defective morphology as those that do not. However, the relation between the morphological disturbance and action of autolytic enzymes in rod mutants requires further studies before definite statements can be made.

TEMPERATURE-SENSITIVE *rod* A MUTANTS

How mutants deficient in the enzymes forming either UDP-glucose or CDP-glycerol can arrive in the situation of having no macroanions in their walls is quite clear. The mechanism in the Boylan-Mendelson temperature-sensitive mutant is much less clear. Examination (3) of the enzymes concerned with the biosynthesis of glycerol teichoic acid showed that they were all present in cells grown at 45°C. Despite this, the proportion of glycerol teichoic acid in the walls (on the basis of either the molar ratios of the components of the polymer to that of mucopeptide constituents or on a wall weight basis) was reduced by about 80% as compared with the mutants grown at 30°C or with the wild type. The proportion of the *N*-acetylgalactosamine-glucose-phosphate polymer (5, 27) was still lower after growth at 45°C. Reexamination of the position (24) showed that the lower proportion of teichoic acid in the walls was in some ways misleading. A switch in the growth temperature of the mutant to 45°C led to an increase in rate of synthesis of mucopeptide relative to protein synthesis (Fig. 2). No such change took place in the wild type. This increase in rate lasted for about three generations. The ultimate result was that, when a steady state at 45°C was realized, there was four to five times as much mucopeptide per unit mass of cells than there was after growth to steady state at 30°C. The amount of D-[14C]alanine, not present in the mucopeptide in the walls but that had been incorporated into polymers removed by hot trichloroacetic acid from the walls of a D-alanine auxotroph, showed no change on a cell mass basis when the temperature was shifted. It was presumed that this D-alanine was associated with the wall teichoic acids. These results suggest that the main effect of the mutation is to regulate the rate of formation of mucopeptide rather than teichoic acids. The incorporation of [2-3H]glycerol into wall teichoic acid has now been studied (H. J. Rogers and C. Taylor, unpublished work). It would appear that there is both an increase in mucopeptide synthesis and some decrease in teichoic acid formation on changing the growth temperature from 30 to 42°C. Chemical determinations of the amounts of mucopeptide constituents and teichoic acid phosphorus in cells grown at 30 and 45°C confirm the work with radioactive precursors (Table 1). How far this inverse change can be explained by competition for some essential intermediate needs further investigation (1).

Mg²⁺ REQUIREMENTS OF *rod* B MUTANTS

The above evidence that gross reduction in the proportion of macroanions in the walls leads to coccal shapes instead of rods seems overwhelming. The reverse statement, namely, that the deformed coccal morphology results exclusively from this reduction in charged polymers, clearly cannot be true, due to the paradoxical status of the *rod* B mutants. These adopt a coccal morphology in inorganic media with glucose as carbon source and are corrected to rods by sodium-L-glutamate or high salt concentrations (19, 20, 31). The amounts of teichoic acid in the walls alter only slightly, relative to each other, but the total macroanion associated with the wall remains the same, whether the bacteria are growing as rods or cocci (22).

The variable and slow growth rates of these particular mutants and their prolonged lags in growth when inoculated into liquid minimal media in the absence of glutamate were problems which repeatedly occurred. This applied to the original minimal medium (21), to Spizizen (28) medium, or to the improved medium of Sargent (25). Results with Spizizen medium were particularly difficult, and often the mutants

TABLE 2. *Low-phosphate, chloride-free minimal medium used to study the effects of Mg²⁺ and anion concentration on growth*[a]

Medium component	Amt per liter of medium (ml)	Final concn
Na⁺/K⁺ phosphate (pH 7.4), 0.12 M	10.0	1.2 mM
[3-(*N*-morpholino)]propane-sulfonic acid, 0.2 M	250.0	0.05 M
Tris, 0.175 M	250	0.044 M
(NH₄)₂SO₄, 0.15 M	10	1.5 mM
Glucose, 10%	50	0.5%
FeSO₄·7H₂O, 0.36 mM	1.0	0.36 μM
MnSO₄, 0.4 mM	1.0	0.4 μM
Na₂SO₄, 1 M	10.0	10 mM
K₂SO₄, 0.4 M	25	10 mM

[a] Solutions of MgSO₄ amino acid auxotrophic requirements and anions as their sodium, potassium, or ammonium salts were added as required. The final volume was adjusted to 1.0 liter with water. The solutions were kept separately, sterilized, and mixed as required.

failed to grow altogether. To examine the reasons for this, a quite different minimal medium was designed (Table 2). The high concentration of phosphate present in earlier media was eliminated because from preliminary experiments it was suspected that the Mg²⁺ concentration was critical. In this medium it was found that two factors were important for rapid growth: (i) the concentration of Mg²⁺; and (ii) the presence of a suitable anion.

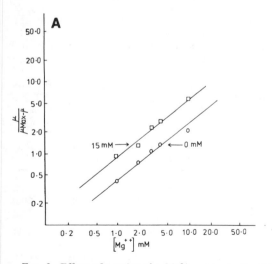
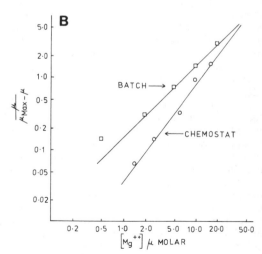

Fig. 3. *Effect of varying the Mg²⁺ concentration (A) upon the growth rate of the mutant at two different NaCl concentrations (○, zero concentration; □, 15 mM); (B) upon the growth rate of the wild type in batch (□) and continuous culture (○). In both, 15 mM Cl⁻ was present. The* K_s *is when the ratio* $\mu/(\mu_{max} - \mu)$ *reaches the value of 1.0, i.e., when the growth rate is half-maximal.*

TABLE 3. *Effect of Cl⁻ ion concentration on the K_s for Mg^{2+} for rod B 104[a]*

Cl⁻ concn (mM)	K_s value (mM)
0	3
15	1.2
30	0.4

[a] The K_s measures the concentration of a medium constituent required to maintain a half-maximal exponential rate of growth.

The Mg^{2+} in the medium could not be replaced by Na^+, K^+, NH_4^+, Ca^{2+}, Sr^{2+}, Ba^{2+}, or Be^{2+}. The latter three ions were toxic at 1 to 3 mM. Figure 3 shows plots of the logarithms of the Mg^{2+} concentrations added to the growth media, against the logarithms of the ratios $\mu/(\mu_{max} - \mu)$, at any given Mg^{2+} concentration and where μ_{max} is the maximum growth rate attainable by varying the Mg^{2+} concentration. It will be seen that the Mg^{2+} required to obtain the half-maximal growth rate of the mutant is between two and three orders of magnitude greater than for the wild type. The K_s for the mutant, however, is dependent on the concentration of anion present, which is in this case chloride. Increasing the chloride concentration decreases the K_s (see Table 3). Further examination of the specificity of the anion effect on growth of the mutant in the presence of 10 mM Mg showed that, whereas Cl⁻, Br⁻, I⁻, NO_3^-, CNS⁻, glutamate, and aspartate were effective, F⁻, SO_4^{2-}, $S_2O_3^{2-}$, $Fe(CN)_6^{4-}$, CO_3^{2-}, $M_2O_3^{2-}$ acetate, and formate were ineffective at concentrations of from 5 to 20 mM. Some substances such as thiocyanate were toxic at the higher concentrations, and optimal rates of growth were obtained with these at 5 to 10 mM. Table 4 summarizes these results.

It was known, of course, from earlier work (21) that the presence of salts such as sodium or potassium chloride at high concentrations of the order of 0.8 to 1.0 M in the growth medium would change the deformed cocci to rods, as would sodium-L-glutamate. Examination of the morphology of the mutant growing at steady maximum rates in media containing 10 mM Mg^{2+} and 15 to 20 mM NaCl showed that all the cells were typical deformed cocci. However, when the other growth-effective inorganic anions were tried, only rods were found with I⁻, Br⁻, or NO_3^-. The morphological effect was, of course, fully reversible by subculturing into media containing 10 mM Mg^{2+} and 15 mM Cl⁻. The morphology in the presence of a constant concentration of any one of this group of anions was entirely controlled by the Mg^{2+} concentra-

TABLE 4. *Effect of different anions on the rate of growth of rod B 104 growing in minimal medium containing sulfate*

Growth-effective anions			Noneffective anions		
Anion	Concn (mM)	Growth rate[a] (min)	Anion	Concn (mM)	Growth rate[a] (min)
SO_4^{2-} only		147[b]	$Fe(CN)_6^{4-}$	5	170
Cl⁻	10	90	$S_2O_3^{2-}$	15	113
	15	75	CO_3^{2-}	15	140
Br⁻	15	70	MO_4^{2-}	15	130
I⁻	1	80	F⁻	5	130
	10	75		15	130
NO_3^-	15	65			
CNS⁻	5	90			
	10	85			
ClO_4^-	15	85			
IO_3^-	15	80			

[a] Doubling time in steady-state exponential growth.
[b] Some variation was found in the absence of effective ions. The result quoted is the mean value from five separate experiments. The range of values was 125 to 185 min.

tion in the medium (see Table 5). Alternatively, if the Mg^{2+} was kept constant and the anion concentration was varied, the morphology was dependent on the concentration of the latter (Fig. 4). The obvious question to be answered, then, was whether L-glutamate, which had originally been thought of as having a specific role as an amino acid, was in fact simply another effective anion. As can be seen from Table 6, the concentrations of L-glutamate required to effect morphological correction of the mutant were considerably lower in the present medium with 10 mM Mg^{2+} than they were in the original minimal medium (19), and the addition of Cl⁻ lowered the requirement still further. Moreover, in the presence of 0.27 mM glutamate, the morphology was directly dependent on the Mg^{2+} concentrations (Table 7). None of these morphological effects were

TABLE 5. *Effect of anions on the morphogenic effect of variable Mg^{2+} concentration[a]*

Mg^{2+} (mM)	L/D[b]				
	Cl⁻	Br⁻	I⁻	NO_3^-	CNS⁻
1		1.19	1.05	1.16	
10	1.14	2.15	2.02	1.98	1.57

[a] The concentration of the anions was 15 mM except I, which was at 5 mM.
[b] L/D = length in micrometers/diameter in micrometers. Both dimensions were measured with a Watson split-image eyepiece at a magnification of ×1,500.

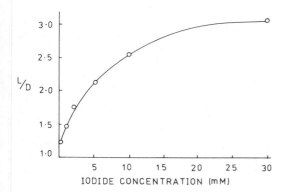

FIG. 4. *Effect of increasing concentration of KI upon the axial ratio (length/diameter) of the* rod *B cells growing in the minimal media containing 10 mM Mg²⁺ (Table 2). The dimensions of formalin cells from exponentially growing cultures were measured at a magnification of ×1,500 with a Watson split-image eyepiece.*

TABLE 7. *Effect of varying the* Mg^{2+} *in the growth medium in the presence of 0.27 mM sodium-L-glutamate upon the morphology of* rod B 104

Mg^{2+} concn (mM)	Length (L) (μm)	Diam (D) (μm)	L/D[a]
1	1.86	1.73	1.08
3	2.05	1.52	1.36
5	2.08	1.28	1.64
7	2.12	1.19	1.78
10	2.25	1.08	2.10

[a] Ratio of the lengths of the axes of the cells in micrometers.

demonstrable with the wild type. Perhaps most significant, L-aspartate that is ineffective in changing morphology as was previously found (19) will, like chloride, increase the growth rate in the presence of Mg^{2+}. Thus it would seem possible that L-glutamate functions principally as a particularly effective anion and changes the morphology in the presence of Mg^{2+} by the same mechanism as inorganic anions like I⁻ or Br⁻. There was no significant change in the wall chemistry under any of the above circumstances.

Genetic examination of these mutants shows that both the morphological changes and the requirement for Mg^{2+} are likely to be the ex-

TABLE 6. *Effect of L-glutamate and chloride ions on the morphology of* rod B 104[a]

Cl⁻ concn (mM)	L-Glutamate concn (mM)	L/D[b]	Doubling time[c] (h)
0	0	1.14	3.1
15	0	1.10	1.3
0	0.12	1.19	1.3
15	0.12	1.90	1.2
0	6.0	1.89	1.2
15	6.0	2.82	

[a] The TRM medium (see Table 2) contained 10 mM Mg^{2+} and was then supplemented with the various concentrations of sodium-L-glutamate with or without 15 mM NH_4Cl.

[b] L/D = length/diameter of cells, both in micrometers and measured with a Watson split-image eyepiece using a magnification of ×1,500.

[c] Doubling time of the mass in the culture measured by optical density.

pression of a single mutation (R. S. Buxton and H. J. Rogers, unpublished work). One further preliminary result of interest is that these mutants growing in the presence of 10 mM Mg^{2+} and 5 mM I⁻ behaved in a temperature-sensitive fashion. Grown at 30 or 35°C, the cells were entirely rods. Grown at 42°C for two to three generations, they were entirely deformed spheres (Fig. 5). In behaving thus, they mimic the *rod* A mutants.

IS THERE A PHYSIOLOGICAL EXPLANATION COMMON TO THE MORPHOLOGICAL EFFECTS OF *rod* GENES?

It is tempting to speculate along lines already suggested by Baddiley (1) and his colleagues that the role of the teichoic acids is to act as ion-exchange resins holding a ready supply of divalent cations, such as Mg^{2+}, available to the wall biosynthetic enzymes. Before considering this hypothesis, it may be useful to recall the known distribution and obviously relevant functions of Mg^{2+} in the gram-positive bacterial cell. Growing in batch culture or in continuous culture but not limited by Mg^{2+}, this cation is found in two fractions from the bacteria. Part of the fixed cation is extractable with dilute salt solutions such as 0.85% NaCl and is presumably held by ionic bonds in the walls (17, 30). The rest is firmly fixed and is stoichiometrically related to the ribosomal content (26, 29). Mg^{2+} is known to be important in maintaining ribosomal organization. Some Mg^{2+} must also be present in the membranes, since if protoplasts are suspended in media containing too little of this cation they are leaky and can lyse (18). Finally, some free ionic Mg^{2+} must presumably exist in the cytoplasm since a number of enzyme systems, including some of those concerned with synthesis of wall polymers, require this cation, although some may use ionic manganese instead.

The *rod* B strains behaved as do other mutants (15) selected as lacking Mg^{2+} uptake systems.

For example, they required very high concentrations of this ion to achieve rapid growth and were more resistant to Co²⁺ than the wild type. A deficiency in magnesium transport could reasonably explain the need both for a very high concentration of Mg^{2+} in the growth medium and for additional diffusible counter-ions like chloride. Glutamate could also serve as a counter-ion, since we have shown that it can be actively transported by *rod* B mutants as well as by the wild type. It is known that, in *B. subtilis*, at least two transport sites exist, a high-affinity site and a low one by which Mg^{2+} is co-transported with citrate (31). The relationship of the stimulation by glutamate to these two known sites and to the glutamate transport system has not yet been explored. The morphological effects controlled by Mg^{2+} in the presence of some inorganic anions and glutamate would seem to be less easily explainable on a simple transport hypothesis. The ultimate concentration of Mg^{2+} inside bacterial cells is not related to the external concentration of Mg^{2+} (11, 15) unless the growth rate is altered. Under all circumstances, the bulk of the internal Mg^{2+} is related to the RNA which is itself, of course, related to the growth rate. Two possible mechanisms exist for the action of the morphologically potentiating anions: (i) they act either more or less effectively than Cl^- as counter-ions and therefore modify the active uptake of Mg^{2+} through the membrane, thus altering the small internal concentration of free ions in the cytoplasm; (ii) the order of effectiveness of the ions is $Cl^- \ll Br < I^-$. This order corresponds both with the size of the ions and with their lipophilic character. It would seem possible that this indicates effects at the level of the cell membrane or wall. The anions might modify interactions of Mg^{2+} with the anionic phospholipid groups, thereby modifying the fluidity of the membrane by altering the lateral mobility of the phospholipids. Alternatively, because of their size, they might modify the distribution of the Mg^{2+} either within the wall or between the wall and the membrane.

One final point that might be made about the effect of Mg^{2+} in modifying the morphology of *rod* mutants concerns the *rod* D, CDP-glycerol pyrophosphorylase-deficient mutant. The Mg^{2+} requirement for maximal growth rate in the same medium as used for *rod* B mutants (see Table 2) was 0.1 mM. Its exponential growth rate was then identical to that of the wild type. When the concentration of the ion was increased to 10 to 20 mM in either this or in a rich tryptone-yeast extract medium, the shape of the cells was corrected to that

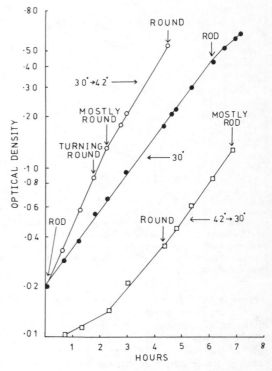

FIG. 5. *Effect on growth rate and morphology of shifting* rod B *cultures growing in minimal medium containing 10 mM Mg²⁺ and 5 mM KI from 30 to 42°C. Shifted from 30 to 42°C at zero time* (○); *kept at 30°C* (●); *shifted from 42 to 30°C at zero time* (□).

of a rod although the dimensions of the cells were not restored to those of the wild type (Rosenberger, unpublished results). Attempts to correct the morphology of *rod* A mutants growing at the restrictive temperature of 42°C have not been successful. On the other hand, the *rod* B mutants growing as rods with 5 mM I⁻ and 10 mM Mg^{2+} at 30°C were also converted to cocci by increasing the growth temperature to 45°C. Thus, the failure with *rod* A mutants may not exclude these mutants from being considered phenomena concerned with the uptake or distribution of Mg^{2+}. Further work is clearly necessary, but it seems not unreasonable to regard all the *rod* mutants of *B. subtilis* as basically disturbed in Mg^{2+} metabolism either through loss of the anionic wall polymers or more directly by loss of transport systems for the ions. In either case, the availability of the cations to the wall biosynthetic enzymes may be disturbed. Mg^{2+}, normally held in the wall by ionic linkages, may be greatly reduced or the amount involved with the membrane or in the cytoplasm may be disturbed.

REVERSION OF PROTOPLASTS OF
BACILLUS LICHENIFORMIS
TO BACILLI

Protoplasts of a number of bacteria, including *B. subtilis*, when plated not too densely on either 25% gelatin or 2.5% agar will revert quite rapidly to bacilli (13, 14). During this process, the cells gradually form walls and pass through a stage where these are of very uneven thickness, the septa running at many angles in the cells which, themselves, have bizarre shapes reminiscent in sectioned material of the *rod* mutants. Recently, we (6, 7) studied the total process of formation of wall polymers biochemically concurrently with a multiply orientated ultrastructural study. The formation of mucopeptide, of teichoic acid, and of cytoplasmic proteins proceeds exponentially and starts immediately when the protoplasts are plated on a modified DP medium of Landman et al. (14) containing 2.5% agar and are incubated at 35°C. In the early stages, patches of fine fibrils of mucopeptide can be seen arranged approximately radially around the somewhat misshapen and swollen protoplasts. Later, thick organized walls are formed with very long, thick fibers of material constituted from all of the wall polymers protruding again radially through the walls. These fibers soon disappear, and later the cells start to be organized in rod shapes and the septa ultimately become regularly spaced and at right angles to the longitudinal axis of the cells. During reversion, the average length of the glycan strands of the mucopeptide is gradually increasing, possibly because new synthetic sites are being inserted in the membrane as well as because the existing chains are extending. Likewise, the average degree of cross-linking of the peptides is increasing during reversion but reaches the same value as that in the walls of the bacilli at an earlier time than the glycan strands are completed.

From the immediate point of view of comparing *rod* mutants with the appropriate intermediate stage in the reversion of protoplasts, the following observations may be made. The latter stage approximately corresponds to the transient appearance of radial fibers of wall material. It also corresponds to a time when the apparent lengthening of the glycan chains and of cross-linking are almost complete. The latter results suggest that the insertion of new synthetic sites no longer accounts for a major part of the exponential increase in mucopeptide in the system. Presumably some extension of the existing chains is still occurring. Cross-linking is completed. Thus, the changes that occur in the morphology between 9 to 12 h of incubation, when the cells look like *rod* mutants, and 16 to 18 h, when they look like normal bacilli, involve the following: (i) the insertion of few or no more new sites for mucopeptide biosynthesis than are present in the walls of exponentially growing bacteria; (ii) no further increase in the degree of cross-linking of the mucopeptide; (iii) the disappearance of radially arranged fibrous material. One other relevant observation is that, whereas there were soluble wall materials in the medium at very early stages, these disappeared in the intermediate stages, preceding the one we are now interested in, but reappeared around this period and persisted. These soluble materials showed clear evidence of being the products of the hydrolytic action of the known autolytic enzymes. They may well be turnover products from the wall. The proportion of the total wall material formed in the system as these soluble products was much higher when the agar concentration in the medium was lowered from 2.5 to 0.8%. Reversion was also much slower and less complete. This evidence suggests that the morphological change is likely to involve a rearrangement of existing wall materials, conceivably with a change in orientation of the mucopeptide from radial to tangential, and not necessarily involving changes in rate or type of wall polymer biosynthesis. Although Mg^{2+} is known to be necessary for reversion, the exact effects of deficiencies at different stages of the process have not been studied. The rate and extent of reversion is likely to be controlled by the action of autolytic enzymes.

ACKNOWLEDGMENTS

My thanks are due to P. F. Thurman, with whom the work on magnesium requirement of *rod* B mutants was done, to C. Taylor for work on the temperature-sensitive *rod* A mutants, and to T. S. J. Elliott for suggesting the possible change of orientation of mucopeptide as an explanation of the morphological change during reversion of protoplasts.

LITERATURE CITED

1. **Baddiley, J.** 1972. Teichoic acids in cell walls and membranes of bacteria. Essays Biochem. **8**:35–77.
2. **Boylan, R. J., and N. H. Mendelson.** 1969. Initial characterization of a temperature-sensitive Rod⁻ mutant of *Bacillus subtilis*. J. Bacteriol. **100**:1316–1321.
3. **Boylan, R. J., N. H. Mendelson, D. Brooks, and F. E. Young.** 1972. Regulation of the bacterial cell wall: analysis of a mutant of *Bacillus subtilis* defective in biosynthesis of teichoic acid. J. Bacteriol. **110**:281–290.
4. **Cole, R. M., T. J. Popkin, R. J. Boylan, and N. H. Mendelson.** 1970. Ultrastructure of a temperature-

sensitive Rod⁻ mutant of *Bacillus subtilis*. J. Bacteriol. **103**:793–810.

5. **Duckworth, M., A. R. Archibald, and J. Baddiley.** 1972. The location of N-acetylgalactosamine in the walls of *Bacillus subtilis* 168. Biochem. J. **130**: 691–696.

6. **Elliott, T. S. J., J. B. Ward, and H. J. Rogers.** 1975. Formation of cell wall polymers by reverting protoplasts of *Bacillus licheniformis*. J. Bacteriol. **124**:623–632.

7. **Elliott, T. S. J., J. B. Ward, P. B. Wyrick, and H. J. Rogers.** 1975. Ultrastructural study of the reversion of protoplasts of *Bacillus licheniformis* to bacilli. J. Bacteriol. **124**:905–917.

8. **Ellwood, D. C., and D. W. Tempest.** 1969. Control of teichoic acid and teichuronic acid biosynthesis in chemostat cultures of *Bacillus subtilis* var niger. Biochem. J. **111**:1–5.

9. **Ellwood, D. C., and D. W. Tempest.** 1972. Effects of the environment on bacterial wall content and composition. Adv. Microbial Physiol. **7**:83–117.

10. **Forsberg, C. W., P. B. Wyrick, J. B. Ward, and H. J. Rogers.** 1973. Effect of phosphate limitation on the morphology and wall composition of *Bacillus licheniformis* and its phosphoglucomutase-deficient mutants. J. Bacteriol. **113**:969–984.

11. **Hurwitz, C., and C. L. Rosano.** 1967. The intracellular concentration of bound and unbound magnesium. J. Biol. Chem. **242**:3719–3722.

12. **Karamata, D., M. M. McConnell, and H. J. Rogers.** 1972. Mapping of *rod* mutants of *Bacillus subtilis*. J. Bacteriol. **111**:73–79.

13. **Landman, O. E., and S. Halle.** 1963. Enzymically and physically induced inheritance changes in *Bacillus subtilis*. J. Mol. Biol. **7**:721–738.

14. **Landman, O. E., A. Ryter, and C. Frehel.** 1968. Gelatin induced reversion of protoplasts of *Bacillus subtilis* to the bacillary form: electron microscopic and physical study. J. Bacteriol. **96**:2154–2170.

15. **Lusk, J. E., R. J. P. Williams, and E. P. Kennedy.** 1968. Magnesium and the growth of *Escherichia coli*. J. Biol. Chem. **243**:2618–2624.

16. **Martin, H. H.** 1964. Composition of the mucopolymer in cell walls of the unstable and stable L-form of *Proteus mirabilis*. J. Gen. Microbiol. **36**:441–450.

17. **Meers, J. L., and D. W. Tempest.** 1970. The influence of growth-limiting substrate and medium NaCl concentration on the synthesis of magnesium-binding sites in the walls of *Bacillus subtilis* var *niger*. J. Gen. Microbiol. **63**:325–331.

18. **Reaveley, D. A., and H. J. Rogers.** 1969. Some enzymatic and chemical properties of the mesosomes and cytoplasmic membranes of *Bacillus licheniformis* 6346. Biochem. J. **113**:67–79.

19. **Rogers, H. J., and M. M. McConnell.** 1970. The role of

glutamine in the phenotypic change of a rod mutant derived from *Bacillus subtilis* 168. J. Gen. Microbiol. **61**:173–181.

20. **Rogers, H. J., M. M. McConnell, and I. D. J. Burdett.** 1968. Cell wall or membrane mutants of *Bacillus subtilis* and *Bacillus licheniformis* with grossly deformed morphology. Nature (London) **219**:285–288.

21. **Rogers, H. J., M. M. McConnell, and I. D. J. Burdett.** 1970. The isolation and characterisation of mutants of *Bacillus subtilis* and *Bacillus licheniformis* with disturbed morphology and cell division. J. Gen. Microbiol. **61**:155–171.

22. **Rogers, H. J., M. M. McConnell, and R. C. Hughes.** 1971. The chemistry of the cell walls of *rod* mutants of *Bacillus subtilis*. J. Gen. Microbiol. **66**:297–308.

23. **Rogers, H. J., H. M. Pooley, P. F. Thurman, and C. Taylor.** 1974. Wall and membrane growth in Bacilli and their mutants. Ann. Microbiol. (Inst. Pasteur) **125B**:135–147.

24. **Rogers, H. J., P. F. Thurman, C. Taylor, and J. N. Reeve.** 1974. Mucopeptide synthesis by *rod* mutants of *Bacillus subtilis*. J. Gen. Microbiol. **85**:335–350.

25. **Sargent, M. G.** 1973. Synchronous cultures of *Bacillus subtilis* obtained by filtration with glass fiber filters. J. Bacteriol. **116**:736–740.

26. **Schmidt, G. B., C. L. Rosano, and C. Hurwitz.** 1971. Evidence for a magnesium pump in *Bacillus cereus* T. J. Bacteriol. **105**:150–155.

27. **Shibaev, U. N., M. Duckworth, A. R. Archibald, and J. Baddiley.** 1973. The structure of a polymer containing galactosamine from walls of *Bacillus subtilis*. Biochem. J. **135**:383–384.

28. **Spizizen, J.** 1968. Transformation of biochemically deficient strains of *Bacillus subtilis* by deoxyribonucleate. Proc. Natl. Acad. Sci. U.S.A. **44**:1072–1078.

29. **Tempest, D. W., J. W. Dicks, and J. L. Meers.** 1967. Magnesium-limited growth of *Bacillus subtilis* in mixed cultures in a chemostat. J. Gen. Microbiol. **49**:139–147.

30. **Tempest, D. W., and R. E. Strange.** 1966. Variation in content and distribution of magnesium and its influence on survival in *Aerobacter aerogenes* grown in a chemostat. J. Gen. Microbiol. **44**:273–279.

31. **Willecke, K., E. M. Gries, and P. Oehr.** 1973. Coupled transport of citrate and magnesium in *Bacillus subtilis*. J. Biol. Chem. **248**:807–813.

32. **Young, F. E.** 1967. Requirement of glucosylated teichoic acid for adsorption of phage in *Bacillus subtilis* 168. Proc. Natl. Acad. Sci. U.S.A. **58**:2377–2384.

33. **Young, F. E., C. Smith, and B. E. Reilly.** 1969. Chromosomal location of genes regulating resistance to bacteriophage in *Bacillus subtilis*. J. Bacteriol. **98**:1087–1097.

Mechanisms of Stability and Reversion of Mass Conversion Stable L-Forms of *Bacillus subtilis*

OTTO E. LANDMAN,[1] MARIA R. DeCASTRO-COSTA,[2] AND ENRIQUETA C. BOND[3]

Department of Biology, Georgetown University, Washington, D.C. 20007

INTRODUCTION

There is a large body of literature in bacteriology concerned with osmotically sensitive spherical or pleomorphic cells that are partly or completely devoid of cell wall. The modes of origin and the properties of these osmotically sensitive forms are quite varied. The vocabulary available to describe the necessary distinctions is very limited and the same words are often used, confusingly, to refer to different objects (8). The various forms and relationships which are at the focus of this paper are shown in Fig. 1.

The portion of the work dealing with the reversion inhibitor and the accumulation of phosphorylated intermediates formed part of a dissertation submitted by M.R.D. to Georgetown University (in 1975) in partial fulfillment of the

[1] Current temporary address: % Dr. Howard Rogers, National Institute for Medical Research, The Ridgeway, Mill Hill, London NW7 1AA, England.
[2] Present address: Ave. Marechal Gomes Da Costa 1051, Porto, Portugal 683125.
[3] Present address: Medical Sciences Dept., Southern Illinois University School of Medicine, Springfield, Ill. 62708.

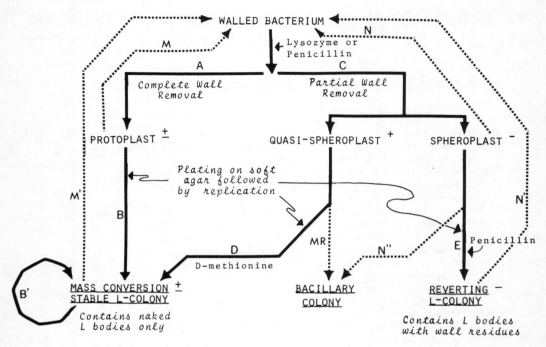

FIG. 1. *Forms and relationships among mass conversion L-forms of gram-positive and -negative bacteria. Solid lines, Pathways leading away from bacillary form; broken lines, pathways of reversion; +, occurs in gram-positive bacteria; −, occurs in gram-negative bacteria. The following are selected literature references to publications dealing with individual pathways (GP, gram positive; GN, gram negative). (i) Pathway A + B B'—14, 18 (GP); 14, 17 (GN). (ii) Pathway C + D, C + MR—14, 22, 27 (GP). (iii) Pathway C + E, N, N', N"—2, 14, 15, 20 (GN). (iv) Pathway M, M'—14, 16, 19 (GP). (v) Pathway N'—1, 14, 17 (GN).*

University's requirements for a Ph.D. degree. The portion of the work dealing with the diaminopimelic acid-lysine pathway formed part of a dissertation submitted by E.C.B. to Georgetown University (in 1969) in partial fulfillment of the University's requirements for a Ph.D. degree.

INHERITANCE OF BACTERIAL CELL WALL FOLLOWS A NON-MENDELIAN (LAMARCK-IAN) INHERITANCE PATTERN

One feature of the systems of Fig. 1 which has been of particular interest to our laboratory is their special heritability behavior. For example, when the cell wall is removed from *Bacillus subtilis* with lysozyme and the resultant protoplasts are plated on hypertonic soft agar medium, each protoplast gives rise to an L-colony consisting of wall-less, irregularly shaped L-bodies (18, 26). In a typical experiment, 2.5 L-colony-forming units (L-CFU) are liberated from each bacillus (3) (Fig. 1, pathways A and B). L-bodies from resuspended L-colonies again give rise to L-colonies in further platings (18) (Fig. 1, pathway B'). Thus, a brief transient enzyme treatment has produced an alteration in each member of the treated population—namely, wall-lessness—which is now passed

on through an indefinite number of cell generations. We call these naked offspring "mass conversion stable L-forms" (Fig. 1) (14). We are quite certain that this induced heritable change does not entail loss or gain of DNA-encoded information: for one thing, there is no case known in all of genetics where a particular environmental treatment produces identical changes in the DNA of all treated cells. However, much more importantly, we have found that the change is completely reversible—that each L-CFU (protoplast or L-body) can be induced to revert to the walled form, or in genetic terms to express again its wall-formation information content (18).

All bacterial strains that were examined experienced difficulty in restarting new wall once all the old wall had been lost. The probability of reversion is very different in different organisms. For example, *Salmonella paratyphi B* mass conversion stable L-forms revert extremely rarely (14, 17), whereas those of *Bacillus megaterium* multiply only briefly in the naked state before reverting (12–14). *B. subtilis* is intermediate in this respect: depending on the plating medium, the individual L-colonies are overgrown in 2 to 20 days by spontaneous revertants originating from within the colonies (18).

FACTORS RESPONSIBLE FOR HERITABLE PERSISTENCE OF NAKED STATE

Wall Residues Act as Primers; Absence of Wall Blocks Continuation of Wall Synthesis

If gain or loss of DNA-encoded information is ruled out as an explanation for the described changes, what then is the mechanism responsible for the long-term, heritably transmitted persistence of wall-lessness? An obvious explanation which comes to mind is that the bacteria need a preformed wall skeleton to build more wall and, as a consequence, if all of the preexisting wall is removed, the building of future wall cannot proceed. That this explanation is certainly part of the answer is indicated by the following observations. In *B. subtilis* suspensions subjected to a brief and gentle lysozyme treatment (4 to 20 μg of lysozyme per ml for 40 min [pathway C of Fig. 1]), a part of the population could be "caught" at the "quasi-spheroplast" stage, a stage where the cells are osmotically sensitive and have assumed spherical shape, and yet still possess wall residues clearly visible in the electron microscope.

If the quasi-spheroplasts were placed on HT medium (27), they gave rise to bacillary colonies (Fig. 1, pathway MR); however, when the cell wall growth inhibitor D-methionine (7, 23) was added to the same medium, they gave rise to L-colonies (Fig. 1, pathway D) (22, 27). Bacilli gave identical plating results on these two media. Yet, in the quasi-spheroplasts the slight inhibition by D-methionine determined that the extant wall residue was shed or autolyzed, that wall rebuilding did not occur, and that future cell propagation proceeded in the naked state.

The concept that the presence of wall residues is a key factor in permitting prompt wall repair after withdrawal of penicillin or lysozyme was also important in understanding the behavior of spheroplasts and reverting L-bodies of gram-negative bacteria (Fig. 1, pathways E, N, N', and N''). These cells retained both lipoprotein and lipopolysaccharide constituents of their wall (often called "outer membrane") (14). Once penicillin or lysozyme was withdrawn, reversion (i.e., wall repair) occurred promptly (2, 15, 20).

To Revert, Naked Cells Must First Be "Conditioned" to a Special Metabolic State

Early in our studies with protoplasts and L-bodies, we discovered that 25% gelatin media were extremely effective in promoting their reversion to the bacillary form (18). As a result of detailed studies, optimal conditions were determined such that 80 to 100% of the inoculated protoplasts or L-bodies reverted within 1 h after transfer to 20 to 25% gelatin medium. In experi-

mental terms this statement means that, at zero time, a properly conditioned suspension of protoplasts plated on HT medium will give rise only to L-colonies, but that, after a 60-min sojourn in 25% gelatin medium, 80 to 100% of the same cells will give rise to bacillary colonies on HT medium (16).

Only protoplasts which were conditioned by 60 to 90 min of incubation in 0.40% casein hydrolysate medium (step 1) gave such efficient reversion; control protoplasts conditioned in the absence of casein hydrolysate, or in casein hydrolysate with chloramphenicol or puromycin, or bacilli protoplasted after casein hydrolysate incubation did not start to revert in gelatin for 3 to 4 h after inoculation. Conditioning, then, means prolonged exposure to a protein synthesis-promoting environment (16). We do not have direct evidence concerning the nature of the preparation for reversion that is made by the protoplasts during conditioning. Most likely, this treatment modifies the naked cells so that they produce wall precursors at a maximal rate during the next step, step 2, incubation in gelatin.

Diffusible Reversion Inhibitor Prevents Reversion at Moderate and High Protoplast Concentrations During Step 2

Discovery of the inhibitor; the inhibitor is a protein (called RIP). To understand the persistence of the L state and the resumption of wall building during reversion, an understanding of the biochemical-molecular events during step 1 and step 2 is essential. At the outset of our recent experiments concerning the early phases of wall deposition during step 2, we had to contend with two formidable difficulties. (i) The reverting cells were embedded in 25% gelatin and, for most chemical and tracer analyses, had to be separated cleanly from this sticky, viscous material. (ii) Synchronous, rapid reversion occurred only at cell concentrations of 10^6 protoplasts/ml or below. Even at concentrations of 10^7 CFU/ml in the gelatin, reversion was delayed for hours (16, 19; DeCastro-Costa and Landman, submitted for publication). In sum, chemical study or reversion required recovery of fragile cells from very dilute suspension and from many liters of (radioactive) 25% gelatin media.

In an attempt to bypass these problems, we undertook a study of the reversion inhibition phenomenon. The possibility seemed remote that a micronutrient required for reversion might already be limiting at a cell concentration of 10^7 CFU/ml; hence, the obvious possibility was that the protoplasts were releasing a reversion inhibitor. This was soon verified in experiments with protoplast extracts: an extract corresponding to 10^8 protoplasts/ml prevented

TABLE 1. *Effect of trypsin, chloramphenicol, and β-mercaptoethanol on reversion*

Line no.	Pretreatment:[a] trypsin, 250 μg/ml	Treatment:[b]		Reversion[c] (%)	
		Chloramphenicol, 100 μg/ml	β-Mercaptoethanol, 1,140 μg/ml	2×10^7 CFU/ml of gelatin	2×10^6 CFU/ml of gelatin
1	−	−	−	1.7	11.3
2	+	−	−	4.1	73.9
3	−	+	−	45.8	75.2
4	+	+	−	78.1	89.8
5	−	−	+	0.7	6.1
6	+	−	+	4.3	15.0
7	−	+	+	4.8	20.3
8	+	+	+	78.5	76.5

[a] Pretreatment administered at the end of conditioning incubation in 0.40% casein hydrolysate medium (step 1).
[b] Reagents present in gelatin medium throughout the incubation period of 1 h (step 2).
[c] 1.7% reversion means that 1.7% of the suspended cells formed bacillary colonies and 98.3% formed L-colonies. The total cell number did not change.

reversion in dilute protoplast suspensions in gelatin medium. The inhibitor in the extract was non-dialyzable, heat sensitive, sensitive to 0.4% sodium lauryl sulfate (but insensitive to 0.1% Triton X-100), and sensitive to trypsin and Pronase, and thus, obviously, was a protein or protein-containing material (M. R. DeCastro-Costa, Ph.D. thesis, Georgetown University, Washington, D.C., 1975). We called it reversion-inhibitory protein (RIP).

Destruction of the RIP by trypsin stimulates reversion. The sensitivity of the RIP to proteinases suggested that it might be possible to destroy the diffusing inhibitor molecules on the way to their target cells. Fortunately, *B. subtilis* protoplasts proved to be quite insensitive to trypsin: in the presence of 600 μg of trypsin per ml, not only did the protoplasts maintain full viability but, as we had hoped, their reversion was stimulated markedly. For example, 60% of the cells suspended at a density of 10^7 CFU/ml reverted in the presence of 600 μg of trypsin per ml, whereas less than 5% reverted in the same suspension without added trypsin.

The stimulation of reversion attainable in this system by trypsin action was limited by the extreme sensitivity of the cells to the RIP which is being produced continuously, and also, we think, because much of the trypsin is bound to the gelatin which is a substrate for trypsin. A more effective way of eliminating the RIP from the system was to use a combination of measures—to pretreat the conditioned protoplasts with trypsin (after step 1) and then to add chloramphenicol to the gelatin medium during step 2 to block further biosynthesis of the RIP (Table 1, compare lines 1 to 4). (Well-conditioned protoplasts were not inhibited in their reversion by the presence of chloramphenicol during step 2 since peptidoglycan synthesis does not require concomitant protein synthesis [9, 16].)

Secretion of inactive RIP can explain reversion inhibition of target cell and non-inhibition of source cell; activation of RIP by β-mercaptoethanol. The diffusing inhibitor hypothesis raised an important question: how can a source cell release a "cloud" of inhibitor molecules which prevent wall synthesis at a target cell about 44 cell radii distant from the source cell and yet not be prevented itself from reverting? (At a cell concentration of 10^7 CFU/ml, a protoplast of radius 1 μm and volume approximately 4 μm³ was an average of about 44 μm distant from its neighbor protoplasts. Molecules of the RIP contained in the 4-μm³ sphere were diluted by a factor of approximately 90,000 when they were evenly distributed throughout a sphere of 44-μm³ radius.) Probably the source cell was releasing the RIP in an inactive form and this protein became activated only after it had gained enough distance from its source cell so that a buildup of active inhibitor near its surface was avoided. Attempting to find experimental evidence for activation, we tested the effect of β-mercaptoethanol, an activator for many reactions involving SH groups. Marked inhibition of reversion by β-mercaptoethanol was observed, presumably due to activation of the RIP (Table 1, lines 5–8). As one would predict, the β-mercaptoethanol effect was least evident in cells which had been most effectively "cleansed" of RIP by the dual treatment with trypsin and chloramphenicol (compare lines 4 and 8, Table 1). In singly treated cells, the effect of mercaptoethanol treatment was considerable (compare lines 3 and 7, and 2 and 6 of Table 1).

The RIP may be an autolysin. What is the nature of the RIP and its mechanism of action? We know, from earlier electron microscope studies and studies with antibiotics and other inhibitors, that the principal reversion activity occurring during step 2 is deposition of peptidoglycan wall (16, 19). The RIP is therefore most probably

TABLE 2. *Effect of cell walls with and without autolysin on reversion*

Type of wall prepn added	Amt (mg dry wt/ml)	Amidase content (U)[a]	Reversion (%) 3×10^7 CFU/ml	2×10^6 CFU/ml	2×10^5 CFU/ml
None			2.0	7.0	42.9
Walls with autolysin	0.75	7.3	0.8	3.7	10.8
Detergent-treated, autoclaved walls	1.0		9.1	28.6	55.8

[a] A unit of amidase is the amount of enzyme required to produce a (linear) decline of 0.001 optical density (450 nm) units/min at 35 C in a suspension of 2 mg of lyophilized cell wall per ml of 0.05 M sodium carbonate buffer (pH 9.5).

destroying either nascent peptidoglycan, intermediates, or enzymes involved in its synthesis. As was already shown earlier by Forsberg and Ward, protoplasts and L-forms of *Bacillus licheniformis* produce and excrete *N*-acetyl-muramyl-L-alanine amidase (6), the chief autolysin of this organism and also that of its close relative, *B. subtilis*. Autolysins are thought to be involved in wall extension, wall turnover, and cell separation of several bacteria, including *B. subtilis* (25). An autolysin is thus a very plausible candidate for our inhibitor, and we made attempts to determine whether the RIP and autolysin are one and the same. Some of our results are shown in Table 2. This table shows that an ordinary cell wall preparation, which contains a considerable amount of autolysin, inhibited reversion at all protoplast concentrations tested (line 2), whereas a cell wall preparation made in the presence of detergent and autoclaved to inactivate all of the autolysin stimulated reversion at all protoplast concentrations (line 3). Such a stimulation is predicted if the RIP has a high affinity for cell wall, as autolysin does (6, 10, 25), and the added wall offers binding sites to the RIP to compete with the sites on the nascent cell wall of the reverting protoplasts. Added wall would not be expected to mitigate reversion inhibition if the RIP were a proteinase. In separate experiments, we also found that cell wall preparations adsorb out RIP activity from crude cell extracts and, in the process, gain in autolytic activity. In sum, we believe our present data support the idea that RIP and autolysin are one and the same, but final proof of this matter remains for the future.

MECHANISMS IN REVERSION

Requirement for a Physically Solid Surface During Reversion Can Be Bypassed if the Reversion Inhibitor Is Partly Removed

Early experiments indicated that the availability of a physically solid surface was an important factor in the induction of reversion (5, 16, 18). After our discovery of the RIP, we reinvestigated the requirement for 25% gelatin under conditions in which the RIP concentration was sharply reduced by trypsin. Results are shown in Table 3. In the presence of 500 μg of trypsin per ml, 60% of the inoculated protoplasts reverted within 1 h in 10% gelatin medium. At 38°C, this medium was only slightly viscous and certainly far from solid. We inferred that the stimulation of reversion by special solid environments was probably due to the ability of these environments to modify the activity of the RIP by altering the diffusion dynamics near the protoplast surface.

The RIP Is Limiting the Rate of Reversion in L-Colonies Growing in Soft Agar Media

The L-forms of *B. subtilis* could be maintained in the L state indefinitely through fairly frequent transfers in osmotically stabilized soft agar media such as DP medium. On this medium, reversion occurred also, however; it began after 3 to 4 days of incubation at 30°C. Characteristically, several L-bodies started to make wall, and their rapidly multiplying progeny overgrew the L-colony. Reversion on 0.7% agar differed from reversion in gelatin in several respects: for example, conditioning was not discernibly involved, reversion was not synchronized and very much slower, and D-methionine inhibited agar reversion but not gelatin-induced reversion. In view of the key role played by the RIP in the gelatin reversion system, it was of interest to determine whether it also influenced reversion in L-colonies. To test

TABLE 3. *Modification of the requirement for gelatin for reversion when the reversion inhibitor is destroyed by trypsin*

Gelatin concn (% wt/vol)	Reversion[a] (%) With trypsin	Without trypsin
25	15	13
20	31	14
15	46	8
10	60	6
5	6	4

[a] Experimental conditions: cell concentration, 10^7 CFU/ml; 500 μg of trypsin per ml; 38°C. Incubation in gelatin media for 1 h.

this question, various concentrations of trypsin or Pronase were incorporated into soft agar media inoculated with protoplasts or were spotted on media 17 h after inoculation. The result was that marked stimulation of reversion occurred. Evidently the RIP can be the rate-limiting factor controlling the reversion rate of L colonies in agar medium.

AN INTEGRATED, SPECULATIVE PICTURE OF THE STABILITY AND THE MECHANISM OF REVERSION OF *B. SUBTILIS* MASS CONVERSION STABLE L-FORMS

Assumptions. To simplify the task of developing a self-consistent view of *B. subtilis* L-form stability and reversion, we accepted certain inferences drawn from the above data in the full realization that future research may not sustain them. In particular, we assumed that the RIP is in fact the amidase, that the various trypsin effects are primarily due to the destruction of the RIP, and that the mercaptoethanol effect is chiefly due to the activation of the amidase. (The autolysin of several group H streptococci is activated by β-mercaptoethanol [24]).

Lipoteichoic acid. A recent publication by Höltje and Tomasz furnished data and concepts important to our hypotheses concerning gelatin reversion (10). These authors provided evidence that, in pneumococcus, a membrane lipoteichoic acid (LTA) preparation is an effective inhibitor of the autolysin amidase. Further, they showed that the amidase has greater affinity for wall teichoic acid (WTA) than for LTA and that it is activated when WTA is added to the inactive autolysin-LTA mixture. Similarly, the N-acetyl-muramidases of both *Streptococcus faecalis* and *Lactobacillus acidophilus* were inhibited by purified LTAs from several bacterial species (4a). A recent review on LTA by Wicken and Knox added further detail to this picture (28). It appears that, in many gram-positive bacteria, LTA is released in considerable quantity from the membrane surface, passing through the cell wall into the culture fluid. Protoplasts of *S. faecalis* release LTA (11), and so does the bacillary form of *B. subtilis* (A. J. Wicken, personal communication); whether *B. subtilis* protoplasts or L-forms release LTA has not been investigated.

Drawing on the foregoing experimental findings, inferences, and results from the literature, we developed the following tentative and speculative picture of protoplast (L-form) stability and reversion in *B. subtilis*.

Mechanism of Stability and Reversion

Basically, the mechanism of stability is that, once the cell wall is removed completely, secre-tion of autolysin (RIP) prevents accumulation of the threshold level of peptidoglycan (the primer) which is necessary to set rapid wall synthesis in motion. Reversion occurs when the balance between the antagonistic processes of peptidoglycan extrusion from the membrane surface and peptidoglycan hydrolysis by autolysin shifts in favor of peptidoglycan accumulation. This shift can be accomplished by (i) increasing the rate of peptidoglycan synthesis and/or accretion, (ii) lowering the quantity of the autolysin, or (iii) lowering the activity of the autolysin at the cell surface. Gelatin medium must somehow act to shift this balance in favor of peptidoglycan accumulation. How can it do this?

(i) Concerning the possibility of an increase in peptidoglycan synthesis or accretion due to the gelatin medium, we believe that well-conditioned protoplasts produce peptidoglycan at a rapid rate, regardless of whether gelatin is present or not. This belief is based on the finding that reversion occurs very rapidly in near-liquid media in the presence of trypsin. (Protoplasts of streptococci have been shown by direct chemical analysis to extrude large amounts of peptidoglycan chain in liquid suspension [25a].)

(ii) Could gelatin medium cause a lowering in the quantity of autolysin accumulating at the cell surface? Since gelatin obviously has the effect of slowing diffusion rather than increasing the diffusion rate, it is predicted that, in gelatin medium, a larger-than-normal quantity of autolysin should accumulate near the source cell. Such an accumulation should lead to more rapid peptidoglycan destruction, not to primer formation.

(iii) We are thus left with the third alternative, that autolysin activity is lower in the presence of gelatin. We postulate that most of the autolysin (the RIP) which is accumulating near the source cell in the gelatin is inactive because it is associated with LTA in a complex. (LTA is also being secreted by the source cell.) As the LTA-autolysin complexes diffuse outward from the source cell to a region of lowered LTA concentration, they dissociate and the autolysin is activated. In this way we can explain the finding that the RIP does not prevent reversion of its source cell whereas it blocks reversion of a distant target cell. In this scheme, β-mercaptoethanol activation of the RIP might be due simply to enhanced dissociation of the LTA-autolysin complex. (We must assume that reassociation of the LTA-autolysin complex does not occur freely, otherwise the autolysin would be again rendered inactive in the vicinity of the target cell. Perhaps, after dissociation and activation, a conformational change occurs in the autolysin so that it can no longer readily reassociate with LTA).

The foregoing picture provides an explanation of events during the phase of reversion when wall synthesis is initiated and a primary quantity of new wall accumulates. However, substantial areas of ignorance remain concerning other phases of reversion. For example, we know that after wall building the reverted cells require a period of protein synthesis to gain the ability to survive on low-osmotic-strength media. The nature of the process for acquisition of osmotic stability is unknown (16). Furthermore, substantial time intervenes between reversion and recovery of normal morphology, especially septation (16, 21). Again, we know very little concerning the mechanism whereby the normal morphogenetic mechanisms recover their function.

DIFFERENCES BETWEEN BACILLARY AND PROTOPLAST METABOLISM IN RELATION TO REVERSION CONDITIONING

Our understanding of the phase of reversion preceding the building of wall primer (step 1 conditioning) is similarly fragmentary. As indicated earlier, conditioning for reversion requires 60 to 90 min of protein and RNA synthesis, but we do not know how this macromolecular synthesis later promotes reversion during step 2.

Accumulation and Excretion of Phosphorylated Intermediates

To explore the effect of the conditioning treatment on protoplasts and, if possible, to detect UDP-activated peptidoglycan precursors, we compared the phosphorylated pool constituents of bacilli with those of protoplasts incubating in high-casein hydrolysate (conditioning) media. A sensitive method was used involving polyethyleneimine (PEI) cellulose chromatography of highly radioactive (^{32}P) cold 1 M formic acid extracts of the walled and wall-less cells (4). Table 4 documents one of the intriguing results of these studies, namely, that high levels of RNA nucleoside triphosphates accumulate in suspensions of protoplasts after conditioning whereas no such accumulation occurs in control bacillary suspensions. This buildup of high nucleoside triphosphate pools in the conditioned protoplasts may well be related to a slowdown in RNA synthesis which occurs in these cells at about the same time. We observed this slowdown in separate experiments comparing [^{3}H]uridine incorporation into the cold trichloroacetic acid-insoluble fraction of protoplasts and bacilli. Protoplasts incubating in medium without casein hydrolysate did not show a slowdown in RNA synthesis relative to the bacillary controls and also had substantially

TABLE 4. *Comparison of nucleoside triphosphate pool accumulation in protoplasts and bacilli incubating in conditioning medium*[a]

Identification of spot	(Counts per min/spot [protoplast extract])/ (counts per min/spot [bacillary extract])			
	10 min[b]	30 min[b]	60 min[b]	90 min[b]
GTP	0.57	0.48	1.63	3.81
ATP	1.24	1.33	2.56	7.56
CTP	1.18	0.94	1.55	3.12
UTP	0.77	0.58	1.74	—
?[c]	0.95	1.06	1.30	6.40

[a] A 1-ml volume of culture at 2×10^8 CFU/ml in 0.4% casein hydrolysate-0.7 mM phosphate-0.66 M sucrose medium was divided into two aliquots, lysozyme was added to a final concentration of 250 μg/ml to one of them, and both aliquots were incubated for 1 h at 34°C. A 400-μCi amount of H^{32}PO$_4$ was added to each tube, and incubation was continued. At the times shown, 50-μl samples were pipetted into 50 μl of 2 M formic acid and stored in an ice bath. A 5-μl volume of the centrifugation supernatant of these samples was subsequently spotted on PEI cellulose sheets and chromatographed along with known standards. The radioactive spots (detected by overnight exposure to X-ray film) were cut out, and the radioactivity was measured by Cerenkov radiation. Assuming that the specific radioactivity of the phosphorus in each phosphorylated pool constituent was the same as the specific radioactivity of the phosphorus in the medium, the absolute amount of phosphorus in each spot on the chromatograms could be determined. Estimates were made of moles of ATP, GTP, etc., per cell (DeCastro-Costa and Landman, manuscript in preparation).
[b] Time of incubation with ^{32}P.
[c] Approximate $R_f = 0.866$.

lower levels of nucleoside triphosphate pools than the conditioned protoplasts.

Conditioned protoplasts also differed from bacilli in their active transport behavior. When analyses of ^{32}P metabolites were done separately on protoplast and bacillary pellets and the conditioning medium in which they had been incubated, it was discovered that the conditioned protoplasts (but not the bacillary controls) had excreted substantial quantities of different phosphorylated intermediates. For example, 5% of the total accumulated ATP, 21% of CTP, and 69% of an unidentified metabolite were in the supernatant fraction 60 min after addition of ^{32}PO$_4$ (M. R. DeCastro-Costa, Ph.D. thesis, Georgetown University, Washington, D.C., 1975).

Modified Response of the Aspartate-Dpm-Lysine Pathway Resulting from Wall Removal

Several years ago, in probing to find an explanation for the heritable persistence of the wall-less condition of mass conversion stable L-

TABLE 5. *Labeled aspartate, diaminopimelic acid, and lysine in whole cell hydrolysates of B. subtilis bacilli and L-forms on semidefined medium in presence of [³H]acetate*

Cell type	Dilution spotted	Amt spotted (µl)	cpm		
			In aspartate spot	In Dpm spot	In lysine spot
Bacilli[a]	1[b]	5		838	
Bacilli	1:50	5	182		638
L-forms[c]	1	50		0	
L-forms	1:50	5	117		0

[a] Bacillary colonies (2.25×10^2) were suspended and hydrolyzed.

[b] Using very concentrated hydrolysates, the separation of lysine on the chromatograms was poor; a 1:50 dilution gave good separation of lysine and aspartate.

[c] L-colonies (2.25×10^4) were suspended and hydrolyzed. There was somewhat more bacillary material than L material. The specific activity of aspartate in the two cell types is fairly similar.

forms, we performed experiments to determine whether cells continued to produce cell wall precursor after removal of the cell wall or whether, perhaps, failure of wall precursor biosynthesis was a factor in preventing reversion (E. C. Bond, Ph.D. thesis, Georgetown University, Washington, D.C., 1969; E. C. Bond and O. E. Landman, Bacteriol. Proc., 1970, G141, p. 36).

Extensive experiments were carried out to find diaminopimelic acid (Dpm) in protoplasts and L-forms. Incubation media (sometimes 10-fold concentrated) were also examined. The outcome of these experiments was that no Dpm was detected in the wall-less forms or in medium supernatants. Comparing whole cell hydrolysates of protoplasts, L-forms, and bacilli, our most sensitive procedures would have detected it if the protoplasts or L-forms had contained 1/500 to 1/1,000 times as much DAP as the bacilli. The presence of about 0.1 µg of Dpm per ml in the medium (free or combined) could have been detected had it been present. Since Dpm is the direct precursor of lysine in *B. subtilis*, these results raised the question of whether wall removal caused loss of ability to synthesize lysine in this organism. The experiment shown in Table 5 was done to answer this question. Bacilli and L-forms were grown in parallel in 0.5 M succinate-stabilized "semisynthetic" soft agar medium with radioactive acetate (the only undefined ingredient in this medium was 2% purified pigskin gelatin). The two types of colonies were harvested, freed of most of the agar, and hydrolyzed, the hydrolysates were chromatogramed, the spots were cut out, and

their radioactivity was measured. Table 5 shows that the specific radioactivity of aspartate, a Dpm precursor, is about the same in walled and wall-less cells, whereas no radioactivity is present in either the Dpm or lysine spots. All lysine in the L-form hydrolysates must therefore be derived from the pigskin gelatin. The most obvious explanation of this drastically reduced flow in the Dpm-lysine pathway is that the pathway is repressed as a result of wall removal (failure to sequester Dpm into its normal site, the totally insoluble cell wall sink,'' could reasonably be expected to alter pool levels and, hence, repression equilibria). So far, our experiments do not provide support for repression. Our colleague, A. Hirvonen, compared Dpm decarboxylase activities in protoplasts, L-forms, and bacilli and found all of them to exhibit similar specific activities (Hirvonen and Landman, unpublished data). The apparent shutoff of the Dpm-lysine pathway in L-forms (also in protoplasts; data not shown) is not absolute. For one thing, protoplasts can grow out into L-colonies on completely defined medium devoid of lysine. Accordingly, the lysine block is leaky. Furthermore, as reported earlier in this paper, well-primed protoplasts can revert rapidly in liquid media and must therefore be presumed to produce substantial amounts of (Dpm-containing) peptidoglycan. In other bacteria, extrusion of peptidoglycan chains from protoplasts has been directly demonstrated (25a).

Taking the data as a whole, we are led to infer that wall removal induces a reduced flow in the Dpm-lysine pathway, contingent upon the state of conditioning of the cell or the growth medium.

Conditioning and Reversion

The differences between protoplast metabolism and bacillary metabolism described in the two preceding sections show that wall removal causes fairly substantial metabolic changes in *B. subtilis*. It is plausible to regard conditioning as a procedure which redresses some of these, bringing the cells to a state where rapid wall biosynthesis can again occur. To understand reversion of mass conversion L-forms adequately, a fuller knowledge of these metabolic shifts is required.

ACKNOWLEDGMENTS

This work was supported by successor grants GB 7204 and GB 27606 from the National Science Foundation and by Public Health Service grant AI 05972 from the National Institutes of Health to O.E.L. M.R.D. was a predoctoral fellow of the Calouste Gulbenkian Foundation and held at a University Fellowship from Georgetown University. E.C.B. was supported for two years by Predoctoral Fellowships from the National Institutes of Health. We thank

Michael Cashel, of the National Institutes of Health, for advice and for extending the hospitality of his laboratory in conjunction with the measurement of pools of phosphorylated intermediates.

LITERATURE CITED

1. **Altenbern, R. A.** 1961. Critical factors influencing growth of L forms of *Proteus mirabilis*. J. Bacteriol. **81**:586–594.
2. **Altenbern, R. A.** 1963. Reversion of L forms and spheroplasts of *Proteus mirabilis*. J. Bacteriol. **85**: 269–272.
3. **Breakefield, X. O., and O. E. Landman.** 1973. Temperature-sensitive divisionless mutant of *Bacillus subtilis* defective in the initiation of septation. J. Bacteriol. **113**:985–998.
4. **Cashel, M., R. A. Lazzarini, and B. Kalbacher.** 1969. An improved method for thin-layer chromatography of nucleotide mixtures containing ^{32}P-labeled orthophosphate. J. Chromatog. **40**:103–109.
4a. **Cleveland, R. F., J. V. Höltje, A. J. Wicken, A. Tomasz, L. Daneo-Moore, and G. D. Shockman.** 1975. Inhibition of bacterial cell lysins by lipoteichoic acids and related compounds. Biochem. Biophys. Res. Commun. **67**: 1128–1135.
5. **Clive, D., and O. E. Landman.** 1970. Reversion of *Bacillus subtilis* protoplasts to the bacillary form induced by exogenous cell walls, bacteria and by growth in membrane filters. J. Gen. Microbiol. **61**:233–243.
6. **Forsberg, C. W., and J. B. Ward.** 1972. *N*-acetylmuramyl-L-alanine amidase of *Bacillus licheniformis* and its L-form. J. Bacteriol. **110**:878–888.
7. **Ghuysen, J. M., and G. D. Shockman.** 1973. Biosynthesis of peptidoglycan, p. 37–130. *In* L. Leive (ed.), Bacterial membranes and walls. Marcel Dekker Inc., New York.
8. **Guze, L. B.** 1968. Preface, p. VII–VIII. *In* L. B. Guze (ed.), Microbial protoplasts, spheroplasts and L forms. The Williams and Wilkins Co., Baltimore.
9. **Higgins, M. L., L. Daneo-Moore, D. Boothby, and G. D. Shockman.** 1974. Effect of inhibition of deoxyribonucleic acid and protein synthesis on the direction of cell wall growth in *Streptococcus faecalis*. J. Bacteriol. **118**:681–692.
10. **Höltje, J.-V., and A. Tomasz.** 1975. Lipoteichoic acid: a specific inhibitor of autolysin activity in *Pneumococcus*. Proc. Natl. Acad. Sci. U.S.A. **72**:1690–1694.
11. **Joseph, R., and G. D. Shockman.** 1975. The cellular localization of lipoteichoic acid in *Streptococcus faecalis* ATCC9790. J. Bacteriol. **122**:1375–1386.
12. **Kawakami, M., and O. E. Landman.** 1966. Retention of episomes during protoplasting and during propagation in the L state. J. Bacteriol. **92**:398–404.
13. **Kusaka, I.**, 1967. Growth and division of protoplasts of *Bacillus megaterium* and inhibition of division by penicillin. J. Bacteriol. **94**:884–888.
14. **Landman, O. E.** 1968. Protoplasts, spheroplasts and L forms viewed as a genetic system, p. 319–332. *In*
15. **Landman, O. E., R. A. Altenbern, and H. S. Ginoza.** 1958. Quantitative conversion of cells and protoplasts of *Proteus mirabilis* and *Escherichia coli* to the L-form. J. Bacteriol. **75**:567–575.
16. **Landman, O. E., and A. Forman.** 1969. Gelatin-induced reversion of protoplasts of *Bacillus subtilis* to the bacillary form: biosynthesis of macromolecules and wall during successive steps. J. Bacteriol. **99**:576–589.
17. **Landman, O. E., and H. S. Ginoza.** 1961. Genetic nature of stable L forms of *Salmonella paratyphi B*. J. Bacteriol. **81**:875–886.
18. **Landman, O. E., and S. Halle.** 1963. Enzymically and physically induced inheritance changes in *Bacillus subtilis*. J. Mol. Biol. **7**:721–738.
19. **Landman, O. E., A. Ryter, and C. Frehel.** 1968. Gelatin-induced reversion of protoplasts of *Bacillus subtilis* to the bacillary form: electron-microscope and physical study. J. Bacteriol. **96**:2154–2170.
20. **Lederberg, J., and J. St. Clair.** 1958. Protoplasts and L-type growth of *Escherichia coli*. J. Bacteriol. **75**: 143–160.
21. **Miller, I. L., W. Wiebe, and O. E. Landman.** 1968. Gelatin-induced reversion of protoplasts of *Bacillus subtilis* to the bacillary form: photomicrographic study. J. Bacteriol. **96**:2171–2174.
22. **Miller, I. L., R. M. Zsigray, and O. E. Landman.** 1967. The formation of protoplasts and quasi-spheroplasts in normal and chloramphenicol-pretreated *Bacillus subtilis*. J. Gen. Microbiol. **69**:513–525.
23. **Neuhaus, F. C., and W. G. Struve.** 1965. Enzymatic synthesis of analogs of the cell wall precursor. I. Kinetics and specificity of uridine diphospho-N-acetylmuramyl-l-alanyl-D-glutamyl-L-lysine: D-alanyl-D-alanine ligase (adenosine diphosphate) from *Streptococcus faecalis R*. Biochemistry **4**:120–131.
24. **Ranhand, J. M.** 1974. Inhibition of the development of competence in *Streptococcus sanguis* (Wicky) by reagents that interact with sulfhydryl groups: discernment of the competence process. J. Bacteriol. **118**:1041–1050.
25. **Rogers, H. J., H. M. Pooley, P. F. Thurman, and C. Taylor.** 1974. Wall and membrane growth in bacilli and their mutants. Ann. Microbiol. (Inst. Pasteur) **125B**:135–147.
25a. **Rosenthal, R. S., D. Junkind, L. Daneo-Moore, and G. D. Shockman.** 1975. Evidence for the synthesis of soluble peptidoglycan fragments by protoplsts of *Streptococcus faecalis*. J. Bacteriol. **124**:398–409.
26. **Ryter, A., and O. E. Landman.** 1964. Electron microscope study of the relationship between mesosome loss and the stable L state (or protoplast state) in *Bacillus subtilis*. J. Bacteriol. **88**:457–467.
27. **Tichy, P., and O. E. Landman.** 1969. Transformation in quasi spheroplasts of *Bacillus subtilis*. J. Bacteriol. **97**:42–51.
28. **Wicken, A. J., and K. W. Knox.** 1975. Lipoteichoic acids: a new class of bacterial antigens. Science **187**: 1161–1167.

Zones of Cell Wall Enlargement in *Bacillus subtilis*

R. J. DOYLE, U. N. STREIPS, AND J. R. HELMAN

Department of Microbiology and Immunology, University of Louisville Schools of Medicine and Dentistry, Louisville, Kentucky 40201

INTRODUCTION

It is axiomatic to consider that bacteria divide in an orderly and reproducible manner. This implies a coordinate synthesis of protein and informational macromolecules along with cell wall and membrane components. In each bacterium, there must be some means of conserving surface components so that they are properly distributed to daughter cells. It has been shown in many bacteria that surface molecules are turned over during cell division so that daughter cells do not inherit exactly one-half of the surface structures of the mother cell. Turnover may be necessary for septum formation and the subsequent modification of cross walls to form caps. Basically, three modes of surface inheritance are possible in bacterial cells, as shown in Fig. 1 for rod-shaped organisms. No evidence exists showing the possibility of conservative surface growth. Thus, the choice lies between the semiconservative mode and the random mode. There is no consistency in the literature on this point with regard to rod-shaped bacteria. On the other hand, in streptococci, wall growth occurs at restricted, well-defined sites at regions of septation (see review by Shockman et al. [29]).

Recently, considerable attention has been given to the role of cell wall in bacterial division. Hirota et al. (14) have proposed a model for cell division in *Escherichia coli* which assumes that the cell wall acts as a primitive mitotic apparatus. In this model, peptidoglycan synthesis occurs in the central zone of the cell and is turned off when DNA replication is complete. Additional wall synthesis can then occur, resulting in septum formation. Thus, in the proposed model, the zones of cell elongation are restricted to the equatorial portions of the cell cylinders. In addition, the model is consistent with the replicon hypothesis of Jacob et al. (16), which assumes that membrane growth also occurs at equatorial regions. In spite of the foregoing, several papers have been published supporting random wall synthesis in *E. coli*. For example, pulse-chase experiments, followed by autoradiography, indicate that newly synthesized peptidoglycan and other surface components are distributed over a large number of sites (17, 24, 31). Moreover, several sites on the surface of *E. coli* appear to be penicillin sensitive (1). Thus, there is conflict in the literature concerning how surface components are distributed after cell division in *E. coli*.

The conflict is even more apparent when *Bacil-*

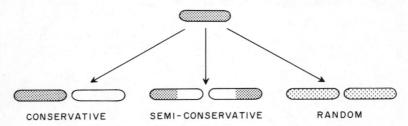

FIG. 1. *Possible inheritance profiles of cell surface molecules in a rod-shaped bacterium.*

TABLE 1. *Surface changes accompanying cell division in* Bacillus *species*

Organism	Expt	Reference
B. subtilis and B. cereus	Fully developed flagella were observed at only one cell pole. Flagella were absent from the other pole or were not fully developed.	3
B. cereus	Cells were permitted to grow in the presence of fluorescent anti-whole cell antibody. New growth areas (unstained) appeared near the poles.	4
B. megaterium	Cells were permitted to grow in the presence of fluorescent anti-whole cell antibody. New growth appeared at one pole and in the center of the cell cylinder.	4
B. anthracis	Stationary-phase cells (encapsulated) were shifted to new growth medium. Subsequent lack of capsular staining was observed in equatorial regions.	23
B. subtilis	Cells were labeled with TeO_3^- and permitted to grow. Sections showed Te crystals at poles, indicating central growth origin of membrane.	27
B. megaterium	Membrane phospholipid was labeled with $[^3H]$- or $[^{14}C]$palmitic acid and examined by autoradiography. Membrane growth was found at one of the poles.	25
B. licheniformis	Cells were grown in rabbit antipeptidoglycan, washed, and then incubated with fluorescent anti-rabbit immunoglobulin. Results show staining on cylinders but not on cross walls.	15
B. cereus	Wall thickened by addition of chloramphenicol; cells were washed and placed in new growth medium. Cells showed random loss of thickened areas during growth.	5
B. subtilis	In ts mutant, flagella synthesis was inhibited at 46°C. Cells shifted to 46°C from lower temperature showed flagella at one of the poles.	28
B. subtilis and B. megaterium	Chloramphenicol-treated cells were washed and placed in new growth medium. Poles remained "thick" whereas cylinders became "thin" during growth. Growth occurred at many regions in the cylinder.	12
B. megaterium	Cells uniformly labeled with α,ϵ-$[^3H]$diaminopimelic acid were permitted to divide. Autoradiography of daughter cells showed random labeling.	20
B. subtilis	Cells pulsed with $[^3H]$glycerol followed by sectioning and autoradiography showed random labeling on membranes.	24
B. megaterium	Progeny of cells labeled with $[^3H]$glycerol showed large numbers of areas which contain the label. Determined by autoradiography.	13
B. subtilis	"Nearest-neighbor analysis" indicated that newly synthesized peptidoglycan was intercalated randomly into preexisting peptidoglycan.	21
B. subtilis	Use of temperature-sensitive *rod⁻ div⁻* mutants showed that cell elongation occurred only in the region of *rod⁻* morphology. Division points were not restricted to *rod⁻* regions. Thus, although elongation occurs at a restricted number of sites, it is not limited to regions of septation.	22
B. subtilis	Electron micrographs of sections of cells and cell walls prior to and after plasmolysis suggested that wall growth occurred randomly. Newly synthesized wall "migrated" from the inner wall face to the outer.	10
B. megaterium	Pulse-labeling of DAP⁻ *lys⁻* mutant with α,ϵ-$[^3H]$diaminopimelic acid and subsequent autoradiography showed diffuse intercalation of new wall into the cylindrical part of the cell. A growth zone observed in the center of the cell was suggested to be the site of cross-wall formation.	6,7

lus species are considered. We have summarized the results from several laboratories in Table 1 and have restricted our comments to the genus *Bacillus*. It is clear that, although several unique approaches to the problem have been employed, no definitive statements can be made regarding the modes of surface distribution on daughter cells. Thus, new experiments are required to

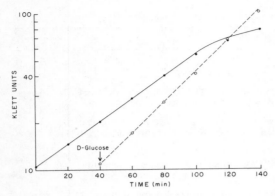

FIG. 2. *Growth of* B. subtilis *gtaC10 in galactose minimal medium. Spizizen minimal medium (30) was supplemented with 0.08% casein hydrolysate and 0.5% D-galactose. At the arrow, a sample of cells was removed, washed twice with minimal salts, and suspended in minimal salts containing 0.5% D-glucose. All operations were at 37°C.*

adequately resolve the question. This paper deals with a novel approach to the study of cell wall growth. The results show that cell wall replication in *Bacillus subtilis* follows a random dis-

tribution pattern. Furthermore, the experiment eliminates problems in interpretation due to cell wall turnover.

BASIC EXPERIMENT TO DETERMINE THE ZONES OF CELL WALL ENLARGEMENT IN *B. SUBTILIS*

Ideally, to determine whether cell wall growth zones are localized or random, it is necessary to monitor the insertion of newly synthesized wall molecules as well as to determine their fate upon cell division. Accordingly, we have developed a method to examine the site(s) of cell wall assembly in *B. subtilis* and to study cell wall distribution in daughter cells. The method makes use of the following observations described by our laboratory and by others. (i) Concanavalin A (Con A) reacts specifically and reversibly with α-D-glucosylated teichoic acids on bacterial surfaces (2, 8, 9). (ii) Newly synthesized teichoic acid is covalently attached only to newly synthesized peptidoglycan (21). (iii) *B. subtilis* gtaC mutants do not glucosylate their cell wall teichoic acids when grown in the presence of glucose, but do synthesize gluco-

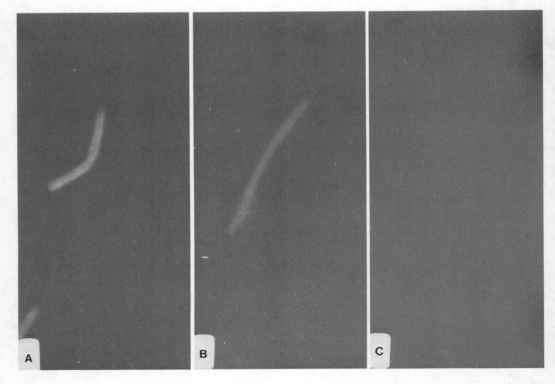

FIG. 3. *Staining of* B. subtilis *with FL-Con A. (A)* B. subtilis *168; (B)* B. subtilis *gtaC10 grown in galactose minimal medium; (C)* B. subtilis *gtaC10 grown in glucose minimal medium. Photography and handling of cells were performed as described earlier (9).*

sylated teichoic acids when grown in the presence of galactose (18, 26, 32; D. C. Birdsell and F. E. Young, Bacteriol. Proc., 1970, G162, p. 39). Class C mutants are deficient in phosphoglucomutase and do not utilize galactose as a carbon energy source (18, 26, 32).

Thus, class C mutants, when shifted from glucose to galactose media, synthesize α-D-glucosylated teichoic acids which can be detected by use of fluorescent Con A (FL-Con A) (9). In addition, when cells grown in the presence of galactose are shifted to glucose, it should be possible to follow the fate of preexisting glucosylated teichoic acid. This constitutes a chase experiment in which it should be possible to discriminate between semiconservative and random cell wall replication.

INTERACTION BETWEEN B. SUBTILIS gtaC MUTANTS AND CONCANAVALIN A

In Fig. 2, the growth characteristics of B. subtilis gtaC10 (provided by D. C. Birdsell and F. E. Young) in Spizizen minimal medium are shown. In the presence of galactose, the generation time was 44 min, whereas when the cells were shifted to glucose the generation time was approximately 31 min.

Figure 3 shows the interaction between FL-Con A and control B. subtilis cells. Figure 3A depicts the interaction between the protein and B. subtilis 168 which is known to possess α-D-glucosylated cell wall teichoic acids. Figure 3B represents the interaction with B. subtilis gtaC10 grown in galactose for four to five generations. The mutant cell binds FL-Con A as well as the wild type, 168. Fig. 3C shows that FL-Con A does not interact with B. subtilis gtaC10 when the cell has been grown in glucose minimal medium for four to five generations. Thus, control experiments established that B. subtilis gtaC10, when grown in glucose minimal medium, does not contain Con A-reactive teichoic acids. On the other hand, when the cells were grown in galactose minimal medium, they interacted readily with the protein and in a manner similar to that for B. subtilis 168 (see also reference 9).

When glucose-grown cells of B. subtilis gtaC10 were shifted into galactose media, it was

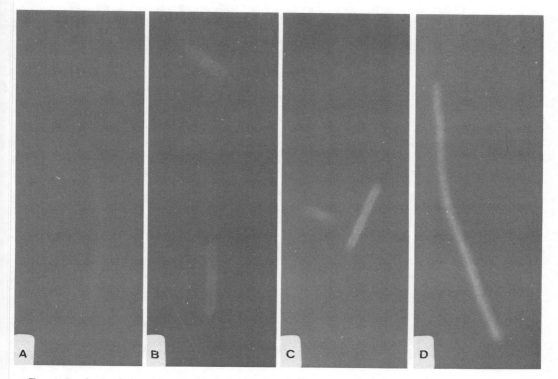

FIG. 4. *Synthesis of glucosylated teichoic acid by* B. subtilis *gtaC10. Cells were grown for nine to ten generations in glucose minimal salts and then shifted to galactose minimal salts. After the shift, cells were removed, washed, and mixed with FL-Con A. (A) At 0.25 generation after the shift from glucose to galactose; (B) 0.5 generation post-shift; (C) 1.0 generation post-shift; (D) 2.0 generations post-shift.*

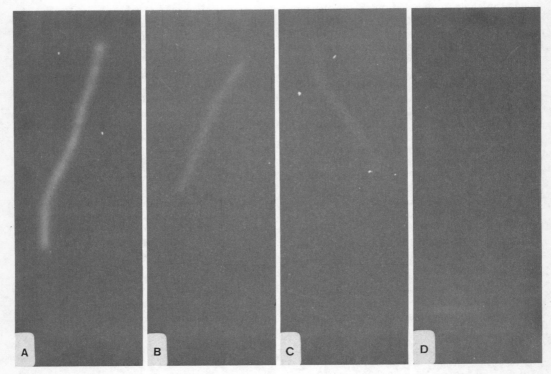

FIG. 5. *Fate of surface teichoic acid in dividing* B. subtilis *gtaC10. Cells were grown in galactose minimal salts and subsequently shifted to glucose minimal salts. (A) At 0.25 generation after shift from galactose to glucose; (B) 0.5 generation post-shift; (C) 1.0 generation post-shift; (D) 2.0 generations post-shift.*

found that FL-Con A could detect the site(s) of insertion of newly synthesized cell wall (Fig. 4). After 0.25 generation, uniform fluorescence around the cells was observed (Fig. 4A). The fluorescence increased in intensity with growth (Fig. 4B–D) until the maximum interaction was reached (two generations, Fig. 4D). These data indicate that newly synthesized cell wall molecules are inserted randomly over the cell surface of *B. subtilis*. However, it should be pointed out that cell wall turnover is occurring (10, 19) and that the observed random staining patterns may reflect not only new growth but replacement of old wall as well.

To circumvent the possibility that turnover may bias the interpretation of fluorescence patterns, the following experiment was performed. *B. subtilis* gtaC10 was grown for nine to ten generations in galactose minimal salts medium and then shifted to glucose minimal medium. If wall replication occurs by a semiconservative mechanism, then fluorescence should be observed only at cell poles and not at division sites. However, if wall replicates by a random mechanism, uniform fluorescence, although weaker, should be observed. The weaker fluorescence would be expected since old wall is "diluted" into new wall, and, in addition,

turnover is constantly occurring. The results show that, as the cells divide, random disappearance of old cell wall material occurs (Fig. 5). In none of the cells are nonfluorescent regions observed. Thus, we conclude that in *B. subtilis* cell wall assembly is a random process which does not involve segregated sites.

CONCLUSIONS

The data presented in this paper show that the cell wall of *B. subtilis* replicates in a random manner. We have taken advantage of the fact that glucosylation of the cell wall teichoic acid of *B. subtilis* strain gtaC depends on the presence of galactose in the growth medium. The use of FL-Con A provides a convenient probe to determine where on the cell wall the teichoic acid molecules are located. We determined that new cell wall material was inserted randomly on the bacterial surface. Moreover, the loss of old cell wall material from the surface followed a random pattern. We have been able to repeat these experiments by electron microscopy using the bacteriophage $\phi25$ as a probe for α-D-glucosylated teichoic acids and have reached the same conclusions (R. J. Doyle, U. N. Streips, and B. S. Giammara, unpublished observations).

Howard Rogers has suggested that dichotomous replication may lead to several distinct sites of wall assembly. If several wall bands were being synthesized, one following the other, from regions of septation, then FL-Con A may not have adequately resolved the resulting patterns. This possibility exists when glucosylated teichoic acid synthesis is being followed (i.e., shift from glucose to galactose medium). However, when the chase experiments were performed (galactose to glucose shift), areas devoid of fluorescence were not observed. If semiconservative wall replication had occurred, it would be expected that FL-Con A-free areas adjacent to septa would have been found, regardless of the rate which the cells were growing. It will be necessary to confirm our results using cells growing at different rates.

ACKNOWLEDGMENTS

We thank D. C. Birdsell and F. E. Young for the bacterial strains. Thanks is also given to H. E. Kubitschek and A. L. Koch for stimulating discussions.

This work was supported in part by an institutional grant from the America Cancer Society.

LITERATURE CITED

1. **Bayer, M.** 1967. The cell wall of *Escherichia coli*; early effects of penicillin treatment and deprivation of diaminopimelic acid. J. Gen. Microbiol. **46**:237–246.
2. **Birdsell, D. C., R. J. Doyle, and M. Morgenstern.** 1975. Organization of teichoic acid in the cell wall of *Bacillus subtilis*. J. Bacteriol. **121**:726–734.
3. **Bisset, K., and C. Hale.** 1960. Flagellar pattern and growth of *Bacillus spp*. J. Gen. Microbiol. **22**:536–538.
4. **Chung, K., R. Hawirko, and P. Isaac.** 1964. Cell wall replication. I. Cell wall growth of *Bacillus cereus* and *Bacillus megaterium*. Can. J. Microbiol. **10**:43–48.
5. **Chung, K. L.** 1971. Thickened cell walls of *Bacillus cereus* grown in the presence of chloramphenicol: their fate during growth. Can. J. Microbiol. **17**:1561–1565.
6. **DeChastellier, C., C. Frehel, and A. Ryter.** 1975. Cell wall growth of *Bacillus megaterium*: cytoplasmic radioactivity after pulse-labeling with tritiated diaminopimelic acid. J. Bacteriol. **123**:1197–1207.
7. **DeChastellier, C., R. Hellio, and A. Ryter.** 1975. Study of cell wall growth in *Bacillus megaterium* by high-resolution autoradiography. J. Bacteriol. **123**:1184–1196.
8. **Doyle, R., and D. Birdsell.** 1972. Interaction of concanavalin A with the cell wall of *Bacillus subtilis*. J. Bacteriol. **109**:652–658.
9. **Doyle, R., M. McDannel, J. Helman, and U. N. Streips.** 1975. Distribution of teichoic acid in the cell wall of *Bacillus subtilis*. J. Bacteriol. **122**:152–158.
10. **Fan, D., B. Beckman, and H. Gardner-Eckstrom.** 1975. Mode of cell wall synthesis in gram-positive bacilli. J. Bacteriol. **123**:1157–1162.
11. **Forsberg, C., P. Wyrick, J. Ward, and H. Rogers.** 1973. Effect of phosphate limitation on the morphology and wall composition of *Bacillus licheniformis* and its phosphoglucomutase-deficient mutants. J. Bacteriol. **113**:969–984.
12. **Frehel, C., A. Beaufils, and A. Ryter.** 1971. Etude au microscope electronique de la croissance de la paroi chez *B. subtilis* et *B. megaterium*. Ann. Inst. Pasteur Paris **121**:139–148.
13. **Green, E., and M. Schaechter.** 1972. Mode of segregation of the bacterial cell membrane. Proc. Natl. Acad. Sci. U.S.A. **69**:2312–2416.
14. **Hirota, Y., A. Ryter, M. Richard, and U. Schwarz.** 1974. Growth of the cell envelope in the *E. coli* cell cycle, p. 407–530. *In* A. L. Kolber and M. Kohiyama (ed.), Mechanism and regulation of DNA replication. Plenum Press, New York.
15. **Hughes, R., and E. Stokes.** 1971. Cell wall growth in *Bacillus licheniformis* followed by immunofluorescence with mucopeptide-specific antiserum. J. Bacteriol. **106**:694–696.
16. **Jacob, F., S. Brenner, and F. Cuzin.** 1963. On the regulation of DNA replication in bacteria. Cold Spring Harbor Symp. Quant. Biol. **28**:329–348.
17. **Lin, E. C. C., Y. Hirota, and P. Jacob.** 1971. On the process of cellular division in *Escherichia coli*. VI. Use of a methocel-autoradiographic method for the study of cellular division in *Escherichia coli*. J. Bacteriol. **108**:375–385.
18. **Maino, V., and F. E. Young.** 1974. Regulation of glucosylation of teichoic acid. I. Isolation of phosphoglucomutase in *Bacillus subtilis* 168. J. Biol. Chem. **249**:5169–5175.
19. **Mauck, J., L. Chan, and L. Glaser.** 1971. Turnover of the cell wall of the gram-positive bacteria. J. Biol. Chem. **246**:1820–1827.
20. **Mauck, J., L. Chan, L. Glaser, and J. Williamson.** 1972. Mode of cell wall growth of *Bacillus megaterium*. J. Bacteriol. **109**:373–378.
21. **Mauck, J., and L. Glaser.** 1972. On the mode of *in vivo* assembly of the cell wall of *Bacillus subtilis*. J. Biol. Chem. **247**:1180–1187.
22. **Mendelson, N., and J. Reeve.** 1973. Growth of the *Bacillus subtilis* cell surface. Nature (London) New Biol. **243**:62–64.
23. **Meynell, G., and A. Lawn.** 1965. Inheritance of capsule and the manner of cell-wall formation in *Bacillus anthracis*. J. Gen. Microbiol. **39**:423–427.
24. **Mindich, L., and S. Dales.** 1972. Membrane synthesis in *Bacillus subtilis*. III. The morphological localization of the sites of membrane synthesis. J. Cell Biol. **55**:32–41.
25. **Morrison, D., and H. Morowitz.** 1970. Studies on membrane synthesis in *Bacillus megaterium* KM. J. Mol. Biol. **49**:441–459.
26. **Rogers, H., M. McConnell, and I. Burdett.** 1970. The isolation and characterization of mutants of *Bacillus subtilis* and *Bacillus licheniformis* with disturbed morphology and cell division. J. Gen. Microbiol. **61**:155–171.
27. **Ryter, A.** 1967. Relationship between synthesis of the cytoplasmic membrane and nuclear segregation in *Bacillus subtilis*. Folia Microbiol. **12**:283–290.
28. **Ryter, A.** 1971. Etude de la croissance de la membrane chez *B. subtilis* au moyen de la distribution des flagelles. Ann. Inst. Pasteur Paris **121**:271–288.
29. **Shockman, G., L. Daneo-Moore, and M. Higgins.** 1974. Problems of cell wall and membrane growth, enlargement, and division. Ann. N.Y. Acad. Sci. **235**:161–197.
30. **Spizizen, J.** 1958. Transformation of biochemically deficient strains of *Bacillus subtilis* by deoxyribonucleate. Proc. Natl. Acad. Sci. U.S.A. **44**:1072–1078.
31. **Van Tubergen, R., and R. Setlow.** 1961. Quantitative radioautographic studies on exponentially growing cultures of *Escherichia coli*. The distribution of parental DNA, RNA, protein and cell wall among progeny cells. Biophys. J. **1**:589–625.
32. **Young, F. E.** 1967. Requirement of glucosylated teichoic acid for adsorption of phage in *Bacillus subtilis* 168. Proc. Natl. Acad. Sci. U.S.A. **58**:2377–2384.

Control of Peptidoglycan Synthesis During Sporulation in *Bacillus sphaericus*

D. J. TIPPER, I. PRATT, M. GUINAND, S. C. HOLT, AND P. E. LINNETT

*Department of Microbiology, University of Massachusetts Medical School, Worcester, Massachusetts 01605;
Laboratoire de Chimie Biologique, Université de Lyon, Villeurbanne, France;
Department of Microbiology, University of Massachusetts, Amherst, Massachusetts 01002; and
Woodstock Agricultural Research Center, Sittingbourne Laboratories, Sittingbourne, Kent, England*

INTRODUCTION

Whereas the bacterial cell wall peptidoglycan of *Bacillus subtilis* is a typical Alγ structure (25) in which residues of *meso*-diaminopimelate (*meso*-Dpm) are directly cross-linked through ᴅ-alanine residues, the cortical peptidoglycan has some unique structural components not found in the peptidoglycan of any bacterial cell wall (Fig. 1A). Even though the tetrapeptides in the cortical peptidoglycan have the same amino acid sequence and cross-linking as the Alγ structure of the cell wall, they substitute only about 30% of the disaccharide subunits of the glycan, while another 20% of the disaccharides are substituted by a single, C-terminal ʟ-alanine residue. The remaining 50% of the disaccharides contain muramic lactam. This unique structure was determined by Warth and Strominger (33, 34), who also showed that its components occur in the spores of several *Bacillus* and *Clostridium* species. All other peptidoglycans are polymerized from disaccharide-peptide subunits that are assembled on membrane-bound lipid intermediates from UDP-GlcNAc and UDP-MurNAc-pentapeptide precursors, highly hydrophilic compounds that are synthesized by soluble cytoplasmic enzymes (27). It is probable that this is also true for the cortical peptidoglycan and that its disaccharide-ʟ-alanine and muramic lactam subunits are produced from a nascent polymer of polymerized disaccharide-pentapeptide by a combination of peptidase activity and transacylation (28, 34). Attempts have been made in several laboratories, including our own, to demonstrate the presence of enzyme activities in sporulating cells of *B. subtilis* and related bacilli capable of performing these functions in vitro, but these attempts have been uniformly unsuccessful.

The impetus behind such studies derives from the fact that enzymes involved in synthesis of the unique elements of cortex peptidoglycan should be specific for sporulation and without obvious function in vegetative growth. These enzyme activities would join the relatively

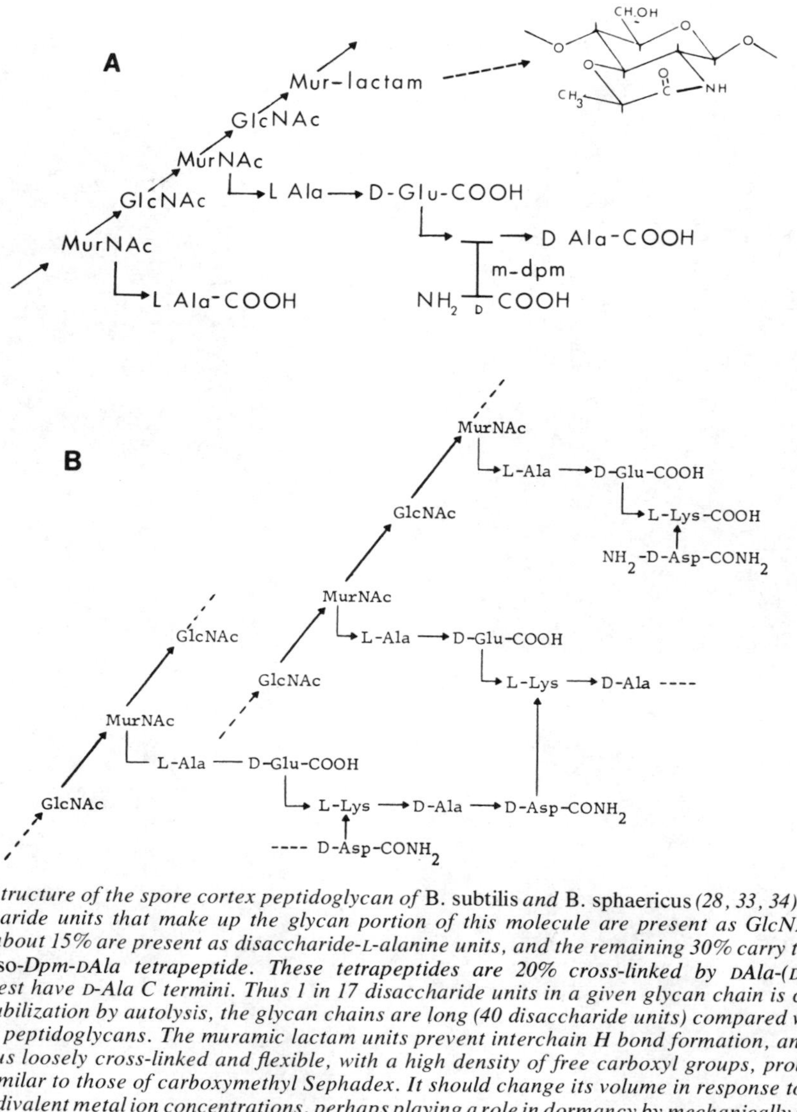

A

Mur-lactam
GlcNAc
MurNAc
GlcNAc → L Ala → D-Glu-COOH
MurNAc → L Ala-COOH
D Ala-COOH
m-dpm
NH_2 - D COOH

CH_2OH — CH_3 — O — C — NH

B

MurNAc → L-Ala → D-Glu-COOH → L-Lys-COOH
NH_2-D-Asp-$CONH_2$
GlcNAc

MurNAc → L-Ala → D-Glu-COOH → L-Lys → D-Ala ----
GlcNAc
GlcNAc

MurNAc → L-Ala — D-Glu-COOH → L-Lys → D-Ala → D-Asp-$CONH_2$
GlcNAc
---- D-Asp-$CONH_2$

FIG. 1. *(A) Structure of the spore cortex peptidoglycan of* B. subtilis *and* B. sphaericus *(28, 33, 34). About 55% of the disaccharide units that make up the glycan portion of this molecule are present as GlcNAc-muramic lactam units, about 15% are present as disaccharide-L-alanine units, and the remaining 30% carry the complete* LAla-DGlu-meso-Dpm-DAla *tetrapeptide. These tetrapeptides are 20% cross-linked by* DAla-(D)meso-Dpm *linkages; the rest have D-Ala C termini. Thus 1 in 17 disaccharide units in a given glycan chain is cross-linked. Even after solubilization by autolysis, the glycan chains are long (40 disaccharide units) compared with those in many cell wall peptidoglycans. The muramic lactam units prevent interchain H bond formation, and the native structure is thus loosely cross-linked and flexible, with a high density of free carboxyl groups, probably giving it properties similar to those of carboxymethyl Sephadex. It should change its volume in response to changes in univalent and divalent metal ion concentrations, perhaps playing a role in dormancy by mechanically compressing the spore core (28). (B) Structure of the vegetative cell wall peptidoglycan of* B. sphaericus *(11). The lower part of the structure shows two glycan chains cross-linked through N*ε(D-alanyl-D-isoasparaginyl)-L-lysine *linkages. The upper part shows an uncross-linked tetrapeptide unit. All peptides end in C-terminal L-lysine, and cross-linkage is 55%. The glycan average chain length is 6 to 8 disaccharide units.*

small group of polypeptides synthesized during sporulation that are clearly sporulation specific. Sporulation-specific polypeptides are those found exclusively in spores or those enzymes whose products are found exclusively in spores (7, 28). They include the structural polypeptides of spore coats and exosporium, the hydrophilic proteins in *B. megaterium* and *B. subtilis* which are rapidly degraded during germination (26; D. J. Tipper and P. Setlow, unpublished observa-

tions), and the enzymes for synthesis of dipicolinate (3) and of sulfolactic acid (35).

Development of the primordial cell wall, cortex, spore coats, and exosporium of *Bacillus* spores occurs only after engulfment of the forespore (5, 10, 22, 24), and accumulation of dipicolinate and sulfolactic acid also occurs only after this stage of sporulation. Thus, investigation of the control of cortex synthesis is a model for understanding the control of events

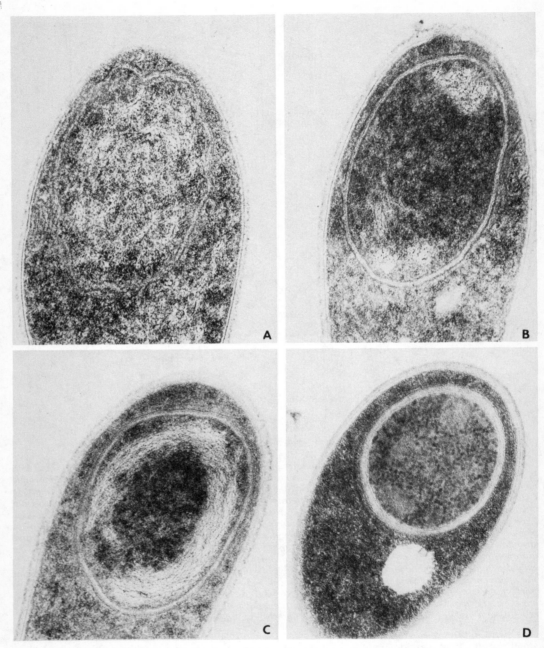

Fig. 2. *Forespore development in B.* sphaericus. *Thin sections of sporulating B.* sphaericus *cells were stained for electron microscopy as previously described (10). (A)* t = 4 h. *A nascent, fully engulfed forespore with flexible inner and outer forespore membranes with no visible intervening structure. The forespore cytoplasm resembles that of the mother cell. (B)* t = 4.2 h. *The forespore outline has become smooth, suggesting some stiffening of its envelope, and a thin line of what may be peptidoglycan material is visible between its membranes. Condensation of the forespore nucleoid is in progress. (C)* t = 4.2 h. *A different section of the same stage in forespore development. The crescent-shaped, condensed nucleoid is clearly visible, but as yet there are no signs of spore coat development. (D)* t = 4.5 h. *The forespore core now has a granular appearance similar to that of the mature spore. The space between inner and outer forespore membranes is now wider and contains primordial cell wall material. The first hint of spore coat assembly can be seen within the mother cell cytoplasm, adjacent to the outer forespore membrane. (E)* t = 5 h. *The forespore core is fully condensed. Primordial cell wall immediately adjacent to the inner forespore membrane is clearly distinguished from the lightly staining cortex layer that now separates it from the outer forespore membrane. The lamellar mid-coat layer can now be seen entirely surrounding the spore, and there is some evidence of outer coat. Exosporium*

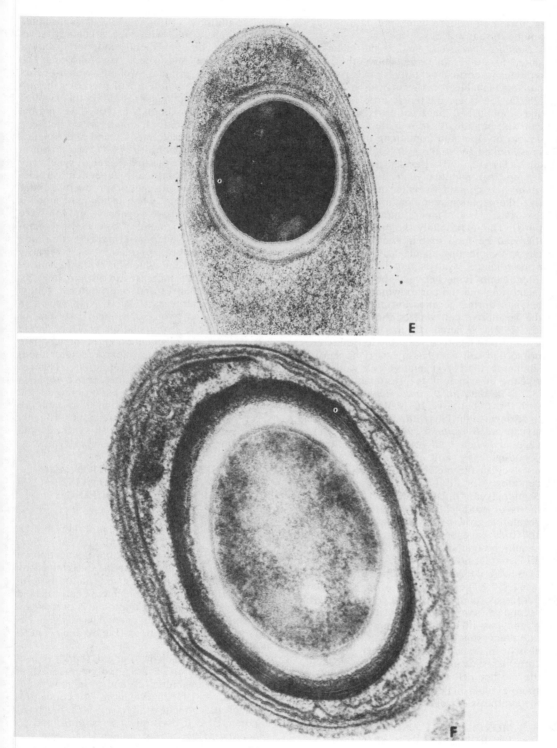

assembly adjacent to the mother cell membrane is also visible. (F) t = 10 h. Transverse section of a mature spore still within its mother cell. The inner forespore membrane is barely discernible within the primordial cell wall, which is now surrounded by a much thickened cortex that is separated from the inner layer of the spore coat by the folded remnants of the outer forespore membrane. The lamellar mid-coat layer lies between the more amorphous inner and outer coat layers, and the spore is separated from the cytoplasmic membrane of the mother cell by the exosporium.

occurring in mid to late sporulation that are unique to that process.

Bacillus sphaericus 9602 is particularly well suited to studies of cortex biosynthesis since, although its cortical peptidoglycan is structurally indistinguishable from that of *B. subtilis* (Fig. 1A) (28; D. J. Tipper, Bacteriol. Proc., p. 24, 1969, and unpublished observations), its vegetative cell wall peptidoglycan is quite different, being devoid of Dpm and containing L-lysyl residues cross-linked by D-alanyl-D-isoasparaginyl residues (11) (Fig. 1B). Besides the Dpm-containing cortical peptidoglycan, the spores of *B. sphaericus* contain a smaller quantity of vegetative-like peptidoglycan containing lysine and D-aspartate (D. J. Tipper, unpublished observations). This is probably the primordial cell wall that can be seen in thin sections of developing spores in this species (10; Fig. 2D). The primordial cell wall is that layer of the spore integuments lying between the inner forespore membrane and the cortex which, unlike cortex, persists during germination and develops into the vegetative cell wall of the outgrowing cell (5, 22, 31). Whereas the cortex peptidoglycan is uniformly highly susceptible to lysozyme, the primordial cell wall has a lysozyme sensitivity similar to that of vegetative cell wall peptidoglycan, of which it is presumably composed (32). The data on *B. sphaericus* are consistent with this hypothesis. It should thus be possible to distinguish the biosynthesis of cortical peptidoglycan in *B. sphaericus* from that of both vegetative cell wall and primordial cell wall peptidoglycans: any enzyme in *B. sphaericus* involved in the metabolism of Dpm-containing peptidoglycan, but not of lysine-containing peptidoglycan, must be specific for cortex synthesis or modification and without function in vegetative growth. To date, two such enzymatic activities have been recognized. The first is a membrane-bound DGlu-*meso*-Dpm peptide hydrolase (6), and the second is a cytoplasmic enzyme, UDP-MurNAc-L-Ala-DGlu:*meso*-Dpm ligase (30). The appearance of the latter activity during sporulation has been correlated with the second of two discrete periods of synthesis of enzymes involved in synthesis of the nucleotide precursors of peptidoglycan (17, 18). It has also been demonstrated (29) that this soluble, cortex-specific enzyme is located exclusively in the mother cell cytoplasm, whereas the forespore cytoplasm is rich in enzymes required for the synthesis of vegetation-type peptidoglycan.

MORPHOLOGY AND KINETICS OF SPORULATION IN *B. SPHAERICUS*

B. sphaericus is a convenient organism for studies of sporulation because, under appropriate conditions (10, 17, 30), it sporulates synchronously and with high efficiency. This process can be conveniently monitored with a phase-contrast microscope by following the appearance of terminal swelling, which occurs after 2.5 h of sporulation and precedes the appearance of refractile spores within this swollen cell terminus by about 3 h (10). The optimal growth temperature for *B. sphaericus* is between 32 and 35°C in rich media, and the kinetics of sporulation in BS broth at 32°C are shown in Fig. 3 (10). The kinetics and degree of synchrony of sporulation are critically dependent on adequate aeration but are quite reproducible under controlled conditions, when an adequate number of prior generations of vegetative growth have resulted in the attainment of balanced exponential growth. The generation time is 35 min, and t_0, the initiation of sporulation, is arbitrarily defined as the time at which the doubling time of turbidity abruptly increases to 80 min (Fig. 3). After t_0, turbidity and morphology follow characteristic patterns (Fig. 3). Also shown in this figure are two biochemical markers of sporulation, the accumulation of Dpm ligase activity and the accumulation of dipicolinate (30). Note that the former is followed, after about 0.5 h, by the appearance of refractility. This occurs at the time at which the forespore cytoplasm is seen in thin sections to have acquired the granular, condensed appearance of mature spores (Fig. 2D, E) and corresponds roughly to the end of primordial cell wall synthesis and the beginning of spore coat and cortex synthesis.

DNA SYNTHESIS, SEPTATION, AND SYNTHESIS OF VEGETATIVE PEPTIDOGLYCAN DURING SPORULATION

Recent studies (G. G. Khachatourians and D. J. Tipper, Abstr. Annu. Meet. Am. Soc. Microbiol. 1975, I19, p. 120) of variation in cell number and cell volume (as determined by the Coulter counter) during sporulation in both *B. sphaericus* and *B. subtilis* have demonstrated that t_0 (as defined turbidimetrically) precedes a final symmetrical cell division. This division occurs at $t_{0.6}$ in *B. sphaericus* (Fig. 4) and $t_{1.5}$ in *B. subtilis*.

6-(*p*-Hydroxyphenylazo)uracil (HPUra) is a selective inhibitor of DNA polymerase III of gram-positive bacteria (2), and so inhibits semiconservative DNA replication. At concentrations of 10 μg/ml it inhibits by 50% the postexponential cell division in *B. subtilis* and *B. sphaericus* (Fig. 4A) if added at $t_{0.7}$ and $t_{0.1}$, respectively. In *B. sphaericus*, the division at $t_{0.6}$ is 50% inhibited by chloramphenicol (Cm) added at $t_{0.4}$ at a concentration that inhibits

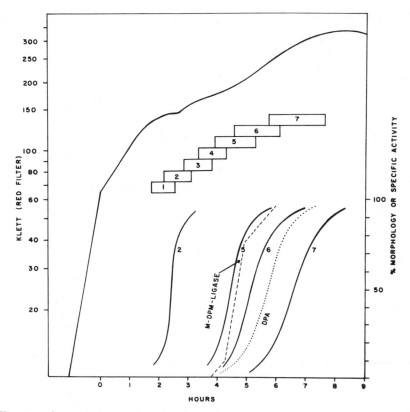

FIG. 3. *Kinetics of sporulation in* B. sphaericus. *The upper curve shows culture turbidity measured with a Klett colorimeter using a red filter (logarithmic scale). The solid lower curves (linear scale) represent morphological events visible in the phase microscope. – – –, meso-Dpm ligase specific activity; . . ., dipicolinate (DPA) accumulation. During vegetative growth, turbidity and cell number (not shown) double each 35 min. The hours of sporulation are measured from* t_0, *defined by the break in the turbidity curve. The boxes represent morphological events visible in electron micrographs (10) or by phase-contrast observations. (1) Appearance of terminal sporulation septa. (2) Terminal swelling (phase contrast) and forespore engulfment (electron micrographs) commence. (3) Engulfment completion; forespore membranes apparently flexible (see Fig. 2A). (4) Rounding up of the forespore and condensation of its nucleoid (see Fig. 2B, C). (5) Primordial cell wall synthesis; early mid-coat synthesis; adoption by the forespore cytoplasm of a granular appearance (see Fig. 2D). (6) Forespores become semirefractile (phase); mid-coat well developed; cortex, outer coat, and exosporium development visible. (7) Phase-bright spores; completion of coats, cortex, and exosporium (Fig. 2F).*

protein synthesis by 98% (Fig. 4B). It is thus probable that all events required for cell division, other than cell separation (autolysis?), are complete by $t_{0.4}$, 20 min after the time of 50% inhibition of cell division by HPUra. Presuming that cell division is coupled to the termination of rounds of chromosomal replication in *B. sphaericus*, as in other organisms (8), and that HPUra inhibits DNA synthesis up to the time of completion of rounds, then cell division is virtually complete 20 min later and actually complete 30 min later. The corresponding period for *Escherichia coli* B/r growing at 37°C is 20 min (8).

All of the cells that undergo postexponential

cell division in the presence of HPUra continue to follow the normal sequence of sporulation events and produce viable, refractile spores. It thus appears that, although postexponential DNA synthesis and segregation are essential for sporulation in both species, this DNA replication occurs before the final symmetrical cell division. Thus the subsequent formation of the sporulation septum occurs in the absence of intervening DNA synthesis. One copy of the genome must be segregated to the terminus of the cell, where it is to be enclosed in the forespore. This segregation occurs either at the time of DNA synthesis, before the previous vegetative cell division, or after this event, in

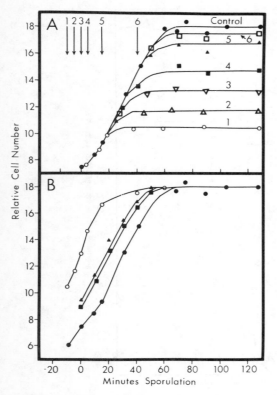

FIG. 4. *Effect of 6-(p-hydroxyphenylazo)uracil (HPUra), chloramphenicol, and vancomycin on post-exponential cell division in* B. sphaericus. *(A) HPUra results. The residual cell division (curves numbered 1–6) after addition of HPUra (10 μg/ml) to a sporulating culture at the indicated times (1–6) was determined by using a Coulter electronic particle counter. This concentration of HPUra was sufficient to completely inhibit vegetative cell division. The control curve (without drug) shows that the total cell count doubles between $t_0 + 10$ min and $t_0 + 60$ min, although this division is only partially distinct from the termination of the round of division initiated before t_0. The postexponential cell division is half complete at about $t_0 + 35$ min. (B) Plateau levels reached in the presence of HPUra are plotted against the time of addition of drug (○). The division at $t_0 + 35$ min is 50% inhibited by HPUra added at $t_0 + 5$ min. Similar data are presented for vancomycin (10 μg/ml; ▲) and chloramphenicol (50 μg/ml; ■). The control data (no drug) are repeated (●).*

the absence of DNA synthesis. It seems likely that nucleoid segregation occurs at the time of DNA synthesis, in the absence of septation, as in the conditional division-defective *B. subtilis* mutant of Mendelson and Cole (21). If so, genome replication shortly after t_0 would result in segregation of genome copies to both ends of the cell. After the cell division at $t_{0.6}$, spore

septa form at the predetermined (older) cell termini, partitioning the spore genome from the mother cell.

Thin sections of vegetative and sporulation septa in *B. sphaericus* (10) indicate that both are initially identical in profile and contain a continuous line of dark-staining material contiguous with the peptidoglycan layer of the cell wall. The vegetative septum develops by a doubling of this peptidoglycan layer and its eventual separation by invagination of the external structural protein layer of the cell wall. In contrast, the nascent sporulation septum loses its structured appearance and becomes flexible from the center toward the edges, and engulfment of the forespore proceeds by proliferation of both membranes of the septum around the forespore cytoplasm (10), as seen in other *Bacillus* species (5, 24). The doubling in cell number at $t_{0.6}$ is sensitive to vancomycin, a specific inhibitor of peptidoglycan polymerization, up to $t_{0.4}$, the time of sensitivity to Cm (Fig. 4B). Also, the swelling and development of semi-refractile forespores that follow sporulation septation are both inhibited by vancomycin added at t_2, the time of spore septum formation (10), and 30 min before swelling becomes visible (Fig. 5). It is thus probable that both septation events involve obligatory peptidoglycan synthesis, probably for formation of a cross wall of vegetative-type peptidoglycan. The sensitivity of spore septum formation to penicillin has previously been described (9, 15, 31). In contrast, Pitel and Gilvarg (23) have shown that incorporation of Dpm into cell wall peptidoglycan ceases at the beginning of sporulation in *B. megaterium* and incorporation into spore integuments commences only after engulfment, at the probable times of primordial cell wall and cortex synthesis. Perhaps incorporation associated with spore septum formation was too transient to be detected.

SYNTHESIS OF UDP-*N*-ACETYLMURAMYL-PENTAPEPTIDE PRECURSORS OF VEGETATIVE AND SPORULATION PEPTIDOGLYCANS IN *B. SPHAERICUS*

The pathways for synthesis of the UDP-MurNAc-pentapeptide precursors of vegetative and cortical peptidoglycans in *B. sphaericus* are shown in Fig. 6. The sequential addition of L-alanine and D-glutamate to UDP-MurNAc produces the nucleotide dipeptide that should be a common precursor for both pathways. The subsequent addition of L-lysine and D-alanyl-D-alanine produces the vegetative precursor, whereas the addition of *meso*-Dpm and D-

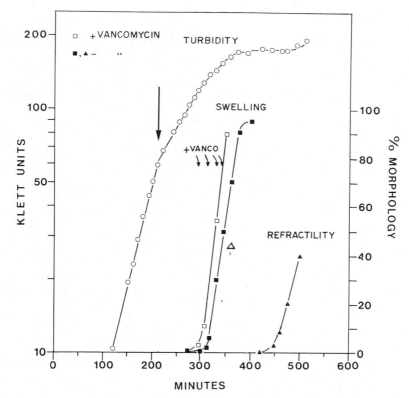

FIG. 5. *Effect of vancomycin (vanco) on spore septum and forespore formation. Data for turbidity (logarithmic scale; ○), percentage of terminally swollen cells (linear scale; □), and percentage of cells having a semirefractile forespore (▲) are shown for the control culture (no drug). t_0 was at 220 min (arrow), and the percentage of cells achieving terminal swelling (□) is plotted against the time of addition of vanco (10 μg/ml; arrows). Swelling, which accompanies forespore engulfment (10), becomes resistant to vanco 30 min before it occurs, that is, at the time of spore septum formation (10). All cells that swell produce semirefractile forespores, but development of this refractility occurs about 15 min later than in the control.*

alanyl-D-alanine produces the cortical precursor. It was already known that the Dpm ligase of *E. coli* is inactive with L-lysine and that the L-lysyl ligase of *Staphylococcus aureus* is inactive with *meso*-Dpm (12). It was therefore expected that a unique and specific Dpm ligase activity would be found in sporulating *B. sphaericus,* and it was also predicted that a unique D-alanyl-D-alanine ligase would be required for the subsequent addition of the dipeptide to the nucleotide tripeptide containing Dpm.

As expected, vegetative cells were completely devoid of Dpm ligase activity, which only appeared at about $t_{4.5}$, increasing up to t_7 (Fig. 7). The appearance of Dpm ligase activity was continually sensitive to concentrations of Cm or streptolydigin (Sln) that were capable of efficiently inhibiting protein and RNA synthesis in sporulating cells of *B. sphaericus* (Fig. 7) (30). The Dpm ligase activity was also fairly

stable in the inhibited cells (Fig. 7) and so was not subject to rapid turnover (14). Thus the accumulation of this activity reflects enzyme synthesis, and this is dependent upon continued transcription and translation, probably of the structural gene for the ligase. The messenger apparently has a half-life of a few minutes only and so is not unusually stable. It is possible, but less probable, that Cm and Sln prevent formation of a short-lived modifier (e.g., a protease) of a polypeptide precursor of Dpm ligase activity.

It was subsequently found that activity catalyzing the addition of DAla-DAla to UDP-MurNAc-tripeptide containing either L-lysine or *meso*-Dpm was continually present throughout vegetative growth and sporulation. The specific activities with the two acceptors varied in parallel and showed the same dependence upon pH, divalent metal ion concentration, and temperature (17). It thus appears that a single enzyme

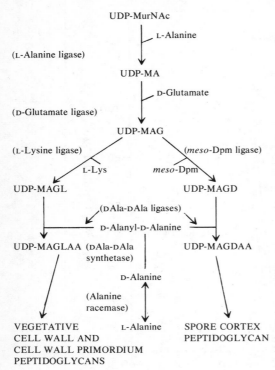

FIG. 6. *Enzymatic reactions involved in synthesis of the nucleotide pentapeptide precursors of vegetative cell wall and spore cortex peptidoglycans. All have been demonstrated in* B. sphaericus *9602. Ligase activities were assayed (12) by incubating the labeled amino acid with the appropriate acceptor nucleotide (e.g.,* [14C]*-meso-Dpm or* L-[14C]*Lys with UDP-MurNAc-LAla-DGlu) and enzyme (17, 30).* D-Alanyl-D-alanine synthetase and alanine racemase activities were assayed in similar enzyme preparations, as previously described (17). Enzymes were normally prepared by precipitation of the supernatants from ultrasonic disruption of cells with ammonium sulfate at 75% saturation (17, 30). This procedure led to disruption of 100% of the cells and isolation of 98% of the soluble protein up to stage* $t_{4.5}$ *of sporulation. After that time, the forespores rapidly developed resistance to ultrasonic disruption. All amino acid ligase activities were stable in these extracts when stored at* −80°C, *and protein recoveries and specific activities were reproducible from experiment to experiment (17, 18, 29). Abbreviations: uridine-diphospho-N-acetylmuramic acid,* UDP-MA; *alanine,* A; D-*glutamate,* G; L-*lysine,* L; *meso-α,ε-diaminopimelic acid,* D. *Conventional amino acid abbreviations are used elsewhere.*

is responsible for the final step in the synthesis of the pentapeptide precursors of both vegetative and cortical peptidoglycans, and that the single event of synthesis of Dpm ligase activity is sufficient to allow production of the cortical peptidoglycan precursor.

The variation in specific activities of all the enzymes involved in synthesis of the two pentapeptide precursors during sporulation in *B. sphaericus* is shown in Fig. 8. With the exception of alanine racemase, all showed a drop of about 50% in specific activity between t_0 and t_2, and all those that were involved in synthesis of the precursor of cortex, i.e., excluding L-lysyl ligase, showed a subsequent increase in specific activity commencing before, but most markedly in parallel with, the appearance of Dpm ligase activity. The D-Glu ligase activity appeared to increase somewhat earlier than the others, but in other experiments it more closely followed the general pattern.

In Fig. 9A, a similar experiment is shown in which the variation in the specific activity of DAla-DAla ligase during sporulation is drawn on a linear scale. The data are very similar to those shown in Fig. 8. Figure 9A also shows the kinetics of sporulation in this experiment. In the lower panel (Fig. 9B), the turbidity and total soluble protein released from these cells are drawn on a linear scale. Total protein increased approximately 2.5-fold between t_0 and t_3, and turbidity increased in parallel. Total protein then reached a plateau from which it gradually declined, commencing at about $t_{5.5}$. Since forespores partially resist ultrasonic disruption after $t_{4.5}$ and totally resist this procedure after $t_{5.5}$, this accounts for a decrease of about 8% in the yield of soluble protein after $t_{5.5}$ (see below). Thus, the data in Fig. 7 through 9 represent the activities in both the mother cell and forespore cytoplasmic compartment up to about t_5, but only the activities of the mother cell after $t_{5.5}$ (18, 29).

Variation in the total activity of DAla-DAla ligase is shown in Fig. 9B. Activity increased exponentially during vegetative growth and until shortly before t_0, but accumulation of activity ceased at t_0 and activity remained constant until t_2. During this period, the 60% drop in specific activity is accounted for by the increase in total protein and is therefore a consequence of dilution. The subsequent renewed accumulation of activity between t_2 and t_4 (Fig. 9B) was largely masked in the specific activity data (Fig. 9A) by the increase in total protein. However, the marked increase in total activity that occurred between t_5 and t_7 occurred in the presence of a constant or slightly decreasing protein content and was seen as a marked increase in specific activity (Fig. 9A). This occurred in parallel with the appearance of the Dpm ligase activity and was separated from the first period of enzyme synthesis by a pause of about 1 h (18).

In Fig. 10, the variation in the total activity of the other enzymes involved in peptidoglycan

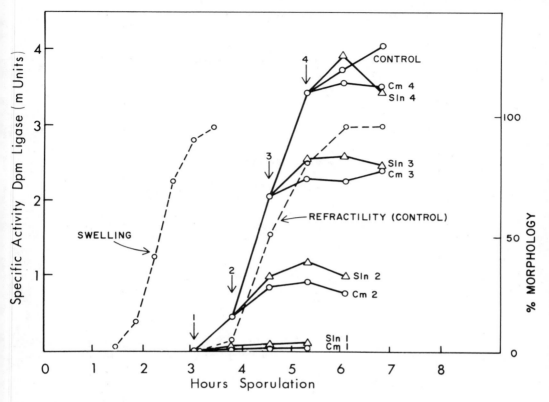

FIG. 7. *Appearance of Dpm ligase activity during sporulation in* B. sphaericus *and its sensitivity to inhibitors of RNA and protein synthesis. Samples of a sporulating culture of* B. sphaericus *were removed at the four times indicated by the arrows and further incubated with either Cm (50 μg/ml) or Sln (100 μg/ml). These cultures and the controls were assayed for Dpm ligase activity at the indicated times. No activity is detectable before* t_3. *Activity (control, no drug) is half-maximal at* $t_{4.5}$, *30 min before 50% of the cells acquire visible refractility. After the addition of Cm, accumulation of activity ceased after an increment equal to that occurring in the control culture in a 10-min period. After addition of Sln, accumulation of activity ceased after an additional 5 to 10 min.*

precursor synthesis is shown in the same experiment. With the exception of racemase, the accumulation of all activities ceased at t_0 and commenced again after a pause of 1.5 to 2.5 h. In the case of L-Ala ligase and DAla-DAla synthetase, two separate periods of subsequent accumulation of total activity were seen. They occurred at the same time as the two periods of accumulation of DAla-DAla ligase activity (Fig. 9). These two periods were not clearly delineated for D-Glu ligase activity, and only the first period of accumulation was seen for L-Lys ligase activity. Again, alanine racemase behaved quite differently in that its total activity increased about sevenfold between t_0 and t_2, followed by a decline and a subsequent increase that partially coincided with the second period of synthesis of the ligase activities. This two-step pattern of increase was seen in repeated experiments (18).

SENSITIVITY OF INCREASES IN DALA-DALA SYNTHETASE AND DALA-DALA LIGASE ACTIVITIES TO INHIBITORS OF MACROMOLECULAR SYNTHESIS

Two cultures of sporulating *B. sphaericus*, A and B, were divided into three equal parts: a control culture containing no drug, and cultures containing Cm (100 μg/ml) or Sln (100 μg/ml). Culture A was divided when about 40% of its spores were swollen ($t_{2.5}$), shortly after the start of the first period of accumulation of DAla-DAla ligase activity. Culture B was divided at about $t_{4.5}$, when most of the sporangia were swollen, a time corresponding to the start of the second period of accumulation of ligase activity. The control data for the two experiments happened to give a continuous curve (Fig. 11), and it can be seen that both Cm and Sln in-

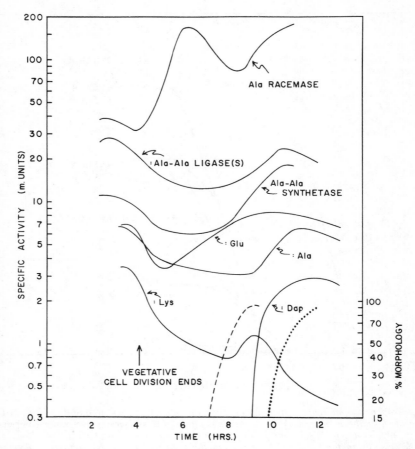

FIG. 8. *Variation in specific activity (logarithmic scale) of enzymes involved in synthesizing the UDP-MurNAc-pentapeptide precursors of vegetative and cortical peptidoglycans during sporulation in B. sphaericus (17). t_0 was at 4.5 h (arrow). Symbols: dashed line, percentage of terminally swollen cells; dotted line, percentage of refractile forespores. From the top, the first five activities represented are alanine racemase, UDP-MurNAc-LAla-DGlu-LLys (or meso-Dpm):DAla-DAla ligase, D-alanyl-D-alanine synthetase, UDP-MurNAc-LAla:DGlu ligase, and UDP-MurNAc:LAla ligase. All five activities are common to the pathways of synthesis of both precursors (Fig. 6). The two lower curves are for the pathway-specific activities, UDP-MurNAc-LAla-DGlu:LLys ligase and the equivalent* meso-*Dpm ligase.*

hibited both early and late stages of accumulation of activity, although the inhibition by Sln was less than complete and took longer to be expressed.

In the same experiment, assays of DAla-DAla synthetase activity gave essentially the same result (Fig. 12). Thus, for these two enzyme activities, as for the single period of increase in Dpm ligase activity (Fig. 7), both periods of increase are dependent upon continued transcription and translation.

VARIATION IN LIGASE ACTIVITIES IN POSTEXPONENTIAL GROWTH IN Spo MUTANTS

After mutagenesis of the parent with nitrosoguanidine, Spo mutants of *B. sphaericus*

were isolated as colonies that failed to show the typical brown pigmentation of sporulating colonies of the parent on BS agar (18). Three of these mutants, Spo3, -4, and -7, grew vegetatively at a rate similar to that of the parent in BS broth and showed variable amounts of sporulation on prolonged incubation. Spo3 failed to produce any swollen sporangia or spores and never showed any accumulation of Dpm ligase activity, nor did it accumulate any dipicolinate. Spo4 and -7 were oligosporogenic, producing 2 to 3% refractile spores, but only after more than 12 h of incubation in stationary phase at 32°C. They showed a similar delayed and fractional accumulation of Dpm ligase activity and dipicolinate accumulation (18). Staining with methylene blue revealed the presence of some sporulation septa in postexponential-phase cells of all mutants, although cells of Spo3, in particular, became misshapen and frequently produced terminal minicells on prolonged incubation. It is probable that this was a consequence of aborted sporulation at stage 2, the stage of spore septum formation. These mutants all showed the continued accumulation of total protein after t_0 seen in the parent. Like the parent, they also ceased accumulation of DAla-DAla ligase activity at about t_0 (Fig. 13) and showed a marked increase in alanine racemase activity between t_0 and t_2. However, they did not show the drop in alanine racemase activity or the increase in Ala-Ala ligase activity seen in the parent after t_2. These mutants thus appear to express at least some of the normal events of sporulation up to t_2 and not to express at least some of the normal events occurring after t_2. This correlates well with the morphological evidence of a block at spore septum formation and corroborates the temporal relationship of swelling and forespore engulfment with the first period of accumulation of ligase activities by showing that the latter does not occur in the absence of the former.

DISTRIBUTION OF DPM AND LYS LIGASE ACTIVITIES BETWEEN MOTHER CELL AND FORESPORE COMPARTMENTS OF SPORULATING CELLS OF *B. SPHAERICUS*

It has been demonstrated that synthesis of peptidoglycan precursor-synthesizing activities during sporulation is a consequence of gene expression at the level of transcription. It remains to be determined whether the genome expressed is that in the forespore or that in the mother cell compartment of the sporulating cell. It seems probable that these two genomes undergo at least partially differential expression from the time of their segregation by spore septum formation, and this must certainly be true after forespore engulfment. In *B. sphaericus* (10), as in other *Bacillus* species (5, 22, 24), spore coats are assembled outside the outer forespore membrane in direct contact with the mother cell cytoplasm, and this is also true for the exosporium, which is assembled close to the mother cell cytoplasmic membrane in the area surrounding the forespore (10). These events must involve a considerable proportion of the protein-synthesizing capacity of the sporulating cells, and presumably are a consequence of transcription and translation within the mother cell cytoplasm. As previously noted, the condensed appearance of the forespore cytoplasm at the time of assembly of these structures also seems to rule out a role for the forespore machinery of macromolecular synthesis in these events at that time. Since this is also the time

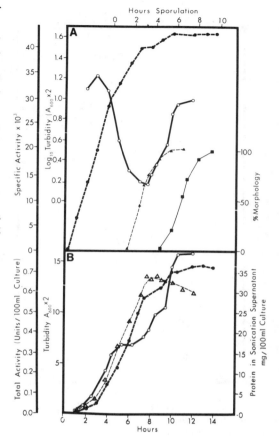

FIG. 9. *Variation in UDP-MurNAc-LAla-DGlu-meso-Dpm:DAla-DAla ligase activity during sporulation (18). (A) Specific activity data (linear scale),* O; *turbidity (logarithmic scale),* ●. *Morphology data: Percentage of terminally swollen cells,* ▲; *percentage of semi-refractile forespores,* ■. *(B) Total activity data,* O; *turbidity (linear scale),* ●; *total soluble protein released by ultrasonic disruption,* △.

during which transcription occurs which leads to accumulation of Dpm ligase activity and of all the other enzymes involved in synthesis of the cortical peptidoglycan precursor, it may also be predicted that these events occur within the mother cell cytoplasm. Moreover, this is consistent with the site of cortex synthesis.

As has frequently been emphasized (5, 18, 28), the topology of forespore engulfment is such that the space between the two forespore membranes is effectively exterior to both mother cell and forespore cytoplasms. Synthesis of the peptidoglycan component of bacterial cell walls involves production of UDP-MurNAc-pentapeptide and UDP-GlcNAc precursors by cytoplasmic enzymes and transfer of these precursors to undecaprenolphosphate at the cytoplasmic (inner) surface of the plasma membrane.

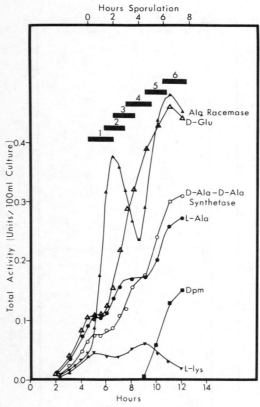

FIG. 10. *Variation in the total activity of L-Lys, meso-Dpm, L-Ala, and D-Glu ligases and of DAla-DAla synthetase and alanine racemase during sporulation. The kinetics of turbidity increase and appearance of swollen and refractile cells were those shown in Fig. 9. L-Lys ligase (▼); meso-Dpm ligase (■); L-Ala ligase (●); D-Glu ligase (△); DAla-DAla synthetase (activity × 0.5), (○); alanine racemase (activity × 0.05), (▲). The bars in this figure represent the periods during which the following morphological events occur (cf. Fig. 3): (1) postexponential cell division (Fig. 4); (2) spore septum formation; (3) terminal swelling and initiation of engulfment; (4) termination of engulfment; (5) primordial cell wall synthesis (Fig. 2D); (6) cortex synthesis (10).*

quence of polymerization by that membrane of precursors of vegetative-type peptidoglycan, synthesized within the forespore cytoplasm. In contrast, the cortex accumulates between the primordial cell wall and the outer forespore membrane, and is probably polymerized by enzymes within the outer forespore membrane from subunits made within the mother cell cytoplasm. As will be shown, the distribution of precursor-synthesizing activities within these two cytoplasmic compartments is quite consistent with this hypothesis.

Although forespores become resistant to sonic disruption after about t_5 and are recovered in the centrifugation pellet after this treatment, these forespores and even mature spores can be disrupted by grinding with alumina. When this treatment is applied to vegetative cells or sporulating cells up to t_5, the specific activities of peptidoglycan precursor-synthesizing enzymes found in the supernatant after this disruption procedure are essentially identical to those found after sonic disruption (29). Neither procedure seems to introduce selective inhibition,

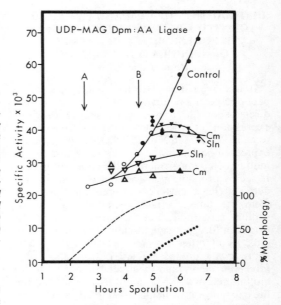

FIG. 11. *Effects of Cm and Sln on the increase in activity of DAla-DAla ligase during sporulation. The data for two separate experiments are presented: A (open symbols), antibiotics added at $t_{2.5}$ (arrow) and B (solid symbols), antibiotics added at $t_{4.5}$ (arrow). Ligase activity in control without drug (○, ●); ligase activity in cultures containing 100 μg of Cm per ml (△, ▲); ligase activity in cultures containing 100 μg of Sln per ml (▽, ▼); percentage of terminally swollen cells (– – –); percentage of semirefractile forespores (· · · ·).*

After addition of other components to complete the repeating subunit of the peptidoglycan, these lipid-disaccharide-peptide subunits are transported to the wall (exterior) surface of the membrane, where they are polymerized (27). The morphology of appearance of primordial cell wall and cortex between the inner and outer forespore membranes is consistent with this normal pattern of events: the primordial cell wall, which appears before cortex in *B. sphaericus* (Fig. 2D), is intimately associated with the inner forespore membrane, and is probably a conse-

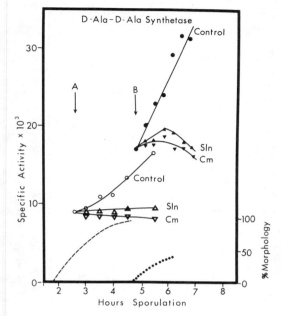

FIG. 12. *Effects of Cm and Sln on the increase in activity of DAla-DAla synthetase during sporulation. The data for the same two experiments depicted in Fig. 11 are given. Synthetase activity in controls without drug (○, ●); synthetase activity in cultures containing 100 μg of Cm per ml (▽, ▼); synthetase activity in cultures containing 100 μg of Sln per ml (△, ▲); percentage of terminally swollen cells (– – – –); percentage of semirefractile forespores (· · · ·).*

activation, or loss of activity that does not occur in the other procedure.

Cells from a sporulating culture of *B. sphaericus* were subjected to two sequential periods of sonic disruption. The first (S1) was brief, in the hope that early forespores could be recovered, and resulted in 50% breakage of the mother cells but no visible enrichment for forespores before $t_{4.5}$. The second period of sonication (S2) was prolonged (10 min) and resulted in 100% mother cell disruption. The pellet from the second disruption was further disrupted by grinding with alumina (G), and so three soluble enzyme preparations (S1, S2, and G) were obtained from each cell sample. Each was analyzed for Dpm and Lys ligase activities (Fig. 14). The proportion of total soluble protein (S1 + S2 + G) found in the supernatant from grinding (G) reached a maximum of about 8% at $t_{5.5}$ (Fig. 14A), at which point the forespores were totally resistant to sonic disruption. Before t_5, the supernatant from grinding (G) contained little soluble protein and was probably a nonspecific fraction. The two sonication supernatants (S1 and S2) were very similar to one another and before $t_{5.5}$ represented both mother cell and forespore compartments, whereas after $t_{5.5}$ they represented only the mother cell compartment (29).

At least 98% of the total Dpm ligase activity was found within the mother cell compartment (Fig. 14A), whereas the forespore compartment, which contained only 8% of the total

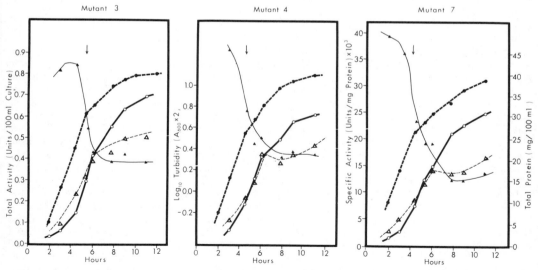

FIG. 13. *Variation in activity of UDP-MurNAc-LAla-DGlu-meso-Dpm:DAla-DAla ligase activity during postexponential growth in Spo mutants 3, 4, and 7. In each case, the presumed end of exponential growth is indicated by the arrow. Turbidity (log scale) (●). Total protein in supernatants from ultrasonic disruption (○); ligase total activity (△); ligase specific activity (▲).*

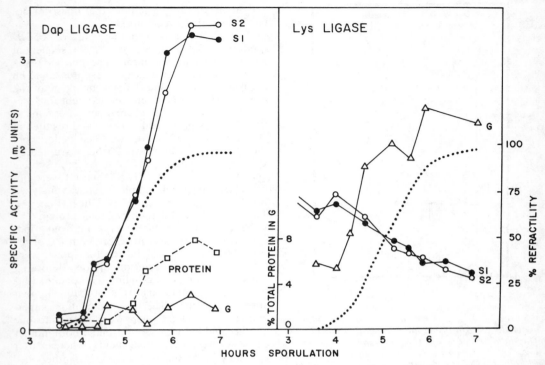

FIG. 14. *Distribution of Dpm and Lys ligase activities between sporangia and forespores during forespore development. Cells at the indicated stage of sporulation were sequentially disrupted by two ultrasonic treatments (preparations S1 and S2) and by grinding with alumina (preparations G). Ligase activities in the supernatant fractions from these procedures are presented, together with the percentage of the total soluble protein in preparations G (□). Percentage of sporangia containing semirefractile forespores (. . . . .); specific activity of Dpm ligase (left) or L-Lys ligase (right) in preparations S1 and S2 (○, ●); specific activity of Dpm ligase (left) or Lys ligase (right) in preparations G (△).*

soluble protein, contained 25% of the L-Lys ligase activity because its specific activity in the forespore fraction was threefold that of the mother cell fraction (Fig. 14B).

Data in previous experiments involving sonic disruption of sporulating cells between t_5 and t_7 (Fig. 7–13) demonstrated that the mother cell cytoplasm contains all of the activities necessary for synthesis of the precursor of cortical peptidoglycan and that all of these activities accumulate as a consequence of synthesis between t_5 and t_7. Similar data were obtained in the current experiment (Fig. 15), which shows the expected increase in specific activity, in the supernatants from sonic disruption, of L-Ala ligase activity, Ala-Ala synthetase activity, and D-Glu ligase activity. These increases occurred in parallel with the appearance of Dpm ligase activity. Since the mother cell contained 92% of the total soluble protein, even late in forespore development (Fig. 14), and all of the mother cell soluble protein

was released in fractions S1 and S2, the variations in specific activity of these fractions reflect mostly variations in mother cell enzyme contents, independent of the degree of contamination by forespore contents before $t_{5.5}$. Since the recovery of total protein in these fractions decreased only slightly between t_5 and t_7, the specific activity data (Fig. 15) also reflect the total activities (29). These data indicate that all of the cortex precursor-synthesizing activities, like that of Dpm ligase (Fig. 14), are synthesized within the mother cell cytoplasm during this period of sporulation. This is consistent with the proposed role of the mother cell in synthesis of the precursor of cortical peptidoglycan. It has been demonstrated in *E. coli* that at least some of the genes whose products are involved in synthesis of UDP-muramyl-pentapeptide are clustered and may form an operon (19, 20). The data in *B. sphaericus* are consistent with coordinate control of expression of these genes in both compartments of the sporulating cell.

In Fig. 15, the activities of Ala-Ala ligase, Ala-Ala synthetase, and D-Glu ligase in the supernatants from grinding are also shown. Although these data show more scatter, due to the greater inherent irreproducibility of this procedure, it is probable that the variations seen during this period of sporulation are not significant. These levels of activity approached those of vegetative cells (Fig. 12), and similar specific activities of all of these enzymes were found in the supernatants from grinding of clean, mature spores (Fig. 16, zero-time data). As expected, these preparations from mature spores contained no detectable Dpm ligase activity. It is thus apparent that the forespores and spores are fully prepared for synthesis of the precursors of vegetative peptidoglycan, and it seems likely that these activities are accumulated during the first period of synthesis of ligase activities in sporulation, i.e., between about t_2 and $t_{3.5}$, parallel with the engulfment of the forespore. They are then apparently stable, persisting at these levels in the mature spore. These activities would be capable of producing the precursors for primordial cell wall synthesis during sporulation and for vegetative cell wall synthesis during outgrowth following germination.

The activity of these precursor-synthesizing enzymes increases much more rapidly than does total protein during the first 30 min of germination of *B. sphaericus* spores (Fig. 16), although again D-Glu ligase appears to behave somewhat differently from the other activities. It is thus possible that coordinate derepression of synthesis of these enzyme activities is associated with the early events in germination, a period during which rapid synthesis of cell wall peptidoglycan is obviously necessary for cell survival. By the first cell division, at 180 min at 32°C, these activities have returned essentially to those of vegetative cells, as found in forespores and mature spores.

MEMBRANE-ASSOCIATED ENZYMES INVOLVED IN LATER STAGES OF PEPTIDOGLYCAN SYNTHESIS

Polymerase and Carboxypeptidases

Membrane preparations from cells of *B. sphaericus* at all stages of vegetative growth and sporulation are capable of polymerizing UDP-GlcNAc with UDP-MurNAc-pentapeptide, containing either *meso*-Dpm or L-lysine, to form lysozyme-sensitive peptidoglycan. There is no discrimination between these substrates in vitro and no reason to suppose that discrimination should occur in vivo at the level of addi-

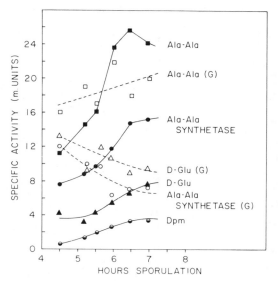

FIG. 15. *Distribution of other peptidoglycan precursor-synthesizing activities between sporangia and forespores during forespore development. The same preparations for which data on Dpm and Lys ligase activities are presented in Fig. 14 were used, but only data for preparations S1 (full lines and solid symbols) and G (dashed lines and open symbols) are presented. Data for preparations S2 were similar to those for S1. UDP - MurNAc - LAla - DGlu - meso- Dpm:DAla - DAla ligase activities (■, □); DAla-DAla synthetase activities (●, ○); UDP-MurNAc-LAla:DGlu ligase activities (▲, △); UDP-MurNAc-LAla-DGlu:meso-Dpm ligase activities (◑).*

tion of GlcNAc and polymerization of the disaccharide-peptide subunits (13). Presumably a new transpeptidase is required for forming DAla-(D)*meso*-Dpm cross-links in the cortex, but this activity was not detected in vitro, nor was there any evidence of muramic lactam synthesis in vitro.

Membranes from all stages of growth contain two carboxypeptidase activities, including an acyl-DAla-DAla carboxypeptidase I activity, which is active on both Dpm- and Lys-containing pentapeptides, and an L-lysyl-D-alanine carboxypeptidase activity, which is totally inactive on the Dpm-containing tetrapeptide (6). This is consistent with the exclusive presence of L-lysyl C termini in vegetative peptidoglycan (11) and of D-alanyl C termini in the cortical peptidoglycan (unpublished observations).

Appearance of a DGlu-*meso*-Dpm Endopeptidase Activity

In the course of studies aimed at finding unique enzyme activities in sporulating cells

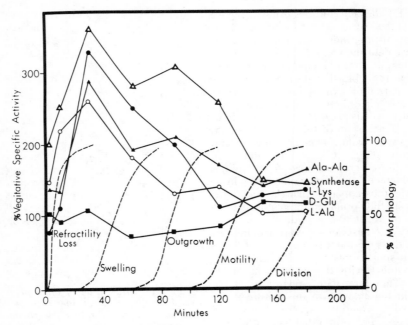

FIG. 16. *Variation in specific activity of the enzymes involved in the synthesis of the UDP-MurNAc-penta-peptide precursor of vegetative cell wall peptidoglycan during germination of* B. sphaericus *spores. B. sphaericus spores were freed of residual sporangia and sporangial fragments by treatment with lysozyme (0.25 mg/ml in 50 mM Tris-hydrochloride, pH 7.5, and 10 mM MgCl₂) for 30 min at 37°C followed by treatment with sodium dodecyl sulfate (2 mg/ml) for 30 min at 37 C. After 10 washes with water, the resultant spores were heat shocked for 1 h at 65°C in water and germinated in BS broth at 33°C. The germination process was reasonably synchronous, as shown by phase-contrast observations of the kinetics of loss in refractility and of appearance of visible swelling, outgrowth (elongation), motility, and cell division (dotted curves). Outgrowing spores did not become totally sensitive to the normal ultrasonic disruption procedure (30) until 120 min, and the data presented here are for soluble enzymes prepared by grinding of cell samples with alumina (29). The zero-time data are for mature, refractile spores after washing and heat shock (29). Total soluble protein increased about 15-fold during the course of this experiment, and culture volumes for cell samples were adjusted to yield approximately equal quantities of soluble proteins.*

of *B. sphaericus* responsible for production of L-alanine C termini, a DGlu-*meso*-Dpm endopeptidase activity was found to appear during sporulation (6; Fig. 17). The product formed by this activity would have D-Glu C termini, which are not found in the cortex. However, these might be intermediates in the formation of L-alanine C termini or muramic lactam. Since this enzyme is without activity on the analogous L-lysine-containing peptides, it is apparently uniquely involved in the metabolism of cortical peptidoglycan and therefore is a sporulation-specific enzyme, as suggested by the time of its appearance (Fig. 17). Its appearance preceded the appearance of refractile spores by about 1.5 h and therefore preceded the appearance of Dpm ligase activity by about 1 h, and mostly occurred during forespore engulfment. To be functional in cortex metabolism, this enzyme activity should be located in the outer forespore membrane, although this has yet to be

demonstrated. It might provide a useful marker for fractionation of the membranes of sporulating *B. sphaericus* cells.

CONCLUSION

The termination of vegetative growth and initiation of sporulation in *B. sphaericus* is accompanied by termination of the transcription of those genes required for synthesizing the enzymes involved in production of the precursor of vegetative cell wall peptidoglycan. These genes remain turned off during the final symmetrical cell division and during spore septum formation, but they are turned on again shortly after formation of the spore septum, probably as a consequence of derepression of the forespore genome. This results in a relatively high specific activity of these enzymes within the forespore, and particularly in a high specific activity of the L-lysyl ligase. This distinguishes the forespore

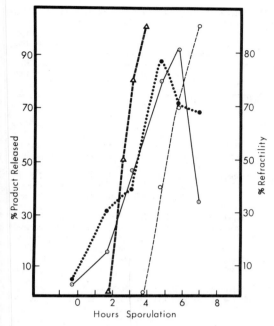

FIG. 17. *Variation in activity of D-Glu:meso-Dpm endopeptidase during sporulation in* B. sphaericus. *Percentage of terminally swollen cells (△); percentage of semirefractile forespores (○). Cells were isolated at the indicated times and were disrupted by shaking (5 min) with glass beads in a Braun MSK homogenizer in 10 mM Tris, pH 8, 20 mM MgCl₂, and 0.1 mM dithiothreitol. Membrane fragments were isolated by differential centrifugation and resuspended in the same buffer (6). Equal quantities of particulate enzyme protein (7 μg) were incubated with MurNAc-LAla-DGlu-meso-Dpm-DAla (labeled with ¹⁴C in the D-Ala residue) at 37°C for 2 h in 10 mM Tris-hydrochloride, 5 mM MgCl₂, pH 8. Substrate and product (meso-Dpm-D-[¹⁴C]Ala) were separated by thin-layer chromatography and quantitated by determination of radioactivity (6). The data are presented as percentage of substrate hydrolyzed (⊙). Equal quantities of enzymes (40 μg) were also incubated with unlabeled MurNAc-LAla-DGlu-meso-Dpm (5 nmol) in the same buffer. After 6 h at 37°C, free Dpm was determined by dinitrophenylation and thin-layer chromatography (6). Again, data are presented as percentage of substrate hydrolyzed (○).*

cytoplasm from that of the mother cell. They persist in the mature spore, and their structural genes are again derepressed during the first 30 min of germination, when there must be a heavy demand for cell wall peptidoglycan synthesis.

The only unique enzyme involved in the synthesis of the precursor of cortical peptidoglycan, Dpm ligase, is synthesized within the mother cell cytoplasm as a consequence of derepression of the mother cell genome late in sporulation.

Coincidentally, synthesis of the other enzyme activities required for cortex precursor synthesis is derepressed. The expression of these genes within the mother cell cytoplasm occurs at about the same time as expression of other sporulation-specific genes, including that responsible for a new DGlu-*meso*-Dpm endopeptidase activity and those involved in dipicolinate synthesis (30) and synthesis of the unique polypeptides involved in spore coat and exosporium production. It is possible, however, as indicated by the data of Aronson and Horn (1), that expression of the latter genes commences well before assembly of their products into morphologically identifiable structures.

The alterations in the machinery of RNA and protein synthesis which have been noted during sporulation (4, 16) are initiated before spore septum formation. It remains to be demonstrated at what point in the sporulation process (immature forespore, mature forespore, germinating spore) this machinery reverts to its vegetative status. Presumably it never does in the mother cell, and the forespore may harbor a sequence of variants from the status in vegetative cells.

ACKNOWLEDGMENTS

This work was supported by NSF Grant GB 6416 and by Public Health Service Grants HD 06518 (from the National Institute of Child Health and Human Development) and AI 10806 (from the National Institute of Allergy and Infectious Diseases).

We would like to thank Bobbye Smith for her excellent technical services.

LITERATURE CITED

1. **Aronson, A. I., and D. Horn.** 1969. Synthesis and regulation of the bacterial spore coat, p. 72–81. *In* L. L. Campbell (ed.), Spores IV. American Society for Microbiology, Bethesda, Md.
2. **Brown, N. C.** 1971. Inhibition of bacterial DNA replication by 6-(p-hydroxy-phenylazo)-uracil: differential effect on repair and semi-conservative synthesis in *Bacillus subtilis*. J. Mol. Biol. **59:**1–16.
3. **Chasin, L. A., and J. Szulmajster.** 1969. Enzymes of dipicolinic acid biosynthesis in *Bacillus subtilis*, p. 133–147. *In* L. L. Campbell (ed.), Spores IV. American Society for Microbiology, Bethesda, Md.
4. **Doi, R. H., and T. J. Leighton.** 1972. Regulation during initiation and subsequent stages of bacterial sporulation, p. 225–232. *In* H. O. Halvorson, R. Hanson, and L. L. Campbell (ed.), Spores V. American Society for Microbiology, Washington, D.C.
5. **Fitz-James, P. C., and E. Young.** 1969. Morphology of sporulation, p. 39–72. *In* G. W. Gould and A. Hurst (ed.), The bacterial spore. Academic Press Inc., New York.
6. **Guinand, M., G. Michel, and D. J. Tipper.** 1974. Appearance of a γ-D-glutamyl-(L)*meso*-diaminopimelate peptidoglycan hydrolase during sporulation in *Bacillus sphaericus*. J. Bacteriol. **120:**173–184.
7. **Hanson, R. S., and A. A. Yousten.** 1970. Unique biochemical events in bacterial sporulation. Annu. Rev. Microbiol. **24:**53–90.
8. **Helmstetter, C. E., and O. Pierucci.** 1969. Cell division

during inhibition of DNA synthesis in *Escherichia coli.* J. Bacteriol. **95:**1627–1633.

9. **Hitchens, A. D., and R. A. Slepecky.** 1969. Antibiotic inhibition of the septation stage in sporulation of *Bacillus megaterium.* J. Bacteriol. **97:**1513–1515.

10. **Holt, S. C., J. J. Gauthier, and D. J. Tipper.** 1975. Ultrastructural studies of sporulation in *Bacillus sphaericus.* J. Bacteriol. **122:**1322–1338.

11. **Hungerer, K. D., and D. J. Tipper.** 1969. Cell wall polymers of *Bacillus sphaericus* 9602. I. Structure of the vegetative cell wall peptidoglycan. Biochemistry **8:** 3577–3587.

12. **Ito, E., S. G. Nathenson, D. N. Dietzler, J. S. Anderson, and J. L. Strominger.** 1966. Formation of UDP-acetyl-muramyl peptides, p. 324–337. *In* E. F. Neufeld and V. Ginsburg (ed.), Methods in enzymology, vol. 8. Academic Press Inc., New York.

13. **Izaki, K., M. Matsuhashi, and J. L. Strominger.** 1968. Biosynthesis of the peptidoglycan of bacterial cell wall. XIII. J. Biol. Chem. **243:**3180–3192.

14. **Kornberg, A., J. A. Spudich, D. L. Nelson, and M. P. Deutscher.** 1968. Origin of proteins in sporulation. Annu. Rev. Biochem. **37:**51–78.

15. **Lawrence, P. J., M. Rogolsky, and V. T. Hanh.** 1971. Binding of radioactive benzylpenicillin to sporulating *Bacillus* cultures: chemistry and fluctuations in specific binding capacity. J. Bacteriol. **108:**662–667.

16. **Leighton, T.** 1974. Sporulation-specific translational discrimination in *Bacillus subtilis.* J. Mol. Biol. **86:** 855–863.

17. **Linnett, P. E., and D. J. Tipper.** 1974. Cell wall polymers of *Bacillus sphaericus*: activities of enzymes involved in peptidoglycan precursor synthesis during sporulation. J. Bacteriol. **120:**342–354.

18. **Linnett, P. E., and D. J. Tipper.** 1976. Transcriptional control of peptidoglycan precursor synthesis during sporulation in *Bacillus sphaericus.* J. Bacteriol. **125:**565–574.

19. **Lugtenberg, E. J. J., and A. Van Schijndel-van Dam.** 1972. Temperature-sensitive mutants of *Escherichia coli* K-12 with low activities of the L-alanine adding enzyme and the D-alanyl-D-alanine adding enzyme. J. Bacteriol. **110:**35–40.

20. **Lugtenberg, E. J. J., and A. Van Schijndel-van Dam.** 1972. Temperature-sensitive mutants of *Escherichia coli* with low activity of the diaminopimelic acid adding enzyme. J. Bacteriol. **110:**41–46.

21. **Mendelson, N. H., and R. M. Cole.** 1972. Genetic regulation of cell division initiation in *Bacillus subtilis.* J. Bacteriol. **112:**994–1003.

22. **Murrell, W. G.** 1967. The biochemistry of the bacterial spore. Adv. Microb. Physiol. **1:**133–251.

23. **Pitel, D. W., and C. Gilvarg.** 1971. Timing of mucopeptide and phospholipid synthesis in sporulating *Bacillus megaterium.* J. Biol. Chem. **246:**3720–3724.

24. **Ryter, A.** 1965. Etude morphologique de la sporulation de *Bacillus subtilis.* Ann. Inst. Pasteur Paris **108:** 40–60.

25. **Schleifer, K. H., and O. Kandler.** 1972. Peptidoglycan types of bacterial cell walls and their taxonomic implications. Bacteriol. Rev. **36:**447–477.

26. **Setlow, P.** 1974. Identification of several unique low molecular weight basic proteins in dormant spores of *Bacillus megaterium* and their degradation during spore germination. Biochem. Biophys. Res. Commun. **61:**1110–1117.

27. **Tipper, D. J.** 1972. Bacterial cell walls, p. 121–205. *In* G. D. Fasman and S. N. Timasheff (ed.), Biological macromolecules, vol. 6B. Marcel Dekker, Inc., New York.

28. **Tipper, D. J., and J. J. Gauthier.** 1972. Structure of the bacterial endospore, p. 3–12. *In* H. O. Halvorson, R. Hanson, and L. L. Campbell (ed.), Spores V. American Society for Microbiology, Washington, D.C.

29. **Tipper, D. J., and P. E. Linnett.** 1976. Distribution of peptidoglycan synthetase activities between sporangia and forespores in sporulating cells of *Bacillus sphaericus.* J. Bacteriol. **126:**213–221.

30. **Tipper, D. J., and I. Pratt.** 1970. Cell wall polymers of *Bacillus sphaericus* 9602. II. Synthesis of the first enzyme unique to cortex synthesis during sporulation. J. Bacteriol. **103:**305–317.

31. **Vinter, V.** 1963. Spores of microorganisms. XII. Non-participation of the pre-existing sporangial cell wall in the formation of the spore envelopes and the gradual synthesis of DAP-containing structures during sporogenesis of Bacilli. Folia Microbiol. **8:**147–155.

32. **Warth, A. D., D. F. Ohye, and W. G. Murrell.** 1963. Location and composition of spore mucopeptide in Bacillus species. J. Cell Biol. **16:**593–609.

33. **Warth, A. D., and J. L. Strominger.** 1969. Structure of the peptidoglycan of bacterial spores: occurrence or the lactam of muramic acid. Proc. Natl. Acad. Sci. U.S.A. **64:**528–535.

34. **Warth, A. D., and J. L. Strominger.** 1972. Structure of the peptidoglycan from spores of *Bacillus subtilis.* Biochemistry **11:**1389–1395.

35. **Wood, D. A.** 1971. Sporulation in *Bacillus subtilis*: the appearance of sulpholactic acid as a marker event for sporulation. Biochem. J. **123:**601–605.

Reversible Formation of Undecaprenyl Glucosaminyl Lipids by Isolated *Bacillus subtilis* Membranes

G. E. BETTINGER[1] AND F. E. YOUNG

Department of Microbiology, University of Rochester School of Medicine and Dentistry, Rochester, New York 14642

INTRODUCTION

The membrane composition of *Bacillus subtilis* has been reported by two groups (5, 16). Membranes from stationary-phase cells contain about 62% protein, 22% RNA, and 16% lipid by weight (5). The lipid fraction is made up of 10% neutral lipid and 75% phospholipid, consisting mostly of diphosphatidyl glycerol and phosphatidyl ethanolamine, with lesser amounts of phosphatidyl glycerol, lipoaminoacids, and diglucosyl diglyceride. The C_{55} polyisoprenyl lipid, undecaprenol, is also present, and may be found in a variety of forms as the free alcohol, undecaprenyl phosphate or pyrophosphate, or even as undecaprenyl muramyl pentapeptidyl *N*-acetylglucosaminyl pyrophosphate (17, 19). No evidence for a hexosaminyl phosphatidyl glycerol, such as exists in *Bacillus megaterium* (15), has been reported. Based on these findings, the only glucosamine-containing lipid phosphate one would expect to find in these membranes is the undecaprenyl disaccharide cell wall intermediate.

During the course of experiments attempting to synthesize peptidoglycan in vitro by isolated membranes of *B. subtilis* 168, Boylan et al. (R. J. Boylan, A. N. Chatterjee, and F. E. Young, Abstr. Annu. Meet. Am. Soc. Microbiol. 1973, p. 153) found that GlcNAc could be incorporated into a lipid fraction by the addition of only UDP-*N*-acetyl-D-glucosamine (UDP-GlcNAc) to the membranes. Moreover, the formation of this lipid reduced the incorporation of UDP-*N*-acetyl-D-muramyl-L-alanyl-D-γ-glutamyl-*meso*-diaminopimelyl-D-alanyl-D-

alanine (UDP-muramyl pentapeptide) into a product, presumably peptidoglycan. Because these glucosaminyl lipids are apparently not formed in quantity in growing cells, we have been studying the chemical composition of glucosaminyl lipids formed in vitro.

CHEMICAL PROPERTIES OF THE GLUCOSAMINYL LIPIDS

Cytoplasmic membranes of *B. subtilis*, prepared as follows, can incorporate UDP-GlcNAc into a lipid fraction (G. E. Bettinger, A. N. Chatterjee, and F. E. Young, manuscript in preparation).

B. subtilis 168 (*lys-3 trpC2 metB10*) was grown in Difco antibiotic medium 3 to an optical density at 585 nm (OD_{585}) of 1.5. Membranes were prepared by differential centrifugation from cells broken by grinding with alumina powder and stored at −70°C in 0.1 M Tris, 0.1 $MgCl_2$, 0.001 M β-mercaptoethanol (pH 8.0). All incubations were done in duplicate or, in one case, triplicate. An equal volume of membranes (15 to 30 mg of protein per ml as measured by the method of Lowry et al. [14]) and either UDP-[1-³H]GlcNAc (10 mM, 5 μCi/μmol), UDP-[6-¹⁴C]GlcNAc (2 mM, 1 μCi/mol), or UDP-[¹⁴C]muramyl pentapeptide (2 mM, 8.2 μCi/μmol), labeled in both the terminal D-alanyl-D-alanine, were mixed for in vitro synthesis. Reactions were stopped and the glucosaminyl lipids extracted by adding a quantity of chloroform:methanol (2:1, vol/vol) equal to four times the reaction volume. The extracted lipids in the organic phase were dried in counting vials before the addition of a toluene-based scintillation cocktail (Omnifluor, New England Nuclear Corp.). Aqueous samples were counted in a

[1] Present address: Microbiology Section, A. I. DuPont Institute, Wilmington, Del. 19889.

TABLE 1. *Chemical properties of the* N-*acetyl-glucosaminyl lipids*[a]

Properties of GlcNAc lipids	
Saponification	No
Acid hydrolysis (0.005 N HCl)	Yes
Hydrogenolysis	Yes
Formation:	
Bacitracin sensitive	Yes
Inhibits UDP-muramyl pentapeptide	
incorporation	Yes
Elution from DEAE-acetate:	
3 mM NH$_4$COOH	No
6 mM NH$_4$COOH	Yes
Chain length (NaBH$_4$):	
Undecaprenyl-P-P-GlcNAc	
Undecaprenyl-P-P-GlcNAc-(GlcNAc)$_3$	
Undecaprenyl-P-P-GlcNAc-(GlcNAc)$_5$	

[a] The properties of the lipids formed in vitro are summarized. See text for complete explanation.

Triton X-100:toluene cocktail (1:2, vol/vol) mixture.

The chemical properties of the extracted glucosaminyl lipids are summarized in Table 1. These lipids are not susceptible to mild alkaline hydrolysis (21) which is designed to remove the fatty acids of glyceryl phospholipids. *B. subtilis* phospholipids, labeled with ^{32}P, were completely deacylated by these conditions, whereas the undecaprenyl ^{32}P-labeled pyrophosphate was not affected.

The glucosaminyl lipids are exquisitely labile to hydrolysis by 0.005 N HCl in 50% n-propanol, and are half hydrolyzed in 45 s at 90°C. Such lability, as noted by Behrens and Leloir (2), is typical of undecaprenyl phosphate derivatives and is attributed to the unsaturated (allelyic) nature of the alpha isoprene unit (11). Catalytic reduction of the unsaturated alpha isoprene unit of undecaprenyl phosphate derivatives leads to hydrogenolysis and the release of the phosphate esterified compound (22). The glucosaminyl lipids are equally susceptible to hydrogenolysis as authentic *B. subtilis* undecaprenyl pyrophosphate or *Staphylococcus aureus* undecaprenyl disaccharide cell wall intermediate, and the glucosamine released bears a net negative charge as predicted for compounds esterified to undecaprenyl phosphate. The glyceryl phospholipids from *B. subtilis* are not affected at all by this treatment.

The in vitro formation of the glucosaminyl lipids is insensitive to bacitracin. However, membranes prepared from cells treated for 60 min with bacitracin (300 μg/ml) before harvesting are severely restricted in their ability to incorporate either UDP-GlcNAc or UDP-muramyl pentapeptide into lipid as compared to control membranes. Bacitracin is known to form a complex with undecaprenyl pyrophosphate (20) and to gradually deplete the available pool of this lipid.

Washed membranes preincubated with UDP-GlcNAc are only able to incorporate half the amount of N-acetylmuramyl pentapeptide into lipid as control membranes. The glucosaminyl lipids can be separated from undecaprenyl muramyl pentapeptidyl pyrophosphate and undecaprenyl muramyl pentapeptidyl-N-acetyl-glucosaminyl pyrophosphate on DEAE-cellulose (acetate form) using the elution scheme of Pless and Neuhaus (18). Thus, the glucosaminyl lipids are distinguishable from the cell wall lipid intermediate.

These data provide strong evidence that glucosamine is linked to the polyisoprenyl undecaprenol lipid by a phosphodiester or a pyrophosphate bond. The lipid could not be eluted from DEAE-cellulose (acetate form) in chloroform:methanol:water (10:10:3) containing 3 mM ammonium formate, but was recovered in this solvent made to 6 mM ammonium formate. Phosphodiester lipid-linked sugars are eluted at 3 mM ammonium formate under these conditions, whereas pyrophosphate-linked sugars are eluted in the higher ammonium formate concentration (3). Therefore, the glucosamine in these lipids would appear to be pyrophosphate linked to undecaprenol.

After mild acid hydrolysis of the isolated glucosaminyl lipids, the aqueous soluble material was treated with bacterial alkaline phosphatase and separated into three well-defined peaks on a column of Bio-Gel P-2. Each peak was concentrated, reduced with NaBH$_4$, and hydrolyzed (4 N HCl, 4 h, 100°C). No evidence of galactosamine was detected in the hydrolysates (10). Glucosamine and glucosaminitol were separated (8), and the chain lengths were determined from the ratio of nonreduced to reduced sugar. These ratios indicated that glucosamine was present as either a monosaccharide, tetrasaccharide, or hexasaccharide, and therefore glucosamine of three different degrees of polymerization is pyrophosphate linked to undecaprenol.

FORMATION AND REVERSAL OF LIPID

The rate of formation of lipid, measured as the total incorporation of label into chloroform:methanol extracts, and the rate of reversal of preformed lipid by 10 mM UMP is shown in Fig. 1. The lipids are formed rapidly, with half-maximal formation at 1.5 min. Once formed, the lipids were not readily chased by added UDP-GlcNAc, and therefore did not exhibit the typical characteristics of an intermediate. However,

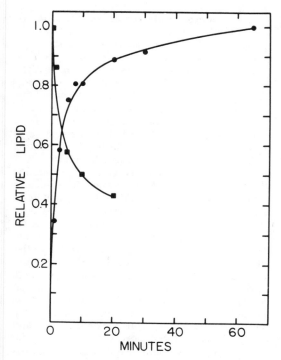

FIG. 1. *Kinetics of lipid formation and reversal. The rate of formation of the [^{14}C]N-acetylglycosaminyl lipid (●) and its rate of reversal by 10 mM UMP (■) are shown.*

the amount of isotope remaining with the membranes after lipid extraction was only 10% of the amount in the lipid, and it too was completely formed by 5 min. If this represents endogenous acceptor, it may be present in limiting amounts and rapidly saturated, thereby precluding a successful chase of the lipid, and might explain the in vitro resistance to bacitracin by limiting the number of lipid cycles possible below a level sufficient to notice an effect. In fact, the addition of 10-fold excess of unlabeled UDP-GlcNAc at 30 s did show a slight but immediate drop in the amount of labeled N-acetylglucosaminyl lipid. Once formed, about 50% of the lipid can be quickly reversed by UMP but then no additional decrease is observed. The reversal of preformed lipid by [^{14}C]UMP leads to recovery of [^{14}C]-UDP-GlcNAc (data not shown).

The inability to completely reverse prelabeled N-acetylglucosaminyl lipid by 10 mM UMP prompted us to investigate the effect of varying UMP levels on both lipid formation and reversal. Inhibition of lipid formation is concentration dependent from 0 to 10 mM UMP and 90% effective at 10 mM (Table 2). The maximum amount of reversal of the preformed lipid oc-

curred at 1 mM UMP, with increasing levels having no additional effect.

The biosynthesis of a polyisoprenyl pyrophosphate-linked sugar commonly results from the reversible transfer of a sugar phosphate from a nucleotide sugar diphosphate (XDP-sugar) onto the lipid monophosphate, with the release of XMP (12, 13). Further polymerization may occur by the addition of sugar from its nucleotide diphosphate to the nonreducing terminus of the lipid linked sugar acceptor. Normally, this transfer results in the formation of a glycoside bond, with XDP as the soluble product. This reaction may be reversed by XDP. As shown in Table 1, glucosaminyl lipids of three different degrees of polymerization are formed, and it seems likely that the partial reversal by UMP (Fig. 1) represents loss of sugar from only the lipid monosaccharide. UDP might be expected to depolymerize the oligosaccharide lipids to form the lipid monosaccharide, and theoretically a mixture of both UMP and UDP would cause complete reversal. We tested the effects of these nucleotides on both the formation and reversal of the glucosaminyl lipids to determine if they are both involved in the synthesis of these lipids.

EFFECT OF UMP AND UDP

The inhibition of the formation of the glucosaminyl lipids by UMP, UDP, or both is shown in Table 3. As was seen before (Table 2), 10 mM UMP inhibits lipid synthesis by 86%, and 10 mM UDP causes 75% inhibition. The observed inhibition by UDP is not due to its hydrolytic cleavage to UMP since less than 5% of the UDP in the reaction mixture was converted to UMP. When both UMP and UDP were added, the

TABLE 2. *Effect of UMP on formation and reversal of N-acetylglucosaminyl lipids*[a]

UMP (mM)	Inhibition of formation (%)	Reversal (%)
20		59
10	90	59
5.0		59
1.0	51	59
0.5	57	
0.1	23	46
0.05	20	
0.01	5	
0	0	0

[a] Different levels of UMP were added to membranes prior to adding UDP-[^{3}H]GlcNAc to assess inhibition of lipid formation, or to washed membranes prelabeled by incubation with UDP-[^{3}H]GlcNAc to measure reversal. The lipid was extracted after 30 min and counted.

TABLE 3. *Effect of UMP and UDP on N-acetyl-glucosaminyl lipid formation* [a]

Reaction	Lipid formed (relative)
Membranes + 10 mM UMP + mM UDP-[^{14}C]GlcNAc	0.14
Membranes + 10 mM UDP + mM UDP-[^{14}C]GlcNAc	0.26
Membranes + 10 mM UMP/UDP + mM UDP-[^{14}C]GlcNAc	0.04
Membranes + mM UDP-[^{14}C]GlcNAc	1.00

[a] UMP and UDP were added to membranes as shown prior to the addition of labeled UDP-GlcNAc. The amount of lipid formed in 30 min from duplicate samples was determined.

formation of the glucosaminyl lipid was inhibited by 96%. The observed pattern of inhibition indicates that the buildup of lipid-linked N-acetylglucosamine oligomer from UDP-GlcNAc occurs in two discrete stages.

The reversal of N-acetylglucosaminyl lipid by UMP, UDP, or both is shown in the two experiments listed in Table 4. Either UMP or UDP (10 mM) is able to reverse the preformed lipid to a comparable extent. However, when both are added simultaneously (Table 4, line 4), an additive effect is observed that is not a mass action effect since UMP is already present at 10 times the level needed for maximum reversal (Table 2). Secondly, at a time when UMP reversal is complete (30 min, as in Fig. 1), UDP addition causes further reversal (Table 4, line 3). These data support the hypothesis that formation of

TABLE 4. *Reversal of N-acetylglucosaminyl lipid by UMP and UDP* [a]

Reaction mixture	Lipid[b]	
	Expt 1	Expt 2
[^{14}C]GlcNAc membranes + 10 mM UMP	0.49	0.42
[^{14}C]GlcNAc membranes + 10 mM UDP	0.51	0.44
[^{14}C]GlcNAc membranes + 10 mM UMP, then 10 mM UDP for 30 min	0.39	0.31
[^{14}C]GlcNAc membranes + 10 mM UMP and UDP	0.37	0.26
[^{14}C]GlcNAc membranes with no additions	1.00	1.00

[a] Membranes were incubated for 30 min with UDP-[^{14}C]GlcNAc, washed, and suspended. UMP and UDP were added as shown, and the amount of lipid remaining after 30 min was determined. The results of two experiments, triplicate samples, are shown.
[b] Relative to control.

the N-acetylglucosaminyl lipids proceeds by two distinct and reversible reactions, with either UMP or UDP as the nucleotide product.

As suggested above, it seems likely that the first step in the biosynthesis of these lipids is the formation of undecaprenyl-N-acetylglucosaminyl pyrophosphate with UMP as a soluble product and further polymerization occurring by the addition of hexosamine at the nonreducing end via a glycosidic linkage and the release of UDP. This hypothesis was tested by incubating membranes, prelabeled with UDP-[^{14}C]-GlcNAc, with either UMP or UDP, extracting the lipid remaining after 20 min, performing a mild acid hydrolysis (0.005 N HCl), and fractionating the products on a Bio-Gel P-2 column. The data are summarized in Table 5. Of the remaining extracted lipid, 90% was hydrolyzed, and essentially all of this was recovered after chromatography. UMP significantly decreased the amount of free glucosamine (peak 3), which corresponds to undecaprenyl-N-acetylglucosaminyl pyrophosphate prior to hydrolysis, and did not affect the glucosamine hexasaccharide (peak 1). Lipid reversal by UDP lowered the amount of (peak 1) material corresponding to undecaprenyl-(N-acetylglucosamine)$_6$ pyrophosphate without markedly disturbing the level of monosaccharide. The increase in peak 2 material (tetrasaccharide) seen with both UMP and UDP compared to control is unexplained. We have not followed the kinetics of formation of each individual species, except to note that the relative amount of material in peak 2 varies from sample to sample. Nevertheless, the data in Table 5 confirm the independent role played by UMP and UDP in N-acetylglucosaminyl lipid formation and reversal as observed in other systems (12, 13).

CONCLUSIONS

Polyisoprenoid lipids have been found in prokaryotic and eukaryotic systems where they apparently play a major role in glycoprotein and polysaccharide biosynthesis by acting as a hydrophobic intermediate (12, 13). In bacteria the formation of cell wall, O antigen, and mannan has been shown to have undecaprenol-linked sugars as an intermediate (13). It has also been proposed that undecaprenol serves as an intermediate in the biosynthesis of teichoic acid (1) and in the formation of a poly N-acetylglucosamine-1-phosphate polymer in *Staphylococcus lactis* (6).

In Fig. 2 we have summarized the data presented here on the in vitro formation of undecaprenyl-N-acetylglucosaminyl lipids by *B. subtilis*. We have not been able to determine whether the

TABLE 5. *Chromatographic analysis of lipid reversal*[a]

Mixture	Lipid remaining	Bio-Gel P-2 column	
		Peak	Relative cpm
[14]C-labeled lipid membranes, no addition	1.00	1	0.47
		2	0.08
		3	0.44
[14]C-labeled lipid membranes + 10 mM UMP	0.48	1	0.52
		2	0.19
		3	0.27
[14]C-labeled lipid membranes + 10 mM UDP	0.61	1	0.29
		2	0.21
		3	0.48

[a] After UMP or UDP reversal, the amount of lipid remaining (shown relative to control) was extracted and hydrolyzed, and the free glucosamine oligosaccharides were separated into three peaks on a Bio-Gel P-2 column eluted with water. Peak 1 consists of hexasaccharide, peak 2 consists of tetrasaccharide, and peak 3 consists of monosaccharide. The distribution of isotope in each peak is displayed as a fraction of the total isotope applied to the column.

undecaprenyl hexasaccharide is transferred to a membrane acceptor and thereby completes a cycle; however, there is some non-lipid-soluble material formed during the in vitro reaction which is not soluble in chloroform:methanol: water (10:10:3, vol/vol/vol). This would seem to eliminate further polymerization of N-acetyl-glucosamine on the isoprenoid, since dolichyl polyglucosyl pyrophosphate formed by liver microsomes is soluble in the latter mixture (4).

We have thus far been unable to demonstrate formation of these lipids in vivo. Treatment of cells with high levels of D-cycloserine in an effort to block wall synthesis prior to formation of the lipid intermediate, thereby making the pool of undecaprenyl phosphate available as an N-acetylglucosamine acceptor, was unsuccessful. A stable L-form derived from this organism (24) and which does not form UDP-muramyl pentapeptide (9) similarly did not synthesize these lipids in vivo.

We have not studied the nonlipid material in detail, other than solubilizing it in 1% sodium dodecyl sulfate and observing its degradation by 0.5 N NaOH, at 30°C, overnight. It is not solubilized by lysozyme. From studies on the lipid it does not seem likely that the isotope is incorporated as N-acetylgalactosamine, thereby

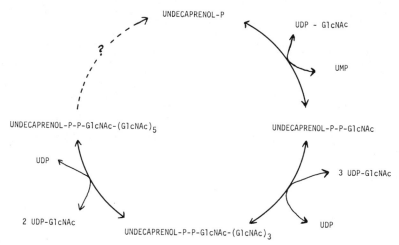

FIG. 2. *Formation sequence of the undecaprenyl N-acetylglucosaminyl lipids. A sequence by which the N-acetylglucosaminyl lipids may be reversibly formed, consistent with the data presented, is shown. The fate of the lipid hexasaccharide has not been established.*

eliminating it from being the glucosyl-N-acetyl-galactosamine polymer found attached to the cell wall in this organism and released during autolysis (7, 23). The possibility that this component is lipoteichoic acid has not been excluded.

The role of the undecaprenyl N-acetylglucosaminyl lipids is unknown. Although thus far we have only been able to identify these lipids from in vitro incubations, the enzymes responsible for their formation are present in exponentially growing cells, and represent a potential alternative to the utilization of UDP-GlcNAc and undecaprenyl phosphate in cell wall biosynthesis. Whether the formation of these lipids leads to the formation of a different polymer than peptidoglycan, or serves to modulate cell wall synthesis, remains to be determined.

ACKNOWLEDGMENTS

We wish to thank J. Tkacz and A. Chatterjee for their suggestions and advice. UDP-[^{14}C]muramyl pentapeptide was prepared by R. J. Boylan, and *S. aureus* cell wall lipid intermediate was prepared by A. Chatterjee. This work was supported by Public Health Service grant AI-0141 to F.E.Y. from the National Institute of Allergy and Infectious Diseases.

LITERATURE CITED

1. Anderson, R. G., H. Hussey, and J. Baddiley. 1972. The mechanism of wall synthesis in bacteria. The organization of enzymes and isoprenoid phosphates in the membrane. Biochem. J. 127:11–25.
2. Behrens, N. H., and L. F. Leloir. 1970. Dolichol monophosphate glucose: an intermediate in glucose transfer in liver. Proc. Natl. Acad. Sci. U.S.A. 66:153–159.
3. Behrens, N. H., A. J. Parodi, and L. F. Leloir. 1971. Glucose transfer from dolichol monophosphate glucose: the product formed with endogenous microsomal acceptor. Proc. Natl. Acad. Sci. U.S.A. 68:2857–2860.
4. Behrens, N. H., A. J. Parodi, and L. F. Leloir. 1972. The structure of the compound formed by glucose transfer from dolichol monophosphate glucose to a microsomal acceptor, p. 189–193. *In* R. Piras and H. Ponti (ed.), Biochemistry of the glycosidic linkage. Academic Press Inc., New York.
5. Bishop, D. G., L. Rutberg, and B. Samuelsson. 1967. The chemical composition of the cytoplasmic membrane of *Bacillus subtilis*. Eur. J. Biochem. 2:448–453.
6. Brooks, D. G., and J. Baddiley. 1969. A lipid intermediate in the synthesis of a poly-(N-acetylglucosamine 1-phosphate) from the wall of *Staphylococcus lactis* N.C.T.C. 2102. Biochem. J. 115:307–314.
7. Duckworth, M., A. R. Archibald, and J. Baddiley. 1972. The location of N-acetylgalactosamine in the walls of *Bacillus subtilis* 168. Biochem. J. 130:691–696.
8. Durda, P. J., and M. A. Cynkin. 1974. A procedure for the separation of glucosamine from glucosaminitol. Anal. Biochem. 59:407–409.
9. Gilpin, R. W., F. E. Young, and A. N. Chatterjee. 1973. Characterization of a stable L-form of *Bacillus subtilis* 168. J. Bacteriol. 113:486–499.
10. Heyworth, R., H. R. Perkins, and P. G. Walker. 1961. Paper chromatography of hexosamines and N-acetyl-hexosamines. Nature (London) 190:261–262.
11. Kandutsch, A. A., H. Paulus, E. Levin, and K. Bloch. 1964. Purification of geranylgeranyl pyrophosphate synthetase from *Micrococcus lysodeikticus*. J. Biol. Chem. 239:2507–2515.
12. Lennarz, W. J. 1975. Lipid linked sugars in glycoprotein synthesis. Science 188:986–991.
13. Lennarz, W. J., and M. G. Scher. 1972. Metabolism and function of polyisoprenol sugar intermediates in membrane-associated reactions. Biochim. Biophys. Acta 265:417–441.
14. Lowry, O., N. Rosebrough, A. Farr, and R. Randall. 1951. Protein measurement with the Folin phenol reagent. J. Biol. Chem. 193:265–275.
15. Op den Kamp, J. A. F., and L. L. M. van Deenen. 1966. On the structure of glucosaminyl phosphatidyl glycerol of *Bacillus megaterium*. Chem. Phys. Lipids. 1:86–89.
16. Op den Kamp, J. A. F., I. Redai, and L. L. M. van Deenen. 1969. Phospholipid composition of *Bacillus subtilis*. J. Bacteriol. 99:298–303.
17. Osborn, M. J. 1969. Structure and biosynthesis of the bacterial cell wall. Annu. Rev. Biochem. 38:501–538.
18. Pless, D. D., and F. C. Neuhaus. 1973. Initial membrane reaction in peptidoglycan synthesis. J. Biol. Chem. 248:1568–1576.
19. Rothfield, L., and D. Romeo. 1971. Role of lipids in the biosynthesis of the bacterial cell envelope. Bacteriol. Rev. 35:14–38.
20. Stone, K. J., and J. L. Strominger. 1971. Mechanism of action of bacitracin: complexation with metal ion and C_{55}-isoprenyl pyrophosphate. Proc. Natl. Acad. Sci. U.S.A. 68:3223–3227.
21. Stone, K. J., and J. L. Strominger. 1972. C_{55}-isoprenyl pyrophosphate, p. 306–309. *In* S. P. Colowick and N. O. Kaplan (ed.), Methods in enzymology, vol. 28B. Academic Press Inc., New York.
22. Wright, A., M. Dankert, P. Fennessey, and P. W. Robbins. 1967. Characterization of a polyisoprenoid compound functional in O-antigen biosynthesis. Proc. Natl. Acad. Sci. U.S.A. 57:1798–1803.
23. Young, F. E. 1966. Fractionation and partial characterization of the products of autolysis of cell walls of *Bacillus subtilis*. J. Bacteriol. 92:839–846.
24. Young, F. E., P. Haywood, and M. Pollock. 1970. Isolation of L-forms of *Bacillus subtilis* which grow in liquid medium. J. Bacteriol. 102:867–870.

Autolysins in *Bacillus subtilis*

W. CLAIBORNE BROWN

Department of Biology, University of California–San Diego, La Jolla, California 92093

INTRODUCTION

Autolysins represent a class of bacterial enzymes that are probably both essential and potentially detrimental to the cell. Thus, when growth of the cell is inhibited, rapid lysis might occur because of the presence of autolysins. The presence of these enzymes during exponential growth has led many investigators to assume that autolysins are important physiologically in such processes as cell division, cell separation, and cell wall biosynthesis. The evidence for these roles has been summarized in recent reviews (16, 18), and will not be considered here. Despite the large number of studies described in the literature, there is still no definitive information on this subject. There are several lines of investigation which might provide more insight into the roles of autolysins. For example, studies with purified enzymes (9, 25, 27) will increase our understanding of the chemical and physical properties of autolysins. A recent report provided evidence that lipoteichoic acid might regulate autolysins in *Diplococcus pneumoniae* (26). Presumably, these studies will be extended to other organisms and will involve screening for other endogenous regulatory molecules. The synthesis and activity of autolysins might also be regulated by nutritional factors and various growth conditions. Comparative studies might be conducted to determine the number, specificity, and distribution of autolysins in various bacteria. It will be interesting to determine if different bacteria will utilize the same or a different type of autolysin for a specific physiological process.

Bacillus subtilis is an ideal model system with which to investigate the physiological roles of autolysins because there is a considerable amount of information already available on the physiology and genetics of this organism. Most of the work on autolysins in *B. subtilis* has been carried out with three strains (Table 1). We have used strain 168 and its derivatives for our studies. This report will focus primarily on some of the approaches used in this laboratory to gain further insight into the physiology, biochemistry, and biological roles of autolysins in *B. subtilis*.

PHYSIOLOGICAL STUDIES

These studies were originally designed to gain some practical information on the formation and distribution of autolysins in batch cultures. It was anticipated that a set of standard conditions of cultivation could be developed which would optimize the production of autolysins and facilitate the comparison of various mutants.

TABLE 1. *Studies on autolysins in* Bacillus subtilis

Strain	Type of autolysin	State of purity	Reference
R	Hexosaminidase	Crude	29
168; Marburg	N-acetylmuramic acid L-alanine amidase	Purified	7,12,13,25,39–41
	Hexosaminidase	Partial	8,14
B	Exo-β-N-acetylglucosaminidase	Purified	27
	Exo-β-N-acetylmuramidase	Partial	11

Distribution of Autolysins

Depending on the organism, autolysins may be cytoplasmic, extracellular, or bound to the cell surface. Several staphylococci have extracellular enzymes. Richmond (29) conducted a systematic study of *B. subtilis* R and found that 80% of the activity was extracellular. Most of the studies conducted with other strains of *B. subtilis* have been based on the assumption that the enzyme was cell bound. There is little published data on the distribution of autolysin in this organism.

We have compared the specific activity of autolysin among the various components of the culture for strain 168 grown in Trypticase soy broth (TSB). Two types of cell preparations were examined. In the first preparation, intact cells were extracted with lithium chloride. The cells were then washed with water and disrupted in a French pressure cell. Another portion of cells was disrupted first in the French pressure cell, and then the cell walls were extracted with lithium chloride. The most active enzyme was found in the cell wall extracts and whole cell extracts, respectively (Table 2). These results indicated that the autolysins were primarily cell bound. Although the cell wall extract showed the highest specific activity, for large-scale purification purposes

this advantage was offset by our earlier finding that 14 times more enzyme can be extracted from whole cells (6).

Effect of Various Nutritional and Physical Factors on Formation of Autolysins in Batch Cultures

There have been no previous reports on the conditions for production of autolysin in *B. subtilis* 168. The purpose of this phase of the investigation was to evaluate the effect of different carbon sources, media, and temperature on growth and formation of autolysins in this strain.

Carbon source. Cells were grown in Spizizen minimal medium supplemented with L-tryptophan, acid-hydrolyzed casein, and different added carbon sources in 1-liter batches. Cells were extracted with lithium chloride and the extracts were assayed using sodium dodecyl sulfate (SDS) heat-inactivated cell walls (substrate walls) as described previously (6). The rate of growth was highest in the glucose and glycerol media (Table 3). However, more autolysin was produced with lactate and succinate as carbon sources. This suggested that autolysins are subject to catabolite repression. Similar results have been reported previously for the exo-β-N-acetylglucosaminidase in *B.*

TABLE 2. *Specific activity of autolysins in the growth medium and among various fractions of* Bacillus subtilis *168 grown in Trypticase soy broth*[a]

Cell prepn	Source of autolysin	Sp act (units/mg)	
		Amidase	Hexosaminidase
	Growth medium	20	7.9
Intact	Salt extract from cells	77	43
Intact	Cytoplasm from salt-extracted cells	2.6	—[b]
Mechanically disrupted	Salt extract from cell walls	276	112
Mechanically disrupted	Cytoplasm	6.6	2.6

[a] Cells were grown to mid-log phase, harvested, and washed. One portion of cells was extracted with LiCl (6). The other portion was suspended in water (20% [wt/vol]) and disrupted mechanically at 20,000 lb/in² with an automatic French pressure cell. All samples were dialyzed against 0.2 M LiCl for 3 h. The dialysis fluid was changed every hour. Enzyme activity was measured using strain 168 walls as substrate (6).

[b] —, Below limit of detection.

TABLE 3. *Effect of various carbon sources on formation of autolysins in* Bacillus subtilis *168[a]*

| Carbon source | Doubling time (min) | Activity (units/50 mg of cells) | |
		Hexos-aminidase	Amidase
Glycerol	41	66	128
Sodium lactate	60	116	350
Sodium succinate	66	200	286
Glucose	35	102	188

[a] Cells were grown to mid-log phase in minimal medium (33) supplemented with 0.02% (wt/vol) acid-hydrolyzed casein, 50 μg of L-tryptophan per ml, and 0.5% (wt/vol) of the appropriate carbon source. Enzyme was extracted from cells and measured as described previously (6).

TABLE 4. *Effect of various media on formation of autolysins in* Bacillus subtilis *168[a]*

| Medium | Doubling time (min) | Activity (units/50 mg of cells) | |
		Hexos-aminidase	Amidase
Trypticase soy broth	23	4	174
Penassay broth	23	30	154
Brain heart in-fusion	20	—[b]	40
MSGT[c]	69	—	34
MSGT + 0.02% acid-hydro-lyzed casein	37	—	148
MSGT + 0.1% yeast extract	27	—	158

[a] Cells were grown to mid-log phase in the medium indicated, extracted, and assayed as described previously (6).

[b] —, Below the level of detection.

[c] MSGT, Minimal salts-glucose medium (33) plus 50 μg of L-tryptophan per ml.

subtilis B (4). However, there have been no previous reports describing catabolite repression of an *N*-acetylmuramic acid L-alanine amidase. Growth of cells in glucose medium plus added cyclic AMP (cAMP) did not increase the amounts of autolysin associated with the walls (data not shown). This result was somewhat expected in view of some earlier findings by Setlow that cAMP did not relieve the catabolite repression in log cells and sporulating cells of several bacilli (31).

Media. Lithium chloride extracts from cells grown in various media were assayed using substrate walls (6). The results are summarized in Table 4. Hexosaminidase was low or not detected in all of the media tested. Earlier findings that this enzyme is rapidly degraded by *B. subtilis* proteases (7) might account for these results. Alternatively, this might have been due to the presence of inhibitors in the media. The growth rate and level of amidase were strongly influenced by the addition of amino acids to the minimal salts medium. The addition of yeast extract to the medium caused rapid growth and high levels of amidase. However, the autolysin formed in the yeast extract medium rapidly lost activity during storage (unpublished findings). Most of the rich media caused rapid growth and the formation of high levels of amidase. The one exception was brain heart infusion (BHI) medium. This medium caused rapid growth, but the amount of amidase formed was significantly lower than in the other rich media. Despite the lower amount of amidase produced in BHI, the cells did not form chains. We investigated the possibility that amidase was produced in BHI-grown cells but retained in the cytoplasm or released to the growth medium. The data (Table 5) did not show an enrichment for amidase in the cyto-

plasm or growth media. The amount of autolysin produced in different experiments varied markedly. However, the ratios of enzyme produced in the various media were the same as indicated in Table 4. Similar ratios were observed when the rates of cell wall autolysis were compared using walls isolated from cells grown in each medium. This suggests that less autolysin was produced in the media, although differences in lithium chloride extractability cannot be ruled out completely.

These preliminary data support the view that certain media might contain compounds which regulate the synthesis of autolysins. Experiments are in progress to determine the chemical nature of these compounds.

Temperature. The effect of temperature on growth and formation of autolysin was tested in the range of 30 to 45°C. Maximum growth

TABLE 5. *Specific activity of autolysins in the growth medium and various fractions of* Bacillus subtilis *grown in brain heart infusion broth[a]*

| Source of autolysin | Sp act (units/mg) | |
	Amidase	Hexosaminidase
Growth medium	1.5	1.6
Salt extract from cells	68	48
Cytoplasm	—[b]	—

[a] The same procedures were used as described in Table 2.

[b] —, Below the limit of detection.

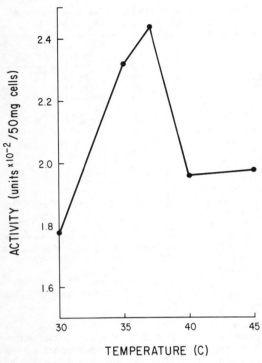

FIG. 1. *Effect of temperature on formation of N-acetylmuramic acid-L-alanine amidase in B. subtilis 168. Cells were grown to mid-log phase with Trypticase soy broth with shaking at the temperature indicated. Cells were harvested and extracted with LiCl (6). The amidase activity was measured at pH 9.5 as described previously (6).*

occurred at 45°C. Extracts from cells grown at 37°C were the most active in these experiments (Fig. 1). The results are shown only for the amidase, but similar results were obtained with the hexosaminidase. The reason for the low activity above 37°C was not clear since the amidase was completely stable for up to 30 min of heating at 50°C. Another confusing observation was that one strain used in these studies (strain BR151) formed more autolysin at 45°C than at 37°C (see Table 8). Studies using thermosensitive mutants must be planned and evaluated carefully in view of these results.

BIOCHEMICAL STUDIES

Purification and Properties of Autolysins

A major development in this field was the recent purification of three autolysins to homogeneity (Table 6). Chan and Glaser (9) purified an N-acetylmuramic acid L-alanine amidase from cell-free extracts of *Bacillus megaterium* 500-fold by salt precipitation, ion-exchange chromatography, and sucrose gradient centrifugation, Ortiz et al. (27) purified an exo-β-N-acetylglucosaminidase 700-fold from *B. subtilis* B by extraction with a high-salt solution, gel filtration, and ion-exchange chromatography. Finally, Herbold and Glaser (25) purified an N-acetylmuramic acid L-alanine amidase from *B. subtilis* 168 by extraction with high salt, chromatography on hydroxylapatite, and gel filtration. These investigators also reported the purification of a second protein (modifier protein) which combines stoichiometrically with the enzyme and stimulates its activity. Aside from its possible role as an activator, this protein might regulate the distribution of autolysins in various organisms. The basis for this idea is described as follows. The purified autolysins studied so far are relatively small molecules (Table 6) that could probably pass through the cell wall easily (R. C. Hughes, P. F. Thurman, and E. Stokes, Abstr. 1st Int. Congr. Bacteriol. 1973, p. 9). However, when the enzyme is bound to modifier protein, the size of the complex increases such that it might no longer pass through the wall into the growth medium (25). Thus, normal modifier might promote binding to cell walls. Conversely, changes in the modifier could cause the autolysins to remain in the cytoplasm or be released from the cell.

Simplified Procedure for the Preparation of Partially Purified Autolysins

Several procedures are now available for the preparation of highly purified autolysins (9, 25, 27). However, for some types of experiments, the use of partially purified enzymes might be adequate and more convenient. For example, partially purified preparations might be used in

TABLE 6. *Some properties of autolysins purified from bacilli*

Organism	Specificity	pH optimum	Mol wt	Isoelectric point	Reference
B. megaterium KM	NAMA[a] L-alanine amidase	6.8	20,000	8.2	9
B. subtilis Marburg	NAMA L-alanine amidase	8.0	50,000	NR[b]	25
B. subtilis B	Exo-β-N-acetylglucosaminidase	5.9	75,000	3.8	27

[a] NAMA, *N*-acetylmuramic acid.
[b] NR, Not reported.

the preliminary screening of different groups of bacteria or mutants for specific autolysins. Currently, we use a column containing cell walls embedded in agarose to prepare partially purified autolysins from *B. subtilis*. This method is a refinement of a previously published technique (5). When 5 M LiCl extracts of intact cells were diluted and added to the column, the autolysin was retained. Nucleic acids and most of the proteins were eluted with 0.25 M lithium or sodium chloride. The autolysin was eluted in a single step with 5 M salt. Only amidase activity was detected in this eluate (Table 7). The hexosaminidase activity present initially in the crude extract was lost during the purification. The SDS-polyacrylamide gel scan patterns (Fig. 2) give an indication of the degree of purification obtained by this procedure. A large number of protein peaks were observed with SDS-gels prepared from the crude extract (Fig. 2A). Most of the protein was removed by passage through the column (Fig. 2B). Routinely the procedure results in a 30-fold purification and 40% recovery of the amidase.

Frequently, the lithium chloride extracts of whole cells (6) contained large amounts of membrane components as indicated by the yellow color present. This reduced the flow rate of the column significantly. These components can be eliminated by a preliminary batch purification with cell walls (5), or by precipitation with 1.M calcium chloride. The latter procedure requires passage over Sephadex G-25 to remove the calcium chloride.

BIOLOGICAL ROLES

Roles in Vegetative Growth: Analysis of Autolysins in Mutants

One approach to the study of the roles of autolysins is the analysis of mutants. Several investigators have isolated and studied various morphological mutants. The primary reason for the emphasis on this class is the assumption that morphological changes might result from changes in autolysins. We have measured the levels of amidase and sensitivity of cell walls to added amidase in two types of morphological mutants of *B. subtilis*. The first type, strain 13, was isolated by J. Ito, Scripps Clinic and Research Foundation, La Jolla, Calif. This mutant forms long chains, lacks protease, and germinates slowly. The second type is represented by the thermosensitive tag mutants (strain RUB1000 and RUB1012) described earlier (2, 3, 10). The amount of amidase extracted from strain 13 was only 14% of that extracted from the wild type (Table 8). Both strains RUB1000 and RUB1012 produced less extractable amidase at the nonpermissive temperature (Table 8).

TABLE 7. *Release of N-terminal groups and reducing groups from SDS-inactivated cell walls by partially purified* N-*acetylmuramic acid* L-*alanine amidase* [a]

Time (h)	N-terminal groups[b] (nmol/mg)	Reducing groups[c] (nmol/mg)
0	24	11
3	263	15
12	501	14

[a] Cell walls (2 mg/ml [dry wt]) were suspended in buffers: 50 mM sodium phosphate (pH 6.0) and 50 mM sodium carbonate (pH 9.5). At zero time, partially purified autolysin was added and samples were removed as indicated. Soluble reducing groups (36) and N-terminal groups (17) were measured.
[b] Reaction carried out at pH 9.5.
[c] Reaction carried out at pH 6.0.

Note that strains RUB1000 and RUB1012 were compared to strain BR151 because the tag markers were introduced into the latter strain by transformation.

Cell walls from the two types of mutants differed in their sensitivity to added amidase (Table 9). SDS walls from strain S13 were as sensitive to added amidase as the wild type. When cell walls from the tag mutants were used as substrate, the sphere walls were 8 to 20 times less sensitive to amidase than the wild type. These results did not provide evidence for a clear-cut relationship between disturbed morphology and defective autolysins. Probably the major reason for this finding is that these mutant strains contain defects in a regulatory gene which control several functions related to the cell surface. More definitive information on the roles of autolysins could be obtained from an analysis of mutants with defects in the primary structure of the enzymes.

There have been no conclusive reports describing mutations in the structural gene for autolysins. Possible candidates have been isolated from *B. subtilis* (15) and *Staphylococcus aureus* (W. Wong, R. W. Gilpin, and A. N. Chatterjee, Abstr. Annu. Meet. Am. Soc. Microbiol. 1975, K109, p. 165). However, these findings have not been substantiated with biochemical and genetic data. One promising approach to this problem is based on findings by Tomasz et al. (37) that the bactericidal action of penicillin and several other cell wall antibiotics require the presence of active autolysins. Subsequently, similar findings were made by Rogers and Forsberg (30). We have used this phenomenon as a basis for selecting potential autolytic defective mutants. We have assumed that, if autolysins are required for penicillin killing, then a population of pencillin-

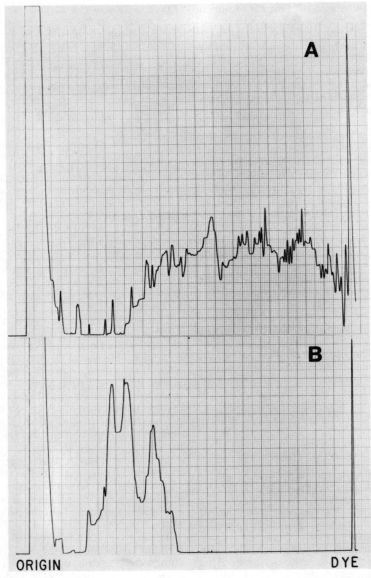

ORIGIN   DYE

FIG. 2. *Densitometry tracings of SDS-polyacrylamide gels of partially purified N-acetylmuramic acid L-alanine amidase from* B. subtilis *168. Gels were prepared and run by the method of Weber and Osborn (38). Gels were analyzed using a Joyce, Loebl Ltd. microdensitometer. (A) Protein pattern before purification on cell wall agarose column. (B) After column purification.*

resistant cells might contain some autolytic-defective mutants. We have used cloxacillin because it is resistant to the pencillinase produced by this organism (C. E. Buchanan, personal communication). The wild type is sensitive to cloxacillin in terms of the minimal inhibitory concentration (0.04 to 0.08 μg/ml).

Several colonies arose spontaneously on plates containing up to 0.4 μg of cloxacillin per ml. About 10 of these were grown to log phase in broth and tested for cellular autolysis. The rate of autolysis for these isolates was the same as for the wild-type strain.

In another experiment, we treated the wild type with nitrosoguanidine and selected for mutants resistant to 1 μg of cloxacillin per ml. One of these isolates was grown to log phase and extracted with lithium chloride. The results are summarized in Table 10. The extracts from wild-type cells contained the normal amount of autolysin. By contrast, there was no detectable enzyme activity in extracts from the mutant. There was no enrichment for autolysins in the growth medium or cytoplasm of the mutant. Though encouraging, these results must be interpreted with caution since the mutants have not been made isogenic with respect to a standard recipient.

Roles in Cell Differentiation: Analysis of Autolysins in Sporulating Cells and Spores

One area of investigation that has been relatively neglected is the role of autolysins in cellular differentiation. The bacilli are particularly attractive for such studies because they have a distinct morphogenetic cycle. Thus, during vegetative growth the peptidoglycan is modified presumably to allow for cell division, cell separation, cell wall synthesis, or rearrangement. During spore formation, lytic enzymes lyse the cell wall of the mother cell to liberate free spores. A major event in spore germination is the lysis of the cortex and the release of soluble peptidoglycan by spore lytic enzymes. Although the

TABLE 9. *Relative sensitivity of wild type and mutant cell walls to added* N-acetylmuramic *acid* L-alanine amidase[a]

Source of enzyme	Source of substrate	Relative sensitivity
S13	168	1.0
S13	S13	1.0
BR151 (30 C)	BR151 (30 C)	1.0
BR151 (30 C)	BR151 (45 C)	1.0
RUB1000 (rods)	RUB1000 (rods)	1.0
RUB1000 (rods)	RUB1000 (spheres)	0.05
RUB1012 (rods)	RUB1012 (rods)	1.0
RUB1012 (rods)	RUB1012 (spheres)	0.12

[a] Lithium chloride extracts (6) were prepared from cells grown to mid-log phase in the media as indicated in the footnotes to Table 8. Substrate cell walls were prepared by treating walls with boiling 2% (wt/vol) sodium dodecyl sulfate (6). Enzyme activity was measured as described previously (6).

precise details have not been determined for these reactions, it is clear that lytic enzymes play prominent roles in the modification of cell surfaces during cell differentiation. Most of the studies have been devoted to the autolysins formed during vegetative growth, whereas the autolysins associated with sporulation have received considerably less attention. Few spore autolysins have been studied and none have been purified to homogeneity. A major problem in this area is that most of the enzymes remain bound to insoluble spore components. To our knowledge, *Bacillus cereus* is the only organism from which a spore autolysin has been solubilized. This was first reported by Strange and Dark (34). They detected lytic activity in buffer extracts from sporulating cells and mechanically disrupted spores.

Several additional reports have appeared describing some of the properties of this enzyme (20–22, 35). We have made several unsuccess-

TABLE 8. *Comparison of relative* N-acetylmuramic *acid* L-alanine *amidase activity in wild type and morphological mutants of* Bacillus subtilis[a]

Strain	Properties	Relative activity	
		Total (units/g)	Specific (units/mg of protein)
168	Wild type	1.0	1.0
S13	Chains, 20 to 30 cells in length	0.14	0.11
BR151	Wild type[b]	1.5[c]	1.6[c]
RUB1000	Rods at 30°C; spheres at 45°C	0.18[c]	0.51[c]
RUB1012	Rods at 30°C; spheres at 45°C	—[d]	NA[e]

[a] Cells were grown to mid-log phase and extracted with LiCl (6). Strains 168 and S13 were grown in Trypticase soy broth. The other strains were grown in minimal salts-glucose medium (33) with added 0.02% acid-hydrolyzed casein and the required amino acids.
[b] A derivative of strain 168 used for the development of the thermosensitive mutants, RUB1000 and RUB1012. The mutant markers were introduced into strain BR151a by transformation.
[c] Extracts from cells grown at 30 and 45°C were measured. The ratio of 45/30°C values is shown.
[d] —, Activity produced at 45°C was below the limit of detection.
[e] NA, Not applicable; see footnote c.

TABLE 10. *Levels of* N-acetylmuramic *acid* L-alanine *amidase present in wild type and a cloxacillin-resistant mutant of* Bacillus subtilis[a]

	Units/50 mg of cells	
Strain	Expt 1	Expt 2
Wild type[b]	96	96
Mutant 1	—[c]	—

[a] Cells were grown in Trypticase soy broth to mid-log phase at 37°C. Enzyme was extracted and measured at pH 9.5 (6).
[b] Strain 168.
[c] —, Below limit of detection.

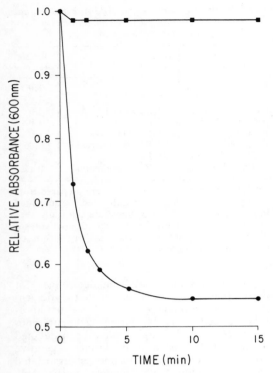

FIG. 3. *Lysis of cortical fragments by a urea-mercaptoethanol extract from spores of* B. cereus T. *The procedures for preparing extracts and cortical fragments and for measuring enzyme activity are described elsewhere (Brown and Cuhel, J. Gen. Microbiol., in press):* (■) *cortical fragments in buffer;* (●) *cortical fragments plus dialyzed urea-mercaptoethanol extract.*

ful attempts to solubilize autolysins from spores of *B. subtilis*. Consequently, we have decided that *B. cereus* T offers the most attractive system at this time for an analysis of spore autolysins. We will attempt to use the information gained from this study to develop a similar system in *B. subtilis*. The latter system will be more amenable to genetic analysis.

Our first series of experiments was designed to develop more efficient procedures for extracting autolysins from spores. The rationale used was based on the assumption that spore autolysins might be localized on the surface. This relationhip was demonstrated previously for many autolysins associated with vegetative cells. Cleaned spores were soaked in a solution containing 7.2 M urea, 10% 2-mercaptoethanol (pH 3). These conditions were shown previously to alter spore coats (19). A small amount of the dialyzed extracts was incubated with cortical fragments at 37°C. The suspension lost 45% of the original turbidity in 15 min

(Fig. 3). By contrast, cortical fragments incubated in buffer alone or with boiled extract lost less than 2% of the original turbidity during this interval. The details of this system will be described elsewhere (6a). These data suggest that spores contain a surface-localized autolysin. This enzyme could be adsorbed onto the cortex or trapped between the various protein coat layers. The physiological significance of the surface-bound autolysin has not been determined but might be related to germination and outgrowth.

Currently, we are investigating the possibility that a cell might utilize specific autolysins at different stages of the morphogenetic cycle. The basis for this hypothesis stems from a comparison of the substrate specificity of the lytic enzymes associated with sporulating cells and spores of *B. cereus* T. The three major systems studied are the "sporangial" enzymes (35), "core" enzymes(s) (21), and "surface" enzyme (W. C. Brown, R. L. Cuhel, and A. Nakamoto, Abstr. Annu. Meet. Am. Soc. Microbiol. 1975, I135, p. 139). Table 11 shows that the "sporangial" enzymes cause the lysis of cell walls and cortical fragments. The "surface" enzyme(s) is highly active against cortical fragments, but does not affect any other substrate. The "core" enzyme(s) has low activity against cortical fragments, and, in addition, promotes germination-like changes in sensitized spores. It is interesting that each of these enzyme systems has some characteristic that distinguishes it from the others.

TABLE 11. *Substrate properties of lytic enzymes from spores and sporulating cells of* Bacillus cereus T[a]

Source of enzyme	Sp act (units/mg of protein)		Germination of sensitized spores
	Cell walls	Cortical fragments	
Spore surface	—[b]	1,217	No
Spore core	—	93	Yes
Sporangia	196	1,463	No

[a] The procedures for preparation of spores, spore enzymes, and cortical fragments, and measurement of enzyme activity are described elsewhere (6a). To prepare "sporangial" enzyme, cells sporulating in G medium (23) were harvested just prior to spore release. The cells were harvested just prior to spore release. The cells were disrupted at 20,000 lb/in² using an automatic French pressure cell. The cytoplasmic fraction was dialyzed and used as the source of enzyme. Cell walls were prepared from cells grown in G medium as described previously (6). Sensitized spores were prepared (32) and assayed (20) as described previously.

[b] —, Below limit of detection.

These data suggest that differences may occur in the specificity and distribution of lytic enzymes during cell differentiation. Studies in progress might help to clarify the physiological roles of these enzymes.

SUMMARY AND FUTURE PROSPECTS

Several dramatic developments have occurred recently in the study of autolysins. At least three purified enzymes are available for study. These are all relatively small molecules, and in one case the enzyme combines with a modifier protein which stimulates its activity. Undoubtedly, purification and analysis of autolysins from various organisms will follow.

Lipoteichoic acid has been proposed as a regulator of autolysin in *Pneumococcus*. We can expect that attempts will be made to extend this finding to other organisms. Likewise, other potential inhibitors will probably be evaluated.

This study showed that conditions of cultivation can markedly influence the synthesis and/or activity of autolysins formed in batch cultures of *B. subtilis*. These findings can be used to great advantage in the preparation and analysis of autolysins from this organism.

To date, most of the mutants studied have probably been of the regulatory class. Mutants which are defective in the structural genes for autolysins are desperately needed. Continued isolation and analysis of large numbers of mutants might produce this class.

Of special interest are the findings which indicate differences in specificity and distribution of autolysins in sporulating cells and spores. Future goals should include detailed studies on the properties and regulation of autolysins formed at each stage of the morphogenetic cycle.

ACKNOWLEDGMENTS

This work was supported by Grant No. GM40035 from the National Science Foundation and an institutional grant from the American Cancer Society.

The technical assistance of Carrie Wilson is gratefully acknowledged.

I am indebted to F. E. Young and J. Spizizen for helpful discussions during this study.

Several students participated in various aspects of this work: Kathy Taylor, Sheila Lukehart, Russell Cuhel, Angie Nakamoto, Cheurchan Chantasuban, and Chris Greer.

LITERATURE CITED

1. **Berkeley, R. C. W., S. J. Brewer, J. M. Ortiz, and J. B. Gillespie.** 1973. An exo-β-N-acetylglucosaminidase from *Bacillus subtilis* B: characterization. Biochim. Biophys. Acta **309:**257–168.
2. **Boylan, R. J., and N. H. Mendelson.** 1969. Initial characterization of a temperature-sensitive rod-mutant of *Bacillus subtilis.* J. Bacteriol. **100:**1316–1321.
3. **Boylan, R. J., N. H. Mendelson, D. Brooks, and F. E. Young.** 1972. Regulation of the bacterial cell wall: analysis of a mutant of *Bacillus subtilis* defective in biosynthesis of teichoic acid. J. Bacteriol. **110:**281–290.
4. **Brewer, S. J., and R. C. W. Berkeley.** 1973. Control of the production of exo-β-N-acetylglucosaminidase by *Bacillus subtilis* B. Biochem. J. **134:**271–281.
5. **Brown, W. C.** 1972. Binding and release from cell walls. A unique approach to the purification of autolysins. Biochim. Biophys. Acta **47:**993–996.
6. **Brown, W. C.** 1973. Rapid methods for extracting autolysins from *Bacillus subtilis.* Appl. Microbiol. **25:**295–300.
6a. **Brown, W. C., and R. L. Cuhel.** 1975. Surface-localized cortex-lytic enzyme in spores of *Bacillus cereus* T. J. Gen. Microbiol. **91:**429–432.
7. **Brown, W. C., D. K. Fraser, and F. E. Young.** 1970. Problems in purification of *Bacillus subtilis* autolytic enzyme caused by association with teichoic acid. Biochim. Biophys. Acta **198:** 303–315.
8. **Brown, W. C., and F. E. Young.** 1970. Dynamic interaction between cell wall polymers, extracellular proteases and autolytic enzymes. Biochem. Biophys. Res. Commun. **38:**546–568.
9. **Chan, L., and L. Glaser.** Purification of N-acetylmuramic acid-L-alanine amidase from *Bacillus megaterium.* J. Biol. Chem. **247:**5391–5397.
10. **Cole, R. M., T. J. Popkin, R. Boylan, and N. H. Mendelson.** 1970. Ultrastructure of a temperature-sensitive rod-mutant of *Bacillus subtilis.* J. Bacteriol. **103:**793–810.
11. **Del Rio, L. A., R. C. W. Berkeley, S. J. Brewer, and S. F. Roberts.** 1973. An enzyme from *Bacillus subtilis* B with exo-β-N-acetylmuramidase activity. FEBS Lett. **37:**7–9.
12. **Fan, D. P.** 1970. Cell wall binding properties of the *Bacillus subtilis* autolysin(s). J. Bacteriol. **103:** 488–493.
13. **Fan, D. P.** 1970. The autolysins of *Bacillus subtilis* as dechaining enzyme. J. Bacteriol. **103:**494–499.
14. **Fan, D. P., and M. M. Beckman.** 1972. New centrifugation technique for isolating enzymes from large cell structures: isolation and characterization of two *Bacillus subtilis* autolysins. J. Bacteriol. **109:**1258–1265.
15. **Fan, D. P., and M. M. Beckman.** 1973. Mutant of *Bacillus subtilis* with a temperature-sensitive autolytic amidase. J. Bacteriol. **114:**798–803.
16. **Ghuysen, J.-M., and G. D. Shockman.** 1973. Biosynthesis of peptidoglycan, p. 37–130. *In* L. Levie (ed.), Bacterial membrane and walls. Marcel Dekker, Inc., New York.
17. **Ghuysen, J.-M., D. J. Tipper, and J. L. Strominger.** 1966. Enzymes that degrade bacterial cell walls, p. 685–699. *In* E. Neufeld and V. Ginsburg (ed.), Methods in enzymology. Academic Press Inc., New York.
18. **Glaser, L.** 1973. Bacterial cell surface polysaccharides. Annu. Rev. Biochem. **42:**91–112.
19. **Gould, G. W., and A. D. Hitchins.** 1963. Sensitization of bacterial spores to lysozyme and hydrogen peroxide with reagents which disrupt disulfide bonds. J. Gen. Microbiol. **33:**413–423.
20. **Gould, G. W., and A. D. Hitchins.** 1965. Germination of spores with Strange and Dark's spore lytic enzyme, p. 213–221. *In* L. L. Campbell and H. O. Halvorson (ed.), Spores III. American Society for Microbiology, Bethesda, Md.
21. **Gould, G. W., A. D. Hitchins, and W. L. King.** 1966. Function and location of a "germination enzyme" in spores of *Bacillus cereus.* J. Microbiol. **44:**293–302.
22. **Gould, G. W., and W. L. King.** 1969. Action and properties of spore germination enzymes, p. 276–286. *In* L. L. Campbell (ed.), Spores IV. American Society for Microbiology, Bethesda, Md.
23. **Hashimoto, T., S. H. Black, and P. Gerhardt.** 1960. Development of fine structure, thermostability and

dipicolinate during sporogenesis in a *Bacillus*. Can. J. Microbiol. **6**:203–212.

24. **Hashimoto, T., W. R. Frieben, and S. F. Conti.** 1972. Kinetics of germination of heat-injured *Bacillus cereus* spores, p. 409–415. *In* H. O. Halvorson, R. Hanson, and L. L. Campbell (ed.), Spores V. American Society for Microbiology, Washington, D.C.

25. **Herbold, J. R., and L. Glaser.** 1975. *Bacillus subtilis* N-acetylmuramic acid L-alanine amidase. J. Biol. Chem. **250**:1676–1682.

26. **Holtje, Joachim-V., and A. Tomasz.** 1975. Lipoteichoic acid: a specific inhibitor of autolysin activity in *Pneumococcus*. Proc. Natl. Acad. Sci. U.S.A. **72**:1690–1694.

27. **Ortiz, J. M., J. B. Gillespie, and R. C. W. Berkeley.** 1972. An exo-β-N-acetylglucosaminidase from *Bacillus subtilis* B; extraction and purification. Biochim. Biophys. Acta **289**:174–186.

28. **Richmond, M. H.** 1959. Formation for a lytic enzyme by a strain of *Bacillus subtilis*. Biochim. Biophys. Acta **33**:78–91.

29. **Richmond, M. H.** 1959. Properties of a lytic enzyme produced by a strain of *Bacillus subtilis*. Biochim. Biophys. Acta **33**:92–101.

30. **Rogers, H. J., and C. W. Forsberg.** 1971. Role of autolysins in the killing of bacteria by some bactericidal antibiotics. J. Bacteriol. **108**:1235–1243.

31. **Setlow, P.** 1973. Inability to detect cyclic AMP in vegetative or sporulating cells or dormant spores of *Bacillus megaterium*. Biochem. Biophys. Res. Commun. **52**:365–372.

32. **Somerville, H. J., F. P. Delafield, and S. C. Rittenberg.** 1970. Urea-mercaptoethanol-soluble protein from spores of *Bacillus thuringiensis* and other species. J. Bacteriol. **101**:551.

33. **Spizizen, J.** 1958. Transformation of biochemically deficient strains of *Bacillus subtilis* by deoxyribonucleate. Proc. Natl. Acad. Sci. U.S.A. **44**:1072–1078.

34. **Strange, R. E., and F. A. Dark.** 1957. A cell-wall lytic enzyme associated with spores of *Bacillus* species. J. Gen. Microbiol. **16**:236–249.

35. **Strange, R. E., and F. A. Dark.** 1957. Cell-wall lytic enzymes at sporulation and spore germination in *Bacillus* species. J. Gen.Microbiol. **17**:525–537.

36. **Thompson, J. S., and G. D. Shockman.** 1968. A modification of the Park and Johnson reducing sugar determination suitable for the assay of insoluble materials: its application to bacterial cell walls. Anal. Biochem. **22**:260–268.

37. **Tomasz, A., A. Albino, and E. Zaneti.** 1970. Multiple antibiotic resistance in a bacterium with suppressed autolytic system. Nature (London) **227**:138–140.

38. **Weber, K., and M. Osborn.** 1969. The reliability of molecular weight determinations by dodecyl sulfate-polyacrylamide gel electrophoresis. J. Biol. Chem. **224**:4406–4412.

39. **Young, F. E.** 1966. Autolytic enzyme associated with cell walls of *Bacillus subtilis*. J. Biol. Chem. **241**:3462–3467.

40. **Young, F. E., and J. Spizizen.** 1963. Biochemical aspects of competence in the *Bacillus subtilis* transformation system. II. Autolytic enzyme activity of cell walls. J. Biol. Chem. **238**:3126–3130.

41. **Young, F. E., D. J. Tipper, and J. L. Strominger.** 1964. Autolysis of cell walls of *Bacillus subtilis*: mechanism and possible relationships to competence. J. Biol. Chem. **239**:PC3600–3602.

Characterization of Patterns of Symmetrical and Asymmetrical Division in Outgrowing Cells of *Bacillus megaterium*

ANDREW M. SLEE, MYRON MYCHAJLONKA,[1] STANLEY C. HOLT,
AND RALPH A. SLEPECKY

*Department of Biology, Syracuse University, Syracuse, New York 13210; and Department of Microbiology,
University of Massachusetts, Amherst, Massachusetts 01002*

INTRODUCTION

A point of view advanced recently suggests that the early stages of sporulation may be a modified type of cell division, a key event in sporulation being the asymmetric division, which is stage II of the sporulation sequence (3, 5, 11). Such a view allows one to construct models of sporulation in which the location of the forespore septum and the timing of its appearance are determined by the same controls operative in cell division modified by step-down conditions. Thus, a sporeforming organism is capable of two types of division (Fig. 1). One type is the symmetrical division typically seen during vegetative growth; its pattern is as found in other gram-positive, rod-shaped organisms. The other observable form is the asymmetrical division which differs from a symmetrical division not only in the location of the septum but also in conditions for its formation. In most cases investigated, cell wall material is not found in the septum, but recently it was shown that the initial spore septum of *Bacillus sphaericus* apparently contains peptidoglycan across its entire width (7).

We have described a system which can be used to study the control of either type of division and their interrelationships (9, 10). In that system, the outgrowing cell after spore germination can proceed to a symmetrical division or, upon shift-down during outgrowth, can be manipulated to proceed to the spore via micro-

cycle sporulation (6, 8, 12). Since the sporulating cell must proceed through an asymmetrical division before it can form a spore, we used microcycle sporulation ability as an assessment of asymmetrical division ability.

Our first report using this system described the techniques employed and indicated that DNA replication must be initiated before cells are able to undergo microcycle sporulation (10). However, that study concluded that DNA replication may not be the only requirement that must be met before the cells can sporulate. Furthermore, under the conditions used, the DNA replicated dichotomously, suggesting that the medium used was not the most minimal for the organism and that other conditions might reveal new insights. In a subsequent study (9), we determined that in sucrose salts medium the attainment of a particular size cell was necessary and that this was accompanied by an increase in surface growth as evidenced by the incorporation of labeled glycerol and diaminopimelic acid. In addition, we used media affording different growth rates to provide other conditions; the higher the growth rate of the cells, the shorter was the time required before the cells could microcycle and later undergo synchronous divisions. The current report expands these latter findings to include the patterns of DNA synthesis in these various media and their relationship with the ability of cells to undergo asymmetric division. Of particular interest is the finding that initiation of DNA is required in all media; in addition, it appears that, in citrate salts medium, where DNA synthesis

[1] Present address: Department of Microbiology, Temple University, Philadelphia, Pa. 19140.

85

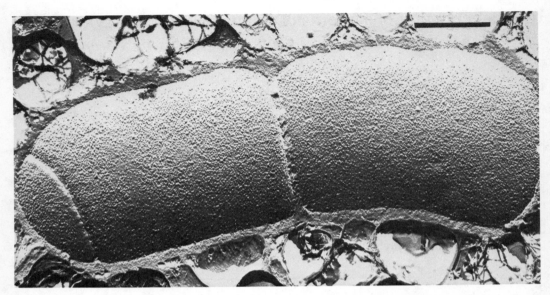

FIG. 1. *Freeze-etched preparation of* Bacillus megaterium *showing both the symmetrical and the asymmetrical (stage II) types of division. Bar = 0.5 μm.*

is discontinuous, the ability to form the asymmetric division declines after termination of DNA synthesis. Data are also presented which indicate that the medium on which the spores are grown influences the subsequent patterns of division during outgrowth.

COMPARISON OF DIVISION PATTERNS AT DIFFERENT GROWTH RATES

Spores of *Bacillus megaterium* harvested from nutrient agar plus manganese and outgrown in media affording different growth rates were examined for their ability to achieve symmetrical division and to form an asymmetrical division upon shift-down to a replacement sporulation medium (Fig. 2, 3, 4, and 5). The observed growth rates (slope of OD versus time), measured in batch cultures for sucrose salts-tryptone, sucrose salts, citrate salts, and succinate salts media, were 0.400, 0.325, 0.158, and 0.150, respectively. Cells achieved at least one synchronous symmetrical division as indicated by the stepwise pattern and doubling of cell number. In all cases a certain point in outgrowth was attained before cells acquired the ability to undergo microcycle sporulation, which showed a gradual rise to peak ability at a time coinciding with about twice the time required in outgrowth prior to initiation. The ability of the cells to sporulate declined as the cells approached the point of initiation of symmetrical

division. This increase and subsequent decrease in sporulation ability was not confined to the first symmetrical division cycle as it could readily be demonstrated in a second synchronous division in sucrose salts medium (Fig. 3) and citrate salts medium (not shown in Fig. 4). If data of all four media were normalized so that the terminations of the first symmetrical division cycle were made equal to 1, the peaks and declines of sporulation abilities occurred at the same points (see Fig. 6). Likewise, in the case of both sucrose salts and citrate salts media, if the end of the second symmetrical division cycle were normalized to 1, then during both cycles the points of peak and low sporulation ability coincided. Thus it appears that cells are only able to sporulate at certain stages of their growth cycle.

DNA SYNTHESIS AND ASYMMETRICAL DIVISION

It has been suggested, based on continuous culture experiments, that sporulation could occur only when the cells were at a particular stage in their division or DNA replication cycle (1). Others have found that cells examined at various stages of their division cycle for their ability to sporulate showed peak periods of susceptibility; however, the peak position was variable and no consistent relationship to a particular point in the division

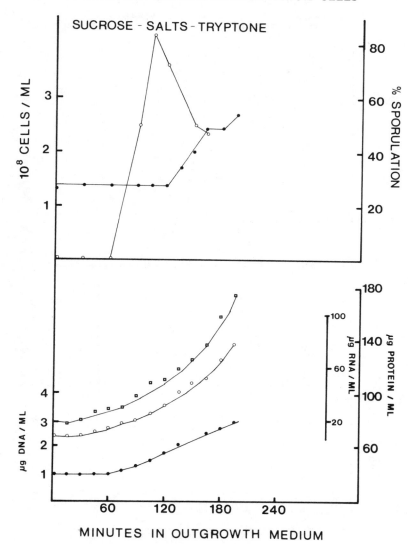

FIG. 2. *(Upper panel) Cell division during outgrowth of nutrient agar spores in sucrose salts-tryptone and the ability of these outgrowing cells to achieve an asymmetric division, and ultimately form a spore, after transfer to R medium. Symbols:* ●, *Cell number per milliliter of culture;* ○, *percent sporulation. (Lower panel) Pattern of macromolecular synthesis during outgrowth in sucrose salts-tryptone. Symbols:* ●, *Micrograms of DNA per milliliter of culture determined by the diphenylamine assay;* ○, *micrograms of RNA per milliliter of culture;* □, *micrograms of protein per milliliter of culture.*

cycle was found (2). Our findings suggest peak susceptibility prior to the onset of symmetrical division.

Previous examinations of events in sucrose salts medium indicated that DNA replication must be initiated before cells can undergo microcycle sporulation (10). The observed increase in cell mass, total RNA, and protein showed no specific correlation with the micro-

cycle pattern (see Fig. 3). Total RNA and protein showed the same pattern for the two other media in which they were determined (Fig. 2 and 4). Although the total DNA as determined chemically showed the same pattern in sucrose salts-tryptone (Fig. 2) as in sucrose salts medium (Fig. 3; reference 10), namely, that initiation of synthesis began coincident with the ability to undergo

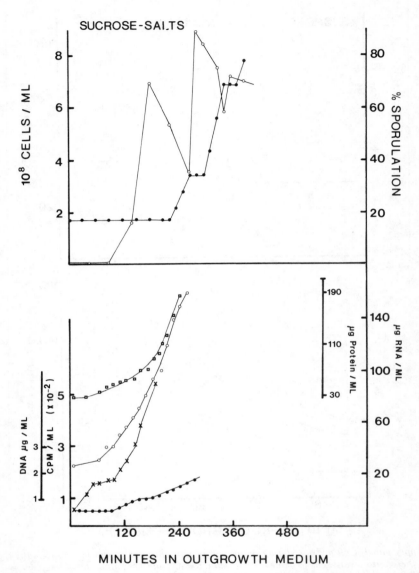

FIG. 3. *(Upper panel) Cell division pattern during outgrowth of nutrient agar spores in sucrose salts and the ability of these cells to achieve an asymmetric division, and ultimately form a spore, after transfer to R medium. Symbols; ●, Cell number per milliliter; ○, percent sporulation. (Lower panel) Pattern of macromolecular synthesis during outgrowth in sucrose salts. Symbols: ●, Micrograms of DNA per milliliter of culture determined by the diphenylamine assay; ×, DNA measured by incorporation of [methyl-³H]thymidine; ○, micrograms of RNA per milliliter of culture; □, micrograms of protein per milliliter of culture.*

microcycle sporulation, such was not the case for citrate salts medium (Fig. 4). In citrate salts medium DNA synthesis as assessed chemically was initiated almost 2 h after the initiation of the ability to undergo asymmetric division. However, if DNA synthesis was assessed by the uptake of labeled thymidine, a more sensitive indicator of DNA synthesis,

then it was seen that initiation of DNA synthesis occurred prior to the time of ability to initiate asymmetric division. Differences in patterns of DNA synthesis when examined chemically and by incorporation of labeled thymidine during outgrowth were described previously (6, 8). When the data on DNA synthesis and ability to form spores were normal-

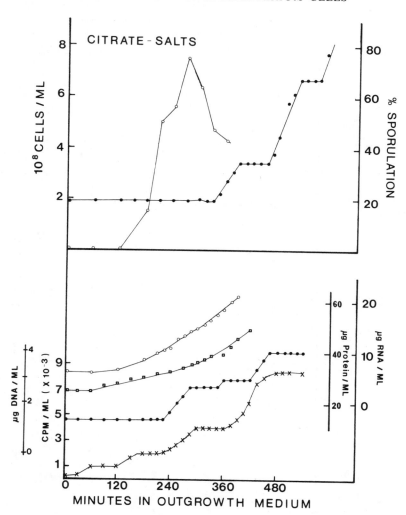

Fig. 4. *(Upper panel) Cell division during outgrowth of nutrient agar spores in citrate salts and the ability of these outgrowing cells to achieve an asymmetric division, and ultimately form a spore, after transfer to R medium. Symbols:* ●, *Cell number per milliliter of culture;* ○, *percent sporulation. (Lower panel) Pattern of macromolecular synthesis during outgrowth in citrate salts. Symbols:* ●, *Micrograms of DNA per milliliter of culture determined by diphenylamine assay;* ×, *DNA measured by incorporation on [methyl-³H]thymidine;* ○, *micrograms of RNA per milliliter of culture;* □, *micrograms of protein per milliliter of culture.*

ized so that the termination of the symmetrical division in sucrose salts-tryptone, sucrose salts, and citrate salts was equal to 1, then, in all cases and regardless of the growth rate af-

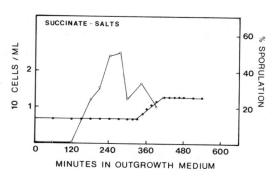

Fig. 5. *Cell division pattern during outgrowth of nutrient agar spores in succinate salts and the ability of these cells to achieve an asymmetric division, and ultimately form a spore, after transfer to R medium. Symbols:* ●, *Cell number per milliliter of culture;* ○, *percent sporulation.*

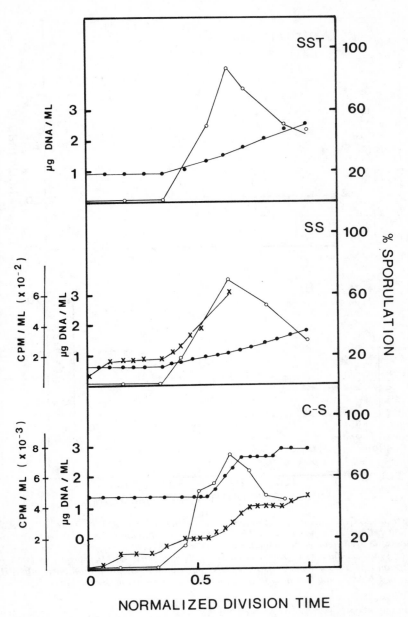

FIG. 6. *Normalized plots of the microcycle sporulation and DNA synthesis data from the previous figures. In all cases the end of the first symmetrical division was made equal to 1. Abbreviations: SST, Sucrose salts-tryptone; SS, sucrose salts; C-S, citrate salts. Symbols:* ●, *Micrograms of DNA per milliliter of culture determined by diphenylamine assay;* ×, *DNA measured by incorporation of* [methyl-^{3}H]*thymidine;* ○, *percent sporulation.*

forded by the outgrowth medium, DNA replication was a prerequisite for asymmetric division and subsequent sporulation (Fig. 6).

Discontinuous synthesis of DNA using both methods of measurement was observed when

citrate salts was the outgrowth medium (Fig. 4). If one assumes that the stepwise pattern indicates initiation and subsequent termination of a round of DNA replication, then under these conditions only one round of DNA

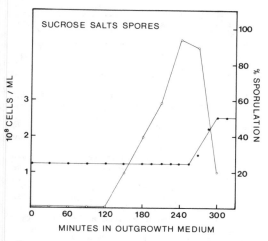

FIG. 7. *Cell division pattern during outgrowth of sucrose salts spores in sucrose salts medium and the ability of these outgrowing cells to achieve an asymmetric division and ultimately form a spore upon shift-down to R medium. Symbols:* ●, *Cell number per milliliter of culture;* ○, *percent sporulation.*

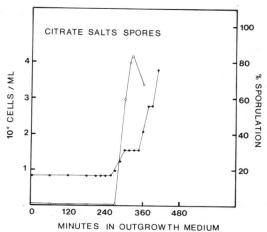

FIG. 8. *Cell division pattern during outgrowth of citrate salts spores in sucrose salts medium and ability of these cells to form an asymmetric division, and ultimately a spore, upon shift-down to R medium. Symbols:* ●, *Cell number per milliliter of culture;* ○, *percent sporulation.*

replication occurs during outgrowth as contrasted with sucrose salts medium, where dichotomous replication was observed (10). Furthermore, if one assumes that the plateau in the curves of DNA synthesis represents the time of termination of a round of DNA synthesis, then at termination the ability of the cells to form the asymmetric division declines (Fig. 4). Obviously, the use of citrate salts outgrowth medium offers much potential for answering other questions about cell cycle relationships and asymmetric versus symmetric division.

EFFECT OF SPORE SOURCE ON DIVISION

The finding that the source of the spores used had a significant effect on the subsequent patterns of division (Fig. 7, 8, and 9) was an unexpected one. The experiments outlined previously were done with spores harvested from nutrient agar supplemented with manganese. When spores were harvested from sucrose salts and sucrose salts was the outgrowth medium, there was considerable delay in subsequent division events, but the ability to microcycle preceded the symmetrical division (Fig. 7). If citrate salts was the source of the spores placed into sucrose salts outgrowth medium, the cells were unable to form asymmetric septations until after symmetric division (Fig. 8). When spores were harvested from succinate salts and outgrown in sucrose salts medium, poor sporulation ability

followed in time the ability to make symmetric divisions (Fig. 9).

The spores in the latter two cases, formed on the most minimal media allowing outgrowth, may be analogous to microcycle spores which have been found not to undergo another round of microcycle sporulation (6, 8, 12). The reason for this deficiency is not known.

CONCLUSIONS

In summary, heat-activated and germinated spores, when placed into complete defined growth media affording different growth rates,

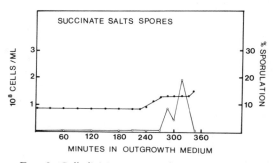

FIG. 9. *Cell division pattern during outgrowth of succinate salts spores in sucrose salts medium and their ability to form an asymmetric division and ultimately a spore upon shift-down to R medium. Symbols:* ●, *Cell number per milliliter of culture;* ○, *percent sporulation.*

outgrew and accomplished at least one synchronous symmetrical division. Cells shifted down to a defined, nitrogen-deficient medium, which supported sporulation but not symmetrical division, accomplished microcycle sporulation at specific times in the cell cycle. That ability was found to occur prior to the onset of the first synchronous symmetrical division and then declined as the cells approached that division. The pattern of microcycle sporulation was cyclic with that ability, upon shift-down from outgrowth medium, increasing again after the completion of the first symmetrical division and subsequently declining concomitant with the onset of the second symmetrical division. The ability to initiate microcycle sporulation (and thus asymmetric division) was found to be coincident with the initiation of DNA synthesis in the various media affording different growth rates. The source of the spores had a pronounced effect on the patterns of division.

ACKNOWLEDGMENT

This investigation was supported by a grant from the National Science Foundation.

LITERATURE CITED

1. Dawes, I. W., and J. Mandelstam. 1970. Sporulation of *Bacillus subtilis* in continuous culture. J. Bacteriol. **103**:529–535.
2. Dworkin, M., J. Higgins, A. Glenn, and J. Mandelstam. 1972. Synchronization of the growth of *Bacillus subtilis* and its effect on sporulation, p. 233–237. *In* H. O. Halvorson, R. Hanson, and L. L. Campbell (ed.), Spores V. American Society for Microbiology, Washington, D.C.
3. Freese, E. 1972. Sporulation of bacilli, a model of cellular differentiation, p. 85–124. *In* A. A. Moscana and A. Monroy (ed.), Current topics in developmental biology, vol. 7. Academic Press Inc., New York.
4. Greene, R. A., and R. A. Slepecky. 1972. Minimal requirements for commitment to sporulation in *Bacillus megaterium*. J. Bacteriol. **111**:557–565.
5. Hitchins, A. D., and R. A. Slepecky. 1969. Bacterial sporulation as a modified procaryotic cell division. Nature (London) **223**:804–807.
6. Holmes, P. K., and H. S. Levinson. 1967. Metabolic requirements for microcycle sporogenesis of *Bacillus megaterium*. J. Bacteriol. **94**:434–440.
7. Holt, S. C., J. J. Gauthier, and D. J. Tipper. 1975. Ultrastructural studies of sporulation in *Bacillus sphaericus*. J. Bacteriol. **122**:1322–1338.
8. MacKechnie, I., and R. S. Hanson. 1968. Microcycle sporogenesis of *Bacillus cereus* in a chemically defined medium. J. Bacteriol. **95**:355–359.
9. Mychajlonka, M., A. M. Slee, and R. A. Slepecky. 1975. Requirements for microcycle sporulation in outgrowing *Bacillus megaterium cells*, p. 434–440. *In* P. Gerhardt, H. L. Sadoff, and R. N. Costilow (ed.), Spores VI. American Society for Microbiology, Washington, D.C.
10. Mychajlonka, M., and R. A. Slepecky. 1974. Requirement of deoxyribonucleic acid synthesis for microcycle sporulation in *Bacillus megaterium*. J. Bacteriol. **120**:1331–1338.
11. Slepecky, R. A. 1969. Synchrony and the formation and germination of bacterial spores, p. 77–99. *In* G. M. Padilla, G. L. Whitson, and I. L. Cameron (ed.), The cell cycle: gene-enzyme interactions. Academic Press Inc., New York.
12. Vinter, V., and R. A. Slepecky. 1965. Direct transition of outgrowing bacterial spores to new sporangia without intermediate cell division. J. Bacteriol. **90**:803–807.

Influence of Ambient pH on the Osmotic Properties of Protoplasts from *Bacillus megaterium*[1]

R. J. BROWN AND T. R. CORNER

Department of Microbiology and Public Health, Michigan State University,
East Lansing, Michigan 48824

INTRODUCTION

Acidic conditions (pH $\leq$ 5.5) fix bacterial protoplasts against osmotic shock. The effects of acid have been detected in two different ways, which may or may not indicate that two different mechanisms with different time frames are operative. One of the mechanisms is clearly immediate protonation of cellular constituents; the other may result from changes in cellular biosynthetic processes.

Lowering the ambient pH to less than 5.5 makes protoplasts of *Bacillus megaterium* (4) or *Streptococcus faecalis* (14) resistant to osmotic stress. Acidic titration of protoplast membranes isolated from *S. faecalis* results in displacement of bound Mg^{2+}, and subsequent neutralization causes Mg^{2+} to bind again to the membranes. According to Weibull (22), Mg^{2+} ions strengthen and maintain the integrity of the membrane. They also are important in the reaggregation of dissociated membranes (1, 19). But the titration studies of *S. faecalis* membranes imply that losses rather than gains of membrane Mg^{2+} ions result in osmotic stability.

Alternatively, growth of *B. megaterium* in a medium in which the pH drops to 5.5 or below results in cells that fail to become spheres, as normal cells do, when their cell walls are digested with lysozyme (mucopeptide *N*-acetylmuramyl hydrolase, EC 3.2.1.17) in a suspending medium

of high osmotic pressure generated by impermeant molecules. Concomitantly, a change in membrane phospholipid content—an increased percentage of diphosphatidyl glycerol—occurs (17). Furthermore, the acid-induced changes in membrane phospholipids have not been shown to be directly involved in the fixation process, and it is difficult to see how an effect that is manifest almost immediately could have its basis in changes that require biosynthetic processes.

Although acid-induced chemical changes in the membrane may be responsible for the observed osmotic fixation, the mechanism remains obscure and further study is warranted. Previous investigations only compared the ability of acid-fixed protoplasts to withstand the rigors of dilution into distilled water, or dilute buffer, with that of untreated, or treated and neutralized, protoplasts. Accordingly, we first examined the effects of acid treatment on the behavior of protoplasts at intermediate osmotic pressures and then examined the effects of acid on proton binding by protoplasts. Our results suggest that acid fixation may occur at the level of the cytoplasm rather than the membrane.

RESULTS AND DISCUSSION

Effects of Ambient pH on Protoplasts

Protoplasts of *B. megaterium* were released into a 2.0-osmol/kg sucrose solution by treatment with lysozyme by the general methods of Corner and Marquis (3). The turbidity (meas-

[1] Journal article no. 7397 of the Michigan Agriculture Experiment Station.

ured as optical density) of protoplast suspensions is inversely related to protoplast volume (10, 12) and shows dramatic changes when protoplasts lyse (5). Determinations of optical densities at 650 nm (A_{650}) were carried out on suspensions of protoplasts treated with various concentrations of H_2SO_4 or NaOH after dilution into several NaCl solutions of different osmotic pressures (Fig. 1). After transfer of the initial protoplast suspension, which had been formed in a 2.0-osmol/kg sucrose solution at pH 7.0, to a 2.0-osmol/kg NaCl solution, the ambient pH was 6.4. These protoplasts showed typical osmotic behavior, swelling and eventually bursting as the osmotic pressure of their suspending medium was lowered (Fig. 1B).

Suspensions of protoplasts in which the ambient pH was adjusted to 6.6 or 7.0, with NaOH, prior to osmotic dilution (Fig. 1C) also showed typical behavior. As the pH was further increased, there was a decrease in the initial turbidity of treated samples which became greater as the rise in pH became higher. Alkaline conditions apparently enhanced the initial bursting response. Treatment with alkali reportedly disaggregates membranes of *B. megaterium* (24), thus likely accounting for the deleterious effects of high pH. However, the osmotic behavior of the survivors of alkali treatment apparently was similar to that of untreated protoplasts.

Moderately acidic conditions, pH 6.4 to 3.0,

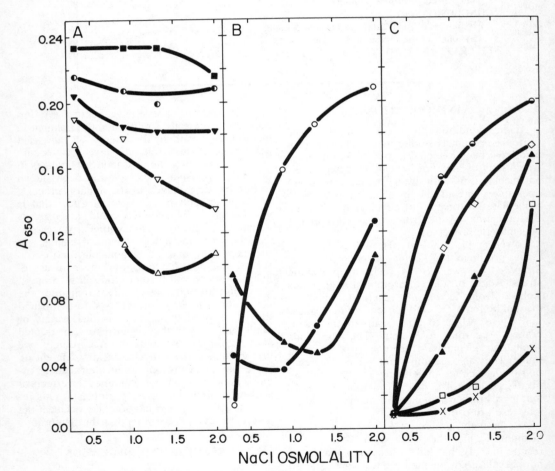

Fig. 1. *Influence of ambient pH on the osmotic properties of protoplasts from* B. megaterium. *Protoplast suspensions in 2.0-osmol/kg sucrose solutions were adjusted by the addition of H_2SO_4 or NaOH to the appropriate pH as follows: (A) 2.4 (■), 2.8 (◑), 3.2 (▼), 3.6 (▽), 4.1 (△); (B) 4.7 (▲), 5.2 (●), untreated (○); (C) 6.66 (◒), 7.0 (◇), 7.4 (▲), 8.3 (□), or 9.3 (×). Optical densities at 650 nm were then determined on samples that had been transferred to NaCl solutions of various osmolalities, which were adjusted to the treatment pH. After transfer to NaCl solution, the pH of untreated suspensions was 6.4.*

caused an initial decrease in turbidity which became progressively less as the pH was lowered (Fig. 1 A and B). On subsequent osmotic dilution, the turbidity changes in suspensions of protoplasts surviving the initial acidification were markedly different from those in suspensions of untreated or alkali-treated protoplasts. As the ambient osmotic pressure was reduced, there was an initial decline in turbidity followed by an increase. The extent of the decline decreased and the extent of the increase became greater as the pH was reduced. Eventually, at pH 4.1, the turbidity of the most osmotically dilute suspension was greater than the turbidity of the initial suspension. The turbidity response curve became progressively modified until, under strongly acidic conditions, the turbidity rose to a plateau value with decreasing ambient osmotic pressure, rather than first declining and rising. All of the effects attributable to acidic conditions were produced by HCl as well as H_2SO_4, but were not produced by LiCl, Li_2SO_4, or Na_2SO_4.

Based on the turbidity determinations, protoplasts treated at pH values in the range 3.5 to 5.2 appeared to swell and then shrink again as the ambient osmolality was reduced. As described below, further study of protoplasts treated at pH 4, hereafter referred to as "acid-treated" protoplasts, indicated that the turbidity determinations were misleading.

Osmotic Stability of Acid-Treated Protoplasts

The osmotic behavior of acid-treated protoplasts was therefore studied with a microscope. Direct counts and volume estimates were made as described by Corner and Marquis (3). Whereas untreated protoplasts swelled and burst in accord with previous observations (5), acid-treated protoplasts neither shrank nor burst when subjected to osmotic shock (Table 1). The initial acidification, however, did result in about 40% bursting in the population; but, after this bursting occurred, no further changes were elicited. Similar results were obtained when sucrose, rather than NaCl, solutions were used.

Because microscope examination revealed that osmotically shocked, acid-treated protoplasts did not change in volume or burst, it is apparent that suspension turbidity did not adequately reflect the osmotic behavior of acid-treated protoplasts. Such determinations were useful, however, in following the fixation process in a qualitative fashion.

The cause of the anomalous turbidity readings, first detected at pH 5.2, is uncertain, but may be due to acid-induced changes in the refractive indices of the protoplasts themselves

TABLE 1. *Effects of acid treatment (pH 4.0) and its reversal (pH 6.3) on the osmotic behavior of* B. megaterium *protoplasts*

Protoplast sample	Optical density ($\times 10^3 A_{650}$)	Intact protoplasts (%)	Avg protoplast vol (μm^3)
Untreated in:			
2.0-osmol/kg NaCl	208	100	2.9
1.3-osmol/kg NaCl	174	87	4.3
0.9-osmol/kg NaCl	138	54	
0.3-osmol/kg NaCl	15	2	
Treated in:			
2.0-osmol/kg NaCl	109	60	2.7
1.3-osmol/kg NaCl	95	59	2.9
0.9-osmol/kg NaCl	113	50	2.5
0.3-osmol/kg NaCl	175	56	2.5
Treated, reversed in:			
2.0-osmol/kg NaCl	47	25	
1.3-osmol/kg NaCl	25		
0.9-osmol/kg NaCl	20		
0.3-osmol/kg NaCl	17	3	

(see reference 11) rather than to acid-induced clumping of protoplasts, which was observed only at pH <4.5. Whatever the source, the effect was reversible. There was little hysteresis in the responses of acid-treated protoplasts that were subjected to osmotic dilution followed by osmotic concentration (Fig. 2). Likewise, the effect of acid treatment was reversible. Protoplasts treated with acid and then returned to pH 6.3 regained osmotic sensitivity and the optical peculiarities were eliminated (Table 1). During the reversal process, additional bursting occurred in the treated population.

Action of *n*-Butanol on Acid-Treated Protoplasts

Lytic agents, such as *n*-butanol, have been used in distinguishing between membrane fixation and general cytoplasmic fixation (2). The enhanced osmotic stability of acid-treated protoplasts could result from an increase in membrane mechanical strength, e.g., the case of formaldehyde treatment (3), or from gelation of the cytoplasm, e.g., the case of hexachlorophene treatment (2). Protoplasts with gelled cytoplasm would no longer need an intact membrane to maintain structural integrity and, therefore, should be less susceptible to butanol-induced lysis than would otherwise be the case. Acid-treated protoplasts were not lysed by treatment with 0.3 M *n*-butanol at any osmotic pressure examined (Fig. 3). Untreated protoplasts were lysed by treatment with the same concentration of *n*-butanol, and the turbidity was

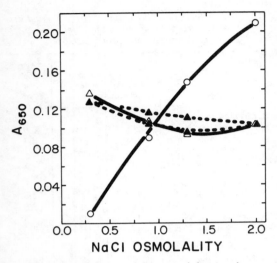

FIG. 2. *Reversibility of the optical density changes elicited from acid-treated* B. megaterium *protoplasts in NaCl solutions. Acid-treated protoplasts suspended in acidified 2.0-osmol/kg NaCl solution were subjected to sequential dilution and concentration of their osmotic environment by the addition of acidified water or acidified 5 M NaCl solution (▲). The results of single-step dilutions of untreated (○) and treated protoplasts (△) are also shown.*

reduced to about the base level achieved by lowering the ambient NaCl concentration from 2.0 to 0.3 osmol/kg.

Subcellular Location of pH Effects

Acid titrations were carried out on various preparations in an effort to determine the site at which changes in pH exert their effects. In all cases, intact protoplasts bound fewer protons than did broken protoplasts (Fig. 4), suggesting the existence of a permeability barrier to hydronium ions. In another series of experiments, broken protoplasts were separated into a soluble fraction and a membrane fraction by centrifugation, and each of these fractions was titrated. Isolated membranes bound very few protons under moderately acidic conditions, but they did show considerable binding in the region between pH 2.5 and 2.0. Since the apparent pK was about 2.35, the groups responsible were probably the phosphate groups of membrane phospholipids. The soluble fraction bound almost as many protons as the entire broken cell preparation, and the response was roughly parallel down to the pH at which membrane phosphate groups began to bind protons. Summing the contributions made by the soluble fraction and the membrane fraction produced a curve that corresponded almost exactly to the curve produced by the entire broken cell preparation. Thus, the major contributors to the observed proton binding were located in the cytoplasm. The difference between the proton binding of the intact protoplasts and that of the disrupted protoplasts must have, therefore, been caused by failure of protons to penetrate the intact protoplast membrane. As the pH of the suspending medium decreased, the number of protons bound by the intact protoplasts increased, not proportionately but in an "accelerating" fashion. Such a divergence from linearity could indicate a progressive breakdown in the permeability barrier.

There is precedent for the view that acidification results in destruction of the protoplast membrane. Exposure of cells of *Micrococcus lysodeikticus* to pH 3.0 permits titration of the cytoplasmic proteins. These proteins are not available to protons at higher ambient pH values (6, 7).

Because protoplasts of *B. megaterium* break during centrifugation (3), cell wall fragments could not be removed from any of the preparations, except the one containing the isolated membranes. Bacterial cell walls are polyelectrolytes capable of binding significant numbers of protons (13, 18), and, consequently, the threshold for the breakdown of membrane permeability cannot be deduced directly from the data in Fig. 4. Proton binding by cell walls of *B. megaterium*

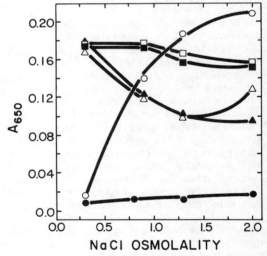

FIG. 3. *Resistance to butanol lysis of acid-treated protoplasts from* B. megaterium. *A final concentration of 0.3 M n-butanol was added to untreated (○,●), pH 4.1- to 4.3-treated (△,▲), and pH 3.6-treated (□,■) protoplasts in NaCl solutions. Open and closed symbols represent optical density determinations before and after butanol treatment, respectively.*

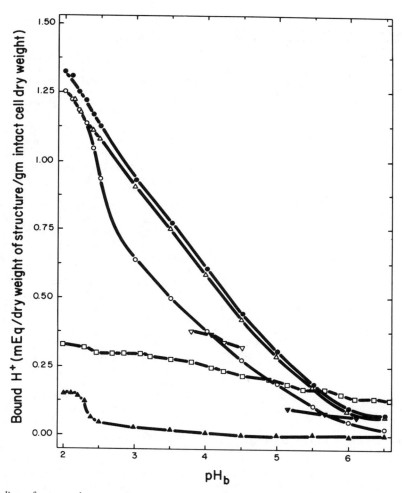

FIG. 4. *Binding of protons by protoplasts and cell components from* B. megaterium. *Intact (○) or burst (●) protoplasts and crude membrane (▲) or soluble (△) fractions were titrated with 0.1 N H₂SO₄. The concentrations of separated fractions were adjusted to be equivalent to their concentrations in the intact protoplast suspensions. The data are corrected for binding by the suspending medium (2.0-osmol/kg sucrose containing 770 μg of lysozyme per ml and 0.04 M potassium phosphate buffer). Binding by cell walls was calculated from data given by Marquis (13) for a wall contribution to the total dry weight of 20% (□), 29% (▽), or 10% (▼).*

can account for all of the protons bound by the intact protoplast suspension down to about pH 4.8 (Fig. 4), but at that pH such binding can account for only about 60% of the protons bound by the broken protoplast suspension. The cell wall binding data were computed from values given by Marquis (13), assuming that the walls comprise 20% of the total cell dry weight (21, 23). The crossover point at which all the binding in the intact protoplast suspension can be attributed to cell wall sites depends on the fraction of cell dry weight that is wall material (Fig. 4). If one uses the 29% value given by Marquis (13), the crossover point occurs at about pH 4.1; if, on the other hand, the cell wall were

to contribute only 10% of the total cell dry weight, then the crossover point would occur at about pH 5.7. It is evident that, in the intact cell, the cell wall represents an important external proton sink.

Since 10% by weight is a low value for the cell wall contribution in *B. megaterium*, the cell wall probably stops acting as a proton sink between pH 4.8 and pH 4.1. In this pH region, the protoplast apparently becomes permeable to protons. After correction for binding by the cell wall in the intact protoplast suspension, the protoplast membrane contributed less than 10% of the total binding capacity of the protoplast. Moreover, the binding capacity of the membrane

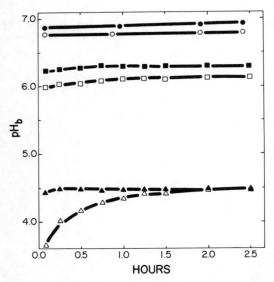

FIG. 5. *Time dependence of pH equilibrium in acid-treated suspensions of* B. megaterium *protoplasts. The bulk pH of untreated (○,●), or acid-treated protoplast suspensions, pH 6 (□,■) or pH 4 (△,▲), was measured at 15-min intervals. Intact protoplasts are represented by open symbols, and broken protoplasts are represented by closed symbols.*

was, at best (pH 2.1), less than 20% of the total capacity expressed by the intact protoplast.

Time Effects in Proton Binding

Further evidence for the existence of a permeability barrier to protons and for the acid-catalyzed breakdown of that barrier stems from comparisons of the times required to reach equilibrium after the addition of different amounts of acid to suspensions of intact or broken protoplasts (Fig. 5). The bulk pH of a suspension of intact protoplasts was initially about 6.8; that of a suspension of broken protoplasts was about 6.9. These values remained essentially constant over the time considered. When sufficient acid was added to lower the pH of an intact protoplast suspension to 6.0, the bulk pH showed only a slow drift to a higher pH, which was also reflected by a similar drift in the pH of a suspension of broken protoplasts. Again broken protoplasts exhibited a greater buffering capacity than intact ones. However, when a greater amount of acid was added, intact and broken protoplasts responded differently. Within 15 min, broken protoplasts had reached a stable pH, but intact protoplasts only slowly attained equilibrium. Furthermore, the equilibrium pH was the same in both cases. Thus, when the pH is reduced to about 4 and adequate time is allowed, the

membrane does not serve as a barrier to proton penetration.

CONCLUSIONS

Mechanism of Acid-Catalyzed Osmotic Stability

Edebo (4) originally proposed that the osmotic insensitivity of acid-treated bacterial protoplasts resulted from the denaturation of cytoplasmic proteins. Later work by Marquis et al. (14) focused on the protoplast membrane as the target for the fixation. The findings presented here seem to point more to the former mechanism than to the latter, in spite of the inherent difficulty in understanding how protein denaturation extensive enough to cause osmotic fixation (i.e., gelation) could be readily reversible. Although the protoplasts do become osmotically sensitive after reversal of the pH, they may not return to their initial state.

The essential observations leading to our tentative support of Edebo's proposal are summarized below. It should be borne in mind, however, that the arguments apply specifically to protoplasts of *B. megaterium* treated at pH 4. Since proton binding is an expression of chemical composition, other bacterial membranes may show different binding characteristics and the proton effects may be somewhat different. It is clear that acid-fixed protoplasts are not sensitive to butanol disruption and that their cytoplasmic contents are not available for dissolution into the suspending medium. Whether this results from the denaturation of cytoplasmic proteins or from a membrane that has become butanol insensitive is uncertain. At pH 4, the membrane binds only a few protons whereas the intact protoplast binds many more. Binding by the membrane, however, is about that expected on a basis of the contribution of membrane proteins to the total cell dry weight. Perhaps the strongest evidence in favor of Edebo's view is that membrane permeability appears to have broken down at pH 4, thereby allowing the protons cytoplasmic access.

Physiology of the Proton in *B. megaterium*

The results presented here suggest that the cell wall can serve as a proton sink, thereby reducing the number of environmental protons that reach the membrane. It may be more than coincidental that the growth of *B. megaterium* is severely limited at about pH 5 (20) because it is just in this pH region, 5 to 4, where the cell wall ceases to protect the protoplast from external protons. Furthermore, the apparent permeability barrier to protons also breaks down in this pH region.

Such a breakdown in membrane permeability

could have consequences not related to acid-catalyzed denaturation of cytoplasmic proteins. One of the prerequisites of the chemiosmotic theory (8, 16) of energy coupling is the presence of a membrane that is relatively impermeable to protons (15). In spite of its controversial nature, recent evidence from Harold's laboratory (9), among others, strongly supports chemiosmotic coupling in substrate transport processes. Therefore, a cell possessed of a faulty proton permeability barrier would encounter severe difficulties transporting substrates needed for growth. Similarly, at the point where the cell wall no longer shields the membrane from protons, the proton gradient may become too steep for the successful extrusion of protons as a result of metabolism. Such a situation would seriously disrupt the smooth functioning of metabolism and growth.

ACKNOWLEDGMENTS

This work was supported by National Science Foundation Grant BMS 71-01493 and by Public Health Service Training Grant GM-09011 from the National Institute of General Medical Sciences.

LITERATURE CITED

1. **Beaman, T. C., H. S. Pankratz, and P. Gerhardt.** 1974. Chemical composition and ultrastructure of native and reaggregated membranes from protoplasts of *Bacillus cereus*. J. Bacteriol. **117:**1335–1340.
2. **Corner, T. R., H. L. Joswick, J. N. Silvernale, and P. Gerhardt.** 1971. Antimicrobial actions of hexachlorophene: lysis and fixation of bacterial protoplasts. J. Bacteriol. **108:**501–507.
3. **Corner, T. R., and R. E. Marquis.** 1969. Why do bacterial protoplasts burst in hypotonic solutions? Biochim. Biophys. Acta **183:**544–558.
4. **Edebo, L.** 1961. Lysis of bacteria. 3. On the stability of protoplasts and spheroplasts in different pH-ranges. Acta Pathol. Microbiol. Scand. **53:**121–128.
5. **Eisenberg, A. D., and T. R. Corner.** 1973. Osmotic behavior of bacterial protoplasts: temperature effects. J. Bacteriol. **114:**1177–1183.
6. **Few, A. V., M. J. Fraser, and A. R. Gilby.** 1957. The intracellular catalase of *Micrococcus lysodeikticus*. Biochim. Biophys. Acta **24:**306–314.
7. **Gilby, A. R., and A. V. Few.** 1958. The permeability of *Micrococcus lysodeikticus* to hydrochloric acid. Biochim. Biophys. Acta **30:**421–422.
8. **Harold, F. M.** 1974. Chemiosmotic interpretation of active transport in bacteria. Ann. N.Y. Acad. Sci. **227:**297–311.
9. **Hirata, H., K. Altendorf, and F. M. Harold.** 1974. Energy coupling in membrane vesicles of *Escherichia coli*. I. Accumulation of metabolites in response to an electrical potential. J. Biol. Chem. **249:**2939–2945.
10. **Kuczynski-Hallman, M., Y. Avi-Dor, and J. Mager.** 1958. Turbidity changes in suspensions of gram-positive bacteria in relation to osmotic pressure. J. Gen. Microbiol. **18:**364–368.
11. **Latimer, P.** 1975. The influence of photometer design on optical-conformational changes. J. Theor. Biol. **51:**1–12.
12. **Marquis, R. E.** 1967. Osmotic sensitivity of bacterial protoplasts and the response of their limiting membrane to stretching. Arch. Biochem. Biophys. **118:**323–331.
13. **Marquis, R. E.** 1968. Salt-induced contraction of bacterial cell walls. J. Bacteriol. **95:**775–781.
14. **Marquis, R. E., N. Porterfield, and P. Matsumura.** 1973. Acid-base titration of streptococci and the physical states of intracellular ions. J. Bacteriol. **114:**491–498.
15. **Mitchell, P.** 1963. The chemical asymetry of membrane transport processes, p. 32–56. *In* H. D. Brown (ed.), Cell interface reactions. Scholar's Library, New York.
16. **Mitchell, P.** 1973. Performance and conservation of osmotic work by proton-coupled solute porter systems. J. Bioenerg. **4:**63–91.
17. **Op den Kamp, J. A. F., W. van Iterson, and L. L. M. van Deenen.** 1967. Studies on the phospholipids and morphology of protoplasts of *Bacillus megaterium*. Biochim. Biophys. Acta **135:**862–884.
18. **Ou, L. T., and R. E. Marquis.** 1970. Electromechanical interactions in cell walls of gram-positive cocci. J. Biochim. Biophys. Acta **135:**862–884.
19. **Rottem, S., O. Stein, and S. Razin.** 1968. Reassembly of Mycoplasma membranes disaggregated by detergents. Arch. Biochem. Biophys. **125:**46–56.
20. **Sakharova, Z. V.** 1970. Growth inhibition in *Bacillus megaterium* by H^+ and OH ions. Microbiology **39:**861–863 (translated from Microbiologiya **39:**978–980, 1969).
21. **Salton, M. R. J.** 1964. The bacterial cell wall. Elsevier Publishing Co., New York.
22. **Weibull, C.** 1956. The nature of the "ghosts" obtained by lysozyme lysis of *Bacillus megaterium*. Exp. Cell Res. **10:**214–221.
23. **Weibull, C.** 1958. Bacterial protoplasts. Annu. Rev. Microbiol. **12:**1–26.
24. **Yamaguchi, T., and S. Sakaguchi.** 1972. Studies on the cytoplasmic membranes of *Bacillus megaterium* KM. I. Fractionation of the cytoplasmic membranes by alkali-treatment. J. Biochem. Tokyo **71:**211–218.

Membrane-Bound Penicillinase and Phospholipid Production in *Bacillus licheniformis* 749/C

BRIAN N. DANCER and J. OLIVER LAMPEN

Waksman Institute of Microbiology, Rutgers University, The State University of New Jersey, New Brunswick, New Jersey 08903

INTRODUCTION

Bacillus licheniformis 749/C produces two penicillinases (β-lactamase, EC 3.5.2.6)—a hydrophilic exoenzyme and a hydrophobic membrane-bound enzyme (8, 12, 13, 15, 16). The latter is a novel type of protein with phosphatidylserine as the NH_2 terminus and can be converted to a form almost identical to the exoenzyme by trypsin treatment (1, 17, 18, 21). In the conversion, the enzyme loses a peptide containing 25 amino acids and the phospholipid from the NH_2 terminus. In vivo, the bulk of the membrane-bound enzyme is not a precursor of the exoenzyme (3). However, from genetic studies it appears that both enzymes are products of the same gene (6, 19). Thus, it is likely that one enzyme is an obligate intermediate in formation of the other or that both are derived from a common precursor. In an attempt to resolve this we have undertaken in vitro protein synthesis experiments to demonstrate the nature of the active polypeptide made by the ribosomes.

IN VITRO SYNTHESIS OF PENICILLINASE IN EXTRACTS OF *B. LICHENIFORMIS*

Davies (4) developed an in vitro amino acid incorporation system for *B. licheniformis* which used S-30 supernatants of cell lysates. This was considered capable only of completing polypeptide chains, not initiating new ones. This system was sufficient for our purpose and, since *B. licheniformis* 749/C is a magnoconstitutive mutant with up to 2% of its protein as penicillinase, it was likely that extracts would produce enough of the enzyme to allow the detection of its activity.

The cell extract was made from cells growing in nutrient broth (200 ml), which had been harvested at mid-exponential phase and suspended in 10 ml of protoplasting medium (14) containing 100 μg of lysozyme per ml. After 5 min of incubation at 30°C, the cells were weakened but retained their shape. They were recentrifuged and resuspended in 0.8 ml of protoplasting medium without lysozyme. This was mixed with a solution (1.2 ml) containing Brij 58 (0.83%), $(CH_3COO)_2$ Mg (17 mM), Tris-hydrochloride (17 mM), KCl (83 mM), and 1.7 μg of DNase (electrophoretically pure) (EC 3.1.4.5). Lysis was allowed to take place for 5 min at 4°C, and then the cloudy lysate was centrifuged at $5,000 \times g$ for 5 min and $30,000 \times g$ for 30 min. Only the topmost portion of the supernatant (1.0 ml of S-30 containing about 6 mg of protein) was used in further experiments.

The incubation mixture for in vitro protein synthesis contained Tris-hydrochloride (10 mM), magnesium acetate (10 mM), KCl (50 mM), 20 L-amino acids (0.04 mM each), ATP (2 mM), GTP (0.2 mM), pyruvate kinase (0.02 mg/ml) (EC 2.7.1.40), dithiothreitol (5 mM), phosphoenolpyruvate (5 mM), and S-30 supernatant (0.4 mg of protein), final pH 7.8. After reaction at 35°C for 60 min, the mixture contained about 60 U of penicillinase per ml compared to about 5 U/ml before incubation or in a control containing chloramphenicol (50 μg/ml). (One unit of penicillinase hydrolyzes 1 μmol of benzylpenicillin per h at 30°C, and the maximum specific activity of *B. licheniformis*

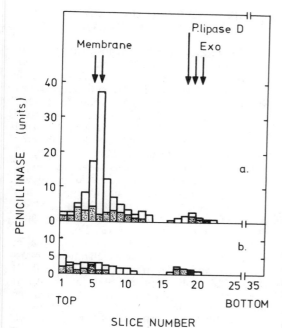

Fig. 1. *Polyacrylamide gel electrophoresis of penicillinase synthesized in a cell-free system. Penicillinase from the in vitro protein synthesis mixture was purified by affinity chromatography on Sepharose 4B-cephalosporin C (3) and lyophilized. The lyophilized material was taken up in 0.3 ml of 0.05 M Tris-hydrochloride (pH 6.7) containing 25% glycerol and 0.005% bromophenol blue. A portion of this (20 μl) was applied to a 7.5% polyacrylamide gel and subjected to electrophoresis at 3 mA per tube until the tracking dye reached the bottom. The gels were cut into 2-mm slices, each of which was macerated with 5 ml of 0.1 M phosphate buffer (pH 7.0) containing 0.1% TDC. Elution was allowed to proceed overnight before penicillinase was assayed in each fraction. (a) Open boxes, Complete in vitro protein synthesis mixture; shaded boxes, unincubated reaction mixture. (b) Open boxes, No energy source in the reaction mixture; shaded boxes, complete mixture with chloramphenicol (50 μg/ml).*

penicillinase is about 340 U/μg of Lowry protein.) The penicillinase produced was purified by affinity chromatography on Sepharose 4B-cephalosporin C (3), concentrated (final volume of 0.3 ml), and subjected to electrophoresis in 7.5% polyacrylamide gels by the procedure of Davis (5). The gels were freed of reactants by prerunning for 1 h at 3 mA per tube. The samples (20 μl) were then introduced, and electrophoresis was continued until the tracking dye reached the bottom of the gel. Under these conditions the membrane-bound enzyme just entered the gel, whereas the exoenzyme reached about the middle of the gel. A sample

of the membrane-bound enzyme which had been treated with phospholipase D to remove the phospholipid group (17) showed almost the same mobility as the exoenzyme. The enzyme made in vitro was all of the membrane-bound type, indicating that the phospholipid was already attached (Fig. 1). The suggestion that penicillinase is synthesized with phosphatidylserine already covalently attached to the enzyme led us to investigate phospholipid metabolism in *B. licheniformis* to elucidate the mode of attachment of phospholipid to the enzyme.

PHOSPHOLIPIDS OF *B. LICHENIFORMIS*

The work of Patterson and Lennarz (11) suggests that, in bacilli, phospholipids are made by the usual bacterial pathways, i.e., CDP-diglyceride is a common precursor of phosphatidylglycerol and cardiolipin in one pathway and of phosphatidylserine and phosphatidylethanolamine in another. Morman and White (10), in investigating the membrane phospholipids

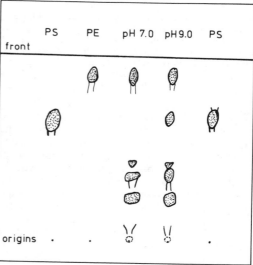

Fig. 2. *Thin-layer chromatography of chloroform-methanol extracts of* B. licheniformis *whole cells. Cultures (1 liter) were harvested at mid-exponential phase and suspended in either 0.1 M phosphate buffer (pH 7.0) or 0.1 M Tris-hydrochloride (pH 9.0) (10 ml). These were extracted with chloroform-methanol (2), and the chloroform-soluble material was applied to a thin-layer chromatography plate (Silica Gel G, 0.25 mm). The plates were developed in chloroform-methanol-acetic acid-water (25:15:4:2, vol/vol/vol/vol) and sprayed with ninhydrin (0.2%) in acetone-lutidine (9:1, vol/vol). The R_f of ninhydrin-reactive spots was compared with those of pure phosphatidylserine (PS) and phosphatidylethanolamine (PE).*

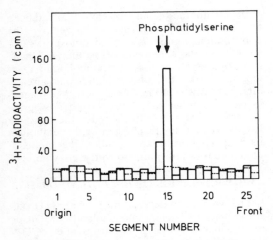

FIG. 3. *Thin-layer chromatography of chloroform extracts of tRNA. Reisolated tRNA which had been treated in a procedure designed to attach phospholipid to [3-³H]serine tRNA (see text) was suspended in either 0.1 M acetate buffer at pH 4.0 or 0.1 M Tris-hydrochloride at pH 9.0 and incubated for 60 min at 35°C. Chloroform extracts were prepared and chromatographed with appropriate standards as described for Fig. 2. The lanes containing standards were sprayed with ninhydrin; those containing the extracts were divided into segments (0.5 cm) which were scraped off, and the radioactivity was measured in Aquasol-water (5 ml:0.5 ml) with a Packard Tri-Carb scintillation counter. Solid line, pH 9.0 extract; broken line, pH 4.0 extract.*

of *B. licheniformis* 749/C, could find no free phosphatidylserine. This possibly indicates the presence of an active decarboxylase causing rapid conversion to phosphatidylethanolamine. To confirm their observation we made extracts by the Bligh and Dyer procedure (2) with the cells initially suspended in 0.1 M phosphate buffer (pH 7.0). The chloroform extracts were applied to thin-layer chromatography plates (Silica Gel G, 0.25 mM) and developed in chloroform-methanol-acetic acid-water (25:15:4: 2, vol/vol/vol/vol) (20). The amino phospholipids were detected with ninhydrin. Under these conditions, no free phosphatidylserine was detectable (Fig. 2). However, if extracts were prepared from cells suspended in 0.1 M Tris-hydrochloride (pH 9.0), phosphatidylserine was now detectable. This seemed to indicate that the phospholipid was normally complexed through an alkali-labile linkage which was probably cleaved non-enzymatically since it occurred with chloroform-methanol present. Such extreme lability is known for the ester linkage between tRNA and amino acids. Accordingly, we examined nucleic acid fractions for bound phosphatidylserine.

PHOSPHATIDYLSERINE CONTENT OF NUCLEIC ACID FRACTIONS

RNA was isolated by phenol extraction and ethanol precipitation (7) from cells grown in broth which were suspended in 1 mM Tris-hydrochloride (pH 7.2) containing 10 mM MgCl₂ and 0.1% taurodeoxycholate (TDC, anionic detergent). The ethanol precipitate was redissolved in 0.3 M sodium acetate (pH 7.0) containing 0.1% TDC and then subjected to 2-propanol fractionation (22).

The tRNA purified in this way was free of high-molecular-weight nucleic acid, as determined by Sephadex G-75 chromatography, and was entirely free of protein as judged by the Lowry technique (9). The ratio of absorbance at 260 nm to that at 280 nm was 2.0.

The tRNA fraction was the only one in this 2-propanol purification which released phosphatidylserine upon treatment at pH 9.0. If the tRNA was kept at pH 4.0 in 0.1 M acetate buffer containing 0.1% TDC, then no phosphatidylserine was detected. It therefore seemed likely that tRNA with phosphatidylserine attached is a normal constituent of cells and that the phospholipid is bound in the same way as the usual amino acids. The phosphatidylseryl tRNA may be present in abnormally large amounts in our strain. However, even here, the quantity present was insufficient for detailed characterization.

IN VITRO ATTACHMENT OF PHOS-PHOLIPID TO tRNA

Presumably, the phosphatidylseryl tRNA extracted from cells represented only a fraction of their maximum content and reflected the physiological condition of the cells. To obtain more material, we have turned our efforts to in vitro production of phosphatidylseryl tRNA from purified *B. licheniformis* tRNA.

By analogy with the usual phospholipid biosynthetic pathway, it seemed likely that synthesis would occur through CDP-diglyceride. We eventually found that we could prepare the phosphatidylseryl tRNA from CTP, phosphatidic acid, and seryl tRNA. The extracted tRNA was deaminoacylated and then reaminoacylated with [3-³H]serine and the other 19 amino acids (7). The product was used in the following incubation mixture: Tris-hydrochloride, 10 mM; magnesium acetate, 10 mM; KCl, 50 mM; CTP, 3 mM; phosphatidic acid (ex-egg yolk lecithin), 1 mg/ml; S-30 supernatant, 1 mg/ml; tRNA, 5 mg/ml; final pH 7.2. This was incubated at 35°C for

60 min and then the tRNA was extracted as before.

The reisolated tRNA was dissolved in 0.1 M acetate buffer (pH 4.0) with 0.1% TDC. Chloroform-methanol extraction showed no phosphatidylserine. However, if the tRNA was dissolved in 0.1 M Tris-hydrochloride (pH 9.0) and incubated for 60 min at 35°C, free phosphatidylserine was detected. Thin-layer chromatography showed that all of the chloroform-soluble radioactivity was phosphatidylserine (Fig. 3). The reaction was dependent on CTP, phosphatidic acid, and intact RNA. RNA degraded with RNase, or an incubation mixture containing ATP in place of CTP, did not produce the phospholipid. A tentative reaction scheme would be:

$$CTP + phosphatidic\ acid \rightleftharpoons$$

$$CDP - diglyceride + PP_i$$

$$CDP\text{-}diglyceride + ser\ tRNA \rightleftharpoons$$

$$CMP + phosphatidyl\ ser\ tRNA$$

(where PP_i is inorganic pyrophosphate).

CONCLUDING REMARKS

It seems likely, then, that there are a number of novel features in the synthesis and secretion of penicillinase. Foremost is the likelihood that the phospholipid is attached before termination of the polypeptide chain. The mode of attachment of the phospholipid is at present unknown, but we feel sure that it must involve the phosphatidylseryl tRNA as a donor. This is probable since it is an activated form of phosphatidylserine and is protected by esterification from decarboxylation to phosphatidylethanolamine. More precise characterization of the tRNA species involved here must await purification and to this end we are currently working.

ACKNOWLEDGMENTS

We thank J. Sohm for her excellent technical assistance.
The work was supported by Public Health Service grant AI-04572 from the National Institute of Allergy and Infectious Diseases. B.N.D. held a Charles and Johanna Busch Postdoctoral Research Fellowship.

LITERATURE CITED

1. **Ambler, R. P., and R. J. Meadway.** 1969. Chemical structure of bacterial penicillinases. Nature (London) **272:**24–26.

2. **Bligh, E. G., and W. J. Dyer.** 1959. A rapid method of total lipid extraction and purification. Can. J. Biochem. Physiol. **37:**911–917.

3. **Crane, L. J., G. E. Bettinger, and J. O. Lampen.** 1973. Affinity chromatography purification of penicillinase of *Bacillus licheniformis* 749/C and its use to measure turnover of cell-bound enzyme. Biochem. Biophys. Res. Commun. **50:**220–227.

4. **Davies, J. W.** 1969. Protein synthesis by cell free extracts of *B. licheniformis* 749/C. Biochim. Biophys. Acta **174:**686–695.

5. **Davis, B. J.** 1964. Disc electrophoresis. II. Method and application to human serum. Ann. N.Y. Acad. Sci. **121:**404–427.

6. **Dubnau, D. A., and M. R. Pollock.** 1965. The genetics of *Bacillus licheniformis* penicillinase. A preliminary analysis from studies on mutation and inter-strain and intra-strain mutations. J. Gen. Microbiol. **41:**7–21.

7. **von Ehrenstein, G.** 1967. Isolation of s-RNA from *Escherichia coli* cells, p. 588–596. *In* L. Grossman and K. Moldave (ed.), Methods in enzymology, vol. 12A. Academic Press Inc., New York.

8. **Kushner, D. A., and M. R. Pollock.** 1961. The location of cell-bound penicillinase in *Bacillus subtilis*. J. Gen. Microbiol. **26:**255–265.

9. **Lowry, O. H., N. J. Rosebrough, R. J. Farr, and R. J. Randall.** 1951. Protein measurement with the Folin phenol reagent. J. Biol. Chem. **193:**265–275.

10. **Morman, M. R., and D. C. White.** 1970. Phospholipid metabolism during penicillinase production in *Bacillus licheniformis*. J. Bacteriol. **104:**247–253.

11. **Patterson, P. H., and W. J. Lennarz.** 1971. Studies on the membranes of bacilli. I. Phospholipid synthesis. J. Biol. Chem. **246:**1062–1072.

12. **Pollock, M. R.** 1961. The measurement of the liberation of penicillinase from *Bacillus subtilis*. J. Gen. Microbiol. **26:**239–253.

13. **Pollock, M. R.** 1961. The mechanism of liberation of penicillinase from *Bacillus subtilis*. J. Gen. Microbiol. **26:**267–276.

14. **Sargent, M. G., B. K. Ghosh, and J. O. Lampen.** 1968. Localization of cell-bound penicillinase in *Bacillus licheniformis*. J. Bacteriol. **96:**1329–1338.

15. **Sargent, M. G., B. K. Ghosh, and J. O. Lampen.** 1970. Characteristics of penicillinase secretion by growing cells and protoplasts of *Bacillus licheniformis*. J. Bacteriol. **97:**820–826.

16. **Sargent, M. G., and J. O. Lampen.** 1970. A mechanism for penicillinase secretion in *Bacillus licheniformis*. Proc. Natl. Acad. Sci. U.S.A. **65:**962–969.

17. **Sawai, T., L. J. Crane, and J. O. Lampen.** 1973. Evidence for phospholipid in plasma membrane penicillinase of *Bacillus licheniformis*. Biochem. Biophys. Res. Commun. **53:**523–530.

18. **Sawai, T., and J. O. Lampen.** 1974. Purification and characteristics of plasma membrane penicillinase from *Bacillus licheniformis* 749/C. J. Biol. Chem. **249:**2688–2694.

19. **Sherratt, D. J., and J. F. Collins.** 1973. Analysis by transformation of the penicillinase system of *Bacillus licheniformis*. J. Gen. Microbiol. **76:**217–230.

20. **Skipski, V. P., R. F. Peterson, and M. Barclay.** 1964. Quantitative analysis of phospholipids by thin-layer chromatography. Biochem. J. **90:**374–378.

21. **Yamamoto, S., and J. O. Lampen.** 1975. Membrane penicillinase of *Bacillus licheniformis*, a phospholipoprotein. J. Biol. Chem. **250:**3212–3213.

22. **Zubay, G.** 1962. The isolation and fractionation of soluble ribonucleic acids. J. Mol. Biol. **4:**347–356.

Phospholipoprotein Membrane Penicillinase of *Bacillus licheniformis* and Its Role in Penicillinase Secretion

J. OLIVER LAMPEN AND SHINPEI YAMAMOTO

Waksman Institute of Microbiology, Rutgers University, The State University of New Jersey, New Brunswick, New Jersey 08903; and Department of Agricultural and Biological Chemistry, Kochi University, Kochi, Japan

INTRODUCTION

The work presented here is part of a general program examining how a microorganism produces proteins (enzyme, toxin, cell wall component, etc.) which ultimately are found outside the membrane permeability barrier of the cell. Our attention has been focused on the step by which the nascent polypeptide chain passes through a membrane, thus becoming separated from the cytosol of the cell. In the eukaryotic cell, separation from the cytosol occurs in the rough endoplasic reticulum where the polypeptide chain, formed on bound ribosomes, is passed into the lumen of the reticulum. The protein, which is now extracytoplasmic, usually undergoes subsequent transport, modification, storage, and controlled release. Several reviews covering the process in eukaryotic microorganisms and in animals have appeared (4, 13, 18, 26).

In the prokaryotic cell, the total process of secretion is considerably simpler and may be considered analogous to the passage of proteins into the lumen of the rough endoplasmic reticulum of higher organisms. The nascent peptide chain is probably formed on membrane-bound polysomes (5, 13) and inserted into the membrane through which it passes in a partially folded form (2, 3, 20). Folding may be completed within the plasma membrane or at its outer surface, and the protein may undergo subsequent modification by proteolytic action. The affinity of the final protein molecule for the membrane usually determines whether it is released or retained at the outer surface.

Secretion by the prokaryotic cell occurs from the cytoplasm out into the surrounding medium, whereas, in the eukaryote, secretion occurs into the lumen of the reticulum. Thus, microsomes obtained from the rough endoplasmic reticulum offer advantages for study of the initiation of the protein chain and perhaps of the factors that cause one enzyme to be made on a membrane-bound ribosome and another on a free cytoplasmic ribosome. With the prokaryotic cell, one is able to examine the passage through the membrane (which we consider to be the actual secretion stage) by determining the nature of the initial products as they appear at the outer membrane surface and the basis of release from the membrane. The prokaryotic system which has seemed the most suitable has been the production of penicillinase (β-lactamase, EC 3.5.2.6) by *Bacillus licheniformis* 749 (penicillinase inducible) and mutant 749/C (constitutive). The reasons for this choice are detailed in the following sections.

PENICILLINASE SECRETION IN *B. LICHENIFORMIS* 749/C

General Properties of System

The bacilli, and many other gram-positive bacteria, commonly secrete a variety of enzymes into the culture fluid. In contrast, the complex cell envelope of most gram-negative organisms traps those proteins that pass through the plasma membrane. Another advantage of the bacilli for secretion studies is that their cell walls can usually be dissolved enzymatically. Thus, one can examine the emerging enzyme proteins directly and, on occasion, chemically or enzymatically modify the outer face of the membrane.

The important characteristics of the *Bacillus* system we have selected are summarized in Table 1. Because penicillinase represents ~2% of the total bacterial protein, purification and characterization of the forms present in various locations are simplified. The existence of a single structural gene for the cell-bound and extracellular enzymes (27) is not surprising since the form released from the cell by trypsin (EC 3.4.21.4) differs in amino acid sequence from the natural exoenzyme only in that it lacks the NH_2-terminal lysine residue (1a). The accessibility of the cell-bound enzyme to substrate (and, in part, to antibody) facilitates its measurement, and the relatively close coupling of secretion and synthesis renders unlikely the existence of any substantial pool of an inactive precursor (6, 22).

The exopenicillinase of *B. licheniformis* 749/C is a highly soluble molecule composed of a single peptide chain (molecular weight ~29,000) whose sequence has been determined by Ambler and Meadway (1a). It lacks cysteinyl residues

TABLE 1. *Properties of penicillinase secretion by* B. licheniformis *749/C*

1. Penicillinase ca. 2% of total protein formed
2. Single structural gene for the soluble exoenzyme and the hydrophobic membrane-bound form
3. Cell-bound enzyme: 80% of total at pH 6, 20% at pH 8
4. Cell-bound enzyme readily accessible to external substrate
5. Secretion relatively closely coupled to synthesis

and has lysyl residues at both the NH_2 and COOH termini. On the basis of its resistance to proteases, its ready renaturation after treatment with guanidine-hydrochloride, and the existence of isoenzymes with modifications at the third position from either terminus (R. J. Meadway, Ph.D. thesis, Univ. of Edinburgh, Edinburgh, Scotland, 1969), the exoenzyme can be visualized as a compact central ball with NH_2 and COOH terminal sequences that are at the surface and subject to enzymatic modification.

The membrane-bound enzyme is associated with the general plasma membrane or with mesosomal vesicles which are released during protoplast formation. The enzyme is relatively concentrated in the vesicles, and it is material from vesicles that is released during incubation of washed cells at pH 8 to 9 (21). Although the vesicle enzyme was initially thought to differ from the general plasma membrane form (23), it is now clear that the two enzymes are essentially identical. The preferential release of exoenzyme from the vesicle fraction probably is the result of the localization of a releasing enzyme in or near the mesosomes (L. Traficante and J. O. Lampen, unpublished results).

We have isolated substantial quantities of apparently pure membrane penicillinase (31, 32) having about the same specific activity as the exoenzyme. Since there is no change in total

TABLE 2. *Differences between membrane and exopenicillinases*

Property	Exo	Membrane	Reference
Mol wt (sodium dodecyl sulfate)	29,000	33,000	8, 32
Solubility in water	Very high	Low	25
TDC[a] bound/mol	0	37 (0.1% TDC)	8
pI	5.1–5.2	4.7–4.8	8
P/mol	0	1 g-atom	24
[2-³H]glycerol incorporated	–	+	24, 25

[a] TDC, Taurodeoxycholate.

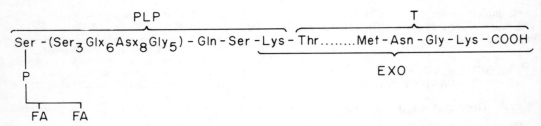

FIG. 1. *Schematic structure of membrane penicillinase. Abbreviations: EXO, exopenicillinase; T, enzyme produced by treatment of exo- or membrane enzyme with trypsin; PLP, phospholipopeptide portion; FA, fatty acids.*

activity when penicillinase is released by trypsin from membrane fragments (12), we consider this value (~350 U/μg of protein) to be the maximum.

Comparison of the Membrane and Exopenicillinases

The two penicillinases are essentially indistinguishable as far as their kinetic properties and substrate specificity are concerned. Both react with antibodies produced in response to the exoenzyme; in fact, the membrane form can completely prevent the binding of exoenzyme to a column of bound antibody to exoenzyme (8). Thus, the membrane enzyme must contain, or be able to assume the configurations of, all the antigenic determinants of the exoenzyme. The major portion of the membrane-bound enzyme, i.e., the portion released from the membrane by treatment with trypsin, is apparently a polar protein with a conformation and a catalytic site essentially identical to that of exopenicillinase.

The two penicillinases differ sharply in their overall polarity (Table 2). The exoenzyme is very soluble in water and does not bind detergents, whereas the membrane enzyme binds large amounts of ionic and nonionic detergents and aggregates in their absence (8, 25). The membrane enzyme has a molecular weight of approximately 33,000 in contrast to the 29,000 of the exoenzyme (8, 32), and its pI is about 0.4 pH units lower than exoenzyme (determined by isoelectrofocusing [8]). The greater acidity and hydrophobicity of the membrane protein prompted a search for phospholipid constituents. The enzyme was purified from organisms grown in a medium containing $H_3{}^{33}PO_4$ or $[2\text{-}{}^3H]$glycerol. The ^{33}P was incorporated into the membrane enzyme at a molecular ratio of 1.3 P:1 enzyme (24). The purified enzyme also contained ^3H activity derived from $[2\text{-}{}^3H]$glycerol, and this activity could not be separated from the enzyme protein by a variety of physicochemical treatments. Exopenicillinase isolated from these cultures contained neither ^{33}P nor ^3H activity.

These observations support our view that the membrane enzyme is comprised of a major polar portion essentially identical with the usual exopenicillinase and an additional hydrophobic "tail" that probably contains a phospholipid residue.

PHOSPHOLIPOPROTEIN NATURE OF MEMBRANE PENICILLINASE

A purified sample of the membrane enzyme labeled by growth in the presence of $[^3H]$glycerol and ^{14}C-labeled amino acids was treated with trypsin to produce the exo-like enzyme and the fragment which apparently constitutes the hydrophobic tail (25, 33). The main protein portion exhibited penicillinase activity and ^{14}C activity, but was not labeled with tritium. The fragment contained both ^3H activity and ^{14}C-labeled amino acids.

A schematic structure of the total membrane enzyme is presented in Fig. 1. The sequences of the first four amino acids at the COOH termini of exoenzyme and the membrane enzyme were identical (32); thus, the extra peptide portion of the membrane enzyme was not attached to the COOH terminus of the usual exoenzyme. The extra fragment yielded phosphatidylserine upon exhaustive digestion with Pronase (*Streptomyces griseus* protease; EC 3.4.21.4 and 3.4.24.4), and acid hydrolysis produced only four different amino acid residues (Ser, Gly, Asp, and Glu) in addition to a single lysine which is the NH_2 terminal residue of the usual exoenzyme. The fragment was therefore termed a phospholipopeptide and the membrane enzyme was called a phospholipoprotein. Since the fatty acids of the phosphatidic acid residue were similar to those of the total membrane phospholipids (32), the phosphatidic acid is probably formed by the usual synthetic pathway for membrane lipids. It should be noted that there is no detectable free phosphatidylserine in the membranes of *B. licheniformis* 749 and 749/C (17; Dancer and Lampen, p. 100) or of most *Bacillus* species. The only stable phos-

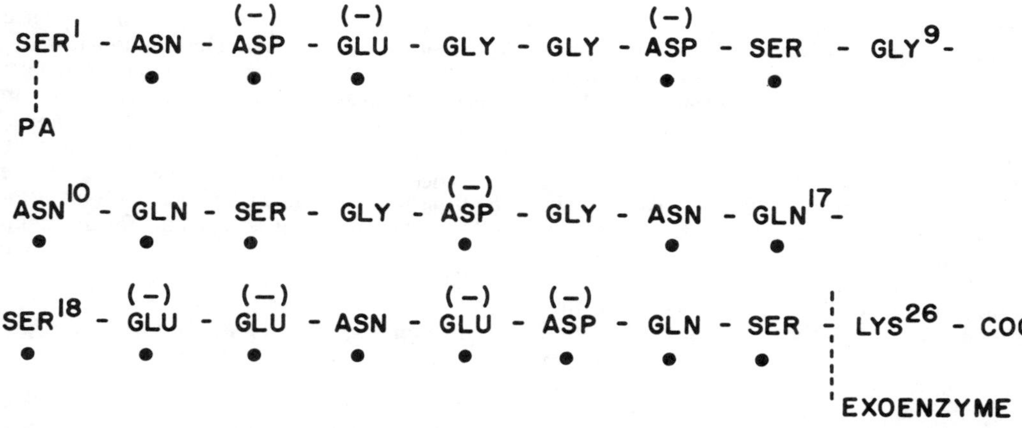

SER¹ - ASN - ASP⁽⁻⁾ - GLU⁽⁻⁾ - GLY - GLY - ASP⁽⁻⁾ - SER - GLY⁹-

PA

ASN¹⁰ - GLN - SER - GLY - ASP⁽⁻⁾ - GLY - ASN - GLN¹⁷-

SER¹⁸ - GLU⁽⁻⁾ - GLU⁽⁻⁾ - ASN - GLU⁽⁻⁾ - ASP⁽⁻⁾ - GLN - SER - LYS²⁶ - COO⁻

EXOENZYME

FIG. 2. *Sequence of the phospholipopeptide from membrane penicillinase. Abbreviations and symbols: PA, phosphatidic acid;* ●, *polar residue;* (—), *negatively charged residue.*

phatidylserine in the membrane may be that bound in peptide linkage; the free compound is presumably decarboxylated to phosphatidylethanolamine by the membrane-bound phosphatidylserine decarboxylase (EC 4.1.1.65) (19).

The exopenicillinase released by the growing organism has lysine as its NH_2 terminus so that the normal release process must involve the cleavage of the Ser^{24}-Lys^{25} linkage. An enzyme cleaving the membrane enzyme to yield an exoform with Lys as its NH_2 terminus has been demonstrated in our laboratory and appears to be localized in or near the mesosome (L. Traficante, personal communication). Its precise specificity and importance in the physiological release process are under investigation.

STRUCTURE OF THE PHOSPHOLIPOPEPTIDE

Amino Acid Sequence

The amino acid sequence of the phospholipopeptide has been determined by Yamamoto and Lampen (34) and is illustrated in Fig. 2. The peptide chain is highly hydrophilic since at least 19 of the 25 amino acids present are considered to be polar. Thus, the hydrophobic character of the total phospholipopeptide must be primarily a function of the NH_2 terminal phosphatidylserine. A closer examination of the chain reveals the existence of three distinct segments. Segment I (residues 1 to 9) contains both hydrophobic residues, including phosphatidylserine, and hydrophilic residues, including three dicarboxylic acids. Segment II (residues 10 to 17) is largely made up of polar amino acids although there is only one ionizable residue (Asp). The final segment (III, residues

18 to 25) is composed entirely of polar residues and includes four dicarboxylic acids. The three segments can be expected to differ substantially in the nature and intensity of their interaction with the lipids of the cell membrane and would therefore determine to a large extent the location and orientation of the total enzyme in the membrane.

Possible Repeating Tetrapeptide Unit

The existence of only six types of amino acid residues (Gly, Ser, Asp, Asn, Glu, and Gln) in the phospholipopeptide suggested that it had arisen by reiteration and modification of an oligopeptide structure. From the arrangement shown in Fig. 3, it seems likely that the repeating unit is -Asp(Asn)-Glu(Gln)-Ser-Gly- and that this occurs seven times but with a number of modifications and deletions. To determine if the proposed modifications are reasonable in that they require only acceptable single-base changes in the corresponding mRNA, the codons for the various amino acids (Fig. 3) were examined. The Asp ↔ Asn exchange requires a simple G ↔ A transition and the Glu ↔ Gln modification requires only a G ↔ C transversion, one which occurs frequently (10). The substitution of Gly by Glu at residue 19 can also take place by a G ↔ A transition. The possible codons for serine are AG^U/C, UC^U/C, and UC^A/G. If one assumes that the original codon for serine was AG^U/C, an A ↔ G transition would yield GG^U/C, one of the glycine codons, thus explaining the Gly at position 5. We have tentatively ruled out the UC^U/C and UC^A/G codons on the basis that the replacement of the Ser by a Gly at this position would then become quite unlikely. In addition to these conversions, all of which appear acceptable, one must postulate a duplication of the Glu[19] residue and six deletions.

If one examines the modifications in relation to the three distinguishable portions of the chain (Fig. 2), it is evident that the highly polar portion (residues 18 to 25) developed by replacement of the nonpolar Gly[19] by a Glu, a duplication of that residue (Glu[20]), and the deletion of two Gly residues and an uncharged Ser residue in the next two repeating units. Since the codon for Lys, which occurs at position 26, is AA^A/G, it is conceivable that the codon GG^A/G for the original Gly at position 26, instead of being deleted, was converted by successive A $\longleftrightarrow$ G transitions (via Glu) to that for Lys. In an opposite series of changes, the loss of charged Glu residues after Asp[7] and Asp[14] and the replacement of a Ser by Gly at position 5 contributed to the greater hydrophobicity and decreased negative charge of segments I and II.

One would predict that retention of the phosphatidylserine residue of the NH$_2$ terminus would be sufficient to insure the attachment of the penicillinase to the membrane and thus that there would have been little selective pressure toward maintaining the precise sequence of the repeating tetrapeptide. Changes in sequence apparently did occur but not in a random fashion. In fact, the mutations conserved appear to have specifically led to a systematic divergence in polarity between the two extreme portions of the phospholipopeptide chain. This indicates the existence of an evolutionary selective pressure favoring this differentiation, especially as it affects the affinity of these segments for the membrane and hence the orientation of the total enzyme molecule.

IN VITRO FORMATION OF MEMBRANE PENICILLINASE

The unusual structure of the membrane penicillinase immediately raises two questions. What is the actual gene product, and when and how is the phospholipid added during the synthetic process? These problems have been investigated in our laboratory by Brian Dancer. Some of this work is presented elsewhere in this volume (Dancer and Lampen, this volume, p. 100); however, those findings are summarized here for completeness.

An in vitro protein-synthesizing system was developed from the constitutive penicillinase-

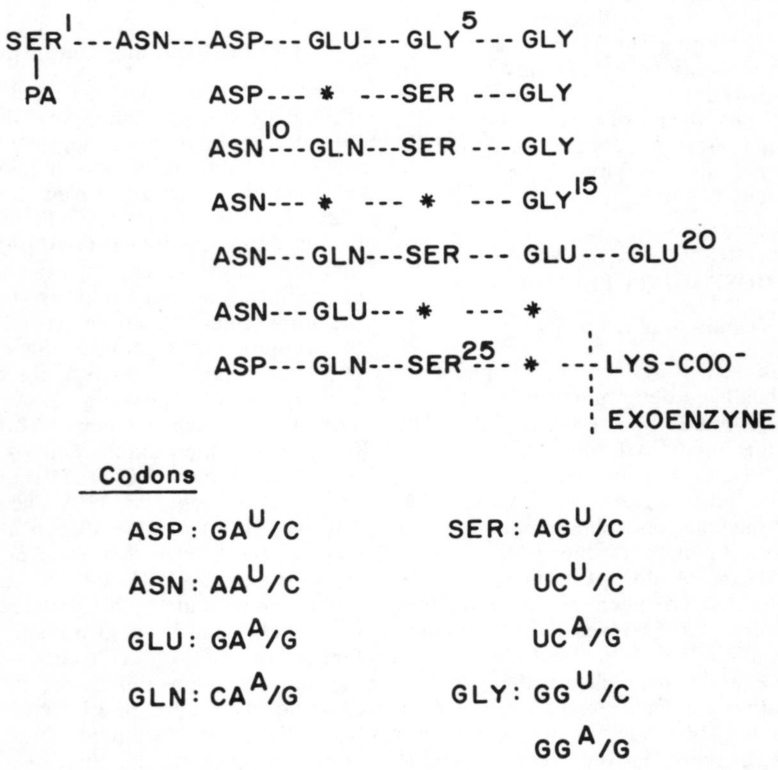

SER^1 --- ASN --- ASP --- GLU --- GLY^5 --- GLY
|
PA   ASP --- * --- SER --- GLY

ASN^{10} --- GL.N --- SER --- GLY

ASN --- * --- * --- GLY^{15}

ASN --- GLN --- SER --- GLU --- GLU^{20}

ASN --- GLU --- * --- *

ASP --- GLN --- SER^{25} - * --- LYS-COO$^-$

EXOENZYNE

Codons

ASP : GA^U/C	SER : AG^U/C
ASN : AA^U/C	UC^U/C
GLU : GA^A/G	UC^A/G
GLN : CA^A/G	GLY : GG^U/C
	GG^A/G

FIG. 3. *Repeating unit in phospholipopeptide. Asterisk indicates residue assumed to have been deleted.*

producing mutant 749/C in which chloramphenicol-sensitive net formation of penicillinase activity could be demonstrated (9). It is likely that this system does not initiate new polypeptides, but rather completes chains already attached to the ribosomes. The only penicillinase detectable with certainty was the hydrophobic enzyme containing the covalently bound phospholipid. We infer from this result that the phospholipid is attached while the nascent enzyme is bound to the polysome. Exopenicillinase then would be a product of cleavage of the membrane phospholipoprotein enzyme, even though the bulk of the membrane-bound enzyme is not a precursor in vivo of the exoenzyme (7).

Dancer and Lampen (this volume, p. 100) have demonstrated the presence of phosphatidylseryl tRNA in membranes of strain 749/C and its formation in vitro from cytidine triphosphate, phosphatidic acid, and [3-^{3}H]seryl tRNA. Thus, the attachment of the phospholipid to the polypeptide probably involves phosphatidylseryl tRNA as the donor, although the mode of attachment and the point in the biosynthesis of the membrane enzyme at which attachment occurs are unknown.

ROLE OF THE PHOSPHOLIPOPEPTIDE PORTION OF MEMBRANE PENICILLINASE IN SECRETION

Our general concept of the secretion of enzymes by microorganisms is that the nascent polypeptide chain is produced on a membrane-attached ribosome and inserted into the membrane, where it undergoes multiple hydrophobic interactions with membrane proteins and lipids and eventually folds either in the membrane or near the aqueous face as it hydrates (13). This secreted protein may then undergo enzymatic alterations, such as the removal of the phospholipopeptide portion of the membrane penicillinase, to produce the hydrophilic exoenzyme. Eventual release is generally a function of whether or not the final form of the protein retains substantial affinity for the membrane.

The phospholipopeptide portion of membrane penicillinase, with its 25 amino acid residues, is probably long enough to reach across the membrane bilayer, especially since the presence of a number of serine and glycine residues would reduce the amount of helical structure. The terminal phosphatidylserine residue could be at the cytoplasmic face of the membrane with the repeating tetrapeptide extending across the membrane and the main hydrophilic protein portion lying in the external aqueous environment (Fig. 4, left). Alternatively, the phosphatidylserine could be on the outer face with the first segments of the repeating tetrapeptide interacting primarily with the membrane and with the last, highly polar, charged segment in the aqueous phase (Fig. 4, right). In either case, the Ser^{24}-Lys^{25}-Thr^{26} bonds should be relatively accessible to trypsin or to the releasing enzyme which appears to be responsible for the physiological cleavage and the subsequent release of the hydrophilic exoenzyme. The alternative arrangements are illustrated in Fig. 4, which also indicates the potential problems that are encountered in movement of the main chain across the membrane because of the presence of the hydrophobic anchor at the NH$_2$ terminus.

If one assumes that the phosphatidylseryl residue is added early in the synthetic process and remains at the cytoplasmic face of the membrane (Fig. 4, left), the major portion of the chain must be moved in some manner through the membrane while the first portion is retained at the cytoplasmic face. If one proposes instead that the phosphatidylserine is eventually situated on the exterior face (Fig. 4, right), it is necessary to explain how the bound phospholipid is moved across the bilayer when movement of free phospholipids is usually slow (15). The answer may lie in the character of the NH$_2$ terminal phosphatidylserine, which is unusual in that it does not react in the standard procedures for determining NH$_2$ terminal residues (32). Partial charge neutralization between the amino group of the serine and the phosphate may facilitate movement of the phosphatidylserine residue across the lipid bilayer.

The fate of the phospholipopeptide fragment in the growing cell after cleavage of the membrane-bound penicillinase and release of the exoenzyme is unknown and clearly warrants careful study. Because of its overall hydrophobic character, one would expect the fragment to remain attached to the cell membrane; its components should eventually be reutilized. The likelihood of this is increased by the observation (1) that the phosphatidylserine-containing tails on certain membrane proteins of strain 749 remained with the membrane fragments after cleavage (and removal) of these proteins by trypsin.

NATURE OF THE mRNA FOR THE PHOSPHOLIPOPEPTIDE

One of the major unsolved problems concerning the mechanism by which enzymes are secreted is why certain mRNA's become attached to membrane-bound ribosomes and are translated there with the nascent peptide chain

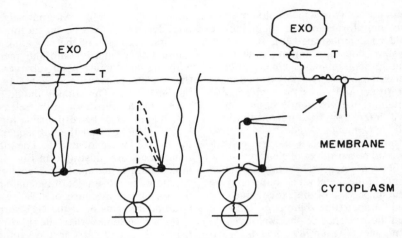

FIG. 4. *Possible modes of formation of membrane penicillinase (schematic). See text for discussion. Abbreviation: T, sites of cleavage by trypsin.*

being inserted into the membrane, whereas other mRNA's appear to be translated almost exclusively on free cytoplasmic polysomes. It has been suggested (4, 13) that there is a signal, either a special sequence or a special structure produced as a result of that sequence, that favors or may actually be required for translation on a membrane-bound ribosome. The signal could be located near the NH_2 terminus of the nascent chain (the first portion inserted into the membrane) or toward the 5' end of the corresponding mRNA.

A feature that may be of considerable significance to this problem is the high purine content of the mRNA corresponding to the phospholipopeptide portion of membrane penicillinase—a minimum of 72% AG and a maximum of 79% (both calculations assume that the condon for Ser is AG^U/C, the only one consistent with the suggested replacements). Also, all of the codons contain at least two purines, and all but three of the pyrimidine residues (those in the CA^A/G codon for Gln) occur in the third or "wobble" position.

A notable property of the purine bases (especially adenine) in the RNA backbone is their tendency to stack (11, 30). As a result, poly(rA) and other purine-rich polynucleotides tend to form ordered helical structures (single or double stranded depending on the pH, temperature, etc.) that are very similar to the typical double-stranded chains [such as poly(rA):poly(rU)] (28, 29). There are several reports that the poly(rA) at the 3' end of eukaryotic mRNA's has an affinity for membranes and when bound is protected against degradation by RNases (14, 16). Since purines constitute almost 80% of the bases in the proposed mRNA sequence cor-

responding to the phospholipopeptide, this stretch (75 nucleotides) of the total mRNA for penicillinase should have properties similar to poly(rA), including an affinity for the plasma membrane.

Both the mRNA for penicillinase and the nascent polypeptide contain structures which should favor translation of the mRNA on membrane-bound rather than on free ribosomes. The NH_2 terminal portion of the membrane enzyme consists of a repeating tetrapeptide terminating (at least soon after initiation) in a highly hydrophobic phosphatidylserine residue which would be expected to orient the growing chain to membranes. In fact, it is possible that translation could not successfully be completed on a cytoplasmic ribosome where there might be no ready source of phosphatidylserine residues. In addition, the corresponding mRNA carries near its 5' end a purine-rich sequence with probable affinity for membranes. The observations made in this single case are adequate only to reveal the possibilities inherent in these structural features, but it is already evident that membrane penicillinase is not the only phospholipoprotein in *B. licheniformis*. Membranes from cells of the inducible strain 749 grown in the presence of [2-³H]glycerol and without inducer (to avoid formation of penicillinase) contain at least six or seven proteins with ³H-labeled "tails" that yield phosphatidylserine on digestion with Pronase (1).

The preceding comments are based on the assumption that the repeated tetrapeptide portion of the enzyme is a part of the actual penicillinase gene product. A more adequate knowledge of the reactions involved in the biosynthesis of the membrane penicillinase is clearly essential if we are to evaluate the precise role of the phospholipopeptide portion in determining the site of synthesis of the penicillinase.

ACKNOWLEDGMENT

The research presented here was supported by Public Health Service Grant AI-04572 from the National Institute of Allergy and Infectious Diseases.

LITERATURE CITED

1. **Aiyappa, P. S., and J. O. Lampen.** 1976. Membrane associated phospholipoproteins of *Bacillus licheniformis* 749. Biochim. Biophys. Acta **448**:401–410.

1a. **Ambler, R. P., and R. J. Meadway.** 1969. Chemical structure of bacterial penicillinases. Nature (London) **272**:24–26.

2. **Bettinger, G. E., and J. O. Lampen.** 1975. Further evidence for a partially-folded intermediate in penicillinase secretion by *Bacillus licheniformis*. J. Bacteriol. **121**:83–90.

3. **Bissell, M. J., R. Tosi, and L. Gorini.** 1971. Mechanism of excretion of a bacterial proteinase: factors controlling accumulation of the extracellular proteinase of a *Sarcina* strain (Coccus P). J. Bacteriol. **105**:1099–1109.

4. **Blobel, G., and D. D. Sabatini.** 1971. Ribosome-membrane interaction in eukaryotic cells, p. 193–195. *In* L. A. Manson (ed.), Biomembranes, vol. 2. Plenum Publishing Corp., New York.

5. **Cancedda, R., and M. J. Schlessinger.** 1974. Localization of polyribosomes containing alkaline phosphatase nascent polypeptides on membranes of *Escherichia coli*. J. Bacteriol. **117**:290–301.

6. **Chesbro, W. R., and J. O. Lampen.** 1968. Characteristics of secretion of penicillinase, alkaline phosphatase, and nuclease by *Bacillus* species. J. Bacteriol. **96**:428–437.

7. **Crane, L. J., G. E. Bettinger, and J. O. Lampen.** 1973. Affinity chromatography purification of penicillinase of *Bacillus licheniformis* 749/C and its use to measure turnover of cell-bound enzyme. Biochem. Biophys. Res. Commun. **50**:220–227.

8. **Crane, L. J., and J. O. Lampen.** 1974. *Bacillus licheniformis* 749/C plasma membrane penicillinase, a hydrophobic polar protein. Arch. Biochem. Biophys. **160**:655–666.

9. **Dancer, B. N., and J. O. Lampen.** 1975. *In vitro* synthesis of hydrophobic penicillinase in extracts of *Bacillus licheniformis* 749/C. Biochem. Biophys. Res. Commun. **66**:1357–1364.

10. **Jukes, T. H.** 1975. Mutations in proteins and base changes in codons. Biochem. Biophys. Res. Commun. **66**:1–8.

11. **Kondo, N. S., H. M. Holmes, L. M. Stempel, and P. O. P. Ts'o.** 1970. Influence of the phosphodiester linkage (3'-5', 2'-5', and 5'-5') on the conformation of dinucleoside monophosphate. Biochemistry **9**:3479–3498.

12. **Lampen, J. O.** 1967. Cell-bound penicillinase of *Bacillus licheniformis*; properties and purification. J. Gen. Microbiol. **48**:249–259.

13. **Lampen, J. O.** 1974. Movement of extracellular enzymes across membranes, p. 351–374. *In* M. A. Sleigh and D. H. Jennings (ed.), Transport at the cellular level. Symp. Soc. Exp. Biol., vol. 28. Cambridge University Press, Cambridge, England.

14. **Lande, M. A., M. Adesnik, M. Sumida, Y. Tashiro, and D. D. Sabatini.** 1975. Direct association of messenger RNA with microsomal membranes in human diploid fibroblasts. J. Cell Biol. **65**:513–518.

15. **McConnell, H. M., P. Devaux, and C. Scandella.** 1972. Lateral diffusion and phase separation in biological membranes, p. 409–426. *In* C. F. Fox (ed.), Membrane research. Academic Press Inc., New York.

16. **Milcarek, C., and S. Penman.** 1974. Membrane-bound polyribosomes in HeLa cells: association of polyadenylic acid with membranes. J. Mol. Biol. **89**:327–338.

17. **Morman, M. R., and D. C. White.** 1970. Phospholipid metabolism during penicillinase production in *Bacillus licheniformis*. J. Bacteriol. **104**:247–253.

18. **Palade, G., P. Siekevitz, and L. B. Caro.** 1962. Structure, chemistry and function of the pancreatic exocrine cell, p. 23–55. *In* A. V. S. de Reuck and M. P. Cameron (ed.), The exocrine pancreas. CIBA Foundation Symposium. J. and A. Churchill, Ltd., London.

19. **Patterson, P. H., and W. J. Lennarz.** 1971. Studies on the membranes of Bacilli. I. Phospholipid synthesis. J. Biol. Chem. **246**:1062–1072.

20. **Sanders, R. L., and B. K. May.** 1975. Evidence for the extrusion of unfolded extracellular enzyme polypeptide chains through membranes of *Bacillus amyloliquefaciens*. J. Bacteriol. **123**:806–814.

21. **Sargent, M. G., B. K. Ghosh, and J. O. Lampen.** 1968. Characteristics of penicillinase release by washed cells of *Bacillus licheniformis*. J. Bacteriol. **96**:1231–1239.

22. **Sargent, M. G., B. K. Ghosh, and J. O. Lampen.** 1970. Characteristics of penicillinase secretion by growing cells and protoplasts of *Bacillus licheniformis*. J. Bacteriol. **97**:820–826.

23. **Sargent, M. G., and J. O. Lampen.** 1970. Organization of the membrane-bound penicillinases of *Bacillus licheniformis*. Arch. Biochem. Biophys. **136**:167–177.

24. **Sawai, T., L. J. Crane, and J. O. Lampen.** 1973. Evidence for phospholipid in plasma membrane penicillinase of *Bacillus licheniformis*. Biochem. Biophys. Res. Commun. **53**:523–530.

25. **Sawai, T., and J. O. Lampen.** 1974. Purification and characteristics of plasma membrane penicillinase from *Bacillus licheniformis* 749/C. J. Biol. Chem. **249**:2688–2694.

26. **Schramm, M.** 1967. Secretion of enzymes and other macromolecules. Annu. Rev. Biochem. **36**:307–320.

27. **Sherratt, D. J., and J. F. Collins.** 1973. Analysis by transformation of the penicillinase system of *Bacillus licheniformis*. J. Gen. Microbiol. **76**:217–230.

28. **Stannard, B. S., and G. Felsenfeld.** 1975. The conformation of polyriboadenylic acid at low temperature and neutral pH. A single-stranded rod-like structure. Biopolymers **14**:299–307.

29. **Thomas, G., Jr., and K. A. Hartman.** 1973. Raman studies of nucleic acids. VIII. Estimation of RNA secondary structure from Raman scattering by phosphate-group vibrations. Biochim. Biophys. Acta **312**:311–322.

30. **Warshaw, M. M., and C. R. Cantor.** 1970. Oligonucleotides interactions. IV. Conformational differences between deoxy- and ribodinucleoside phosphates. Biopolymers **9**:1079–1103.

31. **Yamamoto, S., and J. O. Lampen.** 1975. Membrane penicillinase of *Bacillus licheniformis*, a phospholipoprotein. J. Biol. Chem. **250**:3212–3213.

32. **Yamamoto, S., and J. O. Lampen.** 1976. Purification of plasma membrane penicillinase from *Bacillus licheniformis* 749/C and comparison with exoenzyme. J. Biol. Chem. **251**:4095–4101.

33. **Yamamoto, S., and J. O. Lampen.** 1976. The hydrophobic membrane penicillinase of *Bacillus licheniformis* 749/C. Characterization of the hydrophilic enzyme and phospholipopeptide produced by trypsin cleavage. J. Biol. Chem. **251**:4102–4110.

34. **Yamamoto, S., and J. O. Lampen.** 1976. Membrane penicillinase of *Bacillus licheniformis* 749/C: sequence and possible repeated tetrapeptide structures of the phospholipopeptide region. Proc. Natl. Acad. Sci. U.S.A. **73**:1457–1461.

II. *Pseudomonas aeruginosa* and Related Species

Introduction

RICHARD S. BERK

Department of Immunology and Microbiology, Wayne State University School of Medicine,
Detroit, Michigan 48201

There have been a number of conferences on *Pseudomonas aeruginosa* over the past three years, with each having a major emphasis on the medical and clinical aspects of disease processes and virulence factors. The rapidly growing interest in this opportunistic pathogen attests to its increasing medical importance. More and more clinicians and basic scientists have begun to discover and appreciate this organism's unusual antibiotic resistance, complex genetic organization, biochemical versatility, and unique clinical importance. Consequently, when the American Society for Microbiology approached me to set up this conference, I felt that, in order to really understand the role of this organism in clinical infections, it was important that its biological properties be comprehensively covered along with its ability to cause a variety of disease states. The participants of this conference were of a wide and diverse background as well as nationalities. Nevertheless, each was able to characterize *P. aeruginosa* in such a way as to shed further light on this organism's unusual in vitro and in vivo properties.

The conference was opened by S. G. Wilkinson, who presented an hour-long talk on the chemical composition of the cell envelope of *P. aeruginosa* and related species. He stressed that the one "achilles heel of the organism," so to speak, was its unusual sensitivity to EDTA as opposed to the generally resistant species such as *Pseudomonas diminuta, Pseudomonas maltophilia*, and *Pseudomonas cepacia*. Of particular interest were the unusual amino sugars found in the cell walls of the various species. Some of these were quinovosamine, fucosamine, 3-amino-3,6-dideoxyglucose, and 3-amino-3,6-dideoxygalactose. The high inorganic phosphate content of the *P. aeruginosa* cell envelope was stressed, and it was postulated that the integrity of the membranes was substantially altered by the subsequent removal of phosphate.

David Bradley then described four major types of pili found associated with *P. aeruginosa*. These consisted of flexible PSA pili, rigid RP4 pili, flexible R130 pili, and flexible W-pili. With the exception of the PSA pili, each one was determined by drug resistance plasmids. At present, the genetic origin of the PSA pili remains unknown. Of particular interest was the theory of how nucleic acid enters the cell after phage adsorption to the pili. Bradley theorized that the pili retract approximately 50% after adsorption and thereby pull the virus to the cell surface where nucleic acid penetration takes place. A description of the filamentous phage Pf (single-stranded DNA) and its adsorption to the tips of pili was also discussed and compared with the adsorption of tailed phage. Near the end of the talk, Ray Sarber interrupted the session by stating that we should all leave the building because of a telephoned bomb threat. After a short informal session in the park situated across from the hotel, we returned to complete the morning session.

Bruce Holloway opened the genetics session with a discussion on genetic variation. He characterized *P. aeruginosa* as an organism well endowed with a variety of plasmids. In addition, many strains appear to be multi-lysogenic and aeruginocinogenic. The identification of R plasmids in these organisms has led to a better understanding of genetic variation. Thus, a series of phenotypic properties ranging from antibiotic resistance, growth rates, lysogeny, epidemiological typing, and cell envelope function can be ascribed to the presence of plasmids in *P. aeruginosa*. Of particular interest was the discussion of aeruginocin tolerant (*tol*) mutants and the relationship between the cell envelope and the site of action of aeruginocins. The role of mucoid variants in cystic fibrosis patients was also discussed in an attempt to correlate genetic research with pathogenicity studies.

An introduction to the physiology and metabolism of *P. aeruginosa* was initiated by J. J. R. Campbell. He stressed the unusual and unique metabolic properties of the pseudomonads with major emphasis on pigment formation, carbohydrate metabolism, and isocitratase activity. It was stated that pyocyanin acts as a chelating agent and interferes with keto-acid metabolism.

The sessions ended with a discussion of experimental infections, immune responses, and important *Pseudomonas* species other than *P. aeruginosa*.

The 3-day sessions were dedicated to the memory of Michael Doudoroff, who passed away after the programing and scheduling of the conference.

Genetic Variation in *Pseudomonas aeruginosa*

B. W. HOLLOWAY

Department of Genetics, Monash University, Clayton, Victoria 3168, Australia

INTRODUCTION

The species known as *Pseudomonas aeruginosa* is an aggregate of individuals differing in recognizable characteristics, notably cell envelope properties, bacteriophage and aeruginocin typing properties, and antibiotic resistance, all of which result from genetic variation. The geneticist is concerned with the identification of the range of genetic variation, how it arises, the selective forces imposed upon it, and the interactions of the genetic determinants of the bacterium. The microbial variants which arise by such mechanisms are the interests of medical microbiologists, biochemists, and industrial biologists. The increasing frequency of drug resistance variants, particularly those determined by plasmids, the more frequent occurrence of this organism in the hospital environment, and changes in patterns of epidemiological typing all point to the need for an understanding of how this genetic variation arises.

RESULTS

Sources of Genetic Variation— Particularly Plasmids

Many bacteria have two distinguishable genetic components—the bacterial chromosome and plasmids—and *P. aeruginosa* seems to be well endowed in the latter respect. In addition, almost all strains of *P. aeruginosa* are lysogenic for at least one bacteriophage, and the frequency of aeruginocinogenic strains seems to be equally high (3).

In recent years a veritable harvest of transmissible plasmids for *P. aeruginosa* have been detected. The first of these were sex factors such as FP2, FP5, and FP39, and it has been found that about 30% of hospital strains of *P. aeruginosa* carry a sex factor (11). Some of these sex factors have been shown to carry genetic determinants for mercury resistance (e.g., FP2) or a temperature-sensitive leucine biosynthetic determinant (e.g., FP39) which can complement one of the chromosomal leucine biosynthetic genes. The selective advantage of such determinants for either the plasmids or the bacterial host remains to be understood.

In 1969, R plasmids were identified in *P. aeruginosa* isolated in a burns unit in Birmingham, England (9), and since that time identification of other R factors has been made in many countries. These have many different antibiotic resistance profiles, such that the variety of R factors found in *P. aeruginosa* now rivals that known to occur in the *Enterobacteriaceae* (5).

These plasmids provide a source of genetic variation which has the potential to affect the population structure of this species in several different ways. Firstly, the presence of the plasmid in *P. aeruginosa* can confer a range of bacterial phenotypic effects, including antibiotic resistance, aeruginocin tolerance, epidemiological typing, cell envelope function, UV protection, bacteriophage lysis and lysogeny, and growth rates, all of which are likely to alter the selective advantages or disadvantages of strains carrying one or more of these plasmids. A number of R factors have been shown to promote the transfer of bacterial chromosome, and of particular importance is the fact that some of the P group plasmids are promiscuous, having the widest host range of any known R plasmid, being able to transfer from *P. aeruginosa* to such unrelated genera as *Salmonella, Rhizobium, Acinetobacter, Neisseria,* and *Vibrio*.

R Factors with Chromosome Donor Ability

The range of extensively studied sex factors in *Escherichia coli* and *Salmonella typhimurium* is quite small, due in most part to the success of F in this role. With *P. aeruginosa*, two sex factors, FP2 and FP39, have been mainly studied and, together with several transducing phages, their use in linkage studies has enabled the construction of a chromosome map which at this time embraces about 60 markers. Genetic circularity has not yet been established, due mainly to the fact that FP2 and FP39 have only one origin of transfer, and this has also made the mapping analysis of the so-called "late region" (more than 50 min from the FP2 origin) somewhat difficult (5, 6).

These deficiencies have encouraged the development of other sex factors for mapping purposes. Stanisich and Holloway (12) showed that some R plasmids could promote chromosome transfer in *P. aeruginosa* strain PAT, but that, in the strain in which most chromosomal mapping and other genetic work had been done (strain PAO), recombinant frequency with these R factors was too low for them to be of much use.

In the search for an R plasmid which is an effective sex factor for strain PAO, a series of matings was carried out with PAO.R$^+$ donors and PAO.R$^-$ recipients, with selection for particular chromosomal markers. Recombinants were produced at low frequency (approximately 10^{-8} per donor cell), and these recombinants in turn were then examined as chromosome donors. With one R factor, R68, when selection was made for a certain chromosomal region, recombinants were found with chromosomal donor activity, with comparable or better frequency to that found with FP2 or FP39.

The plasmid from one such recombinant, R68.45, has been studied in detail (D. Haas and B. W. Holloway, Mol. Gen. Genet., in press). It has the following main characteristics. (i) It retains all of the properties of the parent plasmid R68 including carbenicillin, neomycin, kanamycin, and tetracycline resistance; aeruginocin tolerance; and extended host range (1). (ii) Donor ability can be lost spontaneously from strains containing R68.45 without loss of other plasmid characteristics. (iii) Transfer of host chromosome and plasmid occurs on solid but not in liquid media. (iv) The frequency of transfer of all markers averages 10^{-4} per donor cell, in contrast to FP2 matings where the frequency of marker transfer depends upon the marker's position relative to the FP2 origin. (v) Kinetic data from interrupted matings indicate that R68.45 can promote chromosome transfer from a multiplicity of sites in contrast to the single site of origin with FP2 and FP39.

R68.45 has considerable potential as a sex factor. For example, there has been little chromosome mapping of other species of *Pseudomonas*.

Silva and Clarke (personal communication) have shown that R68.45 promotes chromosome transfer in *Pseudomonas putida* at frequencies which should enable mapping in that species. If R68.45 is equally effective with other species of *Pseudomonas*, these results could mean that the advantages of genetic analysis could be extended to other species of *Pseudomonas*. Studies on the evolution of the genus, and the understanding of the regulation of substrate utilization, would benefit greatly from genetic features including mapping data, recombinant analysis, partial diploids, and interspecific hybrids (2, 13).

It is possible that R68.45 may also be effective as a sex factor in genera other than *Pseudomonas*. Unger et al. (L. Unger, J. R. Sokatch, and R. R. Martin, Abstr. Proc. ICN-UCLA Winter Conf. Mol. Cell. Biol., 1975) have shown that the related plasmid RP1 can transfer chromosome at low frequency in *E. coli*. It would be worthwhile to see if variants of R68 could be obtained which promoted chromosome transfer in other genera, thereby enabling the combination of sex factor activity and promiscuous host range to provide the means of genetic analysis in bacterial genera as yet untouched by genetic hands. Furthermore, there is no reason to believe that chromosome transfer mediated by R or FP factors does not take place in nature and thus has the potential for redistributing genes in a natural population, thus contributing to genetic variation.

In addition to phenotypic contributions and chromosome transfer, plasmids possess another mechanism for producing bacterial genetic variation. Krishnapillai (8) has shown that some FP and R plasmids can increase the mutation rate of host chromosomal markers, presumably through their possession of a plasmid DNA repair system active on bacterial DNA.

Genetics of the Cell Envelope

Many of the interesting and important characteristics of *P. aeruginosa* have to do with the cell envelope. This is an area where the available genetic techniques could be profitably used to supplement biochemical and electron microscope investigations (4). One such approach has been the characterization of aeruginocin tolerant (*tol*) mutants (7). It is thought that the site of action of aeruginocin is a membrane component of the cell envelope, so that mutants which are not killed by aeruginocins survive because they have structural or functional changes in the cell membrane or possibly other components of the cell envelope.

One class of *tol* mutant has provided information on the native resistance of *P. aeruginosa* to toxic agents. *tolA* mutants have been shown to be hypersensitive to aminoglycosides but to no other toxic agents, and there is an increase in permeability only to aminoglycosides in these *tolA* mutants. This means that, in *P. aeruginosa*, native resistance to aminoglycosides is specific and not part of a permeability barrier indiscriminately acting on a wide range of compounds (B. Mills and B. W. Holloway, manuscript in preparation).

The role of mucoid variants of *P. aeruginosa* in cystic fibrotic patients is a good example of the importance of the cell surface in the pathogenicity of *P. aeruginosa*. Such variants are commonly found in terminal cases of pulmonary infection in children with this disease. They can be isolated with ease in the laboratory either as survivors of infection by the virulent phage E79, among aeruginocin-tolerant mutants, or as mutants resistant to certain selected levels of carbenicillin (J. Govan, J. Med. Microbiol., in press; J. Govan, Arch. Dis. Child., in press). Govan has also shown that mucoid variants isolated from nature are more resistant to carbenicillin and more sensitive to oxytetracycline than the nonmucoid forms of the same strain, thus demonstrating the importance of selective antibiotic therapy in the treatment of respiratory infections in cystic fibrotic patients.

Bacteriophage and bacteriocin-resistant and -tolerant strains have been successfully used in enterobacteria for the genetic analysis of the cell envelope. There is preliminary evidence that the isolation of such mutants in *P. aeruginosa* could be equally valuable. Eight *tol* loci and two *ese* (E79 resistant) loci are known for strain PAO, and mutants at these loci show an interesting range of pleiotropic properties.

When strain PAO is induced for aeruginocin production by mitomycin C, the survivors show an unexpectedly high frequency of phage-resistant and *tol* mutants, in some cases the increase being 2,000 times greater than the normal mutation frequency (C. Crowther and B. W. Holloway, unpublished data). In view of the high fre-quency with which aeruginocinogenicity is found in *P. aeruginosa* strains, it is possible that this property may exert a role in the formation of cell envelope variants in nature.

ACKNOWLEDGMENTS

Work from my laboratory was supported by the Australian Research Grants Committee. It is a pleasure to acknowledge the contributions of my colleagues to this work: Carol Crowther, Allan Godfrey, John Govan, Dieter Haas, Viji Krishnapillai, Barbara Mills, Tony Morgan, and John Watson.

LITERATURE CITED

1. **Chandler, P. M., and V. Krishnapillai.** 1974. Phenotypic properties of R factors of *Pseudomonas aeruginosa*: R factors readily transferable between *Pseudomonas* and the *Enterobacteriaceae*. Genet. Res. **23:**239–250.
2. **Clarke, P. M., and M. H. Richmond** (ed.). 1974. Genetics and biochemistry of Pseudomonas. J. Wiley & Sons, London.
3. **Holloway, B. W.** 1969. Genetics of *Pseudomonas*. Bacteriol. Rev. **33:**419–443.
4. **Holloway, B. W.** 1971. A genetic approach to the study of the bacterial membrane. Aust. J. Exp. Biol. Med. Sci. **49:**429–434.
5. **Holloway, B. W.** 1975. Genetic organisation of Pseudomonas, p. 133–161. *In* P. H. Clarke and M. H. Richmond (ed.), Genetics and biochemistry of Pseudomonas. J. Wiley & Sons, London.
6. **Holloway, B. W., V. Krishnapillai, and V. Stanisich.** 1971. Pseudomonas genetics. Annu. Rev. Genet. **5:**425–446.
7. **Holloway, B. W., H. Rossiter, D. Burgess, and J. Dodge.** 1974. Aeruginocin tolerant mutants in *Pseudomonas aeruginosa*. Genet. Res. **22:**239–253.
8. **Krishnapillai, V.** 1975. Resistance to ultraviolet light and enhanced mutagenesis conferred by *Pseudomonas aeruginosa* plasmids. Mutat. Res. **29:**363–372.
9. **Lowbury, E. J. L., A. Kidson, H. A. Lilly, G. A. J. Ayliffe, and R. J. Jones.** 1969. Sensitivity of *Pseudomonas aeruginosa* to antibiotics: emergence of strains highly resistant to carbenicillin. Lancet **ii:**448–452.
10. **Olsen, R. H., and P. Shipley.** 1973. Host range and properties of the *Pseudomonas aeruginosa* R factor 1922. J. Bacteriol. **113:**772–780.
11. **Pemberton, J. M., and B. W. Holloway.** 1973. A new sex factor of *Pseudomonas aeruginosa*. Genet. Res. **21:** 263–272.
12. **Stanisich, V. A., and B. W. Holloway.** 1971. Chromosome transfer in *Pseudomonas aeruginosa* mediated by R factors. Genet. Res. **17:**169–172.
13. **Wheelis, M. H.** 1975. The genetics of dissimilarity pathways in *Pseudomonas*. Annu. Rev. Microbiol. **29:**505–524.

Classification of Plasmids in *Pseudomonas aeruginosa*

G. A. JACOBY

Massachusetts General Hospital, Boston, Massachusetts 02114

INTRODUCTION

In recent years a number of plasmids have been found in *Pseudomonas* species. These plasmids can be classified by the particular function they determine, for example, mobilization of the host chromosome for sex factors, antibiotic resistance for R factors, or hydrocarbon utilization for degradative plasmids. These groups can be further subdivided by physical criteria such as plasmid size, DNA composition, and DNA homology, and by biological criteria such as plasmid host range, susceptibility or resistance of plasmid hosts to certain bacteriophages, and plasmid-plasmid interactions, particularly incompatibility relationships. Compatible plasmids coexist stably in the same host whereas incompatible plasmids either eliminate one another or appear to recombine to form plasmid hybrids. Based on my own work and that of Bryan, Holloway, Mitsuhashi, and their co-workers, at least 10 incompatibility groups have so far been found in *Pseudomonas aeruginosa*. Classification by incompatibility agrees well with classification by other criteria. The results leading to these conclusions and some properties of plasmids in *P. aeruginosa* are summarized in this paper.

CLASSIFICATION

P-1 Plasmids

The first R factors discovered in *P. aeruginosa* were found in highly carbenicillin-resistant isolates from a burn unit in Birming-ham, England, in 1969 (42). Antibiotic resistance was transmissible to *Escherichia coli* (17, 57), and in *E. coli* one of these plasmids was used to define incompatibility group P (16). P plasmids determine pili (2, 48) which serve as receptors for P group-specific bacteriophage such as RNA phage PRR1 (48) and also confer susceptibility to DNA phages such as PRD1, PR3, and PR4 (47, 56), which attach to the cell wall of organisms carrying not only P but also N and W group plasmids (3, 47). P group plasmids interfere with the replication of phage G101 (38) and confer tolerance to certain pyocins (11). P plasmids have an exceptionally broad host range (16, 45) and have been found in a variety of gram-negative hosts throughout the world (18, 20–22, 24, 25, 36). Aside from the original outbreak in Birmingham, P plasmids have so far been detected in *P. aeruginosa* strains from Scotland (52), South Africa (58), and Spain (55). Physical and biological properties of some P group plasmids are summarized in Tables 1 and 2.

Other Plasmids Found in P-1-Carrying Strains

On closer examination, the R plasmids found in *P. aeruginosa* strains from Birmingham turned out to be subtly heterogeneous in transfer properties, phage sensitivity, antibiotic resistance, and other properties (11, 12, 30, 38, 56). (Abbreviations for antibiotics are as follows: Ak, amikacin; Cb, carbenicillin; Cm, chloramphenicol; Gm, gentamicin; Km, kanamycin; Sm, streptomycin; Su, sulfonamide; Tc, tetracycline; Tm, tobramycin. Superscript r indi-

TABLE 1. *Physical properties of* Pseudomonas aeruginosa *plasmids*

Plasmid	Mol wt ($\times 10^6$)[a]	G + C content (mol%)[b]	No. of plasmid copies per cell	Reference
RP1	36–40	60	1–3	19, 32
R638	40	61		58
R1033	45			55
R91	35			R. W. Hedges
R931	25	58	18	4
R3108		57		4
pMG2 (R 130)	23	59	16–20	54
RPL11		58		37
R679		60		4
R1162	5.5		11–12	1
R5265		59		4
FP2	59	58	1–2	49
FP39	55	60	1–2	49
Sa	25	62	3–5	26
R7K	20	62	3–5	26
R388	21	62	3–5	26
R46	31			R. W. Hedges
CAM	151			A. M. Chakrabarty
SAL	44, 56			A. M. Chakrabarty

[a] Where plasmid contour length was given in the reference cited, the molecular weight has been calculated from the relationship 1 μm equals 2.07×10^6 (40).

[b] Where plasmid buoyant density in CsCl was given in the citation, the guanine plus cytosine (G + C) content was calculated by the formula of Schildkraut et al. (53).

TABLE 2. *Biological properties of* P. aeruginosa *plasmids*

Plasmid	Incompatibility group[a] P	E	Antibiotic resistance[b]	Resistance[c] to: Hg^{2+}	PHg	UV	Pyo	Phages	Susceptibility PRR1	PRD1[d]	Transfer to E. coli[e]	Fertility inhibition[f] RP1	FP2
RP1	P-1	P	CbKmTc	s	s	s	r	G101	s	s	+		–
R30	P-1		CbKmTc	s	s	s	r	G101	s	s	+		–
R68	P-1	P	CbKmTc	s	s	s	r	G101	s	s	+		–
R638	P-1		CbKmTc	s	s	s	r	G101	s	s	+		–
R1033	P-1		CbCmGm KmSmSuTc	r	s	s	s	G101	s	s	+		–
RP1-1	?		Cb	s	s	s	s	B39	r	r	–	–	–
RP8	?		Cb	s	s	s	s	s	r	r	–	–	–
R91	?		Cb	s	s	s	s	s	r	r	–	–	+
R931	P-2		SmTc	r	s	r	s	B39D3E79 G101M6PB1	r	r	–	+	–
R3108	P-2		SmSuTc	r	r	s	s	B39D3G101	r	r	–	+	–
Rms159	P-2		CmSmTc	r	r	s	s	B39G101 M6PB1	r	r	–	+	–
pMG1	P-2		GmSmSu	r	s	r	s	B39D3E79 G101M6PB1	r	r	–	–	–
pMG2	P-2		GmSmSu	r	s	r	s	B39D3E79 G101M6PB1	r	r	–	–	–

TABLE 2. (*Continued*)

Plasmid	Incompatibility group[a] P	E	Antibiotic resistance[b]	Resistance[c] to: Hg²⁺	PHg	UV	Pyo	Phages	Susceptibility PRR1	PRD1[d]	Transfer to E. coli[e]	Fertility inhibition[f] RP1	FP2
pMG5	P-2		AkKmSuTb	r	r	s	s	B39D3E79 G101M6PB1	r	r	−	+	−
RPL11	P-2		CbCmGm SmSuTc	r	r	s	s	B3	r	r	−	−	−
R38	P-2		SmSuTc	r	r	s	s	B39D3E79 G101M6PB1	r	r	−	+	−
R39	P-2		SmSuTc	r	r	s	s	B39D3E79 G101M6PB1	r	r	−	+	−
CAM	P-2			s	s	r	s	B3D3E79 G101M6PB1	r	r	−	+	−
CAM-OCT	P-2			s	s	r	s	B39G101PB1	r	r		+	−
Rip64	P-3	C	CbCmKm GmSuTm	r	s	s	s	s	r	r	+	+	+
Rip40c	?		Cb	s	s	s	s	s	r	r	−	−	−
R679	P-4		SmSu	s	s	s	s	s	r	r	−	−	
R1162	P-4		SmSu	s	s	s	s	s	r	r	−	−	
R5265	P-4		SmSu	s	s	s	s	s	r	r	−	−	−
Rms163	P-5		CmSuTc	s	s	s	s	s	r	r	−	−	−
Rms149	P-6		CbGmSmSu	s	s	s	s	F116	r	r	−		−
Rms148	P-7		Sm	s	s	s	s	B39C5	r	r	−	−	+
FP2	P-8			r	r	s	s	s	r	r	−		
FP5	?			r	s	s	s	s	r	r	−		
FP39	?			s	s	s	s	s	r	r			
Sa		W	CmGmKm SmSuTm	s	s	s	s	s	r	s	+	+	−
R7K		W	CbSm	s	s	s	s	s	r	s	−	−	
R388		W	SuTp	s	s	s	s	s	r	s	−	+	−
R46		N	CbSmSuTc	s	s	s	s	s	r	r	−		−
R2	?		CbSmSu	s	s	r	s	s	r	r	−	+	+
SAL	?			s	s	s	s	s	r	r		+	−

[a] The incompatibility group as determined in *P. aeruginosa* (P) or *E. coli* (E).

[b] Abbreviations: Ak, Amikacin; Cb, carbenicillin; Cm, chloramphenicol; Gm, gentamicin; Km, kanamycin; Sm, streptomycin; Su, sulfonamide; Tc, tetracycline; Tm, tobramycin, Tp, trimethoprim.

[c] Resistance (r) or susceptibility (s) to HgCl₂, phenylmercuric nitrate (PHg), UV radiation (UV), and the indicated bacteriophages was determined as described previously (33). Tolerance to pyocins (Pyo) 41 and 108 (28) is also indicated.

[d] Strains susceptible to phage PRD1 were also lysed by phages PR3 and PR4.

[e] Transfer to *E. coli* was not observed (frequency less than 10⁻⁸) where minus is indicated but others have obtained transfer at low frequency of RP1-1 (11,30), R91 (12), R679 (6), and R1162 (1,6).

[f] Fertility inhibition was determined as a decrease in transfer frequency for RP1 or FP2 from a donor carrying a second plasmid and for (RP1) (R⁺) doubles by a loss of PRR1, PRD1, PR3, and PR4 susceptibility. Plasmids inhibiting FP2 transfer also inhibit FP2-mediated chromosome mobilization.

cates resistance. Superscript s indicates susceptibility.) For example, strain 1822 can transfer
linked $Cb^r Km^r Tc^r$ (plasmid RP1, also termed R18
or R1822 and probably identical to RP4) and also
Cb^r alone (plasmid RP1-1 or R18-1) (27). RP1-1
transfers at much lower frequency than RP1 to
E. coli, does not confer susceptibility to phages
PRR1, PRD1, PR3, or PR4 by spot test, and
cannot be detected as satellite DNA (11, 30,
56). Strain S8 from Edinburgh gives rise to
a similar Cb^r plasmid RP8 (38), and strain
9169 from Birmingham yields R91, which is
$Cb^r Km^s Tc^s$ in *Pseudomonas* but which in
E. coli (to which it transfers only at low frequency) expresses Km^r and Tc^r as well as Cb^r
(12). Despite these differences there is considerable DNA homology between RP1 and
RP1-1, RP8, and RP91 (29, 30, 52). Furthermore, although R91 does not confer susceptibility
to phages lytic for RP1 hosts, mutants of R91
derepressed for transfer can be selected that are
susceptible to these phages (12, 56), and if a
phage titer increase test rather than a spot test
is employed, RP1-1, RP8, and R91 hosts do
propagate phages PRR1, PR3, and PR4 (56).
Curiously, in view of these close similarities,
RP1 appears compatible with each of these Cb^r
plasmids (11, 30). I have confirmed this finding
using plasmid pMG4 which is a Cb^s mutant of a
$Cb^r Km^r Sm^r Tc^r$ recombinant plasmid formed
between RP1 and a P-2 group plasmid (33). The
entering plasmid pMG4 eliminates RP1, R30,
R68, or R638 in a recipient, confirming its P
group incompatibility, but is quite compatible
with RP1-1, RP8, or R91 since recipient
strains carrying these three plasmids retain Cb^r.
Furthermore, on outcross from a (pMG4)
(RP1-1) or (pMG4) (R91) donor, Cb^r is independently transferred excluding transposition
of Cb^r (23) into pMG4 as an explanation for
apparent compatibility. Possibly, the incompatibility behavior of RP1-1, RP8, and R91 is repressed just as the transfer properties of these
plasmids are repressed. However, unlike the behavior of a repressed plasmid which is temporarily derepressed for transfer on entering a new
host (44), RP1-1, RP8, and R91 are also
compatible with pMG4 in reciprocal crosses
in which they are the entering plasmids. Somewhat similar compatibility relationships have
been observed between a P-2 plasmid, R931,
that determines $Sm^r Tc^r Hg^r$ and plasmids
determining Sm^r or Hg^r alone found together
with R931 in its strain of origin (H. Dryburgh
and V. Stanisich, Proc. Soc. Gen. Microbiol.
2:66, 1975) and between P-3 plasmids and a related Cb^r plasmid (see below).

P-2, P-3, and P-4 Plasmids

The next R plasmid group was found in
resistant *P. aeruginosa* strains isolated in Paris
that could transfer carbenicillin resistance and
other markers to *E. coli* (59). In *E. coli* these R
factors were compatible with P group plasmids
and with members of other established incompatibility groups (7) and hence were assigned to a
new group designated C (15). Rip64, one of these
plasmids, determines resistance to gentamicin
and tobramycin as well as to carbenicillin and
has the interesting property of strongly inhibiting transfer and chromosome mobilization by
Pseudomonas sex factor FP2 (35a). A C group
plasmid has also been found in a gentamicin-resistant *P. aeruginosa* isolate from
Chicago (5). *P. aeruginosa* strain LA277 from
Paris that transfers plasmid $Rip40_a$ determining
$Cb^r Km^r Su^r$ to *E. coli* transfers a plasmid, termed
$R40_c$ in Table 2, determining Cb^r alone to *P.
aeruginosa*. Although $Rip40_a$ belongs to the C
group in *E. coli* (7), $Rip40_c$ and Rip64 are
compatible in *P. aeruginosa*, suggesting a
similar relationship to that observed between
RP1 and RP1-1.

The first plasmids of restricted host range
found in *P. aeruginosa* were detected by Bryan
et al. (6) in isolates from Edmonton, Canada.
Bryan made the important observation that a *P.
aeruginosa* recipient is necessary to detect many
P. aeruginosa R factors. Among streptomycin-
resistant *P. aeruginosa* strains, some transferred
resistance readily to *P. aeruginosa* recipients
but not detectably to *E. coli*, whereas others
gave barely detectable transfer to *E. coli* and
transferred at a slightly higher frequency to
Pseudomonas (6). The R factors that failed to
transfer to *E. coli* showed mutual incompatibility
but were compatible with those in the other group
and with P- and C-type R plasmids (4, 5).
Bryan et al. therefore initiated the classification of incompatibility groups in *P. aeruginosa*
by designating the plasmids transmissible between *P. aeruginosa* but not to *E. coli* as
P-2 plasmids and the plasmids transmissible at
low frequency to *E. coli* that determine linked
$Sm^r Su^r$ as P-4 plasmids. P plasmids like RP1
were renamed P-1 plasmids in *Pseudomonas*
species and C-type plasmids were renamed
P-3 (4, 5, 54).

P-2-type plasmids are among the most frequently found in *P. aeruginosa*. They are widely
distributed geographically, having been found in
isolates from Canada, the United States, South
Africa, and Japan (4, 5, 33, 34, 37). Some
of these plasmids determine resistance to such

clinically important anti-*Pseudomonas* drugs as carbenicillin, gentamicin, tobramycin, and amikacin (5, 33, 34, 37). Their host range is quite limited (33, 54). Although pili have been detected by electron microscopy on P-2 plasmid hosts, phage specific for such strains have not yet been found (54). As a group, P-2 plasmids tend to interfere with the replication of certain phages (see Table 2) including phages used for *Pseudomonas* typing (33, 38). Certain P-2 plasmids also inhibit pyocin production in at least some host strains (5, 33) so that the influence of plasmid carriage needs to be taken into account when phage or pyocin typing is used for epidemiological classification.

P-4 plasmids can be transferred to *E. coli* (1, 6) or *P. aeruginosa* only once and thereafter become nontransmissible. R1161, a representative of this group, has a molecular weight of only 5.5×10^6 (Table 1), so it is not surprising that they are nonconjugative. R1161 demonstrates considerable DNA homology, with other plasmids conferring linked Sm-Su^r isolated in a wide variety of hosts (1). Plasmids with other resistance phenotypes have been found in *P. aeurginosa* that also fail to transfer from the primary recipients (31). Their relationship to the P-4 group remains to be established.

P-5, P-6, and P-7 Plasmids

Recently Mitsuhashi et al. (B. W. Holloway, personal communication) have detected R plasmids in *P. aeruginosa* isolates that, like P-2 plasmids, fail to transfer to *E. coli* but that are compatible with members of the previously established *Pseudomonas* incompatibility groups and with each other. They have thus defined incompatibility groups P-5, P-6, and P-7. Table 2 summarizes the biological properties of these plasmids. Note that Rms149 confers insusceptibility to phage F116 whereas Rms148 gives resistance to phages B39 and C5.

Members of these seven plasmid groups as well as others to be described have been tested for compatibility in derivatives of *P. aeruginosa* PAO. Table 3 summarizes the results, with "C" indicating compatibility and "I" indicating incompatibility. So far as they have been tested, Rms163, Rms149, and Rms148 are compatible with each other and with members of groups P-1 through P-4, confirming the findings of Mitsuhashi et al.

P-8 and FP Factors

In addition to R factors, *P. aeruginosa* strains carry a number of plasmids that act as

TABLE 3. *Compatibility properties of P. aeruginosa plasmids*

Plasmid	P-1	P-2	P-3	P-4	P-5	P-6	P-7	P-8	W	N
				Interaction with plasmid of group:[a]						
P-1	I	C	C	C	C		C	C	C	C
P-2		I	C	C	C	C	C	C	C	C
P-3			C	C	C	C	C	C	C	C
P-4				C	C	C		C	C	
P-5					C	C	C	C	C	
P-6						C	C	C	C	
P-7							C			
P-8									C	C
CAM	C	I	C	C	C	C	C	C	C	C
SAL	C	C	C	C		C		C	C	C
R2	C	C	C		C	C			C	C

[a] "C" indicates compatibility as determined by the stable coexistence of plasmids from the indicated groups in the same host and in some cases by their independent transfer from a strain containing both plasmids. "I" indicates incompatibility as determined by elimination of the resident plasmid when a plasmid of the same group is introduced and in some cases by the formation of apparent plasmid recombinants that serially cotransmit new combinations of parental resistance determinants.

sex factors to promote the oriented transfer of the *Pseudomonas* chromosome (50). These plasmids can be distinguished by other phenotypic properties such as resistance to Hg^{2+} (41), organomercurials (34), and UV radiation (39), and by the ability of RP39 to correct a certain Leu$^-$ defect (50). The best-known FP factor, FP2, is compatible with plasmids of groups P-1 through P-7 (see Table 3) and has been assigned to group P-8. Shahrabadi et al. (54) have reported FP39 to be incompatible with a P-2 plasmid, but, in a different host, I find FP39 compatible with P-2 plasmids R931, R3108, pMG1, and pMG2.

Transfer of *E. coli* R Factors to *P. aeruginosa*

Many R plasmids isolated in *E. coli, Salmonella, Proteus*, and other gram-negative bacteria cannot be transferred to *P. aeruginosa* by conjugation (14, 35), including members of incompatibility groups FI, FII, FIV, A, C, G, H, Iα, Iβ, Iγ, Iζ, Iω, J, K, L, M, N, O, S, T, V, X, and Y. The failure of many group C (or A-C) plasmids to transfer is surprising since C-type plasmids, such as Rip64, have been found in *P. aeruginosa* and these particular plasmids can transfer back from *E. coli*. Plasmids that can be transferred to *P. aeruginosa* include, in addition to P plasmids, W plasmids and a few N group plasmids (35, 54). W plasmids, like many of the plasmids found in *Pseudomonas* (Table 1), have a high G + C content in their DNA, and most W and N plasmids (but not R46) confer susceptibility to DNA phages also active on P plasmid hosts (3, 47). Both W and N plasmids are rather unstable in *P. aeruginosa* and have not yet been detected in natural isolates, although FP39 and several W-type plasmids appear to be incompatible (35a). So far as they have been tested, N and W plasmids (Table 3) are compatible with plasmids of groups P-1 through P-8.

Degradative Plasmids

Plasmids have been detected in soil pseudomonads that allow growth on complex organic compounds as sole carbon sources, including CAM (camphor), OCT (octane), and SAL (salicylate (8, 10, 51). DNA restriction limits transfer of these degradative plasmids to *P. aeruginosa* (8), but once this barrier is overcome, CAM can be established in readily transmissible form. Although CAM has a much higher molecular weight than P-2 R plasmids (Table 1), CAM and P-2 R plasmids are incompatible (35) and readily form what appear to be CAM-R factor recombinants. In *Pseudomonas putida*, CAM and OCT are incompatible (10) and can hybridize to form CAM-OCT recombinants (9, 13) that can be transferred to *P. aeruginosa*, where they also behave as members of the P-2 group. SAL, on the other hand, although transmissible to *P. aeruginosa*, fails to transfer further from a primary *P. aeruginosa* recipient. Its compatibility properties are still under test (Table 3), but clearly SAL is not a P-2 plasmid.

Other Plasmid-Plasmid Interactions

Incompatibility is not the only interaction observed between plasmids in *P. aeruginosa*. Just as in *E. coli* where some plasmids inhibit the fertility function of the F factor (44), plasmids in *Pseudomonas* can inhibit the fertility function of FP2 and depress both chromosome mobilization and FP2 transfer (35a). Plasmids R91, Rms148, and R2 possess this property, although to a less marked degree than Rip64. R2 is also known to inhibit the fertility of FP5 (43). RP1 is also susceptible to fertility inhibition (16, 46, 46; Jacoby, Abstr. Annu. Meet. Am. Soc. Microbiol. 1975, H53, p. 105) as evidenced by loss of susceptibility to phages PRR1, PRD1, PR3, and PR4 and by decreased RP1 transfer on conjugation from a strain carrying RP1 and a second plasmid. Members of groups P-2, P-3, and W as well as the SAL

plasmid (Table 2) and FP5 (56) have this effect, but it is not a uniform enough characteristic of a given compatibility group (Table 2) to serve as a major aid in classification.

FUTURE PROSPECTS

Undoubtedly, other incompatibility groups will be defined as additional plasmids are tested. For example, plasmid R2 has not yet proved incompatible with any of the groups tests (Table 3), and the compatibility behavior of FP factors other than FP2 has yet to be thoroughly worked out. The molecular properties of relatively few *Pseudomonas* plasmids have been determined, and study of DNA homology between members of different plasmid groups has just begun (54). It is not yet known how commonly insertion sequences occur in *Pseudomonas* plasmid DNA (23) nor how often plasmids of different groups can recombine with each other or with the host chromosome. These are some of the prospects for a future conference on *P. aeruginosa*.

ACKNOWLEDGMENTS

I thank the many donors of plasmids and phage used in these studies, Lorraine Sutton for expert assistance, and the National Science Foundation for support.

LITERATURE CITED

1. Barth, P. T., and N. J. Grinter. 1974. Comparison of the deoxyribonucleic acid molecular weights and homologies of plasmids conferring linked resistance to streptomycin and sulfonamides. J. Bacteriol. 120:618–630.
2. Bradley, D. E. 1974. Adsorption of bacteriophages specific for *Pseudomonas aeruginosa* R factors RP1 and R1822. Biochem. Biophys. Res. Commun. 57:893–900.
3. Bradley, D. E., and E. L. Rutherford. 1975. Basic characterization of a lipid-containing bacteriophage specific for plasmids of the P, N, and W compatibility groups. Can. J. Microbiol. 21:152–163.
4. Bryan, L. E., S. D. Semaka, H. M. Van Den Elzen, J. E. Kinnear, and R. L. S. Whitehouse. 1973. Characteristics of R931 and other *Pseudomonas aeruginosa* R factors. Antimicrob. Agents Chemother. 3:625–637.
5. Bryan, L. E., M. S. Shahrabadi, and H. M. Van Den Elzen. 1974. Gentamicin resistance in *Pseudomonas aeruginosa*: R-factor-mediated resistance. Antimicrob. Agents Chemother. 6:191–199.
6. Bryan, L. E., H. M. Van Den Elzen, and J. T. Tseng. 1972. Transferable drug resistance in *Pseudomonas aeruginosa*. Antimicrob. Agents Chemother. 1:22–29.
7. Chabbert, Y. A., M. R. Scavizzi, J. L. Witchitz, G. R. Gerbaud, and D. H. Bouanchaud. 1972. Incompatibility groups and the classification of *fi⁻* resistance factors. J. Bacteriol. 112:666–675.
8. Chakrabarty, A. M. 1972. Genetic basis of the biodegradation of salicylate in *Pseudomonas*. J. Bacteriol. 112:815–823.
9. Chakrabarty, A. M. 1973. Genetic fusion of incompatible plasmids in *Pseudomonas*. Proc. Natl. Acad. Sci. U.S.A. 70:1641–1644.
10. Chakrabarty, A. M., G. Chou, and I. C. Gunsalus.

1973. Genetic regulation of octane dissimilation plasmid in *Pseudomonas*. Proc. Natl. Acad. Sci. U.S.A. **70:**1137–1140.

11. **Chandler, P. M., and V. Krishnapillai.** 1974. Phenotypic properties of R factors of *Pseudomonas aeruginosa*: R factors readily transferable between *Pseudomonas* and the Enterobacteriaceae. Genet. Res. **23:**239–250.

12. **Chandler, P. M., and V. Kirshnapillai.** 1974. Phenotypic properties of R factors of *Pseudomonas aeruginosa*: R factors transferable only in *Pseudomonas aeruginosa*. Genet. Res. **23:**251–257.

13. **Chou, G. I. N., D. Katz, and I. C. Gunsalus.** 1974. Fusion and compatibility of camphor and octane plasmids in *Pseudomonas*. Proc. Natl. Acad. Sci. U.S.A. **71:**2675–2678.

14. **Datta, N., and R. W. Hedges.** 1972. Host range of R factors. J. Gen. Microbiol. **70:**453–460.

15. **Datta, N., and R. W. Hedges.** 1972. R factors identified in Paris, some conferring gentamicin resistance, constitute a new compatibility group. Ann. Inst. Pasteur Paris **123:**849–852.

16. **Datta, N., R. W. Hedges, E. J. Shaw, R. B. Sykes, and M. H. Richmond.** 1971. Properties of an R factor from *Pseudomonas aeruginosa*. J. Bacteriol. **108:**1244–1249.

17. **Fullbrook, P. D., S. W. Elson, and B. Slocum.** 1970. R-factor mediated beta-lactamase in *Pseudomonas aeruginosa*. Nature (London) **226:**1054–1056.

18. **Grant, A. J., and J. Pittard.** 1974. Incompatibility reactions of R plasmids isolated from *Escherichia coli* of animal origin. J. Bacteriol. **120:**185–190.

19. **Grinsted, J., J. R. Saunders, L. C. Ingram, R. B. Sykes, and M. H. Richmond.** 1972. Properties of an R factor which originated in *Pseudomonas aeruginosa* 1822. J. Bacteriol. **110:**529–537.

20. **Hedges, R. W.** 1974. R factors from Providence. J. Gen. Microbiol. **81:**171–181.

21. **Hedges, R. W.** 1975. R factors from *Proteus mirabilis* and *P. vulgaris*. J. Gen. Microbiol. **87:**301–311.

22. **Hedges, R. W., N. Datta, J. N. Coetzee, and S. Dennison.** 1973. R factors from *Proteus morganii*. J. Gen. Microbiol. **77:**249–259.

23. **Hedges, R. W., and A. E. Jacob.** 1974. Transposition of ampicillin resistance from RP4 to other replicons. Mol. Gen. Genet. **132:**31–40.

24. **Hedges, R. W., A. E. Jacob, and J. T. Smith.** 1974. Properties of an R factor from *Bordetella bronchiseptica*. J. Gen. Microbiol. **84:**199–204.

25. **Hedges, R. W., V. Rodriguez-Lemoine, and N. Datta.** 1975. R factors from *Serratia marcescens*. J. Gen. Microbiol. **86:**88–92.

26. **Heffron, F., F. Sublett, R. W. Hedges, A. Jacob, and S. Falkow.** 1975. Origin of the TEM beta-lactamase gene found on plasmids. J. Bacteriol. **122:**250–256.

27. **Holloway, B. W., and M. H. Richmond.** 1973. R-factors used for genetic studies in strains of *Pseudomonas aeruginosa* and their origin. Genet. Res. **21:**103–105.

28. **Holloway, B. W., H. Rossiter, D. Burgess, and J. Dodge.** 1973. Aeruginocin tolerant mutants of *Pseudomonas aeruginosa*. Genet. Res. **22:**239–253.

29. **Ingram, L. C., M. H. Richmond, and R. B. Sykes.** 1973. Molecular characterization of the R factors implicated in the carbenicillin resistance of a sequence of *Pseudomonas aeruginosa* strains isolated from burns. Antimicrob. Agents Chemother. **3:**279–288.

30. **Ingram, L., R. B. Sykes, J. Grinsted, J. R. Saunders, and M. H. Richmond.** 1972. A transmissible resistance element from a strain of *Pseudomonas aeruginosa* containing no detectable extrachromosomal DNA. J. Gen. Microbiol. **72:**269–279.

31. **Iyobe, S., K. Hasuda, A. Fuse, and S. Mitsuhashi.** 1974. Demonstration of R factors from *Pseudomonas*

aeruginosa. Antimicrob. Agents Chemother. **5:**547–552.

32. **Jacob, A. E., and N. J. Grinter.** 1975. Plasmid RP4 as a vector replicon in genetic engineering. Nature (London) **255:**504–506.

33. **Jacoby, G. A.** 1974. Properties of R plasmids determining gentamicin resistance by acetylation in *Pseudomonas aeruginosa*. Antimicrob. Agents Chemother. **6:**239–252.

34. **Jacoby, G. A.** 1974. Properties of an R plasmid in *Pseudomonas aeruginosa* producing amikacin (BB-K8), butirosin, kanamycin, tobramycin and sisomicin resistance. Antimicrob. Agents Chemother. **6:**807–810.

35. **Jacoby, G. A.** 1975. Properties of R plasmids in *Pseudomonas aeruginosa*. p. 36–42. *In* D. Schlessinger (ed.), Microbiology—1974. American Society for Microbiology, Washington, D.C.

35a. **Jacoby, G. A.** 1975. R plasmids determining gentamicin or tobramycin resistance in *Pseudomonas aeruginosa*, p. 287–295. *In* S. Mitsuhashi, L. Rosival, and V. Krěmery (ed.), Drug-inactivating enzymes and antibiotic resistance. Springer-Verlag, New York.

36. **Jobanputra, R. S., and N. Datta.** 1974. Trimethoprim R factors in enterobacteria from clinical specimens. J. Med. Microbiol. **7:**169–177.

37. **Korfhagen, T. R., and J. C. Loper.** 1975. RPL11, an R factor of *Pseudomonas aeruginosa* determining carbenicillin and gentamicin resistance. Antimicrob. Agents Chemother. **7:**69–73.

38. **Krishnapillai, V.** 1974. The use of bacteriophages for differentiating plasmids of *Pseudomonas aeruginosa*. Genet. Res. **23:**327–334.

39. **Krishnapillai, V.** 1975. Resistance to ultraviolet light and enhanced mutagenesis conferred by *Pseudomonas aeruginosa* plasmids. Mutat. Res. **29:**363–372.

40. **Lang, D.** 1970. Molecular weights of coliphages and coliphage DNA. III. Contour length and molecular weight of DNA from bacteriophages T4, T5, and T7, and from bovine papilloma virus. J. Mol. Biol. **54:**557–565.

41. **Loutit, J. S.** 1970. Investigation of the mating system of *Pseudomonas aeruginosa* strain 1. VI. Mercury resistance associated with the sex factor (FP). Genet. Res. **16:**179–184.

42. **Lowbury, E. J. L., A. Kidson, H. A. Lilly, G. A. J. Ayliffe, and R. J. Jones.** 1969. Sensitivity of *Pseudomonas aeruginosa* to antibiotics: emergence of strains highly resistant to carbenicillin. Lancet **2:**448–452.

43. **Matsumoto, H., and T. Tazaki.** 1973. FP5 factor, an undescribed sex factor of *Pseudomonas aeruginosa*. Jpn. J. Microbiol. **17:**409–417.

44. **Meynell, E., G. G. Meynell, and N. Datta.** 1968. Phylogenetic relationships of drug-resistance factors and other transmissible bacterial plasmids. Bacteriol. Rev. **32:**55–83.

45. **Olsen, R. H., and P. Shipley.** 1973. Host range and properties of the *Pseudomonas aeruginosa* R factor R1822. J. Bacteriol. **113:**772–780.

46. **Olsen, R. H., and P. L. Shipley.** 1975. RP1 properties and fertility inhibition among P, N, W, and X incompatibility group plasmids. J. Bacteriol. **123:**28–35.

47. **Olsen, R. H., J. Siak, and R. H. Gray.** 1974. Characteristics of PRD1, a plasmid-dependent broad host range DNA bacteriophage. J. Virol. **14:**689–699.

48. **Olsen, R. H., and D. D. Thomas.** 1973. Characteristics and purification of PRR1, an RNA phage specific for the broad host range *Pseudomonas* R1822 drug resistance plasmid. J. Virol. **12:**1560–1567.

49. **Pemberton, J. M., and A. J. Clark.** 1973. Detection and characterization of plasmids in *Pseudomonas aeruginosa* strain PAO. J. Bacteriol. **114:**424–433.

50. **Pemberton, J. M., and B. W. Holloway.** 1973. A new sex factor of *Pseudomonas aeruginosa*. Genet. Res. **21:**263–272.

51. **Rheinwald, J. G., A. M. Chakrabarty, and I. C. Gunsalus.** 1973. A transmissible plasmid controlling camphor oxidation in *Pseudomonas putida*. Proc. Natl. Acad. Sci. U.S.A. **70**:885–889.

52. **Saunders, J. R., and J. Grinsted.** 1972. Properties of RP4, an R factor which originated in *Pseudomonas aeruginosa* S8. J. Bacteriol. **112**:690–696.

53. **Schildkraut, C. L., J. Marmur, and P. Doty.** 1962. Determination of the base composition of deoxyribonucleic acid from its buoyant density in CsCl. J. Mol. Biol. **4**:430–443.

54. **Shahrabadi, M. S., L. E. Bryan, and H. M. Van Den Elzen.** 1975. Further properties of P-2 R-factors of *Pseudomonas aeruginosa* and their relationship to other plasmid groups. Can. J. Microbiol. **21**:592–605.

55. **Smith, D. I., R. Gomez Lus, M. C. Rubio Calvo, N. Datta, A. E. Jacob, and R. W. Hedges.** 1975. Third type of plasmid conferring gentamicin resistance in *Pseudomonas aeruginosa*. Antimicrob. Agents Chemother. **8**:227–230.

56. **Stanisich, V. A.** 1974. The properties and host range of male-specific bacteriophages of *Pseudomonas aeruginosa*. J. Gen. Microbiol. **84**:332–342.

57. **Sykes, R. B., and M. H. Richmond.** 1970. Intergeneric transfer of a β-lactamase gene between *Ps. aeruginosa* and *E. coli*. Nature (London) **226**:952–954.

58. **Van Rensburg, A. J., and M. J. de Kock.** 1974. A new R factor from *Pseudomonas aeruginosa*. J. Gen. Micribiol. **82**:207–208.

59. **Witchitz, J. L., and Y. A. Chabbert.** 1971. Résistance transférable à la gentamicine. I. Expression du caractère de résistance. Ann. Inst. Pasteur Paris **121**:733–742.

Pili and Associated Bacteriophages of *Pseudomonas aeruginosa*

DAVID E. BRADLEY

*Faculty of Medicine, Memorial University of Newfoundland,
St. John's, Newfoundland, Canada A1C 5S7*

INTRODUCTION

Bacterial pili are filamentous appendages much thinner than flagella and of variable length. A number of different morphological types have been identified (15), the best known being F pili, determined by the *Escherichia coli* sex factor F. Pilus studies on the genus *Pseudomonas*, which has polar flagella, show that the filaments may also be polar or may cover the whole cell, depending on the species (19). With *Pseudomonas aeruginosa* several pilus types have been characterized, including "common" pili, which are polar (1, 22, 36) and whose function is unknown. In addition, pili determined by transferable drug resistance plasmids have been identified (9, 11, 32). These are not necessarily polar. Most *P. aeruginosa* pili act as receptors for a variety of different bacterial viruses, and a study of pilus/bacteriophage interactions provides valuable information on the functional properties of pili.

POLAR PILI OF *P. AERUGINOSA*

Characteristics

Most strains of *P. aeruginosa* have polar pili, designated PSA pili (13), in varying numbers. Despite an apparently identical appearance, pili produced by different strains of *P. aeruginosa* are generally serologically unrelated (13), with no correlation between serotypes of pili and serological groups of bacteria (based on either cell wall or flagellar antigens). PSA pili are flexible filaments 6 nm thick (3, 36) with no visible subunit structure or terminal appendages. Their length ranges between 100 and 5,000 nm, averaging about 2,500 nm. The pilus protein (pilin) of *P. aeruginosa* strain K has a molecular weight of 17,500 compared to the 12,000 of F pili (W. Paranchych, personal communication). PSA pili are produced by *P. aeruginosa* strain PA01 at temperatures between 10 and 44°C (5, 13). As will be described, they act as receptors for various bacteriophages. Some phage isolates are able to adsorb to more than one serotype of pilus (13). Attempts to correlate PSA pilus production with the presence of the FP2 or FP39 sex factors (21) of *P. aeruginosa* showed that PSA pili were not determined by the plasmids. Their genetic origin remains unknown.

Polar Pili as RNA Bacteriophage Receptors

The RNA phages of *E. coli* male strains (26) were found by electron microscopy to adsorb to F pili (17). It was not therefore surprising that the morphologically similar single-stranded RNA phage PP7 was observed attached to the PSA pili of sensitive strains of *P. aeruginosa* (2). The number of virions on a pilus depended on pH (6); usually only one phage (thought to be irreversibly adsorbed) was found on each pilus at the normal pH of the culture (pH 8.4), but there were at least ten times as many at pH 6.8 (thought to be reversibly adsorbed). This route of infection was confirmed when it was found that non-piliated host mutants were resistant to the RNA phage (37).

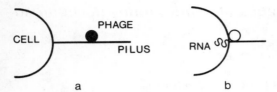

FIG. 1. *Simplified model for the adsorption and RNA penetration of* P. aeruginosa *phage PP7. (a) Virion adsorbs to midpoint (on average) of pilus; (b) pilus retracts to half its length and RNA passes into the cell.*

Retraction of Polar Pili

The F pilus receptors of *E. coli* RNA phages were at first thought to act as tubes down which infecting RNA could pass (15, 16), but the idea that they retracted into the cell has gained favor (27). With *P. aeruginosa* (3), it was suggested that a phage virion attached to a pilus, which then withdrew into the cell, pulling the virus to the surface where nucleic acid penetration took place (Fig. 1). The observation that only one PP7 RNA phage virion adsorbed to each pilus offered a favorable opportunity to test this hypothesis. It was assumed that a virion would adsorb at random anywhere along the length of the pilus so that the average adsorption site for many phages on different pili would be at the midpoint. If the model in Fig. 1 was correct, and the phage particle stopped further pilus retraction when it reached the cell surface, then PP7 adsorption should have reduced the average pilus length by 50%. A suitable control organism for the experiment would be one with nonretractile pili (still able to adsorb the phage), which would show no length reduction. A strain thought to have nonretractile pili was PP7-resistant PAO68, derived from PP7-sensitive PAO1 (3, 6). With PAO1 exponential-phase cultures, it was found that an average pilus length reduction of 43% occurred after RNA phage adsorption, but with PAO68 there was no change (6). In Fig. 2, experimental data (continuous lines) were compared to theoretical curves (broken lines) which showed the expected frequency distribution after a 50% length reduction (4). In the lower graphs, theoretical values were obtained by halving each measurement taken in the absence of phage adsorption. Conversely, theoretical frequency distribution curves for unretracted lengths were obtained by doubling each pilus measurement after PP7 adsorption (top graphs). A remarkably close match of experimental and theoretical curves indicates that the model is correct; PAO1 PSA pili retract but PAO68 pili do not. It

was subsequently found that a characteristic of nonretractile pili was their very large numbers (10), often over 100 pili on a single pole, depending on the strain (Fig. 3).

Further support for the model comes from the electron microscope observation that irreversibly adsorbed PP7 virions (1 per pilus at pH 8.4) are located at pilus bases on the sensitive strain PAO1 (Fig. 4), but are distributed at random along the nonretractile pili of strain PAO68 (Fig. 5). Pilus retraction is apparently stimulated by phage adsorption rather than by the negative staining procedure (6). The possibility that the pili are continuously extending and retracting in the absence of any stimulus is not compatible with experimental data (5).

Adsorption of Filamentous Bacteriophages to Polar Pili

The filamentous bacteriophage Pf, which contains single-stranded DNA, was isolated on *P. aeruginosa* strain K by Takeya and Amako (34), and found to infect only piliated bacteria (7). Pf was shown to adsorb to the tips of isolated pili (7), which were distinguished by antibody labeling (25). However, the electron microscopy of adsorption mixtures of *P. aeruginosa* and Pf

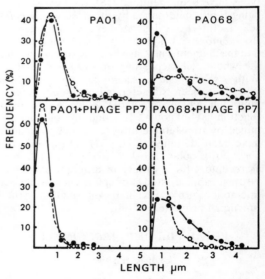

FIG. 2. *Frequency distribution curves for pilus lengths with and without phage PP7 adsorption:* ●, *from direct measurement;* ○, *predicted for 50% length reduction (see text). Curves match with* P. aeruginosa *strain PAO1, indicating retraction, but not with strain PAO68 (experimental values from reference 6).*

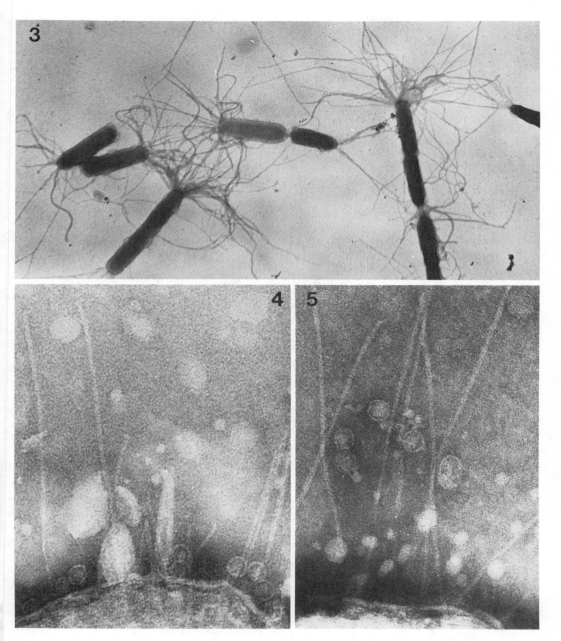

Fig. 3. *Low-magnification micrograph of a* P. aeruginosa *strain K mutant with nonretractile pili in large numbers (10). Contrast was enhanced by antibody labeling. Magnification, ×7,000. Reprinted with permission of Academic Press Inc., New York.*

Fig. 4. *Phage PP7 at bases of retractile PSA pili of strain PAO1 (6). Magnification, ×200,000. Reprinted with permission of* The Journal of General Microbiology.

Fig. 5. *Phage PP7 adsorbed at random on nonretractile PSA pili of strain PAO68 (6). Magnification, ×200,000. Reprinted with permission of* The Journal of General Microbiology.

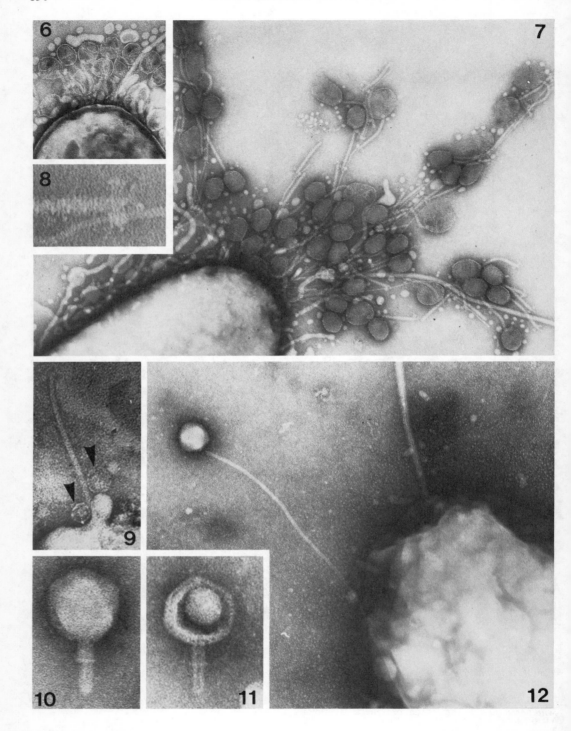

FIG. 6. *Phage M6 adsorbed to the pole of sensitive* P. aeruginosa *strain PAO1 (12) showing empty heads. Magnification,* ×75,000. *Reprinted with permission of* The Journal of General Virology.

FIG. 7. *Phage M6 adsorbed to the nonretractile pili of the resistant strain PAO68 (12) showing full heads. Magnification,* ×75,000. *Reprinted with permission of* The Journal of General Virology.

FIG. 8. *Detail of M6 phage tail attached to pilus (12). Magnification,* ×400,000. *Reprinted with permission of* The Journal of General Virology.

FIG. 9. *RNA phage PRR1 virions (arrowed) at base of RP1 pilus on* E. coli *(9). Magnification,* ×175,000. *Reprinted with permission of Academic Press Inc., New York.*

FIG. 10. *Lipid phage PR4 with full head. Magnification,* ×270,000.

FIG. 11. *Lipid phage PR4 with empty head. Magnification,* ×270,000.

FIG. 12. *Lipid phage PR4 virion adsorbed to the tip of a W pilus on* P. aeruginosa *(R7K); the tail may have been detached during negative staining. Phages were also found on the cell surface. Magnification,* ×115,000.

←——

showed virions adsorbed only to the poles of the cells. This suggested a mechanism whereby virions attached to the tips of pili which then retracted, pulling the phage filaments to the cell surface. It is possible that secondary receptors in the cell wall may be required for DNA penetration. A similar sequence has been suggested for an *E. coli* F-specific filamentous phage (24).

Adsorption of Tailed Bacteriophages to Polar Pili

The investigation of several morphological types of bacteriophages with noncontractile tails revealed that they were pilus dependent (8, 12, 31), and that they could adsorb to PSA pili of more than one serotype (13). Four basic observations established their pilus specificity: (i) they neither adsorbed to nor infected pilusless host mutant strains; (ii) they adsorbed to, but did not infect, host mutants with nonretractile pili; (iii) host mutants resistant to the phages had no pili; and (iv) virus particles were visibly attached to host pili (retractile or nonretractile) in the electron microscope. The last point is illustrated here with reference to phage M6 (12). Empty virions were observed only at the polar surface of sensitive cells (Fig. 6). With an M6-resistant mutant having nonretractile pili, virions adsorbed to the filaments but retained their DNA (Fig. 7). This suggests that pilus retraction is a prerequisite for DNA penetration. The attachment of M6 virions to pili was by means of short tail fibers (Fig. 8).

It therefore seems that the tailed pilus phages, like the RNA and filamentous phages, utilize retractile PSA pili to gain access to the cell.

PILI DETERMINED BY DRUG RESISTANCE PLASMIDS IN *P. AERUGINOSA*

Pili and Bacteriophages of the P Compatibility Group Plasmids

There are four principal groups of drug resistance plasmids occurring naturally in *P. aeruginosa*. Compatibility group nomenclature remains to be clarified, but they are currently called P-1, P-2, etc. (32). The P-1 group contains R factors capable of intergeneric transfer. The "type plasmid" RP4 (18, 20), alternatively designated R1822 (28), determines specific pili (9) which are shorter than the polar PSA pili. Neither their involvement in conjugation nor their ability to retract has been established. They are not strictly polar but prefer that part of the cell. They act as receptors (9) for the P-specific RNA phage PRR1 (30), which attaches to the sides of the pili. Single virions show a tendency to be attached near the bases (Fig. 9), suggesting that the filaments may be retractile like PSA pili. A P-specific filamentous phage Pf3 (33) appears in the electron microscope to adsorb to the cell wall (9), but as we have seen with Pf, this does not preclude a pilus as the primary adsorption site. A unique type of phage (isolates designated PR4 and PRD1) contains lipid (14, 29, 33). PR4 has an easily detached tail with a small sheath (Fig. 10 and 11). Both isolates are able to grow on bacteria carrying plasmids of compatibility groups P, N and W, which are related in genetic homology (23). This type of phage appears to adsorb only to the cell surface of bacteria carrying RP4 (14, 29).

Small numbers of pili have been found on *P. aeruginosa* carrying the plasmid R130 of the P-2 group. They appear similar to PSA pili, but are not polar (32), and have not been studied in any detail. The P-2 group includes the *P. aeruginosa* sex factor FP39.

Pili of the W Compatibility Group Plasmids

The first W plasmid to be isolated apparently originated in *Shigella* (35), but all three members of the group can transfer intergenerically although they are rather unstable in *P. aeruginosa*. They determine long flexible pili 12 nm thick, which are only expressed in small numbers by *P. aeruginosa* (11). Strains carrying W plasmids are sensitive to the lipid phage PR4. Virions adsorb to the tips of W-pili as well as to the cell surface (Fig. 12). Adsorption is accompanied by a 90% drop in piliation for strains of *Salmonella typhimurium* carrying W plasmids, but this remains to be confirmed for *P. aeruginosa*. It is possible that PR4 has a mechanism of infection like the filamentous phage Pf, in which case W pili would have to be retractile. However, cell wall receptors have been identified for the similar isolate PRD1 (J. Siak and R. H. Olsen, Abstr. Annu. Meet. Am. Soc. Microbiol., 1975, S274, p. 259); they could be required to trigger DNA penetration after pilus retraction. The unlikely possibility that PR4 adsorption to pilus tips is nonspecific has not been ruled out.

CONCLUSION

Four different types of pilus have been found associated with *P. aeruginosa*: (i) flexible PSA pili, thickness 6 nm, average length about 1,250 nm, (ii) rigid RP4 pili, thickness 8 nm, average length about 300 nm, (iii) flexible R130 pili, dimensions not yet measured, (iv) flexible W pili, thickness 12 nm, average length about 450 nm. All but PSA pili are determined by drug resistance plasmids. In no case has their involvement in conjugation and drug resistance transfer been established, but in view of the proven requirement for F pili in F plasmid transfer (15), this seems highly likely. The origin of PSA pili is unknown. They may well be plasmid determined (the ease of formation of pilus-less mutants suggests this), but attempts to transfer them from one strain to another have been unsuccessful (D. E. Bradley, unpublished data). One possibility is that the plasmid has lost its ability to transfer. The most important aspects to be investigated are the functional role of plasmid-determined pili in conjugation and the genetic origin of PSA pili.

ACKNOWLEDGMENTS

The most recent of my work described here was supported by the Medical Research Council of Canada (grant no. MA5608). I am grateful to Rosemary Bradley for helping with the manuscript and to Doris Cohen for technical assistance.

LITERATURE CITED

1. **Bradley, D. E.** 1965. The morphology and physiology of bacteriophages as revealed by the electron microscope. J. Roy. Microsc. Soc. **84**:257–316.
2. **Bradley, D. E.** 1966. The structure and infective process of a *Pseudomonas aeruginosa* bacteriophage containing ribonucleic acid. J. Gen. Microbiol. **45**:83–96.
3. **Bradley, D. E.** 1972. A study of pili on *Pseudomonas aeruginosa*. Genet. Res. **19**:39–51.
4. **Bradley, D. E.** 1972. Evidence for the retraction of *Pseudomonas aeruginosa* RNA phage pili. Biochem. Biophys. Res. Commun. **47**:142–149.
5. **Bradley, D. E.** 1972. Stimulation of pilus formation in *Pseudomonas aeruginosa* by RNA bacteriophage adsorption. Biochem. Biophys. Res. Commun. **47**: 1080–1087.
6. **Bradley, D. E.** 1972. Shortening of *Pseudomonas aeruginosa* pili after RNA-phage adsorption. J. Gen. Microbiol. **72**:303–319.
7. **Bradley, D. E.** 1973. The adsorption of the *Pseudomonas aeruginosa* filamentous bacteriophage Pf to its host. Can. J. Microbiol. **19**:623–631.
8. **Bradley, D. E.** 1973. Basic characterization of a *Pseudomonas aeruginosa* pilus-dependent bacteriophage with a long noncontractile tail. J. Virol. **12**: 1139–1148.
9. **Bradley, D. E.** 1974. Adsorption of bacteriophages specific for *Pseudomonas aeruginosa* R factors RP1 and R1822. Biochem. Biophys. Res. Commun. **57**: 893–900.
10. **Bradley, D. E.** 1974. The adsorption of *Pseudomonas aeruginosa* pilus-dependent bacteriophages to a host mutant with nonretractile pili. Virology **58**:149–163.
11. **Bradley, D. E.** 1975. The occurrence of pili associated with a plasmid of the W compatibility group. Biochem. Biophys. Res. Commun. **64**:918–925.
12. **Bradley, D. E., and T. L. Pitt.** 1974. Pilus-dependence of four *Pseudomonas aeruginosa* bacteriophages with non-contractile tails. J. Gen. Virol. **24**:1–15.
13. **Bradley, D. E., and T. L. Pitt.** 1975. An immunological study of the pili of *Pseudomonas aeruginosa*. J. Hyg. **74**:419–430.
14. **Bradley, D. E., and E. L. Rutherford.** 1975. Basic characterization of a lipid-containing bacteriophage specific for plasmids of the P, N, and W compatibility groups. Can. J. Microbiol. **21**:152–163.
15. **Brinton, C. C.** 1965. The structure, function, synthesis and genetic control of bacterial pili and a molecular model for DNA and RNA transport in gram-negative bacteria. Trans. N.Y. Acad. Sci. **27**:1003–1054.
16. **Brinton, C. C.** 1971. The properties of sex pili, the viral nature of "conjugal" genetic transfer systems, and some possible approaches to the control of bacterial drug resistance. Crit. Rev. Microbiol. **1**:105–160.
17. **Crawford, E. M., and R. F. Gesteland.** 1964. The adsorption of bacteriophage R17. Virology **22**:165–167.
18. **Datta, N., R. W. Hedges, E. J. Shaw, R. B. Sykes, and M. H. Richmond.** 1971. Properties of an R factor from *Pseudomonas aeruginosa*. J. Bacteriol. **108**:1244–1249.
19. **Fuerst, J. A., and A. C. Hayward.** 1961. Surface appendages similar to fimbriae (pili) on pseudomonas species. J. Gen. Microbiol. **58**:227–237.
20. **Grinsted, J. J., R. Saunders, L. C. Ingram, R. B.**

Sykes, and M. H. Richmond. 1972. Properties of an R factor which originated in *Pseudomonas aeruginosa* 1822. J. Bacteriol. 110:529–537.

21. Holloway, B. W. 1969. Genetics of *Pseudomonas*. Bacteriol. Rev. 33:419–443.

22. Houwink, A. L., and W. van Iterson. 1950. Electron microscopical observations on bacterial cytology. II. A study on flagellation. Biochim. Biophys. Acta 5: 10–44.

23. Ingram, L. C. 1973. Deoxyribonucleic acid-deoxyribonucleic acid hybridization of R factors. J. Bacteriol. 115:1130–1134.

24. Jacobson, A. 1972. Role of F pili in the penetration of bacteriophage f1 J. Virol. 10:835–843.

25. Lawn, A. M. 1967. Simple immunological labelling method for electron microscopy and its application to the study of filamentous appendages of bacteria. Nature (London) 214:1151–1152.

26. Loeb, T., and N. D. Zinder. 1961. A bacteriophage containing RNA. Proc. Natl. Acad. Sci. U.S.A. 47: 282–289.

27. Marvin, D. A., and B. Hohn. 1969. Filamentous bacterial viruses. Bacteriol. Rev. 33:172–209.

28. Olsen, R. H., and P. Shipley. 1973. Host range and properties of the *Pseudomonas aeruginosa* R factor R1822. J. Bacteriol. 113:772–780.

29. Olsen, R. H., J. Siak, and R. H. Gray. 1974. Characteristics of PRD1, a plasmid-dependent broad host range DNA bacteriophage. J. Virol. 14:689–699.

30. Olsen, R. H., and D. D. Thomas. 1973. Characteristics and purification of PRR1, an RNA phage specific for the broad host range *Pseudomonas* R1822 drug resistance plasmid. J. Virol. 12:1560–1567.

31. Pemberton, J. M. 1973. F116: a DNA bacteriophage specific for the pili of *Pseudomonas aeruginosa* strain PAO. Virology 55:558–560.

32. Shahrabadi, M. S., L. E. Bryan, and H. M. Van Den Elzen. 1975. Further properties of P-2 R-factors of *Pseudomonas aeruginosa* and their relationship to other plasmid groups. Can. J. Microbiol. 21:592–605.

33. Stanisich, V. 1974. The properties and host range of male-specific bacteriophages of *Pseudomonas aeruginosa*. J. Gen.Microbiol. 84:332–342.

34. Takeya, K., and K. Amako. 1966. A rod-shaped pseudomonas phage. Virology 38:163–164.

35. Watanabe, T., C. Furuse, and S. Sakaizumi. 1968. Transduction of various R factors by phage P1 in *Escherichia coli* and by phage P22 in *Salmonella typhimurium*. J. Bacteriol. 96:1791–1795.

36. Weiss, R. L. 1971. The structure and occurrence of pili (fimbriae) on *Pseudomonas aeruginosa*. J. Gen. Microbiol. 67:135–143.

37. Weppelman, R. M., and C. C. Brinton. 1971. The infection of *Pseudomonas aeruginosa* by RNA pilus phage PP7: the adsorption organelle and the relationship between phage sensitivity and the division cycle. Virology 44:1–17.

Localization and Functional Role of the *Pseudomonas* Bacteriophage 2-Associated Depolymerase

PASQUALE F. BARTELL

New Jersey Medical School, Newark, New Jersey 07103

INTRODUCTION

The synthesis of phage-directed enzymes is known to occur shortly after the insertion of phage nucleic acid into a receptive bacterial cell. Most of these enzymes are primarily involved in the production of various structural components that are eventually brought together in the assembly of progeny phage. However, the enzymes themselves are not destined to become an identifiable part of the mature phage particle. Other enzymes are also synthesized in the infected cell, and these ultimately become closely associated with the mature phage particle; they are largely recognized by virtue of their hydrolytic activity on various structural components of the bacterial cell. Among these enzymes are the depolymerases that act on capsular and slime layers (4).

Although the functional role of these enzymes in the phage life cycle remains to be defined, various investigators have presented data suggesting that these enzymes act on interfering exopolysaccharides and thereby assist phage in reaching underlying bacterial cell wall receptor sites. Others believe that these enzymes may assist in the release of phage from infected cells (4). More recent studies have provided strong experimental evidence implicating these enzymes, through interaction with their substrates, as the specific molecular interaction required for phage adsorption (6, 8, 10).

The purpose of this review is to summarize studies dealing with the depolymerase associated with phage 2 infection of *Pseudomonas aeruginosa*, and the functional role of this enzyme in the phage life cycle.

THE PHAGE 2 DEPOLYMERASE

Pseudomonas phage 2 belongs to Bradley's group B, possessing a head with hexagonal outline and a long noncontractile tail with a prominent knoblike structure at the tip. Infection of *P. aeruginosa* strain BI with phage 2 results in the production of a depolymerase (2). On mature lawns of susceptible bacteria, the activity of the enzyme is observed as a halo surrounding phage plaques. The enzyme is routinely found in infective lysates produced in a soft agar layer as well as broth cultures, but is not detectable in uninfected cultures.

The depolymerase has been purified 1,688-fold from crude lysates by salting out with ammonium sulfate, Sephadex gel filtration, and high-speed centrifugation, producing a single band when tested by electrophoresis in acrylamide gel. The molecular weight is estimated to be 180,000 on the basis of gel filtration data. The enzyme recognizes a substrate that is present in a polysaccharide-containing glycolipoprotein fraction obtained from the extracellular slime layer of strain BI. The major constituents of this fraction are amino and neutral sugars (glucosamine, galactosamine, rhamnose, mannose, glucose, galactose). The enzyme specifically hydrolyzes this substrate at an optimum pH of 7.5, reducing the viscosity and releasing amino and neutral sugars (2).

DEPOLYMERASE SPECIFICITY

The phage 2 depolymerase is not unique since, in addition to phage 2, five other *Pseudomonas* phages have been observed to produce depolymerases when they infect susceptible host cells. These enzymes fall into two distinct groups based on their substrate specificities. It is also evident that there are differences in the polysaccharide-containing glycolipoprotein substrate fractions obtained from the extracellular slime layer of various strains of *P. aeruginosa*.

ORIGIN OF THE PHAGE DEPOLYMERASE

Analyses, by construction of phage growth curves, indicate that the depolymerase is synthesized by *P. aeruginosa* strains BI and B after infection with phage 2 (1). The kinetics of biosynthesis of the depolymerase closely parallel the rate of formation of phage-directed virions, and alterations in the experimental conditions of infection are reflected by alterations in the production of enzyme. The presence of active enzyme and mature phage particles is observed in disrupted cells as early as 50 min after infection. Infection of strains BI and B with other phages does not result in the synthesis of depolymerase, nor is the enzyme detectable in supernatant fluids or extracts from uninfected cultures. The results of experiments employing chloramphenicol or an auxotrophic mutant (BI *arg⁻*) suggest that de novo protein synthesis is essential for synthesis of the enzyme. These experiments indicate that depolymerase synthesis is not a general cellular response to infection by phage, but rather is a specific response to phage 2 infection. The isolation of phage mutants with alterations in their ability to produce active enzyme has provided strong evidence to support the role of the phage genome in synthesis of the depolymerase.

RELATIONSHIP BETWEEN DEPOLYMERASE AND THE MATURE PHAGE PARTICLE

The existence of a free and soluble form of the enzyme is evident by its filtration characteristics, its diffusibility in agar, and by centrifugation studies. However, the enzyme also appeared to be in a form that was firmly associated with the phage particle, and subsequent experiments suggested a physical relationship between enzyme and the mature phage particle. Despite exhaustive purification, depolymerase activity bands with phage particles at a density of 1.49 to 1.51 g/ml in a density gradient composed of cesium chloride, indicating a firm association of enzyme with the phage particle. A more precise location of the enzyme on the phage particle has been established through the use of specific antiserum prepared against purified enzyme. When mixed with phage and viewed under the

electron microscope, the phage particles are bound together in a rosette arrangement, with the phage tails oriented towards the center (Fig. 1). In contrast to this, agglutination of the phage occurs in a completely disorganized pattern when phage 2 is mixed with antiserum prepared against purified phage 2 particles. These results indicate that the depolymerase is located at the tip of the tail of phage 2, close to, or forming part of, the base plate structure. The localization of phage-associated enzymes at the tail tip of other phages is well documented (6, 9).

RELATIONSHIP BETWEEN THE ENZYME-SUBSTRATE INTERACTION AND PHAGE ADSORPTION

The localization of the enzyme, and the fact that phage 2 adsorbs to its susceptible host cell in a tail-first manner, has suggested a possible role for the enzyme in phage adsorption. When adsorption of phage 2 is examined under varying conditions of pH, phage 2 adsorbs over a rather broad range, reaching maximum levels around pH 7.5. Interestingly, pH 7.5 is also found to provide optimal pH for activity of the enzyme. The possible relationship between enzyme-substrate interaction and phage adsorption has been suggested by the characteristics of various mutants of strain BI isolated after exposure to nitrosoguanidine (8). When compared to the wild-type strain BI, these mutants (BI/PDB₂ng1) are devoid of substrate for the phage enzyme, and when subsequently tested for their ability to adsorb phage 2, they fail to do so. Spontaneous mutants of strain BI (BI/2s), resistant to phage 2 infection, also have been isolated, and the nature of their resistance was confirmed to be the failure to adsorb phage 2. In each case, the loss in ability to adsorb phage is accompanied by a loss in enzyme substrate.

The relationship between enzyme-substrate interaction and phage adsorption is best seen with *Pseudomonas* phages 2 and 8, which possess depolymerases of different specificities. The phage 2 enzyme interacts with substrate produced by strain BI, but not EI, and accordingly phage 2 adsorbs to strain BI, but not EI. On the other hand, phage 8 enzyme interacts with substrate produced by strain EI, but not BI, and accordingly phage 8 adsorbs to strain EI, but not BI (8).

The ability of phage 2 to adsorb to strain BI indicates the presence of appropriate phage receptor sites on the bacterial cell. Accordingly, the next experiments attempted to demonstrate the presence of phage receptors in the polysaccharide-containing substrate by mixing phage with the substrate and measuring the percentage

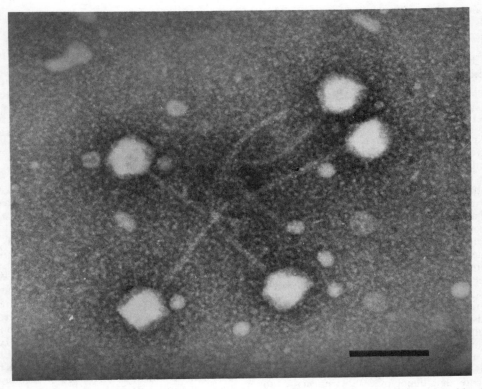

Fig. 1. *Bacteriophage 2 after interaction with anti-depolymerase serum. Note the rosette formed by the phages with their tails oriented toward the center. The bar represents 100 nm.*

of the phage suspension that was inactivated after 10 min of incubation. The results of these experiments make it clear that purified preparations of substrate obtained from strain BI contain phage 2 receptors (3). On the other hand, the polysaccharide-containing glycolipoprotein fraction from a mutant of strain BI (BI/2s1) and strain EI fail to inactivate phage when tested in the same manner. As noted above, the mutant BI/2s1 and strain EI also fail to adsorb phage 2, and also fail to produce a reactive substrate for the phage 2 enzyme. These results indicate that the phage receptor is indeed a component of the polysaccharide-containing glycolipoprotein substrate.

Evidence has been presented indicating a close association of the phage enzyme with the phage particle, and the likelihood that the enzyme functions in the initial attachment of phage to the host cell. Since the phage enzyme is located on a region of the phage involved in the adsorptive process, then the interaction of anti-enzyme serum with phage particles should render the phage incapable of initiating infection. The results of our experiments show that this is exactly what occurs, and the fact that phage 2 is inactivated by anti-depolymerase serum points to the essential nature of this enzyme in the infectious process. In other studies involving *Salmonella* phage ϵ^{15}, it has been suggested that a phage-associated enzyme may be responsible for specific adsorption to bacteria (6, 10).

PDP1 is a haloless mutant of phage 2 that has been found to adsorb, infect, and replicate on strain BI, despite the fact that enzyme activity has not been found to be associated with this mutant. The growth curve of PDP1 is quite similar to that of phage 2, having a latent period of 55 min, a rise period of 20 to 25 min, and an average burst size of 10. The absence of a halo around the plaques of this mutant phage might be interpreted in two ways: (i) an absence of depolymerase, or (ii) the structural presence of a depolymerase that lacks hydrolytic activity. Experiments have been performed to examine these possibilities (Table 1). Antiserum prepared against wild-type phage 2 completely inactivates the mutant PDP1, indicating a strong serological relationship between phage 2 and its mutant. Antiserum prepared against the purified depolymerase also inactivates PDP1. This result has been taken as an indication that a cross-reacting

TABLE 1. *Inactivation of phage mutant PDP1 by anti-phage 2 and anti-depolymerase sera*

Medium	Phage input (PFU × 10⁵/ml)	Phage recovered (PFU × 10⁵/ml)	Inactivation (%)
Buffer[a]	1.95	1.95	0
Anti-phage 2 serum	1.95	0	100
Anti-depolymerase serum	1.95	0	100

[a] Tris, 5 mM (pH 7.4), supplemented with 0.1 M sodium chloride and 0.01 M magnesium sulfate.

polypeptide(s), antigenically similar to those of the depolymerase, are present in PDP1 particles. Further examination under the electron microscope reveals that PDP1 interacts with the anti-depolymerase serum and produces a tail-centered rosette arrangement similar to that observed when the wild-type phage 2 is reacted with anti-depolymerase serum. These results suggest that the PDP1 mutant possesses tail region polypeptides that are antigenically related to the wild-type phage 2 depolymerase polypeptides. Although enzymatically inactive, these polypeptides appear to be in the same structural location as the depolymerase of phage 2. These results may be taken to suggest that active enzyme is not essential in the adsorptive process and that the presence of structural enzyme, although devoid of enzymatic activity, may retain the ability to recognize complementary receptors and allow phage to adsorb to the cell surface. In this connection, coliphage T4D possesses an enzyme, dihydrofolate reductase, as one of the structural components of the base plate, and that this enzyme has been shown to play a role in the adsorption process. Two mutants of T4D, neither of which induces the production of active dihydrofolate reductase, are fully infective. These mutants induce the production of a protein that resembles the enzyme in that it binds to the substrate, but does not reduce free dihydrofolate. Kozloff et al. (7) indicated that the protein may serve a structural role in the phage tail plate rather than an enzymatic one. This hypothesis has also been proposed by Dawes and Goldberg (5), who stated that the dihydrofolate reductase plays no enzymatic role in the virion, but is structurally important during the early stages of phage adsorption.

ACKNOWLEDGMENT

These investigations were supported by Public Health Service Grant AI-08504 from the National Institute of Allergy and Infectious Diseases.

LITERATURE CITED

1. **Bartell, P. F., and T. E. Orr.** 1969. Origin of polysaccharide depolymerase associated with bacteriophage infection. J. Virol. 3:290–296.
2. **Bartell, P. F., and T. E. Orr.** 1969. Distinct slime polysaccharide depolymerase of bacteriophage infected *Pseudomonas aeruginosa*: evidence of close association with the structured phage particle. J. Virol. 4:580–584.
3. **Castillo, F. J., and P. F. Bartell.** 1974. Studies on the bacteriophage 2 receptors of *Pseudomonas aeruginosa*. J. Virol. 14:904–909.
4. **Cohen, S. S.** 1968. Virus-induced enzymes. Columbia University Press, New York.
5. **Dawes, J., and E. B. Goldberg.** 1973. Functions of baseplate components in bacteriophage T4 infection. Virology 55:380–390.
6. **Kangegasaki, S., and A. Wright.** 1973. Studies on the mechanism of phage adsorption: interaction between phage ε¹⁵ and its cellular receptor. Virology 52:160–173.
7. **Kozloff, L. M., C. Verses, M. Lute, and L. K. Crosby.** 1970. Bateriophage tail components. II. Dihydrofolate reductase in T4D bacteriophage. J. Virol. 5:740–753.
8. **Reese, J. F., G. Dimitracopoulos, and P. F. Bartell.** 1974. Factors influencing the adsorption of bacteriophage 2 to cells of *Pseudomonas aeruginosa*. J. Virol. 13:22–27.
9. **Stirm, S., W. Bessler, F. Fehmel, E. Freund-Molbert, and H. Thurow.** 1971. Isolation of spike-formed particles from bacteriophage lysates. Virology 45:303–308.
10. **Takeda, K., and H. Uetake.** 1973. *In vitro* interaction between phage and receptor lipopolysaccharide: a novel glycosidase associated with Salmonella phage ε¹⁵. Virology 52:148–159.

Pseudomonas Plasmid RP1-Encoded Surface Components: a Somatic Receptor for Phage PRD1

RONALD H. OLSEN, JUNE-SANG SIAK,[1] AND PATRICIA L. SHIPLEY[2]

Department of Microbiology, University of Michigan Medical School, Ann Arbor, Michigan 48104

INTRODUCTION

Bacterial plasmids can be transferred between bacteria not known to exchange chromosomal genes and thus afford an opportunity for the study of gene expression in hosts having disparate physiological properties and ecological niches. We have studied plasmid-encoded genes whose products are associated with several levels of cellular organization or location. For this we have used the R factor, RP1, which originated in *Pseudomonas aeruginosa*. This R factor is freely transferred among unrelated gram-negative bacteria (3, 4, 12).

When RP1-encoded β-lactamase activity was compared for several *Pseudomonas* and *Enterobacteriaceae* strains, the enzyme activity encoded by RP1 in these hosts varied at most by a factor of two (12). Thus, the expression of a diffusible periplasmic gene product was not greatly affected by the genetic background of the producing cells. Analogously, when the *Escherichia coli* histidine operon was incorporated into RP1 and its expression was studied in *P. aeruginosa*, we observed gene expression adequate to confer histidine independence on *Pseudomonas* histidine auxotrophs representative of the known chromosomal linkage groups for histidine biosynthesis in *Pseudomonas* (11).

Levy and McMurry (9) reported the presence of tetracycline-inducible protein in membrane fractions from minicells containing R factors of

five different incompatibility groups. Their results associated a decrease in tetracycline accumulation with the presence of a plasmid encoding tetracycline resistance. When we determined the effect of RP1 on tetracycline accumulation by several gram-negative bacterial strains (18), they also showed reduced tetracycline uptake. Thus, the behavior of RP1-encoded tetracycline resistance, presumably associated with inner membrane changes directed by RP1, was similar to the previous observations of Franklin (5). In psychrophilic bacteria, however, tetracycline resistance was observed to be cold sensitive for bacteria growing near 0 C. Perhaps this indicates that mesophilic bacterial strains are the source of RP1-encoded tetracycline resistance.

We considered that expression of phage receptors specified by RP1 would be a convenient indication of bacterial surface alterations encoded by RP1. When we grew bacteria containing RP1 with filtered sewage, we obtained several phages of different plaque morphology and growth characteristics. Two of these phages were selected for further study.

One phage, designated PRR1, contained RNA and was specific for pili produced by bacterial strains maintaining RP1 (12, 14). Phage PRR1 resembles male-specific *Escherichia coli* phages in its growth properties and morphology. However, some bacterial strains containing RP1 are unable to plaque PRR1, although they are normal with respect to their ability to serve as donors of RP1. A similar observation has been made for *Proteus mirabilis* harboring F genotes and unable to plaque F-specific coliphage (6).

Electron microscope observation of another

[1] Present address: Department of Microbiology and Immunology, Hahnemann Medical College, Philadelphia, Pa. 19102.
[2] Department of Microbiology, University of Washington, Seattle, Wash. 98195.

TABLE 1. *Host-influenced adsorption and plating of PRD1[a]*

Host bacterium	PRD1 adsorbed (%)	EOP[b]
Salmonella typhimurium LT2(RP1)	60	(1)
Pseudomonas aeruginosa PAO67(RP1)	40	0.8
Pseudomonas aeruginosa PAT904(RP1)	17	0.4

[a] Experimental conditions were as reported previously (13).
[b] Plating efficiency was determined relative to LT2(RP1).

RP1-specific phage, designated PRD1, when adsorbed to host bacteria indicated a plasmid-encoded surface alteration heretofore not observed. In addition, phage PRD1 was unlike other plasmid-specific phages previously described. It adsorbed to the cell wall of bacteria containing RP1 and contained duplex DNA enclosed in a membranous head structure (13). In this report we focus on the unique properties of this phage with respect to the location of its receptor and consider the utility of this system for the study of plasmid-encoded alterations of the bacterial surface.

RESULTS

In Situ Properties and Removal of the PRD1 Receptor

In a study of phage PRD1 adsorption, we observed that phage PRD1 adsorption and plating efficiency varied with the host bacterium (13). An example of this variance is shown in Table 1. These data indicate that *Salmonella typhimurium* LT2(RP1) optimally expresses the phage PRD1 receptor. When the hosts listed in Table 1 were tested for their phage adsorption kinetics, the adsorption rate was similar although the bacterial strains used varied with respect to the amount of phage they adsorbed. In view of the apparent optimal behavior of *S. typhimurium* LT2(RP1), we chose this strain for more intensive study. However, various procedures described here have been used with *P. aeruginosa* and *E. coli* with similar results.

Previous observations, using electron microscopy, clearly showed phage PRD1 adsorbed to the cell surface of bacteria maintaining RP1. We therefore directed our developmental techniques to the extraction and characterization of cell wall components. We initially observed that the capacity of sensitive bacterial strains

to adsorb phage PRD1 was labile in situ to heat treatment, organic solvents, and the enzymes pepsin and trypsin. When these agents were applied to *S. typhimurium* LT2(RP1) and adsorption of *Salmonella* phage P22 was compared with phage PRD1, the results suggested that a protein constituent of the cell wall might serve as the PRD1 receptor. The adsorption of phage P22, known to be specific for cell wall lipopolysaccharide (16), was not diminished by these treatments. On the other hand, all of the above treatments significantly reduced phage PRD1 adsorption. On the basis of these observations, then, we adopted the tentative view that PRD1 receptor was probably not lipopolysaccharide and accordingly directed our efforts to the isolation of a cell wall protein unique to bacteria containing RP1.

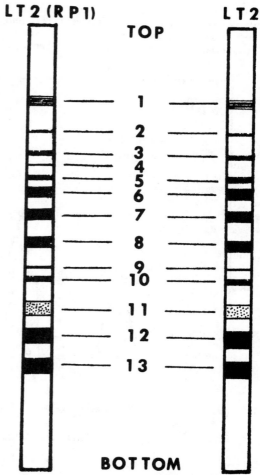

FIG. 1. *SDS-polyacrylamide (10%) gel patterns for the outer membrane proteins of R[+] and R[−] strains of S. typhimurium LT2.*

Mild alkaline treatment of intact cells as described by Braun et al. (2) for removal of coliphage T5 receptor from *E. coli* was tried. However, no phage PRD1 inactivating activity (PIA) was detected in the supernatant fraction of cell suspensions that had been treated and centrifuged. The pelleted cells also had lost their PIA towards phage PRD1 but not phage P22. This result indicated sensitivity to alkaline treatment similar to the report of Weltzien and Jesaitis (22) for coliphages T2 and T6.

We also considered that the phage PRD1 receptor may be juxtaposed within the inner structure of the outer cell wall and hence extracted during procedures promoting the removal of the outer wall. To test this possibility, we employed the procedure of Osborn et al. (15) for the separation of inner and outer cell wall. During the separation of inner and outer cell wall fractions attendant to this procedure, we determined PIA against phage PRD1 and were able to recover, in low yield, a soluble extract (not sedimenting at $105,000 \times g$) capable

of inactivating phage PRD1. This result obtained whether *E. coli* (RP1) or *P. aeruginosa* PAO67(RP1) was used. However, recovery of PIA was erratically low and this prompted consideration that, in point of fact, some constituent of the menstruum was influencing removal of receptor rather than the direct action of mechanical manipulations intrinsic to the Osborn procedure. We therefore determined the effect singly of the menstruum constituents on the recovery of phage PRD1 receptor. When this was done, EDTA or, alternatively, lysozyme treatment of the intact cells did not result in recovery of PIA in the supernatant of treated and pelleted cell suspensions. However, the PIA of the treated cells was significantly reduced when subsequently tested. When we exposed cells to Tris buffer containing sucrose (0.25 M), we solubilized significant amounts of PIA. It therefore appeared that mere exposure of cells maintaining RP1 to sucrose effected removal of the phage PRD1 receptor and also allowed maintenance of PIA towards phage PRD1

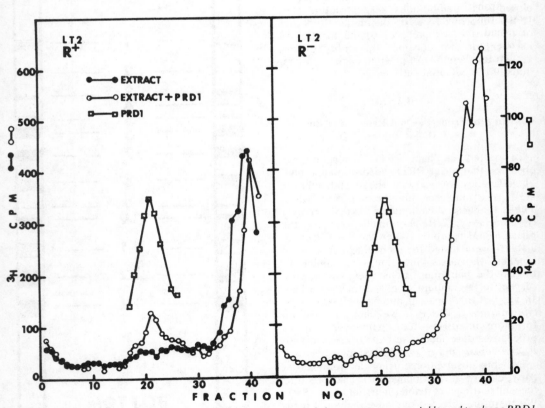

Fig. 2. *Sedimentation profiles in a 5 to 20% sucrose gradient of phage receptor material bound to phage PRD1. Cell wall protein which had been labeled with tritiated amino acids was eluted from cells by exposure to 0.6 M sucrose in Tris-NaCl buffer. Phage PRD1 was labeled with* ^{14}C *in its DNA. Experimental conditions were as described in the text.*

after removal. This observation, then, provided the basis for the subsequent extraction techniques used for more definitive studies. We later determined that exposure of washed cells to 0.6 M sucrose was optimal for removal and recovery of the phage receptor.

Characterization of Extracted PRD1 Receptor

We were interested in the diversity of cell wall modifications mediated by RP1-encoded genes. Therefore, to qualitatively estimate the number of cell surface proteins encoded by RP1, we used the method described by Schnaitman (17) for the extraction and analysis of outer wall protein. This technique was employed to extract the proteins of bacteria with RP1 (R^+) and without RP1 (R^-) for analysis by sodium dodecyl sulfate (SDS)-polyacrylamide gel electrophoresis. A typical result is shown in Fig. 1. The pattern shown in Fig. 1 indicates 12 regions (bands) staining with Coomassie blue which were common to both R^+ and R^- bacteria. Band 4 was unique to extracts obtained from R^+ bacteria. We now wished to identify this material as the PRD1 receptor.

We had observed earlier that the admixture of Tris-sucrose R^+ cell extract to phage PRD1 which contained ^{14}C-labeled DNA did not result in triggering of phage DNA release to the menstruum. Although the association between the receptor and phage was sufficiently irreversible to inactivate phage, it was not complete in the sense of promoting phage DNA release. From this we surmised that the receptor might be recovered from phage PRD1-receptor complexes in its native form. We therefore reasoned that, during centrifugation, the phage receptor would co-sediment with adsorbed phage and thus be concentrated in phage pellets and available for subsequent elution and comparison with the SDS-polyacrylamide gel electrophoresis patterns shown in Fig. 1.

To assess the efficacy of this receptor purification procedure, we labeled cellular proteins of R^+ and R^- bacteria during growth on medium containing tritiated amino acids. The labeled cells were washed and extracted with 0.6 M sucrose as described earlier. These extracts were then mixed with phage PRD1 which had been labeled with ^{14}C in its DNA. These ^{3}H-labeled receptor–^{14}C-labeled phage complexes were then run on a 5 to 20% sucrose gradient. Radioactivity profiles on aliquots of these gradients are shown in Fig. 2 for *S. typhimurium* extracts. The profiles clearly show no significant cell wall radioactivity in the region of the phage peak for R^- extracts. On the other hand, extracts from R^+ bacteria

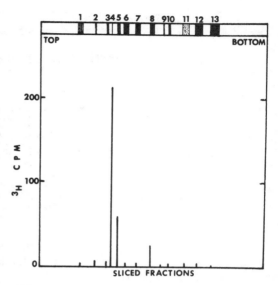

FIG. 3. *Co-migration pattern of purified ^{3}H-labeled phage PRD1-bound material with unlabeled R^+ outer membrane protein extract during 10% SDS-polyacrylamide gel electrophoresis. Gels were stained with Coomassie blue and sliced, and fractions were counted to locate phage receptor radioactivity as described in the text.*

showed a peak of ^{3}H radioactivity corresponding to the phage position denoted by the ^{14}C-labeled peak. We presumed that this correspondence between the ^{3}H-labeled cell wall extract and the ^{14}C-labeled phage peaks indicated the co-sedimentation of receptor adsorbed to phage PRD1. An identical result obtained when we tested extracts derived analogously from R^+ and R^- *E. coli* J53(RP1). We next isolated phage-bound receptor sufficient for further analysis by pooling sucrose gradient fractions in the phage-receptor region from replicate gradients. These were pooled, and phage-receptor was concentrated by ultracentrifugation. Phage-receptor pellets were suspended in buffer with EDTA and incubated at 37°C for 1 h to elute the receptor. Phage was removed by ultracentrifugation and the supernatant was concentrated in a pressurized ultrafiltration cell. Concentrates were stored frozen in 1% SDS and 0.1 M β-mercaptoethanol.

The radioactive receptor eluate described above was now mixed with cell wall material extracted with Triton-100 by the Schnaitman procedure (17) and run on 10% SDS-polyacrylamide gels as before (Fig. 1). After electrophoresis, the gels were stained with Coomassie blue to locate the outer cell wall proteins including band 4 previously presumed to be RP1 encoded. The gels were sliced to include

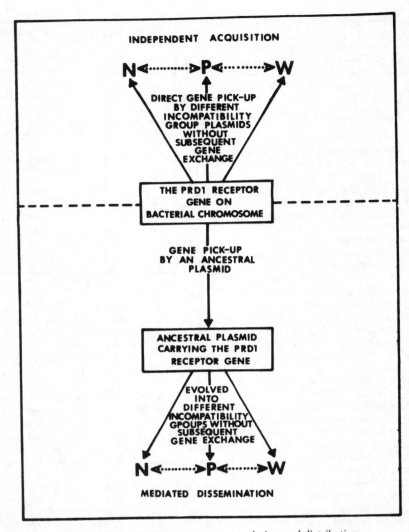

FIG. 4. *Phage PRD1 receptor gene evolution and distribution.*

a stained band in each fraction. The gel slices were dissolved in hydrogen peroxide, and radioactivity from the receptor eluate was located with respect to the corresponding stained slice. The results (Fig. 3) indicate that most of the ^{3}H-labeled receptor eluate migrated to the band 4 position. Minor peaks at fraction 5 and 8 may be radioactive cell wall material associated in situ with the phage PRD1 receptor which copurified. From these results we concluded that band 4 protein is most likely the phage PRD1 receptor.

In the previous experiment, the phage receptor migrated to the high-molecular-weight region of the SDS-polyacrylamide gel. We thus prepared appropriate protein standards for the calibration of gels to determine the molecular weight of the receptor by the procedure of Weber and Osborn (21). When the protein standards were subjected to co-electrophoresis with the phage PRD1-receptor eluate described previously, the molecular weight of the phage PRD1 receptor was estimated to be 51,000 per monomer. We do not presently know, however, if the receptor is multimeric in situ. A detailed summary of the procedures leading to the extraction and characterization of the phage PRD1 receptor will be published elsewhere (manuscript in preparation).

DISCUSSION

Phage PRD1 is clearly unlike other phage described to date when its plasmid-encoded somatic receptor, possible lipid content, DNA content, and broad host range are considered together. The ubiquity of RP1 or related plasmid-specific phages is also apparent from the facility with which these phages have been isolated at geographically remote locations, for example, our report of PRD1 and PRR1 isolation from Kalamazoo, Mich., sewage (R. H. Olsen, P. Shipley, and K. Saffier, Abstr. Annu. Meet. Am. Soc. Microbiol. 1972, P178, p. 165) or the isolation in Australia by Stanisich (19) of tailed phages resembling PRD1 and a filamentous phage designated Pf3. The morphology of the Australian phages has recently been characterized by Bradley and Rutherford (1). Previously described plasmid-dependent phages had their host range confined to bacteria which contain a plasmid of a particular group. For example, bacteria containing the *E. coli* sex factor F or related plasmids plate the male-specific *E. coli* phages (10); the N compatibility group phage, Ike, attacks bacteria containing N plasmids (7); the I compatibility group phage, If1, attacks bacteria containing I-like plasmids (8). However, PRD1 is unique in its plasmid-dependent host range. It will infect bacteria containing not only a P group plasmid, but also bacteria containing either N or W group plasmids (13). Therefore, the genetic information specifying the PRD1 receptor is more widely distributed among plasmids of different incompatibility groups than had been previously observed for other plasmid-dependent phages (13). From this observation we surmise that plasmids specifying the PRD1 receptor may have evolved from a common ancestral plasmid or, alternatively, that the plasmids allowing plating of PRD1 evolved independently through a common host from which was obtained the somatic receptor genetic information requisite for PRD1 adsorption. A summary of these possibilities is shown in Fig. 4.

When we apply the extraction techniques presented here to bacteria containing N or W group plasmids, we obtain significantly less PRD1 receptor. This may indicate, however, that the N and W plasmids encode a different receptor with altered properties or, alternatively, that the N and W plasmids specify yet additional cell wall components which interact with the phage PRD1 somatic receptor and consequently diminish the efficacy of our procedure.

SUMMARY

Phage PRD1 is an example of a new and unique class of phages whose growth requires the expression of a plasmid-encoded phage receptor. Thus, PRD1 susceptibility is con-

tingent on plasmid modification of the cell surface. Pursuant to this, it seems that the critical host bacterium contributions to not only phage synthesis but also host bacterium adaptability to a plasmid-specific cell modification have been genetically conserved. This has occurred throughout the evolution of bacterial hosts otherwise having unique DNA composition, physiological properties, and cell surface determinants peculiar to their genus or species. The simple procedures summarized here may be useful for the description of other cell surface changes encoded by plasmids, e.g., entry exclusion barriers or surface antigens and membrane factors resulting in changed bacteriocin or phage sensitivity.

ACKNOWLEDGMENT

This investigation was supported by Public Health Service Grant AI-07533 from the National Institute of Allergy and Infectious Diseases.

LITERATURE CITED

1. **Bradley, D. E., and E. L. Rutherford.** 1975. Basic characterization of a lipid-containing bacteriophage specific for plasmids of the P, N, and W compatibility groups. Can. J. Microbiol. 21:152–163.
2. **Braun, V., K. Schaller, and H. Wolff.** 1973. A common receptor protein for phage T5 and colicin M in the outer membrane of *Escherichia coli* B. Biochim. Biophys. Acta 323:87–97.
3. **Bryan, L. E., H. M. Van Den Elzen, and J. T. Tseng.** 1972. Transferable drug resistance in *Pseudomonas aeruginosa*. Antimicrob. Agents Chemother. 1:22–29.
4. **Datta, N., R. W. Hedges, E. J. Shaw, R. B. Sykes, and M. H. Richmond.** 1971. Properties of an R factor from *Pseudomonas aeruginosa*. J. Bacteriol. 108:1244–1249.
5. **Franklin, T. J.** 1967. Resistance of *E. coli* to tetracyclines: changes in permeability to tetracyclines in *E. coli* bearing transferable resistance factors. Biochem. J. 105:371–378.
6. **Horiuchi, K., and E. A. Adelberg.** 1965. Growth of male-specific bacteriophage in *Proteus mirabilis* harboring F-genotes derived from *Escherichia coli*. J. Bacteriol. 89:1231–1236.
7. **Khatoon, H., and R. V. Iyer.** 1971. Stable coexistence of R*fi⁻* factors in *Escherichia coli*. Can. J. Microbiol. 17:669–675.
8. **Lawn, A. M., G. G. Meynell, E. Meynell, and N. Datta.** 1967. Sex pili and the classification of sex factors in the *Enterobacteriaceae*. Nature (London) 216:343–346.
9. **Levy, S. E., and L. McMurry.** 1974. Detection of an inducible membrane protein associated with R-factor-mediated tetracycline resistance. Biochem. Biophys. Res. Commun. 56:1060–1068.
10. **Meynell, E., and N. Datta.** 1965. Functional homology of the sex-factor and resistance transfer factors. Nature (London) 207:884–885.
11. **Olsen, R. H., and C. Gonzalez.** 1974. *Escherichia coli* gene transfer to unrelated bacteria by a histidine operon—RP1 drug resistance plasmid complex. Biochem. Biophys. Res. Commun. 59:377–385.
12. **Olsen, R. H., and P. L. Shipley.** 1973. Host range and properties of the *Pseudomonas aeruginosa* R factor R1822. J. Bacteriol. 113:772–780.

PSEUDOMONAS

13. **Olsen, R. H., J. S. Siak, and R. H. Gray.** 1974. Characteristics of PRD1, a plasmid-dependent broad host range DNA bacteriophage. J. Virol. **14:**689–699.

14. **Olsen, R. H., and D. D. Thomas.** 1973. Characteristics and purification of PRR1, an RNA phage specific for the broad host range *Pseudomonas* R1822 drug resistance plasmid. J. Virol. **12:**1560–1567.

15. **Osborn, M. J., J. E. Gander, E. Parisi, and J. Carson.** 1972. Mechanism of assembly of the outer membrane of *Salmonella typhimurium*: isolation and characterization of cytoplasmic and outer membrane. J. Biol. Chem. **247:**3962–3972.

16. **Rapin, A. M. C., and H. M. Kalckar.** 1971. The relation of bacteriophage attachment to lipopolysaccharide structure, p. 267–307. *In* G. Weinbaum, S. Kadis, and S. J. Ajl (ed.), Microbiol toxins IV. Academic Press Inc., New York.

17. **Schnaitman, C. A.** 1973. Outer membrane proteins of *Escherichia coli*. I. Effect of preparative condition on the migration of protein in polyacrylamide gels. Arch. Biochem. Biophys. **157:**541–552.

18. **Shipley, P. L., and R. H. Olsen.** 1974. Characteristics and expression of tetracycline resistance in gram-negative bacteria carrying the *Pseudomonas* R factor RP1. Antimicrob. Agents Chemother. **6:**183–190.

19. **Stanisich, V.** 1974. The properties and host range of male-specific bacteriophages of *Pseudomonas aeruginosa*. J. Gen. Microbiol. **84:**332–342.

20. **Wais, A. C., and E. B. Goldberg.** 1969. Growth and transformation of phage T4 in *Escherichia coli* B/4, *Salmonella, Aerobacter, Proteus,* and *Serratia*. Virology **39:**153–161.

21. **Weber, K., and M. Osborn.** 1969. The reliability of molecular weight estimation by dodecyl sulfate-polyacrylamide gel electrophoresis. J. Biol. Chem. **244:**4406–4412.

22. **Weltzien, H. U., and M. Jesaitis.** 1971. The nature of the colicin K receptor of *Escherichia coli* Cullen. J. Exp. Med. **133:**534–553.

Ultrastructural Alteration of the Outer Membrane of *Pseudomonas aeruginosa* Associated with Resistance to Polymyxin B and to EDTA

H. E. GILLELAND, JR.

Department of Microbiology and Immunology, Louisiana State University Medical Center, School of Medicine in Shreveport, Shreveport, Louisiana 71130

INTRODUCTION

There has been great interest in the structure and function of the outer (cell wall) membrane (OM) of gram-negative bacteria in recent years. The majority of the investigations performed have been biochemical analyses, with few direct ultrastructural studies into the architecture of the OM. This is due in part to the inability to observe any change in the architecture of the OM upon thin-sectioning cells having confirmed OM biochemical changes, such as alterations in the lipopolysaccharide (LPS). However, the freeze-etch technique offers a uniquely suited means for the direct observation of the ultrastructural architecture of biological membranes. A great potential exists for the application of this technique for the direct observance of OM architectural alterations in cells with known or suspected biochemical modification of their OM. Such cells would include certain mutants having modifications in LPS structure or in LPS content or loss of protein from the OM, cells having increased sensitivity or resistance to certain antibiotics where a change in cell envelope permeability to the antibiotic is suspected, and cells after exposure to an agent thought to extract material from the OM. This paper reviews the ultrastructural alterations which occur in the OM of *Pseudomonas aeruginosa* upon the acquisition of resistance to polymyxin B and to EDTA.

CELL ENVELOPE ULTRASTRUCTURE UPON FREEZE-ETCHING

First, it is necessary to review briefly the cell envelope ultrastructure as revealed upon freeze-etching. When cells of *P. aeruginosa* are freeze-etched without the use of a cryoprotectant, the convex surfaces of an internal fracture surface within the cytoplasmic membrane (CM), an internal fracture surface within the OM, and, upon etching, the outer surface of the cell envelope are revealed (9). Because the replica produced upon freeze-etching without cryoprotection is extremely uneven, the concave fracture surfaces which result upon freeze-fracturing of the cell envelope cannot be studied effectively. Therefore, freeze-etching with glycerol cryoprotection is employed for studying the internal architecture of the two membranes of the gram-negative cell envelope. Whereas the outer surface of the cell can no longer be visualized, both the CM and the OM fracture down their hydrophobic centers to reveal two complementary internal surfaces (9). These four fracture surfaces are shown in Fig. 1. In the convex CM fracture, particles which are believed to be proteins are embedded in an underlying smooth layer thought to represent lipid. The complementary concave CM fracture surface is felt to represent the outer half of the lipid bilayer of the CM. Thus the CM is believed to be a lipid-protein-lipid membrane,

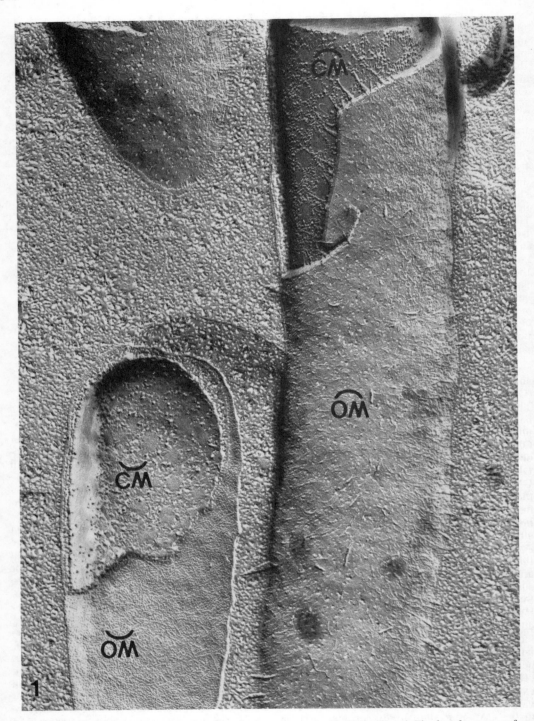

Fig. 1. P. aeruginosa *grown in tryptic soy broth and freeze-etched in 30% glycerol. The four fracture surfaces encountered in glycerol-protected cells are shown: convex outer membrane (OM) layer, convex cytoplasmic membrane (CM) layer, concave outer membrane layer, and concave cytoplasmic membrane layer. The concave outer membrane layer is studded with particles embedded in an underlying smooth layer. Magnification, ×80,500. (From Gilleland et al. [9])*

consistent with the fluid mosaic membrane model (16), with the protein particles associated more firmly with the lipid layer on the cytoplasmic side of the bilayer. The OM also is thought to have a lipid-protein-lipid architecture similar to the CM, except the particles in the OM are more firmly associated with the outer half of the bilayer. Thus, the convex OM fracture appears smooth, whereas the concave OM fracture is studded with particles. The appearance of these four fracture surfaces in *P. aeruginosa* is typical of gram-negative bacteria. *Escherichia coli* (24), *Acinetobacter* sp. (18), and *Salmonella typhimurium* (19) have all been shown to possess four similar fracture surfaces upon freeze-etching with glycerol cryoprotection. However, *P. aeruginosa* does appear to differ from the other gram-negative rods examined in the degree of particle crowding in the concave OM layer. These other organisms have the concave OM layer more tightly packed with particles so that the underlying smooth layer cannot be as easily seen as it is in *P. aeruginosa*. Several different strains of *P. aeruginosa* grown under varying growth conditions have consistently revealed this less crowded particle density in the concave OM (7–9, 12, 20).

OUTER MEMBRANE ALTERATIONS PRODUCED BY EDTA

These studies began as an attempt to determine the cell envelope changes which accompany EDTA lysis of *P. aeruginosa*. *P. aeruginosa* is unusually sensitive to lysis by EDTA. However, osmotically fragile rods, termed "osmoplasts" by Asbell and Eagon (2, 3), result upon treatment with EDTA if the cells are protected from lysis by suspension in hypertonic sucrose. EDTA causes the release of LPS and protein in the form of a LPS-protein complex (9, 13, 14) through a mechanism thought to involve the extraction of divalent cations which hold the LPS-protein in place in the OM. The liberated complex can be visualized in negatively stained preparations as a mixture of spherical units approximately 7 nm in diameter and small rodlets (20 by 7 nm) which are composed of spherical units (9, 14, 21). Roberts et al. (13) reported the complex to be 60% protein, 30% LPS, and 10% loosely bound lipid. The protein of the complex was found to correspond to two OM major proteins (21). Furthermore, the dimensions of the complex match the size of the particles seen in the concave OM. Upon freeze-etching of osmoplasts, approximately one-half of the particles appeared to have been extracted from the concave OM layer (9, 20). Thus, the particles in the concave

OM layer correspond to the site within the cell wall of the EDTA-extractable LPS-protein complex. The osmoplasts could be restored to osmotic stability by the addition of Mg^{2+} in the presence of the supernatant containing the EDTA-extracted material, but not in its absence (9, 20). Freeze-etching of these restored cells revealed the concave OM layer was now crowded with particles in a disorganized array (9). Apparently, reaggregation of the particles had occurred. Restoration is a purely physical process not requiring metabolic activity by the cell (20). More recently, Stinnett and Eagon (20) have shown that osmoplasts suspended in a tryptic soy broth-sucrose mixture for 2 h also can repair the OM damage using an energy-dependent process requiring protein synthesis. Self-repair was evidenced by the regaining of osmotic stability and by the reinsertion of particles into the concave OM layer. Thus, freeze-etching allows the direct visualization of OM damage caused by EDTA treatment and the repair of that damage with restoration of osmotic stability in both restored and repaired cells. The extraction of LPS-protein from the OM, resulting in immediate lysis, must not be the only lethal effect caused by EDTA, however, since both restored and repaired cells remain nonviable upon transfer to fresh medium even though their OM damage is reversed and osmotic stability is recovered (9, 20).

ULTRASTRUCTURAL MODIFICATION OF THE OUTER MEMBRANE AFTER GROWTH IN A Mg^{2+}-DEFICIENT MEDIUM

If the particles in the concave OM layer were, indeed, an EDTA-sensitive site within the cell envelope, it seemed reasonable that in a cell made resistant to the lytic action of EDTA the concave OM layer could be expected to have a modified appearance. Brown and Melling (5, 6) had reported that *P. aeruginosa* grown in basal medium deficient in Mg^{2+} becomes resistant to EDTA. Therefore, cells were grown in basal media containing either sufficient or deficient concentrations of Mg^{2+} and examined by freeze-etching (8). The cells grown in the Mg^{2+}-sufficient medium exhibited a concave OM layer studded with particles similar to that described above for tryptic soy broth-grown cells. The cells retained their sensitivity to lysis by EDTA, and osmoplasts which had particles extracted from the concave OM layer could be formed. The cells grown in the Mg^{2+}-deficient medium, on the other hand, were resistant to lysis by EDTA; osmoplasts could not be formed from them upon EDTA treatment; and the concave OM layer

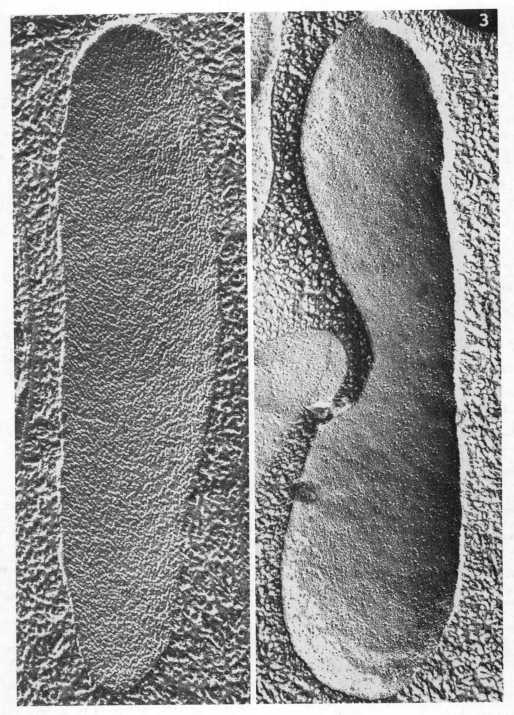

FIG. 2. *Concave outer membrane layer of* P. aeruginosa *grown in a Mg^{2+}-deficient basal medium. This layer appears disorganized and more crowded with particles. Magnification, ×183,000.*

FIG. 3. *Concave outer membrane layer of a polymyxin-resistant isolate grown in basal medium containing 6,000 U of polymyxin B per ml. The number of particles in this layer is greatly reduced, indicating that an alteration in the outer membrane architecture has occurred. Magnification, ×110,000.*

was altered in appearance with the particles in this layer appearing crowded and disorganized (Fig. 2). This appearance remained unchanged upon EDTA treatment. Thus, resistance to the lytic effect of EDTA was correlated with an observable ultrastructural alteration of the OM.

Growth in the Mg^{2+}-deficient medium also produced chemical changes in the cell envelope. Envelopes from these EDTA-resistant cells had 18% less phosphorus, 16.4% more total carbohydrate, 13.3% more 2-keto-3-deoxyoctonate, and qualitative, but not quantitative, differences in OM proteins as compared to envelopes from EDTA-sensitive cells (8).

POLYMYXIN RESISTANCE IN RELATION TO OUTER MEMBRANE ALTERATIONS

Although growth of the cells in the Mg^{2+}-deficient medium did permit the study of OM changes associated with resistance to EDTA, the system was not completely satisfactory since the cells grew slowly and to a very low final cell concentration in such media (8). The lack of sufficient Mg^{2+} undoubtedly resulted in a physiologically abnormal cell. What was desired was a cell which exhibited more typical growth in Mg^{2+}-sufficient medium and yet was resistant to an agent in which resistance involved a modification of the OM. Brown and Melling (5, 6) had reported that the conditions of Mg^{2+} limitation which caused cells of *P. aeruginosa* to become resistant to EDTA also made the cells resistant to polymyxin. Brown, in his recent excellent discussion (4) of how polymyxin is thought to interact with *P. aeruginosa*, gives the primary site of attack by polymyxin on sensitive cells as interaction with the phospholipids in the CM. Furthermore, the LPS in the OM has been indicated as the site of initial interaction of polymyxin with the cell envelope prior to its reaching its primary site of attack (4). Resistance to polymyxin is correlated with a lack of penetration through the cell wall to reach the CM. Thus, it was of interest to examine polymyxin-resistant isolates of *P. aeruginosa* grown in a Mg^{2+}-sufficient medium to determine whether or not the concave OM would be altered. Whereas the sensitive parent was inhibited by 32 U of polymyxin B per ml, resistant isolates were adapted to growth in the presence of 6,000 U of polymyxin B per ml (7). Freeze-etch of the resistant cells grown in basal medium containing 6,000 U/ml revealed that the concave OM layer had a greatly reduced number of particles from the number normally found in this layer (7) (Fig. 3). Thus, resistance to polymyxin was correlated in these cells with a change in OM architecture. Since these particles were previously identified as an EDTA-sensitive site in the OM, these cells in which the particles

were largely absent would be expected to be resistant to lysis by EDTA. This was found to be the case (7). The resistant isolates were not stable mutants but appeared to represent an adaptive response to the presence of polymyxin in the medium. Upon growth of the isolates in basal medium lacking polymyxin, the OM layer reverted to its normal architecture with numerous particles present (7), and the cells regained sensitivity both to polymyxin and to EDTA as would be expected. Resistance to EDTA and to polymyxin both appear to involve the same architectural alteration of the OM. EDTA resistance is probably due to this change in OM architecture which directly alters the primary site of attack by EDTA. Polymyxin resistance more likely involves the same OM component functioning as the initial receptor for polymyxin (4) so that loss of the LPS-protein particles make the cell wall less permeable to polymyxin and prevents it from reaching the primary target site on the CM.

STUDIES WITH OTHER ORGANISMS

The OM of the gram-negative bacteria provides a passive permeability barrier, with the LPS playing an important role in maintaining this barrier (11). The permeability of the OM to antibiotics, lysozyme, and certain other low-molecular-weight compounds is influenced by alterations in LPS in *S. typhimurium* (15) and *E. coli* (22, 23). More recently, alterations in the LPS have been shown to be accompanied by a concomitant decrease in the amount of OM protein in both *S. typhimurium* (1) and *E. coli* (10, 17). Smit et al. (19) performed a freeze-etch analysis of "heptoseless" LPS mutants of *S. typhimurium* which contain reduced amounts of the major OM proteins and found the number of particles in the concave OM layer to be likewise reduced. This was the first study to my knowledge to apply the freeze-etch technique to an organism other than *P. aeruginosa* in order to observe OM ultrastructural alterations in association with LPS and protein changes of the OM.

Freeze-etch analysis provides an additional dimension to studies of OM architecture, and many more freeze-etch studies of OM architecture should follow in the future.

ACKNOWLEDGMENTS

Various portions of the research studies reviewed in this paper were performed in collaboration with I. L. Roth, J. D. Stinnett, R. G. Eagon, and R. G. E. Murray.

LITERATURE CITED

1. Ames, G. F.-L., E. N. Spudich, and H. Nikaido. 1974. Protein composition of the outer membrane of *Sal-*

monella typhimurium: effect of lipopolysaccharide mutations. J. Bacteriol. 117:406–416.

2. Asbell, M. A., and R. G. Eagon. 1966. The role of multivalent cations in the organization and structure of bacterial cell walls. Biochem. Biophys. Res. Commun. 22:664–671.

3. Asbell, M. A., and R. G. Eagon. 1966. Role of multivalent cations in the organization, structure and assembly of the cell wall of *Pseudomonas aeruginosa*. J. Bacteriol. 92:380–387.

4. Brown, M. R. W. 1975. The role of the cell envelope in resistance, p. 71–107. *In* M. R. W. Brown (ed.), Resistance of *Pseudomonas aeruginosa*. John Wiley and Sons, New York.

5. Brown, M. R. W., and J. Melling. 1968. Loss of sensitivity to EDTA by *Pseudomonas aeruginosa* grown under conditions of Mg-limitation. J. Gen. Microbiol. 54:439–444.

6. Brown, M. R. W., and J. Melling. 1969. Role of divalent cations in the action of polymyxin B and EDTA on *Pseudomonas aeruginosa*. J. Gen. Microbiol. 59:263–274.

7. Gilleland, H. E., Jr., and R. G. E. Murray. 1976. Ultrastructural study of polymyxin-resistant isolates of *Pseudomonas aeruginosa*. J. Bacteriol. 125:267–281.

8. Gilleland, H. E., Jr., J. D. Stinnett, and R. G. Eagon. 1974. Ultrastructural and chemical alteration of the cell envelope of *Pseudomonas aeruginosa*, associated with resistance to ethylenediaminetetraacetate resulting from growth in a Mg^{2+}-deficient medium. J. Bacteriol. 117:302–311.

9. Gilleland, H. E., Jr., J. D. Stinnett, I. L. Roth, and R. G. Eagon. 1973. Freeze-etch study of *Pseudomonas aeruginosa*: localization within the cell wall of an ethylenediaminetetraacetate-extractable component. J. Bacteriol. 113:417–432.

10. Koplow, J., and H. Goldfine. 1974. Alterations in the outer membrane of the cell envelope of heptose-deficient mutants of *Escherichia coli*. J. Bacteriol. 117:527–543.

11. Leive, L. 1974. The barrier function of the gram-negative envelope. Ann. N.Y. Acad. Sci. 235:109–129.

12. Lickfeld, K. G., M. Achterrath, F. Hentrich, L. Kolehmainen-Seveus, and A. Persson. 1972. Die Feinstrukturen von *Pseudomonas aeruginosa* in ihrer Deutung durch die Gefrierätztechnik, Ultramikrotomie und Kryo-ultramikrotomie. J. Ultrastruct. Res. 38:27–45.

13. Roberts, N. A., G. W. Gray, and S. G. Wilkinson. 1970. The bactericidal action of ethylenediaminetetraacetic acid on *Pseudomonas aeruginosa*. Microbios 2:189–208.

14. Rogers, S. W., H. E. Gilleland, Jr., and R. G. Eagon. 1969. Characterization of a protein-lipopolysaccharide complex released from cell walls of *Pseudomonas aeruginosa* by ethylenediaminetetraacetic acid. Can. J. Microbiol. 15:743–748.

15. Sanderson, K. E., T. MacAlister, J. W. Costerton, and K.-J. Cheng. 1974. Permeability of lipopolysaccharide-deficient (rough) mutants of *Salmonella typhimurium* to antibiotics, lysozyme, and other agents. Can. J. Microbiol. 20:1135–1145.

16. Singer, S. J., and G. L. Nicolson. 1972. The fluid mosaic model of the structure of cell membranes. Science 175:720–731.

17. Singh, A. P., and R. A. F. Reithmeier. 1975. Leakage of periplasmic enzymes from cells of heptose-deficient mutants of *Escherichia coli*, associated with alterations in the protein component of the outer membrane. J. Gen. Appl. Microbiol. 21:109–118.

18. Sleytr, U. B., M. J. Thornley, and A. M. Glauert. 1974. Location of the fracture faces within the cell envelope of *Acinetobacter* species strain MJT/F5/5. J. Bacteriol. 118:693–707.

19. Smit, J., Y. Kamio, and H. Nikaido. 1975. Outer membrane of *Salmonella typhimurium*: chemical analysis and freeze-fracture studies with lipopolysaccharide mutants. J. Bacteriol. 124:942–958.

20. Stinnett, J. D., and R. G. Eagon. 1975. A model system for studying protein-lipopolysaccharide synthesis, assembly, and insertion in the outer membrane of *Pseudomonas aeruginosa*. Can. J. Microbiol. 21:1834–1841.

21. Stinnett, J. D., H. E. Gilleland, Jr., and R. G. Eagon. 1973. Proteins released from cell envelopes of *Pseudomonas aeruginosa* on exposure to ethylenediaminetetraacetate: comparison with dimethylformamide-extractable proteins. J. Bacteriol. 114:399–407.

22. Tamaki, S., and M. Matsuhashi. 1973. Increase in sensitivity to antibiotics and lysozyme on deletion of lipopolysaccharides in *Escherichia coli* strains. J. Bacteriol. 114:453–454.

23. Tamaki, S., T. Sato, and M. Matsuhashi. 1971. Role of lipopolysaccharides in antibiotic resistance and bacteriophage adsorption of *Escherichia coli* K-12. J. Bacteriol. 105:968–975.

24. Van Gool, A. P., and N. Nanninga. 1971. Fracture faces in the cell envelope of *Escherichia coli*. J. Bacteriol. 108:474–481.

Cell Envelope as a Barrier to Antibiotics

J. W. COSTERTON

Biology, University of Calgary, Calgary, Alberta, Canada

INTRODUCTION

The cell wall and the cytoplasmic membrane constitute the bacterial cell envelope (Fig. 1 and 2) which regulates the complicated molecular traffic between the cell and its environment. Because most antibiotics must penetrate the bacterial cell envelope to reach their metabolic "targets" within the cell, the structure of this cell envelope assumes a major importance in bacterial resistance to antibiotics.

Available evidence indicates that Singer's liquid crystal model of membrane architecture (49) is representative of the actual arrangement of phospholipids and proteins in the cytoplasmic membrane of living bacteria. The penetrability of this membrane is affected by alterations in the chain length and degree of saturation of its component fatty acids (33), and the essential fluidity of the bulk phospholipids is modified (29) by proximity to proteins which "float" in the hydrophobic phase. The cytoplasmic membrane is adpressed against the inelastic peptidoglycan structure of the cell wall by osmotic forces (11), and points of adhesion have been noted between these two structures (40).

Peptidoglycan is the major component of the gram-positive cell wall, and this relatively inelastic compound forms a thick fibrous layer in which other molecules such as teichoic acids, teichuronic acids, and lipids are interspersed (Fig. 1) but do not form coherent or continuous layers. The "periplasmic space" in these organisms occurs between peptidoglycan fibers next to the cytoplasmic membrane, and a variety of degradative enzymes have been localized in this space (38). At their outer surface these bacteria may bear globular protein coats (36), or very extensive fibrillar carbohydrate capsules (9) whose formation is dependent on nutritional and environmental factors.

Because the gram-positive bacterial cell wall is an open fibrillar structure, with a predominantly negative charge, its effect on the passage of ions and molecules is analogous to that of a "bed" of ion-exchange resin. Thus, very large particles are excluded by this structure, and smaller charged molecules may be adsorbed onto structural polymers (5) and impeded by the Donnan effect. This effect also influences proteins which are synthesized at the cytoplasmic membrane and passed through this membrane in a partly folded form, and which assume their native tertiary configuration as they emerge into the periplasmic area (3). These proteins may remain associated with the cytoplasmic membrane, they may become adsorbed to structural molecules within the cell wall, or they may be shed into the menstruum as exoenzymes.

The gram-negative cell wall is a very complex structure (Fig. 2). The innermost element of the gram-negative cell wall is an inelastic peptidoglycan layer (20) which is covalently linked to elongate lipoprotein molecules (6). The lipoprotein molecules extend outward in bundles whose lipid moieties associate with the basically hydrophobic outer membrane (28). The peptidoglycan-lipoprotein complex thus maintains, and partly occupies, a well-defined periplasmic space between the hydrophobic barriers of the cytoplasmic and outer membranes of the gram-negative cell envelope. This periplasmic space also contains a variety of degradative enzymes (12) that are sometimes associated with structural molecules such as lipopolysaccharide (LPS) (15).

The outer membrane of the gram-negative cell wall (Fig. 2) constitutes a basically hydrophobic

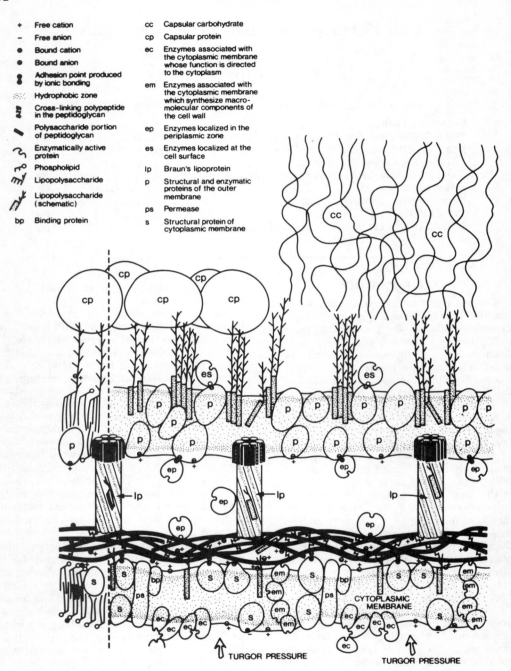

+	Free cation	cc	Capsular carbohydrate
−	Free anion	cp	Capsular protein
●	Bound cation	ec	Enzymes associated with the cytoplasmic membrane whose function is directed to the cytoplasm
●	Bound anion		
	Adhesion point produced by ionic bonding	em	Enzymes associated with the cytoplasmic membrane which synthesize macro-molecular components of the cell wall
	Hydrophobic zone		
	Cross-linking polypeptide in the peptidoglycan		
	Polysaccharide portion of peptidoglycan	ep	Enzymes localized in the periplasmic zone
	Enzymatically active protein	es	Enzymes localized at the cell surface
	Phospholipid	lp	Braun's lipoprotein
	Lipopolysaccharide	p	Structural and enzymatic proteins of the outer membrane
	Lipopolysaccharide (schematic)		
		ps	Permease
bp	Binding protein	s	Structural protein of cytoplasmic membrane

FIG. 1. *Structure of gram-positive cell wall.*

barrier layer which limits both the outward movement of periplasmic molecules and the inward movement of molecules from the environment. This membrane has a hexagonally close-packed arrangement of phospholipids, but it is very penetrable and admits molecules as large as tetrapeptides (41). This high degree of penetrability may result from the outer membrane's content of LPS (26), or from its content of a complex asymmetric system of interconnected structural proteins (25). These LPS molecules, which occupy approximately 25% of the cell's surface

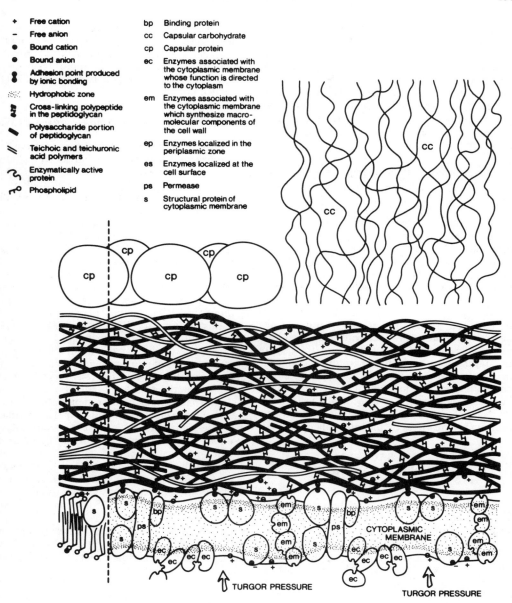

FIG. 2. *Structure of gram-negative cell wall.*

(35), are vital to the integrity of the outer membrane, and their alteration by genetic means (45) or chemical manipulations (12) leads to a loss of the barrier function. The cell wall of *Pseudomonas aeruginosa* is similar to the general gram-negative pattern except that the core region of its LPS is heavily substituted with phosphate (18).

When gram-negative bacteria are examined directly in a variety of natural habitats, the majority of their cells are found to be surrounded by protein coats (13) or by extensive fibrillar

carbohydrate capsules (9, 13). These latter structures surround the cells of *Salmonella typhimurium* growing in the tissues of the mouse (47) and the cells of mucoid strains of *P. aeruginosa* growing in the lungs of cystic fibrosis patients (16). The carbohydrate slime produced by mucoid strains of *P. aeruginosa* is composed of uronic acid polymers (7), and its continued production is stimulated by surfactants in both in vitro and in vivo conditions (23).

Thus, an inward penetrating molecule is subjected to the Donnan effect in all levels of the gram-negative cell wall, to screening by the hydrophobic barrier layer of the outer membrane, and to the action of the degradative enzymes which lurk in their protected niches in the periplasmic space. In this way the immediately external molecular environment of the cytoplasmic membrane is conditioned to a very high degree by the presence of the gram-negative cell wall.

ROLE OF THE BACTERIAL CELL ENVELOPE IN PATHOGENESIS

Capsular material mediates adhesion to host cells and this adhesion appears to be specifically directed at glycoproteins on the host cell's surface (56). This capsule surrounds the bacteria within a lesion and frustrates both antibody attack (51) and phagocytosis by leukocytes, and repeated animal passage selects for bacterial strains which are encapsulated (1). The outer membrane is also important in pathogenesis in that the protruding polysaccharide chains of its LPS molecules react with antibodies at a distance from the cell surface and thus spare the outer and cytoplasmic membranes from the disruptive effect of the C_3 and C_5 complement components (42). Elements of this LPS-containing outer membrane are also detached from infecting cells and these "endotoxins" exert a profound toxic effect on the infected animal (43).

ROLE OF THE BACTERIAL CELL ENVELOPE IN ANTIBIOTIC RESISTANCE

When a given antibiotic has penetrated specific histological barriers, it must overcome the adsorptive effect of cellular detritus (8) and then penetrate all or part of the cell envelope before it reaches its specific "target" in the bacterial cell. The targets of some antibiotics lie within the cell envelope (e.g., bacitracin, polymyxin, and the aminoglycosides), but the targets for the majority of clinically important antibiotics lie in the very metabolically active zone immediately inside the cytoplasmic membrane in which protein synthesis (3) and other important processes are concentrated.

Capsular Materials

The open fibrillar structure of capsular materials does not represent a simple penetrability barrier to antibiotics, but the fact that they consist of predominantly anionic sugar molecules (7) bound in long, insoluble polymers can cause extensive adsorbtion of antibiotic

molecules just as gentamicin is very firmly bound to the cellulose of commonly used microbiological filters (55). Thus, heavily encapsulated cells of *P. aeruginosa* are more resistant to polymyxin (7), gentamicin, and carbenicillin (19) than are nonmucoid cells.

Outer Membrane of the Gram-Negative Cell Wall

The outer membrane of the gram-negative bacterial cell wall is an effective barrier to the penetration of many antibiotics. The approximate "pore size" of this barrier is indicated by its ability to exclude puromycin, benzyl penicillin, actinomycin D, erythromycin, bacitracin, vancomycin, kanamycin, cloxacillin, and pentalysine (41) (of molecular weight 491, 334, 1,250, 734, 1,411, 3,300, 484, 458, and 725, respectively) whereas tetralysine (41) and tetracycline (of molecular weight 580 and 444, respectively) are allowed to pass (12, 45). The outer membrane of *P. aeruginosa* is peculiar in that the core region of its LPS is heavily phosphorylated (58), and this layer is very easily disrupted by the polypeptide antibiotics polymyxin and EDTA (7).

The penetrability of the outer membrane of smooth strains of gram-negative bacteria by antibiotics can be increased by various treatments (12), but as the treatments might also alter the cytoplasmic membrane, the penetrability of the cell walls of selected mutants has been studied, because their cell walls are chemically altered without significant changes in the cytoplasmic membrane. Susceptibility to most antibiotics was increased in LPS-deficient "rough" mutants of *Escherichia coli* (52) and of *S. typhimurium* (45), and this susceptibility was shown to be proportional to the degree of LPS deletion in the latter case (45).

In addition to these rough mutants, there are cells whose penetrability by antibiotics is affected by R factor-mediated changes in the outer membrane. These include cells resistant to sulfonamides (34), streptomycin (32, 54), penicillin (14), chloramphenicol (27), tetracycline (48, 53), and gentamicin and carbenicillin (30). A unique specific antigen has been detected in the outer membrane of some of these resistant bacteria, and two new protein bands have been detected by electrophoresis (39). The effect of this additional outer membrane protein is partly specific since its effect is to increase resistance to actinomycin D, nalidixic acid, rifampin, and lysozyme while it does not affect resistance to cephalosporins (14). On the other hand, cells of *P. aeruginosa* may acquire resistance to polymyxin by the loss of an outer membrane protein (22). Thus, the outer membrane of the gram-negative bacterial cell wall is an important barrier to the penetration of certain antibiotics and this dynamic structure is affected by genetic and nutritional factors (7).

Periplasmic Structures

The peptidoglycan structures which lie just outside the cytoplasmic membrane constitute the "de facto" periplasmic space which conditions the external microenvironment of this membrane (12). These periplasmic structures act as a molecular sieve (46) and may influence the penetration of antibiotics by the adsorptive effect of their structural polymers (53). Periplasmic enzymes play a very important role in the limitation of the penetration of antibiotics in gram-positive cells because the multiple penicillin "targets" are found in the inner regions of the wall (4), or in association with the cytoplasmic membrane (21), and at least two types of protective β-lactamases are found throughout the periplasmic zone of resistant cells (50). Periplasmic enzymes also play an important role in antibiotic resistance in gram-negative bacteria, and specific enzymes within this zone denature streptomycin (32), chloramphenicol (2, 27), gentamicin, kanamycin, and neomycin (17) by either acetylation or phosphorylation, whereas various β-lactamases degrade penicillins and cephalosporins (37). This mode of bacterial resistance to antibiotics is especially effective if the limited penetrability of the outer membrane restricts the number of antibiotic molecules that can reach the periplasmic space, and specific periplasmic enzymes then inactivate these few molecules (32) to provide double protection for the resistant cell (27). For this reason, high levels of resistance to antibiotics can be achieved by gram-negative cells with relatively small amounts of antibiotic-degrading enzymes (44).

Cytoplasmic Membrane

The cytoplasmic membrane differs from the outer membrane in that it contains specific permeases which transport vital nutrients into the cell and antibiotics must pass this membrane via the transport systems or by intercalation among the hydrophobic phospholipid molecules. Polypeptide antibiotics can intercalate into this hydrophobic zone of the membrane and damage its structure (7). The kinetics of the uptake of some antibiotics into sensitive cells resemble those of substrate uptake (48) and the cytoplasmic membrane is the primary barrier in intrinsic resistance of *P. aeruginosa* to streptomycin, tetracycline (53), and actinomycin D, and is also an important barrier to the penetration of actinomycin D into *E. coli* (12). Changes in the cyto-

plasmic membrane which confer tetracycline resistance may involve the deletion of a membrane protein (10) or the addition of a new protein to the membrane (31). This resistance would therefore appear to result from a change in the cytoplasmic membrane which effectively closes the "gate" used by the antibiotic.

CONCLUSIONS

The metabolic "targets" of antibiotics may lie within the bacterial cell or at any level in the complex cell envelope, and to be effective these molecules must penetrate the cell envelope layers which lie between themselves and their target. Since most pathogens are encapsulated, the antibiotics may initially have to pass through a very extensive, primarily anionic, net of carbohydrate fibers. Then, since most gram-negative pathogens are smooth strains, the antibiotic must penetrate through a mat of anionic fibers and a hydrophobic barrier layer. The peptidoglycan layer of the bacterial cell wall serves as an anionic molecular sieve and also contains associated degradative enzymes, some of which can degrade specific antibiotics. Finally, the antibiotic must traverse the cytoplasmic membrane by the use of a transport mechanism. Thus, the bacterial cell envelope comprises a three-phase (gram-positive) or four-phase (gram-negative) protective structure against penetration by exogenous molecules.

Because these cell envelopes are complex and interdependent, the whole protective bacterial envelope can be rendered ineffective by the alteration of one vital component such as the peptidoglycan (37) or the outer membrane (12). Combinations of antibiotics can be designed so that one agent opens up the cell envelope to allow the passage of the other agent (53), and the facilitative molecules need not themselves be antibiotics. Where a bacterium is resistant by virtue of an antibiotic-degrading enzyme, this enzyme can be inactivated by specific inhibitors (24). Thus, a knowledge of this area will allow an intelligent approach to chemotherapy in which we attack the cell wall barriers and enzymes of a specific pathogen as Eagon's group has attacked *P. aeruginosa* using Tris, EDTA, and lysozyme (57) to facilitate the entry of effective antibiotics into the bacterial cells.

LITERATURE CITED

1. **Baechler, C. A., and R. S. Berk.** 1974. Electron microscopic observations of *Pseudomonas aeruginosa*. Z. Allg. Microbiol. **14:**267–281.
2. **Benveniste, R., and J. Davies.** 1973. Mechanisms of antibiotic resistance in bacteria. Annu. Rev. Biochem. **42:**471–506.
3. **Bettinger, G. E., and J. O. Lampen.** 1975. Further evi-

dence for a partially folded intermediate in penicillinase secretion by *Bacillus licheniformis*. J. Bacteriol. **121**: 83–90.

4. **Blumberg, M., and J. L. Strominger.** 1974. Interaction of penicillin with the bacterial cell: penicillin-binding proteins and penicillin-sensitive enzymes. Bacteriol. Rev. **38**:291–335.

5. **Bradley, T. J., and M. S. Parker.** 1968. Binding of aluminium ions by *Staphylococcus aureus* 893. Experientia **24**:1175–1176.

6. **Braun, V., and K. Kantke.** 1975. Biochemistry of bacterial cell envelopes. Annu. Rev. Biochem. **43**:84–121.

7. **Brown, M. R. W.** 1975. The role of the cell envelope in resistance. *In* M. R. W. Brown (ed.), Resistance of *Pseudomonas aeruginosa*. John Wiley and Sons, London.

8. **Bryant, R. E., and D. Hammond.** 1974. Interaction of purulent material with antibiotics used to treat *Pseudomonas* infections. Antimicrob. Agents Chemother. **6**:702–707.

9. **Cagle, G. C.** 1975. Fine structure and distribution of extracellular polymer surrounding selected aerobic bacteria. Can. J. Microbiol. **21**:395–408.

10. **Chopra, I., R. W. Lacey, and J. Connolly.** 1974. Biochemical and genetic basis of tetracycline resistance in *Staphylococcus aureus*. Antimicrob. Agents Chemother. **6**:397–404.

11. **Costerton, J. W., and J. Thompson.** 1972. Induced morphological changes in the stainable layers of the cell envelope of a gram-negative bacterium. Can. J. Microbiol. **18**:937–940.

12. **Costerton, J. W., J. M. Ingram, and K.-J. Cheng.** 1974. Structure and function of the cell envelope of gram-negative bacteria. Bacteriol. Rev. **38**:87–110.

13. **Costerton, J. W., H. N. Damgaard, and K.-J. Cheng.** 1974. Cell envelope morphology of rumen bacteria. J. Bacteriol. **118**:1132–1143.

14. **Curtis, N. A. C., and M. H. Richmond.** 1974. Effect of R factor-mediated genes on some surface properties of *Escherichia coli*. Antimicrob. Agents Chemother. **6**:666–671.

15. **Day, D. F., and J. M. Ingram.** 1975. *In vitro* studies of an alkaline phosphatase-cell wall complex from *Pseudomonas aeruginosa*. Can. J. Microbiol. **21**:9–16.

16. **Diaz, F., L. L. Mosovich, and E. Neter.** 1973. Serogroups of *Pseudomonas aeruginosa* and the immune response of patients with cystic fibrosis. *In* M. E. Fritz (ed.), Cystic fibrosis. M.S.S. Information, New York.

17. **Doi, O., M. Ogura, N. Tanaka, and H. Umezawa.** 1968. Inactivation of kanamycin, neomycin and streptomycin by enzymes obtained in cells of *Pseudomonas aeruginosa*. J. Appl. Microbiol. **16**:1276–1281.

18. **Eagon, R. G., J. D. Stinnett, and H. E. Gilleland, Jr.** 1975. Ultrastructure of *Pseudomonas aeruginosa* as related to resistance. *In* M. R. W. Brown (ed.), Resistance of *Pseudomonas aeruginosa*. John Wiley and Sons, London.

19. **Feary, T. W.** 1975. Review of the biology of *Pseudomonas*. Symposium on basic and clinical research on *Pseudomonas*: abstracts and summaries. Cystic Fibrosis Foundation, Atlanta, Ga.

20. **Forsberg, C. W., M. K. Rayman, J. W. Costerton, and R. A. MacLeod.** 1972. Isolation, characterization and ultrastructure of the peptidoglycan layer of a marine pseudomonad. J. Bacteriol. **109**:895–905.

21. **Forsberg, C. W., and J. B. Ward.** 1972. N-acetylmuramyl-L-alanine amidase of *Bacillus licheniformis* and its L-form. J. Bacteriol. **110**:878–888.

22. **Gilleland, H. E., Jr., and R. G. E. Murray.** 1976. Ultrastructural study of polymyxin-resistant isolates of *Pseudomonas aeruginosa*. J. Bacteriol. **125**:267–281.

23. **Govan, J. R. W.** 1975. Mucoid strains of *Pseudomonas aeruginosa*: the influence of culture medium on the stability of mucus production. J. Med. Microbiol. **8**: 513–522.

24. **Greenwood, D., and F. O'Grady.** 1975. Potent combinations of β-lactam antibiotics using the β-lactamase inhibition principle. Chemotherapy **21**:330–341.

25. **Haller, I., B. Hoehn, and U. Henning.** 1975. Apparent high degree of asymmetry of protein arrangement in the *Escherichia coli* outer cell envelope membrane. Biochemistry **14**:478–484.

26. **Hannecart-Pokorni, E., D. Dekegel, and F. Depuydt.** 1973. Molecular structure of lipopolysaccharides from gram-negative bacteria. Eur. J. Biochem. **38**:6–13.

27. **Ingram, J. M., and H. M. Hassan.** 1975. The resistance of *Pseudomonas aeruginosa* to chloramphenicol. Can. J. Microbiol. **21**:1185–1191.

28. **Inouye, M.** 1974. A three-dimensional molecular assembly model of a lipoprotein from the *Escherichia coli* outer membrane. Proc. Natl. Acad. Sci. U.S.A. **71**:2396–2400.

29. **Jost, P. C., R. A. Capadil, G. Vanderkooi, and O. H. Griffith.** 1973. Lipid-protein and lipid-lipid interactions in cytochrome oxidase model membranes. J. Supramol. Struct. **1**:269–280.

30. **Korfhagen, T. R., J. C. Loper, and J. A. Ferrel.** 1975. *Pseudomonas aeruginosa* R factors determining gentamicin plus carbenicillin resistance from patients with urinary tract colonizations. Antimicrob. Agents Chemother. **7**:64–68.

31. **Levy, S. B., and L. McMurry.** 1974. Detection of an inducible membrane protein associated with R-factor-mediated tetracycline resistance. Biochem. Biophys. Res. Commun. **56**:1060–1068.

32. **Lundbäck, A. K., and K. Nordström.** 1974. Mutations in *Escherichia coli* K-12 decreasing the rate of streptomycin uptake: synergism with R factor-mediated capacity to inactivate streptomycin. Antimicrob. Agents Chemother. **5**:500–507.

33. **McElhaney, R. N., J. DeGier, and E. C. M. van der Neut-Kook.** 1973. The effect of alterations in fatty acid composition and cholesterol content on the nonelectrolyte permeability of *Acholeplasma laidlawii* B cells and derived liposomes. Biochim. Biophys. Acta **298**:500–512.

34. **Mitsuhashi, S.** 1971. *In* Transferable drug resistance factor R. University of Tokyo Press, Tokyo.

35. **Mühlradt, P. F., J. Menzel, J. R. Golecki, and V. Speth.** 1973. Outer membrane of *Salmonella*. Sites of export of newly synthesized lipopolysaccharide on the bacterial surface. Eur. J. Biochem. **35**:471–481.

36. **Nermut, M. V., and R. G. E. Murray.** 1967. Ultrastructure of the cell wall of *Bacillus polymyxa*. J. Bacteriol. **93**:1949–1965.

37. **Nordström, K., and R. B. Sykes.** 1974. Effects of sublethal concentrations of benzylpenicillin on *Pseudomonas aeruginosa*. Antimicrob. Agents Chemother. **6**:741–746.

38. **Okabayashi, K., M. Futai, and D. Mizuno.** 1974. Localization of acid and alkaline phosphatase in *Staphylococcus aureus*. Jpn. J. Microbiol. **18**:287–294.

39. **Olsen, R. H.** 1975. R plasmids and antibiotic resistance in *Pseudomonas*. Symposium on basic and clinical research on *Pseudomonas*: abstracts and summaries. Cystic Fibrosis Foundation, Atlanta, Ga.

40. **Olsen, W. L., H.-G. Heidrich, K. Hannig, and P. H. Hofschneider.** 1974. Deoxyribonucleic acid-envelope complexes isolated from *Escherichia coli* by free-flow electrophoresis: biochemical and electron microscope characterization. J. Bacteriol. **118**:646–653.

41. **Payne, J. W., and C. Gilvarg.** 1968. Size restriction on peptide utilization in *Escherichia coli*. J. Biol. Chem. **243**:6291–6294.

42. **Reynolds, B. L., U. A. Rother, and K. O. Rother.** 1975. Interaction of complement components with a serum-resistant strain of *Salmonella typhimurium*. Infect. Immun. **11**:944–948.

43. **Ribi, E., R. L. Anacher, R. Brown, W. T. Haskins, B.**

Malmgren, K. C. Milner, and J. A. Rudbach. 1966. Reaction of endotoxin and surfactants I. Physical and biological properties of endotoxin treated with sodium deoxycholate. J. Bacteriol. 92:1493–1509.

44. Richmond, M. H. 1975. Antibiotic inactivation and its genetic base. In M. R. W. Brown (ed.), Resistance in Pseudomonas aeruginosa. John Wiley and Sons, London.

45. Sanderson, K. E., T. J. MacAlister, J. W. Costerton, and K.-J. Cheng. 1974. Permeability of lipopolysaccharide-deficient (rough) mutants of Salmonella typhimurium to antibiotics, lysozyme and other agents. Can. J. Microbiol. 20:1135–1145.

46. Scherrer, R., and P. Gerhardt. 1971. Molecular sieving by the Bacillus megatherium cell wall and protoplast. J. Bacteriol. 107:718–735.

47. Shands, J. W. 1966. Localization of somatic antigen on gram-negative bacteria using ferritin antibody conjugates. Ann. N.Y. Acad. Sci. 133:292–298.

48. Shipley, P. L., and R. H. Olsen. 1974. Characteristics and expression of tetracycline resistance in gram-negative bacteria carrying the Pseudomonas R factor RP1. Antimicrob. Agents Chemother. 6:183–190.

49. Singer, S. J. 1974. The molecular organization of membranes. Annu. Rev. Biochem. 43:805–833.

50. Smith, J. T., and J. M. Wyatt. 1974. Relation of R factor and chromosomal β-lactamase with the periplasmic space. J. Bacteriol. 117:931–939.

51. Stendahl, O., C. Tagesson, and L. Edebo. 1974. Influence of hyperimmune immunoglobulin G on the physicochemical properties of the surface of Salmonella typhimurium 395 MS in relation to interaction with phagocytic cells. Infect. Immun. 10:316–319.

52. Tamaki, S., and M. Matsuhashi. 1973. Increase in sensitivity to antibiotics and lysozyme on deletion of lipopolysaccharides in Escherichia coli strains. J. Bacteriol. 114:453–454.

53. Tseng, J. T., and L. E. Bryan. 1974. The effect of complement and other cell wall reagents on tetracycline and streptomycin resistance in Pseudomonas aeruginosa. Can. J. Microbiol. 20:1101–1107.

54. Tseng, J. T., L. E. Bryan, and H. M. van den Elzen. 1972. Mechanisms and spectrum of streptomycin resistance in a natural population of Pseudomonas aeruginosa. Antimicrob. Agents Chemother. 2:136–141.

55. Wagman, G. H., J. V. Bailey, and M. J. Weinstein. 1975. Binding of aminoglycoside antibiotics to filtration materials. Antimicrob. Agents Chemother. 7:316–319.

56. Williams, R. C., and R. J. Gibbons. 1975. Inhibition of streptococcal attachment to receptors on human buccal epithelial cells by antigenically similar salivary glycoproteins. Infect. Immun. 11:711–718.

57. Wooley, R. E., W. D. Schall, R. G. Eagon, and T. A. Scott. 1974. The efficacy of EDTA-Tris-lysozyme lavage in the treatment of experimentally induced Pseudomonas aeruginosa cystitis in the dog. Am. J. Vet. Res. 35:27–29.

58. Zimelis, V. M., and G. G. Jackson. 1973. Activity of aminoglycoside antibiotics against Pseudomonas aeruginosa: specificity and site of calcium and magnesium antagonism. J. Infect. Dis. 127:663–669.

High Temperature as a Probe to Study Cell Division in *Pseudomonas aeruginosa*

J. M. INGRAM, A. R. BHATTI, AND I. W. DEVOE

Department of Microbiology, Macdonald Campus of McGill University, Ste. Anne de Bellevue, Quebec, Canada

INTRODUCTION

Previous studies from our laboratory established that the derepressible alkaline phosphatase (APase) of *Pseudomonas aeruginosa* was located in the region between the cytoplasmic membrane and the outer cell wall, the periplasm (5). The enzyme was purified to homogeneity and shown to be a dimer of molecular weight 68,000 composed of two probably identical monomer units (6). The native dimer is resistant to heat (75 C for at least 1 h) (6) and is completely resistant to digestion by trypsin. The dimer is dissociated by acid pH (below pH 5.0), the monomer is unstable to heat and is sensitive to trypsin digestion (3).

Additional studies showed that the enzyme was released from whole cells after suspension into 0.2 M MgCl$_2$ and that a fractional amount was released by 20% sucrose (4). Sucrose suspension released APase which was bound to the outer surface of the outer cell wall, and MgCl$_2$ released this enzyme plus the periplasm-located enzyme. During the growth cycle, the pH of the medium fell to below pH 5.5 and only the sucrose-released enzyme was pH inactivated (dissociated) whereas the periplasm enzyme remained stable. This observation, coupled with the in vitro pH optimum for activity (about pH 10), led to the suggestion that the hydrophobic microenvironment of the outer cell wall (due mainly to lipopolysaccharide [LPS]) protected the APase against acid denaturation and provided an alkaline environment, due to proton exclusion, for optimum catalytic activity (11). Indeed, APase formed a complex with LPS in vitro, and such a complex exhibited different substrate and thermodynamic properties when compared to the purified enzyme (7).

P. aeruginosa grows slowly at 46°C, and at this temperature the organism forms filaments. Temperature-sensitive mutations in other gram-negative and gram-positive organisms are known, and high-temperature-induced filamentous changes have been documented in normal strains of *Bacillus* (8). Growth in the presence of certain antibiotics (16) and after UV irradiation (12) are also known to induce filament formation. These treatments affect cellular processes such as certain enzymes (13), binding proteins (14), the permeability of the outer cell wall (15), and inhibition of DNA synthesis (10). We should like to report on some studies involving growth of *P. aeruginosa* at 46°C or at 46°C followed by a shift to 37°C. The organism used throughout these studies was *P. aeruginosa* ATCC 9027 which was routinely cultured on inorganic orthophosphate (P$_i$)-deficient, proteose-peptone media (5).

CELL MORPHOLOGY AT HIGH TEMPERATURE

When *P. aeruginosa* was cultured at 46°C and growth was monitored by the absorbance increase at 660 nm, there was slight but significant growth. These results were substantiated by observing the increase in protein during the growth cycle (1). Cells obtained after growth at 37°C were short, motile rods, whereas those observed at 46°C were filaments, plasmolyzed and nonmotile. The results presented in Fig. 1a and b show thin section and freeze-fracture preparations of filaments. The complete absence of cell division points within the filament and the continuous uniform cytoplasmic membrane and outer cell wall are evi-

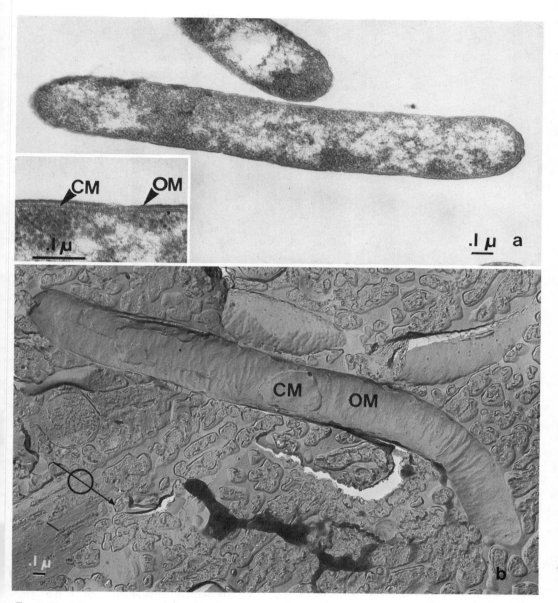

Fig. 1. *Electron micrographs of filaments of* P. aeruginosa *growth at 46°C. (a) Thin-section preparation; (b) freeze-fracture preparation. The cells were cultivated at 46°C on P_i-deficient media and examined immediately.*

dent. Treatment of filaments grown at 46°C with 0.2 M $MgCl_2$ and lysozyme resulted in the production of large spheroplasts which contained more or less regular arrangements of "cytoplasmic packets" on the inner surface of the cytoplasmic membrane (1). The fact that large spheroplasts resulted strengthens the hypothesis that the outer and inner membranes, together with the mucopeptide, of the filaments are continuous. The maximum number of cells observed in a filament was eight.

CELL DIVISION AFTER TEMPERATURE SHIFT

When filaments grown at 46°C were transferred to 37°C they began to fragment after approximately 20 min; the results (Fig. 2A and B)

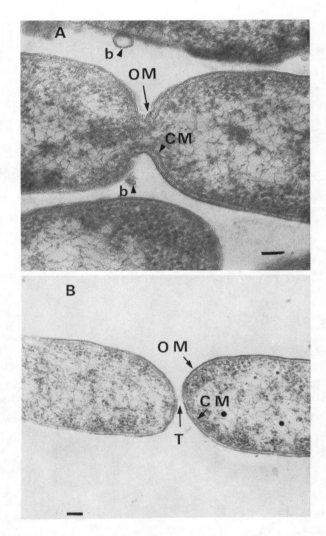

FIG. 2. *Electron micrographs of filaments of* P. aeruginosa *grown at 46°C and transferred to 37°C. (A) A sample after 50 min; (B) a sample after 60 min at 37°C. Abbreviations: OM, Outer membrane; b, blebs; CM, cytoplasmic membrane; T, tubular structure.*

show thin sections of cells in the late stages of division and final separation, respectively. In all cases the outer and cytoplasmic membranes were continuous and the absence of septa was evident (1). Freeze-fracture examination of these cells confirmed these data. Similar results were recently obtained with *Escherichia coli* B/r (17). These results, together with the results of the present study, strongly suggest that *E. coli* and *P. aeruginosa* divide by a constrictive rather than a septal process.

Treatment of filaments obtained at 46°C with penicillin G prior to a shift to 37°C inhibited cell division (Fig. 3). There was no effect observed when cells were grown and treated at 37°C; however, when filaments obtained at 46°C were shifted to 37°C, a ballooning effect at the potential points of fragmentation was observed. These results suggest that there is a disruption in mucopeptide synthesis at these points but that cell wall elongation proceeds normally. Since mucopeptide synthesis was blocked and outer cell wall synthesis continued, there is an overabundance of wall at these points and the probable area of occupation would be in the forms of a "hernia" about the potential division points. The production and manifestation of the "hernia" would be greater if the mucopeptide and the outer cell wall were anchored with a lipoprotein as described by Braun

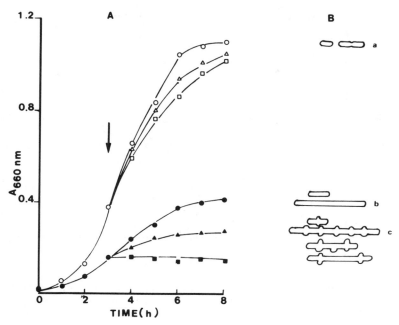

FIG. 3. *Effect of penicillin G on the growth and cell morphology of* P. aeruginosa *grown at 37 and 46°C. (A) Symbols: Hollow and solid symbols represent growth at 37 and 46°C, respectively. Triangles and squares represent cultures containing 25 and 100 µg of penicillin G per ml, respectively. Circles represent controls. An arrow indicates the addition of antibiotic. (B) Diagrammatic presentation of morphology of* P. aeruginosa *observed (a) in the presence and absence of penicillin G at 37°C, (b) in the absence of penicillin G at 46°C, and (c) in the presence of penicillin G at 46°C and shifted to 37°C.*

(1). It is also evident from these data that the permeability of the outer cell wall must be altered at 46°C since penicillin G penetrates to the mucopeptide layer.

ENZYME ALTERATIONS PRODUCED BY HIGH TEMPERATURE

Little, if any, APase appeared in the cells or the culture filtrate (CF) when *P. aeruginosa* was grown at 46°C. This is a surprising observation since, as stated before, the purified enzyme is stable to these temperatures. However, after a shift to 37°C, APase appeared first in the CF and then the cells, and after a short lag the filaments fragmented. When *P. aeruginosa* was grown at 46°C in the same media as above but in the presence of 1 mM P_i, cell growth was almost normal and no filaments were observed (Fig. 4). Similarly, the addition of purified APase was partially successful in reversing the adverse effects of growth at 46°C. The APase concentration was assayed at the termination of the experiment and all of the initial activity was recovered. This observation suggests that if APase was formed after growth at 46°C it would remain stable and be detected.

Additional experiments showed that the rates of DNA, RNA, and protein synthesis in filaments were the same as those observed in cells grown at 37°C (1). However, to achieve comparable rates at 46°C, the concentrations of [^{14}C]uracil or [^{14}C]leucine were increased 10-fold compared to the concentrations at 37°C. It was determined that the K_m for [^{14}C]uracil at 46°C was three- to fourfold greater than that at 37°C. It is probable that a periplasm-located binding or carrier protein was destroyed at 46°C. Other enzyme-specific activity levels such as glucose dehydrogenase and gluconate dehydrogenase were reduced at 46°C (unpublished observations), and the concentration of the cytochromes of electron transport was also decreased at 46°C (2). Assay of typical cytoplasm-located enzymes such as glyceraldehyde-3-phosphate dehydrogenase indicated no differences between cells grown at 46 or 37°C. These observations suggest that only those enzymes and proteins external to the cytoplasm were affected by growth at 46°C.

The observation that APase does not appear in cells grown at 46°C but did after a shift to 37°C was examined in greater detail. Since APase dimer was stable at 46°C, it was apparent that some other inactivating process was operative. When chloramphenicol (CM) was added

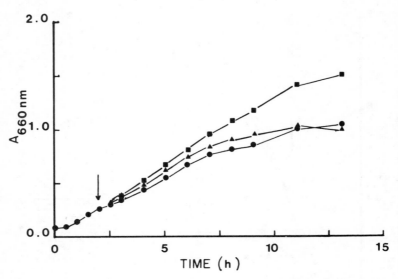

FIG. 4. *Effect of P_i and APase on the growth of* P. aeruginosa *at 46°C. The culture was grown at 46°C for 2 h and aseptically divided into three 20-ml portions in 50-ml flasks. To one was added 0.1 ml of purified APase to give 0.074 U of enzyme activity per ml (▲). To the second was added 0.1 ml of P_i to give a final concentration of 1.0 mM (■), and no addition was made to the third flask (●).*

to the medium at 46°C prior to a shift to 37°C, approximately 10% of the maximum APase appeared. If CM and trypsin were both added prior to the shift to 37°C, no active APase was detected in either the CF or the cells. These data were interpreted to indicate that, in the presence of CM only, preformed APase monomers which are not yet heat inactivated dimerize to yield active enzyme. In the presence of CM and trypsin, preformed monomer from the monomer pool is hydrolyzed (11) and no active dimer appears. These results suggest that APase is exotransported as a monomer and final dimerization occurs when the periplasm location is reached. This result may explain the role of LPS and phospholipid in the APase reaction mechanism (7).

CONCLUDING REMARKS

When *P. aeruginosa* was cultured at 46°C, nonmotile filaments which contain no detectable cell division points were formed. The maximum size of the filaments corresponded to eight single cells. Shifting the temperature to 37°C resulted in fragmentation at one terminus which then proceeded at the opposite terminus. The division process occurred by a mechanism resembling constriction rather than septum formation. A similar conclusion was stated recently for *E. coli* B/r (17). No periplasm APase was synthesized by filaments after growth at 46°C, and cultures grown at 46°C in the presence of P_i did not form

filaments. Purified APase was partially effective in restoring cell division in the absence of P_i. The enzyme APase, or its product P_i, was essential for the cell division process under these conditions. It is possible that P_i was required for the synthesis of additional mucopeptide, lipoteichoic acid, or outer cell wall material. The model which is presented here suggests that filaments do not arise by apparent mutation and that the cell division process is separate from the cell growth and elongation processes (9).

Although filaments cultured at 46°C produced little or no periplasm-located APase, it was found that cytoplasm-located functions such as DNA, RNA, and protein synthesis proceeded normally. In addition, representative enzyme functions of 46°C filaments such as glucose-6-phosphate and glyceraldehyde-3-phosphate dehydrogenases were comparable to those observed in cells grown at 37°C. These results suggest that the cytoplasm possesses insulator characteristics.

ACKNOWLEDGMENT

This research was generously supported by grants from the National Research Council of Canada.

LITERATURE CITED

1. **Bhahi, A. R., I. W. DeVoe, and J. M. Ingram.** 1976. Cell division in *Pseudomonas aeruginosa*: participation of alkaline phosphatase. J. Bacteriol. **126:** 400–409.
1a. **Braun, V.** 1975. Covalent lipoprotein from the outer

membrane of *Escherichia coli*. Biochim. Biophys. Acta **415**:335–377.

2. **Calcott, P. H., A. R. Bhatti, and J. M. Ingram.** 1975. The effect of temperature on the cytochrome pattern and respiration of *Pseudomonas aeruginosa*. FEBS Lett. **56**:318–321.

3. **Cheng, K.-J., D. F. Day, J. W. Costerton, and J. M. Ingram.** 1972. Alkaline phosphatase subunits in the culture filtrate of *Pseudomonas aeruginosa*. Can. J. Biochem. **50**:268–276.

4. **Cheng, K.-J., J. M. Ingram, and J. W. Costerton.** 1970. Release of alkaline phosphatase from cells of *Pseudomonas aeruginosa* by manipulation of cation concentration and of pH. J. Bacteriol. **104**:748–753.

5. **Cheng, K.-J., J. M. Ingram, and J. W. Costerton.** 1970. Alkaline phosphatase localization and spheroplast formation of *Pseudomonas aeruginosa*. Can. J. Microbiol. **16**:1319–1324.

6. **Day, D. F., and J. M. Ingram.** 1973. Purification and characterization of *Pseudomonas aeruginosa* alkaline phosphatase. Can. J. Microbiol. **19**:1225–1233.

7. **Day, D. F., and J. M. Ingram.** 1975. *In vitro* studies of an alkaline phosphatase-cell wall complex from *Pseudomonas aeruginosa*. Can. J. Microbiol. **21**:9–16.

8. **Ferroni, G. D., and W. E. Inniss.** 1973. Thermally caused filament formation in the psychrophile *Bacillus insolitus*. Can. J. Microbiol. **19**:581–584.

9. **Henning, U.** 1975. Determination of cell shape in bacteria. Annu. Rev. Microbiol. **29**:45–60.

10. **Horita, Y., J. Mordoh, and F. Jacob.** 1970. On the process of cellular division in *Escherichia coli*. III. Thermosensitive mutants of *Escherichia coli* altered in the process of DNA initiation. J. Mol. Biol. **53**:369–387.

11. **Ingram, J. M., K.-J. Cheng, and J. W. Costerton.** 1973. Alkaline phosphatase of *Pseudomonas aeruginosa*. II. The mechanism of secretion and release of the enzyme from whole cells. Can. J. Microbiol. **19**: 1407–1415.

12. **Otsuji, N. H., H. Iyekara, and Y. Hideshama.** 1974. Isolation and characterization of an *Escherichia coli ruv* mutant which forms nonseptate filaments after low doses of ultraviolet light irradiation. J. Bacteriol. **117**:337–344.

13. **Smith, H. S., and A. B. Pardee.** 1970. Accumulation of a protein required for division during the cell cycle of *Escherichia coli*. J. Bacteriol. **101**:901–909.

14. **Spratt, B. G.** 1975. Distinct penicillin binding proteins involved in the division, elongation and shape of *E. coli* K$_{12}$. Proc. Natl. Acad. Sci. U.S.A. **72**:2999–3003.

15. **Stone, A. B.** 1973. Regulation of cell division in a temperature-sensitive division mutant of *Escherichia coli*. J. Bacteriol. **116**:741–750.

16. **Strominger, J. L., P. M. Blumberg, H. Suginaka, J. Umbreit, and G. G. Wickus.** 1971. How penicillin kills bacteria: progress and problems. Proc. Roy. Soc. London Ser. B **197**:369–383.

17. **Woldringh, C. L.** 1976. Morphological analysis of nuclear separation and cell division during the life cycle of *Escherichia coli*. J. Bacteriol. **125**:248–257.

Spectrum of Antibiotic Resistance in Clinical Isolates of *Pseudomonas aeruginosa*

L. E. BRYAN AND H. M. VAN DEN ELZEN

Department of Medical Bacteriology, University of Alberta, Edmonton, Canada

INTRODUCTION

In spite of the availability of antimicrobial agents shown to have the capability to inhibit or to kill *Pseudomonas aeruginosa*, the therapeutic efficacy of these drugs for serious pseudomonas sepsis remains disappointing. Fatality rates of 30 to 80% for these infections are commonly reported (5, 8, 10). Individuals who acquire serious pseudomonas infections often have gross impairment of one or more host defense mechanisms. Thus, in these patients the antibiotic is of paramount importance because of the frequent ineffectiveness of an important host defense such as a marked decline in the numbers of polymorphonuclear neutrophils. With these considerations in mind, it is important to recognize that even susceptible strains of *P. aeruginosa* are only relatively susceptible to the most commonly used drugs for pseudomonas infections, carbenicillin and gentamicin. Strains are considered susceptible to carbenicillin if they are inhibited by 100 to 200 μg of the drug per ml. To put this in perspective, it must be noted that these values are near peak levels of the drug in the serum and that compared, for example, to benzylpenicillin susceptibility of *Streptococcus pyogenes*, *P. aeruginosa* is 1,000- to 10,000-fold less susceptible to carbenicillin. Gentamicin susceptibility is even more clouded because of the major influence of pH, cation concentrations, and serum on determinations of minimal inhibitory concentrations (MICs) of the drug. If free cation concentrations are adjusted to those present in serum, the MIC values of gentamicin for even the most susceptible *P. aeruginosa* will be in the range of 2 to 8 μg/ml. Thus, once again MIC values are close to or exceed achievable safe serum levels of the drug. Therapy of "susceptible" strains of *P. aeruginosa* causing severe sepsis is associated with mortality figures which suggest that these strains are not very susceptible to gentamicin.

To perform a meaningful surveillance of antibiotic susceptibility of *P. aeruginosa* at the University of Alberta Hospital (UAH) in Edmonton, we studied strains of *P. aeruginosa* in an attempt to determine those factors which govern its susceptibility to antibiotics. We emphasized the study of aminoglycosides since so many variables affect the determination of MIC values of that group of drugs. It is essential to appreciate that we studied not only resistant strains but also those considered highly susceptible, especially to gentamicin and streptomycin, to understand the differences between such strains. These studies have resulted in the conclusion that aminoglycoside susceptibility of *P. aeruginosa* strains is determined by the permeability of the strain to the aminoglycoside. Some strains which show very high aminoglycoside resistance have the superimposed presence of a drug-modifying enzyme, but many strains showing moderate resistance lack such enzymes.

PROPERTIES AND FREQUENCY OF STRAINS WITH R FACTOR-SPECIFIED GENTAMICIN INACTIVATION

At the UAH we have determined the aminoglycoside susceptibility of over 1,500 strains of *P. aeruginosa* by an agar dilution method with controlled cation concentrations (calcium, 75 mg/liter; magnesium, 20 mg/liter). The results show that 30% of strains have MIC values of 8 μg or greater of gentamicin per ml and 6% require similar values of tobramycin. Twenty-two percent have an MIC of 16 μg or greater of amikacin per ml, and 10% have an MIC of 100 μg or greater of carbenicillin per ml. We have examined selected strains from this group and

TABLE 1. *Gentamicin acetylation specified by R factor R130 in various strains of* Pseudomonas aeruginosa

Enzymatic activity	Strain	MIC of gentamicin[a] (μg/ml)	Sp act[b] (dpm/mg of protein/ 15 min)	R factor DNA[c] (%)	Gentamicin accumulated at 0.5 μg of gentamicin per ml[d] (ng/mg [dry wt] of cells)
Acetylation	PS130(R130)	128	4.8×10^5	18 ± 2	
	280(R130)	2	4.9×10^5	18 ± 2	
	1310(R130)	10	4.8×10^5	18 ± 2	
None	280	0.06	ND[e]	None	96
	1310	0.5	ND	None	10

[a] Using Mueller-Hinton agar with 75 mg of calcium per liter and 20 mg of magnesium per liter.

[b] Using assay method described by Davies et al. (4). Activity in disintegrations per minute of gentamicin-[^{14}C]acetate bound to phosphocellulose paper.

[c] Percentage of total DNA as determined by CsCl density gradient centrifugation.

[d] Accumulation of gentamicin measured by a membrane filter method using repurified [^{3}H]gentamicin (Amersham/Searle) in nutrient broth. Values given are for 20-min accumulation periods.

[e] ND, Not detectable.

from other investigators in detail to determine the factors controlling susceptibility to aminoglycosides, in particular gentamicin. A very small number of strains from the UAH produce gentamicin-acetylating or -adenylylating enzymes. Generally, those which do so have MIC values of 100 μg/ml or greater and frequently contain an R factor. However, even in strains which possess gentamicin-modifying enzymes, it seems that this is not the only factor controlling gentamicin resistance. Table 1 compares MIC values of gentamicin for the original isolate containing R factor R130-specified gentamicin acetylation and of *P. aeruginosa* strains 280 and 1310 containing the same R factor. There is a marked decline of MIC of gentamicin specified by R130 gentamicin acetyl transferase when introduced from strain PS130 to, especially, strains 280. However, as shown in Table 1, there is no significant difference in the amount of R factor DNA nor of enzymatic activity among the three strains shown. Similar results were also obtained for an R factor specifying gentamicin adenylylation, R151. We also determined that the K_m of these enzymes for gentamicin does not vary between strains. Thus, the marked differences in MIC values cannot be explained by differences in the amount or properties of the gentamicin-modifying enzymes in the various strains. Strain 280 is highly permeable to gentamicin (see Fig. 1), and it seems likely that the rate of influx of gentamicin exceeds the capability of gentamicin acetyl transferase to inactivate it, which thus causes the resistance level to be reduced. This is supported by the results obtained with recipient strain 1310, which is less permeable to gentamicin (3), and the MIC of that drug is correspondingly higher than the values obtained for strain 280 (Table 1).

Table 2 illustrates the aminoglycoside resistance profile of strain 280 and of the same strain with various R factors present. Also shown are the resistances of several wild-type strains in which the R factors were originally detected. These results illustrate that resistance to an aminoglycoside in a strain containing a known enzymatic activity may not be accounted for by that form of aminoglycoside modification. For example, strain PS130 appears relatively resistant to SCH 20569, a new aminoglycoside antibiotic. R factor R130 specifies gentamicin and SCH 20569 acetylation although the rate of acetylation of SCH 20569 is one-third to one-half that for gentamicin. Acquisition of R130 by strain 280 is associated with an increase in resistance to gentamicin but not to SCH 20569. Similar reduction of resistance levels specified by other R factors in strain 280 is particularly so for SCH 20569 and amikacin. It is also quite clear from Table 2 that the level of resistance is not wholly a function of enzymatic inactivation, even when the drug is a substrate of the modifying enzyme, but that permeability to the aminoglycoside also plays a very important role. In fact, strain 280, which is highly permeable to gentamicin, would be regarded as susceptible to that drug even with the presence of R factors like R130, R442, and R151 that specify gentamicin modification (Table 2).

AMINOGLYCOSIDE-RESISTANT ENZYME-NEGATIVE STRAINS

We have detected many strains of *P. aeruginosa* at UAH with MIC values varying from 8 to 100 μg of gentamicin per ml, with most being 12 to 50 μg/ml, which do not contain known forms of gentamicin-modifying enzymes. These strains represent nearly 100%

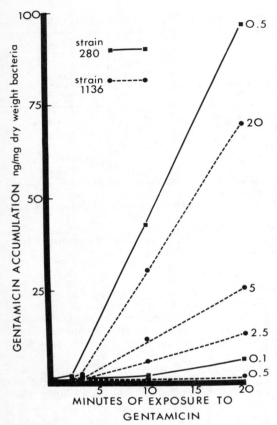

FIG. 1. *Gentamicin accumulation by* P. aeruginosa *strains 280 (■) and 1136 (●) at various gentamicin concentrations. Concentration of gentamicin in micrograms per milliliter used for each accumulation determination is noted on the figure. Accumulation was determined using repurified [³H]gentamicin (Amersham/ Searle) in nutrient broth at a cell density of 10⁹/ml. Samples were removed at the times specified and filtered, using 0.22-μm membrane filters (pretreated with 2.5 ml of cold gentamicin solution [200 μg/ml] to reduce background). Filters were dried and counted in a liquid scintillation system, and the amount of gentamicin accumulated per milligram of cells was determined, using the specific activity of the [³H]gentamicin used (1,000 dpm/ng of gentamicin). Zero-time values have been subtracted (2). The initial zero values for strain 1136 are not shown to improve clarity of the figure.*

of the resistant strains at UAH. Each of these strains has been repeatedly examined using the assay system of Davies et al. (4). We have also used microbiological assays to examine the capability of cell extracts in the presence of various additives to inactivate gentamicin and to look for loss of gentamicin activity in the extracellular fluid of cells grown in broth with subinhibitory concentrations of gentamicin. Finally,

we have chromatographed broth filtrates and cold 10% trichloroacetic acid extracts of these cells and have been unable to detect loss of activity or an inactivated product (1). Ribosomes and soluble components of in vitro amino acid-incorporating systems from these resistant strains are susceptible to gentamicin. Some of these strains possess plasmid DNA, but we have not succeeded in the transfer of this form of resistance to other strains (1). These strains show an increase of resistance to every aminoglycoside we have tested. It would be difficult to account for the last effect on the basis of ribosomal resistance or a single form of enzymatic inactivation. These strains have been termed enzyme-negative strains.

Enzyme-negative resistant and susceptible strains show differential permeability to aminoglycosides, for example, gentamicin. As permeability of aminoglycosides appears to influence strain susceptibility to aminoglycosides, we have undertaken a study of the manner by which gentamicin and streptomycin are accumulated. Accumulation occurs with an initial, rapid, energy-dependent phase and one or more subsequent energy-dependent phases. The energy-dependent form of accumulation is necessary to cause either inhibition of growth or cell death. A wide variety of metabolic inhibitors, including many inhibitors of electron transport and oxidative phosphorylation (e.g., potassium cyanide, 2,4-dinitrophenol, anaerobic conditions), prevent or reduce this form of accumulation. Antibiotic (either streptomycin or gentamicin) can be recovered from cells in an unchanged form and may be apparently concentrated above extracellular concentrations. There is good evidence that the modification of permeability control of intracellular nucleotides (i.e., their loss from cells) which streptomycin or gentamicin causes occurs after energy-dependent streptomycin or gentamicin accumulation is well advanced (2; L. E. Bryan and H. M. Van Den Elzen, submitted for publication). The system is probably best categorized as active accumulation rather than active transport because we have not yet succeeded in testing and confirming all the criteria for the latter. These observations are very interesting and explain the aminoglycoside resistance of obligately anaerobic bacteria and the increase in resistance of facultative bacteria grown anaerobically. Streptococci which have incomplete electron transport chains are relatively resistant to aminoglycosides. Obligate aerobes, for example *Pseudomonas* species and *Mycobacterium* species, tend to be more susceptible to aminoglycosides. In fact, it would appear that *P. aeruginosa* has evolved a system to diminish the remarkable susceptibility

TABLE 2. *Minimal inhibitory concentrations (MICs) of various aminoglycosides for strains of* Pseudomonas aeruginosa *containing various R factors*

R factor	Strain	Enzymatic inactivation	MIC (µg/ml) of:			
			Gentamicin	Tobramycin	Amikacin	SCH 20569
	280		0.062	0.031	0.25	0.062
R130	280	Acetylation[a]	2	0.031	0.25	0.062
R130	PS130	Acetylation	>32	1	8	32
R442	280	Acetylation[a]	2	0.031	0.25	0.062
R442	B442	Acetylation			8	16
R151	280	Adenylylation[a]	4	2	0.25	0.062
R151	POW	Adenylylation	64	16	8	8
R931	280	Phosphorylation[b]	0.125	0.031	0.25	0.062
R931	S-931	Phosphorylation[b]	2	0.5	8	16
R679	280	Phosphorylation[b]	0.125	0.031	0.25	0.062
R679	S679	Phosphorylation[b]	8	2	16	32

[a] Acetylation or adenylylation of gentamicin.
[b] Phosphorylation of streptomycin.

to gentamicin that a few strains of *P. aeruginosa* such as strain 280 can show.

Figure 1 illustrates the comparative accumulation in a very sensitive accumulation system of strain 280 and the relatively gentamicin-resistant strain 1136. These strains clearly show marked differences in their capability to accumulate gentamicin. The reason for this difference is unclear, but it may be a manifestation of a gene like the *tolA* gene described at this symposium by B. Holloway (p. 116). We also know that, in *Escherichia coli*, ATPase-deficient mutants and uncoupling mutants show modified aminoglycoside susceptibility. It is also of interest that the pyocin to which the *tolA* mutant is tolerant has, superficially at least, a similar mechanism of action as colicin K has for *E. coli*. It was recently shown that colicin K exerts an action on some aspect of membrane energization. However, mutants of membrane energization are frequently auxotrophic and have prolonged generation times. Some resistant mutants with properties like this have been isolated, but their importance in nature is unlikely because of their severe metabolic defects. The strains we found at UAH were not characteristically auxotrophic and had normal generation times. We examined the effects on aminoglycoside accumulation of reagents active on the cell wall in an attempt to determine if the outer cell wall represents a permeability barrier in these strains. Results using carbenicillin suggested that the cell wall is a barrier to aminoglycoside accumulation but of similar magnitude in both susceptible and resistant strains, or perhaps of less importance in

resistant strains. Treatment of strain 280 and 1136 with a carbenicillin concentration equal to or above their MIC values caused an increase of gentamicin accumulation in both strains, but somewhat more with strain 280 than 1136. We feel that, in most naturally occurring strains, the cell wall could reduce the rate at which gentamicin reaches the transport site in the membrane. However, our preliminary results suggest that differing capabilities of transport account for much of the widespread difference in susceptibility of strains of pseudomonas to aminoglycosides. This variation resulted in a widespread form of impermeability resistance which is also capable of magnifying the effects of inactivating enzymes. Permeability to aminoglycoside seems dependent to some extent on the cell wall but mainly on an energy-dependent cellular accumulation mechanism which determines the ultimate level of resistance in enzyme-negative or -positive strains. Although not presented here, we have evidence that this mechanism is also influenced by testing conditions such as cation concentrations and thus altered aminoglycoside susceptibility when such conditions are changed.

The isolates which contain an inactivating enzyme in presumably relatively aminoglycoside-impermeable strains have in our experience and in literature reports been isolated only from circumstances where gentamicin concentrations were very high. Two major sources have been urinary isolates and burn units (6, 7, 9). The much more common enzyme-negative strains appeared from all types of isolates and clinical circumstances within a general hospital. In our hospital a major factor in their selection appeared to be the heavy use of gentamicin for nonpseudomonal infections. In these cases the pseudomonas strains which were ubiquitous in our hospital appeared to be treated as bystanders with ineffectual levels of the drug. It would seem that relatively low gentamicin concentrations may be the selective force for primarily permeability-type resistant strains, whereas combined enzyme and permeability-type resistance seems selected by high gentamicin concentrations.

LITERATURE CITED

1. **Bryan, L. E., R. Haraphongse, and M. S. Shahrabadi.** 1974. Gentamicin resistance in *Pseudomonas aeruginosa*. Non-transferable gentamicin resistance, p. 297–312. *In* L. Rosival, V. Kromery, and S. Mitsushashi (ed.), Drug-inactivating enzymes and other problems of resistant bacteria. Springer-Verlag, New York.

2. **Bryan, L. E., and H. M. Van Den Elzen.** 1975. Gentamicin accumulation by sensitive strains of *Escherichia coli* and *Pseudomonas aeruginosa*. J. Antibiot. (Tokyo) **28:**696–703.

3. **Bryan, L. E., H. M. Van Den Elzen, and M. S. Shahrabadi.** 1975. The relationship of aminoglycoside permeability to streptomycin and gentamicin of *Pseudomonas aeruginosa*, p. 475–490. *In* S. Mitsuhashi and H. Hashimoto (ed.), Microbial drug resistance. University of Tokyo Press, Tokyo.

4. **Davies, J., M. Brezezinska, and R. Benveniste.** 1971. R-factors: biochemical mechanisms of resistance to aminoglycoside antibiotics. Ann. N.Y. Acad. Sci. **182:**226–233.

5. **Jackson, G. G., and Louise J. Riff.** 1971. Pseudomonas bacteremia. Pharmacologic and other bases for failure of treatment with gentamicin. J. Infect. Dis. **124** (Suppl):S185–S191.

6. **Kabins, S., C. Nathon, and S. Cohen.** 1974. Gentamicin adenylyl transferase activity as a cause of gentamicin resistance in clinical isolates of *Pseudomonas aeruginosa*. Antimicrob. Agents Chemother. **5:**565–570.

7. **Korfhagen, T. R., J. C. Loper, and J. A. Ferrel.** 1975. Pseudomonas R factors determining gentamicin plus carbenicillin resistance from patients with urinary tract colonizations. Antimicrob. Agents Chemother. **7:**64–68.

8. **McGowan, J. E., M. W. Barnes, and M. Finland.** 1975. Bacteremia at Boston City Hospital. Occurrence and mortality during 13 selected years (1935–1972) with special reference to hospital-acquired cases. J. Infect. Dis. **132:**316–335.

9. **Shulman, J. A., P. M. Terry, and C. E. Hough.** 1971. Colonization with gentamicin resistant *Pseudomonas aeruginosa* pyocine type 5, in a burn unit. J. Infect. Dis. **124**(Suppl):S18–S23.

10. **Tapper, M. L., and D. Armstrong.** 1974. Bacteremia due to *Pseudomonas aeruginosa* complicating neoplastic disease. A progress report. J. Infect. Dis. **130**(Suppl):S14–S23.

Experimental Mouse Infections Caused by
Pseudomonas aeruginosa

RICHARD S. BERK

Department of Immunology and Microbiology, Wayne State University School of Medicine, Detroit, Michigan 48201

INTRODUCTION

Over the past few years the importance of *Pseudomonas aeruginosa* as a human pathogen in a variety of infections has increased dramatically. Of particular interest is its increasing incidence in nosocomial infections of individuals already debilitated by other diseases or by antineoplastic chemotherapy (1–7, 9). A description of three experimental models will be discussed in the present manuscript and will cover (i) infection by gastric intubation, (ii) peroral infection into the lungs, and (iii) eye infections.

RESULTS

Infection by Gastric Intubation

Initial experiments were designed to determine whether normal, undebilitated mice were susceptible to infection when organisms were administered perorally into the stomach. Using a 15-day holding period, it was established that normal mice were susceptible to infection by this route and all three ATCC strains were able to produce lethal infections (Table 1). Of the three strains, the nonencapsulated strain (19660) appeared to be the most virulent on the basis of cell numbers needed to produce death in the animals. The mean lethal dose (LD_{50}) values for strains 19660, 17933, and 17934 were 5.3×10^6, 5×10^7, and 5.6×10^7 colony-forming units (CFU), respectively. All control animals receiving up to 10^9 viable organisms perorally into the lungs did not die.

Although animals were observed for 15 days, all deaths were the result of acute infection and occurred within 72 h after the peroral challenge. Viable *P. aeruginosa* was routinely cultured from the heart, blood, kidney, and other internal organs at necropsy. Those animals which survived the first 72 h spontaneously recovered and showed no subsequent symptoms. For comparative purposes, the mice were also infected by the intravenous (i.v.) and intraperitoneal (i.p.) routes, and the 72-h LD_{50} values of the three ATCC strains were obtained. In all cases the i.v. or i.p. injections yielded LD_{50} values for each respective strain which were greater than the peroral value, indicating that the normal mice appeared to be more susceptible to infection via the stomach than by parenteral routes. In addition, the nonencapsulated strain 19660 appeared to be more virulent than the encapsulated strains regardless of the route of infection. However, the nonencapsulated strain (19660) did not produce any diarrhea in the infected animals whereas the two encapsulated strains (17933 and 17934), although less virulent in terms of LD_{50} than the nonencapsulated strain, produced diarrhea when administered perorally into the stomach. The diarrhea, however, was only observed in animals which eventually died and only in concentrations of organisms at or above the LD_{50} values of the encapsulated strains. The onset of the diarrhea was rapid and occurred within 24 h post-peroral challenge. No diarrhea was produced by these encapsulated strains when they were administered parenterally.

Attempts to increase the susceptibility of mice to peroral infection by treatment with antineoplastic drugs with the nonencapsulated strain (ATCC 19660) and one of the encapsulated strains (ATCC 17933) resulted in the following

TABLE 1. *Comparative summary of* LD_{50} *values for viable* Pseudomonas aeruginosa *in normal mice*

Route of administration	LD$_{50}$ values[a]		
	Strain 17933	Strain 17934	Strain 19660
Peroral (stomach)[b]	5.0×10^7	5.6×10^7	5.3×10^6
Intraperitoneal[c]	1.1×10^8	7.2×10^8	3.6×10^7
Intravenous[c]	3.6×10^8	6.4×10^8	3.3×10^7

[a] Average of duplicate determinations calculated by method of Reed and Muench (8) (minimum of 30 animals per determination).
[b] A 0.01-ml volume of inoculum.
[c] A 0.5-ml volume of inoculum.

observations. The effect of antineoplastic drugs on depressing the natural immunity of animals which were challenged with strain 17933 is shown in Table 2. The greatest increase in susceptibility to a lethal infection was produced in animals treated with a single injection of methotrexate, since drug treatment 24 h prior to and simultaneously with the challenge produced LD_{50} decreases of 208- and 588-fold, respectively. Lower LD_{50} values were also demonstrated in animals which received vincristine sulfate or cytosine arabinoside, but of a lower magnitude, with vincristine sulfate treatment at 24 h prior to challenge exhibiting a 10-fold decrease.

Antineoplastic drug treatment of animals challenged with the nonencapsulated strain 19660 produced results similar to those produced with the encapsulated strain, with methotrexate-treated animals showing the greatest decrease in LD_{50} value but not as great as that which

resulted in strain 17933-challenged animals. Also, little change was produced in animals treated with cytosine arabinoside or vincristine sulfate. Histopathological studies of the acutely ill animals which had received peroral administrations of viable cells revealed no apparent differences between the three strains in the type or magnitude of inflammation.

Infection by Tracheal Instillation

Initial studies attempted to determine whether either acute or chronic systemic infections could be established using peroral administration of *P. aeruginosa* into the lungs of normal animals. Initial studies using *P. aeruginosa* ATCC 19660 did result in an occasional death, but an accurate LD_{50} value could not be established since it was difficult to administer organisms above 2.5×10^9 CFU. Although a 15-day end point was used to observe the animals and calculate the LD_{50} values, when death occurred it was within 72 h in lung-challenged animals. No deaths due to chronic infections nor illnesses were seen in any surviving animals, which appeared to recover uneventfully from the challenge. Also, the challenging of animals perorally into the lungs with high concentrations of heat-killed cells did not result in any deaths (Table 3).

Since LD_{50} values could not be established in normal animals with perorally administered organisms into the lungs, animals were treated with antineoplastic drugs in an attempt to lower their resistance to bacterial infections. The treatment of animals with methotrexate, vincristine sulfate, or cytosine arabinoside simultaneously with peroral challenge into the lungs resulted in LD_{50} values of 4.1×10^7 CFU, 4.8×10^7 CFU,

TABLE 2. *Effect of antineoplastic drugs on the lethality of viable* Pseudomonas aeruginosa *administered perorally into the stomach*

Antineoplastic drug administered	Time of drug administration relative to bacterial challenge	Strain 17933		Strain 19660	
		LD$_{50}$ value[a]	Fold decrease in LD$_{50}$	LD$_{50}$ value[a]	Fold decrease in LD$_{50}$
None	None	5.0×10^7	1.0	5.3×10^6	1.0
Methotrexate, 160 mg/kg	24 h prior	2.4×10^5	208.0	6.1×10^5	8.7
	Simultaneously	8.5×10^4	588.0	1.4×10^5	38.0
Vincristine sulfate, 1.25 mg/kg	24 h prior	4.7×10^6	10.6	6.7×10^5	7.9
	Simultaneously	3.4×10^7	1.5	3.0×10^5	17.7
Cytosine arabinoside, 500 mg/kg	24 h prior	1.3×10^7	4.0	1.9×10^6	3.0
	Simultaneously	8.4×10^6	6.0	3.4×10^6	1.6

[a] Calculated by method of Reed and Muench (8) (minimum of 30 animals per determination).

TABLE 3. *Effect of antineoplastic drugs on the lethality of* Pseudomonas aeruginosa *administered perorally into the lungs of mice*

Antineoplastic drug administration	Time of drug administration relative to bacterial challenge	Drug alone (saline challenge)	Peroral LD_{50} value	Heat-killed cells [a]
Methotrexate, 160 mg/kg	24 h prior	0/5 [b]	2.6×10^8	0/6 [b]
	Simultaneously	0/5	4.1×10^7	0/4
Vincristine sulfate, 1.25 mg/kg	24 h prior	0/5	4.9×10^7	0/5
	Simultaneously	0/5	4.8×10^7	0/4
Cytosine arabinoside, 500 mg/kg	24 h prior	0/5	2.4×10^8	0/5
	Simultaneously	0/5	1.0×10^8	0/4

[a] The heat-killed cell concentration was the equivalent of 1.0×10^9 CFU.
[b] Expressed as total number dead per total number challenged.

and 1.9×10^8 CFU, respectively. Lethality was also observed in these animals when the drugs were given 24 h prior to the challenge into the lung, but the potentiating effect was usually of a lower order in each case as compared to drugs administered at the same time as the bacterial challenge (Table 3). All deaths which occurred in these treated animals, as in the untreated animals, occurred within 72 h, and the surviving animals appeared to resolve the challenge successfully. No lethality was ever observed in control animals when drug treatment was followed by a saline challenge or the equivalent of 10^9 CFU of heat-killed cells at the appropriate time.

Aminoglutethimide and mucin were also used in an attempt to increase the susceptibility of the animals to peroral challenge into the lungs of *P. aeruginosa*. When aminoglutethimide was administered, no potentiating effect was seen since an LD_{50} value could not be established when concentrations of viable organisms as high as 1.3×10^9 CFU were perorally administered into the lungs. When 5% mucin was administered i.p. 24 h prior to the peroral challenge, an LD_{50} value of 7.5×10^7 CFU was established. If the bacterial cells were mixed with 5% mucin and then administered perorally into the lungs, an LD_{50} value of 4.2×10^8 CFU was established. All deaths again occurred within 72 h after challenge in animals treated with aminoglutethimide or mucin.

Ophthalmic Infection

Topical administration of 10^4 to 10^8 cells onto the surface of unwounded corneas failed to produce any pathological changes in two strains of mice. However, changes were observed within 18 to 24 h after inoculation with *P. aeruginosa*

onto the injured corneal surface at dosages of 10^7 and/or 10^8 cells. This damage included (in both animal strains) diffuse conjunctival infiltration, edema, ulceration, and accumulation of a thick, white, purulent exudate. Various degrees of corneal opacity as previously reported also were observed. Swiss-Webster mice recovered from these symptoms within 4 to 6 weeks after wounding and infection. The eyes of BALB/c mice, however, became progressively worse. Infected eyes which had initially appeared swollen and edematous, decreased in size (by day 6) until by 15 days severe microophthalmia was noted. Animals observed after 1 month showed no change in this condition. All cultures plated throughout the experiments performed were pure for *P. aeruginosa*.

Preliminary studies with Swiss-Webster mice which had been thymectomized and later treated with antilymphocytic serum suggests that short-lived T lymphocytes may be associated with natural defense mechanisms of the eye. This was based on the observations that the thymectomized Swiss-Webster mice behaved like normal BALB/c mice and lost their eyes by a process of liquefactive necrosis as the result of bacterial infection.

CONCLUSIONS

Peroral administration of viable *P. aeruginosa* into the stomach of mice resulted in an acute systemic infection, with death occurring within 72 h. One strain, ATCC 19660, a nonencapsulated form of *P. aeruginosa,* had an LD_{50} of 5.3×10^6 CFU, whereas two encapsulated strains, ATCC 17933 and 17934, had LD_{50} values of 5.0×10^7 CFU and 5.6×10^7 CFU, respectively. Each strain required fewer organisms to establish a lethal infection via the stomach than by i.v. and i.p. routes. The nonencapsulated strain, ATCC 19660, did not produce any diarrhea in the infected animals whereas the two encapsulated strains, although less virulent, produced diarrhea when administered perorally. No signs of necrosis were noted within the gastrointestinal tract; however, hematogenous spread of the organism resulted in a vasculitis associated with the pulmonary vessels and bacterial invasion of the renal tissues. Treatment of animals with antineoplastic drugs 24 h before or simultaneously with peroral challenge resulted in an increased susceptibility to infection.

The peroral administration of *P. aeruginosa* into the lungs is a useful method to study the invasiveness of the organism in a host system using the natural route of infection. Although the peroral administration of *Pseudomonas* into the lungs of normal undebilitated animals does not produce disease, neither is clinical pulmonary infection by *P. aeruginosa* often seen in immunocompetent individuals. Our system using a natural mode of infection via the respiratory tract allows the investigator to directly measure the debilitating effect of antibiotics, antineoplastic drugs, hormones, and other virulent-enhancing agents on the respiratory system in combating bacterial infections.

The striking difference in the response of two mice strains as described herein presents an experimental model for studying the natural defense mechanisms of the eye to bacterial invasion. The fact that Swiss-Webster mice spontaneously recover from bacterial challenge whereas BALB/c mice lose their eyes is a dramatic indication that strain differences between the same animal species is an important tool in understanding the mechanisms by which *P. aeruginosa* attacks the susceptible host. In addition, the complete loss of ophthalmic tissue in thymectomized Swiss-Webster mice suggests that the short-lived T lymphocyte plays either a direct or indirect role in the natural defense mechanisms of the eye.

ACKNOWLEDGMENTS

I wish to acknowledge the support of the Office of Naval Research (grant N-00014-69-A-0235-0002), Fight for Sight, Inc., New York, N.Y. (grant-in-aid G-558), and Public Health Service general research support grant 5 S01 RR05384 from the National Institutes of Health. In addition, it is a pleasure to acknowledge the important contributions of Lawrence Schook, Lee Carrick, Jr., Linda Hazlett, and Della Rosen.

LITERATURE CITED

1. **Buck, A. C., and E. M. Cooke.** 1969. The fate of ingested *Pseudomonas aeruginosa* in normal persons. J Med. Microbiol. **2:**521–525.
2. **Finland, M., W. F. Jones, Jr., and M. W. Barnes.** 1969. Occurrence of serious bacterial infections since the introduction of antibacterial agents. J. Am. Med. Assoc. **170:**2188–2197.
3. **Forkner, C. E., Jr.** 1960. *Pseudomonas aeruginosa* infections. Publication **22,** Modern Medical Monographs. Grune and Stratton, Inc., N.Y.
4. **Hammond, C. W., D. Ruml, D. B. Cooper, and C. P. Miller.** 1965. Studies on susceptibility to infection following ionizing radiation. J. Exp. Med. **99:**411–418.
5. **Howerton, E. E., and S. N. Kolmen.** 1972. The intestinal tract as a portal of entry of *Pseudomonas* in burned rats. J. Trauma **12:**355–340.
6. **Hunter, C. A., and P. R. Ensign.** 1947. An epidemic of diarrhea in a new-born nursery caused by *Pseudomonas aeruginosa.* Am. J. Public Health **37:**1166–1169.
7. **Iacocca, V. F., M. S. Sibinga, and G. J. Barbero.** 1963. Respiratory tract bacteriology in cystic fibrosis. Am. J. Dis. Child. **106:**315–324.
8. **Reed, L. J., and H. Muench.** 1938. A simple method of estimating fifty percent endpoints. Am. J. Hyg. **27:**493–497.
9. **Schimpff, S. C., W. H. Greene, V. M. Young, and P. H. Wiernik.** 1974. Significance of *Pseudomonas aeruginosa* in the patient with leukemia or lymphoma. J. Infect. Dis. **130:**s24–s31.

III. NOVEL ASPECTS OF PENICILLIN ACTION

Introduction

ALEXANDER TOMASZ

The Rockefeller University, New York, New York 10021

Some recent insights into the mechanism of action of penicillin prompted the organization of a seminar at the Annual Meeting of the American Society for Microbiology in May of 1976.

During the past two decades, major advances have been made in the identification of penicillin-sensitive bacterial enzymes and in the understanding of their mode of action. However, it seems now that the inhibition of those enzymes of peptidoglycan metabolism is not sufficient to explain the diversity of the biological consequences of penicillin action, such as the selective inhibition of cell division (at low penicillin concentrations) and arrest of cell elongation (at higher concentrations of the drug), the distortion and/or alteration of the unique bacterial shape, the loss of colony-forming ability, the lysis of the cells, and the apparent resistance of nongrowing bacteria to penicillin. Interestingly, all these symptoms of penicillin action were described shortly after the discovery of penicillin. Yet the mechanism of these phenomena still remains a puzzle today. The current renewed interest in these biological symptoms of penicillin action represents, in a way, a shift in emphasis from enzymology "back" towards the more biological-observational concern of early penicillin studies. The elucidation of the mechanism of action of penicillin has emerged as a complex, multilevel task that requires the cooperation of a number of approaches. Figure 1 is intended to illustrate, in a sketchy way, this complexity and also to indicate some of the types of approaches that are being used.

After diffusing through the outermost cell boundary, represented by the cross-hatched band in Fig. 1, the β-lactam molecules seem to attach to penicillin-binding proteins (PBP), indicated as closed and open circles and solid triangles in Fig. 1. At least some of the penicillin-PBP complexes are stable enough to withstand extraction, and, by use of radioactive penicillin, they may be identified as radioactive gel electrophoretic bands. Surprisingly, bacteria seem to have multiple PBPs. In *Escherichia coli*, three of the PBPs appear to have a selective affinity, each for a different β-lactam; and the three specific physiological responses to penicillins (inhibition of cell division, abnormal shape, lysis) could be associated with the inhibition of one or the other of these binding proteins (see the contributions of Spratt and Buchanan).

It is not clear at the present time which of the PBPs correspond to the penicillin-sensitive enzymes of peptidoglycan metabolism (these are reviewed briefly by Strominger and Ghuysen). Studies on the mode of inhibition of these enzymes represent another level of the penicillin problem. The unusual degradation of penicillin (to phenylacetylglycine) is only one of the number of important recent observations made in this field (see the contributions of Ghuysen, Strominger, and Kozarich).

Penicillin treatment induces a variety of physiological effects, some of which are listed in Fig. 1. How the association of penicillin molecules with PBPs or the inhibition of peptidoglycan metabolism may lead to these effects is not understood. Recent studies on this—biological—level of the problem suggest that the irreversible antimicrobial effects (lysis and, at least partly, killing) of penicillin are indirect; they appear to be caused by the upset regulation of a murein hydrolase(s) in the penicillin-treated bacterium. Developments in this area are the discovery of bacterial penicillin tolerance and the identification of membrane teichoic acids as inhibitors of murein hydrolases and the apparent escape of those hydrolase inhibitors into the medium during penicillin treatment of the bacteria (see the contribution of Tomasz and Höltje).

It is hoped that the publication of the contributions to this seminar will further stimulate the interest of our microbiologist colleagues in the mode of action of penicillin.

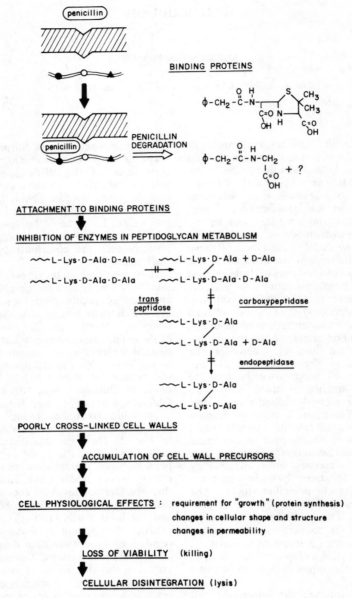

FIG. 1. *Mechanism of action of penicillin.*

How Penicillin Kills Bacteria: a Short History

JACK L. STROMINGER

Department of Biochemistry and Molecular Biology, Harvard University, Cambridge, Massachusetts 02138

It is a privilege for me to have been asked to open this meeting on the mechanisms by which penicillin kills bacteria. Penicillin was discovered by Fleming not long after the time of my birth 50 years ago, and I have spent half of my life working on the mechanism by which it kills bacterial cells. Studies of the mechanism of action of penicillin can be divided into three phases. In the earliest phase (1940–1957), efforts were made to identify the area of microbial physiology in which penicillin exerted its lethal effect. Two independent lines of study led, in 1957, to the hypothesis that penicillin was an inhibitor of bacterial cell wall synthesis and owed its selective toxicity for microbial cells to the fact that they possessed an outer envelope structure not found in animal cells. This conclusion was based both on morphological studies and on chemical studies of a uridine nucleotide which accumulated in penicillin-inhibited bacteria and of the cell wall itself (10, 12, 16).

The cell wall was, however, a recently discovered supramolecular structure whose detailed chemistry and mode of biosynthesis were entirely unknown. The second phase during the next decade was, therefore, spent in elucidating some features of the chemical structure of this gigantic macromolecule and of the mode of its biosynthesis from the uridine nucleotide precursors (15). The cell wall is assembled by a series of enzymatic reactions involving 20 to 30 enzymes. In 1965, it was deduced that penicillins were inhibiting the last step in cell wall synthesis, the cross-linking of the peptidoglycan strands of the bacterial cell wall (18, 19). This reaction was believed to be catalyzed by a transpeptidase, and it was suggested that penicillins were analogues of the natural peptidoglycan substrate, the highly reactive CO-N bond in the β-lactam ring of penicillin being the analogue of the peptide bond involved in the transpeptidation reaction (Fig. 1 and 2; 18). At that time, it was believed that all that remained to be done to complete the study of this problem was to isolate the putative transpeptidase and to study the mechanism of its inhibition by penicillin.

The transpeptidase was, in fact, soon identified in extracts of *Escherichia coli* (7), and this began the third phase of the studies of the mechanism of action of penicillin—the study of the penicillin-sensitive enzymes and the precise mechanism by which they are inhibited by penicillins. The study rapidly became more complicated. First, it was shown that not only is there a transpeptidase whose catalytic activity is inhibited by penicillins, but bacterial cells also contain a D-alanine carboxypeptidase which is penicillin sensitive (7–9). If the transpeptidase was the sole target for penicillin and if its inactivation resulted from penicilloylation of the enzyme, then the membranes of bacterial cells should contain a single protein which reacted with penicillin. Indeed, the binding of penicillin in an irreversible fashion by bacterial cells had been studied in the 1940s and related to the killing of these cells by penicillins (3). It was, therefore, a great surprise to discover that all bacterial cells which have so far been investigated contain not one, but multiple proteins which form stable penicilloyl-protein linkages (1). For example, *Staphylococcus aureus* contains four; *Bacillus subtilis*, five; and *E. coli*, six. Not only has there been a proliferation in discoveries of penicillin-binding components, but there has also been a proliferation in the identification of enzymatic activities which are catalyzed by these penicillin-binding proteins or by the penicillin-sensitive enzymes. These activities include: (i) transpeptidases (Fig. 2); (ii) D-alanine carboxypeptidases (Fig. 2); (iii) endopeptidases (Fig. 3); (iv) penicillinases (Fig. 4); and (v) another recently discovered and novel degradation of penicillins (Fig. 5).

Among these, enzymes which catalyze any of the first three reactions have been considered as possible targets for the killing site(s) of penicillins. However, some pure enzymes catalyze more than one of these reactions. For example, *E. coli* carboxypeptidase IC catalyzes both carboxypeptidase and endopeptidase activity (17); a *Streptomyces* enzyme catalyzes both carboxypeptidase and transpeptidase activities (5); and a recently described enzyme from *S.*

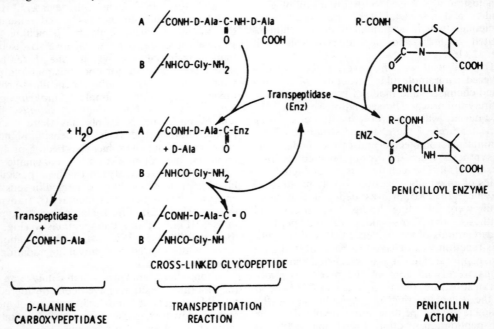

FIG. 1. *Dreiding stereomodels of penicillin (left) and of the D-alanyl-D-alanine end of the peptidoglycan strand (right). Arrows indicate the position of the CO-N bond in the β-lactam ring of penicillin and of the CO-N bond in D-alanyl-D-alanine at the end of the peptidoglycan strand. (From reference 1.)*

aureus catalyzes carboxypeptidase, transpeptidase, and penicillinase activities (Kozarich, p. 203, this volume). Which one of these is the physiological activity of the enzyme in each case? This is an extremely difficult question to answer, and, in my view, only a combination of genetic and biochemical studies can provide a definitive answer. The fourth activity, penicillinase, has in the past few decades been found to be produced in large amounts in some bacteria as a means of protection against the lethal effect of penicillin. However, penicillinases occurred in bacterial cultures which were isolated before large amounts of penicillin were produced in the environment by man. Is this activity a manifestation of a normal function of some of these enzymes in cell wall metabolism? Did the penicillinases produced in large amounts by some penicillin-resistant organisms evolve from enzymes of cell wall metabolism? The fifth enzymatic activity, a novel degradation of penicillin, is clearly the manifestation of the catalytic activity of some enzymes active in cell wall synthesis. It may provide a clue to the detailed mechanisms of these enzymes. The reaction sequence (Fig. 5) involves first the formation of a penicilloyl enzyme followed by its cleavage to phenylacetylglycine and 5,5-dimethylthiazoline carboxylate (6a). A similar cleavage of penicillin occurs in anhydrous trifluoroacetic acid. Both the chemical and enzymatic cleavages may

FIG. 2. *Proposed mechanism of transpeptidation and its relationship to penicilloylation and D-alanine carboxypeptidase activity. A represents the end of the main peptide chain of the glycan strand. B represents the end of the pentaglycine substituent from an adjacent strand. If the acyl enzyme intermediate can react with water instead of the acceptor (left), the enzyme would be regenerated and the substrate would be released. The overall reaction would be the hydrolysis of the terminal D-alanine residue of the substrate (D-alanine carboxypeptidase activity). (From reference 1)*

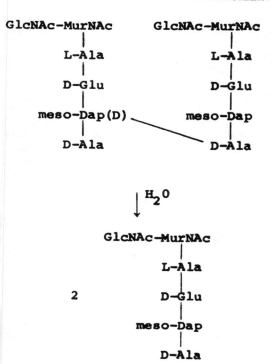

FIG. 3. *Endopeptidase reaction* (E. coli).

there are multiple killing sites for penicillins. Thus, the development of resistance to penicillin is a sequential phenomenon suggesting sequential alteration of different penicillin killing sites (2, 4). The novel penicillin mecillinam kills *E. coli* in a manner different from other β-lactam antibiotics by reacting with a penicillin-binding component (*E. coli* PBC 2) which accounts for only about 1% of the total penicillin bound, whereas other penicillins kill *E. coli* by interactions with PBCs 1 and 3 (13, 14).

Precisely how are these enzymes inhibited by penicillin? To what extent has the previously proposed mechanism (Fig. 1 and 2) been established? Are there other mechanisms of inhibition of some of these enzymes by penicillin? It has been established that the interaction of penicillin with at least some of these enzymes results in penicilloylation. Moreover, the site at which the penicilloyl residue is fixed is clearly a catalytically active site. The penicilloyl residue at this site can be enzymatically transferred to hydroxylamine (J. W. Kozarich et al., J. Biol. Chem., in press), and the novel degradation of the penicilloyl residue to phenacetylglycine and dimethylthiazoline carboxylate is enzymatically catalyzed (6). Is this site the same site as that which catalyzes the reactions of normal substrates for these enzymes? Is there, in fact, an acyl enzyme intermediate in the reaction? In the case of several of these enzymes, kinetic evidence has now been obtained that the reaction proceeds via an acyl enzyme intermediate (Fig. 2; T. Nishino, J. W. Kozarich, and J. L. Strominger, J. Biol. Chem., in press). Moreover, acyl enzymes have recently been isolated from several of these reactions (Kozarich, p. 203, this volume; Kozarich et al., Proc. 9th Rochester Conf. Environmental Toxicity, in press). Penicilloyl peptides have already been obtained by tryptic and Pronase digestion of one of the penicilloyl enzymes, and the penicilloyl residue has been shown to be substituted on a serine residue (4a). The isolation of an

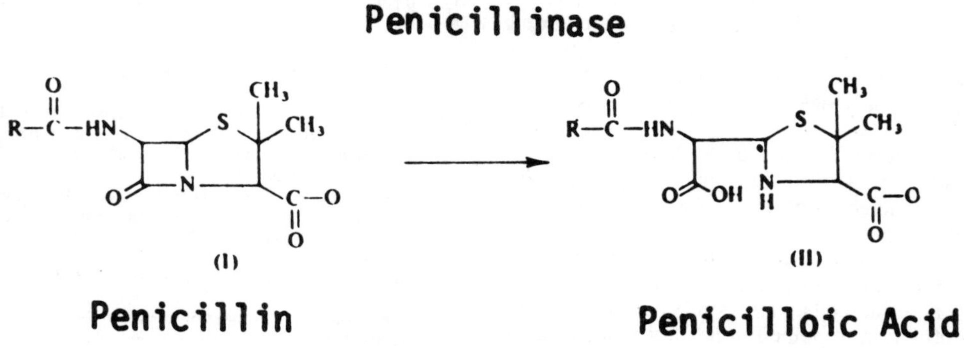

be facilitated by protonation of the thiazolidine ring nitrogen. Conceivably, this is related to the release of D-alanine from the enzyme surface in the normally catalyzed reaction. (For a discussion, see 6.)

In addition to the question of a single enzyme catalyzing several activities, there is also the problem of identification of which one, or ones, of the penicillin-binding components or penicillin-sensitive enzymes (some of the latter bind penicillins reversibly and are thus not detected as components which bind penicillin covalently) is the killing site(s). In fact, much of the presently available data leads to the conclusion that

Penicillinase

(I)

Penicillin

Penicilloic Acid

(II)

FIG. 4. *Penicillinase reaction*.

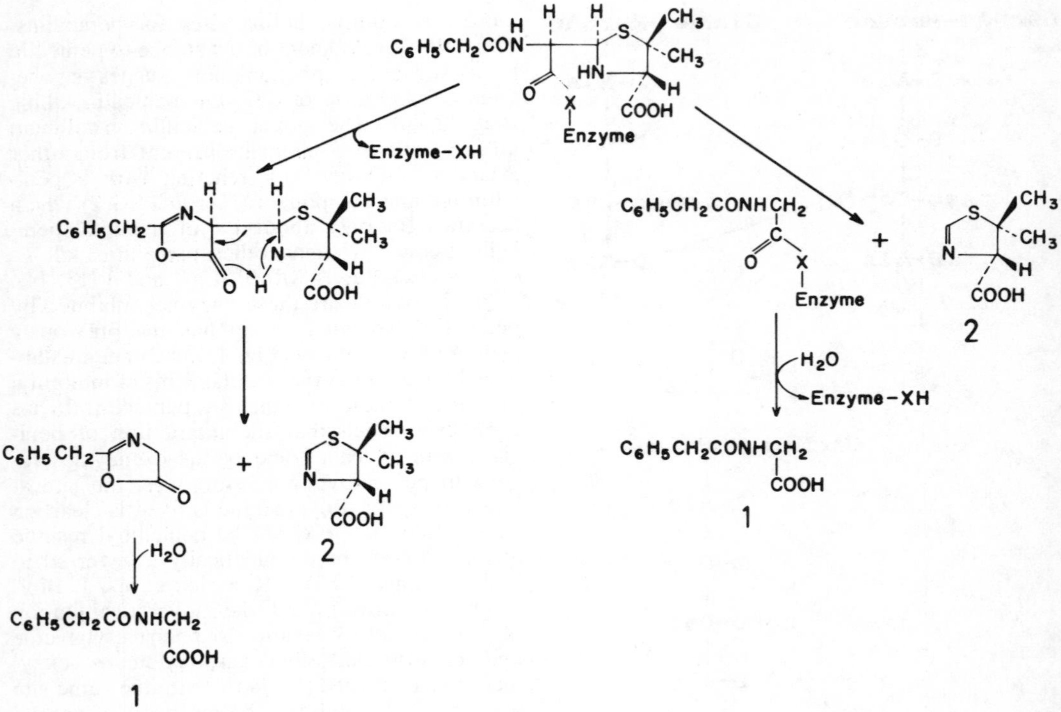

FIG. 5. *Possible mechanisms for the formation of phenylacetylglycine from benzylpenicilloyl-D-alanine carboxypeptidase. (From reference 6)*

acyl peptide would then be a major step in showing whether or not the penicilloyl residue and acyl residue are fixed at the same catalytic site. An alternative proposal has been suggested, namely, that penicillin acts at an allosteric site rather than at the catalytic site (11). Although no compelling evidence in support of this conclusion has been presented, it of course remains possible that different penicillin-sensitive enzymes are inhibited by different mechanisms, and a great deal more work in this area is required. Indeed, a definitive answer might only come from the elucidation of the total structure of a penicillin-sensitive enzyme, for example by X-ray crystallography, and the location of the penicilloyl and acyl residues within that structure. That goal certainly now seems within reach.

Thus, nearly 50 years after Fleming first made his monumental discovery of a small molecule that was selectively toxic for bacterial cells, which has provided the greatest advance in the treatment of illness in the history of mankind, we still do not know precisely how this molecule kills bacterial cells. The study of the mechanism of action of penicillin has led to knowledge of previously unknown aspects of microbial physiology and has been as exciting to microbiologists as the therapeutic use of penicillin has been to physicians. The elucidation of the functions of the different penicillin-binding components and penicillin-sensitive enzymes and studies of their precise mode of inhibition during the next decade should provide an equally challenging period in this work.

ACKNOWLEDGMENTS

This work was supported by National Science Foundation grant PCM 71-01120 and by Public Health Service grant AI 09152 from the National Institute of Allergy and Infectious Diseases.

LITERATURE CITED

1. **Blumberg, P. M., and J. L. Strominger.** 1974. Interaction of penicillin with the bacterial cell: penicillin-binding proteins and penicillin-sensitive enzymes. Bacteriol. Rev. **38**:291–335.
2. **Buchanan, C. E., and J. L. Strominger.** 1976. Altered penicillin binding components in penicillin resistant mutants of *Bacillus subtilis*. Proc. Natl. Acad. Sci. U.S.A. **73**:1816–1820.
3. **Cooper, P. D.** 1956. Site of action of radiopenicillin. Bacteriol. Rev. **20**:28–48.
4. **Demerec, M.** 1945. Production of *Staphylococcus* strains resistant to various concentrations of penicillin. Proc. Natl. Acad. Sci. U.S.A. **31**:16–24.

4a. **Georgapapadakou, N., S. Hammerström, and J. L. Strominger.** 1977. Isolation of the penicillin-binding peptide from D-alanine carboxypeptidase of *Bacillus subtilis*. Proc. Natl. Acad. Sci. U.S.A. **74**:1009–1012.

5. **Ghuysen, J.-M., M. Leyh-Bouille, J. M. Frere, J. Dusart, A. Marquet, H. R. Perkins, and M. Nieto.** 1974. The penicillin receptor in *Streptomyces*. Ann. N.Y. Acad. Sci. **235**:236–268.

6. **Hammarström, S., and J. L. Strominger.** 1975. Degradation of penicillin G to phenylacetylglycine by D-alanine carboxypeptidase from *Bacillus stearothermophilus*. Proc. Natl. Acad. Sci. U.S.A. **72**:3463–3467.

6a. **Hammerström, S., and J. L. Strominger.** 1976. Formation of 5,5-dimethyl-Δ^2-thiazoline-4-carboxylic acid during cleavage of penicillin G by D-alanine carboxypeptidase from *Bacillus stearothermophilus*. J. Biol. Chem. **251**:7947–7949.

7. **Izaki, K., M. Matsuhashi, and J. L. Strominger.** 1966. Glycopeptide transpeptidase and D-alanine carboxypeptidase: penicillin-sensitive enzymatic reactions. Proc. Natl. Acad. Sci. U.S.A. **55**:656–663.

8. **Izaki, K., and J. L. Strominger.** 1968. Biosynthesis of the peptidoglycan of bacterial cell walls. XIII. Peptidoglycan transpeptidase and D-alanine carboxypeptidase: penicillin-sensitive enzymatic reaction in strains of *Escherichia coli*. J. Biol. Chem. **243**:3180–3192.

9. **Izaki, K., and J. L. Strominger.** 1968. Biosynthesis of the peptidoglycan of bacterial cell walls. XIV. Purification and properties of two D-alanine carboxypeptidases from *Escherichia coli*. J. Biol. Chem. **243**: 3193–3201.

10. **Lederberg, J.** 1956. Bacterial protoplasts induced by penicillin. Proc. Natl. Acad. Sci. U.S.A. **42**:574–577.

11. **Leyh-Bouille, M., J.-M. Ghuysen, M. Nieto, H. R. Perkins,** K. H. Schleifer, and O. Kandler. 1970. On the *Streptomyces albus* G DD-carboxypeptidase mechanism of action of penicillin, vancomycin and ristocetin. Biochemistry **9**:2971–2975.

12. **Park, J. T., and J. L. Strominger.** 1957. Mode of action of penicillin. Biochemical basis for the mechanism of action of penicillin and for its selective toxicity. Science **125**:99–101.

13. **Spratt, B. G.** 1975. Distinct penicillin binding proteins involved in the division, elongation, and shape of *Escherichia coli* K12. Proc. Natl. Acad. Sci. U.S.A. **72**:2999–3003.

14. **Spratt, B. G., and A. B. Pardee.** 1975. Penicillin-binding proteins and cell shape in *E. coli*. Nature (London) **254**:516–517.

15. **Strominger, J. L.** 1970. Penicillin-sensitive enzymatic reactions in bacterial cell wall synthesis. Harvey Lect. **64**:179–213.

16. **Strominger, J. L., J. T. Park, and R. E. Thompson.** 1959. Composition of the cell wall of *Staphylococcus aureus*: its relation to the mechanism of action of penicillin. J. Biol. Chem. **234**:3263–3268.

17. **Tamura, R., Y. Imae, and J. L. Strominger.** 1976. Purification to homogeneity and properties of two D-alanine carboxypeptidases I from *Escherichia coli*. J. Biol. Chem. **251**:414–423.

18. **Tipper, D. J., and J. L. Strominger.** 1965. Mechanism of action of penicillins: a proposal based on their structural similarity to acyl-D-alanyl-D-alanine. Proc. Natl. Acad. Sci. U.S.A. **54**:1133–1141.

19. **Wise, E. M., and J. T. Park.** 1965. Penicillin: its basic site of action as an inhibitor of a peptide cross-linking reaction in cell wall mucopeptide synthesis. Proc. Natl. Acad. Sci. U.S.A. **54**:75–81.

Penicillin-Binding Proteins of *Escherichia coli*: General Properties and Characterization of Mutants

BRIAN G. SPRATT

Department of Genetics, University of Leicester, Leicester, LE1 7RH, England

INTRODUCTION

In 1965, penicillin was shown to inhibit the transpeptidation of neighboring pentapeptide side chains of the bacterial peptidoglycan (26, 28). Attempts to study the transpeptidation reaction in an *Escherichia coli* in vitro system led to the identification of two further penicillin-sensitive activities, peptidoglycan endopeptidase and D-alanine carboxypeptidase 1 (1, 4, 11). Recently, progress in the purification of these enzymes has resulted in the realization that *E. coli* contains several distinct forms of transpeptidases, endopeptidases, and carboxypeptidases and that a single enzyme can catalyze more than one of the above reactions (16, 25).

The complexity of the penicillin-sensitive enzymes (PSEs) is paralleled by that of the physiological responses of *E. coli* to β-lactam antibiotics (penicillins and cephalosporins). Different β-lactams, or different concentrations of the same β-lactam, can produce morphological effects which can be classified into four basic types (Fig. 1). It is extremely unlikely, a priori, that these four responses are caused by the inhibition of a single enzyme, and it has been suggested that there are several PSEs which have discrete functions in the synthesis and organization of the peptidoglycan during cell growth and division (3, 7, 8, 16, 20, 21). The identification of which PSE is responsible for each of the physiological responses, and a description of their role in cell growth, is a major aim of current research.

To be able to achieve this aim, we must have a convenient method for studying individual PSEs and preferably one which permits the screening of relatively large numbers of mutants for defects in these enzymes. The fractionation of the individual PSEs is far too laborious for this purpose, and fortunately a more satisfactory method is available. This depends on the knowledge that penicillins bind covalently to the enzymes that they inhibit so that the PSEs can be detected as those proteins which are labeled with [14C]benzylpenicillin (3, 24). These penicillin-binding proteins (PBPs) can be studied readily in crude cell envelope preparations, and mutants with altered PBPs can be detected.

In this article the progress in the identification of the role of the *E. coli* PBPs in the mechanisms of action of β-lactam antibiotics is reviewed.

METHODOLOGY

The methods for the detection and study of the *E. coli* PBPs are presented elsewhere (22a), and only basic details of methodology will be given here.

PBPs are detected as those proteins which bind [14C]benzylpenicillin. Washed cell envelopes (consisting of inner and outer membranes and peptidoglycan) are incubated with [14C]benzylpenicillin, and binding is terminated by the addition of excess unlabeled benzylpenicillin and Sarkosyl NL-97. Addition of the anionic detergent Sarkosyl is important as it denatures the PBPs and prevents the enzymatic release of bound penicillin (see below). It also selectively solubilizes the inner membrane proteins, and these are fractionated on a 10% sodium dodecyl sulfate-polyacrylamide slab gel; the PBPs, which are labeled with [14C]benzylpenicillin, are detected by scintillation autoradiography on X-ray film and can be quantitated by microdensitometry. Fortunately, the penicilloyl-protein linkage is stable throughout these procedures. Binding of other [14C]β-lactams can be measured in a similar way. An estimate of the rate of binding of nonradioactive β-lactams can be obtained by measuring their competition for the binding of [14C]benzylpenicillin to each of the PBPs. The limitations of these latter measurements are discussed elsewhere (22a).

The most satisfactory method of understanding the role of each PBP in cell growth is to isolate mutants which produce an abnormally thermolabile form of the PBP and observe the effects this has on the morphology of the mutant, or on the structure of the peptidoglycan. In practice, temperature-sensitive mutants are

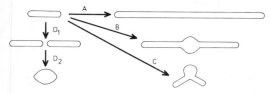

FIG. 1. *Morphological responses of* E. coli *to β-lactam antibiotics. (A) Inhibition of cell division and formation of a filament. (B) Bulge formation. (C) Inhibition of cell elongation, lysis, and extrusion of a spheroplast. (D) Formation of osmotically stable ovoid cell.*

screened for thermolabile PBPs (with this procedure mutants are not likely to be obtained in PBPs which are inessential for cell growth). Envelopes are prepared from cells grown at the permissive temperature (30°C), and the thermostability of the PBPs is measured, in vitro, by comparing the binding of [^{14}C]benzylpenicillin at 30°C with that at 42°C.

PROPERTIES OF PBPs

The PBPs of *E. coli* are located in the inner (cytoplasmic) membrane (22a). No binding of any β-lactam to the outer membrane has been detected (21, 22a). The location of the PBPs is that expected for enzymes involved in the terminal stages of peptidoglycan metabolism. [^{14}C]benzylpenicillin apparently labels all the receptors which bind β-lactams, since no additional PBPs have been detected with ^{14}C-labeled mecillinam, cefoxitin, or cephacetrile (21, 22a). These latter [^{14}C]β-lactams bind to some, or all, of those proteins which bind [^{14}C]benzylpenicillin. All the PBPs are accessible to [^{14}C]benzylpenicillin in whole cells and have been detected in all *E. coli* strains that have been examined, under all growth conditions (22a).

Table 1 gives the apparent molecular weights, the relative abundance, and an estimate of the number of molecules of each PBP per *E. coli* cell.

TABLE 1. *Molecular weights and relative abundance of penicillin-binding proteins (PBPs)*[a]

PBP	Apparent mol wt	Percentage of total binding	No. of molecules of each protein per cell
1	91,000	8.1	230
2	66,000	0.7	20
3	60,000	1.9	50
4	49,000	4.0	110
5	42,000	64.7	1,800
6	40,000	20.6	570

[a] From reference 22a.

cell. Figure 2A shows the pattern of PBPs on a scintillation autoradiograph of a sodium dodecyl sulfate-polyacrylamide slab gel. Six PBPs are invariably detected, and two further PBPs, with molecular weights of 29,000 and 32,000, are sometimes observed (these are designated PBPs 7 and 8 in some figures). PBP 7 is particularly prominent in *E. coli* B/r (see Fig. 7 and 8). Other minor radioactive bands on the gels are irreproducibly obtained and may be proteolytic products of the PBPs.

A comparison of the pattern of the inner membrane proteins, revealed by staining with Coomassie blue, with that of the radioactive bands obtained by autoradiography after [^{14}C]-benzylpenicillin binding, allows the identification of the major PBPs 5 and 6 as minor proteins of this membrane (24). PBPs 1–4 are very minor components of the inner membrane and cannot be identified as stained bands.

Binding of penicillin to PBPs is thought to occur via the mechanism (6):

$$E + P \underset{}{\overset{K}{\rightleftharpoons}} (EP) \overset{k_3}{\to} EP^* \overset{k_4}{\to} E + X$$

Penicillin binds to enzyme (i.e., PBP) to form the reversible complex which can be converted to the penicilloylated enzyme, EP^*. The PBP assay measures the level of EP^*. The latter can regenerate free enzyme and penicillin degradation product(s), X. The k_4 values for different β-lactams, and for different enzymes, are highly variable (6, 22a). A measure of k_4 can be obtained by following the loss of bound [^{14}C]benzylpenicillin from the PBPs. The half-time of release of benzylpenicillin at 30°C in 50 mM phosphate buffer, pH 7.0, was 5 and 19 min, respectively, for PBPs 5 and 6, but much slower for the other PBPs (Fig. 2A–F). Release was stimulated by 2-mercaptoethanol (Fig. 2G–L) and neutral hydroxylamine and was enzymatic; e.g., under nondenaturing conditions all the bound penicillin could be released from PBPs 5 and 6 by 0.14 M 2-mercaptoethanol within 10 min at 30°C, but after denaturation in anionic detergent no loss of penicillin could be detected in samples heated for 3 min in 1.5 M 2-mercaptoethanol at 100°C (22a).

The PBPs should correspond to penicillin-sensitive enzymes. Two distinct D-alanine carboxypeptidases 1 have been purified from *E. coli* (16, 25). Although both are inhibited by penicillin, one of them apparently does not bind penicillin and would not be detected as a PBP; the other, D-alanine carboxypeptidase 1A, also exhibits peptidoglycan transpeptidase activity and forms a doublet on sodium dodecyl sulfate-polyacrylamide gels (25). The two com-

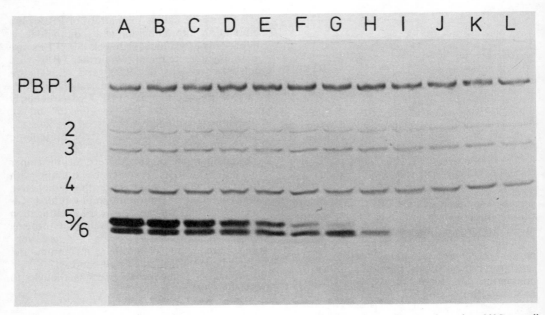

FIG. 2. *Detection of PBPs and release of bound penicillin.* [14C]*benzylpenicillin was bound at 30°C to cell envelopes of KN126 until all PBPs were saturated. A 1,000-fold excess of unlabeled benzylpenicillin was added, and samples were removed into Sarkosyl immediately (A) and after 5 (B), 10 (C), 15 (D), 20 (E), and 30 (F) min of continued incubation at 30°C. Samples were also taken at 0 (G), 5 (H), 10 (I), 15 (J), 20 (K), and 30 (L) min during continued incubation at 30°C in the presence of 0.14 M 2-mercaptoethanol. Samples were applied to a sodium dodecyl sulfate-polyacrylamide slab gel, and the amount of* [14C]*benzylpenicillin remaining bound to each PBP was detected on a scintillation autoradiograph.*

ponents of the doublet have been shown to be identical to PBPs 5 and 6, but it remains to be seen whether one component has exclusively carboxypeptidase activity and the other transpeptidase, or whether each component has both activities (24). It is also not known whether they are distinct polypeptides or only differ by a minor modification of the same polypeptide. They do differ significantly in their k_4 values, and the ratio of PBP 5 to PBP 6 activity varies with the growth conditions; e.g., it is high in actively growing cells but low in stationary-phase cells (unpublished data).

A

B

FIG. 3. *Structures of (A) mecillinam and (B) benzylpenicillin.*

The minor PBPs 1–4 presumably correspond to minor PSEs, and these have yet to be purified.

FUNCTIONS OF PBPs

PBPs and Cell Shape

Growth of *E. coli* in the presence of mecillinam (an amidinopenicillanic acid, Fig. 3A) prevents normal rod-shaped growth (8, 12–14, 17, 22). With *E. coli* KN126, concentrations from 0.05 μg/ml up to at least 200 μg/ml had no effect on cell division for about 40 min at 37°C, but then division ceased while growth continued, and the cells were converted into large osmotically stable ovoid or round forms (22; Fig. 1D). Mecillinam was remarkably specific in its effect on cell shape, and none of the other morphological responses produced by β-lactams (Fig. 1A–C) was observed within the above concentration range. This suggested that mecillinam had a high affinity for a PSE which was required for normal rod-shaped growth of the peptidoglycan and that this enzyme might be detected as a PBP.

The binding of mecillinam to the *E. coli* PBPs was measured by its competition for the

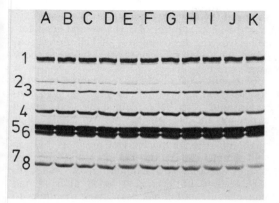

FIG. 4. *Competition of an amidinopenicillanic acid for the binding of* [^{14}C]*benzylpenicillin. The following concentrations of amidinopenicillanic acid were prebound to envelopes of* E. coli *KN126 for 10 min at 30°C, and the residual binding of* [^{14}C]*benzylpenicillin to each of the PBPs was measured: (A) none, (B) 0.0024 μg/ml, (C–K) threefold increasing concentrations up to (K) 47.6 μg/ml. (From reference 22, where further details can be found)*

binding of [^{14}C]benzylpenicillin (23). Only PBP 2 showed competition, and the concentration of mecillinam required to obtain 50% reduction of [^{14}C]benzylpenicillin binding to this protein was almost identical to the minimal inhibitory concentration. Figure 4 shows the competition of

another amidinopenicillanic acid (a morpholino derivative of mecillinam; 22) which, like mecillinam, produces osmotically stable round cells and competes strongly for PBP 2. Mecillinam clearly bound to PBP 2 but apparently not to the other PBPs. However, it was possible that mecillinam bound to other proteins which did not bind benzylpenicillin. Studies with [^{14}C]-mecillinam showed that this was not the case and have confirmed that this derivative binds exclusively to PBP 2 (21, 22; Fig. 5E, F).

The role of this PBP in the regulation of cell shape and in the antibacterial action of mecillinam has been strengthened by the isolation of two types of mutants with altered PBPs 2. The first class of mutants was isolated as resistant to mecillinam; some of these mutants should be resistant because they produce a PBP 2 which no longer recognizes mecillinam. One such mutant (SP 6, previously called B6; 21) has been studied in detail and shown to fail to bind either [^{14}C]mecillinam or [^{14}C]benzyl-penicillin to PBP 2 (21; Fig. 5). This mutant grows slowly as round cells (in the absence of mecillinam) and presumably produces a PBP 2 which not only fails to bind β-lactam antibiotics but also functions extremely poorly in its enzymological role. A revertant of SP 6 has been obtained which regained the normal rod shape at the same time that it regained sensitivity to mecillinam and the ability to bind [^{14}C]mecillinam and [^{14}C]benzylpenicillin (21).

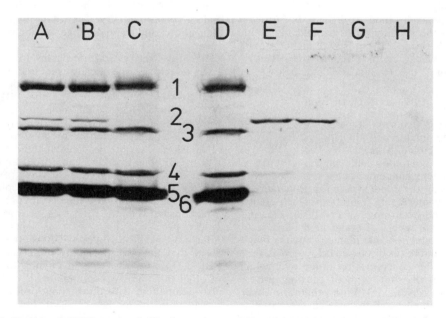

FIG. 5. *Binding of* [^{14}C]*benzylpenicillin to envelopes of* E. coli *KN126 at (A) 30 and (B) 42°C and to SP 6 at (C) 30 and (D) 42°C. Binding of* [^{14}C]*mecillinam to KN126 at (E) 30 and (F) 42°C and to SP 6 at (G) 30 and (H) 42°C. (From reference 21, where further details can be found)*

The rationale behind the isolation of the second class of PBP 2 mutants was the following. Mutants which produce an abnormally thermolabile form of this PBP should grow as rods at 30°C but become converted to osmotically stable round cells at 42°C. We isolated such mutants (designated rod^-) and measured the thermostability of their PBPs. One of these mutants, SP 137, failed to bind [^{14}C]benzylpenicillin to PBP 2 at 30 or 42°C under the normal assay conditions. Since SP 137 was still sensitive to mecillinam at 30°C, it was likely that PBP 2 still bound β-lactams in vivo at this temperature, but that the protein was highly thermolabile and was inactivated during cell envelope preparation. Recently, we have been able to show binding of [^{14}C]benzylpenicillin to PBP 2 at 30°C, but not at 42°C, by taking extra precautions to prevent the inactivation of this protein during envelope preparation (unpublished data). SP 137 therefore has a demonstrably thermolabile PBP 2 and presumably has a missense mutation in the structural gene for this protein.

The temperature-sensitive rod^- mutant studied by Henning et al. (9) has also been shown to have an altered PBP 2 (unpublished data). This mutant maps at 14 min on the E. coli linkage map (2, 9); SP 6 (M. Iwaya, personal communication), SP 137 (unpublished data), and one other rod^- mutant (15), whose PBPs have not been studied, also map in this region and are all presumably allelic.

Benzylpenicillin binds to PBP 2, but it never results in the production of osmotically stable round cells because it binds with higher affinity to PBPs which are involved in the other responses of E. coli to β-lactams (see below).

PBPs and Cell Division

The great majority of penicillins and cephalosporins inhibit cell division at the lowest effective concentrations (7, 20, 21). Cell elongation continues and, in the absence of septation, long filamentous cells are formed (Fig. 1A). Raising the concentration of β-lactams results in an increasing inhibition of cell elongation and the occurrence of cell lysis (Fig. 1C). (Intermediate levels of some penicillins result in the production of filaments with bulges [Fig. 1B], and this is discussed below.) With some β-lactams the concentration range over which they inhibit division, without causing lysis, is large (e.g., cephalexin). With others, however, it is much smaller and in some cases zero; e.g., the lowest concentration of cephaloridine that produces any morphological response in E. coli KN126 or B/r results in cell lysis, and no fila-

ments are seen at any concentration. Cephalexin was the best inhibitor of division, and cephaloridine was the best inhibitor of cell elongation. Most β-lactams have properties between these two extremes (21).

The ability of β-lactams to inhibit division at low concentrations, and elongation at high concentrations, can be explained by two general types of model. In the first of these it is argued that only one PSE is involved, and that slight inhibition of this enzyme prevents division and complete inhibition prevents elongation. The suggestion that slight inhibition of wall synthesis could preferentially block division and cause filamentation has been made by others to explain the inhibition of division when DNA synthesis is prevented (18). A further possibility is that the enzyme located at the septal region is particularly susceptible to inhibition because of increased permeability to penicillin at this region. These types of explanation are difficult to reconcile with the fact that derivatives like cephaloridine have no preferential effect on division at any concentration, whereas cephalexin inhibits division over a wide concentration range. The second, and much more satisfactory, explanation is that inhibition of cell division and inhibition of cell elongation are caused by the inactivation of different PSEs which have distinct roles in peptidoglycan metabolism for these processes (3, 16, 20, 21). Cephalexin would then be predicted to have a high affinity for the enzyme involved in division and a lower affinity for that involved in elongation, and cephaloridine would have the reverse relative affinities.

We have used several approaches to identify a PSE which is specifically required for the division of E. coli. Our initial assumption was that this enzyme was one of the PBPs and that we could obtain some indication of which were the likely candidates by studying the binding of β-lactams which were good inhibitors of division. One of the clearest indications of which PBP was involved came from an experiment in which E. coli KN126 was grown for 15 min at 37°C in the presence of cephalexin and benzylpenicillin, and the distribution of the β-lactams between the PBPs was measured (21). Under precisely the conditions where these β-lactams specifically inhibited division we could show that they were binding preferentially to PBP 3 (Fig. 6). The rate of binding to PBP 3 of other β-lactams which inhibited division was also compatible with the binding protein being involved in this effect (21, 22a), but the most convincing data have been obtained by the isolation of mutants which produce thermolabile PBPs 3.

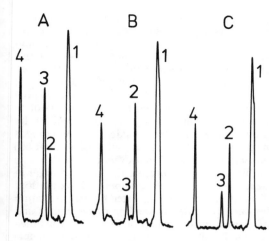

A   B   C

FIG. 6. *Level of PBPs 1–4 after growth in low concentrations of cephalexin and benzylpenicillin. (A) Control cells; (B and C) cells grown for 15 min at 37°C in the presence of 10 μg of cephalexin per ml (B) or 12 μg of benzylpenicillin/ml (C). The level of [¹⁴C]benzylpenicillin bound to the PBPs was quantitated by microdensitometry. The levels of PBPs 5 and 6 were similar under all three conditions and are not shown. (From reference 21, where experimental details can be found)*

Mutants which produce an abnormally thermolabile form of PBP 3 should grow as rods at 30°C but become converted to long filaments on shifting to 42°C (in the absence of any β-lactam); i.e., they will be temperature-sensitive cell division mutants. We have measured the thermostability of the PBPs in 24 temperature-sensitive cell division mutants that we isolated from *E. coli* KN 126 and *E. coli* B/r and in 7 further mutants obtained from other laboratories. None of the latter mutants (which included *fts* A–F [19] and *fts* H [10] mutants) had altered PBPs, but two of the former class had PBPs which were markedly thermolabile.

Mutant SP 63 (previously called 6-30; 21) was isolated from strain KN126; envelopes of the mutant, prepared from cells grown at the permissive temperature, showed a reduced level of [¹⁴C]benzylpenicillin binding to PBP 3 when assayed at 30°C and rapidly lost this binding activity when incubated at 42°C (21). None of the other PBPs was altered, and revertants of SP 63, which grow as normal rods at 42°C, regained the normal level and thermostability of PBP 3 (B. G. Spratt, submitted for publication).

Figure 7 shows the PBPs of a second mutant (SP 25) which was isolated from *E. coli* B/r. All the PBPs of the parent strain were stable at 42°C, but binding of [¹⁴C]benzylpenicillin to

PBP 3 of the mutant was low at 30°C and was rapidly lost at 42°C. SP 25 was isolated, after mutagenesis with nitrosoguanidine, as a mutant which formed filaments at 42°C and then lysed. At first sight the inhibition of cell division and lysis in a strain with a thermolabile PBP 3 would seem to be evidence for a role of this protein in both division and lysis. However, SP 25 is a double mutant since no revertants have been obtained which form colonies on nutrient agar at 42°C (reversion frequency of $<1:10^9$). Mutants which produce thermolabile proteins are almost invariably point mutations and therefore should revert readily. We could separate the lysis defect from the division defect and obtain a derivative (SP 258) which formed long filaments at 42°C but did not lyse. SP 258 now readily produces revertants which form colonies at 42°C on nutrient agar (strains SP 2581 and 2582).

Figure 8 shows that SP 258 still has a thermolabile PBP 3, although it no longer lyses at 42°C, whereas the complete revertants (SP 2581

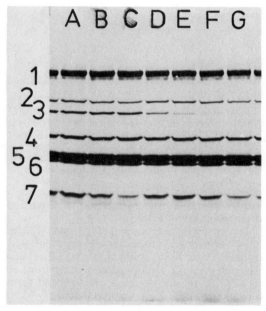

FIG. 7. *Thermolability of PBP 3 in mutant SP 25. Envelopes of E. coli B/r and SP 25 were prepared from cells grown at 30°C. [¹⁴C]benzylpenicillin binding to envelopes of B/r was measured at 30°C (A) and at 42°C after 4 min (B) and 8 min (C) of preincubation at this temperature. Binding to envelopes of SP 25 was measured at 30°C (D) and at 42°C after 0 min (E), 4 min (F), and 8 min (G) of preincubation at this temperature. Membrane proteins were fractionated, and the level of radioactivity bound to each PBP was measured by scintillation autoradiography. (From B. G. Spratt, submitted for publication)*

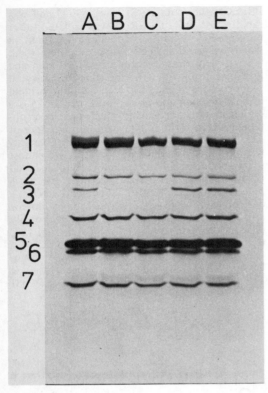

FIG. 8. *PBPs of revertants of strain SP 25. Envelopes were prepared from cells grown at 30°C. [¹⁴C]benzylpenicillin binding to envelopes of SP 25 was measured at 30°C (A). Binding to envelopes of SP 25 (B), SP 258 (C), SP 2581 (D), and SP 2582 (E) was measured at 42°C after 8 min of preincubation at this temperature. (From B. G. Spratt, submitted for publication)*

and 2582) have regained the normal level and thermostability of PBP 3.

The two PBP 3 mutants (SP 63 and SP 258) have very similar properties although one was isolated in a K-12 strain and the other was isolated in a B/r strain. After a shift from 30 to 42°C, both strains cease dividing and form long filaments.

The isolation of revertants which have regained the ability to grow as rods at 42°C at the same time at which they regained the normal thermostability of PBP 3 is very strong evidence that the defect in PBP 3 is the cause of the inhibition of cell division in these mutants. Presumably, PBP 3 is the target at which penicillins and cephalosporins bind to cause filamentation.

PBPs and Cell Elongation and Lysis

High concentrations of essentially all penicillins and cephalosporins inhibit cell elongation and cause cell lysis. At these concentrations they probably inhibit the incorporation of new precursors into the cell wall and thereby prevent all envelope growth. Inhibition of cell elongation should be distinguished from cell lysis; the latter is likely to be a secondary result of the continued action, or activation, of hydrolytic enzymes when wall growth is disturbed (6a, 20, 27). Lysis can be dissociated from the effects of β-lactams on shape, division, and elongation by growth at low pH (6a). Under these conditions high concentrations of the antibiotics inhibit cell elongation in *E. coli*, but do not cause lysis.

PBP 1 has been proposed to be the target at which β-lactams bind to inhibit cell elongation. This attribution was suggested by the correlation between the rates of binding of penicillins and cephalosporins to this protein and their abilities to inhibit cell elongation (21, 22, 22a). Attempts to isolate mutants which produce a thermolabile PBP 1 so far have been unsuccessful.

The enzymes involved in cell lysis may themselves be penicillin sensitive; e.g., peptidoglycan endopeptidases are potentially lytic enzymes (although it is not known whether they act this way in vivo) and are inhibited by β-lactam antibiotics. If this were the case, the extent of lysis with some β-lactams might decrease with increasing concentrations of antibiotics; similarly, inhibition of a D-alanine carboxypeptidase 1 could lead to decreased lysis due to increased levels of peptidoglycan cross-linking and the production of a cell wall that was more resistant to degradation. We have found one cephalosporin that gives increasing amounts of lysis as the concentration is raised, but on continuing to raise it the extent of lysis begins to decrease markedly (unpublished data). Such effects could involve PBPs 4, 5, and 6, or D-alanine carboxypeptidase 1B, for which no roles have yet been ascribed.

PBPs and Penicillin Bulges

Bulge formation (Fig. 1B) is not a universal response of *E. coli* to growth in the presence of β-lactam antibiotics (7, 21). Strain KN126 formed large bulges with ampicillin and closely related derivatives (e.g., amoxycillin), but most other penicillins, and all cephalosporins that we tested, failed to produce this effect at any concentration (21; unpublished data).

There are several reasons to believe that bulge formation is due to the combined effects of the inhibition of PBPs 2 and 3. Division continues, and normal rod-shaped daughter cells are produced during the first 40 min of growth in the presence of mecillinam (inhibition of PBP 2); then each daughter cell starts to become round (12, 17, 22). If cell division were also inhibited (PBP 3), the initial rod-shaped growth would result in a short filament, within which the rounded growth would occur at the region(s) of active wall synthesis. The end result would be a filament with bulges. On this model a β-lactam which formed filaments would also produce bulges, if it bound to PBP 2 at concentrations below those at which lysis occurred. Studies on the rates of binding of penicillins and cephalosporins to the PBPs were compatible with this model. The cephalosporins, which never gave bulges, failed to bind or bound very poorly to PBP 2, whereas those penicillins which gave bulges bound strongly to this protein (21). Further support for this interpretation comes from the simulation of penicillin bulges by conditions which are assumed to specifically suppress the activities of PBPs 2 and 3. The addition of mecillinam (which binds specifically to PBP 2) together with cephalexin (which binds preferentially to PBP 3) gave short filaments with bulges which were similar to those produced by ampicillin (21). Also, the addition of cephalexin to the mutant SP 137 (which has a thermolabile PBP 2) at 30°C gave filaments with bulges. At 25°C SP 137 grew as normal rods, but at 30°C cells were slightly rounded rods. This implies that the thermolabile PBP 2 was partially inactivated even at 30°C and that the addition of cephalexin also inactivated PBP 3 to result in the production of filaments with bulges.

DISCUSSION

The main aim of our work is to identify the targets with which β-lactam antibiotics interact to inhibit the growth of *E. coli*. It is hoped that the identification and eventual purification of these targets will aid in the development of new and more potent penicillins and cephalosporins. These antibiotics are also of interest as inhibitors of bacterial cell shape and division; PBPs 2 and 3 are presumably enzymes which are specifically required for the maintenance of cell shape and for division, respectively, and their study should increase our knowledge of these processes.

Table 2 summarizes our ideas about the involvement of the PBPs in the morphological responses of *E. coli* to β-lactam antibiotics. The evidence that PBP 2 is the target at which mecillinam binds to convert *E. coli* rods into osmotically stable round cells is extremely strong. There is also very strong evidence for the assignment of PBP 3 as the target at which β-lactams bind to inhibit cell division. The most direct and unambiguous method for identifying the role of PBPs in the physiological effects of β-lactam antibiotics is the isolation of temperature-sensitive mutants which produce thermolabile PBPs. The demonstration that revertants which grow normally at the restrictive temperature have regained the normal thermostability of the PBP is almost incontrovertible evidence for a causal role of the altered PBP in the temperature-sensitive phenotype. Although this kind of evidence has been obtained for the involvement of PBPs 2 and 3 in cell shape and cell division, respectively, it has not been obtained for the role of PBP 1 in cell elongation. The latter assignment, therefore, remains speculative and rests on correlations between the concentrations of β-lactams which inhibit cell elongation and those which 50% saturate PBP 1 (21, 22, 22a). The characterization of a temperature-sensitive mutant which stopped elongating and lysed at the restrictive temperature and which produced a thermolabile PBP 1 is the critical test of the function of this PBP.

Efforts are now required to purify the minor PBPs and to examine them for transpeptidase, endopeptidase, and carboxypeptidase activity. Most PSEs show more than one of these activities (3, 16, 25), and if this is the case for the minor PBPs it will be extremely difficult to decide which of these activities is active under in vivo conditions.

It has been suggested (3, 5, 12) that mecillinam may inhibit cross-linking of lipoprotein to peptidoglycan, but attempts to show such inhibition have failed (5; R. James, personal communication). Although PBP 2 may catalyze

TABLE 2. *Effects of β-lactam antibiotics on growth of* E. coli *predicted by their relative affinities for penicillin-binding proteins*[a]

Relative affinities of PBPs 1, 2, and 3 for a β-lactam antibiotic[b]	Morphological effects produced by three arbitrary concentrations of a β-lactam antibiotic			β-Lactam showing this behavior
	Low concn	Medium concn	High concn	
1 > 2 or 3	Lysis	Lysis	Lysis	Cephaloridine
2 > 1 > 3	Ovoid cells	Lysis	Lysis	6-Aminopenicillanic acid
2 > 3 > 1	Ovoid cells	Filaments with bulges	Lysis	None known
2 ≫ 1 or 3	Ovoid cells	Ovoid cells	Ovoid cells	Mecillinam
3 > 1 > 2	Filaments	Lysis	Lysis	Benzylpenicillin
3 > 2 > 1	Filaments	Filaments with bulges	Lysis	Ampicillin

[a] From reference 21.
[b] PBP 1 = cell elongation; PBP 2 = cell shape; PBP 3 = cell division.

a novel reaction in peptidoglycan metabolism, the failure of mecillinam to inhibit markedly total transpeptidase, endopeptidase, or carboxypeptidase activities (14, 17) is still compatible with this protein being a minor species of one of these enzymes.

The functions of PBPs 4, 5, and 6 are unclear. Recently, PBP 4 has been shown to correspond to a PSE, and a mutant has been isolated which lacks this activity (M. Matsuhashi et al., in press). Since this mutant grows normally under all the conditions examined, it appears that PBP 4 does not have a major function in cell growth or in the responses of E. coli to β-lactam antibiotics. Similarly, D-alanine carboxypeptidases 1A (PBPs 5 and 6) and 1B have not been implicated in the effects of β-lactams on cell growth. They may have subtle functions in the regulation of peptidoglycan metabolism, but at present no roles can be ascribed to them.

ACKNOWLEDGMENT

This work was supported by a project grant from the Medical Research Council of Great Britain.

LITERATURE CITED

1. **Araki, Y., A. Shimada, and E. Ito.** 1966. Effect of penicillin on cell wall mucopeptide synthesis in an *Escherichia coli* particulate system. Biochem. Biophys. Res. Commun. **23:**518–525.
2. **Bachmann, B. J., K. B. Low, and A. L. Taylor.** 1976. Recalibrated linkage map of *Escherichia coli* K-12. Bacteriol. Rev. **40:**116–167.
3. **Blumberg, P. M., and J. L. Strominger.** 1974. Interaction of penicillin with the bacterial cell: penicillin-binding proteins and penicillin-sensitive enzymes. Bacteriol. Rev. **38:**291–335.
4. **Bogdanovsky, D., E. Bricas, and P. Dezélée.** 1969. Sur l'identité de la mucoendopeptidase et de la carboxypeptidase 1 d'*Escherichia coli*, enzymes hydrolysant des liasons de configuration D-D et inhibitée par la penicilline. C.R. Acad. Sci. Ser. D **269:**390–393.
5. **Braun, V., and H. Wolff.** 1975. Attachment of lipoprotein to murein (peptidoglycan) of *Escherichia coli* in the presence and absence of penicillin FL 1060. J. Bacteriol. **123:**888–897.
6. **Fuad, N., J. M. Frère, J. M. Ghuysen, C. Duez, and M. Iwatsubo.** 1976. Mode of interaction between β-lactam antibiotics and the exocellular DD-carboxypeptidase-transpeptidase from *Streptomyces* R39. Biochem. J. **155:**623–629.
6a. **Goodell, E. W., R. Lopez, and A. Tomasz.** 1976. Suppression of the beta lactams on *Escherichia coli* and other bacteria. Proc. Natl. Acad. Sci. U.S.A. **73:**3293–3297.
7. **Greenwood, D., and F. O'Grady.** 1973. Comparison of the responses of *Escherichia coli* and *Proteus mirabilis* to seven β-lactam antibiotics. J. Infect. Dis. **128:**211–222.
8. **Greenwood, D., and F. O'Grady.** 1973. The two sites of penicillin action in *Escherichia coli*. J. Infect. Dis. **128:**791–794.
9. **Henning, U., K. Rehn, V. Braun, B. Höhn, and U. Schwarz.** 1972. Cell envelope and shape of E. coli K12. Properties of a temperature-sensitive *rod* mutant. Eur. J. Biochem. **26:**570–586.
10. **Holland, I. B., and V. Darby.** 1976. Genetical and physiological studies on a thermosensitive mutant of *Escherichia coli* defective in cell division. J. Gen. Microbiol. **92:**156–166.
11. **Izaki, K., M. Matsuhashi, and J. L. Strominger.** 1966. Glycopeptide transpeptidase and D-alanine carboxypeptidase: penicillin-sensitive enzymatic reactions. Proc. Natl. Acad. Sci. U.S.A. **55:**656–663.
12. **James, R., J. Y. Haga, and A. B. Pardee.** 1975. Inhibition of an early event in the cell division cycle of *Escherichia coli* by FL1060, an amidinopenicillanic acid. J. Bacteriol. **122:**1283–1292.
13. **Lund, F., and L. Tybring.** 1972. 6 β-amidinopenicillanic acids, a new group of antibiotics. Nature (London) New Biol. **236:**135–137.
14. **Matsuhashi, M., T. Kamiyro, P. M. Blumberg, P. Linnett, E. Willoughby, and J. L. Strominger.** 1974. Study of the mechanism of action and development of resistance to a new amidino penicillin. J. Bacteriol. **117:**578–587.
15. **Matsuzawa, H., K. Hayakawa, T. Sato, and K. Imahori.** 1973. Characterization and genetic analysis of a mutant of *Escherichia coli* K-12 with rounded morphology. J. Bacteriol. **115:**436–442.
16. **Nguyen-Distèche, M., J. J. Pollock, J. M. Ghuysen, J. Puig, P. Reynolds, H. R. Perkins, J. Coyette, and M. R. J. Salton.** 1974. Sensitivity to ampicillin and cephalothin of enzymes involved in wall peptide cross-linking in *Escherichia coli* K12, strain 44. Eur. J. Biochem. **41:**457–463.
17. **Park, J. T., and L. Burman.** 1973. FL-1060: a new penicillin with a unique mode of action. Biochem. Biophys. Res. Commun. **51:**863–868.
18. **Pritchard, R. H.** 1974. On the growth and form of a bacterial cell. Philos. Trans. R. Soc. London **267:**303–336.
19. **Ricard, M., and Y. Hirota.** 1973. Process of cellular division in *Escherichia coli*: physiological study on thermosensitive mutants defective in cell division. J. Bacteriol. **116:**314–322.
20. **Schwarz, U., A. Asmus, and H. Frank.** 1969. Autolytic enzymes and cell division of *Escherichia coli*. J. Mol. Biol. **41:**419–429.
21. **Spratt, B. G.** 1975. Distinct penicillin-binding proteins involved in the division, elongation, and shape of *Escherichia coli*. Proc. Natl. Acad. Sci. U.S.A. **72:**2999–3003.
22. **Spratt, B. G.** 1977. Comparison of the binding properties of two 6 β-amidinopenicillanic acid derivatives that differ in their physiological effects on *Escherichia coli*. Antimicrob. Agents Chemother. **11:**161–166.
22a. **Spratt, B. G.** 1977. Properties of the penicillin-binding proteins of *Escherichia coli* K12. Eur. J. Biochem. **72:**341–352.
23. **Spratt, B. G., and A. B. Pardee.** 1975. Penicillin-binding proteins and cell shape in E. coli. Nature (London) **254:**516–517.
24. **Spratt, B. G., and J. L. Strominger.** 1976. Identification of the major penicillin-binding proteins of *Escherichia coli* as D-alanine carboxypeptidase 1A. J. Bacteriol. **127:**660–663.
25. **Tamura, T., Y. Imae, and J. L. Strominger.** 1976. Purification to homogeneity and properties of two D-alanine carboxypeptidases 1 from *Escherichia coli*. J. Biol. Chem. **251:**414–423.
26. **Tipper, D. J., and J. L. Strominger.** 1965. Mechanism of action of penicillins: a proposal based on their structural similarity to acyl-D-alanyl-D-alanine. Proc. Natl. Acad. Sci. U.S.A. **54:**1131–1141.
27. **Tomasz, A., and S. Waks.** 1975. Mechanism of action of penicillin: triggering of the pneumococcal autolytic enzyme by inhibitors of cell wall synthesis. Proc. Natl. Acad. Sci. U.S.A. **72:**4162–4166.
28. **Wise, E. M., and J. T. Park.** 1965. Penicillin: its basic site of action as an inhibitor of a peptide cross-linking reaction in cell wall mucopeptide synthesis. Proc. Natl. Acad. Sci. U.S.A. **54:**75–81.

Altered Proteins in Penicillin-Resistant Mutants
of *Bacillus subtilis*

CHRISTINE E. BUCHANAN

The Biological Laboratories, Harvard University, Cambridge, Massachusetts 02138

INTRODUCTION

Bacillus subtilis has five penicillin-binding components (PBCs) which can be easily isolated from the solubilized membranes by affinity chromatography (2–4). The major question concerning these different proteins is which of them, if any, corresponds to the lethal target of penicillin. Of the five, only PBC V has so far been found to possess enzymatic activity. It is the D-alanine carboxypeptidase and represents at least 80% of the penicillin-binding protein both in the membranes and in the purified PBCs (1, 3). Since this enzyme is not essential to normal growth of *B. subtilis*, it is not a penicillin killing site (1). However, three of the other proteins, PBCs I, II, and IV, are all candidates for the penicillin killing site, since their antibiotic sensitivity profiles closely resemble that of the killing site (2).

One approach to better understanding the interaction of penicillin with its targets and the role of the individual PBCs in normal cellular growth is to isolate and examine penicillin-resistant mutants. By determining which components become more resistant to penicillin upon mutation of the organism to greater penicillin resistance, one should be able to identify which of them is essential to the cell and thus more likely to be the actual target of penicillin action.

RESULTS AND DISCUSSION

The isolation of highly penicillin-resistant mutants required a stepwise selection (Fig. 1) since a single-step penicillin-resistant mutant shows only a small increase in penicillin resistance (6). Cloxacillin was chosen as the selective penicillin because it is relatively resistant to the β-lactamase of *Bacillus* species. The survival curves of the wild-type *B. subtilis* and five cloxacillin-resistant mutants (Fig. 1) illustrate the relatively small increase in cloxacillin resistance occurring in each step of the selection. The LD_{50} values, defined as the concentrations of cloxacillin required to reduce the number of colony-forming units by 50%, are as follows ($\mu g/ml$): wild type, 0.1; mutant 1, 0.38; mutant 2, 0.88; mutant 3, 2.7; mutant 4, 7.4; mutant 5, 18.0. The cloxacillin-resistant mutants showed a parallel increase in resistance to oxacillin and dicloxacillin but no substantial change in their sensitivities to 6-aminopenicillanic acid (6-APA) or penicillin G (Table 1).

The isolation of the PBCs of *B. subtilis* strain Porton wild type and the five mutants by covalent affinity chromatography has been described previously (5). Two interesting observations were evident in stained sodium dodecyl sulfate-polyacrylamide slab gels (Fig. 2). In mutant 5, PBC I was not present. Either it did not bind to the 6-APA of the affinity column, perhaps because it was insensitive to penicillin, or else the protein was absent in the mutant. This protein could also not be detected in the membranes when [^{14}C]penicillin G was used as a label. When wild-type PBC I is purified, antibody to it can be prepared and used to search for cross-reacting antigenic material in the mutant. In any case, it is clear that the wild-type protein is not essential for normal growth, since mutant 5 has normal morphology and grows, sporulates, and germinates normally. In addition, it is likely that PBC I is not a penicillin killing site since mutant 5 is still quite sensitive to 6-APA and penicillin G, which have been shown not to bind to PBC I. It is also known that the loss of this protein's penicillin-binding activity in mutant 5 is not necessary for increasing cloxacillin resistance beyond mutant 4. When several other fifth-step mutants were isolated from mutant 4 they possessed PBC I, but were just as resistant to cloxacillin as the original mutant 5 (unpublished data).

Another PBC alteration can also be seen on the stained gel (Fig. 2). An examination of PBC II in the series of mutants suggests that there were several discrete changes in the mobility of PBC II, one evident in mutants 4 and 5 as compared with mutant 3. Another slight alteration in PBC II may have occurred in mutant

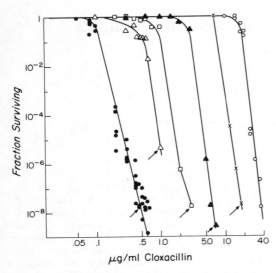

FIG. 1. *Survival curves of* B. subtilis *and the five mutants. The curves (from left to right) correspond to survival of the wild type and mutants 1, 2, 3, 4, and 5. The arrows indicate where a survivor was picked to be used for the isolation of the next-step mutant. (From reference 5)*

1. Such small changes in the electrophoretic mobility could be the result of a single amino acid change affecting the net charge of the protein. Indeed, preliminary results with iso-electric focusing of the PBCs do indicate that the isoelectric points of the mutant 5 and wild-type PBC II are different.

The ability of the individual PBCs to bind cloxacillin was measured indirectly by com-petition for subsequent binding of labeled penicillin G. The details of the binding assays have been published elsewhere (5). The results (Table 2) show that PBC I in mutants 1–4 and PBC IV in mutants 1–5 retained essentially the same sensitivity to cloxacillin as the wild type. PBC II, on the other hand, appeared to undergo three discrete changes in its resistance to cloxacillin, i.e., at mutants 1, 4, and 5. These changes were roughly similar to the changes in the resistance levels of the organisms (Fig. 1). As described above, the change was accom-panied by a change in electrophoretic mobility in mutant 4, and possibly in mutant 1. However, direct proof of the relationship between the altered PBC II and increased penicillin re-sistance requires further genetic studies.

There was no apparent change in PBC II or any other PBC in mutants 2 and 3. Some other change must have occurred in these mutants, possibly a membrane change reflected in altered permeability rather than in an altered PBC. Increased production of a penicillinase was ruled out for all of the mutants.

The affinity of the mutant PBCs for penicillin G was also determined by the competition bind-ing assay. Interestingly, there was no significant change in the sensitivity of PBC II (or any other PBC) to penicillin G despite the obvious alter-ation of the protein's electrophoretic mobility. This corresponds with the fact that the mutants themselves are not more resistant to penicillin G. These findings show that the active sites of penicillin-sensitive proteins may be modified in their sensitivity to one β-lactam antibiotic without any alteration in sensitivity to others. This fact may have implications for therapy with β-lactam antibiotics, and it is paralleled by wide differences in the sensitivity of PBCs in wild-type organisms to different β-lactam antibiotics. A striking example of this is the extreme sensitivity of PBC II in *Escherichia coli* to formamidino penicillin as compared with all other penicillins which have been examined (7).

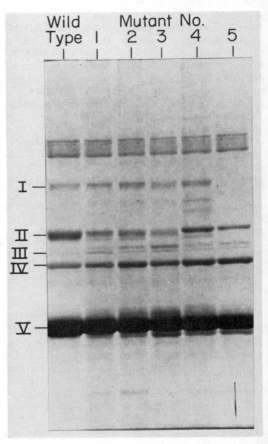

FIG. 2. *Sodium dodecyl sulfate-polyacrylamide slab gel of penicillin-binding components from* B. subtilis *and five cloxacillin-resistant mutants. (From reference 5)*

TABLE 1. *Sensitivity of wild type and mutant 5 to various penicillins*

Penicillin	Structure	LD$_{50}$ (μg/ml, 30°C)	
		WT	Mutant 5
6-Aminopenicillanic acid		7.0	11.0
Benzylpenicillin (Penicillin G)		0.005	0.012
Cloxacillin		0.1	18.0
Dicloxacillin		0.03	3.0
Oxacillin		0.09	3.5

PBCs III and V have previously been eliminated as candidates for the penicillin killing site (1, 2). Here, it has been shown that PBC I is probably not the killing site either, since the protein, if it exists at all, has no affinity for certain penicillins which are still lethal for the organism. It has already been mentioned that the loss of PBC I is not a necessary step for the creation of a fifth-step mutant. It remains to be shown whether alteration of PBC II's resistance is the only means of obtaining mutants 4 and 5 or whether, in fact, other mutations can give the same resistant phenotype. Furthermore, it may not be necessary that more resistant mutants derived from mutant 5, such as

mutants 6, 7, 8, etc., must have an even more penicillin-resistant PBC II. There certainly may be other factors involved in resistance, such as altered permeability or increased hydrolysis of the antibiotic. Based on what has been learned from the mutants described above, however, it is probable that PBC II is the only one of the five PBCs to be truly associated with penicillin's lethal effect on the cell.

ACKNOWLEDGMENTS

This work was supported by Public Health Service research grant AI-09152 from the National Institute of Allergy and Infectious Diseases and National Science Foundation grant BMS71-01120 to J. L. Strominger. C. E. Buchanan was a postdoctoral fellow of the American Cancer Society.

TABLE 2. *In vitro cloxacillin resistance*[a]

PBC[b]	Wild type	Mutants				
		1	2	3	4	5
I	0.54	1.08	1.55	1.04	0.66	—
II	1.75	3.8	2.65	2.18	11.4	72
IV	0.8	0.92	1.62	1.18	0.76	1.43

[a] Resistance is defined as the amount of cloxacillin (μg/ml × min) required to inhibit [^{14}C]penicillin G binding by 50%. (From reference 5)
[b] Penicillin-binding component.

LITERATURE CITED

1. **Blumberg, P. M., and J. L. Strominger.** 1971. Inactivation of D-alanine carboxypeptidase by penicillins and cephalosporins is not lethal in *Bacillus subtilis*. Proc. Natl. Acad. Sci. U.S.A. **68**:2814–2817.
2. **Blumberg, P. M., and J. L. Strominger.** 1972. Five penicillin binding components occur in *Bacillus subtilis* membranes. J. Biol. Chem. **247**:8107–8113.
3. **Blumberg, P. M., and J. L. Strominger.** 1972. Isolation by covalent affinity chromatography of the penicillin binding components from membranes of *Bacillus subtilis*. Proc. Natl. Acad. Sci. U.S.A. **69**:3751–3755.
4. **Blumberg, P. M., and J. L. Strominger.** 1974. Covalent

affinity chromatography as a means of purifying the penicillin binding components from bacterial membranes, p. 401–405. *In* W. B. Jakoby and M. Wilchek (ed.), Methods in enzymology, vol. 34. Academic Press Inc., New York.

5. **Buchanan, C. E., and J. L. Strominger.** 1976. Altered penicillin-binding components in penicillin-resistant mutants of *Bacillus subtilis*. Proc. Natl. Acad. Sci. U.S.A. **73:**1816–1820.

6. **Demerec, M.** 1948. Origin of bacterial resistance to antibiotics. J. Bacteriol. **56:**63–74.

7. **Spratt, B. G., and A. B. Pardee.** 1975. Penicillin-binding proteins and cell shape in *E. coli*. Nature (London) **254:**516–517.

Penicillin-Sensitive Enzymes of Peptidoglycan Metabolism

JEAN-MARIE GHUYSEN

Service de Microbiologie, Faculté de Médecine, Université de Liège, Institut de Botanique, Liège 1, Belgium

In 1940, for the first time, Chain, Florey, and their associates obtained benzylpenicillin in a solid form and demonstrated its efficiency in higher organisms against various pathogenic bacteria. Nine years later, almost all that is known today on the chemistry of penicillin had been discovered (3). In comparison, the unraveling of the mechanisms by which penicillin kills bacteria and exerts its remarkable selective toxicity has been a slow process.

STRUCTURE OF THE WALL PEPTIDOGLYCAN (16, 28)

It was early recognized that penicillin, when acting on growing bacteria, caused damages to the bacterial wall and more precisely to its peptidoglycan moiety. The wall peptidoglycan is a rigid, netlike heteropolymer which is composed of glycan chains cross-linked by peptide chains. Essentially, the glycan moiety consists of linear strands of alternate pyranoside residues of N-acetylglucosamine and N-acetylmuramic acid linked together by $1{\rightarrow}4,\beta$ bonds. All glycans have short tetrapeptide units L-alanyl-D-glutamyl-L-R_3-D-alanine linked to their muramyl carboxyl groups, and the peptide units that substitute adjacent glycan chains are, in turn, covalently linked together by means of interpeptide bridges. These bridges always extend between the C-terminal D-alanine residue of one tetrapeptide and often, but not always, to the ω-amino group of the L-R_3 residue of a second tetrapeptide. The most frequent type of peptidoglycan is that found in the gram-positive bacilli and in the gram-negative bacteria; *meso*-diaminopimelic acid is at the R_3 position in the peptide unit, and the interpeptide bridge is mediated via a direct D-alanyl-(D)-*meso*-diaminopimelic acid linkage.

SYNTHESIS OF NASCENT PEPTIDOGLYCAN (19, 30)

About 30 enzymes are involved in peptidoglycan synthesis. Some of them are cytoplasmic (and soluble). They catalyze the formation of two nucleotide precursors: UDP-N-acetyl-glucosamine and UDP-N-acetylmuramyl-L-Ala-D-Glu-L-R_3-D-Ala-D-Ala. The peptide moiety of the latter is not a tetrapeptide as is found in the completed wall peptidoglycan but a pentapeptide ending in a D-Ala-D-Ala sequence. Once formed, the two precursors are assembled by a membrane-bound, multienzyme system which works in conjunction with a specific, undecaprenyl phosphate carrier. The mechanism is such that chains consisting of multiple disaccharide-peptide units grow by addition of new disaccharide-peptide units on the reducing terminal of the lengthening chain (33, 34). The acceptor on which the nascent glycan chains are assembled may be the undecaprenyl phosphate carrier itself or perhaps another membrane component such as, for example, lipoteichoic acid (W. Wong, F. E. Young, and A. N. Chatterjee, in press). Whatever the exact nature of the membrane acceptor, the nascent, uncross-linked peptidoglycan thus formed emerges on the *exterior* of the plasma membrane, which in fact has been seen by use of isolated protoplasts (5–7).

PEPTIDOGLYCAN CROSS-LINKING REACTION

Insolubilization of the nascent peptidoglycan is achieved by peptide cross-linking and is catalyzed by a membrane-bound transpeptidase (32, 35). The carbonyl group of the penultimate C-terminal D-alanine residue of one pentapeptide (i.e., the donor) is transferred to the ω-amino group of the L-R_3 residue of another pentapeptide (i.e., the acceptor). New peptide bonds are formed, and equivalent amounts of D-alanine residues are liberated from the peptide donors. Such an operation can be performed by cells that, at the onset of the process, completely lack preexisting walls (5–7). The process is slow and appears to be difficult since immobilization of the protoplasts by fixation to the agar in a medium of low fluidity is necessary. In normal cells, the nascent peptidoglycan, probably as its own synthesis proceeds, undergoes insolubilization by attachment to the preexisting wall peptidoglycan. The process is achieved mainly by transpeptidation although, in some bacteria, addition of the nascent peptidoglycan to the glycan strands of the preexisting wall peptidoglycan by transglycosylation may also be a minor pathway of peptidoglycan expansion (23). The direction of the transpeptidation is not uniform among bacteria. Thus, in *Bacillus licheniformis*, the nascent peptidoglycan is the peptide donor and the preexisting wall peptidoglycan is the peptide acceptor (through its amino groups on the D-center of *meso*-diaminopimelic acids; 33, 34). On the contrary, in *Gaffkya homari*, the ϵ-amino groups of lysine residues in the nascent peptidoglycan function as acceptors whereas D-Ala-D-Ala sequences in the preexisting wall function as donors (20a, 20b).

PEPTIDOGLYCAN CROSS-LINKING ENZYME SYSTEM

Basically, three types of enzymes may exist, all of them catalyzing the release of the C-terminal D-Ala residue from D-Ala-D-Ala-ending peptides:

1. Release of D-Ala by transpeptidases is necessarily coupled with the transfer of the residual peptide donor moiety to a proper amino acceptor. These enzymes seem to be exclusively membrane bound.

2. Release of D-Ala by DD-carboxypeptidases is a simple hydrolytic process. These enzymes are often membrane bound, sometimes periplasmic. They probably control the number of peptide donors made available to the transpeptidase activity and, hence, the extent of peptide cross-linking in the wall peptidoglycan. An exact balance between transpeptidase activity and DD-carboxypeptidase activity appears to be a physiologically important parameter (20a, 20b, 24).

3. DD-Carboxypeptidases-transpeptidases also exist that are able to catalyze concomitantly both hydrolysis and transfer reactions. These enzymes are also membrane bound or periplasmic. Strains of actinomycetes, however, excrete such DD-carboxypeptidases-transpeptidases (17). With these enzymes, the channeling of the total enzyme activity into either of these pathways depends upon the environmental conditions (pH, polarity, and acceptor and donor concentrations) (11) as well as upon minor chemical alterations of the peptide substrates (the occurrence of an amide group on the α-carboxyl group of D-glutamic acid; 18). In vivo, a cell-bound DD-carboxypeptidase-transpeptidase might fulfill more than one function, its activity being modulated by the properties of its microenvironment in the cell.

Finally, the situation is made more complex by the fact that, at least in some bacteria, the cross-linking enzyme system or some of its enzyme constituents may occur in two distinct forms that exhibit largely different penicillin sensitivities and, perhaps, are involved in distinct physiological functions such as, for example, wall septation and wall elongation (2, 22, 22a, 25–27, 31).

KILLING TARGET OF PENICILLIN

The peptidoglycan cross-linking enzyme system, considered as a whole, is the target specifically attacked by penicillin. Its complete inhibition causes cessation of growth. The question arises, however, whether all enzyme members are physiologically important, i.e., whether the specific inactivation of one of them may sufficiently impair the peptidoglycan cross-linking machinery to cause serious cell abnormalities and cell death. An approach to the problem rests upon the observation that, in one given organism, the various enzymes involved in peptide cross-linking differ, sometimes drastically, with respect to their penicillin sensitivity. With gram-negative bacteria, low dose levels of penicillin selectively inhibit cell septation, leading to filament formation, whereas higher penicillin concentrations are required to block cell elongation and cause loss of rod shape and, eventually, cell lysis. In *Escherichia coli*, a set of membrane-bound proteins that are able to fix penicillin are apparently specifically involved in cell division, cell elongation, and cell shape, but their possible correlation with specific enzymes remains to be established (29; Spratt, p. 182, this volume). Among gram-positive bacteria, it has been shown that both *B. subtilis* (1) and *G. homari* (20a) possess a highly penicillin-sensitive DD-carboxypeptidase. Specific inactivation of this enzyme has no detectable effect on the growth of *B. subtilis* but seems to be lethal for *G. homari*. At present, a unified view cannot be proposed. Furthermore, killing by penicillin causes cell lysis, and therefore peptidoglycan hydrolases (autolysins) must be actively involved in the process. Under normal conditions of growth, hydrolase action is controlled in such a way that it is only permitted in specific cell areas and at given stages of the cell cycle (G. D. Shockman, unpublished data). Penicillin has no direct action on isolated autolysins, but in its presence triggering of hydrolase activity occurs, resulting in cell lysis. Obviously, the functioning, regulation, and coordination of both peptidoglycan cross-linking and peptidoglycan autolyzing enzyme systems are topics of extreme importance (Tomasz and Höltje, p. 209, this volume).

ISOLATION AND FRACTIONATION OF THE PEPTIDOGLYCAN CROSS-LINKING ENZYME SYSTEM (17)

The isolation of the peptidoglycan cross-linking enzyme system and its fractionation into its individual enzyme components is a difficult task. In particular, substrates must be made available which permit the assay of the various enzymes when uncoupled from their natural substrates. DD-Carboxypeptidase is assayed by action either on isolated UDP-N-acetylmuramyl-pentapeptide or on synthetic L-R_3-D-Ala-D-Ala-ending peptides that closely resemble the corresponding C-terminal part of the natural substrates. Artificial systems of donor and acceptor peptides have been developed that allow transpeptidase activity to be estimated directly and independently of the preceding biosynthetic reactions. The following examples are meant to illustrate the point:

1. In *Streptomyces* sp., transpeptidation occurs between hexapeptides

$$
\begin{array}{c}
\text{L-Ala-D-Glu(amide)} \overset{\text{L}}{\underset{\underset{\text{L}}{\text{Gly-}}}{\rule{1em}{0.4pt}\text{A}_2\text{pm}\rule{1em}{0.4pt}}}\text{-D-Ala-D-Ala}
\end{array}
$$

where D-Ala-D-Ala is the donor group and the N-terminal Gly is the acceptor group. Membrane-bound, periplasmic, and exocellular enzyme preparations have been obtained from various strains of *Streptomyces* which hydrolyze Ac$_2$-L-Lys-D-Ala-D-Ala into D-Ala and Ac$_2$-L-Lys-D-Ala (DD-carboxypeptidase activity) and perform artificial transpeptidations by using the same tripeptide Ac$_2$-L-Lys-D-Ala-D-Ala as donor and, for example, Gly-Gly as acceptor. D-Ala and tetrapeptide Ac$_2$-L-Lys-D-Ala-Gly-Gly are the reaction products.

2. In *Actinomadura* strain R39 (formerly *Streptomyces* R39), transpeptidation occurs between pentapeptides

$$
\begin{array}{c}
\text{L-Ala-D-Glu(amide)} \overset{\text{L}}{\underset{\underset{\text{D}}{}}{\rule{1em}{0.4pt}\text{A}_2\text{pm}\rule{1em}{0.4pt}}}\text{-D-Ala-D-Ala}
\end{array}
$$

where the acceptor group is the amine located on the D-carbon of *meso*-diaminopimelic acid in α-position to a free carboxyl group. This organism produces an exocellular DD-carboxypeptidase-transpeptidase. The isolated enzyme hydrolyzes Ac$_2$-L-Lys-D-Ala-D-Ala into D-Ala and Ac$_2$-L-Lys-D-Ala and carries out transpeptidation with the amidated tetrapeptide

$$
\begin{array}{c}
\text{L-Ala-D-Glu(amide)} \overset{\text{L}}{\underset{\underset{\text{D}}{}}{\rule{1em}{0.4pt}\text{A}_2\text{pm}\rule{1em}{0.4pt}}}\text{-D-Ala}
\end{array}
$$

as acceptor. D-Ala and hexapeptide

$$
\begin{array}{c}
\text{L-Ala-D-Glu(amide)} \overset{\text{L}}{\underset{\underset{\text{D}}{\text{Ac}_2\text{-L-Lys-D-Ala-}}}{\rule{1em}{0.4pt}\text{A}_2\text{pm}\rule{1em}{0.4pt}}}\text{-D-Ala}
\end{array}
$$

are the reaction products. Amidation of the carboxyl group on the D-center of *meso*-diaminopimelic acid abolishes acceptor function. Note that in gram-negative bacteria, the transpeptidation reaction is identical to that which occurs in *Actinomadura* except that the α-carboxyl group of D-glutamic acid is not amidated. However, the specificity profile of the *E. coli* peptidoglycan cross-linking enzyme is such that it does not utilize the tripeptide Ac$_2$-L-Lys-D-Ala-D-Ala for hydrolysis or for transpeptidation. Hence, substrate systems specific for *E. coli* had to be devised.

Through the use of artificial substrates such as those described above and others, transpeptidases, DD-carboxypeptidases, and DD-carboxypeptidases-transpeptidases have been isolated from various organisms. Although very few of them have been purified to protein homogeneity, they have been extremely useful for the study of the mechanisms of transpeptidation and penicillin action at the molecular levels.

INTERACTION BETWEEN PENICILLIN AND EXOCELLULAR DD-CARBOXYPEPTIDASES-TRANSPEPTIDASES FROM *STREPTOMYCES* R61 AND *ACTINOMADURA* R39: THE MODEL (9, 10, 12, 14, 15)

Actinomycetes produce exocellular DD-carboxypeptidases-transpeptidases. Those excreted by *Streptomyces* strain R61 and *Actinomadura* strain R39 were purified to protein homogeneity. They are globular proteins, each consisting of a single polypeptide chain with molecular weights of 38,000 (R61 enzyme) and 53,000 (R39 enzyme). They were selected for the study of the mode of action of penicillin for the following reasons: (i) at present, they are the only enzymes to have been purified to protein homogeneity; (ii) they catalyze artificial hydrolysis and transfer reactions that are almost identical to those which occur in vivo; (iii) these two activities are indistinguishable from each other with respect to their penicillin sensitivity; and (iv) the R39 enzyme is much more sensitive to penicillin than the R61 enzyme, thus offering a way to study the mechanisms through which the enzymes of the peptidoglycan cross-linking system may exhibit large differences in their penicillin sensitivity whether or not they belong to the same organism.

The simplest model which best explains the mode of action of penicillin is

$$E + I \overset{K}{\rightleftharpoons} EI \overset{k_3}{\rightarrow} EI^* \overset{k_4}{\rightarrow} E$$

+ degradation products

Enzyme (*E*) and antibiotic (*I*, for inhibitor) react to form a stoichiometric intermediate complex *EI* characterized by a dissociation constant *K*. Complex *EI* then undergoes isomerization into complex *EI**, in which the enzyme is inactivated and the antibiotic is chemically modified. Depending upon the antibiotic and the enzyme, the *EI** complexes have different half-life values, but in all cases they undergo spontaneous breakdown with regeneration of the enzyme and release of the antibiotic into biologically inactive metabolites. The two last steps are characterized by first-order rate constants, k_3 and k_4, respectively.

The reaction products arising from benzylpenicillin are phenylacetylglycine and *N*-formyl-D-penicillamine (8, 13). Penicillin is thus split into two fragments. Globally, the reaction consists of the addition of two H_2O molecules and results in the hydrolysis of the amide bond and in the rupture of both C_5–C_6 and C_5–S linkages. Enzyme reactivation, release of phenylacetylglycine, and release of *N*-formyl-D-penicillamine during breakdown of complex *EI** are concomitant events. Boiling of complex *EI** (made with the R61 enzyme) stabilizes it and makes it sensitive to Pronase or thermolysin action. By using [^{14}C]benzylpenicillin for complex formation, a radioactive tripeptide Val-Gly-Ser was thus obtained, suggesting that, in the R61 enzyme, serine is the residue involved in penicillin binding (7a). Cephalosporins are also destroyed by both R61 and R39 enzymes, but the degradation products have not yet been characterized.

PENICILLIN AS SUBSTRATE AND INHIBITOR OF THE EXOCELLULAR DD-CARBOXYPEPTIDASES-TRANS-PEPTIDASES (9, 10, 12, 14, 15)

β-Lactam antibiotics are thus substrates of both R61 and R39 enzymes. However, by immobilizing the enzymes, at least transitorily, in the form of complexes *EI**, they also behave as inhibitors. The lower the *K* value is the higher the k_3 value is, and the higher the k_4 value is the better the antibiotic is as a substrate. The lower the *K* value is the higher the k_3 value is, but the lower the k_4 value is the more active

the antibiotic is as an "inhibitor." The importance of the *K* and k_3 constants is obvious since the rate of formation of complex *EI** directly depends on the k_3/K ratio value. The k_4 constant is also important since, at the steady state, the smaller its value, the higher is that part of the total enzyme which is immobilized in the form of complex *EI**. There are two ways to express the efficiency of an antibiotic as inhibitor:

1. A K_i value can be defined as $K_i = k_4 K/k_3$. The lower the K_i is the better the inhibitor is.

2. The level of active enzyme [*E*] which, at the steady state, remains functional as hydrolase and transpeptidase is given by the equation

$$[E] = \frac{E_0}{1 + \dfrac{[I]}{K} + \dfrac{k_3}{K}\dfrac{[I]}{k_4}}$$

If the k_4 is much smaller than k_3 $[I]/K$, then irrespective of the k_4 value, all the enzyme is, at the steady state, immobilized in the form of couple *EI**. However, if both the k_3 and k_4 values are very small, then at an antibiotic concentration equal to the K_i value, formation of complex *EI** may be so slow that within the time used for the experiment it may not occur; i.e., the enzyme may remain active.

Table 1 gives the k_3/K and k_4 values for both R61 and R39 enzymes and a series of β-lactam antibiotics. The k_4 values range from 0.3 × 10^{-6} to 1.4 × 10^{-4} s^{-1}, which correspond to half-lives for the complexes *EI** of 40,000 to 80 min. These variations are important. Nevertheless, even those complexes which have the highest k_4 value are still rather stable. The k_3/K values range from about 100,000 to 3,000 M^{-1}s^{-1} for the R39 enzyme and from 14,000 to 22 M^{-1}s^{-1} for the R61 enzyme. Because of the relatively high stability of all the complexes *EI**, differences between antibiotics with respect to their efficiency as inhibitors should be mainly related to the k_3/K values. If enzyme inhibition is expressed in terms of ID$_{50}$ value (i.e., the antibiotic concentration required to inhibit enzyme activity by 50% under standard conditions), then, irrespective of the antibiotics, the ratio value of k_3/K for the R39 enzyme to k_3/K for the R61 enzyme should be equal to the ratio value of ID$_{50}$ for the R61 enzyme to ID$_{50}$ for the R39 enzyme. Table 2 shows that, within the limits of experimental error, this conclusion is well supported by the experimental data.

Table 3 gives the individual *K* and k_3 values for various enzyme-antibiotic systems characterized by k_3/K values ranging from 66,000 to

TABLE 1. *Interaction between β-lactam antibiotics and the exocellular R61 and R39 enzymes*

Interaction: antibiotic—enzyme	k_3/K $(M^{-1}s^{-1})$	k_4 at 37°C (s^{-1})	Half-life of complexes EI^* at 37°C (min)	ID_{50} at 37°C $(10^{-8}$ M)
Benzylpenicillin—R39	90,000 (20°C)	2.8×10^{-6}	4,100	$(5)^a$
Ampicillin—R39	74,000 (20°C)	4.4×10^{-6}	2,600	$(3)^a$
Cephaloglycine—R39	74,000 (20°C)	0.8×10^{-6}	14,000	$(6)^a$
Cephalosporin C—R39	66,000 (20°C)	0.28×10^{-6}	40,000	$(5)^a$
Benzylpenicillin—R61	13,700 (25°C)	1.4×10^{-4}	80	14
Carbenicillin—R39	2,900 (20°C)	5.4×10^{-6}	2,125	200
Cephalosporin C—R61	1,150 (37°C)	1×10^{-6}	11,200	45
Carbenicillin—R61	820 (37°C)	1.4×10^{-4}	80	800
Ampicillin—R61	107 (37°C)	1.4×10^{-4}	80	2,600
Cephaloglycine—R61	22 (37°C)	3×10^{-6}	3,700	6,900

^{a} In these cases, the k_3/K ratio values are so high and the k_4 values are so low that these determinations are probably equivalent to a simple titration of the enzyme used in the experiments.

TABLE 2. *Relation between the rates of formation of complexes EI^* with the exocellular R61 and R39 enzymes and the corresponding ID_{50} values*

Antibiotic	a $\dfrac{k^3/K \text{ (R39)}}{k_3/K \text{ (R61)}}$	b $\dfrac{ID_{50} \text{ (R61)}}{ID_{50} \text{ (R39)}}$	a/b
Benzylpenicillin	7.3	2.8	2.6
Carbenicillin	3.6	4	0.9
Cephalosporin C ...	31	9	3.4
Ampicillin	626	867	0.7
Cephaloglycine	3,523	1,150	3.1

22 M^{-1}s^{-1}. In no case is the recognition of the antibiotic by the enzyme (as expressed by the K value) exceedingly good, but there is a 20,000-fold variation between the highest and the lowest k_3 value. Note that values of 180 s^{-1} and 13 s^{-1} for the k_3 constant are similar to the k_{cal} value of a true enzymatic reaction (the hydrolysis of a good peptide donor by the R61 enzyme is about 50 s^{-1}).

A last point deserves to be discussed. Both penicillin and D-Ala-D-Ala-ending peptide donor are substrates of the DD-carboxypeptidases-transpeptidases, and therefore one would like to know whether fixation of peptide donor and fixation of penicillin on the same form of enzyme are mutually exclusive. Kinetically, enzyme inhibition by penicillin is competitive with regard to the peptide donor in Lineweaver-Burk plots. However, in a noncompetitive inhibition, linear plots would also be obtained if the dissociation constant for the ternary complex ESI would be roughly equal to that of the binary complex EI. They would then be indistinguishable from those obtained from a classical competitive inhibition. It is thus impossible to make a choice

between the two alternatives, and a structural analogy between penicillin and donor substrate cannot be justified on the basis of a "competitive" inhibition.

INTERACTION BETWEEN PENICILLIN AND CELL-BOUND ENZYMES

The above model applies to cell-bound enzymes. Formation of an inactive enzyme-antibiotic complex is followed by spontaneous breakdown, enzyme reactivation, and release of antibiotic degradation product(s). For technical reasons, it has not yet been possible to show whether or not complex formation is a two-step reaction, but the bimolecular rate constant k for the interaction $E + I \xrightarrow{k} EI^*$ has been measured in several cases (k is also expressed in M^{-1}s^{-1} and, for $[I] << K$, is equivalent to the k_3/K ratio value in a two-step reaction).

Isolated membranes of *Streptococcus faecalis* possess a DD-carboxypeptidase which, apparently, also performs simple transfer reactions (J. Coyette and J. M. Ghuysen, unpublished data). The half-life values of all the complexes formed with various penicillins exceed the generation time of this organism, but the k values exhibit large differences, from 560 M^{-1}s^{-1} with

TABLE 3. *Effect of K and k_3 constant values on the formation of complexes EI^* with the exocellular R61 and R39 enzymes*

Interaction: antibiotic—enzyme	k_3/K $(M^{-1}s^{-1})$	K (mM)	k_3 (s^{-1})
Cephalosporin C—R39 ..	66,000	0.19	12.5
Benzylpenicillin—R61 ..	13,700	13	180
Carbenicillin—R61	820	0.11	0.09
Ampicillin—R61	107	7.2	0.77
Cephaloglycine—R61 ..	22	0.4	0.009

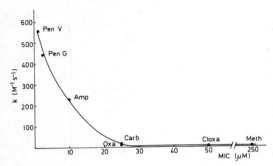

FIG. 1. *Effects of penicillins on* Streptococcus faecalis *ATCC 9790. Relationship between the minimal inhibitory concentration (MIC) values of penicillins and the bimolecular rate constant (k) values for their interaction with the membrane-bound DD-carboxypeptidase. Pen V = phenoxymethylpenicillin; Pen G = benzylpenicillin; Amp =ampicillin; Oxa = oxacillin; Carb = carbenicillin; Cloxa = cloxacillin; Meth = methicillin.*

phenoxymethylpenicillin to 0.7 $M^{-1}s^{-1}$ with methicillin. There exists a relationship (Fig. 1) between the k values and the in vivo activity of various penicillins (expressed as minimal inhibitory concentrations), demonstrating that this membrane-bound enzyme is physiologically important and may be the killing target of penicillin in *S. faecalis*.

Biosynthesis of chemically normal (but functionally defective) peptidoglycan in the unstable spheroplast L-form of *Proteus mirabilis* continues during growth in the presence of 200 to 1,000 units of penicillin/ml. Current studies (22, 22a; H. H. Martin, W. Schilf, and P. Gruss, L-Form Symp., INSERM, Montpelier, 1976) suggest that in normal *Proteus* bacteria at least two isoenzymes of transpeptidase and DD-carboxypeptidase are involved in peptidoglycan synthesis, and that conversion to the L-form by penicillin causes permanent inactivation of the isoenzyme with high penicillin sensitivity. L-form growth and peptidoglycan synthesis in the presence of penicillin would thus continue with the isoenzyme of low penicillin sensitivity. A DD-carboxypeptidase has been isolated from the L-form which interacts with benzylpenicillin with a k value of about 3,500 $M^{-1}s^{-1}$ (unpublished data) and a k_4 value of 4.16 $\times$ $10^{-3}s^{-1}$. Hence, the half-life value of the complex thus formed is of 2.8 min! Such a rapid breakdown may well be sufficient to maintain a high level of functional DD-carboxypeptidase in the continuous presence of penicillin. Another interesting feature of this enzyme is that, kinetically, its inhibition by penicillin is noncompetitive, strongly suggesting that the ternary complex ESI can be formed.

Streptomyces sp. have a membrane-bound transpeptidase. Cetyltrimethylammonium bromide has been used to solubilize it directly from mycelia of strains K15 and *rimosus* (as well as from other strains (4, 21; unpublished data). With strain K15, the same treatment also solubilizes a DD-carboxypeptidase (its location in the cell is still uncertain). These partially purified enzymes interact with benzylpenicillin to form complexes of rather long half-lives (40 to 900 min at 37°C, depending upon the enzyme). The k values for complex formation are 340 $M^{-1}s^{-1}$ for the transpeptidase of *S. rimosus* and 30 and 5,000 $M^{-1}s^{-1}$ for the transpeptidase and the DD-carboxypeptidase of strain K15, respectively. Hence, in strain K15, the inactivation of the DD-carboxypeptidase is considerably faster than the inactivation of the transpeptidase, a situation reminiscent of that of *G. homari* and *B. subtilis*, where DD-carboxypeptidase activity is more sensitive than transpeptidase activity (see above). *S. rimosus* has no detectable DD-carboxypeptidase activity, and its isolated transpeptidase has a penicillin sensitivity intermediate to those of the transpeptidase and DD-carboxypeptidase of strain K15. The physiological significance of these observations is still obscure.

Phenylacetylglycine is the main degradation product arising from benzylpenicillin by interaction with the cetyltrimethylammonium bromide-solubilized *Streptomyces* enzymes, the membranes of *S. faecalis*, and those of *B. stearothermophilus* (20). However, splitting of the antibiotic molecule into two fragments does not always occur. After interaction with the membranes of *Streptomyces* sp. and the isolated DD-carboxypeptidase of the L-form of *P. mirabilis* (unpublished data), the main degradation product is penicilloic acid (and perhaps other degradation products with intact $C_5 - C_6$ linkage; unpublished data). In this respect, one should note that breakdown of the complex formed between benzylpenicillin and the exocellular enzyme from *Streptomyces* R39 yields phenylacetylglycine when breakdown occurs in a medium of high ionic strength under conditions of enzyme reactivation. In a medium of low ionic strength where the enzyme does not recover its activity as DD-carboxypeptidase-transpeptidase, breakdown of the complex apparently yields penicilloic acid (unpublished data). The mechanism of these reactions remains to be discovered.

CONCLUSIONS

Qualitatively, penicillin is, at the same time, a substrate and an inhibitor of the peptidoglycan cross-linking enzyme system. Quantitatively, this double property can be expressed by the values of the kinetics constants involved in the interaction.

Comparison of the "penicillin sensitivity" of the exocellular R61 and R39 enzymes that have been used as models in the present study (Tables 1–3) and of other enzymes demonstrates that "intrinsic" resistance of the penicillin target may result either from a lack of recognition (a high K value) or from a rapid degradation of the antibiotic molecule (a high k_3/K ratio value and a high k_4 value). When considered as penicillin-degrading agents, the enzymes of the peptidoglycan cross-linking system catalyze either the complete splitting of the antibiotic molecule into two fragments with rupture of the $C_5 - C_6$ linkage or the simple hydrolysis of the β-lactam ring, thus suggesting a possible relationship with classical penicillinases.

LITERATURE CITED

1. **Blumberg, P. M., and J. L. Strominger.** 1971. Inactivation of D-alanine carboxypeptidase by penicillins and cephalosporins is not lethal in *Bacillus subtilis*. Proc. Natl. Acad. Sci. U.S.A. **68:**2814–2817.

2. **Blumberg, P. M., and J. L. Strominger.** 1974. Interaction of penicillin with the bacterial cell: penicillin-binding proteins and penicillin-sensitive enzymes. Bacteriol. Rev. **38:**291–335.

3. **Clarke, H. T., J. R. Johnson, and R. Robinson.** 1949. The chemistry of penicillin. Princeton University Press, Princeton, N.J.

4. **Dusart, J., A. Marquet, J. M. Ghuysen, and H. R. Perkins.** 1975. The catalytic activity and penicillin sensitivity in the liquid and frozen states of membrane-bound and detergent-solubilized transpeptidases of *Streptomyces* R61. Eur. J. Biochem. **56:**57–65.

5. **Elliott, T. S. J., J. B. Ward, and H. J. Rogers.** 1975. Formation of cell wall polymers by reverting protoplasts of *Bacillus licheniformis*. J. Bacteriol. **124:**623–632.

6. **Elliott, T. S. J., J. B. Ward, P. B. Wyrick, and H. J. Rogers.** 1975. Ultrastructural study of the reversion of protoplasts of *Bacillus licheniformis* to bacilli. J. Bacteriol. **124:**905–917.

7. **Fitz-James, P.** 1974. Discussion of paper: Studies on the elongation of bacterial cell wall peptidoglycan and its inhibition by penicillin (D. Mirelman, R. Bracha, and N. Sharon). Ann. N.Y. Acad. Sci. **235:**345–346.

7a. **Frère, J. M., C. Duez, J. M. Ghuysen, and J. Vandekerhove.** 1976. Occurrence of a serine residue in the penicillin-binding site of the exocellular DD-carboxypeptidase-transpeptidase from *Streptomyces* R61. FEBS Lett. **70:**257–260.

8. **Frère, J. M., J. M. Ghuysen, J. Degelaen, A. Loffet, and H. R. Perkins.** 1975. Fragmentation of benzylpenicillin after interaction with the exocellular DD-carboxypeptidase-transpeptidases of *Streptomyces* R61 and R39. Nature (London) **258:**168–170.

9. **Frère, J. M., J. M. Ghuysen, and M. Iwatsubo.** 1975. Kinetics of interaction between the exocellular DD-carboxypeptidase-transpeptidase from *Streptomyces* R61 and β-lactam antibiotics. A choice of models. Eur. J. Biochem. **57:**343–351.

10. **Frère, J. M., J. M. Ghuysen, and H. R. Perkins.** 1975. Interaction between the exocellular DD-carboxypeptidase-transpeptidase from *Streptomyces* R61, substrate and β-lactam antibiotics. A choice of models. Eur. J. Biochem. **57:**353–359.

11. **Frère, J. M., J. M. Ghuysen, H. R. Perkins, and M. Nieto.** 1973. Kinetics of concomitant transfer and hydrolysis reactions catalysed by the exocellular DD-carboxypeptidase-transpeptidase of *Streptomyces* R61. Biochem. J. **135:**483–492.

12. **Frère, J. M., J. M. Ghuysen, P. E. Reynolds, R. Moreno, and H. R. Perkins.** 1974. Binding of β-lactam antibiotics to the exocellular DD-carboxypeptidase-transpeptidase of *Streptomyces* R39. Biochem. J. **143:**241–249.

13. **Frère, J. M., J. M. Ghuysen, H. Vanderhaeghe, P. Adriaens, and J. Degelaen.** 1976. Fate of thiazolidine ring during fragmentation of penicillin by exocellular DD-carboxypeptidase-transpeptidase of *Streptomyces* R61. Nature (London) **260:**451–454.

14. **Frère, J. M., M. Leyh-Bouille, J. M. Ghuysen, and H. R. Perkins.** 1974. Interaction between β-lactam antibiotics and exocellular DD-carboxypeptidase-transpeptidase of *Streptomyces* R61. Eur. J. Biochem. **50:**203–214.

15. **Fuad, N., J. M. Frère, J. M. Ghuysen, C. Duez, and M. Iwatsubo.** 1976. Mode of interaction between β-lactam antibiotics and the exocellular DD-carboxypeptidase-transpeptidase from *Streptomyces* R39. Biochem. J. **155:**623–629.

16. **Ghuysen, J. M.** 1968. Use of bacteriolytic enzymes in determination of wall structure and their role in cell metabolism. Bacteriol. Rev. **32:**425–464.

17. **Ghuysen, J. M.** 1976. The bacterial DD-carboxypeptidase-transpeptidase enzyme system: a new insight into the mode of action of penicillin, p. 1–164. *In* W. E. Brown (ed.), E. R. Squibb lectures on chemistry and microbial products. University of Tokyo Press, Tokyo, Japan.

18. **Ghuysen, J. M., P. E. Reynolds, H. R. Perkins, J. M. Frère, and R. Moreno.** 1974. Effects of donor and acceptor peptides on concomitant hydrolysis and transfer reactions catalysed by the exocellular DD-carboxypeptidase-transpeptidase from *Streptomyces* R39. Biochemistry **13:**2539–2547.

19. **Ghuysen, J. M., and G. D. Shockman.** 1973. Biosynthesis of peptidoglycan, p. 37–130. *In* L. Leive (ed.), Bacterial membranes and walls, vol. 1. Dekker Inc., New York.

20. **Hammarstrom, S., and J. L. Strominger.** 1975. Degradation of penicillin G to phenylacetylglycine by D-alanine carboxypeptidase from *Bacillus stearothermophilus*. Proc. Natl. Acad. Sci. U.S.A. **72:**3463–3467.

20a. **Hammes, W. P.** 1976. Biosynthesis of peptidoglycan in *Gaffkya homari*. The mode of action of penicillin G and mecillinam. Eur. J. Biochem. **70:**107–113.

20b. **Hammes, W. P., and O. Kandler.** 1976. Biosynthesis of peptidoglycan in *Gaffkya homari*. The incorporation of peptidoglycan into the cell wall and the restriction of transpeptidation. Eur. J. Biochem. **70:**97–106.

21. **Marquet, A., J. Dusart, J. M. Ghuysen, and H. R. Perkins.** 1974. Membrane-bound transpeptidase and penicillin binding sites in *Streptomyces* R61. Eur. J. Biochem. **46:**515–523.

22. **Martin, H. H., C. Maskos, and R. Burger.** 1975. D-Alanyl-D-alanine carboxypeptidase in the bacterial form and L-form of *Proteus mirabilis*. Eur. J. Biochem. **55:**465–473.

22a. **Martin, H. H., W. Schilf, and C. Maskos.** 1976. Purification of the membrane-bound DD-carboxypeptidase of the unstable spheroplast L-form of *Proteus mirabilis* by affinity chromatography. Non-competitive inhibition of the enzyme by penicillins and low stability of the enzyme-inhibitor complex. Eur. J. Biochem. **71:**585–593.

23. **Mirelman, D., R. Bracha, and N. Sharon.** 1974. Studies on the elongation of bacterial cell wall

peptidoglycan and its inhibition by penicillin. Ann. N.Y. Acad. Sci. **235**:326–347.

24. **Mirelman, D., Y. Yashow-Gan, and U. Schwarz.** 1976. Growth pattern of peptidoglycan: biosynthesis in a thermo-sensitive division mutant of *Escherichia coli*. Biochemistry **15**:1781–1790.

25. **Nguyen-Distèche, M., J. M. Ghuysen, J. J. Pollock, P. E. Reynolds, H. R. Perkins, J. Coyette, and M. R. J. Salton.** 1974. Enzymes involved in wall peptide crosslinking in *Escherichia coli* K12, strain 44. Eur. J. Biochem. **41**:447–455.

26. **Nguyen-Distèche, M., J. J. Pollock, J. M. Ghuysen, J. Puig, P. E. Reynolds, H. R. Perkins, J. Coyette, and M. R. J. Salton.** 1974. Sensitivity to ampicillin and cephalothin of enzymes involved in wall peptide crosslinking in *Escherichia coli* K12, strain 44. Eur. J. Biochem. **41**:457–463.

27. **Pollock, J. J., M. Nguyen-Distèche, J. M. Ghuysen, J. Coyette, R. Linder, M. R. J. Salton, K. S. Kim, H. R. Perkins, and P. E. Reynolds.** 1974. Fractionation of the DD-carboxypeptidase-transpeptidase activities solubilized from membranes of *Escherichia coli* K12, strain 44. Eur. J. Biochem. **41**:439–446.

28. **Schleifer, K. H., and O. Kandler.** 1972. Peptidoglycan types of bacterial cell walls and their taxonomic implications. Bacteriol. Rev. **36**:407–477.

29. **Spratt, B. G.** 1975. Distinct penicillin binding proteins involved in the division, elongation and shape of *Escherichia coli* K12. Proc. Natl. Acad. Sci. U.S.A. **72**:3117–3127.

30. **Strominger, J. L.** 1970. Penicillin-sensitive enzymatic reactions in bacterial cell wall synthesis. Harvey Lect. **64**:179–213.

31. **Tamura, T., Y. Imae, and J. L. Strominger.** 1976. Purification to homogeneity and properties of two D-alanine carboxypeptidases I from *Escherichia coli*. J. Biol. Chem. **251**:414–423.

32. **Tipper, D. J., and J. L. Strominger.** 1965. Mechanism of action of penicillins: a proposal based on their structural similarity to acyl-D-alanyl-D-alanine. Proc. Natl. Acad. Sci. U.S.A. **54**:1133–1141.

33. **Ward, J. B., and H. R. Perkins.** 1973. The direction of glycan synthesis in a bacterial peptidoglycan. Biochem. J. **135**:721–728.

34. **Ward, J. B., and H. R. Perkins.** 1974. Peptidoglycan biosynthesis by preparations from *Bacillus licheniformis*: cross-linking of newly synthesized chains to preformed cell wall. Biochem. J. **139**:781–784.

35. **Wise, E. M., and J. T. Park.** 1965. Penicillin: its basic site of action as an inhibitor of a peptide crosslinking reaction in cell wall mucopeptide synthesis. Proc. Natl. Acad. Sci. U.S.A. **54**:75–81.

Penicillinase, Carboxypeptidase, and Transpeptidase Activities from *Staphylococcus aureus* H

JOHN W. KOZARICH

The Biological Laboratories, Harvard University, Cambridge, Massachusetts 02138

INTRODUCTION

The isolation of distinct penicillin-binding components from bacterial cell membranes has made possible the study of a number of in vitro reactions catalyzed by them. Using affinity chromatography, Strominger and co-workers have studied the penicillin-sensitive activities of the carboxypeptidases of *Bacillus subtilis*, *B. stearothermophilus*, and *Escherichia coli* (4). Transpeptidase activities of exocellular carboxypeptidases and of a membrane-bound and detergent-solubilized transpeptidase of *Streptomyces* have been extensively investigated by Ghuysen, Perkins, and co-workers (7). In all cases, the intimate relationship between these activities and their inhibition by penicillins remains difficult to interpret by complex kinetics. In addition, the large amounts of carboxypeptidase in *B. subtilis*, *B. stearothermophilus*, and *E. coli* have prevented the direct study of minor components. Moreover, the physiological significance of the carboxypeptidases is unclear, and at least one (*B. subtilis*) has been shown to be unessential for cell viability (1).

In the present study *Staphylococcus aureus* strain H was chosen for the solubilization and purification of a transpeptidase activity (J. W. Kozarich and J. L. Strominger, submitted for publication) for three reasons: (i) no major carboxypeptidase or penicillinase activity has been detected for this strain (9, 12); (ii) initial penicillin G binding studies to the particulate membranes indicated the presence of two penicillin-binding components (2); and (iii) a previous study with a particulate membrane fraction of *S. aureus* revealed a strong transpeptidase activity (11).

RESULTS AND DISCUSSION

Purified penicillin binding components from *S. aureus* H were prepared by penicillin affinity chromatography (3) of Triton X-100-solubilized membranes. The purified components were identical to those detected in the particulate membrane fraction with respect to

mobility by sodium dodecyl sulfate (SDS)-polyacrylamide gel electrophoresis (Fig. 1) and sensitivity to penicillin G (J. W. Kozarich et al., submitted for publication). The major and minor components, detected by their essentially irreversible reaction with penicillin G, had molecular weights of ~100,000 and ~115,000, respectively.

Coomassie brilliant blue staining for protein revealed a more complex pattern (Fig. 2). The major component now appeared as a doublet, and an additional protein with a molecular weight of 46,000 (46K protein) which was not detected by normal penicillin-binding procedures was also present. Sequential elutions of the affinity column with neutral hydroxylamine confirmed that the 46K protein bound penicillin less strongly than the higher-molecular-weight components (Fig. 2).

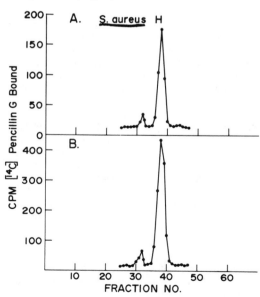

FIG. 1. *Binding of [¹⁴C]penicillin G to the penicillin-binding components of* S. aureus *H. (A) Membranes of* S. aureus. *(B) Purified components. (From Kozarich et al., submitted for publication)*

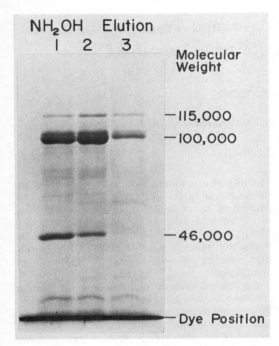

NH₂OH Elution
1   2   3

Molecular
Weight

—115,000
—100,000

—46,000

—Dye Position

FIG. 2. *SDS-polyacrylamide gel electrophoresis of the penicillin-binding components of* S. aureus *H released from the affinity column by three successive column volumes of neutral hydroxylamine. (From Kozarich and Strominger, submitted for publication)*

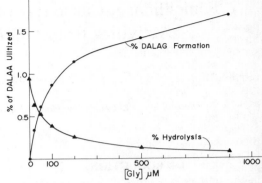

FIG. 3. *Transpeptidation of DALAA to DALAG (●) and inhibition of hydrolysis to DALA (▲) by glycine. Products were isolated by paper electrophoresis. (From Kozarich and Strominger, submitted for publication)*

These fractions were assayed for transpeptidase activity by the conversion of diacetyl-L-Lys-D-Ala-D-Ala (DALAA) to diacetyl-L-Lys-D-Ala-Gly (DALAG) in the presence of glycine (14). Activity as determined by this assay corresponded directly to the amount of the 46K protein in each fraction.

The results of penicillin binding and affinity chromatography suggested that the 46K protein interacted reversibly with penicillin. This possibility was utilized in the selective purification of this protein. Affinity chromatography of solubilized membranes prebound with penicillin G resulted in the retention of the 46K protein on the support while the other components were not retained. The purified protein remained active in the in vitro transpeptidation assay discussed above.

In the absence of glycine, the protein exhibited a carboxypeptidase activity affording diacetyl-L-Lys-D-Ala as the end product (Fig. 3). Increasing concentrations of glycine (to 1 mM) resulted in virtually complete suppression of hydrolysis and concomitant formation of DALAG with an overall rate acceleration (Fig. 3). An apparent K_m for glycine of 40 μM

was obtained. Under identical reaction conditions, 7 mM hydroxylamine was required to give 50% formation of diacetyl-L-Lys-D-Ala hydroxamate, the corresponding transpeptidation product (Kozarich and Strominger, submitted for publication). The higher reactivity of glycine over hydroxylamine, the stronger nucleophile, suggests that the transpeptidation is not merely a chemical partitioning of a reactive intermediate between acceptor and water. Clearly, a high degree of enzymatic selectivity is involved. Along these lines, carboxypeptidase activity is markedly inhibited by low concentrations of D-alanine ("K_m" = 50 μM) and not by L-alanine, indicating stereochemical specificity (Fig. 4). Recent studies of the inhibition by D-alanine of transpeptidation are consistent with the formation of a reactive intermediate in the reaction and a single binding site for D-alanine and glycine (Kozarich and Strominger, submitted for publication). Kinetic evidence of a reactive acyl-enzyme inter-

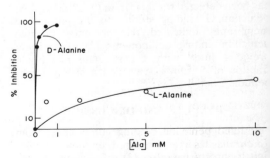

FIG. 4. *Inhibition of hydrolysis of DALAA to DALA (carboxypeptidase activity) by D-alanine (●) and L-alanine (○). (From Kozarich and Strominger, submitted for publication)*

mediate for the carboxypeptidases of *B. subtilis* and *B. stearothermophilus* has recently been reported (T. Nishino, J. W. Kozarich, and J. L. Strominger, J. Biol. Chem., in press) and is consistent with our findings for this protein. However, the much lower concentrations of glycine required for complete transpeptidation with this enzyme than with the carboxypeptidases argues against the physiological significance of the hydrolytic activity.

The reversible nature of the interaction of the enzyme with penicillin G was actually due to a weak penicillinase activity. Incubation of penicillin G with the purified enzyme resulted in the formation of penicilloic acid. Inhibition of transpeptidation by penicillin G was observed at relatively high concentrations, and the amount of suppression corresponded well with the time required for degradation of penicillin G to the inactive penicilloic acid. At low concentrations of penicillin G similar to those required for irreversible binding to other components, degradation of penicillin was completed quickly (<10 min) compared with the time scale required for the detection of transpeptidation products (~180 min). These data suggest that both the transpeptidase and penicillinase activities are occurring on the same enzyme. This possibility is also supported by the kinetic parameters of the reactions (Table 1). The high K_m for DALAA (100 mM) is consistent with one reported (6) for a detergent-solubilized transpeptidase activity from *Streptomyces* (40 mM). Perhaps the most striking kinetic feature is the similarity of the V_{max} values of the individual activities. This coincidence suggests that, if transpeptidation and penicillin degradation are occurring on the same enzyme, one can infer that both reactions may be occurring at the same site and that the rate-determining step is similar for each process. A possible step could be the deacylation of a penicilloyl- or acyl-enzyme intermediate.

The possible coincidence of these catalytic activities at a single enzymatic site is attractive from an evolutionary standpoint. If penicillin is recognized as an analogue of the D-alanyl-D-alanine terminus of the peptidoglycan (15), then one might expect the resulting penicilloyl-enzyme intermediate to be activated in a manner similar to a corresponding acyl-enzyme intermediate during transpeptidation (Nishino et al., in press). Although the penicilloyl-enzyme intermediate would be sterically inaccessible to a transpeptidase acceptor, such as glycine, since the acceptor binding site would be blocked by the portion of the penicilloyl moiety corresponding to the terminal D-alanine, the activated penicilloyl-enzyme bond

TABLE 1. *Kinetic parameters of transpeptidase, carboxypeptidase, and penicillinase activities*

Activity	K_m	V_{max} (nm/min per mg of protein)	Turnover no.
Transpeptidase	100 mM (DALAA)	400	20
Carboxypeptidase	—	240	12
Penicillinase	20 μM (PenG)[a]	500	25

[a] PenG, Penicillin G.

may be accessible to smaller nucleophiles. Sufficient activation and accessibility of the bond could result in the sensitivity of the intermediate to hydrolysis, affording a penicillinase activity. Such an enzyme would have transpeptidase, carboxypeptidase, and penicillinase activities, and may have served as a prototype in other strains for the evolution of much more potent penicillinases. Along these lines, we have found that glycine is not an acceptor in the penicillinase action of the 46K protein.

Strong support for the enzymatic activation of the penicilloyl-enzyme intermediate has been provided by studies of the hydroxylamine-induced release of the penicilloyl moiety from the native complex (Kozarich et al., submitted for publication). Early work (8, 13) suggested that the formation of penicilloyl hydroxamate from penicilloyl-enzyme complexes by treatment with neutral hydroxylamine, a small, reactive nucleophile, supported a thiolester linkage for the attachment of penicillin to the enzyme. This conclusion was based on the chemical reactivity of thiolesters to hydroxylamine. Boiling the complex resulted in the inhibition of the release. This was explained by the possible transacylation of the penicilloyl moiety from a thiol group to another amino acid, e.g., the ε-amino group of a lysine, resulting in a more stable linkage. Recent experiments (Kozarich et al., submitted for publication) using milder denaturing conditions have revealed that the release is an enzymatically catalyzed process. Pretreatment of the penicilloyl-enzyme complexes from the major components of *S. aureus* and the carboxypeptidase of *B. subtilis* (Fig. 5) by heat (55°C) or detergent (1% SDS) results in the time-dependent inhibition of penicilloyl hydroxamate formation. The rate of inhibition corresponds closely to the loss of enzymatic activity of the components as determined by penicillin binding and carboxypeptidase activity under the same denaturing conditions. Trichloroacetic acid precipitation of the complex, which prevents transacylation of thiolesters, also inhibits the release. These data strongly suggest that the release is largely due to activation of the penicilloyl-enzyme bond

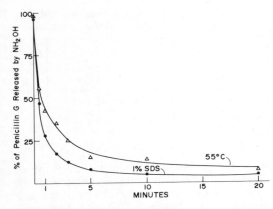

FIG. 5. *Kinetics of inactivation of hydroxylamine-induced [14C]penicillin G release from penicilloylated B.* subtilis *carboxypeptidase by denaturation at 55°C (△) or by 1% SDS at 25°C (●). (From Kozarich et al., submitted for publication)*

by the native complex. This phenomenon bears a striking similarity to the formation of hydroxamic acid from acetyl chymotrypsin, which contains a serine ester linkage (5, 10).

Experiments on the chemical reactivity of the denatured penicilloyl-carboxypeptidase complex support an ester linkage (Table 2). The release of [14C]penicillin from the heat- or trichloroacetic acid-denatured complex with sodium borohydride or at pH 12 is consistent with the cleavage of a carboxylic ester bond and not a more stable linkage, such as an amide bond. A thiolester appears to be excluded by the inertness of the denatured complex to neutral hydroxylamine. The chemical properties of penicilloyl-amino acid model compounds are currently being investigated to further substantiate these points.

Two important conclusions may be drawn from these experiments. First, even components which bind penicillin "irreversibly" contain a relatively high degree of activation of the penicilloyl-enzyme bond. Second, the penicilloyl-enzyme bond is chemically rather stable for a number of enzymes. These conclusions suggest that the broad range of sensitivities of penicilloyl-enzyme complexes to hydrolysis, i.e., penicillinase activity, results from varying degrees of enzymatic activation and not from different types of chemically reactive linkages. Clearly then, depending upon the rate of deacylation and of denaturation of the complex, one could conceivably trap a stable penicilloyl-enzyme complex for highly reactive penicillinases. Along these lines, a stable quinicillin-S. aureus penicillinase complex has recently been isolated by rapid denaturation (16).

The chemical stability of the complex is consistent with an ester or amide linkage.

Denaturation by acetone precipitation has been used to isolate a penicillin complex of the 46K protein (Fig. 6). Penicillin binding followed by heat denaturation (boiling) permitted the release of penicillin from this protein, thereby preventing its detection as discussed above. However, rapid acetone denaturation (Fig. 6-1) of *S. aureus* components treated with [14C]-penicillin G resulted in the isolation of the complex for the 46K protein in addition to the other components as determined by fluorography of an SDS-polyacrylamide gel. Addition of unlabeled penicillin G prior to precipitation resulted in the dilution of radioactivity in the 46K protein only (Fig. 6-2). This graphically il-

TABLE 2. *Chemical reactivity of [14C]penicillin G-B.* subtilis *carboxypeptidase. (From Kozarich et al., submitted for publication)*

Treatment[a]	[14C]penicillin G bound[b] (cpm)	[14C]penicillin G released (%)
Control (pH 7.5)	4,670	—
Boiled (pH 7.5)	4,800	—
NH₂OH (pH 7.5)[c]	160	96.5
Boiled + NH₂OH (pH 7.5)[c]	4,450	5.8
Boiled + Tris-hydrochloride (pH 9.3)[d] ..	4,240	9.2
Boiled + NaBH₄ (pH 9.3)[d]	40	99.0
Trichloroacetic acid + NH₂OH (pH 7.5)[e] ...	4,490	4.0
Trichloroacetic acid + Tris-hydrochloride (pH 9.3)[e]	4,180	10.5
Trichloroacetic acid + NaBH₄ (pH 9.3)[e]	30	99.4
Trichloroacetic acid + NH₂OH (pH 12.0)[e] ..	20	99.6
Trichloroacetic acid + NaOH (pH 12.0)[e]	15	99.7

[a] [14C]penicillin G binding was carried out in the following manner. To 50 μl of carboxypeptidase solution (~10 μg) was added 5 μl of 0.25 M ZnSO₄, 5 μl of 1 M KPO₄, pH 7.5, and 5 μl of [14C]penicillin G (5 g). The solution was maintained at 25°C for 5 min.
[b] [14C]penicillin G remaining bound was determined by paper chromatography.
[c] Penicillin G binding solutions were treated with 30 μl of 2 M neutral hydroxylamine at 25°C for 30 min. Boiling of samples is performed prior to addition of reagents.
[d] Solutions were treated with concentrated solutions of Tris-hydrochloride or sodium borohydride to pH 9.3. Samples were maintained at 25°C for 30 min.
[e] Solutions were treated with 5 μl of 6 M trichloroacetic acid for 3 min at 25°C. Samples were then treated with reagents as described above.

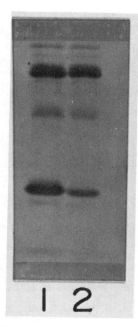

FIG. 6. *Fluorography of an SDS-polyacrylamide gel of [¹⁴C]penicillin G-protein complexes of* S. aureus *components denatured by acetone precipitation. (1) [¹⁴C]penicillin G at 10 µg/ml for 5 min followed by acetone to 80%. (2) [¹⁴C]penicillin G at 10 µg/ml for 5 min followed by a 10-fold dilution with un-labeled penicillin G for 1 min followed by acetone to 80%. (From Kozarich and Strominger, submitted for publication)*

lustrates the penicillinase activity of the component. The large amount of complex isolated (60%) indicates that deacylation is most likely the slow step. Once denatured, the complex is stable to boiling SDS, as are the complexes of the other components.

The detection of the [¹⁴C]penicilloyl-enzyme complex for the 46K protein provides a convenient method for determining the inhibition of its formation by transpeptidase substrate (DALAA). The binding of [¹⁴C]penicillin G to the 46K protein is inhibited by concentrations of DALAA approaching the K_m for this substrate (Fig. 7). This suppression of complex formation establishes the interaction of the 46K protein with the transpeptidase substrate. The requirement of K_m concentrations of DALAA for inhibition further verifies the 46K protein as the site of transpeptidation.

Implicit in the above discussion has been the formation of a reactive acyl-enzyme intermediate in the transpeptidation reaction. Although kinetic data are consistent with its formation (Kozarich and Strominger, submitted for publication; Nishino et al., in press), the iso-

lation of the native complex seems infeasible considering the instability of the native penicilloyl-enzyme complex. However, if both reactions are occurring at the same site, one might expect the denatured acyl-enzyme complex to have a chemical stability comparable to the corresponding penicilloyl-enzyme complex. Acetone precipitation of a reaction mixture of *S. aureus* penicillin-binding components and di-[¹⁴C]acetyl-L-Lys-D-Ala-D-Ala results in the association of radioactivity with all of the components, as determined by fluorography of an SDS-polyacrylamide gel (Kozarich and Strominger, submitted for publication). The complexes are stable to boiling SDS. Mild alkaline hydrolysis (pH 12) of the complexes affords di-[¹⁴C]-acetyl-L-Lys-D-Ala as the released product, confirming the presence of a covalent acyl-enzyme bond formed via cleavage of the terminal D-alanine of the initial substrate. The detection of complexes for the larger components suggests that they may have physiological functions in cell wall synthesis and that the inability to determine any in vitro catalytic activity may be the result of assay conditions or partial loss of activity due to detergent solubilization and affinity chromatography. The sensitivity of the acyl-enzyme bond to alkali is similar to that of the penicilloyl-enzyme bond, suggesting a comparable type of linkage, i.e., an ester.

The isolation of both complexes has made feasible the characterization of acyl- and penicilloyl-peptide fragments to determine the active sites of both reactions. We hope that this method will provide a definitive answer to the question of the site of penicillin action since kinetic analysis has been unable to distinguish between one or two individual sites for transpeptidation and penicillin action. This technique

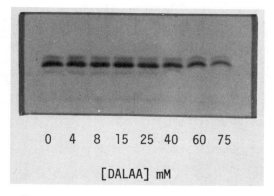

FIG. 7. *Fluorography of an SDS-polyacrylamide gel of [¹⁴C]penicillin G-46K protein complex in the presence of DALAA. (From Kozarich and Strominger, submitted for publication)*

is also being extended to other well-characterized penicillin-binding components, such as the carboxypeptidases of *B. subtilis* and *B. stearothermophilus*.

The question of the physiological significance of the 46K protein is difficult to answer. The work of Mirelman and Sharon (11), however, provides a possible explanation. Using a particulate membrane fraction of *S. aureus*, they found that transpeptidation was inhibited 60% by penicillin G at 0.5 μg/ml. The remaining activity was quite insensitive to further inhibition by penicillin G, requiring at least 25 μg/ml for 50% inhibition. These results are consistent with two separate transpeptidases, one which is sensitive to penicillin and one which is not. It is very reasonable that the 46K protein is responsible for the penicillin-resistant transpeptidation. The observed resistance, however, could be due to the weak penicillinase activity of this component as discussed above. Although no in vitro transpeptidation has been demonstrated for the larger components, it is clear that they play some role in cell wall synthesis since at least one penicillin-sensitive transpeptidase activity needs to be accounted for. This type of inhibition is easily explained by an irreversible binding of penicillin to one of these components. In addition, spontaneous cloxacillin-resistant mutants of *S. aureus*, currently being isolated in our laboratory, reveal alterations in these larger components.

ACKNOWLEDGMENTS

This work was supported by Public Health Service research grant AI-09152 from the National Institute of Allergy and Infectious Diseases and National Science Foundation grant BMS71-01120 to J. L. Strominger. J.W.K. is a postdoctoral fellow of the National Institutes of Health.

LITERATURE CITED

1. Blumberg, P. M., and J. L. Strominger. 1971. Inactivation of D-alanine carboxypeptidase by penicillins and cephalosporins is not lethal in *Bacillus subtilis*. Proc. Natl. Acad. Sci. U.S.A. **69**:3751–3755.

2. Blumberg, P. M., and J. L. Strominger. 1972. Five penicillin binding components occur in *Bacillus subtilis* membranes. J. Biol. Chem. **247**:8107–8113.

3. Blumberg, P. M., and J. L. Strominger. 1974. Covalent affinity chromatography as a means of purifying the penicillin binding components from bacterial membranes, p. 401–405. *In* W. B. Jakoby and M. Wilshek (ed.), Methods in enzymology, vol. 34. Academic Press Inc., New York.

4. Blumberg, P. M., and J. L. Strominger. 1974. Interaction of penicillin with the bacterial cell: penicillin-binding proteins and penicillin-sensitive enzymes. Bacteriol. Rev. **38**:291–335.

5. Dixon, G. H., and H. Neurath. 1957. An intermediate in the deacylation of mono-acetyl-α-chymotrypsin having the properties of acetyl-imidazolyl. J. Am. Chem. Soc. **79**:4558–4559.

6. Dusart, J., A. Marquet, J. M. Ghuysen, and H. R. Perkins. 1975. The catalytic activity and penicillin sensitivity in the liquid and frozen states of membrane-bound and detergent-solubilized transpeptidase of *Streptomyces* R 61. Eur. J. Biochem. **56**:57–65.

7. Ghuysen, J. M., J. M. Frere, M. Leyh-Bouille, J. Dusart, M. Nguyen-Disteche, J. Coyette, A. Marquet, H. R. Perkins, and M. Nieto. 1975. Bacterial transpeptidases and penicillin. Bull. Inst. Pasteur Paris **73**:101–140.

8. Lawrence, P. J., and J. L. Strominger. 1970. Biosynthesis of the peptidoglycan of bacterial cell walls. XV. The binding of radioactive penicillin to the particulate enzyme preparation of *Bacillus subtilis* and its reversal with hydroxylamine of thiols. J. Biol. Chem. **245**:3653–3659.

9. Matsuhashi, M., C. P. Dietrich, and J. L. Strominger. 1967. Biosynthesis of the peptidoglycan of bacterial cell walls. III. The role of soluble ribonucleic acid and of lipid intermediates in glycine incorporation in *Staphylococcus aureus*. J. Biol. Chem. **242**: 3191–3206.

10. Matthews, B. W., P. B. Sigler, R. Henderson, and D. M. Blow. 1967. Three-dimensional structure of tosyl-α-chymotrypsin. Nature (London) **214**:652–656.

11. Mirelman, D., and N. Sharon. 1972. Biosynthesis of peptidoglycan by a cell wall preparation of *Staphylococcus aureus* and its inhibition by penicillin. Biochem. Biophys. Res. Commun. **46**:1909–1917.

12. Park, J. T., M. E. Griffith, and I. Stevenson. 1971. Resistance to penicillin in mutants of a penicillinase-negative organism, *Staphylococcus aureus* H. J. Bacteriol. **108**:1154–1160.

13. Suginaka, H., P. M. Blumberg, and J. L. Strominger. 1972. Multiple penicillin-binding components in *Bacillus subtilis*, *Bacillus cereus*, *Staphylococcus aureus*, and *Escherichia coli*. J. Biol. Chem. **247**:5279–5288.

14. Tamura, T., Y. Imae, and J. L. Strominger. 1976. Purification to homogeneity and properties of two D-alanine carboxypeptidases I from *Escherichia coli*. J. Biol. Chem. **251**:414–423.

15. Tipper, D. J., and J. L. Strominger. 1965. Mechanism of action of penicillins: a proposal based on their structural similarity to acyl-D-alanyl-D alanine. Proc. Natl. Acad. Sci. U.S.A. **54**:1133–1141.

16. Virden, R., A. F. Bristow, and R. H. Pain. 1975. The active site of penicillinase from *Staphylococcus aureus* PC 1. Isolation of a specific covalent complex with the substrate quinacillin. Biochem. J. **149**:397–401.

Murein Hydrolases and the Lytic and Killing Action of Penicillin

ALEXANDER TOMASZ AND JOACHIM V. HÖLTJE

*The Rockefeller University, New York, New York 10021, and Institute für Biologie,
University Tübingen, Tübingen, Germany*

The superb antimicrobial effectiveness of β-lactams is due to a unique property of these drugs, not shared by many other antibacterial agents—namely, that β-lactams not only inhibit microbial growth but also kill and lyse the great majority of bacteria. It was the spectacle of lysing staphylococci on an agar plate in the vicinity of a contaminating mold colony that led Fleming to the discovery of penicillin 40 years ago; yet the mechanism of this bacteriolytic effect has remained largely obscure. In fact, it seems that most of the efforts over the past two decades were concentrated on the identification of penicillin-sensitive enzymatic reactions in the cell wall metabolism of bacteria (Ghuysen, p. 195, this volume), and relatively little attention has been paid to the question of why and how interference with the murein metabolism might precipitate the irreversible physiological effects of penicillin. The present treatise is addressed to that very question. We shall summarize four sets of relatively recent observations (most of them gathered in experiments with pneumococci) that throw light on the complex nature of the lytic and cytocidal effects of penicillin. The key observations may be summarized as follows:

1. Penicillin-induced lysis is caused by the activity of a bacterial murein hydrolase(s). Bacteria in which the activity of this enzyme is suppressed (by mutation or by physiological manipulation) exhibit a peculiar response to penicillin, called "tolerance." In a tolerant bacterium, penicillin simply inhibits cellular growth but does not cause lysis; the rate of loss of viability is also substantially decreased.

2. Treatment of bacteria with penicillin and other cell wall inhibitors can trigger the activity of latent murein hydrolase.

3. The lipid-containing membrane teichoic acids ("lipoteichoic acids") present in pneumococci and in many other gram-positive bacteria are powerful inhibitors of murein hydrolases.

4. Treatment of bacteria with penicillin and other cell wall inhibitors causes a rapid release, into the surrounding medium, of a macromolecular complex that contains the murein hydrolase inhibitor lipoteichoic acid.

On the basis of these observations, we have proposed a mechanism for the lytic and cytocidal action of penicillins (29). It was suggested that in vivo in the bacterial cells murein hydrolases are under the negative control of inhibitory lipopolysaccharides; inhibition of peptidoglycan synthesis by penicillin causes (for reasons not clearly understood) a loss of these inhibitors from the cells, leading to the triggering of murein hydrolase activity which, in turn, destroys the structural integrity of the cell.

Next, we shall discuss each one of the key observations in some detail.

1. ROLE OF MUREIN HYDROLASES ("AUTOLYSINS") IN PENICILLIN-INDUCED LYSIS

Suppression of the murein hydrolase(s) causes a peculiar form of resistance ("tolerance") against the lytic action of penicillin and other cell wall inhibitors. Evidence for this conclusion has mainly come from three experimental systems.

A. Ethanolamine-Grown Pneumococci

Pneumococci have a nutritional requirement for choline. About 80 to 85% of the incorporated choline ends up in the cell wall teichoic acid that is covalently attached to the peptidoglycan (22); the rest of the 15 to 20% of choline is in the pneumococcal Forssman antigen (2), a lipid-containing polysaccharide that has several properties similar to those of the conventional lipoteichoic acids and that has a primary chemical structure similar if not identical to that of the wall teichoic acid of the same bacterium (4, 9).

It has been shown (15) that the choline residues of the wall teichoic acid serve as specific ligands for the catalytic activity of the pneumococcal murein hydrolase (an N-acetyl-muramic acid-L-alanine amidase, to be referred to also as "amidase" or "autolysin").

If choline is replaced by ethanolamine (EA) in the growth medium, the pneumococci will utilize this amino alcohol and biosynthesize EA-containing wall teichoic acids (25). Such cultures grow with normal generation times. However, the EA-grown bacteria exhibit a peculiar response to penicillin that is strikingly different from the response of the choline-grown pneumococci. In contrast to the choline-grown cells, EA-grown pneumococci are not lysed by penicillin, not even at very high penicillin concentrations (several thousand times higher than the minimal inhibitory concentration). Nevertheless, the EA-grown bacteria retain the high penicillin sensitivity typical of pneumococci, but instead of lysis the EA-grown cells simply stop growing at the minimal inhibitory concentration of penicillin (27). Thus penicillin, a typical bacteriolytic agent for the choline-grown cultures, acts as a bacteriostatic drug with the EA-grown bacteria, while the dose responses of the two types of cultures to penicillin remain identical. A further unique aspect of this phenomenon is that it lacks specificity with respect to the inhibitory agent: the EA-grown cells show lysis resistance not only with penicillin G, but with *all* cell wall inhibitors tested (D-cycloserine, β-chloro-D-alanine, vancomycin, cephalexin, etc.) irrespective of their chemical nature or site of inhibition. We suggested the term "multiple antibiotic tolerance" for this phenomenon (26).

The tolerant response of EA-grown pneumococci to penicillin seems to be the consequence of two well-characterized biochemical defects in the autolytic system of EA-grown bacteria: (i) the EA-containing cell wall is completely resistant to the hydrolytic action of the pneumococcal autolysin (22); (ii) EA-grown bacteria contain only an abnormal, low-molecular-weight, low-catalytic-activity (E-form) autolysin (31) that appears to be the subunit of the high-molecular-weight and high-catalytic-activity (C-form) enzyme characteristic of choline-grown pneumococci.

The antibiotic tolerance of EA-grown pneumococci is quickly reversible to the lytic response by the readdition of choline to the growth medium (27). Under these conditions there is a rapid "correction" of the defective autolytic system: pneumococci promptly shift to choline utilization; within minutes after choline addition, one can observe the incorporation of choline-containing (autolysin-sensitive) wall polymers at the cell wall growth zone and also the appearance of catalytically active (C-form) autolysin in the cells (32).

B. Autolysin-Defective Mutant of Pneumococcus

A typical tolerant response to penicillin and other cell wall inhibitors is also exhibited by a pneumococcus mutant (18) which has greatly lowered levels of residual amidase activity (5 to 10% of the wild-type level) but possesses "normal" (i.e., amidase-sensitive and choline-containing) cell walls (12).

C. pH-Dependent Antibiotic Tolerance

A recent collaborative work between our laboratory and the laboratory of R. Lopez in Madrid (Instituto di Immunologia y Biologia Microbiana) yielded an interesting new approach to the study of penicillin-induced lysis. It was found that the lytic effect of β-lactams is a function of the pH of the growth medium in several species of bacteria (19). Lysis of pneumococcal cultures was found to change to a tolerant response if the medium pH was below 6.0 at the time of penicillin treatment. In *Bacillus subtilis*, growth at pH 6.6 prevented penicillin-induced lysis. For each bacterial species (shown in Fig. 1) there exists a unique growth medium pH value at which the particular bacterium shows lytic response to penicillin (10). These pH values correspond to the in vitro pH optima of the major autolysin. At pH values below or above the range "permissive" for lysis, the bacteria exhibit typical features of antibiotic tolerance: (i) they retain normal sensitivity to penicillin and other cell wall inhibitors (i.e., their dose-response curves to these drugs are identical at both the lysis-permissive and lysis-nonpermissive pH values) but respond to cell wall inhibitors by a halt in growth, instead of lysis (Fig. 2); (ii) the loss of lytic response is independent of antibiotic dose and of the chemical nature of the antibiotic; (iii) protection against lysis at the nonpermissive conditions is reversible: lysis of the cells and loss of viability may be triggered by a post-incubation of the drug-treated bacteria at the pH permissive for lysis (19).

A plausible mechanism for the pH dependence of penicillin-induced lysis is that pH values nonpermissive for lysis inhibit the activity of a murein hydrolase which, under permissive conditions, is responsible for the antibiotic-induced destruction of the bacteria.

The observations summarized clearly invalidate an early model of penicillin lysis in which the "imbalance" between an increasing cytoplasmic mass and an inhibited cell wall

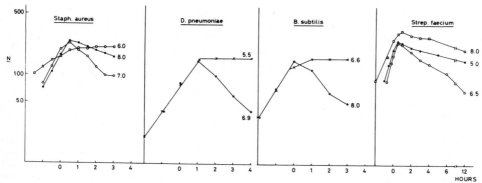

FIG. 1. *pH-dependent penicillin tolerance of four gram-positive bacterial species. Bacteria were grown in the appropriate culture media at the pH values indicated. Antibiotic was added at 0 min of incubation. Benzylpenicillin was used for pneumococci (0.1 μg/ml) and streptococci (10 μg/ml); staphylococci and B. subtilis received cloxacillin at 1 and 0.2 μg/ml, respectively. Growth and lysis were monitored by nephelometry (Coleman nephelometer). (Reproduced from reference 10)*

mass was supposed to cause rupture of the wall by the mechanical-osmotic pressure of the cytoplasm. Our data confirm earlier suggestions (23, 24, 33) that the penicillin-induced lysis is catalyzed by an enzyme.

2. TRIGGERING OF MUREIN HYDROLASE ACTIVITY

It has been shown recently that purified wild-type autolysin can be adsorbed into the surface of the live mutant cells without any apparent effect on the growth, growth rate, or other essential properties of the bacteria (30). Since the adsorption of enzyme molecules is *not* followed by lysis of the cells, we must assume that immediately upon attach-

ment to the cell surface the enzyme molecules are "silenced." A plausible mechanism for such a rapid inhibition of activity would be the attachment of enzyme molecules to an inhibitor. A likely candidate for such an inhibitor is the Forssman antigen ("Fag"), the lipid-containing teichoic acid of pneumococci (2). These molecules are known to traverse the space between wall and membrane and be accessible from the outside in the intact bacteria. The Fag has been shown to be a powerful and specific inhibitor of the pneumococcal amidase (14), and recent studies show that purified amidase can physically associate with Fag in vitro (see section 3).

This system has already yielded extremely valuable information concerning the role of

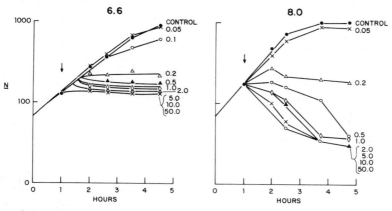

FIG. 2. *Effect of cloxacillin on cultures of* B. subtilis *168 growing at pH 6.6 and pH 8. In the exponential phase of growth at cell concentrations of about 5 × 10⁷ viable cells per ml, the cultures received cloxacillin (arrow) at the concentrations (micrograms per milliliter of growth medium) indicated by the numbers, and the growth response of the cultures was followed by nephelometry. (Reproduced from reference 19)*

autolysin in penicillin-induced lysis. In short, the experimental introduction of the missing enzyme (autolysin) into the mutant cells has made these bacteria immediately "revert" to the wild phenotype in their response to penicillin and other cell wall inhibitors (30). In contrast to the enzyme-defective mutant cells, the enzyme-coated mutant bacteria lysed upon exposure to cell wall inhibitors. Apparently, penicillin treatment of the enzyme "carrier" bacteria can in some way release the inhibition of cell-adsorbed enzyme molecules and trigger their activity. A plausible biochemical correlate of this triggering (i.e., the release into the growth medium of an enzyme inhibitor) will be discussed in section 4.

The artificially "reconstructed" amidase-containing cells mimic the true wild-type bacteria in another property also: pretreatment of the reconstructed cells with inhibitors of protein or RNA synthesis inhibits lysis by a subsequent treatment with penicillin. One must assume, therefore, that inhibition of protein synthesis in the enzyme-carrier bacteria somehow inhibits the activity (or the triggering) of the adsorbed enzyme molecules. Alternatively, the *consequence* of triggered amidase activity (i.e., cellular lysis) may be blocked by inhibitors of protein synthesis. The mechanism of this protection phenomenon is not yet understood. However, the experiments described strongly suggest that the well-known phenomenon of protection of bacteria against penicillin-induced lysis by protein synthesis inhibitors is *not* caused by a deficiency in the number of hydrolase molecules at the cell surface—contrary to a common notion frequently quoted in the literature.

3. LIPOTEICHOIC ACIDS AS INHIBITORS OF MUREIN HYDROLASES

Most gram-positive bacteria examined are known to contain lipopolysaccharides in their plasma membranes. The chemical "backbone" structure of these macromolecules seems to be composed of a polymer of glycerophosphate units (pGp) with various carbohydrate substituents attached to the free hydroxyl group plus a (presumably terminally located) glycolipid. Because of the resemblance of the polysaccharide portion of these polymers to the cell wall teichoic acids, the names "membrane teichoic acid" (6) and, more recently, "lipoteichoic acid" (34) have been coined. Pneumococcal membranes also contain a lipopolysaccharide (Forssman antigen) in which the polysaccharide seems to have a structure closely similar to that of the isologous wall

teichoic acid: the "C-polysaccharide," a complex substance composed of ribitol and choline phosphate and other components (4, 22).

In spite of its complex chemical composition, the Forssman antigen of pneumococci resembles the conventional (polyglycerophosphate) type of lipoteichoic acids in several respects, such as physicochemical properties (2), cellular localization (2), and its relationship to the pneumococcal wall teichoic acid (3). The pneumococcal Forssman antigen (to be called here "lipid-containing teichoic acid" or L_cTA) is a powerful and specific inhibitor of the murein hydrolase of pneumococcus (14). The mechanism of this inhibition seems to involve attachment of enzyme molecules to the L_cTA (manuscript in preparation) at a site which is not identical to the catalytic site of the enzyme protein (16).

In a collaborative effort with A. J. Wicken, G. D. Shockman, and their colleagues, we were able to extend the validity of the pneumococcal findings to three additional species of bacteria which contain pGp-type lipoteichoic acid. The muramidases of *Streptococcus faecium* and *Lactobacillus acidophilus* and the amidase of *Bacillus subtilis* were found to be inhibited by pGp-type lipoteichoic acids (5).

There are four experimental observations suggesting that in vivo the murein hydrolase of pneumococci is under the inhibition of the L_cTA. (i) Addition of high concentrations (3 to 5 mg per ml) of L_cTA to the growth medium of pneumococci protects the culture against penicillin-induced lysis (14). (ii) Pneumococci growing in the presence of high concentrations of L_cTA form long chains (13); such an inhibition of cell separation at the end of cell division is a frequent symptom of an inhibited murein hydrolase in bacteria. (iii) Addition of L_cTA to the growth medium also inhibits triggering of the pneumococcal hydrolase absorbed onto live mutant cells (30). (iv) L_cTA in the medium can inhibit the release of progency bacteriophage in the case of the pneumococcal phage Dp1 which requires host autolytic activity for the exit of progeny phage particles from the infected bacteria (13).

4. RELEASE OF A LIPID-CONTAINING TEICHOIC ACID MUREIN HYDROLASE INHIBITOR FROM BACTERIA DURING PENICILLIN TREATMENT

Treatment of pneumococci with low concentrations of penicillin does not inhibit synthesis of cell wall teichoic acids. However, in the presence of the drug, both the cellular

L_cTA and the newly made wall teichoic acids are secreted into the growth medium (29). This secretion phenomenon is best illustrated by the use of lysis-defective bacteria (such as the amidase-defective mutant pneumococcus or wild-type cells grown under conditions nonpermissive for lysis). The medium of such cultures becomes enriched in an autolysin inhibitor that has properties similar to those of the L_cTA with the exception of an increased precipitability by cold trichloroacetic acid and partial precipitation by antiserum against wall teichoic acids (C-polysaccharide; 29).

It is not clear what the relationship may be between the penicillin-induced secretion and the extensive "shedding" of lipoteichoic acids which has been described in both the exponential phase and the stationary phase of growth of some streptococci (20). The secretion observed in pneumococci is specifically induced by cell wall inhibitors; it occurs only to a limited degree in control bacteria or in cells treated with inhibitors of other cellular polymer syntheses (e.g., chloramphenicol, rifamycin, mitomycin C). Secretion is rapid and is observable at the minimal inhibitory concentrations of the cell wall inhibitors. Only limited leakage of other cellular polymers (nucleic acids and protein) appears to accompany the massive penicillin-induced release of wall and membrane teichoic acids (29).

The exact chemical nature and the more precise physiological correlates of the secreted lipid-containing polysaccharides remain to be determined. For our discussion the relevant aspect of the secretion phenomenon is the fact that an inhibitor of murein hydrolase is lost from the bacteria during treatment with agents that can induce lysis of wild-type cells or can trigger the activity of hydrolase molecules adsorbed onto live mutant bacteria.

MODEL FOR THE MECHANISM OF THE IRREVERSIBLE EFFECTS OF PENICILLIN

According to our model, the mechanism of antibacterial action of penicillin may be broken down into two main phases.

Primary Phase

Penicillin molecules inhibit the activity of an enzyme of peptidoglycan metabolism—presumably a transpeptidase or carboxypeptidase (Ghuysen, p. 195, this volume). (This enzyme should correspond to one or more of the penicillin-binding proteins [Buchanan, p. 191, and Spratt, p. 182, this volume].) We suggest

that the primary physiological response to this inhibition is inhibition of bacterial growth. The exact biochemical mechanism of this growth inhibition is *not* known. It may be a more or less trivial consequence of the perturbation of the cell surface replication. Alternatively, it may involve a specific and unique regulatory signal between the biosynthesis of wall polymers and other cytoplasmic syntheses, in analogy with the coordinate regulation of protein and RNA synthesis (see 17 for the role of the R_c locus in cell wall synthesis). This primary physiological response to penicillin can only be observed in lysis-defective bacteria such as the amidase-defective mutants or bacteria grown under physiological conditions of antibiotic tolerance. A further example for this type of response is the case of *Streptococcus sanguis H* (Wicky), which is only inhibited by penicillins (and other cell wall inhibitors) but is never lysed. Loss of viability of this species is also very limited (maximum of 80% of colony-forming units is lost; Horne and Tomasz, in preparation).

Secondary Phase

In most wild-type bacteria the primary response (inhibition of growth) is followed by secondary (irreversible) effects of penicillin. The key element at the center of this secondary phase of penicillin action is the bacterial murein hydrolase(s) and the in vivo control of this enzyme(s). We suggest, as part of a working hypothesis, that the main biochemical events of this second phase are as follows:

1. Inhibition of peptidoglycan biosynthesis (by "early" inhibitors, such as D-cycloserine or fosfonomycin) or inhibition of the incorporation of peptidoglycan oligomers (e.g., by penicillin; 7, 21) appears to labilize the cellular lipoteichoic acid complex with the resultant loss of these molecules into the medium. The biochemical mechanism of this important phenomenon is not known. Just as in the case of the mechanism of growth inhibition, we do not know whether the labilization of L_cTA complex is a trivial or a unique biochemical event. Labilization (and secretion into the medium) are clearly not assisted by hydrolase activity since lysis-defective bacteria (e.g., mutant pneumococci or *S. sanguis H*) exhibit this phenomenon. The possible involvement of the lipoteichoic acid carrier (first described by Glaser's group [8]) and the possible role of a form of the bactoprenol carrier-lipid (1, 11) in the mechanism of secretion has been considered (29). The understanding of the molecular mechanism of this process seems critical since

it may provide ways to improve the pharmacologically most important aspects of penicillin action.

2. In bacteria containing murein hydrolases, the loss of the endogenous enzyme inhibitor results in the triggering of the hydrolase activity which leads to hydrolysis of covalent bonds in the cell wall followed by the exposure of plasma membrane and an eventual osmotic explosion (lysis) of the cell. Again, we would like to emphasize that point 2 is part of a hypothesis rather than an experimental fact.

One of the physiological roles of the bacterial autolysins seems to be in the physical separation of daughter cells at the end of cell division. It is conceivable that this physiological activity is triggered, on a small scale and at a strictly confined area of the cell surface, by a cyclic, genetically programmed halt in peptidoglycan synthesis at the end of bacterial cell division, i.e., by a mechanism similar to that observable in penicillin-treated bacteria. In this sense one may define the cause of the irreversible effects of penicillin as the premature triggering of an enzyme (murein hydrolase) activity, the physiological role of which is at the end of cell division.

LYTIC ACTION VERSUS KILLING OF BACTERIA BY PENICILLIN

It is well known that during penicillin treatment of bacteria the rate of loss of viability (colony-forming ability) is much faster than culture lysis. The discrepancy is only in part explainable by the superior sensitivity of viability determination as compared with that of turbidity measurements. It should also be recalled that loss of viability is only slowed down but is never completely eliminated in the various tolerant bacteria (10, 19, 26, 27). It is conceivable that in some bacteria irreversible loss of colony-forming ability reflects the irreversible nature of the primary inhibition (for instance, irreversible inhibition of transpeptidation). However, it is known that in many bacteria the primary inhibition is reversible (Ghuysen, p. 195, this volume). For this reason, one has to entertain additional explanations for the bactericidal effect of penicillin. Two alternatives appear plausible: (i) there might exist a unique "killing" event (perhaps a lesion at the plasma membrane level, an amplification of the damage caused by the loss of membrane teichoic acid); (ii) loss of colony-forming ability may be caused by limited damage to the cell wall in the form of nicks (caused by the triggered murein hydrolase) which is not sufficient to cause culture lysis but which may be irreparable under the conditions of the viability assay. Although such limited damage may not cause a complete collapse of cell structure in the liquid culture, the treated bacteria may exaggerate this damage beyond repair on the agar plates during their attempt to enter the first cell division. Such a delayed lysis of drug-treated bacteria on the agar plates has actually been documented (28).

CLINICAL IMPLICATIONS

It has been predicted that lysis-defective mutant bacteria may accumulate in clinically "persistent" infections (27). Recent reports indicate that antibiotic-tolerant bacteria may indeed exist in isolates from patients with recurring infections (L. D. Sabath et al., Prog. Abstr. Intersci. Conf. Antimicrob. Agents Chemother., 16th, Chicago, Abstr. 320, 1976). The pH-dependent antibiotic tolerance described recently adds a further possible physiological cause for the survival (persistence) of pathogenic bacteria in appropriate microenvironments of an infected host. One should expect that among the antibiotic-tolerant bacteria there should be not only autolysin-defective mutants but also regulatory-type mutants with an overproduction of murein hydrolase inhibitor (lipoteichoic acid).

LITERATURE CITED

1. **Bracha, R., and L. Galser.** 1976. In vitro system for the synthesis of teichoic acid linked to peptidoglycan. J. Bacteriol. **125:**872–879.
2. **Briles, E., and A. Tomasz.** 1973. Pneumococcal Forssman antigen: a choline containing lipoteichoic acid. J. Biol. Chem. **248:**6394–6397.
3. **Briles, E., and A. Tomasz.** 1975. Membrane lipoteichoic acid is not a precursor to wall teichoic acid in pneumococci. J. Bacteriol. **122:**335–337.
4. **Brundish, D. E., and J. Baddiley.** 1968. Pneumococcal C-substance, a ribotol teichoic acid containing choline phosphate. Biochem. J. **110:**573–582.
5. **Cleveland, R. F., J. V. Höltje, A. J. Wicken, A. Tomasz, L. Daneo-Moore, and G. D. Shockman.** 1975. Inhibition of bacterial wall lysins by lipoteichoic acids and related compounds. Biochem. Biophys. Res. Commun. **67:**1128–1135.
6. **Critchley, P., A. R. Archibald, and J. Baddiley.** 1962. The intracellular teichoic acid from Lactobacillus asabinosus 17-5. Biochem. J. **85:**420–431.
7. **Elliott, T. S. J., J. B. Ward, and H. J. Rogers.** 1975. Formation of cell wall polymer by reverting protoplasts of Bacillus licheniformis. J. Bacteriol. **124:**623–632.
8. **Fiedler, F., J. Mauck, and L. Glaser.** 1974. Problems in cell wall assembly. Ann. N.Y. Acad. Sci. **235:**198–209.
9. **Fujiwara, M.** 1967. The Forssman antigen of pneumococcus. Jpn. J. Exp. Med. **37:**581–592.
10. **Goodell, E. W., R. Lopez, and A. Tomasz.** 1976. Suppression of the lytic effect of beta lactams on E. coli and other bacteria. Proc. Natl. Acad. Sci. U.S.A. **73:**3293–3297.

11. Hancock, I., and J. Baddiley. 1976. In vitro synthesis of the unit that links teichoic acid to peptidoglycan. J. Bacteriol. 125:880–886.

12. Höltje, J. V., and A. Tomasz. 1974. Teichoic acid phosphorylcholine esterase: a novel enzyme activity in pneumococcus. J. Biol. Chem. 249:7032–7034.

13. Höltje, J. V., and A. Tomasz. 1975. Biological effects of lipoteichoic acids. J. Bacteriol. 124:1023–1027.

14. Höltje, J. V., and A. Tomasz. 1975. Lipoteichoic acid: a specific inhibitor of autolysin activity in Pneumococcus. Proc. Natl. Acad. Sci. U.S.A. 72:1690–1694.

15. Höltje, J. V., and A. Tomasz. 1975. Specific recognition of choline residues in the cell wall teichoic acid by the N-acetyl-muramyl-L-alanine amidase of Pneumococcus. J. Biol. Chem. 250:6072–6076.

16. Höltje, J. V., and A. Tomasz. 1976. Purification of the pneumococcal N-acetyl-muramyl-L-alanine amidase to biochemical homogeneity. J. Biol. Chem. 251:4199–4207.

17. Ishiguro, E., and W. D. Ramey. 1976. Stringent control of peptidoglycan synthesis in Escherichia coli K-12. J. Bacteriol. 127:1119–1127.

18. Lacks, S. 1970. Mutants of Diplococcus pneumoniae that lack deoxyribonucleases and other activities possibly pertinent to genetic transformation. J. Bacteriol. 101:373–383.

19. Lopez, R., C. R. Lain, A. Tapia, S. B. Waks, and A. Tomasz. 1976. Suppression of the lytic and bactericidal effects of cell wall-inhibitory antibiotics. Antimicrob. Agents Chemother. 10:697–706.

20. Markham, J. L., K. W. Knox, A. J. Wicken, and M. J. Heirett. 1975. Formation of extracellular lipoteichoic acid by oral streptococci and lactobacilli. Infect. Immun. 12:378–386.

21. Mirelman, D., R. Bracha, and N. Sharon. 1972. Role of the penicillin-sensitive transpeptidation reaction in attachment of newly synthesized peptidoglycan to cell walls of Micrococcus luteus. Proc. Natl. Acad. Sci. U.S.A. 69:3355–3359.

22. Mosser, J. L., and A. Tomasz. 1970. Choline-containing teichoic acid as a structural component of pneu-mococcal cell wall and its role in sensitivity to lysis by an autolytic enzyme. J. Biol. Chem. 245:287–298.

23. Prestidge, L., and A. Pardee. 1957. Induction of bacterial lysis by penicillin. J. Bacteriol. 74:48–59.

24. Rogers, H. J. 1968. Killing of staphylococci by penicillin. Nature (London) 213:31–33.

25. Tomasz, A. 1958. Biological consequences of the replacement of choline by ethanolamine in the cell wall of pneumococcus: chain formation, loss of transformability and loss of autolysis. Proc. Natl. Acad. Sci. U.S.A. 59:86–93.

26. Tomasz, A. 1974. The role of autolysins in cell death. Ann. N.Y. Acad. Sci. 235:439–448.

27. Tomasz, A., A. Albino, and E. Zanati. 1970. Multiple antibiotic resistance in a bacterium with suppressed autolytic system. Nature (London) 227:138–140.

28. Tomasz, A., and E. Borek. 1962. The mechanism of an osmotic instability induced in E. coli K12 by 5-fluorouracil. Biochemistry 1:543–552.

29. Tomasz, A., and S. Waks. 1975. Mechanism of action of penicillin-triggering of the pneumococcal autolytic enzyme by inhibitors of cell wall synthesis. Proc. Natl. Acad. Sci. U.S.A. 72:4162–4166.

30. Tomasz, A., and S. Waks. 1976. Enzyme replacement in a bacterium: phenotypic correction by the experimental introduction of the wild type enzyme into a live enzyme-defective mutant pneumococcus. Biochem. Biophys. Res. Commun. 65:1311–1319.

31. Tomasz, A., and M. Westphal. 1971. Abnormal autolytic enzyme in a pneumococcus with altered teichoic acid composition. Proc. Natl. Acad. Sci. U.S.A. 68:2627–2630.

32. Tomasz, A., M. Westphal, E. B. Briles, and P. Fletcher. 1975. On the physiological functions of teichoic acids. J. Supramol. Struct. 3:1–16.

33. Weidel, W., and H. Pelzer. 1964. Bagshaped macro-molecules—a new outlook at bacterial cell walls. Adv. Enzymol. 26:193–232.

34. Wicken, A. J., and K. W. Knox. 1975. Lipoteichoic acids, a new class of bacterial antigen. Science 187:1161–1167.

IV. BACTERIAL ANTIGENS AND HOST RESPONSE

Introduction

L. JOE BERRY

Department of Microbiology, University of Texas, Austin, Texas 78712

A number of conferences on endotoxin have been held during the past 20 years, the most recent in 1973. Research concerned with this material has continued with undiminished interest and has recently taken new turns. The chemistry of bacterial lipopolysaccharides (LPS) continues to be investigated at the Max Planck Institute for Immunobiology in Freiburg and in other laboratories throughout the world. The importance of lipid A as the principal biologically active moiety of endotoxin is by now well established, and its possible value in conferring broad-spectrum immunity against gram-negative infections offers promising clinical implications. There is continuing evidence, however, that components of LPS other than lipid A possess interesting properties that merit consideration. Even though the present conference could have been another in the endotoxin series, exciting new developments in the structure and in the immunological and the biological properties of cell walls of gram-positive organisms are sufficiently related to those of gram-negative bacteria to make their inclusion a logical departure from the past.

Discussion was focused on recent studies dealing with the genetics and cellular aspects of host response to endotoxin, especially as it relates to immune phenomena. Through studies of inbred strains of mice, some of which have B cells that are known to be refractory to mitogenic stimulation by LPS whereas others fail to manifest expected reactions, new insights into the mode of action of endotoxin seem near. The isolation and partial chemical characterization of receptor sites for LPS on erythrocytes suggest that the first step in eliciting biological responses to LPS depends upon its binding to cells. Thus, the differential behavior of some inbred animals should make it possible to elucidate something about the fine structure of LPS and the nature of its mitogenicity and adjuvancy in the immune response and in the cellular requirements for release of the mediators responsible for many of its effects.

Endotoxin is not the only substance of bacterial origin that modulates the immune response. Components of *Bordetella pertussis* are known to be active, as are cholera enterotoxin, Freund-type adjuvants, and synthesized preparations recently developed. The changes produced by these materials are capable of enhancing as well as suppressing immunity, and their consideration seemed to comprise a logical part of the conference deliberations.

The cell wall antigens of gram-positive bacteria have received a great deal of recent attention. The chemistry of the peptidoglycans is about as far advanced as that of LPS and their antigenicity is established. Moreover, the biological properties of these preparations are similar in many ways to those of endotoxin. Protein A from staphylococci is of interest for several reasons. It is known to bind the Fc portion of immunoglobulin G, thereby leaving the antigen-combining sites of the molecule free. This property has been exploited for immunodiagnostic purposes. Protein A also activates the classical and alternate pathways of complement, thereby making protein A a chemotactic substance. Lipoteichoic acids also possess interesting immunochemical and biological properties.

Bacterial adherence was included as a conference topic because surface antigens, or at least surface structures, are involved in the process. The significance of attachment as an essential step in the initiation of pathogenic changes has been established for periodontal disease and gonorrhea even though the details of the mechanisms by which adherence occurs remain unresolved. Even though this has been the subject of a number of recent meetings, progress has been sufficiently rapid to make it a part of the conference.

I am indebted to Stephan Mergenhagen and Erwin Neter for their help and cooperation during the 2 years that went into the planning of the conference. Their judgment, advice, and guidance have been invaluable. We are most appreciative of the generous support provided by the National Institute of Dental Research. It has permitted us to select participants from anywhere in the world whose work best covered the subject. We are also indebted to the ASM for serving as a recipient of the NIDR grant.

It greatly simplified the management of the conference, thanks to the help of Raymond Sarber.

We appreciate the assistance of David Schlessinger, editor of the *Microbiology* series, in making space available to us in the 1977 volume. Such prompt publication is unusual.

The support of the following industrial firms, whose generosity made certain amenities possible, is gratefully acknowledged: Bellco Glass, Inc.; Biomedical Products, Inc.; Difco Laboratories; Flow Laboratories; Scimetrics Sales and Service; New Brunswick Scientific Co.; and Fisher Scientific Co.

Last, but by no means least, I owe my wife, Virginia Berry, the greatest of thanks because without her help it could not have been done.

The History of Pyrogen Research

OTTO WESTPHAL, URSULA WESTPHAL, AND THOMAS SOMMER

*Max-Planck-Institut für Immunbiologie, Freiburg-Zähringen, and English Seminar,
University of Freiburg i.Br., Freiburg, West Germany*

IDEAS AND EXPERIENCE TILL THE EARLY 18TH CENTURY

Observations of physicians and those who were ill on the manifestations of fever are as old as the study of medicine itself. For 2,500 years, views about the meaning of fever have moved between two extremes: fever as a symptom and expression of disease, which the physician should fight against, and fever as an indication of activated defense, which the physician should not counteract but promote. Great masters of medicine, again and again throughout history, have vehemently claimed that fever is highly conducive to recovery. Thus, early in medical history the idea emerged that the physician should induce fever artificially in all kinds of diseases and wherever possible (1).

About 500 B.C. the famous Greek physician Parmenides declared: "If only I had the means of creating fever artificially, I should be able to cure all illnesses." Ruphos of Ephesos, about 100 A.D., taught: "One should not only not counteract fever; on the contrary, it is a great remedy. It would be desirable to be able to induce it artificially." These ideas were supported by observations such as those of Galen (ca. 130–200), who reported the cure of insanity by intermittent fever (malaria) and the favorable influence of fever on spasmic conditions, epilepsy, and asthma.

At the end of the Renaissance, these considerations of eminent physicians were taken up again (2). Thomas Sydenham (1624–1689) (ref. 3, p. 104), frequently called the "English Hippocrates" and an enthusiastic propagator of the natural means of curing disease: "Fever is a desirable natural curative." Hermann Boerhaave (1668–1738) (ref. 3, p. 124), the great Dutch master of medicine in Leyden, more than 2,000 years after Parmenides: "I should be the greatest physician if I were able to create, and as easily dispel, intermittent fever." His famous pupil Gerhard van Swieten (1700–1772), who was appointed medical advisor to the Empress Maria-Theresa in Vienna and who founded the "Old Vienna School of Medicine": "Through fever Nature often cures such illnesses as have proved resistent to all the best curatives." The school of Boerhaave introduced the fever thermometer into daily clinical treatment.

With the development of experimental medicine and physiology during the late 18th and early 19th centuries, the old notion of inducing fever artificially was realized. Already Albrecht von Haller (1708–1777) (ref. 3, p. 132), like van Swieten a pupil of Boerhaave, mentioned in his important eight-volume work on human physiology (4) that the intravenous injection of putrid fluid into animals would evoke the manifestations of illness and fever. Mateo-José-Bonaventura Orfila (1787–1853) (ref. 3, p. 203), Spanish-born and later a naturalized Frenchman, became the founder of scientific toxicology in Paris. In 1813 to 1815 the first edition of his *Traité des Poisons* appeared, in which he described (p. 106) the verification of von Haller's experiments. Stimulated by these observations, two scientists in Paris performed careful and extended studies on the physiological and pathological effects caused by injections of putrid fluids into experimental animals, especially dogs.

Gaspard (5), in his review of 1822, referred to the history of experimental intravenous injections of solutions containing foreign matter ("substances étrangères") in general: such injections had already started in 1642, when J.-G. Wahrendorff (quoted in ref. 5) injected wine into the veins of dogs. Gaspard, in experiments performed between 1809 and 1822, injected putrid and other fluids into dogs. He suggested that material from purulent processes occurring in the circulation was probably responsible for all kinds of fever and he stressed the differences of the routes of injection of the fever-producing material: high efficiency by intravenous injection, no effect by oral administration. In addition, he stated that fresh cow's milk, beef bouillon, or human urine did not show the symptoms elicited by small amounts of putrid fluids:

La plupart des symptômes qui s'observent dans toutes les fièvres lentes ou phthisies, semblent pouvoir être rapportés à la présence du pus dans l'économie, puisque dans tous les cas il y a toujours suppuration abondante et profonde, avec trouble général des sécrétions (ref. 5, p. 7). . . . Mais pour que ce fluide étranger puisse circuler avec le sang, et causer alors, comme je le pense, la fièvre hectique dans les divers phthisies ou suppurations profondes, il faut nécessairement qu'il soit absorbé et transporté dans les vaiseaux sanguins. (ref. 5, p. 8).

François Magendie (1783–1855) (6), who can be called the founder of experimental pharmacology (ref. 3, p. 200), followed Gaspard's work with great interest. In 1823, he pointed to the frequent observations of physicians about the unhealthy influence of unhygienic conditions like those in and around many harbors. Here masses of material of plant and animal origin undergo deterioration and putrefaction; and here above all severe illnesses occur, including plague, typhoid fever, intermittent fever, dysentery, cholera, yellow fever, etc. Magendie asked whether there might be a possible common cause of these processes, of which fever is so characteristic. In his experiments he found that the extract of putrid fish was extraordinarily potent in inducing fever and the symptoms of illness:

J'ai répété avec le plus grand soin les experiences de M. Gaspard, et je les ai poursuivies sous le point de vue de leur application à la médicine. J'affirme, et on le croira sans peine, que ses résultats sont parfaitement exacts: de plus, j'ai observé que les diverses sortes de chairs n'avaient pas la même activité dans leur putréfaction" . . . "la matière délétère par excellence, c'est l'eau putride du poisson; quelque gouttes de cet eau injectées dans les veines produisent, en moins d'une heure, les symptômes qui ont la plus grande analogie avec le typhus et la fièvre jaune (ref. 6, p. 83).

Magendie then showed that filtration, through what he called "Papier Joseph," of his putrid fish water resulted in less acute but prolonged action of the putrid fluid (ref. 6, p. 84). In conclusion he stated again, first, that without putrid decomposition of organic matter no symptoms of fever and disease could be elicited experimentally; and second, that the poison must be absorbed through the veins to become active.

Since then, the preferred procedure for inducing experimental fever in laboratory animals during nearly all of the 19th century was the intravenous injection of fluid from putrid organic matter.

At the same time (1820) two French pharmacists, Pierre-Joseph Pelletier (1788–1842) and Joseph-Bienaimé Caventue (1795–1877), isolated quinine as the pure antipyretic drug from cinchona bark. In animal experiments which, under the influence of Magendie, progressed mainly in France, pyresis and antipyresis could now be experimentally produced and analyzed.

FEVER-PRODUCING PRINCIPLE IN PUTRID AND SEPTIC INFECTION

Of great importance and relevance was the Contribution to the Doctrine about the So-Called Putrid or Septic Infection, published in 1856 by the Dane Peter L. Panum (1820–1885) (7), then Associate Professor of Physiology and Pathology at Kiel (Fig. 1 and 2). Because it was published in a Danish journal (8) (Fig. 2), his work did not receive the general attention it deserved. Only a short abstract appeared in German (9). After the Prusso-Danish War in 1866, Panum was Professor of Physiology in Copenhagen, but he did not continue these important investigations. It was 18 years after his first publication, when the subject had been considerably further studied, that, with the help of the famous and influential German pathologist Rudolf Virchow (1821–1902) (who was an earlier teacher of Panum and since then kept up a friendly contact with him) an extensive report on Panum's observations appeared (10). Here he presents the history of the subject and demonstrates that many later investigators generally confirmed his earlier findings. What he published in 1856 (7) can be summarized as follows:

1. The putrid poison is not volatile and is not a known simple end product of putrefaction or fermentation (as described by Justus von Liebig). It can be differentiated from living microorganisms, which may be a source but not the cause.
2. The toxin resists heat and thus differs from typical enzymes ("Fermente").
3. It is insoluble in pure alcohol but soluble in water.
4. The protein-like substances frequently present in putrid fluids are not toxic by themselves, but they absorb ("condense") the toxin on their surface when precipitated. The toxic principle can be at least partially eluted from the precipitates.
5. Injection of a few milligrams of the concentrate suffices to produce high fever and kill a dog.

The struggle of Ignaz Philipp Semmelweiss (1818–1865) (ref. 3, p. 277) in Budapest and especially in Vienna to create an understanding of the infectious nature of puerperal fever, which caused so many deaths, provides a chapter in the well-known history of heroic pioneering in medicine (Fig. 3 and 4) (11). In his now often-cited contribution "On the Etiology of Puerperal Fever," which appeared in 1861 (12), he supported his concept with data from animal experiments. By introducing endometrial secretions of patients with puerperal fever, or putrid fluids of other patients, into female rabbits immediately after delivery, he observed the fever and sepsis from which the animals died. He finally stated: "Based on my experience I take puerperal fever to be a resorption fever caused by the absorption of a decomposing organic substance. . . . The source of that organic substance, which strikes the individual from outside causing puerperal fever, is organic matter that—not obeying the laws that govern normal life—has decomposed to some extent. . . . It is the degree of putrefaction that counts."

Consequently he tried to convince his co-workers and medical students to wash their hands before investigating the patients in the hospital in order to avoid infection. But many medical authorities at that time did not accept his viewpoint (11). However, in Boston, Oliver Wendell Holmes (1809–1894), well known as a writer, had independently developed the same concept by 1843.

In the 1860s, research on fever and fever-producing substances was greatly influenced by surgeons who daily had to fight against septic fever, which developed from open wounds. What was the cause of wound fever? The subject was taken to be of such importance that several medical faculties of universities gave prizes for the best work in this direction. In 1866, for example, the University of Munich proposed the subject "The Effect of Putrid Material and Fluids on the Higher Organism." The prize essay was won by a Dr. Schweninger, whose report (13) still makes worthwhile reading. Eminent surgeons, supported more and more by physiologists and pathologists, pioneered in efforts to clarify the mechanisms of septic fever.

Theodor Billroth (1829–1894) (ref. 3, p. 327), son of a Lutheran parson's family on the Baltic island of Rügen, was Professor of Surgery in Zurich from 1860–1867 and then in Vienna (Fig. 5). A highly educated man, a great surgeon, and an excellent pianist, he was a leading figure in the cultural and scientific life of Vienna. His close friendship with Johannes Brahms (1833–1897) is well known, and many of the letters they exchanged about music and medicine give a lively picture of the spirit of Vienna at that time (14). He was the first to perform stomach surgery. In Zurich, Billroth concentrated on the question of whether a fever-producing principle exists or develops in putrid fluids. In his 1862 publication "Observations on Fever Caused by Wounds and Accidental Wound Diseases" (15) he stated: . . . "the *pyrogenic substances* are equally present in dried putrid material and dried pus as well as in putrid fluids and in fresh pus." This seems to be the first time that the terms "pyrogen" and "pyrogenic substance(s)" were used. Later Billroth isolated bacteria, which he called *Coccobacteria septica*, as the causative agent of septic wound infection (16).

Another great surgeon in this field was Ernst von Bergmann (1836–1906) (17), also the son of a Lutheran minister in East Prussia (Fig. 6). From 1854 to 1877 he lived and taught in the Esthonian town of Dorpat, where he studied medicine at the German university and later became Professor of Surgery. Then after 4 years in Würzburg, he became head of the Surgical Hospital of the University of Berlin (1882–1906). He was certainly one of the most eminent surgeons of his time. von Bergmann believed that a chemically defined substance, which appeared to occur in all putrefying nitrogenous materials of animal and plant origin, was responsible for the putrid intoxication. His important publications appeared in 1868: "The Putrid Poison and the Putrid Intoxication" (18); "On Sepsin, the Poison of Putrid Substances" (19); and "On Fever Caused by Products of Putrefaction and Inflammation" (see ref. 17). In 1872 he published "The Teaching of the Putrid Intoxication" (20).

In his work on sepsin he made the—for his time—remarkable attempt to purify an imputed principle from putrid fluid filtrate, which would produce the syndrome of sepsis in animal experiments. His sepsin was first produced from putrefying yeast. For its further purification, von Bergmann decided in 1870 to go to the famous laboratory of the physiological chemist Wilhelm Kühne in Amsterdam (1837–1900), who was well known for his studies on pancreatic enzymes and the discovery of trypsin, ". . . in an effort to solve the fever question and the cause of the noxious effects of putrefying substances" (ref. 17, p. 249). In a letter to his father he wrote: "I strolled through Amsterdam and found rather mad its innumerable drawbridges and the many winding water drains which flow through the town and sometimes stink even more than putrefying yeast, from which I take such pains to prepare my putrid toxin" (ref. 17, p. 250).

The outbreak of the Franco-Prussian War

(1870–71) interrupted his work. von Bergmann was called to arms. He was soon appointed a top medical officer in the Prussian army and had the credit of ordering strict antiseptic wound treatment, under the influence of Joseph Lister's 1867 report (see below). He never returned to his studies on sepsin, due to other official duties; but he continued as a great pioneer of Lister's method in Germany. He introduced the sterilization of all surgical material by steam.

In fact, priorities in this field of research now shifted considerably with the work of Lister, based on the new advances in microbiology.

BEGINNING OF PYROGEN PHYSIOLOGY

Before entering the period dealing with the microbial aspects of pyrogens and fever, we should mention the work of Bernhard Naunyn (1839–1925) (Fig. 7), Professor of Internal Medicine from 1869 to 1871 in Dorpat, in Bern from 1871–72, in Königsberg from 1872–88, and finally in Strassburg till 1904.

In Bern and Königsberg, Naunyn worked on the physiology of experimental fever. He worked with guinea pigs, rabbits, and dogs, standardizing the pyrogenic material (using filtrates from putrefying muscle) and especially demonstrating the great importance of the surrounding temperature for changes in body temperature brought about by standard intravenous pyrogen injections. In a very clearly written publication (Fig. 8), with V. Dubczanski (Bern) he demonstrated that animals kept at lower temperatures (5 to 15°C), after a standard injection of pyrogenic fluid, tended to show a fall in body temperature, whereas with the same experiment performed at higher temperature (about 25 to 30°C), a rise of body temperature was often observed. In Fig. 9 several original fever curves from his publication (21) are shown.

Summarizing his results, Naunyn writes (ref. 21, p. 27–28): "After these experiments it is apparent that the pyrogenic substances do not only *enhance* body temperature." On the one hand, they induce the production of heat by activating the metabolism of certain organs; on the other hand, they lead to an increase of the loss of heat through the skin:

Under certain, so to say, neutral conditions for heat loss, which are experimentally verifiable by a moderate environmental temperature, the (febrile) state of the animal will not be expressed by any appreciable change of body temperature. . . . Three factors influence the loss of heat through the skin: (1) The difference between the temperature of the skin and the surrounding atmosphere; (2) Covering the skin

with media which facilitate loss of heat (by radiation or transmission) or render it more difficult; (3) The size of the animal; that is, the proportion between its body surface and the mass of its heat-producing inner organs. It is a condition of labile equilibrium of the body temperature to which the animals are brought by the pyrogenic substance. . . .

Naunyn used the term "pyrogenic substance" throughout the whole publication (see title), indicating that he believed in a defined fever-producing principle.

Naunyn demonstrated the function of the animal's skin—with or without fur—in determining response to a pyrogen. He used shorn animals which, later, were wrapped in tin foil or cotton wool in order to restore insulation from the environmental air. Challenged with pyrogen, the conditioned animals reacted differently from controls.

Around the same time, numerous investigations on the metabolism of animals and man under conditions of experimental or clinical fever were performed. One can recognize in these attempts the beginning of pyrogen physiology (see also ref. 37).

MICROBIAL ORIGIN OF FEVER-PRODUCING SUBSTANCES

Before microorganisms were discovered to be infectious agents, it was thought that infection was brought about by a "contagion" responsible for miasmatic-contagious diseases. As early as 1546, the famous Italian physician Hieronymus Fracastoro (1478–1553) wrote three books in which he described in a masterly and clear-cut fashion the nature of contagion and how to treat contagious diseases (22). Three hundred years later, in 1840, Jakob Henle (1809–1885) in Berlin was the first to formulate the criteria for *contagia* as organic, living matter . . . "und zwar mit individuellem Leben begabt, welche zu dem kranken Körper im Verhältnis eines parasitischen Organismus stehen." These criteria are the following. (i) They possess the ability to multiply by assimilation of foreign matter, which is known to be an ability of living beings only. (ii) As with the causative agents of fermentation, their effect can be brought about by a minimal quantity due to their ability to multiply. (iii) Miasmatic-contagious diseases have an exact and typical course of development (23).

But Henle's ideas were soon forgotten. It took almost 25 years until his criteria were generally accepted as a proof of the microbial cause of an infectious disease.

As a 37-year-old surgeon in Glasgow, discarding the popular concept of miasma (direct infection by "bad air"), Joseph Lister (1827–1912) (24) (Fig. 10) postulated that sepsis might be caused by a pollen-like dust. In the course of the same year (1865) he became acquainted with Louis Pasteur's (1822–1895) conception that microorganisms cause fermentation and also disease by putrefaction. First Lister thought that the microorganisms would infect the wounds only through the air. But it did not escape Pasteur that germs could precipitate or be adsorbed on all solid and fluid matter.

Pasteur's findings on fermentation and putrefaction impressed Lister tremendously. Suddenly he understood their prime importance for the question of suppuration and wound infection. Now he learned from Pasteur that these processes of disintegration were in reality a kind of fermentation generated by microscopically small animate beings which, on the ever-present floating dust in the air, could be transported everywhere, and that it was possible to clean the air from dust by filtration, heat, or other means. If Pasteur was right, the secret of wound infection could be solved!

Even more important was Pasteur's observation that material taken from the animal's body, like blood or urine, is normally germfree if it is collected under special precautions in presterilized vessels. Under these conditions it could be kept for an indefinite time without decomposition. According to Pasteur, "The spontaneous origin of life is a phantasmagoria." At the remarkable session of the Sorbonne in Paris on 7 April 1864, Pasteur (Fig. 11) spoke on his experiments. A newspaperman reported: "It was a great day, all Paris gathered to hear him, it was the most distinguished audience to which Pasteur has ever spoken." His lecture was directed against Dr. Pouchet, Director of the Museum of Natural History in Rouen, who since 1858 claimed again and again that he had succeeded in the spontaneous generation of life (24, 25):

Therefore, gentlemen, I could point to this fluid and say to you as follows: Here I have a drop of water taken from the infinity of creation, and it is filled with the bricks with which the lower orders of creation are constructed—and now I am waiting, I am observing, I am questioning this little drop, and I beg of it to repeat once again for me the wonderful drama of God's first creation! But my drop remains silent—silent since I began these experiments a few years ago; it remains silent because I have kept it away from the only thing that humanity cannot produce: that is from the germs floating in the air, from life. Life is the germ, and the germ is life. Never, never again will the teaching of the spontaneous creation

of life recuperate from the deathblow which has been given it by this simple experiment. . . .

One year later, on 12 August 1865, the first successful antiseptic operation (using carbolic acid, i.e., phenol) was performed at Glasgow, and the first series of cases was published by Lister beginning in March 1867 in *Lancet* and *The British Medical Journal* (26). During 1865 to 1869, the mortality in his clinic in Glasgow dropped from 45 to 15%! Nevertheless, it took quite some time until, especially in England and the United States, Lister's "germ theory" was fully accepted. Semmelweiss was certainly a lonely forerunner! The experience of physicians who treated wounded soldiers in the Franco-Prussian War (1870–71) aseptically—on the recommendation and advice of Ernst von Bergmann—was highly convincing, and in 1875 Lister made a triumphant tour through the surgical centers of Germany.

From 1874 on (ref. 24, p. 182–195) there was continuous correspondence between Lister and Pasteur (Fig. 12). (Lister had an excellent command of French.)

But only on the occasion of Pasteur's 70th birthday did the two great men meet personally. The celebration took place on 27 December 1892 at the Sorbonne before 2,500 guests and in the presence of the President of the Republic, Sadi Carnot (1837–1894), also known as a famous engineer and physicochemist (the "Carnot cycle"). Lord Lister represented British science. His address ended as follows: "Monsieur Pasteur, les maladies infectieuses constituent, vous le savez, la grande majorité des maladies qui affligent le genre humain. Vous pouvez donc bien comprendre que la Médicine et la Chirurgie s'empressent à cette occasion solenelle de vous apporter l'hommage profond de leur admiration et de leur reconnaissance." The dramatic scene which then followed has been caught by the painter Rixens in a picture, the middle part of which is shown in Fig. 13 (taken from ref. 24, p. 384). Led by President Carnot, Pasteur approaches Lister. Rixens says "The embrace of these two men was a lively allegory of the union of the sciences in the endeavor to help mankind."

With the final breakdown of the teaching of the spontaneous creation of life and with the characterization of microorganisms (in tissues, body fluids, and in pure cultures) as causative agents of diseases, we find ourselves at the beginning of modern general hygiene. In an address on "The Fight Against Infectious Diseases, Especially the Epidemics of War" (27), given before the Military Academy of Medicine in Berlin on the occasion of its annual foundation day, 2 August 1888, Robert Koch (1843–1910) said:

Since hygiene as a science is honoured today by being represented here for the first time, I may be allowed to stress its significance by talking on the fight against infectious diseases [ref. 27, p. 6]. . . . The future way of fighting epidemics will differ from the hitherto exercised practice considerably. As a rule, in the past one did not take any serious action until the losses were high and the prognosis became very bad. Isolation of the first cases at the beginning of an infectious disease was not recommended, because physicians thought that the disease was not caused by importation, but rather by autochthonic development. Therefore, it was felt senseless to act against individual cases. Now we take the opposite point of view based on the assumption that epidemics—insofar as they are not endemic at a certain place—*must have been imported* [ref. 27, p. 32–33].

Let us realize that these words were spoken less than 90 years ago!

Robert Koch himself contributed greatly to the understanding of microbial participation in wound sepsis by his "Investigations on the Aetiology of Infectious Wound Diseases," from 1880 on, drawing on experience with thousands of wounded soldiers in wartime and supported by animal experiments in which he used pure cultures of bacteria as infectious agents.

From that time on, research on the mechanisms of fever concentrated on the question of the bacterial origin of pyrogenic substances.

THE TERM "PYROGEN"

On the threshold of the new bacteriological era, a pioneer was Sir John Burdon-Sanderson (1828–1905) (Fig. 14), who, after studying medicine in England, spent some time working with Claude Bernard (1813–1878) in Paris before concentrating on questions of fever. From 1871 to 1882 he held the chair of physiology at University College, London, and from 1882 to 1895 he had the same position at the University of Oxford, until he became Regius Professor of Medicine in Oxford for his last 10 years.

In June 1876 he summarized his experience and conclusions in a review "On the Process of Fever" (28). With the concept of a pyrogenic principle as a defined substance (or substances) in mind, he discussed whether it originated from microbes (exogenous) or from tissues (endogenous). With regard to the latter he said:

The alternative is that fever originates in the living tissues, that it is from first to last a disorder of protoplasm, and that all the systemic disturbances

are secondary. In both hypotheses it is tacitly assumed that fever is the product of a material fever-producing cause contained in the blood or tissue juice, the morbitic action of which on the organism is antecedent to all functional disturbances whatever. At bottom we are all humoralists, and believe in infection. It is not until we have to say where and how infection acts that questions arise.

Twenty years later, Burdon-Sanderson wrote a further review in *A System of Medicine* (28), where he takes the question up again (ref. 28, p. 156):

At that early period (1872) the methods now familiar to the pathologist of discriminating between different kinds of bacteria were unknown. When some eight years later Dr. Koch taught us how to do this, it seemed likely that the fever-producing property would turn out to be an endowment of particular species, and that by using pure cultivations it would be possible to induce fever experimentally with much greater certainty than had before been possible.

Further elaborating on that problem, he stressed, however, the well-known observation that severe injuries, such as fractures that are attended with a certain amount of disintegration of tissue, are known to be followed by febrile reactions even when the skin is not broken, thus obviously eliminating bacterial contamination as the cause of fever (29). He concluded that these phenomena seem to confirm the inference of Albert Charrin (1856–1907), who, greatly influenced by Claude Bernard, had claimed (29, 30) that in almost all cells "thermogenic substances, or rather substances from which they can be generated, are contained." One is reminded of the modern concept of endogenous mediator(s) of the febrile response. Charrin (30) also claimed that microbes are not pathogenic in themselves, but rather by their excretion of toxins into the organism (ref. 3, p. 393).

In 1975 the Pharmaceutical Society of Great Britain organized a symposium on pyrogens (29) to celebrate "a hundred years of pyrogen," referring to Burdon-Sanderson's statement in his review of 1896 (28), in which he wrote (ref. 28, p. 157):

The question whether the microorganisms themselves or their products produce fever is an old one. *In 1875 I prepared a substance which I ventured to call pyrogen, from putrid extract of flesh*, by first destroying all bacterial life by the addition of alcohol in sufficient quantities to precipitate most of the protids it contained, separating the precipitate by filtration, *evaporating the clear filtrate, and redissolving it in water. This sterile product produced fever* . . .

(it is) perhaps a body analogous to the unformed ferments or enzymes . . . .

It certainly does not in any way detract from Burdon-Sanderson's merits as an eminent physiologist and pathologist if we remind the reader that the term "pyrogen" was not actually defined in his 1875 publication, since Billroth in 1862 (16), von Bergmann in 1872 (20, p. 386–387), and Naunyn in 1873 (21) had used the term "pyrogenic substance" with exactly the same meaning as proposed by Burdon-Sanderson. It may well be that he used the term as a routine abbreviation in the laboratory, independently of the others.

As to the nomenclature of the term pyrogen, Whittet elaborated on it on the occasion of the Pyrogen Symposium in London (1975) (29), citing the Oxford English Dictionary and Marcoveccio's "*Lingua nostra*" (1968), tracing the etymology of the prefixes "pyro" and "pyreto"; both are derived from Greek, but "pyro" means fire or burning, and "pyreto" was used for fever. Thus, a fever-producing substance should be termed a "pyretogen." In the 17th century "pyretology," according to Whittet (29), was used to describe "that branch of medical science which treats fevers," and the term "pyretica" was used for "a medicine that cures fever."

SEARCH FOR PYROGENIC PRINCIPLES

The status of the fever problem 100 years ago can be characterized as follows (31): experts believed that fever in higher animals and man was induced by a fever-producing principle, pyrogen. However, it was not clear whether the pyrogenic substance (i) was produced by *bacteria* and, if so, whether it was inherent in or excreted by them; or (ii) was formed in the tissue under certain conditions like fermentation or putrefaction due to trauma or infection. It appeared clear that the pyrogenic principle manifested itself by going into the circulation.

The study of fever-producing substances was furthered by the development of biochemical methods for the isolation and purification of natural organic substances. It was also furthered by microbiological methods of growing pure microbial cultures in bulk for use as starting material. However other approaches were also used.

From products of putrefying animal organs, Ludwig Brieger (1849–1919) was able to isolate and purify the low-molecular-weight, basic ptomaines (32) as crystalline derivatives (putrescine, cadaverine; later neurin and neurinin, etc.). They were highly poisonous but nonpyrogenic in pure form. First the ptomaines

were compared with the alkaloids from plants because of the basic and poisonous character they shared with them. In attempts to explain the origin of ptomaines as products of bacterial activity, Brieger also analyzed bacterial cultures. In 1880, typhoid bacilli had just been discovered by Joseph Eberth (1835–1926), a friend of Billroth from the time they spent together at Zurich and a great admirer of Pasteur. In broth cultures of typhoid bacilli, Brieger demonstrated the generation of a ptomaine which he called "typhotoxin" (33). Investigations on cultures of other bacilli followed (34). In these experiments, a higher-molecular-weight toxic substance of protein-like nature could also be enriched and prepared as a sterile, white powder which the authors (34) called toxalbumin. The concept that practically all bacterial toxins were proteins was accepted for quite some time and was strongly supported by the isolation of diphtheria toxin in 1888–90 from culture filtrates by Pierre-Paul-Emile Roux (1853–1933) and Alexandre Yersin (1863–1943) at the Pasteur Institute in Paris. "Toxalbumines" were isolated from many bacterial culture fluids (34, 35). These toxalbumines (or albumoses) often proved to be pyrogenic in animal experiments, and Hans Buchner (1850–1902) (36) pointed to the strong leukocytic reactions (leukocytoses) after their injection. But Ludolf von Krehl (1861–1937), in extended and careful investigations (37, 38), showed that the albumoses, such as those isolated from *Escherichia coli* cultures, were of significantly lower pyrogenicity than the starting material containing whole bacteria. Bacteria grown for 48 to 72 h on agar and potatoes were isolated, washed, suspended in water, and sterilized at 98°C. A 0.1-g amount of this material, after subcutaneous injection into dogs, produced a rise of body temperature from 38.0 to 41.0°C. In contrast, 0.1 g of the purified albumose produced only a rise of temperature up to 39.6°C, with fewer symptoms of illness. von Krehl, therefore, considered the methods for isolating the pyrogenic principle to be inadequate. "Who tells us," he continues, "that during lysis of the bacterial bodies *in vivo* substances may not be generated which are pyrogenically different" (from the albumoses)? (37).

An additional remark may be allowed here. Hans Buchner had a brother 10 years his junior, Eduard (1860–1917). Hans took the greatest interest in Eduard, especially after the early death of their father, when Eduard was only 11 years old. Later, for his studies on sterile bacterial extracts (toxalbumines, etc.), Hans Buchner developed the method of high-pressure extraction of microbial cells. During holidays which Hans and Eduard spent together in Munich, they tried to stabilize the labile extract from yeast cells by the addition of sucrose, which Eduard had learned about while working in the marmalade industry (to earn money for his university studies). In these experiments Eduard observed the production of gas, carbon dioxide, and he soon recognized the phenomenon to be an expression of fermentation in the absence of living cells. Eduard Buchner's publication on "The Alcoholic Fermentation Without Yeast Cells" appeared in 1896; he was then associate Professor of Chemistry in Tübingen. The impact in the scientific world was great, and Eduard Buchner received the Nobel Prize for Chemistry in 1907: "The active principle in the high-pressure extract of yeast is a chemical substance which I have called Zymase. From now on one can do experiments with it as with other chemical substances" (Nobel Lecture). Around the same time (1896) Hans Buchner, a microbiologist, described the bacteriolytic activity of fresh serum. He called the causative agent "alexin," the heat-labile part of which was later termed complement by Paul Ehrlich. Hans Buchner, also an enthusiastic crusader for general hygiene, widely championed the idea that hygiene means more than preventing disease. In 1896 he said "We must also think of a positive promotion of health by positive hygiene" (36a). The concept arises that the body's defense mechanisms can be trained in healthy people, for example by the stimulating effects of injection of bacterial extracts (pyrogens).

FEVER THERAPY

At the same time, we witness the beginning and advance of fever therapy. In psychiatric and other cases, physicians induced fever either by provoking an artificial bacterial infection or by injecting suspensions of killed bacteria. On the basis of their observations and suggestions, artificial fever was now recommended as an important remedy.

A. S. Rosenblum in Odessa had already described in 1876 the favorable effect of artificial *Erysipelas* fever on psychiatric conditions (39). Ten years later (1887), Julius Wagner von Jauregg (1857–1940) (ref. 3, p. 299; Fig. 15), working as a neuropathologist in Vienna, started his systematic investigations on fever treatment of paralytic patients with typhoid vaccine, later with combinations of typhoid vaccine and tuberculin, and finally (1917) by inoculation of malaria-causing organisms (40). For his fundamental studies and results he received the Nobel Prize in Medicine in 1927.

Of no less significance was the development of fever therapy in the field of cancer. There are very ancient observations of physicians that septic fever may often lead to a concomitant, spontaneous regression and cure of established cancer. In 1774 a case of a mammary carcinoma (case Schwenke) was described in which, finally, the physicians produced an abscess with fever on one leg of the patient by induced suppuration. The protocol says (41):

Female adult, inoperable mammary carcinoma; patient had been treated by all the most effective remedies then in use . . . without effect. Having lost all hope of cure she ceased treatment. . . . As suppuration became more abundant, cancer diminished, then disappeared. Against advice patient allowed ulcer to heal; cancer at once recurred; new "issue" then opened at site of former abscess on leg; when suppuration was well established breast cancer gradually disappeared. . . .

In 1881 Friedrich Fehleisen (1854–1924), an assistant of Ernst von Bergmann (17) in Würzburg, treated many patients suffering from carcinoma through the injection of streptococcal cultures (from *Erysipelas*) (42). In his carefully documented treatments he found that chills and fever started regularly within 15 to 61 h. The fevers with peaks up to 41.6°C had a duration of 5 to 18 days. According to his curriculum vitae, kept at the library of the University of Würzburg, Fehleisen joined von Bergmann in Berlin and in 1889 emigrated to the United States.

We owe much to William Bradley Coley (1862–1936) in New York (Fig. 16), who abandoned the production of pyrogenic effects by acute artificial infection and instead used the pyrogenically highly active mixture of killed *Bacillus prodigiosus (Serratia marcescens)* and *Streptococci* (43). The preparation introduced by Coley has been applied as "Coley's toxin" in thousands of cancer cases and is still commercially available for that purpose in the United States. In the Cancer Research Institute, New York, Dr. Coley's daughter, Helen Coley-Nauts, keeps the memory of her father alive by sponsoring relevant cancer research and by organizing and making available one of the largest collections of protocols on fever therapy in cases of cancer and on the spontaneous regression and cure of cancer during processes of natural fever.

With the advancement of vaccine and fever therapy, and based on a vast mass of medical experience, the method of inducing artificial or "sterile" clinical fever developed further and further during the first half of our century. The dream of the ancient physicians became reality. The fever treatment of gonorrhea came into fashion after it was recognized that gonococci are very sensitive to elevated temperature (>37°C). In addition, extended clinical experience was also gained because fever therapy—then also called "nonspecific" or "retuning" therapy ("Umstimmungs" therapy)—was applied in cases where more specific means had failed. A great number of more or less defined new remedies were brought on the market for clinical use.

Besides the nonspecific or fever treatment of cancer, the more general application of artificial clinical fever as a remedy was tried out principally in Germany, Austria, and Russia. Before the era of chemotherapy, antibiotic therapy, and the use of corticoids, fever therapy became very popular in these countries. The vast experience collected throughout these decades of our century (44) may still be of considerable value for more advanced clinical investigations in our time.

After Robert Koch introduced tuberculin for immunization against tuberculosis, a new type of pyrexia was discovered: tuberculin fever, which was found to be most pronounced in tuberculous patients or in animals that had been preinfected with tubercle bacilli. Later it was termed "allergic fever." Here tuberculin is pyrogenic only in sensitized individuals, similar to later findings about the pyrogenic action of extracts from *Brucella* strains only in individuals who had suffered from brucellosis.

ENDOTOXIN

In 1892, during the course of investigations on cholera toxin and on cholera immunity, Richard Pfeiffer (1858–1945) (Fig. 17), a coworker of Robert Koch in Berlin, observed that cholera vibrios, besides the toxin they excreted into the culture medium—the exotoxin—produced a second quite different toxin that was tightly anchored to the bacterial cell and for which he proposed the term endotoxin. In his first publication on the matter (45) he stated (p. 411): "In very young aerobically grown cholera cultures a specific toxic substance is contained which exerts extraordinarily intense toxic effects. This primary cholera toxin is closely attached to, and probably an integral part of, the bacterial body. By chloroform, thymol, or by drying, the cholera vibrios can be killed without any detectable change of the toxin." In the following years it was found that many bacteria produce a similar endotoxin.

During research on the specific staining of bacteria, which was so greatly stimulated by Robert Koch and Paul Ehrlich, the Danish

microbiologist Hans Christian Joachim Gram (1853–1939) (Fig. 18), working as a guest scientist in the laboratories of the General Hospital of the City of Berlin, discovered the "Gram staining method" (46). By this method, two large groups of microorganisms can be distinguished: the gram-positive and the gram-negative bacteria (47). The method has become a very important screening test for bacteria and is widely used in microbiological practice and research. Using the Gram stain, microbiologists found that Pfeiffer's endotoxin was only produced by gram-negative bacilli like *E. coli*, typhoid, cholera, etc. Today we know that almost all gram-negative bacteria, pathogenic or nonpathogenic, produce endotoxin or endotoxin-like material (see ref. 47).

In 1904, in a general microbiological review (48), we find the following (since then generally accepted) definition of endotoxin:

Richard Pfeiffer (1892–95) gave a specific name to the bacterial substrate exerting a toxic action which is definitely different from the already known toxin. He called it endotoxin. The creator of this name based his concept on the correct opinion that his toxic principle is not excreted from the living bacteria, but firmly fixed to the body constituents. In contrast to typical toxins, these poisonous substances are not secreted into the culture medium, but they will be set free if the bacteria undergo lysis, called bacteriolysis.

PYROTOXINA BACTERICA

The time was now ripe for the chemical, physiological, and pharmacological definition of the pyrogenic principle of bacteria. For this, we have to go to Bologna, Europe's oldest university, where the Italian Eugenio Centanni (1863–1948) (Fig. 19) worked at the Institute of General Pathology, of which he later became the director. In 1894 he started to publish a series of papers, the first of which was entitled "Investigations on Infectious Fever—the Fever Toxin of Bacteria" (49). He started, with great enthusiasm, as follows: "I have undertaken a general investigation about infectious fever using the newest achievements of the sciences. It comprises three sets of investigations: (1) on the agents which induce infectious fever, (2) on mechanisms by which they act on the organism, and (3) on therapeutic questions with regard to fever." In Chapter 1 ("The Fever Toxin of Bacteria") he describes the preparation of what he called the pyrotoxina bacterica (49). In principle he used long-term (up to 10 days) autolysis of pure bacterial cultures, working up the sterile filtrate by alcoholic and other fractionation procedures and ending up with a sterile white powder. He was able to produce more or less the same highly pyrogenic material from a large variety of bacteria, including *E. coli*, typhoid, and others. At the end he stated: "Thus, we can conclude that the whole family of bacteria possess essentially the same toxin, a poison which is tied inseparably to their existence and upon which depends the typical picture of the general disturbances caused by bacterial infections." Centanni's statement that his pyrotoxina is not protein in nature and is quite stable to heat (in contrast to the toxalbumins) is noteworthy. On the basis of his data for the pyrogenicity of his preparations, one might assume that he had reached a rather high state of purification.

Although according to present knowledge some of Centanni's claims appear somewhat too generalized, there is no question that he was the first to recognize the intimate relationship between the pyrogenic and the endotoxic principle of bacteria, which he found chemically inseparable, a fact expressed by the term "pyrotoxina."

In addition, Centanni was also the first to observe the induction of what was later called pyrogenic tolerance (50) (see ref. 51, 52): after repeated injections, the animals responded less and less to a given dose of pyrogen. Centanni called it "the third type of immunity" (50, 53). From the documents he has left behind, we find that he corresponded about the "antitoxin of bacterial fever" (50) with Paul Ehrlich, who confirmed the general importance of his observations (54).

Furthermore, Centanni found a substance in bacterial autolysates that was not toxic, as was his pyrotoxina, but was highly active in inducing pyrogenic immunity. This he called "stomosine" (53). In clinical trials he observed antipyretic properties of stomosine, perhaps similar to the observations of A. Chelmonski and later of F. O. Höring (55). For some time the material was produced commercially (called Resolutin). Interestingly, Centanni claimed that stomosine-like material could also be produced from autolysates of gram-positive bacteria such as pneumococci (56).

Because most of his work was published in Italian and in specialized Italian journals that were not widely distributed in the scientific world, it is probable that Centanni did not gain the recognition he deserved. It might be still worthwhile to undertake a careful survey of his papers, both for historical interest and to stimulate some of today's work on pyrogens and fever. As an emeritus, during the Second World War, Centanni summarized his experience and ideas in several articles in German (57).

CHEMISTRY OF BACTERIAL PYROGEN

With the development and advancement of pharmaceutical preparations, especially ampoules containing drugs for injection, such as glucose for infusion, the problem of undesired "injection fever" arose and was soon recognized as a real technical problem. It was Florence Seibert in the United States who, in 1922 to 1925 (58), clearly demonstrated that bacterial contamination was the cause of these "fever shots." She also realized that unweighable, tiny amounts of material were active. Later, in 1951, she recalled sometimes having felt endotoxin to be a ghost rather than a substance, and used to call it her "little blue devil" (59). These untoward effects of bacterial endotoxin, indicated by unexpected fever, attracted for quite some time more investigators, especially in the pharmaceutical industry, than those concerned with the clinically desired induction of artificial ("sterile") fever.

Because, as Centanni had already pointed out, bacterial endotoxin and pyrogen could not be separated, the chemistry of bacterial pyrogen has also been very much based on investigations concerned with bacterial endotoxin. In addition, in attempts to purify and characterize the antigens in bacterial vaccines responsible for antibacterial immunity, it was found that the somatic (or O) antigen was also intimately connected with the endotoxic and pyrogenic principle. It became obvious that the relevant gram-negative bacteria produce a high-molecular-weight complex as part of their outer membrane, or cell wall, termed the "endotoxic complex," which, as a whole, may induce toxic, pyrogenic, and all kinds of immunological effects, depending upon the dose, the route of application, and the relative sensitivity of the species under investigation. In the 19th century, dogs were the preferred experimental animals for pyrogen research, but Naunyn (see ref. 21) and von Krehl (see ref. 37) showed that different animal species may react quite differently to the same dose of pyrogenic material. In the 20th century the animal of choice undoubtedly became the rabbit.

Searching for contributions dealing with the chemistry of bacterial pyrogen, we find many important investigations not primarily concerned with this aspect. A great pioneer was the French microbiologist André Boivin (1895–1949) (Fig. 20), who, together with the Rumanian Lydia Mesrobeanu, devised in 1932 for the first time a generally applicable procedure for extracting the endotoxic complex from many gram-negative bacteria (60): trichloroacetic acid extraction. On the basis of his analyses, he called his purified, antigenic, and toxic extracts "antigènes glycido-lipidiques" to indicate that their main components are polysaccharidic and lipoidic in nature, with only small amounts of additional protein.

In a similar approach, Walter T. J. Morgan in London (61) and Walther F. Goebel in New York (62) developed further extraction procedures, using mixtures of organic solvents and water. Their purified substances, similar to Boivin's products, were composed of polysaccharide, lipid, and protein. Morgan's extracts from *Salmonella* and *Shigella* appeared physicochemically homogeneous and as a uniform substance. In their extended studies on tumor necrosis induced by endotoxin, Murray J. Shear and his co-workers (63) demonstrated that the active principle of *Serratia marcescens* and other bacteria resided in the endotoxic complex. In addition, the substance was highly pyrogenic and had a composition very similar to that of the endotoxin preparations of Boivin, Morgan, and Goebel. The Shear group used the term "lipopolysaccharide" to point to the general chemical composition of the complex. All these preparations formed colloidal dispersions in water with particle sizes on the order of several million.

A comprehensive and critical review on all aspects of bacterial pyrogens appeared in 1950 (64). This excellent review is highly recommended to the reader. The further, more recent history of the subject has been reviewed extensively (65). O. Westphal and O. Lüderitz in 1952 produced pure and protein-free lipo-polysaccharides by applying the phenol/water extraction method (66) to many *Enterobacteriaceae*. The preparations were pyrogenic in rabbits after intravenous doses in the order of less than 0.001 μg/kg. It took nearly 20 years until these authors and their co-workers were finally able to prove that it is the firmly bound, ubiquitous lipid component of lipopolysaccharides, called lipid A (67), which is responsible for the pyrogenic and most of the other endotoxic activities of bacterial endotoxin (see Table 1) (68, 70).

With the purification (66, 68), structural analysis (68, 70), and standardization (69) of this unique natural lipid component, the question of the pyrogenic principle of gram-negative bacteria has received a partial answer.

Many substances other than bacterial endotoxin were found to possess pyrogenic properties (71, 78). They include synthetic or natural double-stranded nucleic acids (RNA) and certain viruses. In these cases endotoxin contamination could be excluded. On the other hand, several other pyrogenic substances have been extracted from microorganisms (nucleic acid and glycopeptide preparations), but quantitatively they do not attain anything like the activity of lipopolysaccharides or lipid A.

The new phase of pyrogen research will certainly deal with extended investigations on the mode of pyrogen action; with the fate of bacterial pyrogen in vivo both in endotoxin-sensitive and -insensitive species (72); and with endotoxin (pyrogen) pharmacology. Besides other questions, the problem of the selective suppression of certain endotoxic manifestations or the enhancement of others is of prime importance, and positive results may be crucial for a new wave of interest in clinical "fever

TABLE 1. *Endotoxic reactions given by lipid A*[a]

Pyrogenicity	Mitogenic lymphocyte stimulation
Lethal toxicity	Induction of immunoglobulin G synthesis in newborn
Toxicity increased by adrenalectomy	mice
Toxicity increased by BCG pretreatment	Macrophage activation
Shwartzman phenomenon	Colony-stimulating factor
Bone marrow necrosis	Complement activation
Embryonic bone resorption	Hagemann factor activation
Leukopenia	Plasminogen activator
Leukocytosis	Induction of prostaglandin synthesis
Depression of blood pressure	Induction of interferon production
Tumor necrotic activity[b]	Nonspecific resistance to infection
Enhanced dermal reactivity to epinephrine	Early refractory state to endotoxin pyrogenicity
Adjuvant activity	Induction of endotoxin tolerance
	Limulus lysate gelation

[a] Data collected by Ch. Galanos, E. Th. Rietschel, and O. Lüderitz (from Westphal [65]).
[b] In several experimental mouse tumor systems, lipopolysaccharides are more active than free lipid A.

therapy." As is well known, humans are very sensitive to endotoxin. After intravenous injections the threshold doses of highly purified substances for leukocytic and pyrogenic reactions are on the order of <0.001 μg/kg. However, therapeutically efficient doses may be considerably above that level and cause a series of untoward side effects. Thus, endotoxin therapy, although in many cases most effective, has hitherto been regarded as "heroic therapy" and is therefore often recommended only in desperate cases. Such patients, on the other hand, may be even more sensitive to its action than normal healthy persons (see ref. 44).

In this context, finally, the question of endogenous mediators (73) induced by endotoxin, such as the endogenous pyrogen released from phagocytizing cells (granulocytes, macrophages) (74), and the recent findings about the pyrogenic activity of prostaglandins (75) and their release from phagocytes by endotoxin action (76), as well as the pyrogenicity of cAMP (77), can now be followed with defined pyrogenic substances and with refined physiological and pharmacological techniques. We cannot resist once again (65) citing one of the pioneers of modern pyrogen research, Ivan L. Bennett, who, opening one of the many endotoxin conferences within the last 20 years (New Brunswick, 1964), said: "Endotoxins possess an intrinsic fascination that is nothing less than fabulous. They seem to have been endowed by Nature with virtues and vices in the exact and glamorous proportions needed to render them irresistible to any investigator who comes to know them" (79).

Endotoxin and bacterial pyrogen act as an ever-present, highly active biological signal. We are surrounded with, and at birth immediately "infected" by, endotoxin-producing bacteria which accompany practically all living organisms throughout life. Experimentally, it has hitherto been almost impossible to produce endotoxin-free life. During evolution, animal life has certainly adapted itself somehow to the continuous stimulus of endotoxin and to the cellular and humoral reactions elicited by the interaction of the unique structural determinants of bacterial lipid A with receptors of the higher organism. Thus, research about this aspect of host-microbe interrelationship will continue to attract scientists in the future as they have been attracted in the past described here.

ACKNOWLEDGMENTS

We wish to thank the following colleagues for their kind help in collecting original literature and dates, and by supplying photographic material: N. Brock, Asta-Werke, Brackwede/Westfalen; E. Bonetti, Istituto di Pathologia Generale, University of Bologna; L. and Gloria Centanni, Bologna (Fig. 19); Helen Coley-Nauts, Cancer Research Institute Inc., New York (Fig. 16); B. Diamant, Department of Pharmacology, University of Copenhagen (Fig. 1, 2, 18); P. Kallos, Helsingborg; A. L. Olitzki, Hebrew University, Jerusalem (Fig. 17); H.-J. Raettig, Robert-Koch-Institut, Berlin; H. Schipperges, Institute f. Geschichte der Medizin, University of Heidelberg (Fig. 3); H. G. Schwick, Behringwerke AG, Marburg; Theodor Wagner von Jauregg, Zofingen, Switzerland (Fig. 15); T. D. Whittet, Chief Pharmacist, Department of Health and Social Security, Alexander Fleming House, London (Fig. 14).

REFERENCES

1. **Winter, D.** 1947. Die Lehre von der Heilkraft des Fiebers im Altertum (The teaching of the curative power of fever in early history). Pharmacie 2:512.
2. **Winter, D.** 1950. Die Lehre von der Heilkraft des Fiebers. II (The teaching of the curative power of fever). Pharmacie 5:131.
3. **Mazenod, L. (ed.).** 1968. Médecins célèbres (part of the collection "La Galérie des Hommes célébres," Paris, 2nd ed. German translation: Die berühmten Ärzte, Aulis-Verlag Deubner und Co., Cologne.
4. **von Haller, A.** Elementa physiologiae corporis humani (1757–1766), vol. III, p. 154 (cited after ref. 5, p. 45).
5. **Gaspard, B.** 1822. Mémoire physiologique sur les maladies purulentes et putrides, sur la vaccine etc. J. Physiol. (Paris) 2:1–45.
6. **Magendie, F.** 1823. Remarques sur la notice précédente (de Dupre), avec quelque expériences sur les effets des substances en putréfaction. J. Physiol. (Paris) 3:81–88.
7. *See* **A. Gjedde.** 1971. Peter Ludvig Panum's videnskabelige indsats. Saertryk af Bibliothek for Laeger, Copenhagen (summary in English, p. 223–225).
8. **Panum, P. L.** 1856. Bidrag til Laeren om den saakaldte putride eller septiske Infection. Bibliothek for Laeger, April, p. 253–285 (see Fig. 2).
9. **von den Busch.** 1859. *In* Schmidt's Jahrb. 101:213–217.
10. **Panum, P. L.** 1874. Das putride Gift, die Bakterien, die putride Infektion oder Intoxikation und die Septikämie (The putrid poison, the bacteria, the putrid infection or intoxication and the septicaemia). Arch. Pathol. Anat. Physiol. Klin. Med. (Virchow's Arch.) 60:301–352.
11. **Antall, J., et al.** 1972. Der Lebensweg des Ignaz Semmelweiss, 1818–1865 (The life of Ignaz Semmelweiss, 1818–1865). *In* Aus der Geschichte der Heilkunde, Museum, Bibliothek und Archiv für die Geschichte der Medizin "Ignàc Semmelweis" and the Motesz Ungarische Gesellschaft für die Geschichte der Medizin, p. 75–90, Budapest.
    Hegar, A. 1882. Ignaz Philipp Semmelweiss—Sein Leben und seine Lehre, zugleich ein Beitrag zur Lehre der fieberhaften Wundkrankheiten (I. P. Semmelweiss—His life and teaching, with a contribution to the teaching of the febrile wound diseases). Freiburg i.Br.-Tübingen.
12. **Semmelweiss, I. D.** 1861. Die Ätiologie, der Begriff und die Prophylaxe des Kindbettfiebers (The aetiology, the notion and the prophylaxis of puerperal fever). C. A. Hartleben's Verlags-Expedition, Pest, Vienna and Leipzig (see Fig. 4).
13. **Schweninger, F.** 1866. Über die Wirkung faulender organischer Substanzen auf den lebenden thierischen Organismus. Gekrönte Preisschrift (On the action of putrefying organic substances on the living organism. Publication carrying off the prize). J. J. Leutner'sche Buchhandlung (F. Stahl), Munich.
14. Briefe von Theodor Billroth (Letters of Th. Billroth),

1st ed. (1895), 9th ed. (1922). Hahn'sche Buchhandlung, Hannover.

15. **Billroth, Th.** 1862. Beobachtungsstudien über das Wundfieber und accidentelle Wund-Krankheiten. Arch. Klin. Chir. **2**:578–667.

16. **Billroth, Th.** 1873. Untersuchungen über die Vegetationsformen von Cocco-bacteria septica und den Antheil, welchen sie an der Entstehung und Verbreitung der accidentellen Wundkrankheiten haben. G. Reimer-Verlag, Berlin. See Arch. Exp. Pathol. Pharmakol. **2**:206–209, 1974.

17. **Buchholtz, A.** 1911. Ernst von Bergmann, 2nd. ed. F.C.W. Vogel, Leipzig.

18. **von Bergmann, E.** 1868. Das putride Gift und die putride Intoxikation. I. Vol. 1. Dorpat.

19. **von Bergmann, E., and O. Schmiedeberg.** 1868. Schwefelsaures Sepsin (Sepsin sulphate). Centralbl. Med. Wisschenschaften, no. 32.

20. **von Bergmann, E.** 1872. Zur Lehre von der putriden Intoxikation. Dtsch. Z. Chir. **1**:373–398.

21. **Dubczanski, V., and B. Naunyn.** 1873. Beiträge zur Lehre von der fieberhaften (durch pyrogene Substanzen bewirkten) Temperaturerhöhung (Contributions to the teaching of the febrile elevation of temperature, provoked by pyrogenic substances). Arch. Pathol. **1**: 1–32 (see Fig. 8).

22. **Fracastoro, H.** 1546. De contagionibus et contagionis morbis et lorum curatione libri tres (The three books on the contagiae, the contagious diseases and their treatment). Translated into German and introduced by V. Fossel, in K. Sudhoff (ed.), Klassiker der Medizin, vol. 5. 1910. Joh. Ambrosius Barth, Leipzig.

23. **Henle, J.** 1840. Von den Miasmen und den miasmatisch-kontagiösen Krankheiten. Reprinted with an introduction by F. Marchand, in K. Sudhoff (ed.), Klassiker der Medizin, vol. 3. 1910. Joh. Ambrosius Barth, Leipzig.

24. **Godlee, R. J.** 1917. Lord Lister. London. German translation by E. Weisschedel, 1925. F.C.W. Vogel, Leipzig.

25. Pasteur und die Generatio spontanea, aus Werken von Pasteur, ausgewählt, übersetzt und eingeleitet von J. Tomcsik. Huber's Klassiker der Medizin und Naturwissenschaften, vol. III, 1964. H. Huber, Bern and Stuttgart.

26. **Lister, J.** Lancet i:326–329, 357–359, 387–389, 507–509; ii:95–96, 353–356 (1867). Br. Med. J. **2**:53–56, 101–102, 461–463, 515–517 (1868); **1**:301–304 (1869).

27. **Koch, R.** 1888. Die Bekämpfung der Infektionskrankheiten, insbesondere der Kriegsseuchen. Buchdruckerei Otto Lange, Berlin.

28. **Burdon-Sanderson, J.** 1876. On the process of fever, part III: Pyrexia. Practitioner, p. 417–31.
—1896. Aetiology of fever, chap. 6. In T. C. Albutt (ed.), A system of medicine. Macmillan and Co., New York.

29. **Whittet, T. D.** 1976. Chairman's opening Address. In International Symposium on Pyrogens. Mallinckrodt Inc., St. Louis, Mo.

30. **Charrin, A., and G. E. H. Roger.** Les fatigues et les maladies microbiennes. Semaine Med. no. 4, (1890); C. R. Acad. Sci., Sept. 1892 (cited after ref. 31; p. 75, ref. 107).

31. **Lenhartz, H.** 1903. Erysipel, die septischen Erkrankungen (Erysipelas, the septic diseases), p. 1–78. In H. Nothnagel (ed.), Spezielle Pathologie und Therapie, vol. III/2, I. H. Holder, Vienna.

32. **Brieger, L.** 1883. Zur Kenntnis der Fäulnisalkaloide (On alcaloids of putrefaction). Ber. Dtsch. Chem. Ges. **16**:1186–1191, 1405–1407.

33. **Brieger, L.** 1886. Untersuchungen über Ptomaine (Investigations on ptomaines), 3rd part, p. 85. Hirschwald, Berlin.

Kobert, R. 1880. Beiträge zur Kenntnis der Ptomaine (Contributions to the knowledge about ptomaines). Schmidt's Jahrb. **185**:123–130.

34. **Brieger, L., and C. Fraenkel.** 1890. Untersuchungen über Bakteriengifte (Studies on bacterial toxins). Berliner Klin. Wochenschr. **27**:241–246, 268–271.

35. **Buchner, H.** 1890. Über pyogene Stoffe in den Bakterienzellen (About pyogenic substances in bacterial cells). Berliner Klin. Wochenschr. **27**:673–677.
—1897. Die Gewinnung von plasmatischen Zellsäften niederer Pilze (Manufacture of plasmatic cell extracts from microorganisms). Muench. Med. Wochenschr., no. 48.

36. **Buchner, H.** 1890. Die chemische Reizbarkeit der Leukocyten und deren Beziehung zur Entzündung und Eiterung (The chemical stimulation of leucocytes and their relation to inflammation and to pus formation). Berliner Klin. Wochenschr. **27**:1084–1089.
See also F. Roemer. 1891. Darstellung und Wirkung protein-haltiger Bakterien-Extrakte (Preparation and activity of protein extracts of bacteria). Berliner Klin. Wochenschr. **28**:1189.

Kanthack, A. A. 1892. Acute leucocytosis produced by bacterial products. Br. Med. J. **1**:1301.

36a. **Buchner, H.** 1896. Biologie und Gesundheitslehre Biology and the teaching of health), p. 40–56. Verh. Ges. Dtsch. Naturforsch. Aertze, 68th Assembly in Frankfurt, 1–2 September.

37. **von Krehl, L.** 1895. Versuche über die Erzeugung von Fieber bei Thieren (Experiments on the production of fever in animals). Arch. Exp. Pathol. Pharmakol. **35**: 222–268.

von Krehl, L., and M. Matthes. 1897. Wie entsteht die Temperatursteigerung des fiebernden Organismus? (What is the mechanism of temperature elevation in organisms under fever?). Arch. Exp. Pathol. Pharmakol. **38**:284–320.

38. **von Krehl, L., and M. Matthes.** 1896. Über febrile Albuminosurie (On febrile albuminosuria). Dtsch. Arch. Klin. Med. **22**:501–514.

39. **Rosenblum, A. S.** 1876. Zum Verhältnis der Fieberkrankheiten zu den Psychosen (The relation of febrile reactions to psychotic illnesses). Trudi Odessaer Klin., p. 90. Cited after A. A. Studnizin. 1976. Die Anwendung der Pyrogen-Therapie in der Dermato-Venerologie (The application of pyrogen therapy in the dermato-venerology). Dermatol. Monatsschr. **162**:801.

40. **Wagner von Jauregg, J.** 1887. Über die Einwirkung fieberhafter Erkrankungen auf Psychosen. Jahrb. Psychiatr. **7**:94–131.
—1912. Über die Behandlung der progressiven Paralyse mit Bakterien-Toxinen. Wiener Klin. Wochenschr. **25**: 61–63.
—1928. Die Behandlung der progressiven Paralyse mit Malaria. Les Prix Nobel, Stockholm.

41. **Dupre de Lisle.** 1774. Traité du Vice cancereux. Couturier Fils, Paris.

42. **Fehleisen, F.** 1882. Über die Züchtung der Erysipelkokken auf künstlichen Nährböden und die Übertragbarkeit auf den Menschen (On the cultivation of cocci from Erysipelas on artificial media and their transfer to man). Dtsch. Med. Wochenschr. **8**:553.
See also Dtsch. Z. Chir., vol. 16, 1882; Aetiologie des Erysipels, 1883, Berlin (cited after H. Lenhartz, l.c. ref. 31).

43. **Coley, W. B.** 1891. Contribution to the knowledge of sarcoma. Ann. Surg. **14**:199–220.
—1893. The treatment of malignant tumors by repeated inoculation of Erysipelas. Am. J. Med. Sci. **105**:487–511. See also Am. J. Med. Assoc. **31**:389, 456 (1889).
For a review with the historic literature of the subject, see **H. Coley-Nauts, W. E. Swift, and B. L. Coley.** 1946. The treatment of malignant tumors by bacterial

toxins as developed by the late William B. Coley, M.D., revised in the light of modern research. Cancer Res. 6:205–216.

U.S. Council on Pharmacy and Chemistry, New and non-official remedies. Erysipelas and Prodigiosus toxins (Coley). J. Am. Med. Assoc. 54:290 (1910); 103:1067–1069 (1934).

Brues, A. M., and M. J. Shear. 1944. Chemical treatment of tumors. X. J. Natl. Cancer Inst. 5:195–208.

44. Asta-Werke, A. G. 1951. Wegweiser durch die Pyrifer-Literatur (Guide through the literature on Pyrifer), with summaries and references of over 800 publications. Brackwede, Westfalia.

Hoff, H. 1957. Fieber, unspezifische Abwehrvorgänge, unspezifische Therapie. G. Thieme, Stuttgart.

45. Pfeiffer, R. 1892. Untersuchungen über das Choleragift (Investigations about the cholera poison). 11:393–412.

46. Gram, Ch. 1884. Über die isolierte Färbung der Schizomyceten in Schnitt- und Trockenpräparaten (The specific staining of Schizomycetes in histological sections). Fortschr. Med. 2:185–189.

47. Davis, B. B., R. Dulbecco, H. N. Eisen, H. S. Ginsburg, and W. Barry Wood (ed.). 1970. Microbiology, p. 22. Harper International Ed., New York.

Boivin, A., and L. Mesrobeanu. 1937. Sur les rapports existant entre la constitution chimique de l'antigène somatique des bactéries et la colorabilité de ces bactéries par la méthode de Gram. C. R. Soc. Biol. 124:1176.

48. Wolff, M. 1904. Beiträge zur Immunitätslehre (Contributions to the teaching of Immunity). Zentralbl. Bakteriol. Parasitenkd. Infektionskr. Hyg. I Orig. 37: 392.

49. Centanni, E. 1894. Untersuchungen über das Infektionsfieber—das Fiebergift der Bakterien. Dtsch. Med. Wochenschr. 20:148.

50. Centanni, E., and A. Bruschettini. 1894. Untersuchungen über das Infektionsfieber—das Antitoxin des Bakterienfiebers. Dtsch. Med. Wochenschr. 20:270.

51. Beeson, R. B. 1946. Development of tolerance to typhoid bacterial pyrogen and its addition to reticulo-endothelial blockade. Proc. Soc. Exp. Biol. Med. 61:248–250.

—1947. Tolerance of bacterial pyrogens. II. Role of the reticulo-endothelial system. J. Exp. Med. 86:39–44.

52. Rietschel, E. Th. 1975. Chemical structure and biological activity of endotoxins (lipopolysaccharides) and lipid A. Naunyn-Schmiedeberg's Arch. Pharmacol. 287: 73–84.

53. Centanni, E. 1921. Trattato di Immunologia, chapter IV: La Immunità stomogene (Terza immunità), p. 149–227. Società Editrice Libraria, Rome, Milan, Naples.

—1897. Les stomosines, nouveaux produits immunisants. Arch. Ital. Biol. 28:220–230.

54. Bonetti, E. (Director of the Istituto di Patologia Generale, Bologna). Personal communication.

55. Chelmonski, A. 1896. Klinische Untersuchungen über den Einfluss des Fäulnisextraktes auf den Verlauf mancher Infektionskrankheiten (Clinical investigations on the course of certain infectious diseases under the influence of extracts from putrid material). Dtsch. Arch. Klin. Med. 57:37–64.

Höring, F. O., and F. Burmeister. 1946. Die Pyrifer-Behandlung der typhösen Erkrankungen (The Pyrifer treatment of typhoid infections). Klin. Prax. 1:1–5.

56. Centanni, E. 1897. Sui vaccini depurati (stomosine). II. Memoria, la stomosina dello Pneumococco. Riforma Med. 13:782.

57. Centanni, E. 1940. Weitere Beiträge zur Kenntnis des pyrogenen Wirkstoffs des Fiebers (Further contributions to the understanding of the pyrogenic principle of fever). Dtsch. Med. Wochenschr. 66:263.

—1942. Immunitätserscheinungen im experimentellen Fieber mit besonderer Berücksichtigung des pyrogenen Stoffes aus Typhusbazillen (Immune phenomena in experimental fever with special reference to the pyrogenic substance from typhoid bacilli). Klin. Wochenschr. 21:664.

58. Seibert, F. B. 1923. Fever-producing substance found in some distilled waters. Am. J. Physiol. 67:90–104.

—1925. The cause of many febrile reactions following intravenous injections. Am. J. Physiol. 71:621–652.

59. Seibert, F. B. 1951. In Proceedings of the Research Conference on Activities of Bacterial Pyrogens, Philadelphia, p. 58.

60. Boivin, A., and L. Mesrobeanu. 1933. Contribution à l'étude de la composition chimique des bactéries. Les substances phosphorées au cours de l'autolyse bactérienne. C. R. Soc. Biol. 112:611.

—1933. Substances azotées et phosphorées "acido-soluble." C. R. Soc. Biol. 112:76.

Boivin, A. 1946. Travaux récents sur la constitution chimique et sur les propriétés biologiques des antigènes bactériens. Schweiz. Z. Pathol. Bakteriol. 9:505–541.

61. Morgan, W. T. J. 1937. Biochem. J. 31:2003.

Morgan, W. T. J., and S. M. Partridge. 1942. Br. J. Exp. Pathol. 23:151.

62. Goebel, W. F., F. Binkley, and E. Perlman. 1945. J. Exp. Med. 81:315.

Baker, E. E., W. F. Goebel, and E. Perlman. 1949. J. Exp. Med. 89:325.

63. Shear, M. J., and F. C. Turner. 1943. Chemical treatment of tumors. V. Isolation of the hemorrhage-producing fraction from Serratia marcescens (Bacillus prodigiosus) culture filtrates. J. Natl. Cancer Inst. 4:81–97.

Hartwell, J. L., M. J. Shear, and J. R. Adams. 1943. VII. Nature of the hemorrhage-producing fraction from Serratia marcescens (Bac. prodigiosus) culture filtrate. J. Natl. Cancer Inst. 4:107–122.

64. Bennett, J. L., and P. B. Beeson. 1950. The properties and biologic effects of bacterial pyrogens. Medicine 29:365–400.

65. Kadis, S., G. Weinbaum, and S. J. Ajl (ed.). 1971. Endotoxins. In Microbial toxins, vol. 4 and 5. Academic Press Inc., New York.

Westphal, O. 1975. Bacterial endotoxins (2nd Carl Prausnitz Memorial Lecture). Int. Arch. Allergy Appl. Immunol. 40:1–43.

66. Westphal, O., O. Lüderitz, and F. Bister. 1952. Z. Naturforsch. 7B:148.

Westphal, O., and K. Jann. 1965. Methods Carbohydr. Chem. 5:83.

67. Westphal, O., and O. Lüderitz. 1954. Chemische Erforschung von Lipopolysacchariden gram-negativer Bakterien (Chemical elaboration of lipopolysaccharides from gram-negative bacteria). Angew. Chem. 66: 407–417.

68. Lüderitz, O., et al. 1973. Lipid A. J. Infect. Dis. 128(Suppl.):17–29.

69. Galanos, Ch., and O. Lüderitz. 1975. Electrodialysis of lipopolysaccharides and their conversion to uniform salt forms. Eur. J. Biochem. 54:603–610.

70. Galanos, Ch., O. Lüderitz, E. Th. Rietschel, and O. Westphal. 1977. Newer aspects of the chemistry and biology of bacterial lipopolysaccharides, with special reference to their lipid A component. Int. Rev. Biochem., in press.

71. Eichenberger, E., P. P. Foa, and T. A. J. Grillo. 1966. In O. Eichler (ed.), Erzeugung von Krankheitszuständen durch das Experiment (The experimental production of states of disease), part 15, p. 280–322 (Fever); with an almost complete collection of the relevant

literature. Springer-Verlag, Berlin, Heidelberg, New York.

72. **Sulzer, B. M.** 1972. Genetic control of host responses to endotoxin. Infect. Immun. **5**:107–113.

73. **Menkin, V.** 1953. Modern views of inflammation. Int. Arch. Allergy Appl. Immunol. **4**:131–168.

1956. Biochemical mechanisms of inflammation, 2nd ed. Charles C Thomas, Springfield, Ill.

74. **Atkins, E.** 1960. Pathogenesis of fever. Physiol. Rev. **40**:580–646.

Dinarelli, C. A., N. P. Gordin, and S. M. Wolff. 1974. Demonstration and characterization of two distinct human leukocytic pyrogens. J. Exp. Med. **139**:1369–1381.

75. **Feldberg, W.** 1975. Body temperature and fever: changes in our views during the last decade (The Ferrier Lecture 1974). Proc. R. Soc. London B **191**:199–229.

76. **Fischer, H., M.-L. Lohmann-Matthes, B. Peskar, E. Th. Rietschel, D. Inter, M. Weidemann, and H. Weckerle.** 1977. Eur. Surg. Res., in press.

77. **Woolf, C. J.** 1957. Neuropharmacology **14**:397.

Woolf, C. J., G. H. Willies, and C. Rosendorff. 1976. Naturwissenschaften **63**:94.

78. **Siegert, R., W. K. Philipp-Dormston, K. Radsak, and H. Menzel.** 1976. Mechanism of fever induction in rabbits. Infect. Immun. **14**:1130–1137.

79. **Bennett, J. L.** 1964. Approaches to the mechanisms of endotoxin action, p. XIII–XVI. *In* M. Landy and W. Braun (ed.), Bacterial endotoxins. Rutger's University Press, New Brunswick, N.J.

Identification of the figures is as follows: (1) *Peter Ludwig Panum (1820–1885)*. (2) *First page of Panum's publication in 1856*. (3) *Ignaz Philipp Semmelweis (1818–1865)*. (4) *Cover page of Semmelweiss's publication in 1861*. (5) *Theodor Billroth (1829–1894)*. (6) *Ernst von Bergmann (1836–1906) (from ref. 17)*. (7) *Bernhard Naunyn (1839–1925)*. (8) *Cover page of Naunyn's publication in 1873*. (9) *Records of two pyrogenic experiments, taken from ref. 21. Curve no I: Rabbit (1,200 g), intramuscular injection of 2 ml of putrid muscle extract at 14°C (experiment 25) and 30°C (experiment 26) environmental temperature. Curve no. II: Guinea pig (400 g), intramuscular injection of 1 ml of putrid muscle extract at 16°C (experiment 32) and 30°C (experiment 31) environmental temperature*. (10) *Joseph Lister (1827–1912)*. (11) *Louis Pasteur (1822–1895) (from ref. 24)*. (12) *In his garden, Pasteur dictates a letter to his wife*. (13) *Scene at the celebration of Pasteur's 70th birthday in Paris. Pasteur, led by President Carnot, and Lister have risen to embrace each other (from ref. 24)*. (14) *Sir John Burdon-Sanderson (1828–1905)*. (15) *Julius Wagner von Jauregg (1857–1940)*. (16) *William Bradley Coley (1862–1936)*. (17) *Richard Pfeiffer (1858–1945)*. (18) *Hans Christian Joachim Gram (1853–1939)*. (19) *Eugenio Centanni (1863–1948)*. (20) *André Boivin (1895–1949)*.

Die Ätiologie, der Begriff

und

die Prophylaxis

des

Kindbettfiebers.

Von

Ignaz Philipp Semmelweis,

Dr. der Medizin und Chirurgie, Magister der Geburtahilfe, o. ö. Professor der
theoretischen und praktischen Geburtshilfe an der kön. ung. Universität zu Pest
etc. etc.

Pest, Wien und Leipzig.
C. A. Hartleben's Verlags-Expedition.
1861.

Bibliothek for Læger.
April 1856.

Videnskabelig Afdeling.

Experimentelle Bidrag
af
Professor Dr. *P. L. Panum.*

6. Bidrag til Læren om den saakaldte putride
eller septiske Infection.

Forat komme til nærmere Kundskab om det Stof (eller
de Stoffer) i de qvælstofholdige Substantsers Forraadnel-
sesprodukter, som indbragt i Blodet virker saa giftigt og
fremkalder den saakaldte putride eller septiske Infection,
kunde man slaae ind paa to forskjellige Veie. Efterat
have studeret de Symptomer, som opstaae efter Injection
af forskjellige raadne Vædsker, kunde man nemlig enten
analysere de raadne Substantser, saavidt som Kemiens
nærværende Standpunkt tillader det, og undersøge den

17

BEITRÄGE

ZUR LEHRE VON DER FIEBERHAFTEN

(DURCH PYROGENE SUBSTANZEN BEWIRKTEN)

TEMPERATURERHÖHUNG

VON

v. DUBCZCANSKI UND B. NAUNYN
IN BERN.   IN KÖNIGSBERG.

MIT 1 TAFEL.

LEIPZIG,
DRUCK VON J. B. HIRSCHFELD.
1873.

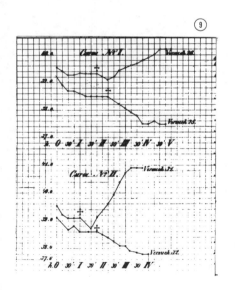

Endotoxins and Other Cell Wall Components of Gram-Negative Bacteria and Their Biological Activities

Position Paper

OTTO LÜDERITZ

Max-Planck-Institut für Immunobiologie, D-78 Freiburg, West Germany

Lipopolysaccharides are known to represent the endotoxic principle of gram-negative bacteria (12, 23). Investigations on other compounds of the cell wall, however, have clearly demonstrated that at least some of them are also endowed with endotoxin-like activities (see the following in this volume: Braun, p. 257; Heymer and Rietschel, p. 344; Schleifer and Seidl, p. 339). It is one of the aims of this symposium to discuss our present knowledge regarding endotoxins and endotoxin-like constituents of the gram-negative cell wall, their antigenic properties, and their mode of action in higher animals. Ideally, all these compounds and their immunological and biological properties ought to be discussed in relation to their structure, their location on the cell surface, and their function for the cell.

Figure 1 shows a most simplified schematic representation of a section through the cell envelope of a capsulated gram-negative bacterium. It consists of a capsule surrounding the cell and three layers, the cytoplasmic or inner membrane, the peptidoglycan, and the outer, plastic membrane. This outer membrane is characteristic of gram-negative bacteria. Certainly, in the course of this symposium, other, more elaborate pictures of the architecture of the outer layer will be shown, but at the moment this simple diagram will serve our purpose. Those building blocks which have so far been identified in the cell envelope are listed. These include the phospholipids, three or four major and some minor proteins (1, 21, 22), the lipoprotein of Braun (p. 257, this volume), the lipopolysaccharide (23), and the enterobacterial common antigen (ECA) (15a). These antigens and their isolation, purification, and structural analysis form the subject of intensive investigations by many research groups. These investigations have provided much information regarding the composition of the outer membrane and the topography of its constituents, but a great deal has still to

be learned, especially about the function and cooperation of these compounds which maintain the viability of the cell. In addition to the antigens of Fig. 1, I shall mention briefly the murein and the lipoteichoic acids of gram-positive bacteria, since their biological properties will be discussed later in this symposium (see the following in this volume: Heymer and Rietschel, p. 344; Knox and Wicken, p. 356; Schleifer and Seidl, p. 339; Wicken and Knox, p. 360).

In this symposium, we are interested mainly in those constituents which, because of their immunological properties, play a role in the interaction of the bacterium and the host during infection, and in those components which show biological, endotoxin-like activities when introduced into the higher animal in an isolated form. In these discussions lipopolysaccharides certainly will occupy a central position, and in studies on the other cell wall constituents the results obtained with lipopolysaccharides will often serve as a comparative basis.

This is because lipopolysaccharides, on account of their prominent endotoxic and immunological properties, have been studied extensively for many years. Much is therefore known about their general structural architecture, its genetic determination, and its biosynthesis. Best explored are the *Salmonella* and *Escherichia coli* lipopolysaccharides (23). They contain a heteropolysaccharide chain of repeating oligosaccharide units, the O-specific chain, which is linked to a central acidic heterooligosaccharide, the core, which in turn is linked to a lipoidal, acylated glucosamine-disaccharide, termed lipid A (Fig. 2).

Comparatively, less is known about the other macromolecules of the cell envelope. The study of their immunological and endotoxic activities has always been hampered by the difficulties encountered in avoiding contamination with endotoxin. This is due to the well-known property of lipopolysaccharides of forming complexes

239

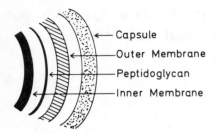

← Capsule

Outer Membrane

Peptidoglycan

Inner Membrane

Components of Outer Membrane:

Lipopolysaccharide

Phospholipids

Proteins

Lipoprotein

Enterobacterial Common
                    Antigen

FIG. 1. *Section through the cell envelope of a capsulated gram-negative bacterium: schematic representation.*

with almost every partner. In fact, it was only recently that Galanos developed a method which allows the extraction from the bacterial cell of a mixture of proteins shown to be free from endotoxin by chemical and biological tests (16). The method of isolation consists in treatment of bacterial cells with EDTA. In the case of S and most R forms, this procedure is known to result in the release of soluble lipopoly-saccharide-protein complexes (13). When this method, however, is applied to R-mutant cells of the Re type in the presence of high salt concentration, the Re lipopolysaccharide remains insoluble in the cell wall, and lipo-polysaccharide-free proteins are released. This investigation led to the discovery of mitogenic effects of cell wall constituents other than lipopolysaccharides (16). It has since been shown by Melchers et al. (16) that at least one mitogenic factor of this mixture is the lipoprotein, which was subsequently tested in a pure form. It is not yet known whether proteins other than lipoprotein are endowed with mitogenic or other biological activities. What is known, however, is that at least some of these cell wall proteins exhibit antigenic activities and, moreover, that some serological specificities are shared by many gram-negative bacteria (2; C. Galanos, unpublished data).

Considering the dominant role lipopoly-saccharides have played in the past, Barber and Eylan (2) used as the title of a recent publication the statement, "The unfortunate role of precedent in bacteriology," with the addition, "the main antigens of *Salmonella* are proteins." These authors concluded that the over-

emphasis on lipopolysaccharide in the past was not to the advantage of bacteriology. To some degree this may be true, and it is hoped that methods of isolation of pure, undenatured envelope proteins will lead to investigations of their biological properties and resolve whether, in addition to the lipoprotein of Braun, other protein molecules of gram-negative bacterial cell walls are also endowed with endotoxin-like properties.

On first sight, similarities in the general structure of lipoprotein and lipopolysaccharide seem to offer a good explanation for common biological properties (see Fig. 2). Both molecules contain a hydrophilic backbone carrying at one end amide- and ester-linked fatty acyl residues rendering this region lipophilic. Both show high affinity for cell surfaces and both are able to sensitize erythrocytes for subsequent reaction with antiserum, properties which are lost after treatment with alkali. The mechanisms of B-lymphocyte stimulation must, however, be different, since lipoprotein acts as a mitogen for lymphocytes derived from the lipopoly-saccharide-resistant C3H/HeJ mouse strain, whereas lipopolysaccharide does not stimulate these cells (16). Moreover, lipoprotein is neither toxic in mice nor pyrogenic in rabbits. The question of whether the lipid region of lipoprotein, by analogy to lipid A, represents

Lipopolysaccharide (Endotoxin)

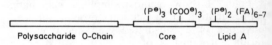

Lipoprotein (B-cell mitogen)

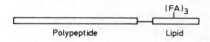

Lipoteichoic Acid (Shwartzman +)

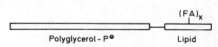

Peptidoglycane (Endotoxin-like)

FIG. 2. *Schematic structures and biological activities of bacterial antigens (FA = fatty acids).*

the active center of the molecule will certainly be investigated soon.

Figure 2 also shows the schematic structures of lipoteichoic acids (Knox and Wicken, p. 356, this volume; Wicken and Knox, p. 360, this volume) and peptidoglycans (Heymer and Rietschel, p. 344, this volume; Schleifer and Seidl, p. 339, this volume). The former structurally resemble endotoxin and lipoprotein in that they contain a long polar main chain to which a hydrophobic lipid portion is attached. Furthermore, they also share physicochemical and essential biological properties with lipopolysaccharide and lipoprotein. The lipoteichoic acids associate in solution to form micelles, and they are able to react with cell surfaces and sensitize erythrocytes, again properties dependent on the presence of fatty acids. Lipoteichoic acids are active in the Shwartzman reaction, and they stimulate bone resorption. Typical endotoxin reactions like fever and B-cell mitogenicity are, however, absent. Peptidoglycans, on the other hand, have no obvious structural similarities to endotoxins, but they exhibit typical endotoxin-like activities.

These data show that it is not possible at the moment to identify structural principles in these molecules which can be related to the different biological activities exhibited by them.

The ECA and the capsular (K) antigens do not exhibit endotoxic activities. I would like, however, to mention one interesting aspect, which has been investigated recently for K polysaccharides by Jann and Westphal (11) and for the ECA by Mayer, Neter, and Mäkelä and their colleagues (see 15a). Both these classes of antigens are transferred under defined conditions to the core of the respective lipopolysaccharide produced by the cell. Core lipid A, therefore, can function as acceptor for capsular antigens and ECA. Under these conditions, the cells produce a lipopolysaccharide in which the original O-specific chain is replaced by a capsular polysaccharide or by the common antigen, respectively. We do not know why the bacteria have developed this capacity to replace O-specific chains by molecules of different specificity. We can only speculate that, in the case of the T1 and T2 antigens, which have been studied previously (3, 5), this replacement may serve as a disguise mechanism for escaping immune recognition and defense by the host.

It is not only the common antigen that exhibits an immunological specificity which is shared by many bacterial groups (in this case by all *Enterobacteriaceae*); this is true also for some of the outer membrane proteins (2), for the lipoprotein (Braun, p. 257, this volume),

and for the inner structures of lipopolysaccharides (23). All these envelope structures which are obviously widely distributed among gram-negative bacteria are cryptic and barely available for antibodies on S-form cells, where they are hidden by the long O-specific chains of the S-form lipopolysaccharides. They only become immunogenic and available for the respective antibodies in R-form strains with a deep lipopolysaccharide defect.

In those cases in which antibodies against these common structures of the cell wall have been found to play a protective role in infection, one has to assume that, during growth and division of the infective cells, these structures become temporarily exposed and thus available for the antibodies.

I would like to mention now two procedures which have been introduced as valuable steps for the isolation and purification of lipopolysaccharides and other antigens. The phenolchloroform-petroleum ether (PCP) method of Galanos et al. (10), which had been elaborated for the selective isolation of R-form lipopolysaccharides, has now been extended by Galanos for further purification of S-form lipopolysaccharides, for the isolation of common antigen (15a), and for the isolation of incomplete lipid A (V. Lehmann, in preparation). Combinations of the PCP and phenol-water methods have proved most valuable and flexible purification methods. The second procedure is the technique of electrodialysis of lipopolysaccharides which was introduced by Galanos (8a, 9). By this treatment, the majority of mono- and divalent metal cations and polyamines, which naturally neutralize the negative charges of the core and the lipid A region, are removed (Fig. 3). The S- and R-form lipopolysaccharides are thus converted into their acid form. After neutralization with a base, uniform salt forms of the lipopolysaccharides can be prepared. This is true also for free lipid A. Interestingly enough, physicochemical properties, such as the sedimentation coefficient and the solubility, and, even more importantly, some biological properties of these salt forms are determined by the nature of the cations associated with the phosphate and carboxyl groups (9; Galanos et al., p. 269, this volume). Since complete solubility is a prerequisite for reproducible biological tests, these factors are of prime importance and can now be handled at will.

In Fig. 4 are depicted the series of incomplete lipopolysaccharides which have been isolated from Ra- to Re-form *Salmonella* mutants (23). The formulas represent intermediate structures in the pathway of lipopolysaccharide biosynthesis. This scheme is well known, and until

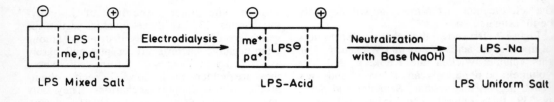

FIG. 3. *Conversion of lipopolysaccharide (LPS) into uniform salt form by electrodialysis and neutralization of the acidic lipopolysaccharide (according to 8, 8a).*

recently the Re lipopolysaccharide containing only ketodeoxyoctonate (KDO) and lipid A was the most reduced natural lipopolysaccharide structure available. Since free lipid A does not occur in nature, the Re lipopolysaccharide has served as a convenient source for the preparation of free lipid A (6, 14, 23). The linkages of KDO are very acid labile and can be cleaved to liberate lipid A under mild conditions. Free lipid A has been studied in many laboratories, and it has proved to be the active principle for endotoxicity in the lipopolysaccharide molecule (14). Several reports in this symposium will be concerned with the chemistry and biology of lipid A. I will therefore restrict myself here to only a few questions of principle.

I would first like to give an up-to-date definition of lipid A. What is lipid A? This question has often been raised, and it is true that with the increasing amount of chemical information the definition of what should be called lipid A has occasionally changed. About 25 years ago, we gave the designation lipid A to the lipoidal precipitate which formed after treatment of lipopolysaccharide with acid (24). However, the term lipid A was also often used for the lipoidal region of lipopolysaccharides from which the precipitate derived. Because of newer results, which have provided an insight into a broader range of lipopolysaccharide structures, it is now justified, and more logical, to restrict the designation lipid A to the genuine lipoidal region of lipopolysaccharide. Certainly, there exist in nature a number of lipid A types. However, compared with the various core types and the innumerable types of O-specific chains occurring in nature, the structure of the lipid A region is the most invariable part of the lipopolysaccharide molecule and it is constant for larger groups of bacteria. In the group *Enterobacteriaceae*,

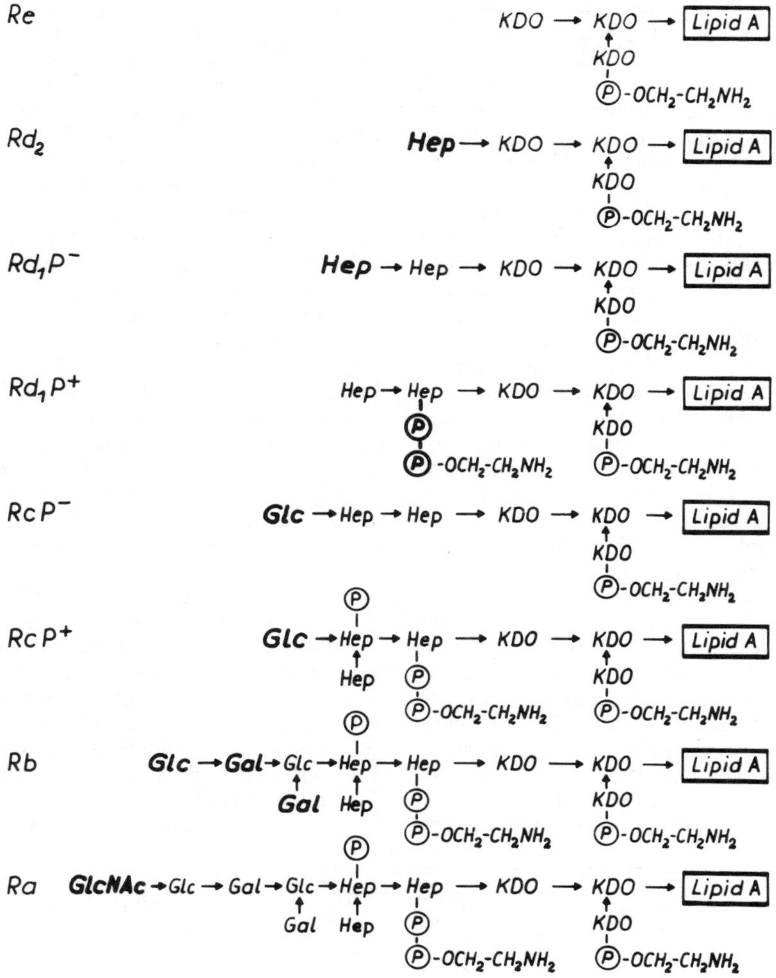

Re
$$KDO \rightarrow KDO \rightarrow \boxed{Lipid\ A}$$
$$\uparrow$$
$$KDO$$
$$|$$
$$\textcircled{P}\text{-}OCH_2\text{-}CH_2NH_2$$

Rd$_2$
$$\textbf{Hep} \rightarrow KDO \rightarrow KDO \rightarrow \boxed{Lipid\ A}$$
$$\uparrow$$
$$KDO$$
$$|$$
$$\textcircled{P}\text{-}OCH_2\text{-}CH_2NH_2$$

Rd$_1$P$^-$
$$\textbf{Hep} \rightarrow Hep \rightarrow KDO \rightarrow KDO \rightarrow \boxed{Lipid\ A}$$
$$\uparrow$$
$$KDO$$
$$|$$
$$\textcircled{P}\text{-}OCH_2\text{-}CH_2NH_2$$

Rd$_1$P$^+$
$$Hep \rightarrow Hep \rightarrow KDO \rightarrow KDO \rightarrow \boxed{Lipid\ A}$$
$$\textcircled{P} \qquad \uparrow$$
$$| \qquad\quad KDO$$
$$\textcircled{P}\text{-}OCH_2\text{-}CH_2NH_2 \quad \textcircled{P}\text{-}OCH_2\text{-}CH_2NH_2$$

RcP$^-$
$$\textbf{Glc} \rightarrow Hep \rightarrow Hep \rightarrow KDO \rightarrow KDO \rightarrow \boxed{Lipid\ A}$$
$$KDO$$
$$|$$
$$\textcircled{P}\text{-}OCH_2\text{-}CH_2NH_2$$

RcP$^+$
$$\textbf{Glc} \rightarrow Hep \rightarrow Hep \rightarrow KDO \rightarrow KDO \rightarrow \boxed{Lipid\ A}$$
$$\textcircled{P} \quad \uparrow \qquad \uparrow$$
$$| \quad Hep \quad \textcircled{P} \qquad KDO$$
$$\textcircled{P} \qquad \textcircled{P}\text{-}OCH_2\text{-}CH_2NH_2 \quad \textcircled{P}\text{-}OCH_2\text{-}CH_2NH_2$$

Rb
$$\textbf{Glc} \rightarrow \textbf{Gal} \rightarrow Glc \rightarrow Hep \rightarrow Hep \rightarrow KDO \rightarrow KDO \rightarrow \boxed{Lipid\ A}$$
$$\uparrow \qquad\qquad \uparrow \qquad\qquad \uparrow$$
$$\textbf{Gal} \qquad Hep \quad \textcircled{P} \qquad KDO$$
$$\textcircled{P} \qquad \textcircled{P}\text{-}OCH_2\text{-}CH_2NH_2 \quad \textcircled{P}\text{-}OCH_2\text{-}CH_2NH_2$$

Ra
$$\textbf{GlcNAc} \rightarrow Glc \rightarrow Gal \rightarrow Glc \rightarrow Hep \rightarrow Hep \rightarrow KDO \rightarrow KDO \rightarrow \boxed{Lipid\ A}$$
$$\uparrow \qquad\qquad \uparrow \qquad\qquad \uparrow$$
$$Gal \quad Hep \quad \textcircled{P} \qquad KDO$$
$$\textcircled{P}\text{-}OCH_2\text{-}CH_2NH_2 \quad \textcircled{P}\text{-}OCH_2\text{-}CH_2NH_2$$

FIG. 4. *Structures of incomplete lipopolysaccharides derived from* Salmonella *Ra to Re mutants (23).*

for instance, we have no evidence for gross variations in the lipid A structure (23).

To differentiate it from the genuine lipid A of lipopolysaccharide, the precipitated lipid A obtained after acid hydrolysis should be called free or isolated lipid A. In case of *Salmonella* we know that during liberation of lipid A no gross degradation reactions occur. Lipid A and free lipid A are structurally quite similar, although a certain degree of degradation certainly occurs.

Free lipid A from *Salmonella* contains only glucosamine, phosphate, and fatty acids (14). KDO and other core sugars are absent, as well as amino acids and phospholipids. Free lipid A from *Salmonella* does not, however, represent a uniform molecule. Because of its lipophilic character and depending on the types of cations present, lipid A, and hence lipopolysaccharides,

form aggregates of different sizes (9). In addition to this kind of physicochemical heterogeneity, lipid A is also heterogeneous with respect to composition and structure.

Microheterogeneity is an attribute of all regions of the lipopolysaccharide molecule. This is true for the O chains, where the chain length and the number of substitutions (acetyl, glycosyl residues) are not constant.

Microheterogeneity has also been shown to reside in the core region of lipopolysaccharide. This is due to the fact that the constant central core oligosaccharide chain carries side chains in nonequimolar ratios, like residues of galactose, phosphate, phosphoethanolamine, and pyrophosphoethanolamine.

A similar kind of heterogeneity also seems to reside in the lipid A region of lipopolysaccharides. Evidence for such an intrinsic heterogeneity in lipid A derives from recent results with a new class of lipopolysaccharide-defective mutants. This class of *Salmonella* mutants, which was recognized for the first time by Osborn and Lehmann (18; V. Lehmann, in preparation; V. Lehmann, E. Rupprecht, and M. J. Osborn, in preparation), carries a lethal, temperature-sensitive defect in the synthesis of KDO. At the nonpermissive temperature, when KDO is not synthesized, these strains stop making lipopolysaccharide and instead synthesize, for a limited period of time, incomplete lipid A. The isolation of the lipid A precursor from these mutants and the evaluation of its structure revealed the presence of an incompletely acylated free lipid A (Fig. 5). Furthermore, heterogeneity with respect to the substituents linked to the constant backbone has been established. These substituents are phosphate and pyrophosphate residues, ethanolamine, and 4-aminoarabinose, which are present in nonequimolar ratios (Rietschel et al., p. 262, this volume). The same is true for lipid A in lipopolysaccharides, and an analogous heterogeneity resides in free lipid A, where an additional heterogeneity is introduced by the hydrolysis procedure. Thus, the amount of 4-aminoarabinose and ethanolamine is significantly decreased in free lipid A. Furthermore, an occasional loss of a fatty acid residue may occur during hydrolysis. In any case, each of the three compounds, lipid A precursor, lipid A in lipopolysaccharides, and free lipid A, exhibits microheterogeneity. They all include corresponding families of genuine structures, whose respective members are closely related and differ mainly by the presence and absence of charged substituents of a constant backbone.

It is certainly possible that the heterogeneity of lipid A and the core represents a dynamic state which is physiologically important for the cell. The core lipid A regions of lipopolysaccharide may act as an ion-exchange barrier which regulates the ion supply for the cell.

The separation and isolation of the lipid A fractions, their chemical identification, and their biological analysis for endotoxic activities were commenced several years ago by Nowotny and his group (7). Although many results have been obtained, there still remain many questions to be posed. Up to now, most investigators have been working with the (natural) mixture of lipid A and lipopolysaccharide entities.

From the foregoing it is evident that the distinction between lipid A, as the lipoidal structure of lipopolysaccharide, and free lipid A is not of great importance in the case of *Salmonella* lipid A. This definition, however, does become important in the case of lipopolysaccharides with different lipid A structures. In such cases the liberation of lipid A from lipopolysaccharide may be accompanied by more or less drastic degradation reactions, so

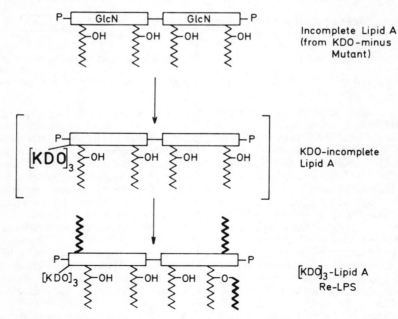

FIG. 5. *Final steps in the biosynthesis of Re lipopolysaccharide (according to Lehmann, in preparation).*

that the lipid A can be tested only in the degraded form. Lipid A of this kind will be described by Rietschel et al. (p. 262, this volume).

Some years ago, we thought that the biosynthesis of a lipid A unit might represent the first step in the pathway of lipopolysaccharide biosynthesis. We speculated that perhaps free lipid A would exist as a pool in bacterial cells, to which, in the case of urgency, the polysaccharide chains could be added quickly. We have spent a great deal of time in efforts to isolate free lipid A from S- and R-form bacteria. These efforts were without success. The results of Osborn and Lehmann have now shown that free lipid A does not, in fact, exist in nature as a precursor of lipopolysaccharides (18). The pathway of biosynthesis involves incomplete lipid A, to which KDO is transferred, followed by the transfer of fatty acids (Fig. 5). Thus, the Re lipopolysaccharide is the first structure of the pathway containing complete lipid A. Since natural free lipid A is not therefore available, acid hydrolysis of lipopolysaccharides represents the only way to obtain it. It would be most valuable if an enzyme could be found which specifically cleaves the KDO linkages and simultaneously would release complete unaltered free lipid A.

Lipopolysaccharides are immunogenic. It has long been known that antibodies are directed against specific determinant oligosaccharide groups residing in the O-specific chain, which determine the O specificity. In incomplete lipopolysaccharides of R mutants, the respective terminal saccharide of the core represents the immunodominant sugar to which the bulk of antibodies are formed (23). Antibodies directed against lipid A have been identified only recently by Galanos et al. (p. 269, this volume). They are stimulated under defined conditions in rabbits, dogs, goats, mice, and other animals. Furthermore, natural antibodies with lipid A specificity have been detected in the sera of various species, including man. Since these natural antibodies react with free lipid A from *Salmonella*, this is taken as additional evidence that the immunological specificity of free lipid A is not an artifact.

Lipid A can be identified by means of sensitive tests. Chemical methods are available, and β-hydroxymyristic acid has proved to be a good marker which can be detected with high sensitivity (19). As shown by Galanos, serological methods can be used for the detection of lipid A, and, with the aid of anti-lipid A serum, the passive hemolysis (inhibition) test will detect minute amounts of free lipid A. Finally, Rietschel and Galanos have described a biological assay in which lipid A- and lipopolysaccharide-induced fever is specifically suppressed by lipid A serum (19a). These assays are useful for many purposes, and, in particular, they allow a distinction between preparations whose biological activities are caused by contaminating endotoxin and preparations which by themselves exhibit endotoxin-like activities, such as murein, viral products, double-stranded RNA, and others.

Regarding lipid A as the biologically active principle of lipopolysaccharides, I would like to mention a recent observation which is important, provided it is confirmed and its interpretation is correct. In the past, the finding that, in a given system, free lipid A exhibits a biological activity identical to that of lipopolysaccharide has automatically led to the assumption that both free lipid A and the parent lipopolysaccharide exercise this activity by the same mechanism. The customary conclusion has been that lipid A is the active principle of endotoxins. The recent results of Morrison and Kline (16a) have demonstrated, however, that this is not always a correct conclusion. In the case of complement activation, these authors have shown that S-form and most R-form lipopolysaccharides activate complement through the alternate pathway, whereas Re endotoxin and free lipid A activate complement through the classical pathway in the absence of antibody. As had also been suspected by our group, the polysaccharide chain of lipopolysaccharides may not only function as a solubilizing carrier for lipid A, but may also, in some cases, modulate its action. Furthermore, the isolated polysaccharides themselves, in the absence of lipid A, may occasionally express endotoxin-like reactions. This has been shown by Nowotny et al. to be the case for the activation of the colony-stimulating factor under specified conditions (17).

On the other hand, investigations on *Rhodospirillaceae* performed by Mayer and his group have shown that the lipopolysaccharide of *R. tenue* exhibits very low lethal toxicity in contrast to other species of this group (Galanos et al., unpublished data). Free lipid A isolated by mild acid hydrolysis of this lipopolysaccharide resembles *Salmonella* free lipid A with respect to chemical and serological properties and toxicity. In this case it seems that lipid A, as present in the complete lipopolysaccharide, is masked and its expression is suppressed either by the presence of the polysaccharide chain or by some unknown substituents which are removed during liberation of the lipid A.

The main features of the structure of *Sal-*

monella lipid A have been evaluated. It has been found that the lipid A precursor of Osborn and Lehmann, whose structure lacks non-hydroxylated fatty acids, is highly toxic for mice and moderately pyrogenic in rabbits. These and other findings have stimulated investigations in various laboratories to identify the minimal structural conditions for endotoxicity (4, 15, 20; Nowotny et al., in preparation; Rietschel et al., p. 262, this volume). Various approaches can be used. Selective stepwise degradation of endotoxin or lipid A may lead to the identification of the smallest fragments still exhibiting biological activities. Inactive fragments of lipid A can be used for restoration of activity by partial chemical re-synthesis. Model substances may be synthesized. Investigations on lipid A from species other than *Salmonella* may represent a further route for exploring biologically essential structures. Work on all these lines is in progress.

LITERATURE CITED

1. **Ames, G. F.-L., E. Spudich, and H. Nikaido.** 1974. Protein composition of the outer membrane of *Salmonella typhimurium*: effect of lipopolysaccharide mutations. J. Bacteriol. **117**:406–416.

2. **Barber, C., and E. Eylan.** 1976. The unfortunate role of precedent in bacteriology. I. The main antigens of *Salmonellae*: the proteins. Zentralbl. Bakteriol. Parasitenkd. Infektionskr. Hyg. Abt. 1 Orig. Reihe A **234**:53–59.

3. **Berst, M., O. Lüderitz, and O. Westphal.** 1971. Studies on the structure of T1 lipopolysaccharides. Eur. J. Biochem. **18**:361–368.

4. **Bradley, S. G.** 1976. Endotoxic activity of complexes of myristic acid and proteins. Proc. Soc. Exp. Biol. Med. **151**:267–270.

5. **Bruneteau, M., W. A. Volk, P. P. Singh, and O. Lüderitz.** 1974. Structural investigations on the Salmonella T2 lipopolysaccharide. Eur. J. Biochem. **43**:501–508.

6. **Chang, C. M., and A. Nowotny.** 1975. Relation of structure to function in bacterial O-antigens. VII. Endotoxicity of lipid A. Immunochemistry **12**:19–28.

7. **Chen, C. H., and A. Nowotny.** 1974. Direct determination of molar ratios of various chemical constituents in endotoxic glycolipids in silicic acid scraping from thin-layer chromatography-plates. J. Chromatogr. **97**:39–45.

8. **Galanos, C.** 1975. Physical state and biological activity of lipopolysaccharides. Toxicity and immunogenicity of the lipid A component. Z. Immunitaetsforsch. **149**:214–229.

8a. **Galanos, C., and O. Lüderitz.** 1975. Electrodialysis of lipopolysaccharides and their conversion to uniform salt forms. Eur. J. Biochem. **54**:603–610.

9. **Galanos, C., and O. Lüderitz.** 1976. The role of the physical state of lipopolysaccharides in the interaction with complement. High molecular weight as prerequisite for the expression of anti-complementary activity. Eur. J. Biochem. **65**:403–408.

10. **Galanos, C., O. Lüderitz, and O. Westphal.** 1969. A new method for the extraction of R lipopolysaccharides. Eur. J. Biochem. **9**:245–249.

11. **Jann, K., and O. Westphal.** 1975. Microbial polysaccharides, p. 1–125. *In* M. Sela (ed.), The antigens, vol. 3. Academic Press Inc., New York.

12. **Kadis, S., G. Weinbaum, and S. J. Ajl (ed.).** 1971. Microbial toxins, vol. 5: Bacterial endotoxins. Academic Press Inc., New York.

13. **Leive, L., and K. Shovlin.** 1968. Physical, chemical, and immunological properties of lipopolysaccharide released from *Escherichia coli* by ethylenediaminetetraacetate. J. Biol. Chem. **243**:6384–6391.

14. **Lüderitz, O., C. Galanos, V. Lehmann, M. Nurminen, E. T. Rietschel, G. Rosenfelder, M. Simon, and O. Westphal.** 1973. Lipid A: chemical structure and biological activity. J. Infect. Dis. **128**:17–29.

15. **Lugowski, C., and E. Romanowska.** 1974. Biological properties of lipid A from *Shigella sonnei*. Eur. J. Biochem. **48**:81–87.

15a. **Mäkelä, P. H., and H. Mayer.** 1976. Enterobacterial common antigen. Bacteriol Rev. **40**:591–632.

16. **Melchers, F., V. Braun, and C. Galanos.** 1975. The lipoprotein of the outer membrane of *E. coli*: a B-lymphocyte mitogen. J. Exp. Med. **142**:473–482.

16a. **Morrison, D. C., and L. F. Kline.** 1977. Activation of the classical and properdin pathways of complement by bacterial lipopolysaccharides. J. Immunol. **118**:362–368.

17. **Nowotny, A., U. H. Behling, and H. L. Chang.** 1975. Relation of structure to function in bacterial endotoxins. VIII. Biological activities in a polysaccharide-rich fraction. J. Immunol. **115**:199–203.

18. **Osborn, M. J., P. D. Rick, V. Lehmann, E. Rupprecht, and M. Singh.** 1974. Structure and biogenesis of the cell envelope of gram-negative bacteria. Ann. N.Y. Acad. Sci. **235**:52–65.

19. **Rietschel, E. T., H. Gottert, O. Lüderitz, and O. Westphal.** 1972. Nature and linkages of the fatty acids present in the lipid A component of *Salmonella* lipopolysaccharides. Eur. J. Biochem. **28**:166–173.

19a. **Rietschel, E. T., and C. Galanos.** 1977. Lipid A antiserum-mediated protection against lipopolysaccharide- and lipid A-induced fever and skin necrosis. Infect. Immun. **15**:34–58.

20. **Rosenstreich, D. L., J. Asselineau, S. E. Mergenhagen, and A. Nowotny.** 1974. A synthetic glycolipid with B-cell mitogenic activity. J. Exp. Med. **140**:1404–1409.

21. **Schmitges, C. J., and U. Henning.** 1976. The major proteins of *Escherichia coli* outer cell envelope membrane. Heterogeneity of protein I. Eur. J. Biochem. **63**:47–52.

22. **Schnaitman, C. A.** 1974. Outer membrane proteins of *Escherichia coli*. IV. Differences in outer membrane proteins due to strain and cultural differences. J. Bacteriol. **118**:454–464.

23. **Weinbaum, G., S. Kadis, and S. J. Ajl.** 1971. Microbial toxins, vol. 4: Bacterial endotoxins. Academic Press Inc., New York.

24. **Westphal, O., O. Lüderitz, E. Eichenberger, and W. Keiderling.** 1952. Über bakterielle Reizstoffe. I. Reindarstellung eines Polysaccharid-Pyrogens aus Bacterium Coli. Z. Naturforsch. **7b**:536–548.

Relation of Structure to Function in Bacterial Endotoxins

A. NOWOTNY[1]

Temple University School of Medicine, Philadelphia, Pennsylvania 19140

The relationship of structure to function in endotoxins has been dealt with in detail in a review which summed up the work of our laboratory, compared it with results obtained by others, and stated our views on this subject in 1969 (21). The present short survey will review only a few of our selected recent findings relevant to the topic indicated by the title. The names of the associates and students involved in this research are listed here in alphabetical order: Ulrich H. Behling, R. Christopher Butler, Chungming Chang, Helena Liang Chang, Chen-lo H. Chen, Jonathan Grohsman, Ah-kau Ng, and Cynara Yang. I gratefully acknowledge here again their devoted work and their contributions, by which they made the results reported in this review possible.

"LIPID A" VERSUS "LIPID MOIETY"

That endotoxin consists of a lipid and a polysaccharide moiety, and that the lipid seems to be responsible for the endotoxic effects, has been shown by a number of laboratories, using a variety of approaches (3, 4, 16). The most extensive work on the importance of this lipid has been carried out by the school of Otto Westphal and Otto Lüderitz, and their associates and students (31, 33). It was this research team which precipitated the lipid-rich hydrolytic fragment of the lipopolysaccharide (LPS) using 1 N HCl at 100°C for 30 min and named this precipitate "lipid A" (32). Later, the same designation was used by them, as well as by many other investigators, to indicate the lipid moiety of the intact endotoxic LPS molecule both in smooth and in rough mutants of gram-negative bacteria (10, 11, 14, 15). Furthermore, the same term was used to identify acidic hydrolytic products of various mutant endotoxins (27).

We considered the use of the same term to describe different preparations inappropriate, and we proposed that a more descriptive identi-

fication of the various lipid-rich preparations obtainable from endotoxins should be established (8, 19–21, 26). We were pleased to hear at this meeting that Dr. Lüderitz proposed restricting use of the term "lipid A" to describe the firmly bound lipids in the endotoxic lipopolysaccharide which form the lipid moiety of this structure.

At the same time, we must disagree with his statement claiming that only minor changes occur during the liberation of "lipid A" by acidic hydrolysis. Chromatographic analysis of various such liberated lipid preparations was carried out (5, 8, 13, 19, 23, 26). The results showed that these were all different from one another, not only in the number of chromatographically distinguishable components, which exceeded 40 in some preparations, but also in biological potency. Under no conditions can one consider the hydrolytic breakdown products of a macromolecule to be quite similar to the parent macromolecule. To use one term such as "free lipid A" to describe such diverse mixtures of partial and complete hydrolytic products may be useful as laboratory jargon, but it is highly inadequate to identify these chemically distinct compounds.

DIFFERENCES IN THE LIPID MOIETY OF VARIOUS ENDOTOXINS

It may now sound obvious to all of us that various hydrolytic procedures applied to different LPS preparations will result in chemically as well as biologically distinct breakdown products. What is apparently not obvious to endotoxicologists is the difference in the chemical structure and also in the biological effectiveness of the lipid moieties of various intact endotoxins. The studies we carried out in this field were made possible through the use of five heptoseless rough mutant (Re) endotoxic glycolipids. The results reported (17) indicated that thin-layer chromatographic patterns of the preparations were similar but not identical. (Figure 1 in reference 17 shows the differences.) Molar ratio determinations carried out on chromatographically pure preparations

[1] Present address: University of Pennsylvania, School of Medicine and School of Dental Medicine, Philadelphia, Pa. 19104.

showed significant differences in the glucos-amine–fatty acid–phosphorus-3-keto-2-deoxy-octonic acid ratios. The greatest differences were established in the biological activities, as measured by their enhancement of antitumor and antibacterial resistance. Further dissimilar-ities among these Re mutant endotoxic glyco-lipids, as well as among other endotoxin preparations, were found by measuring the in-duction of the so-called bone marrow cell colony-stimulating factor. Table 1 summarizes the relevant findings. Based on these results, we assume that not only the polysaccharide part of the various LPS preparations is differ-ent, but significant differences can be found in their lipid moieties as well.

We were glad to hear at this meeting from Dr. Lüderitz as well as from Dr. Rietschel that they identified some bacteria which produce lipid moieties with considerable structural dif-ferences. These very important findings support what has been said above, and we are now anxious to learn how these differences affect the biological potency of such variants, as well as the substantiating details of the chemical structural proposals presented by Dr. Rietschel.

SYNTHETIC GLYCOLIPIDS SHOW SOME ENDOTOXIN-LIKE ACTIVITIES

The most characteristic subunits of LPS structure are glycolipids, described for the first time by us, in which the OH and NH_2 groups of hexosamines are substituted with either ester- or amide-bound long-chain carboxylic acids (18, 26).

During our efforts to synthesize endotoxin-like compounds, in collaboration with J. Assel-

TABLE 1. *Effectiveness of endotoxic glycolipid (GL) compared with smooth endotoxic LPS in nonspecific resistance enhancement against TA3-Ha tumor and S. typhi O-901 bacterial infection and in colony-stimulating factor (CSF) induction*

Pretreatment	Resistance to tumor (% survival)	Resistance to S. typhi O-901 (PD$_{50}$)^a	CSF index
None	5		
S. marcescens O8 LPS	76	3.1×10^{-3}	4.8
S. minnesota S1114 LPS	67	1.6×10^{-3}	4.5
S. minnesota R595 GL	12	4.3×10^{-4}	1.0
E. coli F515 GL	64	1.7×10^{-1}	—
E. coli D31m4 GL	66	3.9×10^{-2}	2.7
E. coli D21f2 GL	56		3.1
S. typhimurium 1102 GL	7		1.0

^{a} PD$_{50}$ is the protective dose of LPS or GL, expressed in milli-grams, which protects 50% of the mice from lethal viable challenge with S. typhi O-901.

TABLE 2. *Adjuvant effect of various preparations on the anti-sheep red blood cell immune response of ICR mice*

Adjuvant prepn^a	Assay		
	HA^b	PFC^c	RFC^d
Endotoxic LPS	2^7	8.2	11.0
NOG	2^7	1.8	1.7
NDG	2^6	0.7	3.2
NLG	2^7	6.3	3.1
NMG	2^5	1.6	1.0
NPG	2^9	2.4	6.0
NOLG	2^8	1.3	6.4
NSG	2^6	1.9	2.5
None	2^4	1.0^e	1.0^f

^{a} NOG = N-octanoyl-D-glucosamine; NDG = N-decanoyl-D-glucosamine; NLG = N-lauroyl-D-glucos-amine; NMG = N-myristoyl-D-glucosamine; NPG = N-palmitoyl-D-glucosamine; NOLG = N-oleyl-D-glucosamine; NSG = N-stearoyl-D-glucosamine.

^{b} Hemagglutination titer.

^{c} Plaque-forming cells, adjuvant index.

^{d} Rosette-forming cells, adjuvant index.

^{e} Control PFC response: 42.3 ± 4.9 PFC/10^6 spleen cells.

^{f} Control RFC response: 6.1 ± 1.1 RFC/10^3 spleen cells.

ineau, we prepared a D-glucosamine derivative in which the primary amino group was acylated with palmitic acid. This compound was found to be nonendotoxic in mice or chick embryos or rabbits. When the mitogenic effect of this preparation was tested in athymic nude mice, a definite activity could be measured (28). Later, we prepared other carboxylic acid homologues of the above preparation and tested them for adjuvant effect against sheep red blood cell or bovine gamma globulin immuno-gens. The results were positive, but only if these synthetic glycolipids were injected in the form of liposomes. Our procedures for the preparation of liposomes and their use as im-mune adjuvants was described very recently (2). Table 2 shows excerpts of the data ob-tained. Although these two biological reactions are not characteristic of endotoxins alone, we think that the findings indicate that the highly unique glucosamine-carboxylic acid compounds present in the lipid moiety are essential partic-ipants in the active site of endotoxins.

BIOLOGICAL ACTIVITIES ARE PRESENT IN POLYSACCHARIDE-RICH FRACTIONS OF ENDOTOXINS

LPS hydrolyzed with 1 N HCl for 30 min at 100°C gives a "lipid A" precipitate and a clear, water-soluble supernatant fluid (32). The latter is rich in partially degraded polysaccharides; it also contains a few percent amino acids and small peptides, and all other components of the starting material which became soluble under the above hydrolytic conditions. No detectable amount of fatty acids could be demonstrated in this water-soluble product. Such a preparation, neutralized by ion exchanger and lyophilized, was inactive in a total of six characteristic endotoxicity assays, including mitogenicity (29). Later, we found and reported that it was active in the production of bone marrow cell colony-stimulating factor (9) and in protection against lethal irradiation (24). It is reported here for the first time that such a nonmitogenic preparation (called PS in our protocols) is a good in vivo immune adjuvant to sheep red blood cell immunogens if given on a proper schedule. Figure 1 shows the findings. Furthermore, some of the PS preparations made from certain gram-negative strains could provide a marginal but significant resistance to transplantable TA3-Ha ascites tumors in mice. Table 3 shows some of our findings in LPS- and PS-induced tumor resistance.

POSTENDOTOXIN SERUM, RICH IN COLONY-STIMULATING FACTOR, MEDIATES RESISTANCE AGAINST EXPERIMENTAL TUMORS

As we reported earlier (12), microgram quantities of endotoxin can enhance tumor resistance in mice against the nonspecific TA3-Ha tumor line which grows in ascites form in syngeneic and allogeneic recipients. The optimal conditions for this endotoxin-induced tumor resistance (TUR) were elaborated (34). More recent studies dealt with the mechanism of this resistance (R. C. Butler, H. Chang, and A. Nowotny, Fed. Proc. **35:**

TABLE 3. *Tumor protection by different PS preparations: correlation to colony-stimulating factor (CSF) production*

Chronic PS (20 μg on days -2, -1, 0, $+1$, $+3$, $+5$, $+7$, $+9$)	Survivors/ total $(P)^a$	CSF index $(CFU)^b$
Saline	4/50	1.0 (43)
PS 665 (*Serratia marcescens*)	6/20; 9/20 (0.005); 5/20 (0.05)	5.0 (258)
PS 734 (*Salmonella typhi* O-901)	5/20 (0.05)	4.3 (191)
PS 733 (*Escherichia coli* O111)	2/20	1.9 (82)
"Native hapten" (*E. coli* O111)	14/20 (0.001)	5.4 (273); 4.8 (476)

^{a} Numbers in parentheses indicate P values of statistical analyses.

^{b} Numbers in parentheses indicate the numbers of colonies, determined in triplicate.

2466, 1976). Using athymic nude mice which have a fully functioning B-cell-mediated immune system, we found that they could be rendered resistant to the above tumor by endotoxin, indicating that the absence of T-cell function in these animals did not interfere with the inducibility of TUR. Using C3H/HeJ mice which have a genetic defect in their B-cell activation and in their general response to endotoxins, we saw that these animals could not be rendered resistant to tumors. Table 4 summarizes the above findings, which seem to indicate that B-cell activation induced by endotoxic LPS is a significant contributing factor to TUR.

If the colony-stimulating factor activity of LPS or PS stimulates bone marrow cells, they could be active in radiation protection, and, as the above-described experiments showed, both preparations were quite active in inducing resistance to radiation. Next, we wanted to see whether bone marrow cell stimulation will reflect on tumor resistance, since, as Table 4

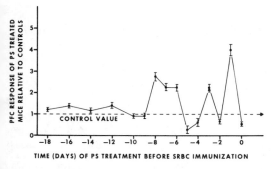

FIG. 1. *Effect of PS treatment on the immune response to sheep red blood cells.*

TABLE 4. *Effect of endotoxin on resistance to tumor in C3H/HeJ and in athymic BALB/c nu/nu mice*

Species	Pretreatment (-1 day)	Challenge dose of TA3-Ha	No. of survivors/ total
C3H/HeJ	None	1,000	6/22
C3H/HeJ	*S. marcescens* LPS, 25 μg	1,000	7/22
BALB/c nu/nu	None	500	1/10
BALB/c nu/nu	*S. marcescens* LPS, 10 μg	500	7/10^a

^{a} $P = 0.005$, determined by the x^2 test.

TABLE 5. *Enhancement of tumor resistance in C57Bl/6J and ICR mice by colony-stimulating factor-rich serum (CSF)*

Species	Pretreatment (−2 h)	Challenge dose of TA3-Ha	No. of survivors/ total	P
C57B1/6J	Saline, 0.3 ml	7×10^4	2/20	
C57B1/6J	Normal serum, 0.3 ml	7×10^4	2/20	
C57B1/6J	CSF serum, 0.3 ml[a]	7×10^4	9/20	0.025
C57B1/6J	LPS, 10 μg	7×10^4	7/10	0.015
ICR	Saline, 0.5 ml	1,600	3/10	
ICR	Normal serum, 0.5 ml	1,600	4/10	
ICR	CSF serum, 0.5 ml[a]	1,600	10/10	0.01

[a] Endotoxin: <0.001 μg/ml.

shows, B-cell activation is a determining factor in TUR induced by endotoxin.

In a series of experiments, we tried first to induce tumor resistance with PS preparations. The results have already been mentioned in this paper, and Table 3 summarizes the results. Subsequently, we attempted to transfer TUR to normal mice by transferring colony-stimulating factor-rich serum obtained from normal mice 2 h after injecting them with 10 to 50 μg of LPS or PS preparations.

The antitumor resistance induced by intravenous (i.v.) passive transfer of post-LPS or post-PS, colony-stimulating factor-rich sera was tested in two systems. One was the induction of resistance to subsequent challenge with TA3-Ha cells, and the other was induction of hemorrhage and necrosis of 7-day-old, approxi-

mately 1 cm in diameter, palpable sarcoma 37 grown subcutaneously in mice. As Table 5 shows, significant resistance could be transferred to subsequent TA3-Ha challenge. Furthermore, passive transfer of colony-stimulating factor-rich serum caused hemorrhage of established sarcoma 37, as shown in Table 6. A short publication from our laboratory reported some of these experiments (6).

Our findings indicate that colony-stimulating factor may be involved in the induction of TUR. In addition to the above-mentioned results, this statement is based on the following additional information:

1. Those LPS and PS preparations which were particularly active in tumor resistance induction were also active in colony-stimulating factor induction. Table 1 summarizes these findings.

2. The "protoplasmic hapten" preparation, which has also been called "native hapten" by Ribi and associates, was also quite active in the induction of both TUR as well as colony-stimulating factor. This "native hapten" preparation was provided to us by Dr. Ribi, for which we express our gratitude here. This preparation is an incompletely assembled precursor of LPS in which the percentage of carboxylic acids is extremely low but the polysaccharide moiety seems to be fully synthesized. This preparation is nontoxic, as was reported in detail by Ribi and associates (1). The colony-stimulating factor index and the antitumor effects of this preparation are shown in Table 3.

3. Following in the footsteps of Old and associates (7), we combined the application of LPS or PS with BCG infection. The colony-stimulating factor-rich sera harvested from BCG-infected and LPS- or PS-injected animals were particularly active in the colony-stimulating factor assay and were eminently active in TUR.

LPS-INDUCED EFFECTS SHOW AN OSCILLATION-LIKE CHANGE WITH TIME

The first time we saw both positive and negative (or zero) effects of previously in-

TABLE 6. *Sarcoma 37 tumor necrosis by colony-stimulating factor (CSF) serum from BCG-infected ICR mice*

Treatment[a]	No. of tumors necrotized/ total	Percent necrotized	P	CSF index
Saline, 0.5 ml	3/33	9		1.0
Normal serum, 0.5 ml	4/33	12		1.0
LPS-CSF serum, 0.5 ml[b] . .	9/25	36	0.01	13.6
PS-CSF serum, 0.5 ml	19/28	45	0.005	10.8
BCG serum, 0.5 ml	5/18	28		6.7
BCG + PS serum, 0.5 ml . .	19/25	76	0.005	15.7
Endotoxin, 20 μg	10/14	70	0.005	

[a] Administered intravenously except that the 20 μg of endotoxin was injected intraperitoneally.

[b] Endotoxin content of the serum: <0.001 μg/ml.

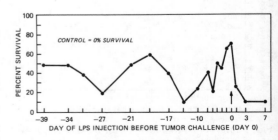

FIG. 2. *Time curve for LPS-induced protection from TA3-Ha tumor.*

jected LPS samples was when we measured the duration of radiation protection induced by endotoxic LPS or by its nontoxic PS derivative (24). An even more puzzling pattern was seen when we studied the duration of LPS- or PS-induced adjuvant effect. Here, the time between adjuvant and immunogen injections was varied. Figure 1 shows such a pattern obtained by using PS as an immune adjuvant in ICR mice. This indicates that either an immune enhancement or an immune suppression can be elicited by these preparations, depending only on the time of their application.

Figure 2 depicts the duration of endotoxin-induced tumor (TA3-Ha) resistance in ICR mice. This is the third biological effect in which a single LPS injection induces such a wavelike, alternating response in the host.

We think that the practical aspects of these observations are obvious. In addition to these, we believe that the similarity of these time-dependent effects may indicate similar mechanisms involved in the elicitation of these three phenomena, thus showing a relationship between these beneficial effects of endotoxic reactions.

The possible explanations for the observed biological oscillations triggered by a single shot of endotoxin are much less obvious. It is possible that LPS acts on more than one target, thus triggering more than one chain reaction, some of which reach their peak early and some later. This very likely possibility was discussed by us earlier (21, 22, 25, 30). Another similarly feasible explanation may lie in a certain degree of synchrony in the maturation level of cell types induced by endotoxin. It is very plausible that the cells involved in these "beneficial" effects of LPS are capable of performing positively at one level of their maturation while they fail to produce protection and/or adjuvant at another level.

LITERATURE CITED

1. **Anacker, R. L., R. A. Finkelstein, W. J. Haskins, M. Landy, K. C. Milner, E. Ribi, and P. W. Stashak.** 1964. Origin and properties of naturally occurring hapten from *Escherichia coli*. J. Bacteriol. **88:** 1705–1720.

2. **Behling, U. H., B. Campbell, C. M. Chang, C. Rumpf, and A. Nowotny.** 1976. Synthetic glycolipid adjuvants. J. Immunol. **117:** 847–851.

3. **Bendich, A., and E. Chargaff.** 1946. The isolation and characterization of two antigenic fractions of Proteus OX-19. J. Biol. Chem. **166:** 283–312.

4. **Boivin, A., J. Mesrobeanu, and I. Mesrobeanu.** 1933. Extraction d'un complexe toxique et antigenique a partir du bacille d'Aertrycke. C. R. Soc. Biol. **114:** 307–310.

5. **Burton, A. J., and H. E. Carter.** 1964. Purification and characterization of the lipid A component of the lipopolysaccharides from *Escherichia coli*. Biochemistry **3:** 411–418.

6. **Butler, R. C., and A. Nowotny.** 1976. Colony stimulating factor (CSF)-containing serum has anti-tumor effects. IRCS Med. Sci. **4:** 206.

7. **Carswell, E. A., L. J. Old, R. L. Kassel, S. Green, N. Fiore, and B. Williamson.** 1975. An endotoxin-induced serum factor that causes necrosis of tumors. Proc. Natl. Acad. Sci. U.S.A. **72:** 3666–3670.

8. **Chang, C.-M., and A. Nowotny.** 1975. Relation of structure to function in bacterial O-antigens. VIII. Endotoxicity of "lipid A." Immunochemistry **12:** 19–28.

9. **Chang, H., J. J. Thompson, and A. Nowotny.** 1974. Release of colony stimulating factor (CSF) by nonendotoxic breakdown products of bacterial lipopolysaccharides. Immunol. Commun. **3:** 401–409.

10. **Dröge, W., V. Lehmann, O. Lüderitz, and O. Westphal.** 1970. Structural investigations on the 2-keto-3-deoxyoctonate region of lipopolysaccharides. Eur. J. Biochem. **14:** 175–184.

11. **Galanos, C., E. T. Rietschel, O. Lüderitz, O. Westphal, Y. B. Kim, and D. W. Watson.** 1972. Biological activities of lipid A complexed with bovine serum albumin. Eur. J. Biochem. **31:** 230–233.

12. **Grohsman, J., and A. Nowotny.** 1972. The immune recognition of TA3 tumors, its facilitation by endotoxin, and abrogation by ascites fluid. J. Immunol. **109:** 1090–1095.

13. **Kasai, N.** 1966. Chemical studies on the lipid component of endotoxin, with special emphasis on its relation to biological activities. Ann. N.Y. Acad. Sci. **133:** 486–507.

14. **Lehmann, V., O. Lüderitz, and O. Westphal.** 1971. The linkage of pyrophosphorethanolamine to heptose in the core of *Salmonella minnesota* lipopolysaccharides. Eur. J. Biochem. **21:** 339–347.

15. **Lüderitz, O., C. Galanos, H. J. Risse, E. Ruschmann, S. Schlecht, G. Schmidt, H. Schulte-Holthausen, R. Wheat, and O. Westphal.** 1966. Structural relationships of Salmonella O and R antigens. Ann. N.Y. Acad. Sci. **133:** 349–374.

16. **Miles, A. A., and N. W. Pirie.** 1939. The properties of antigenic preparations from *Brucella melitensis*. I. Chemical and physical properties of bacterial fractions. Br. J. Exp. Pathol. **20:** 83–98.

17. **Ng, A.-K., C. Butler, C. H. Chen, and A. Nowotny.** 1976. Relationship of structure to function in bacterial endotoxins. IX. Differences in the lipid moiety of endotoxic glycolipids. J. Bacteriol. **126:** 511–515.

18. **Nowotny, A.** 1961. Chemical structure of a phosphomucolipid and its occurrence in some strains of Salmonella. J. Am. Chem. Soc. **83:** 501–503.

19. **Nowotny, A.** 1963. Relation of structure to function in bacterial O antigens. II. Fractionation of lipids present in Boivin-type endotoxin of *Serratia marcescens*. J. Bacteriol. **85:** 427–435.

20. **Nowotny, A.** 1965. Relation of chemical structure to pathologic activity of endotoxins, p. 425–430. *In* L. J. Mills and J. H. Moyer (ed.), Shock and hypotension: pathogenesis and treatment. Grune & Stratton, Inc., New York.

21. **Nowotny, A.** 1969. Molecular aspects of endotoxic reactions. Bacteriol. Rev. **33:** 72–98.

22. **Nowotny, A.** 1971. Chemical and biological heterogeneity of endotoxins, p. 309–329. *In* G. Weinbaum, S. Kadis, and S. J. Ajl (ed.), Microbial toxins, vol. 4. Academic Press Inc., New York.

23. **Nowotny, A.** 1971. Relationship of structure and biological activity of bacterial endotoxins. Naturwissenschaften **58:** 397–409.

24. **Nowotny, A., U. H. Behling, and H. L. Chang.** 1975. Relation of structure to function in bacterial endotoxins. VIII. Biological activities in a polysaccharide-rich fraction. J. Immunol. **115:** 199–203.

25. **Nowotny, A., K. Cundy, N. Neale, A. M. Nowotny, R. Radvany, S. Thomas, and D. Tripodi.** 1966. Relation of structure to function in bacterial O-antigens. IV. Fractionation of the components. Ann. N.Y. Acad. Sci. **133:** 586–603.

26. Nowotny, A., S. Thomas, and O. S. Duron. 1963. Chemistry of firmly-bound cell-wall lipids in gram-negative bacteria. Biochim. Biophys. Acta Library 1:422–424.

27. Risse, H. J., W. Dröge, E. Ruschmann, O. Lüderitz, and O. Westphal. 1967. Eine neue Gruppe von Salmonella R-Mutanten. Serologische und biochemische Analyse des Heptosekerns von Lipopolysacchariden aus Salmonella minnesota- und Salmonella ruiru-Mutanten. Eur. J. Biochem. 1:216–232.

28. Rosenstreich, D. L., J. Asselineau, S. E. Mergenhagen, and A. Nowotny. 1974. A synthetic glycolipid with B-cell mitogenic activity. J. Exp. Med. 140:1404–1409.

29. Rosenstreich, D. L., A. Nowotny, T. Chused, and S. E. Mergenhagen. 1973. In vitro transformation of mouse bone-marrow-derived (B) lymphocytes induced by the lipid component of endotoxin. Infect. Immun. 8:406–411.

30. Tripodi, D., and A. Nowotny. 1966. Relation of structure to function in bacterial O-antigens. V. Nature of active sites in endotoxic lipopolysaccharides of Serratia marcescens. Ann. N.Y. Acad. Sci. 133:604–621.

31. Westphal, O. 1960. Recentes recherches sur la chimie et la biologie des endotoxines des bacteries a gram negative. Ann. Inst. Pasteur Paris 98:789–813.

32. Westphal, O., and O. Lüderitz. 1954. Chemische Erforschung von Lipopolysacchariden gram negativer Bakterien. Angew. Chem. 66:407–417.

33. Westphal, A. Nowotny, O. Lüderitz, H. Hurni, E. Eichenberger, and G. Schönholzer. 1958. Die Bedeutung der Lipoid-Komponente (Lipoid A) für die biologischen Wirkungen bakterieller Endotoxine (Lipopolysaccharide). Pharm. Acta Helv. 33:301–411.

34. Yang, C., and A. Nowotny. 1974. Effect of endotoxin on tumor resistance in mice. Infect. Immun. 9:95–100.

Protective Properties of Antisera to R Core

ABRAHAM I. BRAUDE, ELIZABETH J. ZIEGLER, HERNDON DOUGLAS,
AND J. ALLEN McCUTCHAN

*Departments of Medicine and Pathology, School of Medicine, University of California at San Diego,
San Diego, California 92103*

After 1960, the major interest in bacterial infections shifted from highly communicable gram-positive bacteria to endogenous or resident gram-negative flora of the bowel. The preeminence of the gram-negative bacteria in the past 15 years can be explained by a versatility in achieving antibiotic resistance not encountered with the gram-positive pathogens, and by the growing number of immunosuppressed patients who become susceptible even to the bacteria normally present in their bowel. The result has been a high incidence of bacteremias due to antibiotic-resistant gram-negative organisms and a mortality rate in these infections of 35 to 60% (9). This failure of antibiotics, as well as the toxic properties of gram-negative bacteria, raised the question of antiserum, or antitoxin, as an approach to treatment. At first this idea seemed impractical because of the apparent antigenic heterogeneity of the multiple species and serotypes of pathogenic gram-negative bacilli. By a fortunate coincidence, however, bacterial chemists also turned their interest to gram-negative bacteria in the early 1960s and came up with a discovery that offered a potential solution to the problem of antigenic diversity (11, 13, 17).

Some of the key observations were made on rough mutants of gram-negative bacilli that were blocked at different steps in the biosynthesis of their lipopolysaccharide (LPS). Analysis of these mutants in several laboratories led to the conclusion that the polysaccharide portion consists of two regions, the central R core and the side chains carrying the determinants of O-antigen specificity (11, 13, 17). Although the structure of O-antigenic side chains varies widely among the different species and serotypes of gram-negative bacilli, the structure of the core region appears to be similar in all species, especially in the "backbone" containing only heptose, phosphate, ketodeoxyoctonate (KDO), and hexosamine. This uniformity of structure in the core LPS of different species of gram-negative bacteria provided a plausible basis for developing one antiserum that might be active against all gram-negative bacteria involved in serious human infections.

On this basis, we set out to develop an antiserum to core LPS that would protect against the toxicity of LPS and against bacteremia. To prepare core antisera, we used vaccines made from R mutants of *Escherichia coli* O113 or *E. coli* O111B$_4$ whose cores possessed only "backbone" sugars plus glucose. The R mutant of *E. coli* O113 was prepared in our laboratory, and the O111B$_4$ mutant, known as *E. coli* J5, was obtained from E. C. Heath (11, 20). Both mutants lack the enzyme UDP-galactose-4-epimerase and are therefore incapable of converting glucose to galactose (8). The O113 mutant was also incapable of incorporating galactose when grown in media containing galactose, whereas the J5 mutant when first obtained from Heath incorporated galactose from the medium and produced complete LPS with the same "O" side chains as the smooth parent strain of *E. coli* O111B$_4$. From the J5 strain we derived a new mutant that could no longer incorporate galactose from the medium, and we used this new mutant for preparing protective antisera against R core. These antisera have been systematically examined for their ability to protect against various manifestations of endotoxin and against lethal bacteremia (3, 4, 20, 23, 24).

PREVENTION OF DEATH FROM ENDOTOXIN WITH ANTISERUM: COMPARISON OF S AND R ANTISERA

Antisera against the endotoxins in smooth and rough bacteria, as well as antisera against the endotoxins in heterologous organisms, prevent death when given intraperitoneally to mice challenged with lethal intravenous doses of smooth endotoxin (7, 10, 22). Homologous smooth antiserum reduced the lethal potency of *E. coli*, *Serratia marcescens*, and *Salmonella abortus-equi* endotoxin by 50 to 80%. Antiserum against *E. coli* prevented death from intravenous (i.v.) *S. abortus-equi* and *S. marcescens* endotoxins. This cross-protection by a serum against heterologous endotoxin was always as good as that against the homologous endotoxin and demonstrated that different species of gram-negative bacteria share a common protective antigen unrelated to "O" antigen. Rabbit or human antiserum against the core LPS in the galactose-deficient rough mutant of E. coli O113 and the J5 mutant of E. coli O:111 also protected mice from endotoxin. Both antisera gave as good protection against smooth endotoxins as antisera prepared against homologous smooth endotoxins, providing further proof that "O" antibody was not necessary for preventing death from endotoxin.

PREVENTION OF THE DERMAL SHWARTZMAN REACTION WITH ANTISERUM

Rabbit antiserum to smooth E. coli O:111 endotoxin reduced the frequency of Shwartzman reactions from 98% to 9.6% in experiments comprising more than 65 rabbits in test and control groups (3). Good protection against the local Shwartzman reaction was also obtained with homologous antisera against smooth S. typhimurium and S. marcescens endotoxins, and with heterologous antisera. The homologous protection lasted at least 1 month, was conferred with the 19S fraction, and was accompanied by accelerated clearance of ^{51}Cr-labeled endotoxin from the circulating blood (3). Heterologous protection was not accompanied by accelerated clearance of endotoxin and bore no relationship to "O" antibody. Antiserum to the J5 core LPS gave better protection against heterologous endotoxin than antiserum to the parent E. coli O:111 smooth endotoxin. These results indicate that antiserum prevents the Shwartzman reaction by action against a toxic antigen common to endotoxins from unrelated bacterial genera, that loss of "O"-antigenic units may enhance the production of protective antisera, and that accelerated clearance of endotoxin from the circulation is not necessary for protection.

TREATMENT AND PREVENTION OF INTRAVASCULAR COAGULATION WITH ANTISERUM TO ENDOTOXIN

Rabbit antiserum injected i.v. 2 h before the second dose (prevention) decreased the incidence of renal cortical necrosis from 90% to 18% (4). Disseminated intravenous coagulation (DIC) and renal cortical necrosis were also prevented with heterologous antisera and J5 (core LPS) antiserum, by 19S and 7S immunoglobulins of antisera, and by hyperimmune globulin treated with mercaptoethanol (to eliminate complement binding sites) and iodoacetate (to prevent reaggregation of 7S dimers). As in the case of the dermal Shwartzman reaction, passive protection lasted for at least 30 days. Antiserum prevented the precipitous drop in fibrinogen and platelets that accompanies deposition of fibrin in the glomerulus and elsewhere. These findings indicate that prevention of DIC and renal cortical necrosis, like prevention of the dermal Shwartzman reaction and death from endotoxin, is independent of antibody to O antigen. They also show that complement is not required for this protection.

TREATMENT OF BACTEREMIA IN AGRANULOCYTIC ANIMALS WITH J5 ANTISERUM COLIFORM BACTEREMIA

When nonimmune rabbit serum was given i.v. to agranulocytic rabbits at the onset of bacteremia due to E. coli O4, E. coli O17, or Klebsiella pneumoniae, only 3.1 to 5.7% survived. In contrast, survival rates in animals given rabbit J5 antiserum were 33.3% from E. coli O4, 40% from K. pneumoniae, and 69.2% from the multiply antibiotic-resistant E. coli O17 (combined $P < 0.0005$; 23). Antiserum to E. coli O:111, the parent strain from which the J5 mutant is derived, gave no significant protection. The protection against death from E. coli O17 by J5 antiserum was greater than that obtained with gentamicin (50%), the only antibiotic to which this strain was sensitive. This protection by J5 antiserum was associated with a twofold increase in clearance of ^{51}Cr-labeled bacteria. The results with rabbit antiserum were duplicated with human J5 antiserum in lowering the death rate from E. coli O4 bacteremia.

The titers of bacterial agglutinins of rabbit J5 antiserum against E. coli O4 and O17 were 1:8 and 1:16, respectively. There were no agglutinins to K. pneumoniae in E. coli J5 antiserum or E. coli O:111 antiserum. Nonimmune rabbit serum had no agglutinins to any of the organisms tested. In passive hemagglutination tests with red cells sensitized with endotoxin, the titers of E. coli J5 antiserum were 1:2,048 against E. coli J5 endotoxin, 1:256 against the smooth parent E. coli O:111 endotoxin, 1:16 against E. coli O4, and 1:512 against E. coli O17. The hemagglutinin titers of nonimmune serum were 1:4 against E. coli O4 and E. coli J5 and 1:16 against E. coli O17. Serum from coliform-free rabbits before and after administration of nitrogen mustard had no bactericidal activity against any of the organisms tested, and treatment with J5 antiserum failed to produce such activity.

Pseudomonas Bacteremia

J5 antiserum prepared in both humans and rabbits lowered the death rate from *Pseudomonas* bacteremia in agranulocytic rabbits (24). In a typical experiment, only 4 of 26 (15%) control rabbits survived after treatment with 10 ml of nonimmune serum, whereas rabbit J5 antiserum increased the number of survivors to 16 of 27 (59%, P < 0.002). Upon incubation in vitro with *Pseudomonas* endotoxin or *Pseudomonas* organisms, J5 antiserum possessed increased opsonic activity, gave occasional positive reactions in immunodiffusion tests, and neutralized the pyrogenic activity of both cells and LPS, as determined by subsequent i.v. injection in rabbits. The opsonic activity was evident from a threefold rise in phagocytosis of *P. aeruginosa* and was comparable to opsonization by specific *Pseudomonas* antiserum.

A fourfold increase in survivors was obtained by treatment of *Pseudomonas* bacteremia with J5 antiserum obtained from human subjects. The survival rate was only 7 of 67 (10.4%) in bacteremic rabbits given human serum obtained before immunization but increased to 31 of 73 (42%, P < 0.0005) after treatment with human J5 antiserum. The results were not significantly different from those obtained by treating rabbits with type-specific *Pseudomonas* rabbit antiserum prepared by immunization with the strain of *Pseudomonas* used for producing the bacteremia (24).

Passive protection with antiserum was compared with protection induced by active immunization of rabbits with J5 vaccine. Rabbits were actively immunized by the same schedule as that used for preparation of antiserum: six i.v. injections of 1.0 ml (10^9 bacteria) of J5 vaccine, given three times weekly for 2 weeks. Seven days after the last vaccine injection and 72 h after nitrogen mustard, they received inoculations of *Pseudomonas* in the eye. Active immunization with J5 vaccine increased survival to 92%, a level equal to that obtained with type-specific *Pseudomonas* vaccine. The degree and duration of neutropenia was identical in actively immunized and nonimmunized animals. It is important to note that a vaccine composed of *E. coli* O:111, the parent of J5, did not significantly improve survival. This failure of *E. coli* O:111 vaccine can be explained by the concept that the core LPS is concealed by O:111 oligosaccharides so that the core cannot function as an immunogen.

MECHANISM OF PROTECTION

These experiments and those from other laboratories provide impressive evidence that immunization with "core" LPS antigens can induce protection against gram-negative bacteria belonging to different genera and against their LPS (6, 15, 21). There would seem to be little question now that the protective antigen in *E. coli* J5 lies somewhere in the complex composed of lipid A, KDO, and polyheptose phosphate. The studies of Chedid et al. (6) and McCabe (15) demonstrate that protective antigens are also found in rough *Salmonella* mutants. McCabe protected mice with antiserum to the Re mutant of *S. minnesota* against bacteremia from *K. pneumoniae*. Since KDO is the only core sugar in the Re mutant, it is possible that it is the protective antigen. An important feature of inducing protection against gram-negative bacteria and their endotoxins is that "O" antigen is not necessary and may even be detrimental. By comparing the ability of *E. coli* O:111 with that of its R mutant *E. coli* J5 to stimulate protection, we found that loss of "O" antigen in J5 actually enhanced its ability to stimulate protection against heterologous gram-negative bacteria and their endotoxin. Similar results have been obtained by McCabe with *Salmonella* R mutants in preventing death from bacteremia. The clinical implications of these findings have been brought out by his observation that high titers of R, rather than O, antibody were associated with less frequent shock and death in human gram-negative bacteremia (16).

A consideration of the mechanism of protection by antiserum must take into account its opsonic and antitoxic properties. Antiserum against LPS facilitates removal of circulating gram-negative organisms by enhancing phagocytosis by the reticuloendothelial system (RES). In the case of *E. coli*, for example, Benacerraf et al. (1, 2) found that phagocytosis by the RES was a linear function of the amount of antibody against *E. coli* LPS, and Rowley (18) showed that antibody enhanced the destruction of gram-negative bacilli within RES macrophages. The opsonic activity of J5 antibody is evident from its opsonic action against *P. aeruginosa* and by the doubled rate of clearance of *E. coli* O4 from the circulation after treatment of agranulocytic rabbits with J5 antiserum (23). In the absence of polymorphonuclear (PMN) leukocytes, opsonization would still promote phagocytosis by the RES. Even with normal numbers of PMN leukocytes, the RES is largely responsible for removing gram-negative bacilli from the blood, and the avidity with which they can be extracted by RES cells depends on the antibody level (1, 2). Benacerraf et al. found that in the absence of antibody phagocytosis was very inefficient.

Antiserum to LPS also reduces or nullifies its toxic properties. Our studies have shown that J5 antiserum prevented death of animals from endotoxin, as well as the local and generalized Shwartzman reactions. We found that antiserum to endotoxin can prevent not only renal cortical necrosis but also disseminated intravascular coagulation during the evolution of the generalized Shwartzman reaction. The generalized Shwartzman reaction is accompanied by irreversible shock and hemorrhage, and results from three effects of endotoxin: (i) intravascular coagulation, (ii) depression of RES function so that fibrin polymers are not cleared from the circulation, and (iii) vascular collapse with sluggish blood flow so that fibrin aggregates are trapped in the glomeruli and other vessels. These effects could be arrested with J5 antiserum as late as 16 h after the preparative doses of endotoxin. Antiserum also prevented the precipitous drop in platelets that accompanies fibrin deposition in glomerular and other vessels, thus halting intravascular coagulation after it has been initiated by endotoxin (4).

In view of the fact that the same antiserum protects against both endotoxin and living bacteria, it is possible that bacteremic deaths are actually deaths from endotoxin. This is a reasonable idea because endotoxin is at the surface of gram-negative bacilli and in continuous contact with body fluids during bacteremias. Chedid has proposed that serum enzymes remove smooth antigenic determinants from the surface of gram-negative bacilli and expose R-antigenic sites common to many bacterial strains and species. In this way antibodies to rough determinants common to many species could react with rough endotoxin and protect against smooth bacteria possessing unrelated "O" antigens. This type of reaction between E. coli J5 antibody and exposed R sites could provide it with both antitoxic and opsonic properties.

LITERATURE CITED

1. Benacerraf, B., E. Kivy-Rosenberg, M. M. Sebestyen, and B. W. Zweifach. 1959. The effect of high doses of x-irradiation on the phagocytic, proliferative, and metabolic properties of the reticuloendothelial system. J. Exp. Med. 110:49–64.

2. Benacerraf, B., M. M. Sebestyen, and S. Schlossman. 1959. A quantitative study of the kinetics of blood clearance of P^{32}-labelled Escherichia coli and staphylococci by the reticuloendothelial system. J. Exp. Med. 110:27–48.

3. Braude, A. I., and H. Douglas. 1972. Passive immunization against the local Shwartzman reaction. J. Immunol. 108:505–512.

4. Braude, A. I., H. Douglas, and C. E. Davis. 1973. Treatment and prevention of intravascular coagulation with antiserum to endotoxin. J. Infect. Dis. 128:S157–164.

5. Braude, A. I., H. Douglas, and J. Jones. 1969. Experimental production of lethal Escherichia coli bacteremia of pelvic origin. J. Bacteriol. 98:979–991.

6. Chedid, L., M. Parant, F. Parant, and F. Boyer. 1968. A proposed mechanism for natural immunity to enterobacterial pathogens. J. Immunol. 100:292–301.

7. Davis, C. E., K. R. Brown, H. Douglas, W. J. Tate, and A. I. Braude. 1969. Prevention of death from endotoxin with antisera. I. The risk of fatal anaphylaxis to endotoxin. J. Immunol. 102:563–572.

8. Davis, C. E., S. D. Freedman, H. Douglas, and A. I. Braude. 1969. Analysis of sugars in bacterial endotoxins by gas-liquid chromatography. Anal. Biochem. 28:243–256.

9. DuPont, H. L., and W. W. Spink. 1969. Infections due to gram-negative organisms: an analysis of 860 patients with bacteremia at the University of Minnesota Medical Center, 1958–1966. Medicine 48:307–332.

10. Freedman, H. H. 1959. Passive transfer of protection against lethality of homologous and heterologous endotoxins. Proc. Soc. Exp. Biol. Med. 102:504–506.

11. Heath, E. C., R. M. Mayer, R. D. Edstron, and C. A. Beaudreau. 1966. Structure and biosynthesis of the cell wall lipopolysaccharide of Escherichia coli. Ann. N.Y. Acad. Sci. 133:315–333.

12. Kabat, E. A., and M. M. Mayer. 1961. Experimental immunochemistry, 2nd ed. Charles C Thomas, Publisher, Springfield, Ill.

13. Luderitz, O., C. Galanos, H. J. Risse, E. Ruschmann, S. Schlecht, G. Schmidt, H. Schulte-Holthausen, R. Wheat, and O. Westphal. 1966. Structural relationships of Salmonella O and R antigens. Ann. N.Y. Acad. Sci. 133:349–374.

14. Luderitz, O., A. M. Staub, and O. Westphal. 1966. Immunochemistry of O and R antigens of Salmonella and related Enterobacteriaceae. Bacteriol. Rev. 30:192–255.

15. McCabe, W. R. 1972. Immunization with R mutants of S. minnesota. I. Protection against challenge with heterologous gram-negative bacilli. J. Immunol. 108:601–610.

16. McCabe, W. R., B. E. Kreger, and M. Johns. 1972. Type-specific and cross-reactive antibodies in gram-negative bacteremia. N. Engl. J. Med. 287:261–267.

17. Osborn, M. J. 1966. Biosynthesis and structure of the core region of the lipopolysaccharide in Salmonella typhimurium. Ann. N.Y. Acad. Sci. 133:375–383.

18. Rowley, D. 1958. Bactericidal activity of macrophages in vitro against Escherichia coli. Nature (London) 181:1738–1739.

19. Ryan, J. L., A. I. Braude, and M. Turck. 1973. Galactose-deficient endotoxin from urinary Escherichia coli. Infect. Immun. 7:476–478.

20. Tate, W. J., III, H. Douglas, and A. I. Braude. 1966. Protection against lethality of E. coli endotoxin with "O" antiserum. Ann. N.Y. Acad. Sci. 133:746–762.

21. Young, L. S., P. Stevens, and J. Ingram. 1975. Functional role of antibody against "core" glycolipid of Enterobacteriaceae. J. Clin. Invest. 56:850–861.

22. Ziegler, E. J., H. Douglas, and A. I. Braude. 1973. Human antiserum for prevention of the local Shwartzman reaction and death from bacterial lipopolysaccharides. J. Clin. Invest. 52:3236–3238.

23. Ziegler, E. J., H. Douglas, J. E. Sherman, C. E. Davis, and A. I. Braude. 1973. Treatment of E. coli and Klebsiella bacteremia in agranulocytic animals with antiserum to a UDP-GAL epimerase-deficient mutant. J. Immunol. 111:433–438.

24. Ziegler, E. J., J. A. McCutchan, H. Douglas, and A. I. Braude. 1975. Prevention of lethal Pseudomonas bacteremia with epimerase-deficient E. coli antiserum. Trans. Assoc. Am. Physicians 88:101–108.

Lipoprotein from the Outer Membrane of *Escherichia coli* as Antigen, Immunogen, and Mitogen

VOLKMAR BRAUN

Lehrstuhl Mikrobiologie II, Universität Tübingen, D 7400 Tübingen, West Germany

INTRODUCTION

Immunological studies on the lipoprotein of the cell envelope of *Escherichia coli* (3) were first performed because there was no known biological activity. Therefore, immunological techniques were required to determine the distribution of the lipoprotein between the cytoplasmic membrane and the outer membrane of *E. coli* (2). With the finding that lipoprotein was exclusively localized in the outer membrane, it became of interest to see whether the lipoprotein was exposed to the cell surface. The answer to this question was important for the construction of an outer membrane model. Provided lipoprotein is exposed at the cell surface, antibodies should be produced upon infection which could be used for the purpose of diagnosis and for rapid serological typing of all lipoprotein-containing strains. If, however, it is buried in the outer membrane, anti-lipoprotein antisera could be a tool to detect mutants with altered cell surfaces.

The isolation of lipoprotein includes the use of boiling 4% sodium dodecyl sulfate. Despite this rough detergent treatment, antibodies raised against the isolated lipoprotein react with the native lipoprotein in the cell. We therefore also studied the antigenic sites of the lipoprotein and the conformational stability of the polypeptide chain.

STRUCTURE OF LIPOPROTEIN

Those parts of the lipoprotein primary structure relevant to discussion of the immunological properties are shown in Fig. 1. Most studies have been done with lipoprotein released from murein (peptidoglycan) by degrading the murein with lysozyme or by cleaving the peptide bonds at lysine residue number 55 and arginine residue number 57 with trypsin. The latter release of lipoprotein results in a polypeptide chain shortened by three amino acid residues (Tyr-Arg-Lys; 4, 5). The lysozyme treatment yields a lipoprotein on which two to three murein subunits remain bound (4). Two-thirds of the total

lipoprotein is not bound to murein (13) and ends with the sequence -Tyr-Arg-Lys (8). The free form and the murein-bound form are probably structurally identical. Both contain a covalently linked lipid whose structure was elucidated (12). The lipid is composed of a fatty acid residue linked with the α-amino group and a diglyceride residue bound as thioether to the mercapto group of the N-terminal cysteine (Fig. 1). The fatty acids are distinct from those present in lipopolysaccharide in that no β-hydroxymyristic acid occurs in the lipoprotein. The highly repetitive amino acid sequence comprises 58 amino acids. The conformation of the lipoprotein is mainly α-helical (8). The lipoprotein aggregates in aqueous solution because of the attached lipid moiety and probably also because of the arrangement of the hydrophobic amino acids along one side of the α-helical portion. The lipoprotein is, in molecular terms, the most abundant protein in *E. coli*.

LIPOPROTEIN AS ANTIGEN AND IMMUNOGEN

First attempts to raise antibodies against isolated lipoprotein by injecting samples with Freund adjuvant into rabbits failed. We then adopted techniques used in the immunochemical studies of lipopolysaccharide (6). Lipoprotein could be solubilized in alkali without destroying the antigenic sites. Human or rabbit erythrocytes could be coated with lipoprotein without pretreatment with tannic acid. Rabbits were immunized by injecting lipoprotein fixed to autologous erythrocytes. By passive hemagglutination, immune hemolysis, and immune hemolysis inhibition, we measured the antigen-antibody reactions quantitatively. These techniques, although very sensitive, favor the determination of immunoglobulin M (IgM). The response curve accordingly rose rapidly between days 13 and 19 after the first immunization and fell off between days 19 and 26. To test whether IgM's are preferentially evoked, the antiserum was fractionated on a column of

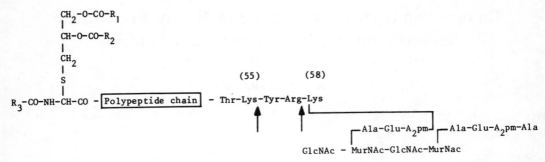

FIG. 1. *Structure of the lipoprotein of the outer membrane of* E. coli B. *The sequence of the polypeptide chain is known (3–5), but only the N-terminal lipid and the C-terminal murein attachment site is shown in detail in order to explain the immunological results.* R_1, R_2, *and* R_3 *are fatty acid residues. MurNAc (=N-acetylmuramic acid) and* A_2pm (=meso-2,6-diaminopimelic acid) *of the murein subunit remain attached to the lipoprotein after degradation of murein with lysozyme. The arrows indicate the cleavage sites of trypsin.*

Sephadex G-200, superfine. Most antibody activity was eluted in the molecular weight region of IgM and only a little in the region of IgG (Fig. 2). To support the predominance of IgM activity, the antiserum was reduced with 2-mercaptoethanol under mild conditions which cleave mainly interchain disulfide bonds (15). A mixture of 0.75 ml of antiserum, 0.75 ml of 0.15 M sodium-potassium phosphate buffer, pH 7.2, and 0.15 μl of 2-mercaptoethanol was incubated for 2 h at room temperature; it was then dialyzed at 4°C for 48 h against the above phosphate buffer and afterwards treated with 4 mg of iodoacetamide. This treatment, known to destroy mostly IgM activity, led to a strong reduction of the antiserum titer. The remaining activity corresponded, within the accuracy of the titer determination by immune hemolysis (2), to the original IgG titer. In the following studies, we worked therefore mainly with IgM antibodies.

ANTIGENIC DETERMINANTS

When lipoprotein containing two or three attached muropeptides (Fig. 1) was injected into rabbits, antibodies were obtained which were specifically directed against the muropeptide region (6). Muropeptides alone or lipoprotein after degradation with Pronase did not react with these antibodies. The muropeptides apparently have to be bound to the polypeptide chain in order to act as hapten. However, in regard to this a word of caution is necessary. Although the basis of specificity of this antiserum seemed to be clear in *E. coli*, it turned out that this antiserum reacted quite well with *Bacillus brevis* murein after lysozyme digestion and to a lesser extent with the lysozyme-digested murein of other gram-positive bacteria (V. Bosch, thesis, Free University of Berlin,

1974). No evidence for the presence of lipoprotein in these organisms has been found. We argue, without having any positive evidence yet, that muropeptides cut out of the murein by lysozyme but still bound to macromolecules can serve as antigenic determinants. This would mean that the carrier molecule of the hapten muropeptide is not of primary importance for the reactivity with this antiserum. This carrier molecule could be lipoprotein but also may be undigested portions of murein or murein-teichoic acid complexes. This finding is especially relevant for serological studies of the occurrence of lipoprotein in other strains such as *Proteus* and *Rhodospirillaceae* (H. Mayer, S. Schlecht, and V. Braun, Abstr. Joint Meet. Eur. Soc. Immunol., Strasbourg, France, 1973).

Lipoprotein released from murein with trypsin has been cleaved at lysine residue 55 (Fig. 1). Antibodies evoked upon infection of this lipoprotein specifically recognize this lysine residue, since its removal by carboxypeptidase B abolishes the antigen-antibody reaction. Interestingly, the free lipoprotein ends with a lysine residue only three amino acids away from lysine 55. However, only slight reactivity was found with the free lipoprotein. These results show that a single amino acid residue is essential but only in the appropriate amino acid environment which determines its stereochemistry. When lysine residue 55 was removed, we obtained a lipoprotein ending with threonine. Antibodies against this lipoprotein reacted with all the lipoprotein samples described so far. This shows that this antibody must be directed towards the common polypeptide chain or the lipid at the N-terminal end. Anti-lipoprotein antibodies in antisera against whole cells also cross-react with all lipoprotein samples with alterations at the carboxyl-terminal end. Such antibodies are therefore suitable for the study of the surface

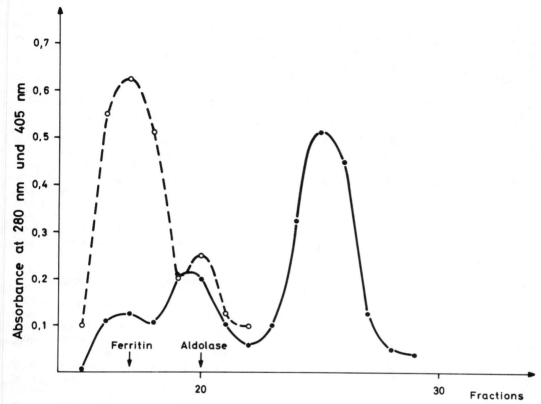

FIG. 2. *Antiserum (1 ml) against isolated lipoprotein ending with threonine residue 54 was fractionated on a Sephadex G-200, superfine, column (100 by 1.8 cm). The protein concentration in the fractions was monitored at 280 nm; the antiserum titer was determined by hemolysis of erythrocytes coated with lipoprotein in the presence of guinea pig complement. The column was eluted with 0.15 M phosphate buffer (pH 7.2)-0.9 M NaCl.*

exposure of lipoprotein in whole cells and for the determination of the occurrence of lipoprotein in other bacterial genera.

AVAILABILITY OF LIPOPROTEIN IN WHOLE CELLS

When antisera against cells of *E. coli*, *Salmonella*, *Arizona*, *Shigella*, and *Citrobacter* were tested for antibodies against purified lipoprotein, various titers were noticed. First, infection of rabbits with heat-killed strains gave rise to two to four times higher titers than infection with living strains. Second, we obtained a distinct gradation of titers between smooth strains with a complete lipopolysaccharide structure at the cell surface and various rough forms. In antisera against heat-killed mutants with an incomplete R core, reciprocal hemagglutination titers of 1,280 to 5,120 were obtained. The antiserum titers of mutants with a complete R core were in the range of 80 to 640. The greatest titer increase was found between the *Salmonella* mutants Ra and Rb$_2$ (6). This is of special interest with regard to the recently observed substantial change in the overall organization of the outer membrane of lipopolysaccharide-deficient mutants of *E. coli* and *Salmonella* (16, and literature cited therein). The ratio of the amounts of protein to lipopolysaccharide to phospholipids in the outer membrane remains nearly constant in going from smooth strains to Rc mutants. In contrast, Rd and Re mutants of *S. typhimurium* LT2 contain 60% less protein and 70% more phospholipid per unit of surface area than the wild type (16). Taking these data and the results of freeze-fracture studies into account, Smit et al. (16) proposed a model in which additional phospholipids appeared in deep rough Rd and Re mutants in the outer leaflet of the outer membrane, whereas they were not present in the wild type. The lipoprotein, however, according to our immunological studies, already becomes exposed at the surface of Rb$_2$ and Rc mutants, i.e., before the drastic outer membrane change occurs. That the production of lipoprotein-specific antibodies really reflects its exposure in whole cells was corroborated by absorption studies of antibodies produced against isolated lipoprotein to living and heat-killed wild-type and Re mutant cells. Only the Re form absorbed the antibodies (6). The immunogenicity parallels the antigenicity of lipoprotein, and in the whole cell both are related to defects in cell surface structures. In wild-type cells the lipoprotein is buried in the outer membrane, shielded by other membrane structures of which the most important one seems to be the saccharide chains of lipopolysaccharide. When the O antigens are

missing (Ra mutants), lipoprotein becomes partially exposed, but the steepest increase in antigenicity was obtained in Rb_2 mutants lacking N-acetyl glucosamine and glucose of the core saccharide (7). Rb_1 mutants were not tested. Coming back to the question posed at the beginning of this paper, it seems that the immunological activity of lipoprotein can be used to define cell surface and outer membrane mutants of *E. coli* and *Salmonella*.

So far, lipoprotein has been detected unequivocally, both chemically and serologically, in *E. coli*, *Salmonella*, *Arizona*, *Serratia marcescens*, *Citrobacter*, and *Shigella* (3, 6, 9), but not in *Proteus*, *Pseudomonas fluorescens*, and *P. aeruginosa* (9, 11). Lipoprotein antisera can be used for strain typing, but in the case of wild-type cells they have to be pretreated to expose lipoprotein. The details of this procedure are at present being worked out.

LIPOPROTEIN AS MITOGEN

Murein-free and muropeptide-containing lipoprotein (Fig. 1) both stimulate splenic lymphocytes from C3H/Tif and from BALB/c nu/nu mice, but not thymus cells from C3H/Tif mice (14). Thymidine incorporation into DNA was increased by a factor of 100 over the control without added lipoprotein. The number of plaque-forming cells against densely coupled trinitrophenylated sheep red blood cells in 2.5×10^6 cultured cells was 1,500 with 4 μg of lipoprotein per ml and 3,000 with 10 μg of lipoprotein per ml, compared with 28 without lipoprotein or 770 with 50 μg of added lipopolysaccharide per ml. Synthesis of [³H]leucine-labeled IgM was stimulated by a factor of 5 and secretion of cellular proteins by a factor of 25 over the control without added lipoprotein. The specific stimulation of B lymphocytes was independent of T lymphocytes, of serum factors, and of adherent cells. Mice which responded poorly to the mitogen lipopolysaccharide (C3H/HeJ) were stimulated equally as well by lipoprotein as high-responder mice (C3H/Tif and BALB/c nu/nu). Anti-IgG antibodies inhibited the mitogenic stimulation of B cells by lipoprotein. Thus, a complex of lymphocyte cell surface structures including the IgG receptor molecules and the lipopolysaccharide and lipoprotein receptors are apparently involved in the regulation of mitogenic stimulation of B lymphocytes to proliferation and differentiation to IgM-secreting cells.

In contrast to the immunogenic and antigenic determinants which reside at the C-terminal end of the lipoprotein, the lipid at the N-terminal end of the polypeptide chain seems to be es-

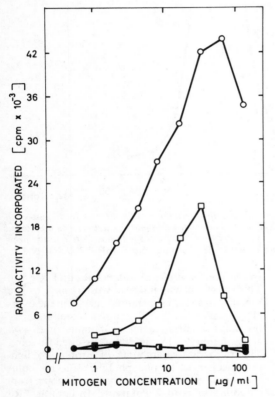

FIG. 3. *Dose-response plot for thymidine uptake in DBA mouse spleen cells after stimulation with lipoprotein (○), lipopeptide (□), alkali-hydrolyzed (0.03 M NaOH in 90% ethanol, 4 h, 37°C) lipoprotein (●), and lipopeptide (■). Cells were cultured for 72 h in microtiter plates (Falcon 3040) in 150-μl amounts at a cell density of 4×10^6/ml in RPMI 1640 medium supplemented with 10% human serum (Flow Laboratories), fresh glutamine (2 mmol/ml), penicillin (100 units/ml), streptomycin (100 μg/ml), and 2-mercaptoethanol (5×10^{-5} M). Before harvesting, the cells were pulsed for 24 h with 0.5 μCi of [³H]thymidine (Amersham-Buchler). Data of W. Bessler (unpublished).*

sential for the mitogenic properties. Release of the ester-linked fatty acids by mild treatment with alkali abolished the mitogenic effect (14). However, upon standing of an alkali-treated lipoprotein solution for at least 1 day, mitogenicity was partially recovered. In this case at least aggregation, which occurs upon longer standing because of the amide-linked fatty acid still bound to the polypeptide chain (Fig. 1), is probably essential for the mitogenic action of lipoprotein. Lipopeptides consisting of three to six amino acids bound to the fatty acids-glycerylcysteine residue were isolated from Pronase digests of lipoprotein (12). They stimulate the uptake of [³H]thymidine into DNA and [³H]uridine into RNA of mouse spleen cells similarly to the complete lipoprotein (Fig. 3). [¹⁴C]oleate incorporation into the lecithin of lymphocyte plasma membranes was increased 60 min after addition of lipoprotein or lipopeptide (W. Bessler, K. Hantke, and K. Resch, unpublished data).

Lymphocytes of beef lymph nodes and of rabbit and rat spleens were stimulated by lipoprotein to an extent similar to lymphocytes of mice. However, calf thymus lymphocytes and peripheral human lymphocytes could only be insignificantly stimulated by lipoprotein concentrations as great as 300 μg/ml (1).

Pyrogenicity assays of lipoprotein revealed a febrile response in rabbits (E. T. Rietschel, personal communication). The dose-response curve was similar to that obtained for lipoid A. Since the rise in temperature (1.5°C per 3 h per 100 μg of lipoprotein per ml) could be largely suppressed by lipoid A-specific antiserum, one has to assume that the pyrogenicity of lipoprotein is due to lipoid A contamination in the range of 1%. The same conclusion may apply to the finding that lipoprotein protects mice against nasal infection by influenza A virus, as does lipopolysaccharide.

The clear-cut antigenic determinants at the C-terminal end of the polypeptide chain, based in one instance on a single amino acid residue, the mitogenic activity of the covalently linked lipid at the N-terminal end, and the possibility of identifying, by serological means, cell wall mutants and *E. coli*-related *Enterobacteriaceae* makes lipoprotein an interesting and useful tool both in immunochemistry and in bacteriology.

ACKNOWLEDGMENT

Part of this work was supported by the Deutsche Forschungsgemeinschaft (SFB 76).

LITERATURE CITED

1. **Bessler, W., and V. Braun.** 1975. Mitogenität von Lipoprotein aus der äusseren Membran von *E. coli* gegenüber Lymphozyten verschiedener Spezies. Z. Immunitaetsforsch. **150:**193.
2. **Bosch, V., and V. Braun.** 1973. Distribution of murein-lipoprotein between the cytoplasmic and outer membrane of *Escherichia coli*. FEBS Lett. **34:**307–310.
3. **Braun, V.** 1975. Covalent lipoprotein from the outer membrane of *Escherichia coli*. Biochim. Biophys. Acta (Reviews in Biomembranes) **415:**336–377.
4. **Braun, V., and V. Bosch.** 1972. Repetitive sequences in the murein-lipoprotein of the cell wall of Escherichia coli. Proc. Natl. Acad. Sci. U.S.A. **69:**970–974.
5. **Braun, V., and V. Bosch.** 1972. Sequence of the murein-lipoprotein and the attachment site of the lipid. Eur. J. Biochem. **28:**51–69.
6. **Braun, V., V. Bosch, E. R. Klumpp, I. Neff, H. Mayer, and S. Schlecht.** 1976. Antigenic determinants of murein lipoprotein and its exposure at the surface of Enterobacteriaceae. Eur. J. Biochem. **62:**555–566.
7. **Braun, V., and K. Hantke.** 1974. Biochemistry of bacterial cell envelopes. Annu. Rev. Biochem. **43:** 89–121.
8. **Braun, V., K. Hantke, and U. Henning.** 1975. Characterization of the free form of murein-lipoprotein from the outer membrane of Escherichia coli B/r. FEBS Lett. **60:**26–28.
9. **Braun, V., K. Rehn, and H. Wolff.** 1970. Supramolecular structure of the rigid layer of the cell wall of *Salmonella*, *Serratia*, *Proteus* and *Pseudomonas fluorescens*. Biochemistry **9:**5041–5049.
10. **Braun, V., and H. Wolff.** 1970. The murein-lipoprotein linkage in the cell wall of *Escherichia coli*. Eur. J. Biochem. **14:**387–391.
11. **Halegoua, S., A. Hirashima, and M. Inouye.** 1974. Existence of a free form of a specific membrane lipoprotein in gram-negative bacteria. J. Bacteriol. **120:**1204–1208.
12. **Hantke, K., and V. Braun.** 1973. Covalent binding of lipid to protein. Diglyceride and amide-linked fatty acid at the N-terminal end of the murein-lipoprotein of the *Escherichia coli* outer membrane. Eur. J. Biochem. **34:**284–296.
13. **Inouye, M., J. Shaw, and C. Shen.** 1972. The assembly of a structural lipoprotein in the envelope of *Escherichia coli*. J. Biol. Chem. **247:**8154–8159.
14. **Melchers, F., V. Braun, and C. Galanos.** 1975. The lipoprotein of the outer membrane of *Escherichia coli*: a B-lymphocyte mitogen. J. Exp. Med. **142:** 473–482.
15. **Morris, J. E., and R. P. Inman.** 1968. Isolation of the monomeric subunit of immunoglobulin M with its interchain disulfide bond intact. Biochemistry **7:**2851–2857.
16. **Smit, J., Y. Kamio, and H. Nikaido.** 1975. Outer membrane of *Salmonella typhimurium*: chemical analysis and freeze-fracture studies with lipopolysaccharide mutants. J. Bacteriol. **124:**942–958.

Chemical Structure of Lipid A

ERNST T. RIETSCHEL, SUMIHIRO HASE, MING-TZAN KING,
JOHN REDMOND, AND VOLKER LEHMANN

Max-Planck-Institut für Immunbiologie, Freiburg i. Br., West Germany

Lipid A represents the common, covalently bound lipid component of lipopolysaccharides of gram-negative bacteria (16, 31; O. Lüderitz, p. 239, this volume). The significance of lipid A for the functional and structural integrity of the bacterial cell membrane (21) and the central role it plays in the endotoxicity of lipopolysaccharides (16; Galanos et al., p. 269, this volume) prompted studies on its chemical composition and structure more than a quarter century ago. In this communication it is intended to summarize the present knowledge on the chemical structure of lipid A.

The first systematic investigations on the composition of free lipid A were initiated in the laboratories of Westphal (31) and Niemann (12, 13). These workers found that free lipid A from *Escherichia coli* and *Salmonella* consisted of D-glucosamine (~22%), phosphate (~10%), and long-chain fatty acids (~60%, mainly D-3-hydroxytetradecanoic acid). In subsequent studies, glucosamine-4-phosphate and N-3-hydroxytetradecanoyl-D-glucosamine residues were isolated, indicating that phosphorylated N-acylglucosamine residues form the backbone of lipid A. The fact, however, that the molecular weight of free lipid A was found to be on the order of 2,000 (4, 17) suggested that more than one substituted glucosamine residue is present in a lipid A unit. Structural models were therefore proposed to indicate the linkage of several glucosamine-phosphate residues. Nowotny postulated that glucosamine residues are interlinked by 1',4-phosphodiester bonds (19). Burton and Carter, on the other hand, provided evidence for glycosidically interlinked glucosamine residues (4). Final proof for the existence of glucosamine disaccharides in *Salmonella* lipid A was provided by Gmeiner et al. in 1969 (8). They showed for the first time that there are present β1',6-linked D-glucosamine disaccharides which carry phosphate residues in positions 1 and 4'. This structure is referred to in this article as the "lipid A backbone."

These latter results were obtained by investigations on highly defective lipopolysaccharides (glycolipids), isolated from *Salmonella*

minnesota Re mutants. Recently, a procedure was devised in our laboratory for the analysis of the lipid A backbone of both R- and S-form lipopolysaccharides (10). This procedure allowed the isolation of the (reduced) lipid A backbone, which was then studied by methylation analysis involving gas-liquid chromatography–mass spectrometry (9) and by N-acetylglucosaminidase. With this method the lipid A backbone of a series of lipopolysaccharides has been investigated (Table 1; 10, 10a). In all cases lipid A is made up, as in *Salmonella*, of β1',6-linked D-glucosamine disaccharides, which carry one phosphate group in glycosidic linkage and a second phosphate that is ester linked to the nonreducing glucosamine residue (Fig. 1A).

When the same degradation procedure was applied to lipopolysaccharides of *Chromobacterium violaceum* NCTC 9694, the presence of the same phosphorylated β1',6-linked D-glucosamine disaccharides in lipid A was demonstrated. Furthermore, the phosphate groups of the *C. violaceum* lipid A backbone are substituted (S. Hase and E. T. Rietschel, Eur. J. Biochem., in press). The phosphate group, which is glycosidically linked to the glucosamine disaccharides, is substituted by a (nonacylated) glucosaminyl residue. To our knowledge this is the first time that a glucosaminyl-1-phosphoryl-1-glucosaminide structure has been detected in natural products. Moreover, the ester-linked phosphate group, bound to the nonreducing glucosamine residue, is substituted by 4-aminoarabinose (Fig. 1B). L-4-Aminoarabinose has been previously identified in various lipopolysaccharides including the lipopolysaccharide (glycolipid) of *S. minnesota* Re mutants (29). The experiments on *C. violaceum* lipid A suggested that this amino sugar may be a constituent of other lipid A's. Recent analysis on glycolipids from *S. minnesota* Re mutants indeed suggests that 4-aminoarabinose is linked in a way analogous to that in *C. violaceum*. In the glycolipid, however, only 10 to 20% of the phosphate groups are substituted by 4-aminoarabinose.

Recently, a new class of mutants (*S. typhimur-*

ium) was isolated, being temperature sensitive both in ketodeoxyoctonate (KDO)-8-phosphate synthetase and in growth (21, 22; V. Lehmann, E. Rupprecht, and M. J. Osborn, in preparation). Under nonpermissive conditions these mutants accumulate a polysaccharide-free lipid A-precursor molecule. The chemical analysis of this precursor shows that it contains, like the lipid A's discussed so far, phosphorylated $\beta 1',6$-linked D-glucosamine disaccharides (which are *N*- and partially *O*-acylated by D-3-hydroxytetradecanoic acid [V. Lehmann, in preparation]). This acidic lipid A precursor is extractable from bacteria grown on Merck medium. If, however, a different culture medium (Loeb) is used, the mutant synthesizes, in addition to the acidic precursor, a neutral precursor molecule. It appears to consist of the usual glucosamine backbone carrying both a glycosidically bound and an ester-bound phosphate residue. These phosphate groups, however, are substituted: the glycosidically bound, by phosphoethanolamine, and the ester-bound, by 4-aminoarabinose.

Studies carried out in other laboratories have shown that $\beta 1',6$-linked glucosamine residues also form the backbone of lipid A in other lipopolysaccharides (Table 1; 2, 6, 14, 18). Furthermore, glucosamine disaccharides were found to be present in lipid A of *Myxococcus fulvus* (28) and *Vibrio cholerae* (J. Redmond, S. Hase, and E. T. Rietschel, unpublished data).

Some authors have postulated that phosphate bridges interlink lipid A units (4, 19). This problem was studied recently by Lehmann et al. (cited in 16), who performed partial hydrazinolysis on model compounds containing phosphate or pyrophosphate bridges. Their results of chemical analysis performed on various lipopolysaccharide-(lipid A) degradation products obtained after hydrazinolysis and gel chromatography could be best explained by assuming the presence of pyrophosphate linkages; direct proof for their existence, however, is still lacking. Very recently, studies with ^{31}P nuclear magnetic resonance spectroscopy have been initiated to study the nature of pyrophosphate linkages in lipopolysaccharides and lipid A (V. Lehmann and P. Mühlradt, unpublished data). First experiments with *Salmonella* R-form lipopolysaccharides (Re-Rc) suggest that pyrophosphate groups may be present in the lipid A component, but further studies are needed to elucidate their quantity and location. Recently, pyrophosphate bridges have also been identified in lipid A of *E. coli* (M. Rosner et al., Fed. Proc. **35**:1700, 1976).

TABLE 1. *Lipopolysaccharides containing $\beta 1',6$-linked D-glucosamine disaccharides in their lipid A component*

Lipopolysaccharide	Reference
Salmonella minnesota (Re)	8,10
S. minnesota (S)	10
Escherichia coli BB9 (Rd$_2$)	10
E. coli EH 100 (Ra)	10
E. coli O86 (S)[a]	10
E. coli O111 (S)	10
Shigella flexneri 5b (Re)	10
S. flexneri 5b (S)[a]	10
S. sonnei	18
Proteus mirabilis D52(I)	—[b]
Serratia marcescens	2
Yersinia enterocolitica Ye75R,IA (R)	—[c]
Fusobacterium nucleatum Fev1	10a
Pseudomonas aeruginosa	6
P. alcaligenes	6
Xanthomonas sinensis	10
Rhodopseudomonas gelatinosa 29/1	10
Selenomonas ruminantium	14
Chromobacterium violaceum NCTC 9694	—[d]

[a] Adams et al. (1, 3) identified $\beta 1',4$-linked glucosamine oligomers in *E. coli* O86, *Neisseria sicca*, and a nonclassified *Shigella flexneri* strain.

[b] M. King, S. Hase, J. Gmeiner, and E. T. Rietschel, unpublished data.

[c] M. King, S. Hase, and E. T. Rietschel, unpublished data.

[d] S. Hase and E. T. Rietschel, Eur. J. Biochem., in press.

Some lipid A's differ in their backbone composition from those discussed so far. Thus, in lipid A of *Pseudomonas diminuta* (32), *Rhodopseudomonas viridis*, and *R. palustris* (27), glucosamine is absent. Instead, in the two *Rhodopseudomonas* strains, 2,3-diamino-2,3-dideoxy-D-glucose is present (Fig. 1C). Phosphate is absent in lipopolysaccharides (and thus in lipid A) of some groups of bacteria and blue-green algae (7, 14, 27, 30). Furthermore, recent investigations on lipopolysaccharides of *Brucella* strains indicate that their lipid component exhibits unique structural features (15; S. Hase and E. T. Rietschel, unpublished data).

Lipid A owes its lipoidal character to the presence of long-chain fatty acids. These are bound to the lipid A backbone through ester and amide linkages. Depending on the

TABLE 2. *Nature, absolute configuration, and type of linkage of 3-hydroxy fatty acids present in lipopolysaccharides*[a]

Lipopolysaccharide	3-Hydroxy acid	Linkage[b]
Rhodopseudomonas gelatinosa	D-3-OH-C 10	E + A
Rhodospirillum tenue	D-3-OH-C 10	E + A
Chromobacterium violaceum	D-3-OH-C 10	E
	D-3-OH-C 12	A
Pseudomonas aeruginosa	D-3-OH-C 10	E
	D-3-OH-C 12	A
Xanthomonas sinensis	D-3-OH-C 10	E
	D-3-OH-C 12	E + A
	D-3-OH-9-Me-C 10	E
	D-3-OH-11-Me-C 12	E + A
Bordetella pertussis	D-3-OH-C 10	E
	D-3-OH-C 12	E
	D-3-OH-C 14	A
Vibrio metchnikovii	D-3-OH-C 12	E
	D-3-OH-C 14	A
V. cholerae	D-3-OH-C 12	E
	D-3-OH-C 14	A
Salmonella abortus-equi	D-3-OH-C 14	E + A
S. typhi	D-3-OH-C 14	E + A
S. minnesota (Re)	D-3-OH-C 14	E + A
Escherichia coli	D-3-OH-C 14	E + A
E. coli BB9 (Rd₂)	D-3-OH-C 14	E + A
Shigella sonnei	D-3-OH-C 14	E + A
S. flexneri 5b (Re)	D-3-OH-C 14	E + A
Proteus mirabilis D52 (I)	D-3-OH-C 14	E + A
Yersinia enterocolitica	D-3-OH-C 14	E + A
Rhodopseudomonas viridis	D-3-OH-C 14	A
Veillonella	3-OH-C 13	E + A
	3-OH-C 15	A
Fusobacterium nucleatum Fev 1	D-3-OH-C 14	E
	D-3-OH-C 16	A
Myxococcus fulvus	3-OH-C 14	E
	3-OH-C 16	E + A
	3-OH-13-Me-C 14	E
	3-OH-15-Me-C 16	E + A
Anabaena variabilis	3-OH-C 14	A
	3-OH-C 16	A
	3-OH-C 18	A

[a] Data are from references 10a, 16, 23, 24, 26, and 30.
[b] E = ester; A = amide.

source of lipid A, various kinds of *ester-bound* fatty acids may be present. Thus, long-chain even- or odd-numbered, isobranched, L-2-hydroxy and D-3-hydroxy fatty acids have been identified (16, 24, 26). In some bacterial groups the 3-hydroxyl group of ester-bound 3-hydroxy fatty acids (Table 2) are acylated by other fatty acids (6, 10a, 18, 25), whereas in other groups they are free (24, 26, 28, 32). Cyclopropane and unsaturated fatty acids have only occasionally been detected in lipid A.

In contrast to the broad spectrum of different types of fatty acids involved in ester bonds, only one type of fatty acids is *amide linked*, namely, D-3-hydroxy fatty acids. These 3-hydroxy acids are generally even numbered, with chain lengths differing in individual bacterial groups (23, 24; Table 2).

The 3-hydroxyl group of N-acyl hydroxy acids has been postulated to be free (25), but recent experiments suggest that it is (partly) substituted (M. King, S. Hase, and E. T. Rietschel, unpublished data). It was found that, on treatment of *S. minnesota* Re glycolipids with alkali, amide-bound Δ^2-tetradecenoic acid is formed. In model experiments involving alkali treatment of N-3-hydroxytetradecanoyl-D-glucosamine and N-3-acetoxytetradecanoyl-D-glucosamine, it was found that the α,β-unsaturated acid was only formed from the 3-O-acylated material. It is therefore believed that Δ^2-tetradecenoic acid is derived from amide-bound, 3-O-substituted 3-hydroxytetradecanoic acid by an alkali-induced β elimination of an as yet unknown residue. This matter is currently under investigation.

As a rule, D-3-hydroxy acids (ester and amide bound) predominate in the fatty acid moiety of lipid A (*Brucella* being an exception [15]). Since they are in general missing in other cell wall lipids of gram-negative bacteria, they are unique to lipid A and represent characteristic lipid A markers.

Some lipid A's contain, in addition to glucosamine, other saccharide components, such as D-arabinose (*Rhodospirillum tenue* [7]) and D-mannose (*Chromatium vinosum* [11]). Phosphoethanolamine (and ethanolamine) is frequently encountered in lipid A. In the neutral lipid A precursor, phosphoethanolamine is linked to the glycosidically bound phosphate group of the backbone. The type and site of attachment of this amine in other lipid A's have yet to be determined.

It has been suggested that covalent linkages exist between lipid A and peptides or protein (19, 33, 34). It is possible, however, that proteins (which are present in only minor amounts in lipopolysaccharide preparations extracted by phenol-water or phenol-chloroform-petroleum ether) are complexed to lipid A through ionic or hydrophobic interactions. A basic outer-membrane protein with high affinity for lipid A has recently been isolated from *S. minnesota* Re bacteria and partially characterized (R. Geyer and C. Galanos, unpublished data).

The chemical studies carried out so far allow a preliminary structural classification of lipid A's into two distinct classes (Fig. 1). The first class (class I) of lipid A is characterized by the presence of a $\beta 1',6$-linked D-glucosamine disaccharide backbone, which carries amide-bound D-3-hydroxy fatty acids. Depending on the presence or absence of phosphate groups

and the degree of their substitution, several types of lipid A, exhibiting distinct structural features, are recognized within this class.

Lipid A of *Selenomonas ruminantium* appears to be free from phosphate groups (14).

The lipid A of a large group of bacteria (e.g., *Enterobacteriaceae*, Fig. 1A) contains phosphate residues, which are substituted not at all or only to a minor extent. In general, two phosphate residues are bound to the glucosamine disaccharide backbone: one in ester linkage (in *Salmonella*: C-4') and one in a glycosidic linkage (C-1). This type of lipid A was first detected in *Salmonella* (8). It is this structure which has been studied most extensively and which has been identified in a

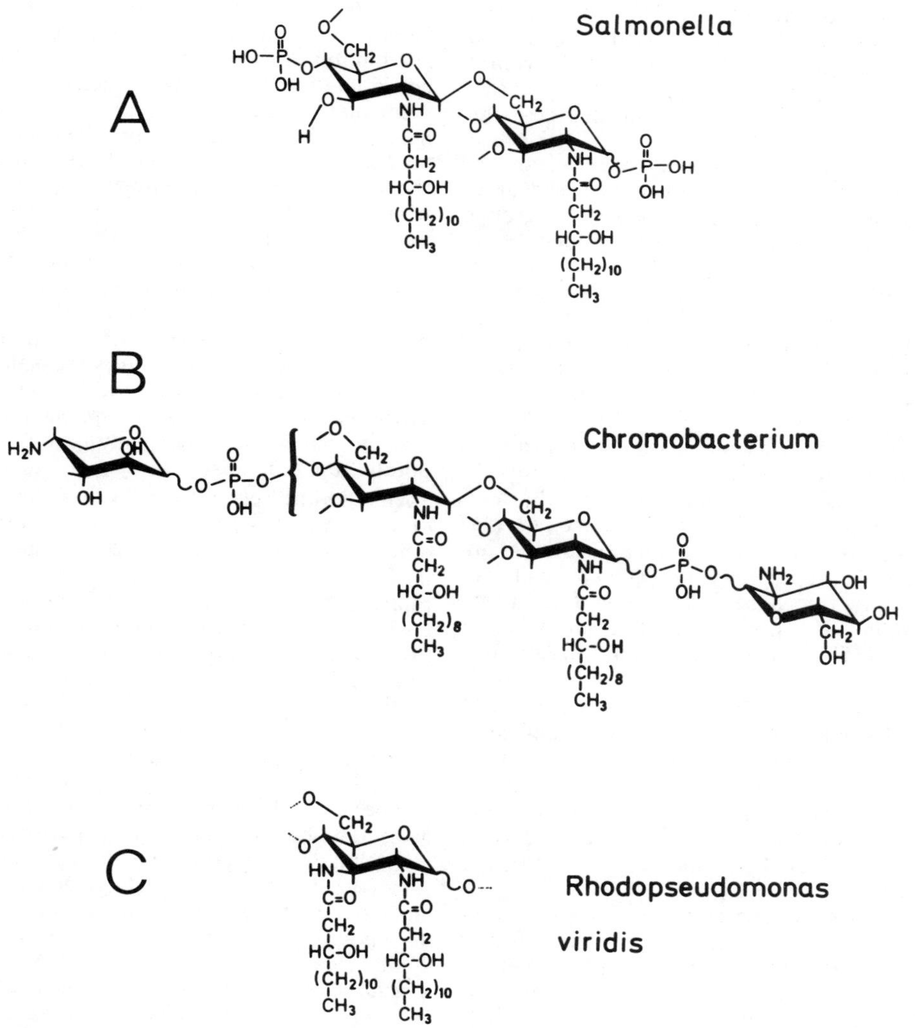

FIG. 1. *Chemical structures of lipid A of* Salmonella *(A),* Chromobacterium violaceum *(B), and* Rhodopseudomonas viridis *(C).*

great variety of bacterial groups (Table 1; 2, 6, 8, 10, 10a, 14, 18). The hydroxyl groups at positions C-3, C-4, and C-6' are acylated by fatty acids. In *Salmonella* these are dodecanoic, hexadecanoic, and D-3-tetradecanoxytetradecanoic acid (of each acid about 1 mol/mol of disaccharide) with additional smaller amounts of D-3-hydroxytetradecanoic acid (25). In other bacterial groups, these or other ester-bound fatty acids are present. The positions of the individual *O*-acyl residues in the sugar backbone are not known at present. The amino groups of the glucosamine backbone are substituted by D-3-hydroxy fatty acids. In *Salmonella*, D-3-hydroxytetradecanoic acid is present, which appears to be (partially) 3-*O* substituted. In other lipid A's, the corresponding D-3-hydroxydecanoic to D-3-hydroxyoctadecanoic acids occur (Table 2). In *Salmonella* lipid A, the hydroxyl group at C-3' represents the point of attachment of the polysaccharide portion of the lipopolysaccharide molecule.

The lipid A of *Chromobacterium violaceum* (and the neutral lipid A precursor) is characterized by the fact that the phosphate groups of the backbone are largely substituted (Hase and Rietschel, in press). In *C. violaceum* (Fig. 1B) the ester-bound phosphate carries (nonacylated) 4-aminoarabinose. To the glycosidically bound phosphate group, a (nonacylated) glucosamine residue is bound in glycosidic linkage (phosphoethanolamine in the neutral lipid A precursor).

Lipid A's of the second class (class II) do not contain glucosamine. Instead, in *Rhodopseudomonas viridis* and *R. palustris* (Fig. 1C) nonphosphorylated 2,3-diamino-2,3-dideoxy-D-glucose is present. Its two amino groups are acylated by D-3-hydroxytetradecanoic acid residues; only traces of ester-bound fatty acids were found. It is not known at present whether in *R. viridis* one or more diaminoglucose residues form a lipid A unit (7, 27).

The structural distinction between class I and class II lipid A is supported by recent serological studies with lipid A antiserum. These show that free lipid A preparations of class I cross-react with one another. No cross-reaction, however, was found between free lipid A of class I and class II (Galanos et al., p. 269, this volume).

It has been documented in several studies that free lipid A is heterogeneous (20). In contrast to this known, partly artificial heterogeneity of free lipid A, it has only recently become appreciated that lipid A also exhibits a certain degree of intrinsic heterogeneity. This first became evident when Re mutant glyco-

lipids were fractionated by thin-layer chromatography (5). The chemical analysis of the corresponding compounds, however, did not reveal significant differences in their content of glucosamine, phosphate, KDO, and fatty acid esters (5).

Recently, new light was shed on lipid A heterogeneity when 4-aminoarabinose was recognized as an occasional, nonobligatory component of *Salmonella* lipid A. Semiquantitative analyses showed that in glycolipid preparations only 10 to 20% of the ester-bound phosphate groups of the lipid A backbone are substituted with the amino sugar. This partial substitution could represent one aspect of intrinsic lipid A heterogeneity. A genuine heterogeneity of the lipid A backbone with regard to ester-bound (C-4') phosphate residues has been postulated by Gmeiner et al. (8). A disproportionate distribution of ester-bound fatty acids may also contribute to lipid A heterogeneity.

Further insight into the problem of lipid A heterogeneity was gained by chemical studies on lipid A precursors. As discussed earlier, the acidic precursor molecule, as extracted from bacteria grown on Merck medium, contains the usual *Salmonella* lipid A backbone with nonsubstituted phosphate groups at C-1 and C-4'. When the mutant was grown on Loeb medium, however, in addition a neutral lipid A precursor was synthesized. Structural analyses show that this molecule differs from the acidic precursor in that the glycosidically linked phosphate is substituted by phosphoethanolamine and the ester-linked phosphate groups are substituted by 4-aminoarabinose.

This finding seems to indicate a dependence of the lipid A structure on the culture conditions. So far, this dependence seems to relate mainly to the substitution of both phosphate groups of the lipid A backbone with basic substituents. In *Selenomas ruminantium*, however, the chain length of the 3-hydroxy fatty acid in lipid A is determined by the nature of the fatty acid added to the culture medium as an external supply (14), and in *Proteus mirabilis* the pattern of nonhydroxylated fatty acids of lipid A depends on the cultivation temperature (S. Rottem, personal communication). The central disaccharide (phosphorylated $\beta1',6$-linked D-glucosamine disaccharides with amide-bound D-3-hydroxy fatty acids) appears not to be affected by external factors. This backbone has been found in systematically quite remote bacteria such as *Salmonella*, *Pseudomonas*, *Fusobacterium nucleatum*, and *Rhodopseudomonas gelatinosa* (Tables 1 and 2). It therefore seems that, at least in these bacterial groups, the lipid A backbone represents a conservative structure and a non-variable portion of the lipopolysaccharide molecule which, in contrast to the *O*-specific chains, has not been subjected to major modifications during evolution.

The chemical investigations performed in recent years on the structures of lipid A from various bacterial groups have shown that these structures exhibit close relationships but are not identical. Lipid A, therefore, represents a *family* of bacterial lipids. Consequently, a chemical structure can only be assigned to a lipid A of an individual, defined bacterial group, where lipid A possesses a characteristic composition. But, even in this case, lipid A exhibits a certain degree of heterogeneity. Structural formulas, therefore, should only be regarded as models showing the general architecture and the structure of the major part of a lipid A molecule.

As outlined earlier in this symposium (Lüderitz, p. 239), the term *lipid A* should be used for the designation of the lipid component as it is present in the lipopolysaccharide molecule, whereas the term *free lipid A* should be used for the designation of isolated lipid A, as it is obtained from lipopolysaccharides by mild acid hydrolysis. In many cases (e.g., *Salmonella*, *E. coli*, *Shigella flexneri*) the structure of free lipid A resembles that of lipid A. In other cases, however (*Chromobacterium violaceum*), the respective structures are quite different. The *lipid A precursor* is a form of native lipid A which lacks naturally the polysaccharide portion. Since acid hydrolysis is not required for its isolation, the lipid A precursor represents an ideal material for further structural and biological studies on lipid A.

The chemical structure of lipid A indicates that it is an amphipathic molecule with a hydrophobic center (acylated disaccharide) and a hydrophilic periphery (phosphate). It furthermore may be an amphoteric molecule, carrying both acidic and basic functional groups. Its unique chemical architecture endows lipid A with affinities and specificities which make it a vital constituent of the bacterial membrane and one of the most potent biologically active (nonprotein) molecules expressing a great variety of distinct (endotoxic) activities.

Although the elucidation of its chemical structure has furthered our understanding of the physicochemical properties of lipid A, knowledge of those components, groups, structures, or conformations which confer endotoxic activity to lipid A remains fragmentary. There is evidence that fatty acids are essential for endotoxicity, but it is likely that other constituents and factors play a significant role in lipid A

activity. It is hoped that further studies on the chemical structure of lipid A will increase our knowledge of the molecular basis of its biological activities.

ACKNOWLEDGMENTS

We thank the Alexander-von-Humboldt Stiftung (S.H., J.R.), the Cancer Research Institute, Inc. (E.T.R.), and the Deutsche Forschungsgemeinschaft (V.L., E.T.R.) for financial support.

LITERATURE CITED

1. **Adams, G. A.** 1971. The chemical composition of a cell wall lipopolysaccharide from *Neisseria sicca*. Can. J. Biochem. **49:**243–250.
2. **Adams, G. A., and P. P. Singh.** 1970. The chemical constitution of lipid A from *Serratia marcescens*. Can. J. Biochem. **48:**55–62.
3. **Adams, G. A., and P. P. Singh.** 1970. Structural features of lipid A preparations isolated from *Escherichia coli* and *Shigella flexneri*. Biochim. Biophys. Acta **202:**553–555.
4. **Burton, A. J., and H. E. Carter.** 1964. Purification and characterization of the lipid A component of the lipopolysaccharide from *E. coli*. Biochemistry **3:**411–418.
5. **Chen, C. H., A. G. Johnson, N. Kasai, B. A. Key, J. Levine, and A. Nowotny.** 1973. Heterogeneity and biological activity of endotoxic glycolipid from *Salmonella minnesota* R595. J. Infect. Dis. **128** (Suppl.): S35–S43.
6. **Drewry, D. T., J. A. Lomax, G. W. Gray, and S. G. Wilkinson.** 1973. Studies of lipid A fractions from the lipopolysaccharides of *Pseudomonas aeruginosa* and *Pseudomonas alcaligenes*. Biochem. J. **133:**563–572.
7. **Drews, G., J. Weckesser, J. Mayer, and H. Mayer.** 1977. Cell envelopes, chap. 22. *In* R. K. Clayton and W. R. Sistrom (ed.), The photosynthetic bacteria. Plenum Press, New York.
8. **Gmeiner, J., O. Lüderitz, and O. Westphal.** 1969. Biochemical studies on lipopolysaccharides of *Salmonella* R mutants. 6. Investigations on the structure of the lipid A component. Eur. J. Biochem. **7:** 370–379.
9. **Hase, S., and E. T. Rietschel.** 1976. Methylation analysis of glucosaminitol and glucosaminyl-glucosaminitol disaccharides. Formation of 2-deoxy-2-(*N*-acetylacetamido)-glucitol derivatives. Eur. J. Biochem. **63:**93–99.
10. **Hase, S., and E. T. Rietschel.** 1976. Isolation and analysis of the lipid A backbone. Lipid A structure of lipopolysaccharides from various bacterial groups. Eur. J. Biochem. **63:**101–107.
10a. **Hase, S., T. Hofstad, and E. T. Rietschel.** 1977. Chemical structure of the lipid A component of lipopolysaccharides from *Fusobacterium nucleatum*. J. Bacteriol. **129:**9–14.
11. **Hurlbert, R. E., J. Weckesser, H. Mayer, and J. Fromme.** 1976. Isolation and characterization of the lipopolysaccharide of *Chromatium vinosum*. Eur. J. Biochem. **68:**365–371.
12. **Ikawa, M., I. B. Koepfli, S. C. Mudd, and C. Niemann.** 1953. An agent from *E. coli* causing hemorrhage and regression of experimental mouse tumor. III. The component fatty acids in the phospholipid moiety. J. Am. Chem. Soc. **75:**1035–1038.
13. **Ikawa, M., J. B. Koepfli, S. G. Mudd, and C. Niemann.** 1953. An agent from *E. coli* causing hemorrhage and regression of an experimental mouse tumor. IV. Some nitrogenous components of the phospholipid moiety. J. Am. Chem. Soc. **75:**3439–3442.
14. **Kamio, Y., K. C. Kim, and H. Takahashi.** 1971.

Chemical structure of lipid A of *Selenomonas ruminantium*. J. Biochem. **70**:187–191.

15. **Lacave, C., J. Asselineau, A. Serre, and J. Roux.** 1969. Comparison de la composition chimique d'une fraction lipopolysaccharidique et d'une fraction polysaccharidique isolées de *Brucella melitensis*. Eur. J. Biochem. **9**:189–198.

16. **Lüderitz, O., C. Galanos, V. Lehmann, M. Nurminen, E. T. Rietschel, G. Rosenfelder, M. Simon, and O. Westphal.** 1973. Lipid A: chemical structure and biological activity. J. Infect. Dis. **128**(Suppl.):9–21.

17. **Lüderitz, O., K. Jann, and R. Wheat.** 1968. Somatic and capsular antigens of gram-negative bacteria, p. 105–228. *In* M. Florkin and E. H. Stotz (ed.), Comprehensive biochemistry, vol. 26A. Elsevier Publishing Co., Amsterdam.

18. **Lugowski, C., and E. Romanowska.** 1974. Chemical studies on *Shigella sonnei* lipid A. Eur. J. Biochem. **48**:319–323.

19. **Nowotny, A.** 1961. Chemical structure of a phosphomucolipid and its occurrence in some strains of *Salmonella*. J. Am. Chem. Soc. **83**:501–503.

20. **Nowotny, A.** 1971. Chemical and biological heterogeneity of endotoxins, p. 309–329. *In* G. Weinbaum, S. Kadis, and S. J. Ajl (ed.), Microbial toxins, vol. 4. Academic Press Inc., New York.

21. **Osborn, M. J., P. D. Rick, V. Lehmann, E. Rupprecht, and M. Singh.** 1974. Structure and biogenesis of the cell wall envelope of gram-negative bacteria. Ann. N.Y. Acad. Sci. **235**:52–65.

22. **Rick, P. D., and M. J. Osborn.** 1972. Isolation of a mutant of *Salmonella typhimurium* dependent on D-arabinose-5-phosphate for growth and synthesis of 3-deoxy-D-mannoctulosonate (ketodeoxyoctonate). Proc. Natl. Acad. Sci. U.S.A. **69**:3756–3760.

23. **Rietschel, E. T.** 1976. Absolute configuration of 3-hydroxy fatty acids present in lipopolysaccharides from various bacterial groups. Eur. J. Biochem. **64**:423–428.

24. **Rietschel, E. T., C. Galanos, and O. Lüderitz.** 1975. Structure, endotoxicity, and immunogenicity of the lipid A component of bacterial lipopolysaccharides,

p. 307–314. *In* D. Schlesinger (ed.), Microbiology—1975. American Society for Microbiology, Washington, D.C.

25. **Rietschel, E. T., H. Gottert, O. Lüderitz, and O. Westphal.** 1972. Nature and linkages of the fatty acids present in the lipid A component of *Salmonella* lipopolysaccharides. Eur. J. Biochem. **28**:166–173.

26. **Rietschel, E. T., O. Lüderitz, and W. A. Volk.** 1975. Nature, type of linkage and absolute configuration of (hydroxy) fatty acids in lipopolysaccharides from *Xanthomonas sinensis* and related strains. J. Bacteriol. **122**:1180–1188.

27. **Roppel, J., H. Mayer, and J. Weckesser.** 1975. Identification of a 2,3-diamino-2,3-dideoxyhexose in the lipid A component of lipopolysaccharides of *Rhodopseudomonas viridis* and *Rhodopseudomonas palustris*. Carbohydr. Res. **40**:31–40.

28. **Rosenfelder, G., O. Lüderitz, and O. Westphal.** 1974. Composition of lipopolysaccharides from *Myxococcus fulvus* and non-fruiting myxobacteria. Eur. J. Biochem. **44**:411–420.

29. **Volk, W. A., C. Galanos, and O. Lüderitz.** 1970. The occurrence of 4-amino-4-deoxy-L-arabinose as a constituent in *Salmonella* lipopolysaccharide preparations. Eur. J. Biochem. **17**:223–229.

30. **Weckesser, J., A. Katz, G. Drews, H. Mayer, and I. Fromme.** 1974. Lipopolysaccharide containing L-acofriose in the filamentous blue-green alga *Anabaena variabilis*. J. Bacteriol. **120**:672–678.

31. **Westphal, O., and O. Lüderitz.** 1954. Chemische Erforschung von Lipopolysacchariden gram-negativer Bakterien. Angew. Chem. **66**:407–417.

32. **Wilkinson, S. G., L. Galbraith, and G. A. Lightfoot.** 1973. Cell wall, lipids and lipopolysaccharides of *Pseudomonas species*. Eur. J. Biochem. **33**:158–174.

33. **Wober, W., and P. Alaupović.** 1971. Studies on the protein moiety of endotoxin from gram-negative bacteria. Eur. J. Biochem. **19**:357–367.

34. **Wu, M.-C., and E. C. Heath.** 1973. Isolation and characterization of lipopolysaccharide proteins from *Escherichia coli*. Proc. Natl. Acad. Sci. U.S.A. **70**:2572–2576.

Biological Activities and Immunological Properties
of Lipid A

CHRIS GALANOS, MARINA FREUDENBERG, SUMIHIRO HASE,
FRANCES JAY, AND ELLEN RUSCHMANN

Max-Planck-Institut für Immunbiologie, Freiburg i. Br., West Germany

The presence of biologically active components in gram-negative bacteria was recognized nearly 100 years ago. Later, it was found that these were firmly bound constituents of the cell wall, and because of their toxicity they were named endotoxins. Since then, many workers of different scientific disciplines have invested much effort in isolating endotoxins, characterizing them, and studying their biological activities.

Early attempts at isolation led to preparations of crude mixtures containing proteins, phospholipids, and lipopolysaccharide; consequently, the precise identity of the biologically active component remained the subject of considerable speculation for many years. The role of the lipopolysaccharide in the biological activity of such preparations became apparent when these could be finally obtained in pure form. With the improvement of isolation procedures, lipopolysaccharides free from proteins and other cell wall components were prepared, and their investigation in different biological tests provided evidence for the endotoxic activity of these macromolecules (12, 24). Lipopolysaccharides are heteropolymers containing polysaccharide bound covalently to lipid, a phospholipid in nature that was termed lipid A (14). The question then arose concerning the biologically active part of this complex heteropolymer.

Already many years ago, it was postulated by Westphal and Lüderitz that lipid A represents the biologically active part of the lipopolysaccharides (26). Support for this hypothesis was provided with the isolation of the R mutants which synthesize lipopolysaccharides lacking the O-specific polysaccharide and parts of the core polysaccharide (15). These incomplete lipopolysaccharides containing predominantly lipid A exhibited all biological activities that were expressed by intact lipopolysaccharides (14, 24). Thus, it could be shown that the O polysaccharide and parts of the core were not important for the expression of the endotoxic activity of lipopolysaccharides.

Direct evidence for the biological activity of lipid A was obtained when soluble lipid A was prepared by complexing with bovine serum albumin (BSA; 8). This provided a reasonably stable form of soluble lipid A that could be prepared in large amounts, and its activity was tested in many biological tests (4, 9, 14). Such soluble forms of lipid A proved highly active in many different endotoxic assays. Table 1 summarizes the results of biological tests with lipid A-BSA complexes obtained in different laboratories.

A new form of soluble lipid A has been prepared recently which does not make use of solubilizing carriers (5). This is obtained from lipopolysaccharides deionized by electrodialysis whereby the unpredictable mixture of metal cations and extensive reduction in polyamines and basic amines always present in lipopolysaccharides is removed and the lipopolysaccharide is converted to the free acid form (Lüderitz, p. 000, this volume). When lipid A is prepared by acid hydrolysis or autohydrolysis from such free acid preparations and subsequently neutralized with triethylamine or sodium hydroxide, soluble forms of lipid A are obtained. The solubility of the lipid A seems to be due to the absence of divalent cations which are removed from the parent lipopolysaccharide during electrodialysis. The biological activity of one such lipid A preparation derived from a *Salmonella minnesota* R345 (Rb) mutant has been compared with that of *Salmonella abortus-equi* S form and *S. minnesota* R595 Re lipopolysaccharides. Table 2 summarizes the results of lethal toxicity, local Shwartzman reaction, complement inactivation, and mitogenicity for B lymphocytes. It can be seen that the activity of the free lipid A is comparable to that of intact lipopolysaccharides.

TABLE 1. *Biological activities of free lipid A*

Activity	Reference
Pyrogenicity	See 4
Lethal toxicity in mice	See 4
Leucopenia	See 4
Leucocytosis	See 4
Local Shwartzman reaction	—[a]
Bone marrow necrosis	See 4
Abortive activity in mice	—[b]
Embryonic bone resorption	See 4
Complement activation	See 4
Depression of blood pressure	See 4
Limulus lysate gelation	See 4
Toxicity enhanced by adrenalectomy	See 4
Toxicity enhanced by BCG	See 4
Induction of nonspecific resistance to infection	See 4
Induction of tolerance to endotoxin	21
Induction of early refractory state to endotoxin pyrogenicity	22
Adjuvant activity	See 4
Mitogenic activity for cells	See 4
Tumor necrotic activity	—[a]
Macrophage activation	See 4
Induction of colony-stimulating factor	2
Induction of immunoglobulin G synthesis in newborn mice	See 4
Induction of prostaglandin synthesis	See 4
Induction of interferon production	See 4
Induction of tumor-necrotizing factor	—[a]

[a] Unpublished data.
[b] F. Rioux-Darrieulat et al., in preparation.

BIOLOGICAL ACTIVITIES OF LIPOPOLYSACCHARIDES IN DEFINED SALT FORMS

Resolution of Endotoxic Activities

The endotoxic activities of lipopolysaccharides injected into experimental animals are manyfold and complex. In the past, it has not been possible to modify lipopolysaccharides so that individual activities could be selectively suppressed or preserved.

Recently, Galanos and Lüderitz were able to abolish selectively in vitro anticomplementary activity by converting lipopolysaccharides to a form exhibiting low molecular weight (low aggregation; 6). Other endotoxic activities are thereby preserved. This was achieved by electrodialyzing lipopolysaccharides and neutralizing the free acid form obtained with different bases (5). Uniform salt forms of the lipopolysaccharides are thus obtained which exhibit characteristic differences in their molecular weight measured by sedimentation coefficient determination. Two such salt forms representative of low and high molecular weight are the triethylamine and sodium salts, respectively.

The biological activities of *S. abortus-equi* and *S. minnesota* R595 in the above two forms are shown in Table 3. It can be seen that the two salt forms of both lipopolysaccharides are highly toxic for rats and adrenalectomized mice and are pyrogenic for rabbits. In complete contrast, anticomplementary activity is expressed only by the sodium form, the triethylamine form being almost completely inactive.

In a recent communication, the R595 lipopolysaccharide was reported to retain its anticomplementary activity in the triethylamine form (15). Since that time, it was found that this was due to incomplete deionization during electrodialysis. The thoroughness of electrodialysis is more critical in the case of R-form lipopolysaccharides, as residual traces of divalent cations lower the threshold of reaggregation, leading to an active form.

The effects of the sodium and triethylamine forms of *S. abortus-equi*, *S. minnesota* R595, and of free lipid A in the sodium form have also been compared in vivo (M. Freudenberg and C. Galanos, in preparation). Figure 1 shows the pattern of complement inactiva-

TABLE 2. *Biological activities of free soluble lipid A*

	Lethality in:			Local Shwartzman phenomenon, positive reaction with (μg):	Complement inactivation with 30 μg (%)	B-lymphocyte mitogenicity (stimulation index with 10 μg
Prepn	Rats (mg)	BCG-treated mice (μg)	Adrenalecto-mized mice (μg)			
Lipid A	3.24[a]	0.45[b]	0.004[a]	20[a,b]	85[a]	17[a]
S. abortus-equi	5.75	0.42	0.002	20[c]	65	14
S. minnesota R595 (Re)	5.35	0.50	0.021	ND[d]	90	12

[a] Lipid A tested as sodium salt.
[b] Lipid A tested as triethylamine salt.
[c] Lower concentrations not tested.
[d] Not determined.

TABLE 3. *Biological activities of lipopolysaccharides in uniform salt forms*

Prepn	Sedimentation coefficient ($S = 10^{-13}$s)	Complement inactivation with 30 μg (%)	Lethality (LD_{50}) in adrenalecto- mized mice (μg)	Lethality (LD_{50}) in rats (mg)	Pyrogenicity (MPD-3)[a] in rabbits (μg/kg)
S. abortus-equi triethylamine	10	0	0.002	6.24	0.00075
S. abortus-equi sodium	105	98	0.004	5.25	0.0019
S. minnesota R595 triethylamine ..	9.5	12	0.0017	6.42	0.0002
S. minnesota R595 sodium	104	100	0.010	4.28	0.006

[a] Minimal pyrogenic dose.

tion in rats over a period of 48 h following injection of 6 mg of each preparation.

The two lipopolysaccharides show an almost identical pattern of anticomplementary activity in their corresponding salt forms. Distinct difference, however, exist between the two forms. The Na^+ form of both lipopolysaccharides shows a biphasic fall in complement hemolytic activity shortly after injection (10 min) and 6 to 9 h later. Thereafter, a slow increase takes place, and in surviving animals complement titers are back to pre-injection levels about 48 h after injection.

The sodium form of lipid A behaves in a similar way; injection of 6 mg leads to a dramatic decrease in hemolytic activity measured 10 min and 6 h later. All animals receiving the above concentration died within 7 h, and changes in complement hemolytic activity after 6 h could not be followed.

A distinctly different pattern of complement inactivation is shown by the triethylamine form of both preparations. Here, the biphasic fall in hemolytic activity is absent, and only a low gradual fall is seen, with lowest titers recorded also in this case at 6 to 9 h after injection. The hemolytic activity then starts to rise and with both lipopolysaccharides preinjection titers in surviving animals are reached after 24 h.

Lower concentrations (600 and 60 μg; not shown in Fig. 1) of both the sodium and triethylamine forms of the *S. abortus-equi* and the *S. minnesota* R595 lipopolysaccharides induced only the 6-h drop in hemolytic activity.

The first drop in hemolytic activity induced by the sodium form probably corresponds to the loss of hemolytic activity observed in vitro. This is supported by the fact that both are absent from the triethylamine form preparations. Also, the kinetics of the in vitro interaction of the sodium form of *S. abortus-equi* with complement show that loss of hemolytic activity at 37°C takes place after 10 min, which coincides with the first in vivo fall in complement titers.

Regarding the 6-h fall in hemolytic activity obtained with both lipopolysaccharides, it is not clear whether the lipopolysaccharide itself is directly involved or whether the fall is due to more indirect mechanisms generated in the course of manifestation of endotoxicity.

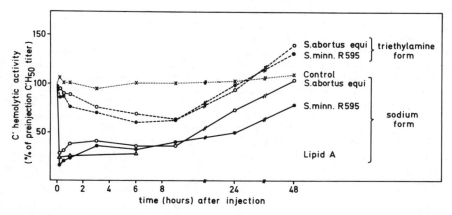

FIG. 1. *In vivo anticomplementary activity with 6 mg of lipopolysaccharide and of lipid A in the triethylamine and sodium forms.*

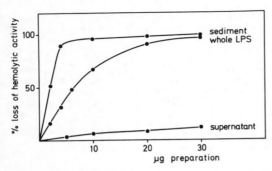

FIG. 2. *Anticomplementary activity of* Salmonella abortus-equi *lipopolysaccharide before and after fractionation. The three preparations were tested in the sodium form.*

It is not known what role the early complement consumption plays in lethal toxicity. However, the lethality of the sodium form preparations was in all cases reproducibly higher than that of the corresponding triethylamine preparations. Thus, the early complement activation may represent an additional but not essential toxicity factor.

Distribution of Anticomplementary Activity in Fractionated Lipopolysaccharides

Although the property that allows lipopolysaccharides to interact with complement is embedded in the lipid A, many lipopolysaccharides express low or no anticomplementary activity (6, 8, 11). This is an intrinsic property of some lipopolysaccharides and is not related to a low molecular weight. It was found recently to be due to the presence of two species of lipopolysaccharide that are distinct in their anticomplementary activity: an active and an inactive one (unpublished data). Their separation was achieved by centrifugation after electrodialysis, whereby ionic cross-linkages are disrupted through removal of divalent cations.

In the present example, the *S. abortus-equi* smooth form lipopolysaccharide was converted to the free acid form by electrodialysis. Centrifugation of the material in distilled water at $12,000 \times g$ resulted in a sediment (approximately 25%) and a clear supernatant fluid. Both fractions were neutralized with NaOH and tested for anticomplementary activity. As can be seen in Fig. 2, the anticomplementary activity was absent from the fraction of lipopolysaccharide remaining in the supernatant fluid and was present exclusively in the sediment.

The presence of an active and inactive fraction has also been demonstrated in the case of the *S. minnesota* R595 lipopolysaccharide. Studies on other biological activities and on the chemical structure of the above preparations are in progress.

General Conclusions

The endotoxic activities expressed by lipopolysaccharides are embedded in the lipid A part of the molecule. Lipid A made soluble by complexing with BSA or by conversion into the triethylamine or sodium form exhibits all biological activities expressed by intact lipopolysaccharides.

Anticomplementary activity may be selectively abolished from lipopolysaccharides. Thus, the in vitro anticomplementary activity and the early in vivo decomplementation induced by lipopolysaccharides could be completely abolished by conversion into uniform salt forms of low molecular weight, without altering the chemical structure of the lipopolysaccharide. Other endotoxic activities remained intact. As far as we know, this was the first time that one biological activity was selectively dissociated from the intact lipopolysaccharide molecule.

In a given lipopolysaccharide preparation, two fractions may be present that are distinct in their ability to interact with complement. The relative proportion of the active and nonactive fractions in the mixture determines whether the activity of the entire preparation is high, medium, or low.

IMMUNOGENIC PROPERTIES OF LIPID A

In the past, the immunogenicity of lipopolysaccharides was associated exclusively with the O-specific chains and the core polysaccharide (16, 17). Recently, we were able to show that lipid A also exhibits immunogenic properties eliciting the production of specific anti-lipid A antibodies (7).

Lipid A becomes immunogenic when exposed in the bacterial cell (7). This is achieved by mild acid treatment of whole cells, whereby the linkage of ketodeoxyoctonate (KDO) to the glucosamine backbone of lipid A is cleaved. The polysaccharide is thus released into the supernatant fluid and is removed by washing while the lipid A is retained on the cell surface. The injection of such acid-treated cells into animals leads to the production of antibodies that may be measured by the passive hemolysis of lipid A-coated erythrocytes.

Under certain conditions other classical methods such as hemagglutination, immune precipitation, and the Ouchterlony gel diffusion method may be used. Here, however, the choice of buffers employed becomes critical because of the precipitating properties of lipid A. Also, nonspecific phenomena due to the property of lipid A to aggregate with proteins may prove hazardous, especially when dealing with sera of low titer. Recently, the enzyme-linked immunosorbent assay (ELISA; 3) has been successfully used for the detection and quantitation of anti-lipid A antibodies (F. Jay and C. Galanos, unpublished data; L. Hanson, personal communication).

Immune Responses of Different Animal Species to Lipid A

After a single immunization, rabbits (7, 13), goats (7), dogs (25), rats, vervets, and baboons (Helm et al., in preparation) respond promptly to acid-treated bacteria, with the formation of anti-lipid A antibodies.

In contrast, mice (6 to 8 weeks old) show no detectable anti-lipid A antibodies after a single immunization, but do so after a second injection carried out preferably 4 to 6 weeks later. High anti-lipid A hemolytic titers may then be obtained; however, their persistence is often short-termed and may disappear within 2 weeks. In many cases the hemolytic activity of the antibodies is completely lost after heating the serum at 56°C for 30 min. All mice strains tested (NMRI, CBAH, C3Hf/Tif, and the endotoxin-resistant strain C3H/HeJ; 20, 23) showed very similar responses to lipid A immunization. Thus, the response of mice to lipid A as an antigen seems to be independent of their sensitivity to the lethal effects of endotoxin and of their responses to lipid A as a mitogen (1).

The absence of anti-lipid A response after a single immunization seems to suggest that mice, in contrast to the animals mentioned above, are not sensitized to the antigen lipid A. This is supported by the finding that rabbits, goats, rats, etc., may in principle contain in their serum naturally occurring anti-lipid A antibodies, whereas these are completely absent from normal mouse serum. This is interesting because antibodies of different O specificity are abundantly present in normal mouse serum.

Cross-Reactions of Lipid A Among Gram-Negative Bacteria

When anti-lipid A antibodies were first prepared (7), it was shown that cross-reactions existed among the lipid A components of different Salmonella and E. coli strains. These studies have since been extended to lipid A preparations from other gram-negative microorganisms.

It can be seen from Table 4 that cross-reactions in the lipid A component are widely present among gram-negative bacteria. It is striking that they also exist between enteric bacteria and certain strains (Rhodopseudomonas gelatinosa and Rhodospirillium tenue; 9a) of photosynthetic bacteria which from the point of evolution are very remote from Enterobacteriaceae.

The above cross-reactions are due to similarities in the chemical structure of the lipid A, which have been confirmed for a large number of the strains listed in Table 4 (Rietschel et al., p. 000, this volume).

Non-cross-reacting lipid A preparations have also been identified. Thus, Rhodopseudomonas viridis and Rhodopseudomonas palustris show no serological cross-reactions in their lipid A with enteric bacteria (9a). This is in agreement with the results of chemical analysis which have revealed that the chemical compositions of the two lipid A preparations are distinctly different from that of Salmonella lipid A (J. Roppel, thesis, University of Freiburg, Freiburg i. Br., West Germany).

The use of the lipid A serological assay in cross-reaction tests is a useful preliminary tool for establishing differences or similarities in the basic structure of lipid A of different gram-negative bacteria. The antigenic deter-

TABLE 4. Serological cross-reactions of the lipid A among gram-negative bacteria[a]

Organism	Cross-reaction[b]
Salmonella (all strains tested)	+
Escherichia coli (all strains tested)	+
Shigella flexneri	+
Proteus mirabilis	+
Proteus vulgaris	+
Agrobacterium tumefaciens	+
Yersinia enterocolitica	+
Pseudomonas fluorescens	+
Xanthomonas sinensis	+
Vibrio cholerae	+
Rhodopseudomonas gelatinosa	+
Rhodopseudomonas viridis	−
Rhodopseudomonas palustris	−
Rhodospirillum tenue	+
Chromobacterium violaceum	+
Neisseria gonorrhoeae	+
Rickettsia canada	+
Rickettsia prowazekii	+
Coxiella burnetii (phase I)	+

[a] Tested with Salmonella anti-lipid A antiserum.

[b] Symbols: +, cross-reaction present; −, no cross-reaction.

minants of lipid A are currently under investigation. The cleavage of the ester-bound fatty acid components or the removal of phosphate from free lipid A does not seem to alter its serological reactivity. So far, the minimal lipid A substructure exhibiting haptenic activity (inhibition of passive hemolysis) has been found to contain glucosamine carrying at least one amide-bound 3-hydroxymyristic acid. Thus, the antigenic specificity of lipid A seems to be embedded in the part of the molecule that represents a basic structure for the lipid A of most gram-negative bacteria.

We are aware of the inhomogeneity of free lipid A (19). However, since the above structure is part of the intact lipid A and is preserved in the large majority of fractions obtained by fractionation of free lipid A (F. Jay and C. Galanos, unpublished data), inhomogenicity as such becomes meaningless for the purpose of serological studies.

Recently, incomplete lipid A from temperature-sensitive lipid A mutants has been isolated which contains a diphosphorylated glucosamine disaccharide substituted by two amide and two ester-bound 3-D-hydroxymyristoyl residues (V. Lehmann, in preparation). This naturally occurring incomplete form of lipid A and the antiserum prepared against it cross-react completely with free lipid A and anti-lipid A antibodies.

Protective Properties of Anti-Lipid A Antisera Against Infection

Several workers involved in studies of the protective properties of anti-lipid A antisera came to the unanimous conclusion that anti-lipid A antibodies confer no protection in mice challenged with gram-negative pathogens (10, 18; W. R. McCabe et al., this volume, p. 293).

Recent studies in our laboratory of mice immunized with lipid A as described above showed a reproducible 50 to 60% protection against *S. typhimurium* (Fig. 3). This protection could be increased to nearly 100% by supplementing the treatment with rabbit complement preabsorbed with *S. typhimurium*. Also, in normal mice injection of fresh rabbit serum increased their threshold resistance to infection.

The use of rabbit complement in the above experiments was prompted by an observation made in our laboratory that addition of nonlytic amounts of fresh rabbit serum to mouse serum leads to an active hemolytic system (M. Freudenberg and C. Galanos, unpublished data). This is also true in vivo when rabbit serum is injected into mice.

Therefore, the higher protection seen in mice receiving fresh rabbit serum may be due to the generation of an active complement hemolytic system otherwise absent from normal mouse serum. Although further studies will be necessary, it is nevertheless interesting since the above findings suggest that humoral mechanisms may play a protective role in *Salmonella* infections.

BIOLOGICAL SIGNIFICANCE OF ANTI-LIPID A ANTIBODIES

Since the identification and preparation of anti-lipid A antibodies was first described, many groups have studied the immunochemical, biological, and clinical aspects of lipid A immunity.

Unlike anti-O and anti-R antibodies, anti-lipid A antibodies are directed against the toxic principle in the lipopolysaccharide molecule. Their biological activities can therefore be expected to be of two types, protective and harmful. Studies so far seem to suggest that both types of activity may be possible. Thus, in

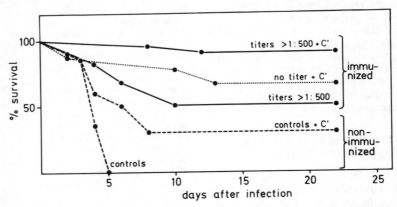

FIG. 3. *Protection against* Salmonella typhimurium *in mice immunized with lipid A and supplemented with rabbit complement.*

adrenalectomized mice anti-lipid A antisera showed both protection against and enhancement of the lethal toxicity of lipid A and of intact lipopolysaccharide. In rabbits no protective effects could be demonstrated. Rabbit anti-lipid A antisera either were ineffective or enhanced the lethal toxicity of free lipid A and lipopolysaccharide.

Similarly, a dual role of anti-lipid A antibodies is suggested in recent studies designed to investigate the effect of free lipid A on the kidneys of dogs. Lipid A was found to induce interstitial nephritis (25), and its development could be both enhanced and partially suppressed by preimmunization of the animals with lipid A (Westenfelder et al., p. 277, this volume) under two different schemes.

Recently, Rietschel demonstrated a protective effect of anti-lipid A antisera against the pyrogenic effects of lipid A and intact lipopolysaccharides (20a, 22). This protection requires pretreatment of the animals with lipid A or lipopolysaccharide. Rabbits treated with a pyrogenic dose of lipid A on day 0 and administered anti-lipid A antiserum on day 1 become immune to the pyrogenic effects of a dose 100 times the minimal pyrogenic dose of endotoxin administered on day 2. This phenomenon is highly specific for lipid A; in the case of intact lipopolysaccharides, pyrogenic tolerance is obtained only if the preparations used for the preparative and challenging injections are cross-reacting in their intact lipid A component (20a).

The finding that lipid A exhibits immunogenic properties provides evidence that immune-mediated mechanisms associated with the lipid A component of endotoxins may be involved in both endotoxic activities and endotoxin tolerance. The presence of anti-lipid A antibodies in normal animals and humans and their increased concentrations in the sera of patients with urinary tract infections emphasize the biological significance of these antibodies. Further, the high reactivity of naturally occurring anti-lipid A antibodies with free lipid A underlines the biological importance of free lipid A as an antigen.

Because of the wide cross-reactions of lipid A among endotoxins, the lipid A serological assay may prove useful as a diagnostic test for the presence of lipid A, and thereby endotoxin, in serum. In current investigations it was shown that free lipid A is detectable in the serum of rats in concentrations of sub-microgram amounts per milliliter.

LITERATURE CITED

1. Andersson, J., F. Melchers, C. Galanos, and O. Lüderitz. 1973. The mitogenic effect of lipopolysaccharide on bone-marrow derived lymphocytes. Lipid A as the mitogenic part of the molecule. J. Exp. Med. 137: 943–953.

2. Apte, R. N., C. Galanos, and D. V. Pluznik. 1975. Lipid A, the active part of bacterial endotoxins in inducing serum colony stimulating activity and macrophage progenitor cells. J. Cell. Physiol. 87:71–78.

3. Engvall, E., and P. Perlmann. 1972. Enzyme-linked immunosorbent assay, ELISA. III. Quantitation of specific antibodies by enzyme-labelled anti-immunoglobulin in antigen coated tubes. J. Immunol. 109:129.

4. Galanos, C. 1975. Physical state and biological activity of lipopolysaccharides. Toxicity and immunogenicity of the lipid A component. Z. Immunitaetsforsch. 149: 214–229.

5. Galanos, C., and O. Lüderitz. 1975. Electrodialysis of lipopolysaccharides and their conversion to uniform salt forms. Eur. J. biochem. 54:603–610.

6. Galanos, C., and O. Lüderitz. 1976. The role of the physical state of lipopolysaccharides in the interaction with complement. High molecular weight as prerequisite for the expression of anti-complementary activity. Eur. J. Biochem. 65:403–408.

7. Galanos, C., O. Lüderitz, and O. Westphal. 1971. Preparation and properties of antisera against the lipid A component of bacterial lipopolysaccharides. Eur. J. Biochem. 24:116–122.

8. Galanos, C., E. T. Rietschel, O. Lüderitz, and O. Westphal. 1971. Interaction of lipopolysaccharides and lipid A with complement. Eur. J. Biochem. 19:143–152.

9. Galanos, C., E. T. Rietschel, O. Lüderitz, O. Westphal, Y. Kim, and D. W. Watson. 1972. Biological activities of lipid A complexed with bovine serum albumin. Eur. J. Biochem. 31:230–233.

9a. Galanos, C., J. Roppel, J. Weckesser, E. Th. Rietschel, and H. Mayer. 1977. Biological activities of lipopolysaccharides and lipid A from Rhodospirillaceae. Infect. Immun. 16:407–412.

10. Hodgin, L., and J. Drews. 1975. Effect of active and passive immunization with lipid A and Salmonella minnesota Re 595 on gram-negative infections in mice. Infection 34/5.

11. Janossy, G., J. H. Humphrey, M. B. Perys, and M. F. Greaves. 1973. Complement independence of stimulation of mouse splenic B lymphocytes by mitogens. Nature (London) New Biol. 245:108–112.

12. Kadis, S., G. Weinbaum, and S. J. Ajl. 1971. Microbial toxins, vol. 5. Academic Press Inc., New York.

13. Lücowski, C., and E. Romanowska. 1974. Biological properties of lipid A from Shigella sonnei. Eur. J. Biochem. 48:81–87.

14. Lüderitz, O., C. Galanos, V. Lehmann, M. Nurminen, E. T. Rietschel, G. Rosenfelder, M. Simon, and O. Westphal. 1973. Lipid A: chemical structure and biological activity. J. Infect. Dis. 128(Suppl.):9–21.

15. Lüderitz, O., C. Galanos, H. J. Risse, E. Ruschmann, S. Schlecht, G. Schmidt, H. Schulte-Holthausen, R. Wheat, O. Westphal, and J. Schlosshardt. 1966. Structural relationships of Salmonella O and R antigens. Ann. N.Y. Acad. Sci. 133:349–374.

16. Lüderitz, O., K. Jann, and R. Wheat. 1968. Somatic and capsular antigens of gram-negative bacteria. Comp. Biochem. 26A:105–228.

17. Lüderitz, O., A. M. Staub, and O. Westphal. 1966. Immunochemistry of O and R antigens of Salmonella and related Enterobacteriaceae. Bacteriol. Rev. 30: 192–255.

18. Mullan, N. A., P. A. Newsome, P. G. Cunnington, G. H. Palmer, and M. E. Wilson. 1974. Protection against gram-negative infections with antiserum to lipid A from Salmonella minnesota Re 595. Infect. Immun. 10: 1195–1201.

19. Ng, Ah-Kau, R. C. Butler, C.-L. H. Chen, and A. Nowotny. 1976. Relationship of structure to function in bacterial endotoxins. IX. Differences in the lipid

moiety of endotoxic glycolipids. J. Bacteriol. **126:** 511–515.

20. **Rank, W. R., U. Flügge, and R. DiPauli.** 1969. Inheritance of the lipid A-induced 19S plaque-forming cell response in mice: evidence for three antigen recognition mechanisms. Behringwerk-Mitt. **49**(Suppl.):222.

20a. **Rietschel, E. Th., and C. Galanos.** 1977. Lipid A antiserum-mediated protection against lipopolysaccharide- and lipid A-induced fever and skin necrosis. Infect. Immun. **15:**34–58.

21. **Rietschel, E. T., Y. B. Kim, D. W. Watson, C. Galanos, O. Lüderitz, and O. Westphal.** 1973. Pyrogenicity and immunogenicity of lipid A complexed with bovine serum albumin or human serum albumin. Infect. Immun. **8:**173–177.

22. **Rietschel, E. T., and O. Lüderitz.** 1975. Chemical structure of lipopolysaccharides and endotoxin immunity. Z. Immunitaetsforsch. **149:**201–213.

23. **Sultzer, B. M.** 1972. Genetic control of host responses to endotoxin. Infect. Immun. **5:**107–113.

24. **Weinbaum, G., S. Kadis, and S. J. Ajl.** 1971. Microbial toxins, vol. 4. Academic Press Inc., New York.

25. **Westenfelder, M., C. Galanos, and P. O. Madsen.** 1975. Experimental lipid A-induced nephritis in the dog. Invest. Urol. **5:**337–345.

26. **Westphal, O., and O. Lüderitz.** 1954. Chemische Erforschung von Lipopolysacchariden gramnegativer Bakterien. Angew. Chem. **66:**407–417.

Pathological Activities of Lipid A: Experimental Studies in Relation to Chronic Pyelonephritis

MARTIN WESTENFELDER, CHRIS GALANOS, PAUL O. MADSEN,
AND WALTER MARGET

*Abteilung für Urologie, Klinikum der Universität Freiburg, Max-Planck-Institut für Immunbiologie,
Freiburg, West Germany; Urology Section, Veterans Administration Hospital,
University of Wisconsin School of Medicine, Madison, Wisconsin 53705;
and Universitätskinderklinik, Munich, West Germany*

Lipid A, the endotoxic principle of the lipopolysaccharides of gram-negative bacteria, exhibits a variety of biological activities as outlined in the preceding paper, when used in a water-soluble form (3). Shwartzman reaction, pyrogenicity, and an influence on the cardiovascular, respiratory, and blood-clotting systems cause the clinical symptoms related to gram-negative septicemia and septic shock that may often lead to death.

Lipid A effects which appear during and after urinary tract infection seem to be related to the development of the inflammatory response and the development of chronic pyelonephritis (5).

We investigated the effect of lipid A in a dog model in which the lipid A was injected into the renal pelvis, which was temporarily ligated for 4 h (Fig. 1). Radioactive lipid A was isolated from *Escherichia coli* EH100 Re mutant, grown on tritiated glucose. The lipid was made soluble by complexing with dog serum albumin in a 1:1 ratio (7). Concentrations of 12 to 230 μg/kg were injected into 24 animals which were followed for a period of 10 weeks. Before lipid A injection and at 2, 4, 6, and 10 weeks thereafter, kidney tissue was obtained by needle biopsies and autopsy. At the same time, urine and tissue were tested bacteriologically, and the occurrence of anti-lipid A antibodies was measured in the serum by the passive hemolysis test (2).

Kidney specimens were investigated for histological alterations and for the presence of lipid A by autoradiography.

It was found that, whereas four control animals which received normal saline did not show any pathological findings, all dogs treated with lipid A developed histological alterations best described as abacterial focal interstitial nephritis. An increase in the number of interstitial cells, wedge-shaped leukocyte infiltrates, and degenerative and atrophic altera-

tions could be distinguished, and 6 weeks after lipid A injection fibrosis occurred. Whereas before lipid A treatment no anti-lipid A antibodies could be detected, 22 of 24 dogs developed significant titers after injection, which persisted in four animals up to the 10th week. Lipid A radioactivity could be detected in 21 of 24 animals and persisted in 16 of 20 dogs up to the 10th week.

Higher concentrations of lipid A had no effect on the intensity of the histological alterations. Thus, in 10 dogs which received lipid A in concentrations of 200 to 600 μg/kg, the intensity of the reaction was comparable to that obtained with the lower concentrations. It should be mentioned, however, that with the higher concentrations the development of the response was accelerated.

In addition to adult dogs, 34 puppies in their first week of life received lipid A in their renal pelvis by use of the same technique as above. Following this treatment, 16 puppies died within 10 days and 4 more developed infected hydronephrosis. The remaining 14 puppies were followed over 1 to 6 weeks. In these animals, in contrast to adult dogs, no lipid A radioactivity or histological alterations were detectable in the kidney. Further anti-lipid A antibodies were absent from the sera during the time of observation.

To investigate whether kidney ischemia might occur during the 4-h ligation time and cause the pathological alterations, renal blood flow and blood pressure were measured with a pulsed logic blood flow meter and Statham pressure transducers in eight dogs after ureteral occlusion and lipid A injection. It was found (7) that ureteral occlusion and lipid A injection into the renal pelvis was followed by a temporary increase in the renal blood flow. In comparison, lipid A injection into the renal artery had a similar effect but without an ef-

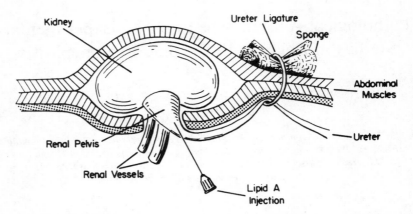

FIG. 1. *Illustrations of interposition of the kidney between the abdominal muscles and the technique of the ureter ligation by a sling through the abdominal wall.*

fect on the blood pressure, whereas the intravenous lipid A injection either had no effect or decreased the renal blood flow. The increase in the renal blood flow after injection into

the renal artery was independent of the blood pressure and the ureteral occlusion. A temporary ischemia as a cause of the histological alterations therefore could be excluded.

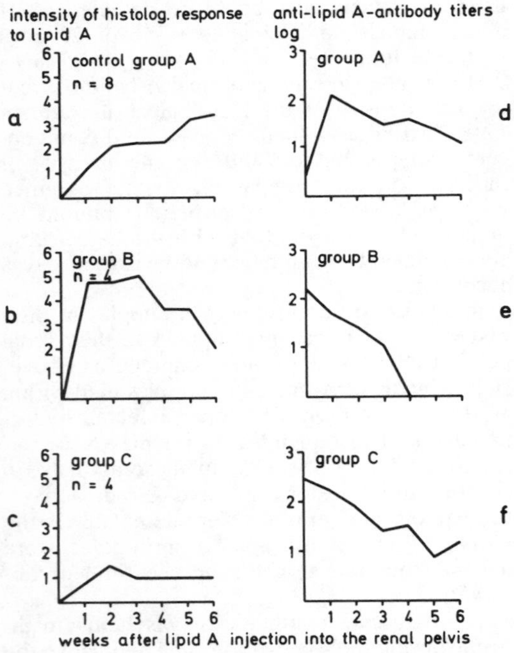

It was assumed that lipid A induced nephritis by a pathological immune process. The role of the anti-lipid A immune response in the induction of the above nephritis was investigated in two groups of dogs (groups B and C, Fig. 2) which were immunized with lipid A immunogen (1) before the induction of lipid A nephritis (5; M. Westenfelder and C. Galanos, unpublished data). Their histological and serological response was compared with that of a group of eight nonimmunized dogs (group A). Group B received intravenously a single injection of 50 μg of lipid A immunogen 6 days before lipid A injection. Group C received four intravenous injections of 50, 100, 200, and 400 μg of lipid A immunogen at days 21, 16, 11, and 6 before lipid A treatment. The histological and serological response of the three animal groups was evaluated over 6 weeks as described. Characteristic and distinguished histological alterations were marked with a number, and mean values for the animal groups per week were calculated and expressed graphically (Fig. 2a–c). This was also done with the geometric mean values of the anti-lipid A serum titers which were expressed as the logarithm (Fig. 2d–f).

As can be seen in Fig. 2, the severity of the histological alterations of the control group (Fig. 2a) increased up to the 6th week and was paralleled by the development of anti-lipid A antibodies (Fig. 2d). Group B (immunized once) revealed an accelerated and stronger histological response which decreased after 3 weeks (Fig. 2b). In contrast, the response in group C (immunized four times) was mild but persistent (Fig. 2c). No further increase (booster effect) of the anti-lipid A titers was observed in groups B and C after the lipid A injection

FIG. 2. *Histological and serological response 1 to 6 weeks after injection of lipid A into the temporarily occluded renal pelvis of three groups of dogs. Group A: Eight control dogs (nonimmunized). Group B: Four dogs which received one injection of lipid A immunogen 6 days before lipid A injection. Group C: Four dogs immunized four times before lipid A injection. (a–c) Intensity of histological response expressed in numbers: 0 = no response; 1 = increase in the number of interstitial cells; 2 = leukocyte infiltrates; 3 = degenerative and/or atrophic alterations; 4, 5, and 6 occur through combinations of 1, 2, and 3. (d–f) Logarithm of anti-lipid A antibody titers. All results are mean values.*

TABLE 1. *Occurrence of anti-lipid A antibody titers in 535 patients*

Age group	Infection[a]	Total no.	No. with positive titers[b]	Percent
Newborns	—	23	0	0
Children	—	50	5	10
Adults	—	70	9	13
Children	Wound	50	20	40
Adults	UTI	262	129	50
Adults	Acute UTI	188	71	38
Adult women ...	Recurrent UTI	74	58	75
Children	CPN	80	60	75

[a] UTI = urinary tract infection; CPN = chronic pyelonephritis.

[b] Titers in uninfected control patients were not higher than 1:16; those in patients with CPN ranged up to 1:512.

TABLE 2. *Occurrence of chronic pyelonephritis (CPN) and proteinuria in adult patients with urinary tract infections who had positive anti-lipid A titers or no anti-lipid A titers*[a]

Anti-lipid A titers	No. of patients	No. with:	
		CPN	Proteinuria
Positive	68	31 (46%)	40 (60%)
None	72	17 (24%)	6 (8%)

[a] Significance: $t = 7.496$, $P < 0.01$.

(Fig. 2e and f). Here, however, a rapid fall of the titers was observed, possibly indicating a process of antibody consumption, following the injection of the antigen (lipid A).

We concluded from these experiments that lipid A can be absorbed from the renal pelvis into the renal tissue, where it becomes attached to tissue structures. The development of lipid A antibodies leads to an immune reaction at the side of lipid A fixation. Through activation of cellular and humoral (complement) defense mechanisms, inflammation and cell damage are induced, leading to abacterial nephritis. This pathological immune process may be stimulated by the persistence of lipid A, even in the absence of infecting bacteria.

Since in urinary tract infections with gram-negative bacteria, endotoxin, and thereby lipid A, is released, a comparable lipid A mechanism may arise. In this case, anti-lipid A antibodies should be detectable in patients with urinary tract infections. We therefore investigated the presence of anti-lipid A antibodies in 535 patients (Table 1; 6). Whereas no titers were found in 23 newborn babies, in about 10% of the healthy population titers up to 1:16 did occur. Low titers were also found in about 40% of children with wound infections. In a group of 262 adult patients with a history of urinary tract infection, 50% revealed significant titers. In acute urinary tract infections, the percentage of positive titers was 38%, whereas the percentage in children with chronic pyelonephritis and in women with recurrent urinary tract infections was 75%. Of these women with positive titers, 93% were infected. As shown in Table 2, patients who are infected and reveal positive titers are significantly more likely to show evidence of chronic pyelonephritis (46%) and proteinuria (60%) compared with patients who are infected but without anti-lipid A titers (24% and 8%, respectively, $P < 0.01$).

In summary, there is experimental evidence for a mechanism by which lipid A may cause damage to the kidney, most probably by the induction of a pathological immune process. In patients there is good correlation between urinary tract infection and the development of anti-lipid A antibodies, especially in those with chronic pyelonephritis and proteinuria. This suggests that a lipid A-dependent immune mechanism may be playing a role in the development of chronic pyelonephritis.

LITERATURE CITED

1. Galanos, C., O. Luderitz, and O. Westphal. 1971. Preparation and properties of antisera against the lipid A-component of bacterial lipopolysaccharides. Eur. J. Biochem. 24:116–122.
2. Galanos, C., E. T. Rietschel, O. Lüderitz, and O. Westphal. 1971. Interaction of lipopolysaccharides and lipid A with complement. Eur. J. Biochem. 19:143–152.
3. Galanos, C., E. T. Rietschel, O. Lüderitz, O. Westphal, Y. B. Kim, and D. W. Watson. 1972. Biological activities of lipid A complexed with bovine-serum albumin. Eur. J. Biochem. 31:230–233.
4. Mergenhagen, S. E., R. Snyderman, H. Gewurz, and H. S. Shin. 1969. Significance of complement to the mechanism of action of endotoxin. Curr. Top. Microbiol. 50:37.
5. Westenfelder, M., and C. Galanos. 1974. Experimental lipid A-induced nephritis in the dog. II. A possible role of lipid A in the pathogenesis of abacterial pyelonephritis. Infection 2:174–177.
6. Westenfelder, M., and C. Galanos. 1976. Lipid A-antibody-titers, their significance in the pathogenesis of chronic pyelonephritis. Verhandlungsbericht der Deutschen Gesellschaft für Urologie, 1975. Springer-Verlag, Berlin-Heidelberg.
7. Westenfelder, M., C. Galanos, and P. O. Madsen. 1975. Experimental lipid A-induced nephritis in the dog. I. Invest. Urol. 12:337–345.

Natural History of the Immune Response to *Salmonella* Polysaccharides in Inbred Strains of Mice

RAIMUND DI PAULI

Immunology Unit, Division of Biology, University of Konstanz, Konstanz, West Germany

INTRODUCTION

Polysaccharides from the cell wall of bacteria play an important role as antigens in the immune response against bacteria. They are useful tools not only in the elucidation of the defense mechanisms of higher organisms but also in the search for solutions of basic immunological problems. Polysaccharides occur ubiquitously in many bacterial species, and they may well have played a primary selective role in the evolution of the immune system as a whole, because of the need of higher organisms to develop a defense mechanism against the intrusion of bacteria. For these reasons, it is of interest to study the various aspects of the immune response to these antigens. I shall discuss the following aspects of the humoral response of mice against the polysaccharides from *Salmonella anatum* (PSan) and *S. strasbourg* (PSstr): (i) immunoglobulin G (IgG) response in different strains, including congenic strains differing by immunoglobulin allotype; (ii) clonal patterns of the response in certain strains as judged by isoelectric focusing (IEF); and (iii) characteristics of adoptive immunity after lymphoid cell transfer to isogenic and congenic mice.

IgG RESPONSE TO PSan AND PSstr

All mice in this study were injected twice intraperitoneally (i.p.) at 1-week intervals and boosted again after 3 to 4 weeks with 0.6 mg of lyophilized, phenol-killed *Salmonella* cells suspended in saline. The booster injection was necessary in the majority of cases for obtaining antibodies of the IgG classes. Since our main goal was to analyze the variability pattern of antibodies, the IEF method was chosen as our system of assay. Under the conditions used, only IgG antibodies enter the gel. The specific antibody bands were visualized with ^{125}I-labeled polysaccharide (9), obtained by acid hydrolysis of lipopolysaccharide (10).

In Table 1 are listed some representative strains tested and the total number of mice in each strain showing IEF bands with ^{125}I-labeled polysaccharide from the immunizing *S. anatum* or *S. strasbourg* antigen. IEF is mainly a qualitative method. The lack of antigen-labeled antibodies does not imply that the animals do not produce antibodies at all, but, judging from dilution experiments, the absence of visible binding in IEF requires at least a 10- to 20-fold lower titer or lower affinity of the negative sera. By simplification, we will call these negative mice low responders and the positive ones responders.

The frequencies of responders vary between strains when immunized with *S. strasbourg*. In the BALB/c strain only 10 of 44 mice were positive in the IEF. A higher proportion (89%) was positive in the BALB/c-Ig^b and in the C57BL/6 strain (97%). Since the BALB/c-Ig^b strain differs from the BALB strain only by the immunoglobulin allotype, which is that from C57BL, it is conceivable that the immunoglobulin gene complex plays a role in the responses of these strains. Other genes might be involved too because the C57BL/6-Ig^a, carrying the BALB allotype, is not as low as BALB/c.

TABLE 1. *Number of mice in different strains, per total number of tested animals, whose sera bound ^{125}I-labeled polysaccharides in isoelectric focusing*

Mouse strain	Immunizing and test antigen[a]	
	PSstr	PSan
BALB/c..........	10/44 (23)[b]	20/20 (100)
BALB/c-Ig^b	58/65 (89)	13/16 (81)
C57BL/6	31/32 (97)	28/33 (85)
C57BL/6-Ig^a	25/38 (66)	17/25 (68)
C3H/HeNIcr	1/20 (5)	20/20 (100)
(C3H × C57)F$_1$	18/20 (90)	ND[c]
BALB/c nu/nu....	0/1 (14 died)	0/11
BALB/c-Ig^b nu/nu	0/5 (10 died)	ND

[a] PSstr = polysaccharide from *Salmonella strasbourg*; PSan = polysaccharide from *S. anatum*.
[b] Percentage of responders.
[c] Not determined.

280

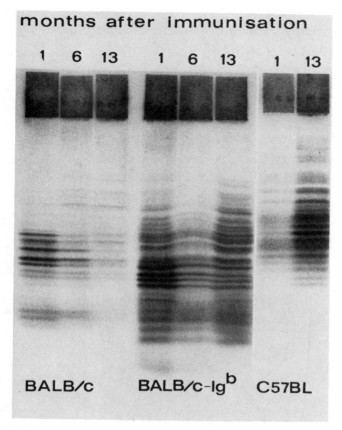

FIG. 1. *Isoelectric focusing of sera from mice of various strains immunized with* Salmonella anatum *and tested with* ^{125}I*-labeled polysaccharide from* S. anatum *at different time periods after immunization. A booster injection of antigen was given 10 days before each bleeding. The pH range is from 3.5 at the top to 10 at the bottom.*

Only one of the 20 C3H mice immunized with *S. strasbourg* was positive in the IEF assay with only a few faint bands. In contrast, when C3H mice were immunized with *S. anatum*, they, like the other mouse strains, all showed a positive and heterogeneous response in IEF. When the C3H low responders were crossed with C57BL responders, all the F1 progeny showed a responder-type IEF; i.e., responsiveness was dominant. We do not know as yet the genetic basis of this phenomenon. A further analysis will be of interest, since in the case of bacterial polysaccharide only few cases of genetic unresponsiveness have been analyzed. It should be noted that this C3H/ HeNIcr strain gives a normal mitogenic response to lipid A.

Two further features of the response of mice to polysaccharide should be mentioned. One is that the IgG response to PSan and PSstr is strictly thymus dependent. None of the geneti-

cally thymusless nude mice immunized with *S. anatum* or *S. strasbourg* showed any sign of antibodies in the IEF (Table 1). Five of nine nudes reconstituted, 1 day prior to immunization, with 10^7 thymus cells were positive in the IEF. These results suggest that T-cell helper function is necessary to obtain an IgG response to these polysaccharides. It will be of interest to study whether polysaccharides or other structures on the bacterial surface are the carrier determinants recognized by the T cells. The second feature is the constancy of clonal patterns. Several mice were boosted 7 months after the first course of immunization and then again after 1 year. Figure 1 shows such an example of IEF patterns of sera from individual mice at different times. It is evident that they do not change their clonal pattern up to 1 year. Among 25 mice observed for this period, there were only two that had changed part of their clonal pattern. We have

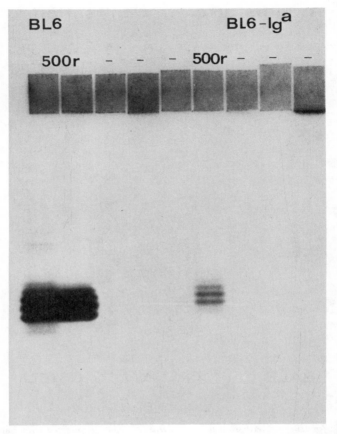

FIG. 2. *Isoelectric focusing of sera from BALB/c-Ig^b and C57BL/6 mice. Only the C57BL are indicated. The numbers are labels of individual mice. Same number means same mouse. The pH range is from 5 at the top to 9 at the bottom.*

shown previously (4) that the fine specificity (which has been used as a marker of the antibody combining site) of the IgM and IgG classes remains constant over similar periods of time. Bacterial polysaccarides thus do not appear to follow a rule, established with certain haptenes (11), according to which the response "matures," as reflected by a gradual increase in antibody affinity. The situation with *Salmonella* polysaccharides is analogous to that found with streptococcal carbohydrate (3).

GENETICS OF ANTIPOLYSACCHARIDE CLONES

The genetic analysis of antibody variability is of primary interest in elucidating the basic mechanism leading to antibody diversity. Several markers for the variable portion of the antibody molecule are available (6). The one applied here is IEF. Although identical isoelectric points, e.g., overlapping of bands in the IEF, do not demonstrate sequence identity,

such antibodies must share at least a major sequence similarity. The method of fine specificity could not be applied in this context, since only a minority of sera showed cross-reactivity to several heterologous polysaccharides tested by the IEF method.

Very striking banding patterns were regularly obtained with BALB/c-Ig^b anti-PSstr sera. These sera consistently displayed relatively few bands, and the same IEF patterns were found with different mice of that strain. To compare these sera, they were focused on gels with a pH gradient from 5 to 9 for the greater resolving power of this pH range. In Fig. 2 selected sera are shown. We compared a total of 33 sera from different BALB/c-Ig^b mice in various combinations, side by side, to substantiate the notion of identity. Taking a typical array of two to four bands as indicating a clone (12), we deduce that BALB/c-Ig^b expresses usually only four to six clones per individual. Through this extensive comparison, we could identify at least four clones expressed in more than one in-

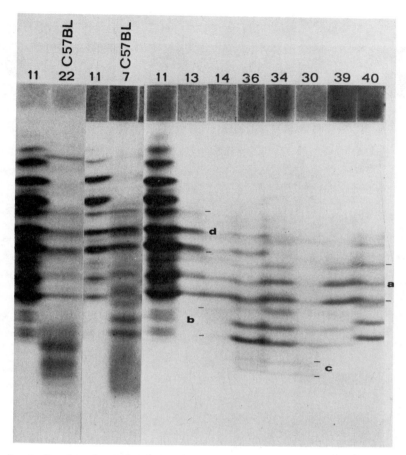

FIG. 3. *Isoelectric focusing of sera from a transfer experiment. The recipients were irradiated (500 rads) syngenic C57BL mice and nonirradiated (−) syngenic or congenic C57BL/6-Ig^a mice. The clone is specific for polysaccharide from* Salmonella anatum. *The pH range is from 3.5 at the top to 10 at the bottom.*

dividual. They are labeled a, b, c, and d in Fig. 2. In 20 of 33 mice, clone a was found in 16, clone b in 14, clone c in 8, and clone d in 7 mice. Thus, individual sera often had more than one of the four "public clones," as shown in Fig. 2. Thirteen mice did not share these public clones. In addition, the individual mice expressing public clones also had private clones not found in other mice. The total number of clones counted in these experiments, including both public and private ones, was of the order of 60. Since each mouse expresses only few, the repertoire of this strain must be much larger than that of the individual.

What is the basis, then, for (i) the restricted expression of only four to six clones per individual and (ii) the very frequent recurrence of the public clones? First, we should add that, until now, two of the public clones were found also in C57BL/6 mice (one, the d clone, is shown in Fig. 2). Thus, it appears that the factor

determining their expression is linked to the heavy-chain allotype and might well be the gene(s) coding for the variable portion of the antibody molecules. It has been shown also in other systems (5) that, when so-called germ line genes are found, they represent only part of the total antibody repertoire to the antigen. Thus, in our view, germ line antibodies are not substantiating the germ line theory. The restricted expression of only few antibody species and the high frequency of given clones are in agreement with a theory of ontogenetic generation of antibody diversity by somatic mutation (1).

ADOPTIVE TRANSFER OF ANTIPOLYSACCHARIDE CLONES

Antipolysaccharide memory spleen cells can be transferred to irradiated recipients. In some cases there is segregation of clones; e.g., the

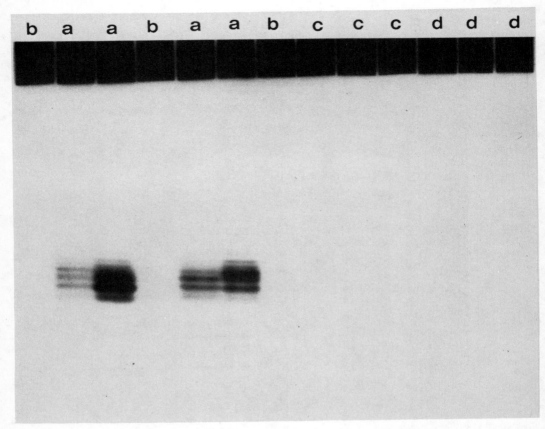

FIG. 4. *Isoelectric focusing of sera from irradiated recipients of the clone shown in Fig. 3. (a) recipients of 2 × 10⁷ memory cells alone. (b) Recipients of 2 × 10⁷ memory cells mixed with 10⁷ normal syngenic spleen cells. (c) Recipients of 2 × 10⁷ memory cells mixed with 10⁷ nylon wool-eluted T cells. (d) Recipients of 10⁷ normal spleen cells alone. The pH is as in Fig. 3.*

recipients do not display the total repertoire of the donor, but only one or two clones. The clone shown in Fig. 3 is a C57BL/6 anti-PSan clone at the third transfer generation. In the experiments shown in Fig. 3, 2 × 10⁷ spleen cells from one donor were transferred into irradiated syngenic, nonirradiated syngenic, or allotype congenic C57BL/6-Igᵃ mice. It is evident that the clone is expressed only in the three irradiated mice. It has been shown that successful transfer of antibody-producing cells is possible only into mice with a permissive immune system; these are irradiated mice, new-born mice (2), or thymusless nude mice (8). In recent years, it has become clear not only that the immune system is under positive effector control but also that negative regulatory systems are involved (7). The cells responsible are probably thymus-derived suppressor cells (7). One explanation for the lack of expression of the C57BL clone in unirradiated syngenic re-

cipients could be the presence of suppressor T cells, as has been suggested (8). For these reasons, we transferred the clone shown in Fig. 3 to further irradiated recipients; 2 × 10⁷ memory spleen cells were transferred either alone or mixed with spleen cells (10⁷) from normal syngenic donors or with nylon wool column-eluted T cells (10⁷) also from normal donors. All recipients received one injection of *S. anatum* antigen. In the IEF of Fig. 4, sera of the different groups of recipients were tested. Only the recipients (a) which received memory cells alone are expressing the donor clone. The other recipients, whether they were injected with a mixture of memory cells and normal spleen cells (b), with memory cells and T cells (c), or with only normal spleen cells, all were negative. These results suggest that in a normal cell population there are cells which can actively suppress an immune response. These cells probably are T cells since nylon wool-isolated cells are active, whereas the treatment of spleen cells (experiments not shown here) removes the suppressive activity. It is unknown what the specificity of the suppressive activity is and whether it is directed to the antigen or to the idiotype of the antibody as others have suggested (8). At least in the anti-*S. anatum* system, the production of donor antibodies was always suppressed in unirradiated recipients. This was independent of whether a single clone or a heterogeneously antibody set-producing cell population was transferred. It was also independent of the mouse strain used. Interestingly, the same is not valid for the transfer of cells producing antibodies to PSstr. The transfer of cells producing antibodies against this antigen to unirradiated syngenic mice results in antibody production with donor IEF patterns.

CONCLUSIONS

I am aware that more questions have been raised with these results than solutions offered. But the immune system is intricate and does not offer simple all or none mechanisms. As shown by the immune responses to these polysaccharides, even within a genetically homogeneous mouse strain, each individual can differ not only in the quantity but also in the quality of the response. On the other hand, as is the case for BALB/c-Ig^b, certain molecules out of the repertoire of the strain are expressed with an exceptionally high frequency. Elucidation of the laws that govern these complex phenotypic displays will still require considerable thought and effort.

LITERATURE CITED

1. **Adam, G., and E. Weiler.** 1976. Lymphocyte population dynamics during ontogenetic generation of diversity, p. 1–20. *In* A. J. Cunningham (ed.), The generation of antibody diversity: a new look. Academic Press Inc., London.
2. **Celada, F.** 1966. Quantitative studies of the adoptive immunological memory in mice. I. An age-dependent barrier to syngeneic transplantation. J. Exp. Med. **124:** 1–14.
3. **Cramer, M., and D. G. Braun.** 1975. Immunological memory: stable IgG patterns determine in vivo responsiveness at the clonal level. Scand. J. Immunol. **4:**63–70.
4. **Di Pauli, R.** 1975. Cross reactivity patterns of IgM and IgG anti-lipopolysaccharide antibodies in individual mice. Eur. J. Immunol. **5:**689–694.
5. **Eichmann, K.** 1972. Idiotype expression and the inheritance of mouse antibody clones. J. Exp. Med. **137:**603–621.
6. **Eichmann, K.** 1975. Genetic control of antibody specificity in the mouse. Immunogenetics **2:**491–506.
7. **Gershon, R. K.** 1975. Immunoregulation by T cells, p. 267–283. *In* E. E. Smith and D. W. Ribbons (ed.), Molecular approaches to immunology. Academic Press Inc., New York.
8. **Kobow, U., and E. Weiler.** 1975. Permissiveness of athymic ("nude") mice toward congenic memory cells. Eur. J. Immunol. **5:**628–632.
9. **Mitchell, G. F., J. H. Humphrey, and A. R. Williamson.** 1972. Inhibition of secondary anti-hapten responses with the hapten conjugated to type 3 pneumococcal polysaccharide. Eur. J. Immunol. **2:**460–467.
10. **Schmidt, G., B. Jann, and K. Jann.** 1969. Immunochemistry of R lipopolysaccharides of Escherichia coli. Different core regions in the lipopolysaccharides of O group 8. Eur. J. Biochem. **10:**501–510.
11. **Siskind, G. W., and B. Benacerraf.** 1969. Cell selection by antigen in the immune response. Adv. Immunol. **10:**1–50.
12. **Williamson, A. R.** 1971. Antibody isoelectric spectra. Analysis of the heterogeneity of antibody molecules in serum by isoelectric focusing in gel and specific detection with hapten. Eur. J. Immunol. **1:**390–394.

Some Aspects of Microcirculatory and Metabolic Changes in Endotoxemia and in Endotoxin Tolerance

BERNHARD URBASCHEK AND RENATE URBASCHEK

Abteilung für Immunologie und Serologie am Institut für Hygiene und Medizinische Mikrobiologie der Universität Heidelberg, Mannheim, West Germany

Invasion of gram-negative as well as of gram-positive bacteria into the circulation of humans is followed by shock in about 25% of patients. Up to the present, septic shock has resulted in death in 50 to 80% of patients, of which two-thirds is caused by bacteremia due to gram-negative bacteria.

The main feature of shock in general is the circulatory failure in the periphery induced by a decreased circulating blood volume. Also, septic shock can be defined as an acute hemodynamic insufficiency with the characteristics of an impairment of capillary exchange with its metabolic consequences. In endotoxic shock the frequent finding of fibrin monomers in patients is characteristic, contrary to other forms of shock (7). In comparison with all other forms of shock, high polymeric fibrin deposits as signs of decompensation of the coagulation system are characteristic in experimental endotoxic shock (for example, in miniature pigs) as well as in septic shock in patients. However, a pathognomonic morphological equivalent of endotoxic shock is presently unknown; it is a manifestation of multifactoral effects.

It should be pointed out that in the initial phase vasoactive mediators of endotoxins play a decisive role in the reaction of the microvascular bed. Decreased perfusion, insufficient oxygen supply, and impaired capillary exchange are the prerequisites for the metabolic disturbances, including the coagulation system.

Aside from the decrease in number of platelets and leukocytes in the peripheral blood, the disturbances in the microcirculation, as observed in the content of the vessels, the vessel wall, and the perivascular space, are among the earliest detectable changes caused by endotoxins (16; B. Urbaschek, Habilitationsschrift, Heidelberg University, Heidelberg, Germany, 1967). The vital microscopic changes registered in the initial phase of endotoxemia, or after administration of mediators of endotoxins, such as histamine and serotonin, have been described in detail (16; Urbaschek, Habilitationsschrift) and were documented in a movie film (B. Urbaschek and R. Urbaschek, E 1927, *in* G. Wolf, Encyclopaedia Cinematographica, Institut für den Wissenschaftlichen Film, Göttingen, Germany, 1975).

By means of microkymography (4), by which an objective measurement of the observed changes in the blood-flow velocity in the microvascular bed is possible, we recently documented the decrease in blood-flow velocity occurring as the first registrable change in the microcirculation after administration of endotoxin or of the biogenic amines mentioned. This method has the advantage, as compared with the flying spot method (3), of also allowing measurements of flow velocities of more than 0.5 mm/s, thus including measurements of the flow through arterioles and partly through precapillaries. According to the principle of the stripe-microkymographion, a film is transported across the longitudinal axis of a slit opening in the camera, which is brought into congruence with the longitudinal axis of a vessel. The corpuscular elements flowing through the vessel cause stripes on the film, the angle (α) of which is related to their velocity. Thus, the velocity (a) can be measured by the calculation $a = (\alpha \times b)/F$, where b is the velocity of the transported film and F is the magnifying factor of the microscope. Also, subtle changes in the caliber of the vessels can be documented in the microvascular bed by perpendicular positioning of the slit opening to the longitudinal axis of the vessel. Until this method was used, the interpretation of the initial decrease in blood flow occurring after endotoxin administration was insufficient, since changes in the caliber of the vessels of up to 30% and slight changes of the sphincters cannot be perceived by vital microscopic observation. Thus, for the first time the initial decrease in blood flow in the microvascular bed following endotoxin could be explained by changes in vascular caliber.

One of the major characteristics of vital microscopic observations of the microvascular bed in the initial phase of endotoxemia is the alterations of the endothelial layer, which are of special significance for initiating the pathogenetic course of endotoxemia. Within the first hour, swelling of endothelial cells and occasionally deviations of these cells occur.

In cooperation with Forssmann and Irwin (17), we studied the effect of endotoxin on the microcirculation in the rabbit ear chamber by means of electron microscopy performed by Forssmann. Endothelial cells are severely damaged, as expressed by discontinuity of the endothelial layer (Fig. 1) and by fragmentation and vacuolization of the cells (Fig. 2 and 3). In a postcapillary venule (Fig. 3) the barrier of permeability seems to be abolished. In some areas the endothelial cells are almost completely destroyed, and only the lamina densa of the basement membrane is still existing, as shown in a capillary in Fig. 4. In Fig. 5 mitochondria of an endothelial cell and a pericyte (Rouget cell) show swelling of the matrix and cristolysis. Fibrinoid depositions can be observed mainly in the pericapillary areas (Fig. 2 and 6) and also within the vessels (Fig. 1 and 3). The pericapillary fibrinoid depositions and the edema observed are comparable to reactions of the connective tissue to acute nonspecific inflammation. In Fig. 4 an activated macrophage with many lysosomes can be seen in the pericapillary area. Extravascular erythrocytes also occur (Fig. 3 and 4). In Fig. 1 platelets can be observed between the discontinuous endothelial cells of a postcapillary venule. Several platelets are attached to the basement membrane (Fig. 6); the endothelial wall of this postcapillary venule is in the process of disintegration. Vacuoles occurred in the platelets as an equivalent of the release reactions that took place.

The vital microscopic and electron microscopic observations of the damaged endothelial cells are supported by the studies of McGrath and Stewart (10) and Gaynor et al. (6) who used electron microscopy of the aorta after endotoxin administration. Gaynor (6) found that the majority of animals develop circulating endothelial cells. Studying whether the margination of granulocytes, which we also observed in the microvascular bed by vital microscopy (16; Urbaschek, Habilitationsschrift), causes intimal injury or is a response to it, Gaynor (5) used neutropenic rabbits to demonstrate that leukocytes are not involved in the pathogenesis of the primary endothelial lesion in endotoxemia. From our studies in miniature pigs, which are described below, it can be concluded that the initial drop in the number of leukocytes is not indicative of the further course of endotoxemia.

Gaynor (5) suggested that endotoxin may have a direct effect on endothelial cells without considering the effect of vasoactive mediators involved.

The endotoxin-caused alterations of the endothelial cells can be explained by studying the effect of biogenic amines on these cells. By vital microscopy we observed these changes after administration of histamine or serotonin (16; Urbaschek, Habilitationsschrift). In electron microscopic studies Majno (11) demonstrated similar changes, such as swelling, contraction, and deviation of endothelial cells after histamine administration.

Without discussing the significance of the activation of the complement system by endotoxin, we point out that it represents an initially available source of histamine. By endotoxin-caused activation of C5, the fragment C5a, which is identical to anaphylatoxin, is generated.

We showed that the activity of histamine and serotonin is enhanced in the isolated organ and in the intact animal (18; Urbaschek, Habilitationsschrift). Zweifach et al. (21) described a dose-dependent potentiation of epinephrine activity after endotoxin administration and a synergism between serotonin and bradykinin in the microcirculation (20). The question remains open whether the severe damage of the endothelial cells is induced by vasoactive mediators of endotoxic effects alone, or in addition by enzymes, such as neuraminidase. In preliminary studies with Spelger (manuscript in preparation), this enzyme caused damage of the endothelial cell in the microvascular bed of the hamster cheek pouch, especially at increased body temperatures of these animals.

Besides the consequences of the increased permeability, the changes of the endothelial layer are of significance in regard to the activation of intravascular coagulation in several ways. It is assumed that the activation of the extrinsic system is based on the availability of tissue thromboplastin from damaged leukocytes and endothelial cells, although the release of this potent phospholipoprotein from the latter cells has not yet been proved. Platelets can adhere to slightly injured endothelial cells, and irreversibly aggregated platelets also function as activators of blood coagulation. The deviation of endothelial cells exposes subendothelial collagen to the content of the vessels, so that factor XII is activated through the contact of collagen with plasma. Thus, the damaged endothelial cells induce activation of the blood coagulation through the intrinsic system.

Since detoxified endotoxin protects animals

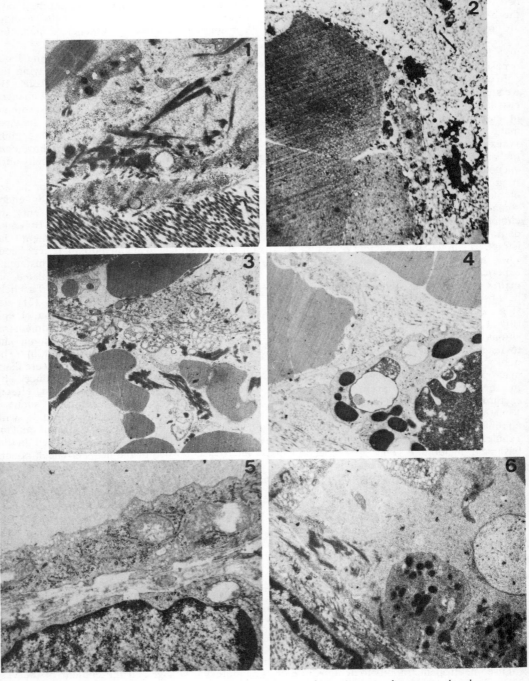

FIG. 1–6. *Electron microscopic studies of the microcirculation in a translucent ear chamber after endotoxin administration.*

against lethal doses of endotoxins from various gram-negative bacteria (19; Urbaschek, Habilitationsschrift), against X irradiation (Urbaschek, Habilitationsschrift), and against microcirculatory changes due to endotoxins (16; Urbaschek, Habilitationsschrift), we studied several clinico-chemical parameters in 54 miniature pigs. One of these experiments is de-

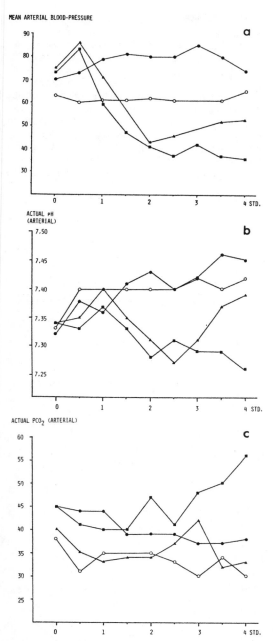

FIG. 7. *Changes in (a) the mean arterial blood pressure, (b) the actual arterial pH, and (c) the actual arterial pCO$_2$ of miniature pigs after 1-h intravenous infusion of (■) endotoxin, (●) detoxified endotoxin, (▲) detoxified endotoxin plus endotoxin, or (○) saline (controls). Measurements were made for 4 h, beginning at the start of the infusion period.*

scribed here. Detoxified endotoxins were prepared from *Escherichia coli* O55 with potassium methylate according to the method of Nowotny (13). Four groups, each of four pigs,

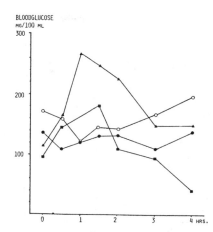

FIG. 8. *Changes in the blood glucose of miniature pigs after 1-h intravenous infusion of (■) endotoxin, (●) detoxified endotoxoid, (▲) detoxified endotoxin plus endotoxin, or (○) saline (controls). Measurements were made for 4 h, beginning at the start of the infusion period.*

were observed in halothane-N$_2$O anesthesia for 4 h from the beginning of the intravenous infusion, which lasted for 1 h. One group received endotoxin from *E. coli* O111 extracted by Boivin's trichloroacetic acid method (250 μg/kg), another group received detoxified endotoxin (150 μg/kg), another group received endotoxin (250 μg/kg) 24 h after pretreatment with detoxified endotoxin (150 μg/kg), and the fourth group served as a control. In cooperation with Storck and Huth, the groups were studied in this way to find those parameters which are unchanged or mitigated in the state of endotoxin tolerance induced by detoxified endotoxin in comparison with the effects of endotoxins. We shall discuss briefly the results of the parameters measured, first describing the effects of endotoxins in these experiments.

The arterial blood pressure (Fig. 7a) increased within the first 30 min in all experiments in miniature pigs. After this time, a marked decrease occurred until the end of the experiment, simultaneously with a drop in arterial actual pH (Fig. 7b), indicating the development of the characteristics of endotoxic shock. Although the respiratory rate was increased, the actual pCO$_2$ (Fig. 7c) increased, with a maximum at the end of the experiment, and the pO$_2$ decreased. As a further sign of shock, the blood glucose (Fig. 8) decreased after an initial increase; the lactate level increased continuously (Fig. 9), and the pyruvate increased with a peak at 2 h postinfusion. In other experiments in miniature pigs, we found a marked increase in the serum glutamic oxalacetic and pyruvic transaminases from the fourth hour on, with the highest level at 24 h,

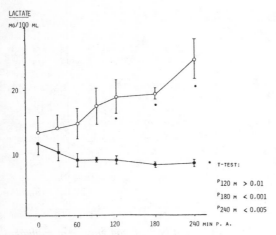

FIG. 9. *Increase in lactate in (○) endotoxin-treated miniature pigs versus (●) controls.*

the end of the observation. As can be seen from these studies the alkaline phosphatase (Fig. 10a), glutamate dehydrogenase (Fig. 10b), and γ-glutamyl transpeptidase (Fig. 10c) increased during the 4 h of observation. The fat metabolism showed a marked increase of free fatty acids (Fig. 11a), free glycerol (Fig. 11b), and triglycerides between the third and fourth hours postinfusion.

Studying the metabolites in our experiments, Lundsgaard-Hansen et al. (8) found an increase in hexose monophosphates, glucose-1-phosphate, and glucose-6-phosphate in heart and skeletal muscle; in liver tissue we observed a decrease in liver glycogen and in the adenyl phosphates and adenosine tri-, di-, and monophosphates. These changes, determined 4 h after the beginning of the infusion by sampling the tissues by the freeze-stop technique, correlated with the decrease in blood pressure, arterial actual pH, and blood glucose at this time. In the group of pigs that were pretreated with detoxified endotoxin, the described changes in metabolites, blood pressure, actual pH, and glucose failed to appear, so that the shock-inducing effect of endotoxin was abolished (Fig. 7a, 7b, 8). Detoxified endotoxin also inhibited the increase in the described enzymes (Fig. 10a–c) and in free fatty acids and free glycerol (Fig. 11a and b). The endotoxin-induced increases in hemoglobin and hematocrit were mitigated by pretreatment with detoxified endotoxin.

The drop in the number of leukocytes and platelets after endotoxin is not prevented by pretreatment with detoxified endotoxin. Also, the changes in blood coagulation, i.e., the beginning of acute consumption coagulopathy and in par-

ticular the endotoxin-induced fibrinogenopenia, are not altered by detoxified endotoxin.

Another experiment with six miniature pigs should be mentioned which was performed in cooperation with Neuhof. After endotoxin infusion, an acute initial reaction occurred as measured by a decrease of the cardiac output during the first hour and an increase of the peripheral vascular resistance. The decrease in cardiac output is compensated by an early enhanced arteriovenous utilization. All the initial hemodynamic reactions described failed to appear in pigs pretreated with detoxified endotoxin.

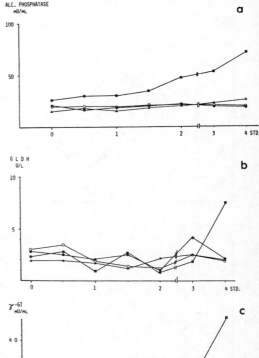

FIG. 10. *Changes in (a) alkaline phosphatase, (b) glutamate dehydrogenase, and (c) glutamyl transpeptidase of miniature pigs after 1-h infusion of (■) endotoxin, (●) detoxified endotoxin, (▲) detoxified endotoxin plus endotoxin, or (○) saline (controls). Measurements were made for 4 h, beginning at the start of the infusion period.*

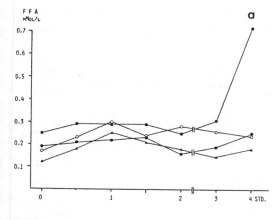

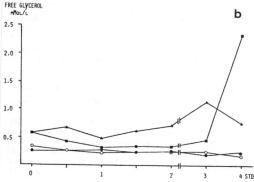

FIG. 11. *Changes in (a) free fatty acids (FFA) and free glycerol of miniature pigs after 1-h infusion of (■) endotoxin, (●) detoxified endotoxin, (▲) detoxified endotoxin plus endotoxin, or (○) saline (controls). Measurements were made for 4 h, beginning at the start of the infusion period.*

It was reported by Berry and Smythe (2) in 1960, who studied an experimental mouse typhoid model, that one of the first metabolic alterations in the experimentally infected mice, as well as in mice after administration of endotoxin, is a rapid depletion of carbohydrates. Berry (1) demonstrated a gluconeogenesis-inhibiting effect in mice after endotoxin administration, as did McCallum and Berry (9) and Schumer (14), and a simultaneous shifting of the lactate/pyruvate ratio. The initial increase in glucose in our experiments in miniature pigs will not be discussed here since it reflects the action of adrenaline released at this time. The successive decrease in blood glucose fails to appear in animals pretreated with detoxified endotoxin; in these animals the decrease in liver glycogen was also prevented. In previous experiments performed with Lundsgaard-Hansen (8), metabolic blood parameters, energy-rich phosphates, and glucose metabolites in the heart, skeletal muscle, and liver were studied in rabbits in compensated and decompensated shock after intravenous injection of endotoxin. By multiple regression-correlation analysis it was shown that the state of shock as such was the major determinant of tissue metabolite changes, the pattern of which reflected a progressive hypoxia and accelerated glycolysis. Over a period of 8 h, some modest alterations in the liver only were possibly attributable to direct intracellular effects of endotoxin, the decisive target of which is concluded to be the vascular system.

Mela (12) described an inhibition of energy production after endotoxin administration, although the oxygen utilization and the ion transfer were unchanged in mitochondria of liver and kidney in rats. It should be pointed out that in our experiments in miniature pigs described above the endotoxin-caused changes in the liver were prevented in the state of endotoxin tolerance.

Detoxified endotoxin per se causes slight changes of some of the parameters, such as in platelet and leukocyte count and in body temperature.

In regard to the participation of zinc ion in the stabilization of membranes, Snyder and Walker (15) found that zinc chloride effectively protected against lethal doses of endotoxins, as measured by mortality at 24 h, and significantly reduced the endotoxin-caused elevation of β-glucuronidase. They also observed a protective effect of zinc chloride on the microcirculation after endotoxin (personal communication).

If in hemorrhagic shock a decrease in blood glucose occurs in the preterminal phase, it is to be explained by the extreme oxygen deficit and the attempt to compensate with glucose the total energy requirements. The decrease in blood glucose develops regularly in endotoxemia, in which the oxygen debt occurs much earlier, since the perfusion of the periphery is decreased initially because of the microcirculatory disturbances, and since the lung is affected at an early stage by mediators of endotoxin, so that in addition the oxygen uptake is decreased. Thus, glucose utilization can already be intensified in the early phase, so that a decrease in glucose results thereafter. In this connection a dependence of the metabolic changes on the circulatory and hemodynamic system is understandable.

LITERATURE CITED

1. **Berry, L. J.** 1971. Metabolic effects of bacterial endotoxin, p. 165–208. *In* S. Kadis, G. Weinbaum, and S. J. Ajl (ed.), Microbial toxins, vol. 5. Academic Press Inc., New York.
2. **Berry, L. J., and D. S. Smythe.** 1960. Some metabolic

aspects of host-parasite interactions in the mouse typhoid model. Ann. N.Y. Acad. Sci. **88**:1278–1286.

3. **Brånemark, P.-I., and I. Jonsson.** 1963. Termination of the velocity of corpuscles in blood capillaries. Biorheology **1**:143–146.

4. **Castenholz, A.** 1973. Kymographie mit dem Vitalmikroskop. Microsc. Acta **74**:89–109.

5. **Gaynor, E.** 1973. The role of granulocytes in endotoxin-induced vascular injury. Blood **41**:797–808.

6. **Gaynor, E., C. Bouvier, and T. H. Spaet.** 1970. Vascular lesions: possible pathogenetic basis of the generalized Shwartzman reaction. Science **170**:986–988.

7. **Heene, D. L., H. G. Lasch, and F. R. Matthias.** 1976. Gerinnungsstörungen und Verbrauchskoagulopathie bei polytraumatisierten Patienten. Intensivbehandlung **1**:42–48.

8. **Lundsgaard-Hansen, P., E. Pappova, B. Urbaschek, L. Heitmann, A. Laederach, N. Molnes, M. Oroz, and U. Wirth.** 1972. Circulatory deterioration as the determinant of energy metabolism in endotoxin shock. J. Surg. Res. **13**:282–288.

9. **McCallum, R. E., and L. J. Berry.** 1973. Effects of endotoxin on gluconeogenesis, glycogen synthesis, and liver glycogen synthase in mice. Infect. Immun. **7**:642–654.

10. **McGrath, J. M., and G. J. Stewart.** 1969. The effects of endotoxin on vascular endothelium. J. Exp. Med. **129**:833–848.

11. **Majno, G., S. M. Shea, and M. Leventhal.** 1969. Endothelial contraction induced by histamine-type mediators. An electron microscopy study. J. Cell Biol. **42**:647–672.

12. **Mela, L.** 1975. Mitochondrial metabolic alterations in experimental circulatory shock, p. 288–295. *In* B. Urbaschek, R. Urbaschek, and E. Neter (ed.), Gram-negative bacterial infections and mode of endotoxin actions. Pathophysiological, immunological, and clinical aspects. Springer-Verlag, New York.

13. **Nowotny, A.** 1963. Endotoxoid preparations. Nature (London) **197**:721–722.

14. **Schumer, W.** 1975. Assessment of studies in the biochemistry and immunology of endotoxemia, p. 278–280. *In* B. Urbaschek, R. Urbaschek, and E. Neter (ed.), Gram-negative bacterial infections and mode of endotoxin actions. Pathophysiological, immunological, and clinical aspects. Springer-Verlag, New York.

15. **Snyder, S. L., and R. I. Walker.** 1976. Inhibition of lethality in endotoxin-challenged mice treated with zinc chloride. Infect. Immun. **13**:998–1000.

16. **Urbaschek, B.** 1971. The effects of endotoxins in the microcirculation, p. 261–275. *In* S. Kadis, G. Weinbaum, and S. J. Ajl (ed.), Microbial toxins, vol. 5. Academic Press Inc., New York.

17. **Urbaschek, B., W. G. Forssmann, and R. Urbaschek.** 1976. Endotoxin-induced microcirculatory disturbances, p. 176–178. *In* Microcirculation, vol. 2. Plenum Press, New York.

18. **Urbaschek, B., H. Kotowski, and H. Bäurle.** 1961. Immunologische Studien an Brucellen. II. Die Wirkung von Brucella abortus Bang sowie dreier Fraktionen dieser Bakterien auf den Uterus unvorbehandelter Meerschweinchen. Z. Immunitaetsforsch. **122**:343–357.

19. **Urbaschek, B., and A. Nowotny.** 1968. Endotoxin tolerance induced by detoxified endotoxin (endotoxoid). Proc. Soc. Exp. Biol. Med. **127**:650–652.

20. **Zweifach, B. W.** 1966. Microcirculatory effects of polypeptides, p. 451–462. *In* E. G. Erdös, N. Back, and F. Sicuteri (ed.), Hypotensive peptides. Springer-Verlag, New York.

21. **Zweifach, B. W., A. L. Nagler, and L. Thomas.** 1956. The role of epinephrine in the reactions produced by the endotoxins of gram-negative bacteria. II. The changes produced by endotoxin in the vascular reactivity to epinephrine, in the rat mesoappendix and the isolated, perfused rabbit ear. J. Exp. Med. **104**:881–896.

Clinical Implications of Enterobacterial Antigens

WILLIAM R. McCABE, MARGARET A. JOHNS, DONALD E. CRAVEN, AND SCOTT C. BRUINS

University Hospital, Boston University, School of Medicine, Boston, Massachusetts 02118

The progressively increasing prevalence of infections caused by gram-negative bacilli and their importance as a cause of morbidity and mortality among hospitalized patients have been emphasized in an earlier presentation (Braude et al., p. 253, this volume). Although the magnitude of the problem of hospital-acquired infections, especially bacteremia, caused by gram-negative bacilli is well recognized by infectious disease clinicians, it is often not appreciated by those who do not have immediate responsibility for patient care. The actual number of deaths each year cannot be accurately determined, but it has been estimated to range from as many as 100,000 deaths (10) to as few as 18,000 deaths per year (18). Irrespective of the exact numbers, however, it is clear that the magnitude of this problem is sufficient to prompt major concern.

Although survival rates from gram-negative bacteremia have increased in recent years, this has failed to compensate for the increasing rate of occurrence of such infections, and the total number of fatalities annually from this cause has continued to increase. Epidemiological control methods and the introduction of new antibiotics have not effectively stemmed the increasing rate of gram-negative bacillary infections. The relative ineffectiveness of other control measures has logically led to consideration of the possible utilization of immunological methods for the enhancement of resistance to infections caused by gram-negative bacilli.

ENTEROBACTERIAL ANTIGENS AND THE ETIOLOGY AND EPIDEMIOLOGY OF GRAM-NEGATIVE BACILLARY INFECTIONS

Consideration of the antigenic composition of *Enterobacteriaceae* and *Pseudomonadaceae* is necessary before progressing to discussion of the role of individual species and serotypes in the etiology of infections. Although it is well recognized that gram-negative bacilli possess three major antigens, capsular or K, O, and H antigens, the extremely large number of individual antigenic types present in each species of gram-negative bacilli is often not appreciated. This extreme antigenic diversity among gram-negative bacilli is illustrated in Table 1, which lists the number of specific capsular or K, O, and H antigen types which have been identified to date in *Escherichia coli*, *Klebsiella* sp., *Enterobacter* sp., *Serratia* sp., species of *Proteus*, and *Pseudomonas aeruginosa* (5). As can be seen, 92 K, 148 O, and 51 distinct H antigen types have been identified among strains of *E. coli*. The large number of antigen types could result in an almost unlimited number of strains with mosaics of these three major antigens. In contrast, with only 13 O and 10 H antigen types among *P. aeruginosa* strains, the potential number of combinations of O and H antigen types is more limited.

This extreme antigenic variation among members of the same species of *Enterobacteriaceae* makes it apparent that simple biochemical separation of gram-negative bacilli into species is not adequate to determine whether only a few or a large number of serological types of an individual species are involved in hospital-acquired infections. This has important clinical implications: the finding of only a small number of serological types would suggest single sources of infection, whereas the finding of multiple serotypes would suggest endogenous infections or multiple sources for infection. In addition, knowledge of the species and antigenic types of organisms causing infection would be essential to any approach to immunization against such infections.

Table 2 shows the etiological agents isolated in 776 episodes of gram-negative bacteremia observed at University Hospital in Boston. As can be seen, *E. coli* was the most frequent etiological agent, causing 35% of 776 episodes of bacteremia. Serological typing for O antigen only, however, demonstrated that a large number of serological types of *E. coli* were involved. Of 86 consecutive strains of *E. coli* isolated from blood cultures, 23 different O-antigenic types were identified, 10 strains were nontypable with available O antiserum, and 4 strains were

TABLE 1. *Antigens of species of* Enterobacteriaceae

Bacterial species	No. of specific antigens		
	Capsular or K	O	H
Escherichia coli	92	148	51
Klebsiella pneumoniae	72	5	—
Enterobacter sp.	—	68	34
Serratia sp.	?	15	13
Proteus sp.	—	117	44
Pseudomonas aeruginosa[a]..	—	13	10

[a] Verder and Evans antigenic schema.

rough. Six O-antigenic types constituted 50% of the strains isolated. Thus, if one were to attempt to immunize high-risk patients with these six O-antigenic types, and if this were entirely effective, it would result in only an 18% reduction in the frequency of gram-negative bacteremia. Similar studies carried out with 30 strains of *K. pneumoniae* revealed that 16 different capsular types were involved as causes of bacteremia and 3 strains were nonencapsulated. No single serotype was responsible for more than two bacteremic episodes.

These studies indicate that a large number of serological types, among the members of each species of *Enterobacteriaceae*, are responsible for bacteremia caused by gram-negative bacilli. Although specific serological types may produce localized outbreaks of infection, these findings demonstrate that almost all gram-negative bacilli are capable of producing serious infections. This basal level of hospital-acquired infections may be further increased by clusters of infections caused by individual serological types. These observations also suggest that there is similar, but limited, invasive capacity among most non-*Salmonella Enterobacteriaceae* and that gram-negative bacilli function primarily as "opportunistic" pathogens.

These findings also have important implications for any considerations of immunization for the control or prevention of gram-negative bacillary infections. The extremely large num-

TABLE 2. *Etiological agents in gram-negative bacteremia*

Bacterial species	No. of isolates
Escherichia coli	274 (35%)
Klebsiella-Enterobacter-Serratia	201 (26%)
Pseudomonas	90 (12%)
Proteus sp.	91 (12%)
Bacteroides	64 (8%)
Other species	56 (7%)

bers of serological types of *Enterobacteriaceae* involved in such infections would preclude any attempts at active or passive immunization which were dependent on the use of either O-specific or capsular (or K) antigens.

ENTEROBACTERIAL ANTIGENS INDUCING IMMUNITY

Earlier studies have demonstrated that immunization with gram-negative bacilli protected a number of species of experimental animals against subsequent infections with homologous bacteria. These studies indicated that immunization with both O-specific and capsular, or K, antigens afforded significant protection but have not demonstrated which of these antigens is most effective in protecting against experimental infections (6, 7, 12, 15, 17). In contrast to the well-documented evidence of the protective effects of immunization with O-specific or capsular, or K, antigens in animals, there is little evidence that humoral antibody exerts any protective effect against gram-negative bacillary infections in humans.

Since the previous demonstration of the involvement of multiple species and diverse serological types as causes of gram-negative bacillary infections appeared to preclude any attempt at immunization against these infections with type-specific antigens, the possibility of immunization utilizing shared, cross-reactive antigens common to gram-negative bacilli was considered. The development of a series of rough mutants of *Salmonella* by bacterial geneticists (13) and the subsequent delineation of the chemical structure of the cell wall lipopolysaccharide (LPS) resulted in the demonstration that the core portion of the LPS of most *Enterobacteriaceae* was of markedly similar chemical composition (8, 14). These findings suggested that antigenic determinants in the core portion of LPS might be shared by most gram-negative bacilli. If such shared antigenic determinants were exposed on the bacterial surface, antibody might exhibit protective activity against infections caused by a large number of heterologous bacilli.

Chedid et al. were the first to demonstrate that immunization with rough (R) mutants of *S. typhimurium* protected mice against challenge with heterologous *Enterobacteriaceae*, but they did not extend these initial observations (4). These observations provided a stimulus for further evaluation of the effect of immunization with R mutants of *Salmonella minnesota* against infections with heterologous smooth gram-negative bacilli in our laboratory. Initial studies evaluated the relative protective ef-

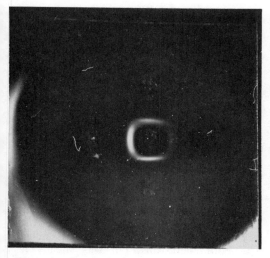

FIG. 1. *Serological comparison of lipid A preparations from several gram-negative bacilli. The center well contains antiserum to lipid A from the Re 595 mutant of* Salmonella minnesota; *top well, lipid A from Re 595; left well, lipid A from* Citrobacter freundii; *bottom well, lipid A from* Chromobacterium violaceum; *and right well, lipid A from* Pseudomonas aeruginosa. *All lipid A preparations were complexed to rabbit albumin for solubility. A precipitin line of identity can be seen between the antiserum and all four lipid A preparations.*

fects of immunization with various chemotype R mutants, Ra, Rb, Rc, Rd_1, Rd_2, and Re, of *S. minnesota*. Rabbits were immunized with the parent *S. minnesota* S218 and its Ra, Rb, Rc, Rd_1, Rd_2, and Re mutants, and 0.3 ml of each antiserum, 0.3 ml of saline, or 0.3 ml of normal rabbit serum was given to individual mice in lots of 40 animals. These mice were challenged intravenously 60 min later with 100 LD_{50} of mouse-virulent strains of *K. pneumoniae* (20 mice) or *P. morganii* (20 mice). Passive immunization with antiserum against the Re mutant afforded significant enhancement of survival during the 3-day observation period against infection with both *K. pneumoniae* ($\chi^2 = 13.8$; $P < 0.01$) and *P. morganii* ($\chi^2 = 45$; $P < 0.001$). Passive transfer of antiserum raised against the other Ra, Rb, Rc, Rd_1, and Rd_2 mutants, and against the parent *S. minnesota* S-218 strain, failed to protect against infections produced by *K. pneumoniae* or *P. morganii*. Studies of the effects of active immunization in protecting against infection with these two challenge strains were also carried out. Active immunization with the Re mutant again proved to be most effective and provided a significant increase in survival rates after infection with *K. pneumoniae* ($P < 0.001$) and *P. morganii* ($P < 0.001$) over

those observed in controls. Subsequent studies compared the effectiveness of type-specific immunization with that of immunization with the shared antigens of the Re mutant. As anticipated, type-specific immunization was much more effective and induced a 10,000-fold increase in the number of *K. pneumoniae* and a 100-fold increase in the number of *P. morganii* required to produce 1 LD_{50}. Immunization with the Re mutant increased the number of *K. pneumoniae* and *P. morganii* by 150-fold and 15-fold, respectively. Additional investigations also demonstrated that the protective effect of antiserum prepared by immunization with whole Re bacilli could be negated by absorption of this antiserum by purified Re LPS, detoxified by sodium hydroxide hydrolysis (9).

Concomitant studies carried out in A. I. Braude's laboratory provided further evidence that immunization with R mutants protected against heterologous gram-negative bacilli. Utilizing the J-5 mutant of *E. coli*, this group was able to demonstrate that immunization with this R mutant protected experimental animals against the local and generalized Shwartzman reactions and endotoxin-induced lethality produced by heterologous endotoxin (1, 2, 16). Braude et al. also developed a model for bacteremia in rabbits colonized by gram-negative bacilli and made neutropenic by injection of nitrogen mustard (3). This model was used by Ziegler et al. to demonstrate that passive immunization with the J5 mutant of *E. coli* protected rabbits against bacteremia from *E. coli*, *K. pneumoniae*, and *P. aeruginosa* (19, 20).

Since ketodeoxyoctonate (KDO) and lipid A are the only recognized antigenic determinants which are present in the LPS of both the J5 mutant of *E. coli* and the Re mutant of *S. minnesota*, attempts have been made to delineate which of these antigens was responsible

TABLE 3. *Survival in spontaneous bacteremia in granulocytopenic rabbits*

	Challenge strains		
Immunizing agent	*Escherichia coli* 166	*E. coli* O:4	*Enterobacter aerogenes*
Re mutant ...	12/19[a] (63%)	8/11 (73%)	6/11 (55%)
Lipid A	5/15 (33%)	2/10 (20%)	0/10 (0%)
Pseudomonas aeruginosa ..	2/10 (20%)	1/10 (10%)	2/10 (20%)
Saline	4/16 (25%)	2/9 (22%)	0/10 (0%)

[a] Number of survivors/number challenged.

for the induction of protective antibodies. The initial portion of these studies, carried out by Margaret Johns, provided evidence of extreme antigenic similarity or identity between lipid A derived from a large variety of gram-negative bacteria. Figure 1 illustrates reactions of identity in agar-gel precipitation between lipid A from the Re mutant of *S. minnesota*, *Citrobacter freundii*, *P. aeruginosa*, and *Chromobacterium violaceum* when antiserum to lipid A from the Re mutant was used. Similar reactions of immunological identity were also obtained with lipid A from *P. vulgaris*, *P. rettgeri*, *K. pneumoniae*, *S. typhosa*, *S. enteritidis*, *Haemophilus influenzae* type B, and *Neisseria meningitidis* types A, C, W-135, and Z.

These studies were then extended to compare the protective effects of immunization with the Re mutant of *S. minnesota* and lipid A against both lethal bacterial infections and heterologous endotoxin. The effects of active immunization with the Re mutant and lipid A were compared with those of *P. aeruginosa*- and saline-injected controls in protection against lethal bacteremia due to two strains of *Escherichia coli* and *Enterobacter aerogenes* in granulocytopenic rabbits by use of the model described by Braude et al. (3). Immunization with the Re mutant afforded significant protection against lethal bacteremia ($P < 0.05$) in comparison with that observed in control animals (Table 3). In contrast, immunization with lipid A did not increase survival rates over those observed in control animals.

The effect of passive transfer of 0.3 ml of

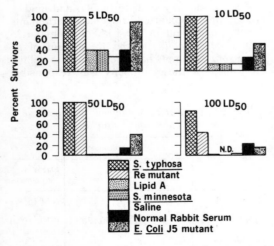

FIG. 2. *Survival rates in mice, passively immunized with 0.3 ml of antiserum to the antigens shown at the bottom of the figure, after intravenous challenge with 5, 10, 50, and 100* LD_{50} *of* Salmonella typhosa *endotoxin. (Reproduced from J. Infect. Dis., in press)*

rabbit antiserum to the Re mutant, to *S. typhosa*, to *S. minnesota*, and to the J5 mutant of *E. coli*, or of normal rabbit serum or saline, upon subsequent challenge with 5, 10, 50, and 100 LD_{50} of *S. typhosa* and *S. minnesota* endotoxin in actinomycin D-treated mice has also been evaluated. Antiserum to lipid A provided no protection against challenge with 5, 10, 50, or 100 LD_{50} of either *S. typhosa* (as shown in Fig. 2) or *S. minnesota* endotoxin. Homologous antiserum and antiserum to the Re mutant provided similar high survival rates, 80 to 100%, against challenge with 5, 10, and 50 LD_{50} of both *S. typhosa* and *S. minnesota* endotoxin. Homologous antiserum was more protective than Re antiserum with 100 LD_{50} challenges with both endotoxins, however. Antiserum to the J5 mutant of *E. coli* also protected against challenge with both endotoxins, but was slightly less effective than antiserum to the Re mutant (W. R. McCabe et al., J. Infect. Dis., in press).

These experiments provide convincing evidence that immunization with R mutants of gram-negative bacilli does not mediate its protective activity as a result of antibody to lipid A. In addition, they suggest, but do not establish, that KDO is the antigenic determinant responsible for the induction of antibodies which protect against lethal challenge with heterologous bacilli and endotoxin.

Concomitant studies have been carried out in 350 patients with bacteremia due to gram-negative bacilli to determine whether these experimental observations could be related to infections in humans. These investigations involved the measurement of levels of antibody in serum obtained at the onset of bacteremia and the relation of titers of antibody to the subsequent severity of the bacteremia. These studies made the assumption that high levels of antibody, if protective, should be associated with a diminution in the frequency with which shock and death subsequently occurred (11). A significant correlation between high titers of immunoglobulin G O-antigenic specific antibody at the onset of bacteremia and the subsequent development of shock and death was demonstrated. An even more striking correlation was demonstrated between high titers of antibody to Re mutants and a diminution in the severity of bacteremia. Shock and death occurred only one-third as often in patients with high titers, $\geq 1:80$, of Re antibody as in those with lower titers, and this apparent protective activity was independent of any protective effect of O-specific immunoglobulin G antibody (21).

These observations obviously have important clinical implications. The demonstration that antibody to cross-reactive antigens, shared by most *Enterobacteriaceae*, protects experimental animals both against heterologous bacillary infections and against lethal endotoxin challenge and that it is associated with a diminution in the severity of bacteremia in humans suggests that it may ultimately prove feasible to immunize humans against such infections.

ACKNOWLEDGMENTS

These studies were supported by Public Health Service research grants AI-11116 and AI-09584 and training grant 5T01-AI-213 from the National Institute of Allergy and Infectious Diseases.

LITERATURE CITED

1. **Braude, A. I., and H. Douglas.** 1972. Passive immunization against the local Shwartzman reaction. J. Immunol. **108:**505–512.
2. **Braude, A. I., H. Douglas, and C. E. Davis.** 1973. Treatment and prevention of intravascular coagulation with antiserum to endotoxin. J. Infect. Dis. **128**(Suppl.): S157–S164.
3. **Braude, A. I., H. Douglas, and J. Jones.** 1969. Experimental production of lethal *Escherichia coli* bacteremia of pelvic origin. J. Bacteriol. **98:**979–991.
4. **Chedid, L., M. Paraut, F. Paraut, and F. Boyer.** 1968. A proposed mechanism for natural immunity to enterobacterial antigens. J. Immunol. **100:**292–301.
5. **Edwards, P. R., and W. H. Ewing.** 1972. Identification of Enterobacteriaceae, 3rd ed. Burgess Publishing Co., Minneapolis, Minn.
6. **Kaijser, B., J. Holmgren, and L. A. Hanson.** 1972. The protective effect against *E. coli* of O and K antibodies of different immunoglobulin classes. Scand. J. Immunol. **1:**27–32.
7. **Kaijser, B., and S. Olling.** 1973. Experimental hematogenous pyelonephritis due to *E. coli* in rabbits: the antibody response and its protective capacity. J. Infect. Dis. **128:**41–49.
8. **Lüderitz, O., A. M. Staub, and O. Westphal.** 1966. Immunochemistry of O and R antigens of *Salmonella*

and related *Enterobacteriaceae*. Bacteriol. Rev. **30:** 192–255.
9. **McCabe, W. R.** 1972. Immunization with R mutants of *S. minnesota*. I. Protection against challenge with heterologous gram-negative bacilli. J. Immunol. **108:** 601–610.
10. **McCabe, W. R.** 1973. Gram-negative bacteremia. DM Disease-a-Month, December. Year Book Medical Publishers, Inc., Chicago.
11. **McCabe, W. R., B. E. Kreger, and M. Johns.** 1972. Type-specific and cross-reactive antibodies in gram-negative bacteremia. N. Engl. J. Med. **287:**261–267.
12. **Markley, K., and E. Smallman.** 1968. Protection by vaccination against *Pseudomonas* infection after thermal injury. J. Bacteriol. **96:**867–874.
13. **Nikaido, A., K. Nikaido, T. V. Subbaih, and B. A. D. Stocker.** 1964. Rough mutants of *Salmonella typhimurium*. Nature (London) **201:**1298–1302.
14. **Osborn, M. J., S. M. Rosen, L. Rothfield, L. D. Zeleznick, and B. L. Horecker.** 1964. Lipopolysaccharide of the gram-negative cell wall. Science **145:**783–789.
15. **Sanford, J. P., B. W. Hunter, and L. L. Souda.** 1962. The role of immunity in the pathogenesis of experimental hematogenous pyelonephritis. J. Exp. Med. **115:**383–410.
16. **Tate, W. J., III, H. Douglas, and A. I. Braude.** 1966. protection against lethality of *E. coli* endotoxin with "O" antiserum. Ann. N.Y. Acad. Sci. **133:**746–762.
17. **Wolberg, G., and C. W. DeWitt.** 1969. Mouse virulence of K(L) antigen-containing strains of *Escherichia coli*. J. Bacteriol. **100:**730–737.
18. **Wolff, S. M., and J. V. Bennett.** 1974. Gram-negative rod bacteremia. N. Engl. J. Med. **291:**733–734.
19. **Ziegler, E. J., H. Douglas, and A. I. Braude.** 1974. Experimental bacteremia due to Pseudomonas in agranulocytic animals. J. Infect. Dis. **130**(Suppl.): S145–S148.
20. **Ziegler, E. J., H. Douglas, J. E. Sherman, C. E. Davis, and A. I. Braude.** 1973. Treatment of *E. coli* and Klebsiella bacteremia in agranulocytic animals with antiserum to a UDP-Gal epimerase-deficient mutant. J. Immunol. **111:**433–438.
21. **Zinner, S. H., and W. R. McCabe.** 1976. Effects of IgM and IgG antibody in patients with bacteremia due to gram-negative bacilli. J. Infect. Dis. **133:**37–45.

Genetic and Cellular Aspects of Host Response to Endotoxin

Position Paper

JAMES WATSON, KATHLEEN KELLY, AND MICHAEL LARGEN

Department of Medical Microbiology, California College of Medicine, University of California, Irvine, California 92717

POSITION

The C3H/HeJ mouse strain differs in responsiveness to endotoxin when compared with other strains of mice, and as a result has become an important tool for analyzing the genetic and cellular aspects of endotoxin responses. Lipopolysaccharide (LPS) isolated from gram-negative bacteria can be viewed as a composite of two distinct functional moieties: the O polysaccharide, which has been characterized as the major antigen, and the lipid A structure, which is responsible for its endotoxic and various immunological activities (19). We consider here how the C3H/HeJ mouse strain has been used to investigate the genetic control of the immunological properties of LPS.

Endotoxins exert a diverse range of physiological responses which do not involve the immune system (20). The defect in C3H/HeJ mice that limits LPS responsiveness is due to a single gene and leads to a means of analyzing the genetic control of nonimmune responses. The position we take here is that the expression of a single common gene in different cell types may be responsible for many of the diverse physiological responses elicited by endotoxins.

IMMUNOLOGICAL ACTIVITIES OF LPS

Lipid A acts as a specific mitogen for bone marrow-derived (B) lymphocytes in mice (4, 34). This results in the polyclonal expression of these cells (2). In addition, lipid A acts as an adjuvant for the specific antibody response to the O-polysaccharide antigens in LPS, stimulating a more rapid response which reaches a greater titer than that to the polysaccharide antigen alone (30).

The C3H/HeJ mouse strain is unique because it is refractive to the mitogenic (29) and poly-

clonal effects of LPS (32). This defect in C3H/HeJ mice appears specific in that other B-cell mitogens such as polyinosinic acid [poly(I)], dextran sulfate, and a purified protein derivative from tuberculin stimulate mitogenic responses in this strain (32). Immune responses to LPS are restricted to only those B lymphocytes that possess surface immunoglobulin receptors capable of binding the O-polysaccharide antigens, whereas mitogenic responses involve most B lymphocytes and require interactions with lipid A at nonimmunoglobulin receptor sites. Although C3H/HeJ mice support immune responses to the O-polysaccharide antigens, the adjuvant effects of the lipid A moiety apparent in other strains of mice are not observed (31–33; J. Watson, R. Riblet, and B. Taylor, J. Immunol., in press). It is the immunological activities of the lipid A moiety that are defective in C3H/HeJ mice.

The adjuvant activity of lipid A is also assayed by the enhancement of immune responses to soluble antigens, such as bovine serum albumin (23), and the capacity to modulate the induction of a specific state of tolerance in mice to several thymus-dependent antigens into a specific state of immunity (7, 18). In C3H/HeJ mice these assays of adjuvant effects are not observed (23) in response to LPS.

The diverse nature of the immunological properties of LPS leads to various questions. For example, how many genes are responsible for the defective LPS responses in C3H/HeJ mice? Also, what are the cellular aspects involved in supporting these LPS responses?

GENETICS OF MITOGENIC RESPONSES TO LPS

Early studies in our laboratory demonstrated that the F_1 hybrids (C3H.SW-Ig-1^b × C3H/HeJ) exhibited a mitogenic response to LPS which was as high as that of the C3H.SW-Ig-1[b] (CWB/13) parent (31). This argued for the dominant expression of the LPS responsiveness gene. However, other workers (9, 28) and later studies in our own laboratory have indicated that the F_1 hybrids between CWB/13 and C3H/HeJ are unique in the dominant expression of LPS responsiveness. Using a number of responder strains as parents, we found that F_1 hybrids between C3H/HeJ and a responder parent show an intermediate mitogenic response. This was true with the following strains as responder parents: C3H/DiSn, C3HeB/FeJ, C57BL/6J, BALB/c, and DBA/2J (Fig. 1). These data are similar to findings with F_1 hybrids between C3H/HeJ and C3H/Tif or B10.5M (9). This argues for the co-dominant expression of LPS responsiveness. At the present time, we have no adequate explanation for the unique (CWB/13 × C3H/HeJ) F_1 hybrids.

A technical point worth noting is that we have found that the day of the mitogenic assay after LPS stimulation is important in determining dominance or co-dominance of LPS responsiveness. This is true because responder and F_1 cultures show different kinetic patterns. Responder parents show a peak of thymidine incorporation into DNA on day 2 which drops sharply on day 3, whereas F_1 progeny show approximately equivalent thymidine uptake on days 2 and 3. Consequently, mitogenic responses assayed on day 2 show an optimal response for the responder parent and result in an interpretation of co-dominant inheritance of LPS responsiveness. Mitogenic responses assayed on day 3 result in an interpretation of dominance, since F_1 hybrid and parental cultures show similar DNA synthetic responses (K. Kelly and J. Watson, Immunogenetics, in press).

Backcrosses of F_1 hybrid mice to C3H/HeJ parents resulted in approximately equal numbers of nonresponder and responder progeny (9, 28, 31, 33). Backcrosses to high-responder parents showed equivalent numbers of intermediate and high-responder progeny (19, 28, 31). F_2 mice segregated into high-responder, intermediate-responder, and nonresponder phenotypes in a ratio consistent with the segregation of a single autosomal gene. These data, together with the backcross data, indicate that LPS responsiveness is probably controlled by a single locus (9, 28).

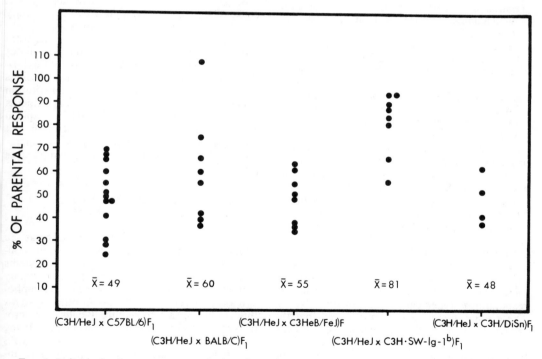

FIG. 1. *Individual spleens were set up in the microculture system with minimal essential media containing 5% fetal calf serum and 10 μg of K235 LPS per ml. Each well was pulsed with 0.25 μCi of [³H]thymidine (14.3 Ci/mmol) from 42 to 48 h after the initial LPS stimulation, and incorporation of radioactivity was determined. The results are expressed as a percentage of the appropriate responder parent values tested in the same experiment.*

GENETICS OF ADJUVANT RESPONSES

The immune response difference to LPS between C3H/HeJ mice and other C3H strains is a quantitative difference. Doses of 1.0 to 25 μg of LPS elicit immunoglobulin M (IgM) responses in C3H/HeJ mice; however, higher doses of LPS show inhibitory effects (23, 31). In contrast, other C3H strains elicit a much greater immune response to LPS over a much wider dose range (0.1 to 200 μg). The immune response difference can be regarded as a result of the adjuvant properties of lipid A.

The linkage relationships of mitogenic and adjuvant responsiveness to LPS have been investigated in backcross (C3H/HeJ × CWB/13) F_1 × C3H/HeJ mice (31). Two conclusions were reached. First, mitogenic and adjuvant responsiveness always segregated together, as all backcross mice that supported high in vivo immune responses to LPS also showed in vitro mitogenic responses to LPS. Second, the defect in C3H/HeJ mice that limits these two responses is due to a single autosomal gene (31).

In mice, an immune response to human IgG (HGG) requires cell collaboration between B and T lymphocytes, and immunization with an aggregated form of HGG (AHGG; 5). The injection of a deaggregated form of HGG (DHGG) results in the induction of tolerance to HGG as revealed by the failure to respond to a subsequent challenge with AHGG (3). Mice treated with LPS shortly after the injection of a tolerogenic dose of DHGG not only fail to become tolerant to HGG, but demonstrate a delayed primary response to HGG and also respond to a subsequent immunogenic challenge of AHGG (13, 18). C3H/HeJ mice can be rendered tolerant to DHGG in a manner identical to that observed in other strains of mice. However, when C3H/HeJ mice are treated with DHGG and a dose of LPS that interferes with tolerance induction in other strains, the LPS has no effect in altering the induction to tolerance (23).

In mice that were the progeny of a backcross between the nonresponder C3H/HeJ parent and the responder (C3H/HeJ × CWB/13) F_1 hybrid, it was found that LPS interfered with tolerance induction to DHGG in vivo only in backcross mice whose spleen cells were also capable of responding mitogenically to LPS in vitro (24, 33). These experiments also demonstrated that the adjuvant and mitogenic properties of LPS are genetically linked. The subcellular mode of action of LPS as an adjuvant may involve the delivery of a signal to B cells which is the same as the stimulus for mitogenesis. Alternatively, this linkage may be a reflection of a single common gene in a different cell type.

CELLULAR ASPECTS OF THE DEFECTIVE MITOGENIC RESPONSE

LPS stimulates B lymphocytes to mitogenesis, but not thymocytes, cortisone-resistant thymocytes, peripheral T cells (11), or macrophages (22). However, there is evidence that T lymphocytes and macrophages influence the activation of B lymphocytes by LPS. B lymphocytes from Peyer's patches of athymic mice (17) are not mitogenically stimulated by LPS unless T lymphocytes and macrophages are added. Similar cellular requirements appear to exist with lymph node B lymphocytes (16). There are several possible cellular locations for the expression of the defect in C3H/HeJ mice, namely, B lymphocytes, T lymphocytes, and macrophages, and these involve either the absence of helper cells or the presence of suppressor cell activity. A variety of in vivo and in vitro reconstitution experiments have been reported which indicate that the defect in C3H/HeJ mice that restricts mitogenic responsiveness is expressed in the B lymphocytes (8, 12, 32). Thus, in adult thymectomized C3H/HeJ mice that were irradiated and reconstituted with various combinations of C3H/HeJ and LPS responder C3HeB/FeJ bone marrow and thymus cells, C3H/HeJ B lymphocytes consistently failed to support mitogenic responses to LPS. In addition, the presence of thymus cells from C3H/HeJ or C3HeB/FeJ mice neither stimulates nor inhibits significantly the response of C3HeB/FeJ bone marrow cells (32). Similar findings have been reported for in vitro reconstitution experiments (8, 12, 32). These experiments indicate that the failure of C3H/HeJ spleen cells to respond mitogenically to LPS is not due to a defect in T lymphocytes or macrophages, but to a defect in the B-lymphocyte population.

CELLULAR BASIS OF ADJUVANT EFFECTS

The cellular site of action of LPS as an adjuvant has become a matter of some controversy since in some experimental systems LPS appears to exert its effect on antibody responses by a direct interaction with B lymphocytes (2, 23, 24, 31), whereas in other systems this effect appears to require T cells or macrophages (1, 21). In backcross experiments utilizing C3H/HeJ mice, the adjuvant properties of LPS segregate with the mitogenic properties, indicating they are controlled by the same gene (24, 31). The coordinate expression of mitogenic and adjuvant effects of LPS suggests that the cellular site of action of LPS as an adjuvant may be restricted to B lymphocytes. This conclusion depends upon showing that the adjuvant effects of LPS in C3H/HeJ mice do not involve a defect in T lymphocytes or macrophages. In thymectomized and irradiated C3H/HeJ mice that had been reconstituted with LPS responder C3HeB/FeJ bone marrow cells, immune responses to LPS were similar to those in normal C3HeB/FeJ mice (32). Since in vivo C3HeB/FeJ thymus cells did not enhance the immune response of C3H/HeJ bone marrow cells to LPS (32), the results support the conclusion that accessory cell types are not involved in at least two of the adjuvant effects exerted by LPS, these being tolerance induction by HGG (24) and immune responsiveness to the O-polysaccharide antigens on LPS (33).

LINKAGE ANALYSIS OF LPS RESPONSIVENESS

A series of recombinant inbred (RI) strains between C3H/HeJ and C57BL/6J mice were examined for the association of LPS responsiveness and various other genetic markers. These RI strains are bred by randomly pairing F_2 brother and sister, and then inbreeding is continued for a number of generations until all loci are homozygous. Each of these F_2 brother-and-sister pairs gives rise to a strain that has a unique combination of genes, since all nonlinked genes have segregated at random in the F_2 generation. These RI strains are homozygous at all loci for the alleles of one or the other parent. Fourteen of the strains were examined for various phenotypes: H-2 haplotype, heavy-chain allotype, and LPS responsiveness (Watson et al., in press). These mice were all screened for a variety of other traits including an electrophoretic variant major urinary protein (Mup-1; 10, 15). Of 14 RI strains, 10 showed a correlation between heavy-chain allotype and LPS responsiveness, whereas the correlation between Mup-1 and LPS responsiveness was even more striking (13 of 14; Table 1). There was no correlation between LPS responsiveness and any of the other traits examined (Watson, Riblet, and Taylor, in press). However, even the association of two genes in an RI strain is not conclusive evidence for genetic linkage. Other genetic evidence, for example backcross and F_2 segregation analysis, is necessary to confirm genetic linkage. Indeed, with another strain combination, C3H/HeJ × CWB/13, it has been previously shown with backcross and allotype congenic mice that there is no linkage between heavy-chain allotype and LPS responsiveness. Thus, the association of the two loci in the RI strains may be fortuitous.

TABLE 1. Summary of H-2, Ig-1 allotype, and major urinary protein (Mup) characteristics of recombinant inbred C57BL/6J × C3H/HeJ lines[a]

Recombinant inbred line	Generations tested	H-2	Ig-1	Mup-1	LPS (responder/non-responder)
BXH-2	F_{14}, F_{23}	k	a	a	NR
BXH-3	F_{16}, F_{23}	k	b	a	NR
BXH-4	F_{15}, F_{20}	b	a	a	NR
BXH-5	F_{16}, F_{27}	k	b	b	R
BXH-6	F_{15}, F_{22}	k	a	a	NR
BXH-7	F_{15}	k	a	a	NR
BXH-8	F_{12}, F_{19}	b	b	a	NR
BXH-9	F_{14}, F_{23}, F_{26}	b	a	a	NR
BXH-10	F_{15}, $F_{19}BC_4F_5$	b	b	b	R
BXH-11	F_{15}, F_{23}, F_{28}, F_{29}	b	b	b	R
BXH-12	F_{14}	k	a	a	NR
BXH-14	F_{15}, F_{22}, F_{28}	k	b	a	NR
BXH-18	F_{14}, F_{20}	k	a	b	NR
BXH-19	F_{15}, F_{22}, F_{28}	b	a	b	R

[a] Parental types: C57BL/6 H-2[b], Ig-1[b], Mup-1[b]
C3H/HeJ H-2[k], Ig-1[a], Mup-1[a]

We have now tested for linkage of LPS responsiveness in the backcross F_1 (C3H/HeJ × C57BL/6J) × C3H/HeJ. In this cross all the progeny exhibit either the C3H/HeJ (Mup-1[a]) or heterozygote (Mup-1[a]/Mup-1[b]) phenotype. The major urinary protein is synthesized in the liver and excreted into the urine, where it is the predominant protein (10, 15). The parental and heterozygote patterns for Mup-1 can be scored by use of polyacrylamide gel electrophoresis. The LPS responsiveness is then assayed with the use of individual spleen cultures. The results of such an analysis are presented in Table 2. As can be seen, there is approximately the 50:50 segregation of both markers expected for a single autosomal gene in a backcross. In at least 57 of 63 mice examined, LPS responsiveness segregates with the heterozygous Mup-1[a]/Mup-1[b] pattern, whereas the nonresponder mice carry the C3H/HeJ allele for Mup-1. There thus

TABLE 2. Summary of backcross linkage analysis[a]

Genotype	No. of high-responder mice	No. of low-responder mice
Mup-1[a]/Mup-1[a]	2	28
Mup-1[a]/Mup-1[b]	29	4

[a] (C3H/HeJ × C57BL/6J) F_1 mice were backcrossed to C3H/HeJ, and the progeny were tested for electrophoretic variants of the major urinary protein. C3H/HeJ is Mup-1[a]; C57BL/6J is Mup-1[b]. Backcross mice were either homozygous (Mup-1[a]/Mup-1[a]) or heterozygous (Mup-1[a]/Mup-1[b]) at this locus.

exists a genetic linkage between the two loci. Since *Mup-1* has previously been mapped to the fourth chromosome of the mouse (15), we may conclude with reasonable certainty that the gene for LPS responsiveness (*Lps*) is also located on the fourth chromosome.

The recombination frequency for *Mup-1* and *Lps* can be calculated from both the RI strains and the backcross progeny. To obtain the recombination frequency for the RI strains, it is necessary to use the following formula (14). The probability of fixing a recombinant genotype (*R*) is $4r/(1 + 6r)$, where r is the probability of recombination in a single meiosis. With $R = 1/14$, a value of 2.0% is obtained. When the backcross data are used, it is necessary to assign a range for the recombination frequency. There were four clear cases of recombination and two more cases in which the *Mup-1* phenotype was questionable. Thus, one can use 4/61 (6.5%) or 6/63 (9.5%) as a recombination frequency. We are now engaged in a more extensive mapping of *Lps* with other genes previously mapped to chromosome IV of the mouse.

INTRACELLULAR RESPONSE TO LPS

The genetic studies lead to the concept that the LPS-related defects in B lymphocytes from C3H/HeJ mice are due to a common biochemical lesion. Although LPS readily binds to cell surfaces, it is not known whether this event leads to the initiation of an intracellular change. LPS may randomly intercalate into the membrane (6), or there may exist specific LPS-binding receptors (25). No difference in the binding of radioactive LPS to spleen cells from C3H/HeJ and other C3H strains can be detected (32). Although the subcellular site of action is unknown, it is important to determine in C3H/HeJ lymphocytes whether interaction with LPS results in no intracellular changes or whether changes do occur and this leads to an altered biochemical response. In LPS-responsive strains of mice, the mixture of mitogenic concentrations of LPS and poly(I) have additive effects on mitogenesis. In contrast, in C3H/HeJ mice, LPS inhibits the response of B lymphocytes to poly(I) (12). The possibility exists that in C3H/HeJ mice the interaction of LPS with B lymphocytes leads to an altered biochemical response which is inhibitory to mitogenesis. It is also possible that LPS and poly(I) merely compete with each other for binding sites on the B-cell surface.

OTHER ENDOTOXIC RESPONSES

Thus far, we have emphasized immunological activities of endotoxin and considered the genetic control of responses that appear to result from the interaction of lipid A with B lymphocytes. There are many other responses in mice which appear to result from cell types other than B lymphocytes. For example, LPS is highly toxic and has pyrogenic properties in mice (19, 20). LPS induces many metabolic changes resulting from the release of vasoactive amines and enzymes contained in lysosomes, affects glycolysis in many cell types, and causes the release of interferon and other biologically active agents (20). It has been reported that C3H/HeJ mice are highly resistant to the pyrogenic effects of LPS and also display an abnormal pattern of leukocyte changes during an intraperitoneal inflammatory response to LPS (26, 27). The finding that the *Lps* gene is linked to the *Mup-1* locus on chromosome IV now permits the genetic analysis of various non-immune endotoxic responses. For example, the involvement of the *Lps* gene in pyrogenic and toxic responses in mice can be investigated. The increased resistance of C3H/HeJ mice to these endotoxic properties (26, 27) may result from involvement of the expression of the *Lps* gene. In preliminary experiments using backcross F_1 (C3H/HeJ × C57BL/6J) × C3H/HeJ mice, we have observed that increased resistance to the pyrogenic and toxic effects of LPS maps with the *Lps* locus. The expression of this locus would appear to be a necessary component of many endotoxic responses.

CONCLUSION

A single locus (*Lps*) on chromosome IV is responsible for the defective responses to LPS in C3H/HeJ mice. There appears to be co-dominant expression of LPS responsiveness at this locus. Genetic analysis of immunological responses to LPS in C3H/HeJ mice reveals that these responses are all controlled by the *Lps* gene. The expression of the *Lps* gene in different cell types may be involved in many non-immune endotoxic responses in mice. The use of C3H/HeJ mice and *Mup-1* as a genetic marker will enable an analysis of the involvement of the *Lps* gene in many diverse endotoxic responses.

ACKNOWLEDGMENTS

This work was supported by Public Health Service grant AI-13383 from the National Institute of Allergy and Infectious Diseases, and by grant 1-469 from the National Foundation. J.W. is supported by a Research Career Development Award (AI-00182) from the National Institute of Allergy and Infectious Diseases; K.K. is supported by National Cancer Institute Training Grant CA 09054; and M.L. is supported by National Institutes of Health Training Grant GM 07307. We thank B. Taylor and R. Riblet for their generous collaborative efforts during the course of this work.

LITERATURE CITED

1. **Allison, A. C., and A. J. S. Davies.** 1971. Requirement of thymus-dependent lymphocytes for potentiation by adjuvants of antibody formation. Nature (London) **233:**330–332.
2. **Andersson, J., G. Möller, and O. Sjöberg.** 1972. Selective induction of DNA synthesis in T and B lymphocytes. Cell. Immunol. **4:**381–393.
3. **Chiller, J. M., G. Habicht, and W. Weigle.** 1970. Cellular sites of immunologic unresponsiveness. Proc. Natl. Acad. Sci. U.S.A. **65:**551–556.
4. **Chiller, J. M., B. J. Skidmore, D. C. Morrison, and W. O. Weigle.** 1973. Relationship of the structure of bacterial lipopolysaccharide to its function in mitogenesis and adjuvanticity. Proc. Natl. Acad. Sci. U.S.A. **70:**2129–2133.
5. **Chiller, J., and W. Weigle.** 1973. Termination of tolerance to human gamma globulin in mice by antigen and bacterial lipopolysaccharide (endotoxin). J. Exp. Med. **138:**740–750.
6. **Ciznár, I., and J. W. Shands.** 1971. Effect of alkali-treated lipopolysaccharide on erythrocyte membrane stability. Infect. Immun. **4:**362–367.
7. **Clamen, H.** 1963. Tolerance to a protein antigen in adult mice and the effect of nonspecific factors. J. Immunol. **91:**833–839.
8. **Coutinho, A.** 1976. Genetic control of B-cell responses. II. Identification of the spleen B-cell defect in C3H/HeJ mice. Scand. J. Immunol. **5:**129–140.
9. **Coutinho, A., G. Möller, and E. Gronowicz.** 1975. Genetic control of B cell responses. IV. Inheritance of the unresponsiveness to lipopolysaccharides. J. Exp. Med. **142:**253–258.
10. **Finlayson, J. S., M. Potter, and C. R. Runner.** 1963. Electrophoretic variation and sex dimorphism of the major urinary protein complex in inbred mice: a new genetic marker. J. Natl. Cancer Inst. **31:**91–97.
11. **Gery, I., J. Krüger, and S. Z. Spiesel.** 1972. Stimulation of B-lymphocytes by endotoxin. Reactions of thymus-deprived mice and karyotypic analysis of dividing cells in mice bearing T_6T_6 thymus grafts. J. Immunol. **108:**1088–1091.
12. **Glode, L. M., I. Scher, B. Osborne, and D. L. Rosenstreich.** 1976. Cellular mechanism of endotoxin unresponsiveness in C3H/HeJ mice. J. Immunol. **116:**454–461.
13. **Golub, E. S., and W. O. Weigle.** 1967. Studies on the induction of immunologic unresponsiveness. I. Effects of endotoxin and phytohemaglutinin. J. Immunol. **98:**1241–1247.
14. **Haldane, J. B. S., and C. H. Waddington.** 1931. Inbreeding and linkage. Genetics **16:**357–374.
15. **Hudson, D. M., J. S. Finlayson, and M. Potter.** 1967. Linkage of one component of the major urinary protein complex of mice to the brown coat color locus. Genet. Res. **10:**195–198.
16. **Janossy, G.** 1976. Heterogeneity of murine and human B lymphocytes responding to polyclonal mitogens, p. 191–209. *In* J. J. Oppenheim and D. L. Rosenstreich (ed.), Mitogens in immunobiology. Academic Press Inc., New York.
17. **Kagnoff, M. F., P. Billings, and M. Cohn.** 1974. Functional characteristics of Peyer's patch lymphoid cells. III. Lipopolysaccharide is thymus dependent. J. Exp. Med. **139:**407–413.

18. **Louis, J., J. Chiller, and W. Weigle.** 1973. The ability of bacterial lipopolysaccharide to modulate the induction of unresponsiveness to a state of immunity. J. Exp. Med. **138:**1481–1495.
19. **Lüderitz, O., O. Westphal, A. M. Staub, and H. Nikaido.** 1971. Isolation and chemical and immunological characterization of bacterial lipopolysaccharides, p. 145–234. *In* G. Weinbaum, S. Kadis, and S. J. Ajl (ed.), Microbial toxins, vol. 5. Academic Press Inc., New York.
20. **Milner, K. C., J. A. Rudbach, and E. Ribi.** 1971. General characteristics, p. 1–66. *In* G. Weinbaum, S. Kadis, and S. J. Ajl (ed.), Microbial toxins, vol. 5. Academic Press Inc., New York.
21. **Newburger, P. E., T. Hamaoka, and D. J. Katz.** 1974. Potentiation of helper T cell function in IgE antibody responses by bacterial lipopolysaccharide (LPS). J. Immunol. **113:**824–829.
22. **Shands, J. W., D. L. Peavy, B. J. Gormius, and J. McGraw.** 1974. In vitro and in vivo effects of endotoxin on mouse peritoneal cells. Infect. Immun. **9:** 106–112.
23. **Skidmore, G., J. Chiller, D. Morrison, and W. Weigle.** 1975. Immunologic properties of bacterial lipopolysaccharide (LPS): correlation between the mitogenic, adjuvant and immunogenic activities. J. Immunol. **114:**770–775.
24. **Skidmore, B. J., J. M. Chiller, W. O. Weigle, R. Riblet, and J. Watson.** 1976. Immunologic properties of bacterial lipopolysaccharide (LPS). III. Genetic linkage between the in vitro mitogenic and in vivo adjuvant properties of LPS. J. Exp. Med. **143:**143–150.
25. **Springer, G. F., J. C. Adye, A. Bezhoravainy, and B. Hirgenson.** 1974. Properties and activity of the lipopolysaccharide receptor from human erythrocytes. Biochemistry **13:**1379–1389.
26. **Sultzer, B. M.** 1968. Genetic control of leucocyte responses to endotoxin. Nature (London) **219:**1253–1254.
27. **Sultzer, B. M.** 1972. Genetic control of host responses to endotoxin. Infect. Immun. **5:**107–113.
28. **Sultzer, B. M.** 1976. Genetic analysis of lymphocyte activation by lipopolysaccharide endotoxin. Infect. Immun. **13:**1579–1584.
29. **Sultzer, B. M., and B. S. Nilssen.** 1972. PPD tuberculin—a B-cell mitogen. Nature (London) New Biol. **240:** 198–200.
30. **Von Eschen, K. B., and J. A. Rudbach.** 1974. Immunological responses of mice to native protoplasmic polysaccharide and lipopolysaccharide. J. Exp. Med. **140:**1604–1614.
31. **Watson, J., and R. Riblet.** 1974. Genetic control of responses to bacterial lipopolysaccharides in mice. J. Exp. Med. **140:**1147–1161.
32. **Watson, J., and R. Riblet.** 1975. Genetic control of responses to bacterial lipopolysaccharides in mice. J. Immunol. **114:**1462–1468.
33. **Watson, J., R. Riblet, M. Cohn, B. Skidmore, J. Chiller, and W. Weigle.** 1976. The mitogenic activity of bacterial lipopolysaccharide as a probe for T cell function, p. 245–260. *In* J. J. Oppenheim and D. L. Rosenstreich (ed.), Mitogens in immunobiology. Academic Press Inc., New York.
34. **Watson, J., E. Trenkner, and M. Cohn.** 1973. The use of bacterial lipopolysaccharides to show that two signals are required for the induction of antibody synthesis. J. Exp. Med. **138:**699–714.

Characteristics of Endotoxin-Resistant Low-Responder Mice

BARNET M. SULTZER AND GAIL W. GOODMAN

Department of Microbiology and Immunology, State University of New York
Downstate Medical Center, Brooklyn, New York 11203

The numerous pathophysiological effects produced by endotoxin have long been known to be subject to intraspecies variation. However, the role of genetic factors in such variation has only recently been appreciated. Our investigations on the genetic control of host responses to endotoxin originated with the recognition that the intraspecies or strain variation in mice we had observed in endotoxin-induced nonspecific resistance to bacterial infections was probably genetically determined (26). It seemed reasonable, therefore, that a genetic approach might be useful for analyzing the mechanism of endotoxin activity at the cellular and eventually the molecular level. This rationale led in turn to the discovery that the leukocyte reactions to endotoxin of the resistant C3H/HeJ mouse are radically different from those of strains of mice which are ordinarily susceptible to endotoxin (27). The subsequent finding that the lymphocytes of this strain were not stimulated appreciably to DNA synthesis by lipopolysaccharide endotoxin (LPS), as occurred with cells from virtually all other strains (32), led to the adoption of the C3H/HeJ mouse as a useful analytical tool for examining the interaction of LPS and mammalian cells. Subsequently, a significant number of expressions of endotoxin activity including antibody production, polyclonal activation, mitogenicity, and action as an adjuvant, as well as the inflammatory cellular response and toxicity, have been found to be under genetic control (3, 19, 22, 28–30, 34, 35).

In this report, our intention is to discuss both in vivo and in vitro studies which will further characterize the responses of this variant mouse strain to endotoxin and may provide some new clues about the multifarious activities of endotoxin in the mammalian host.

IN VIVO RESPONSES

Since our previous studies indicated that the inflammatory response to endotoxin contributed to protection against an experimentally induced bacterial peritonitis, we first directed our efforts at describing the leukocyte response to LPS in C3H/HeJ mice as compared with that in endotoxin-susceptible strains. The results of a representative experiment are shown in Fig. 1. Few, if any, polymorphonuclear cells (PMN) are present in the normal peritoneal cavity of mice. After the intraperitoneal injection of 10 μg of *Escherichia coli* O127:B8 LPS prepared by phenol-water extraction (36), a significant influx of PMN occurs by 24 h in CBA/J mice, whereas an even more striking increase in PMN is apparent by 12 h in C3H/HeJ mice. In contrast, the normal peritoneal cavity of mice contains mononuclear cells consisting of macrophages and lymphocytes. After LPS is given, the level of mononuclear cells decreases in CBA/J mice over the first 24 h, whereas it remains essentially unchanged in C3H/HeJ mice. Indeed, at 48 to 96 h these cells actually increase above normal levels in C3H/HeJ mice while only returning to normal in endotoxin-susceptible mice (28). We chose to review this phenomenon to emphasize that, in terms of the inflammatory leukocyte response to LPS, the C3H/HeJ mouse is *not* a low responder. Also, by morphological criteria, the macrophages from these mice given LPS are activated in that the cell membranes are ruffled and the cytoplasm is spread, with the concomitant appearance of numerous vacuoles. Undoubtedly, this series of cellular events in the peritoneal cavity does not simply reflect the interaction of LPS with each cell type, although this may occur, but most likely involves the occurrence of complex processes including vasoactive and chemotactic effects which influence both the diapedesis and recruitment of extravascular leukocytes.

That chemotaxis of PMN and macrophages plays an important role in the inflammatory response to endotoxin has been supported by those studies which have shown that complement-dependent chemotactic activity, mediated through the cleavage product complement 5a, is obtained from the interaction of complement with endotoxin (23–25). It was of interest, therefore, to measure complement levels in C3H/HeJ mice. Using the method of Terry et al. (33), we found that pooled sera from C3H/HeJ mice

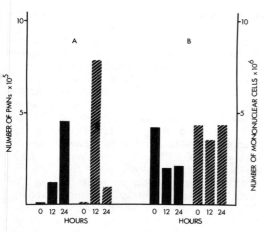

FIG. 1. *Mean number of leukocytes recovered from the peritoneal cavity of CBA/J mice (closed bars) and C3H/HeJ mice (striped bars) given 10 μg of E. coli O127:B8 LPS. (A) Polymorphonuclear cells; (B) mononuclear cells.*

TABLE 1. *Effect of mouse serum on the toxicity of endotoxin[a]*

Serum endotoxin mixture	Survivors/total (% survivors)		
	Day 1	Day 2	Day 3
Buffer, LPS, AcD	18/20 (90)	15/20 (75)	1/20 (5)
A/HeJ serum, LPS, AcD ...	20/20 (100)	17/20 (85)	2/20 (10)
C3H/HeJ serum, LPS, AcD..	20/20 (100)	20/20 (100)	11/20 (45), $P = 0.05$[b]
AcD control..............	20/20 (100)	19/20 (95)	19/20 (95)

[a] The reaction mixture consisted of 1 volume of serum added to 1 volume of endotoxin in Veronal buffer (pH 7.2) to give a final endotoxin concentration of 20 μg/ml. The mixture was incubated at 37°C for 5 h. Amounts of 1.0 ml of the mixture were injected intraperitoneally into Swiss (Albany) mice simultaneously with 10 μg of actinomycin D (AcD) to test for residual endotoxin toxicity.

[b] Statistical evaluation by the fourfold contingency test (11), represents the significance of the difference between A/HeJ and C₃H/HeJ serum.

had relatively high levels of complement, amounting to as much as 29 50% hemolytic complement units. A/HeJ serum was essentially deficient in hemolytic complement, as expected, since this strain is deficient in complement 5 (16). It is possible that the rapid influx of PMN and the sustained levels of mononuclear cells seen in endotoxin-treated C3H/HeJ mice reflect at least in part the consequence of complement activation.

Other serum factors, as well as complement, may contribute to host defense against endotoxicosis by detoxifying endotoxin (5, 9, 12, 21). To determine whether the serum of C3H/HeJ mice could degrade endotoxin more effectively than serum from susceptible A/HeJ mice, endotoxin was incubated with serum from both strains for 5 h at 37°C. Residual endotoxin activity in the serum mixture was measured by a lethality test in actinomycin D-treated mice (17). The pooled data from two trials are shown in Table 1. C3H/HeJ serum reduced the toxicity of endotoxin, whereas A/HeJ serum was ineffective. Passive transfer of protection against an endotoxin challenge was also demonstrable. As shown in Table 2, approximately 50% of normal A/HeJ mice that received 1.0 ml of C3H/HeJ serum 3 h before challenge with 5 LD₅₀ of *Salmonella typhosa* O-901 endotoxin survived.

In view of the type of inflammatory response and the innate resistance to endotoxin shown by C3H/HeJ mice, the possibility existed that these animals might be more resistant to an acute lethal infection with gram-negative bacteria. To test this idea, two types of inocula were used: (i) a washed suspension of organ-

isms from an 18-h culture of *E. coli* O127:B8 and (ii) a 5-h log-phase culture. C3H/HeJ mice clearly were more resistant than A/HeJ mice at all the infective doses used (Table 3). With a log-phase culture, the LD₅₀ was about 3.6 × 10⁶ organisms for A/HeJ mice and 4.1 × 10⁷ organisms for C3H/HeJ mice. On this basis, approximately a 10-fold difference in susceptibility to a lethal *E. coli* peritonitis exists between these strains of mice. However, endotoxin-resistant C3H/HeJ mice have been shown to be highly susceptible to an intracellular-type lethal infection with *S. typhimurium* (34). Therefore, the role of innate endotoxin resistance as a protective mechanism against a lethal gram-negative infection would appear to depend upon the pathogenesis of the particular infecting organism.

In another approach to the study of endotoxin resistance in C3H/HeJ mice, pertussis vaccine was used for its capacity to enhance the susceptibility of mice to the lethal effect of endotoxin (10). Although some evidence suggests that pertussis acts via histamine and serotonin

TABLE 2. *Passive transfer of protection against endotoxicosis in mice with normal C3H/HeJ serum*

Treatment[a]	Survivors/total[b]	Cumulative percent survivors
Saline	0/30	0
Serum	14/30	47

[a] Amounts of 1.0 ml of serum were injected intraperitoneally into A/HeJ mice 3 h before intraperitoneal challenge with 5 LD₅₀ of *S. typhosa* O-901 endotoxin (250 μg in 0.5 ml).

[b] Recorded at 72 h. Data pooled from three trials.

TABLE 3. *Susceptibility of endotoxin-resistant C3H/HeJ mice to a lethal infection with E. coli O127:B8*

Mouse strain	Mean no. of viable organisms injected[a]	Survivors/ total[b]	Percent survivors
A/HeJ	20×10^7	0/12	0
	10×10^7	2/12	17
	5×10^7	3/12	25
C3H/HeJ	20×10^7	9/12	75
	10×10^7	11/12	92
	5×10^7	11/12	92

[a] Washed cells from an 18-h culture standardized turbidimetrically at 540 nm and plate counted. Amounts of 0.5 ml of each dilution were injected intraperitoneally into mice of each strain.
[b] Deaths recorded at 72 h. No deaths occurred after 72 h. The data are pooled from two such experiments.

sensitization, the mechanism underlying the pertussis-endotoxin effect is not clear (2, 18). Nevertheless, the question arose as to whether the resistance of C3H/HeJ mice could be altered by pertussis pretreatment as is the case with other strains. In two separate trials, C3H/HeJ mice were given approximately 7×10^9 killed pertussis cells intraperitoneally, and 5 days later the mice were challenged by the same route with various doses of either *E. coli* O127:B8 or *S. typhosa* O-901 endotoxin. The LD_{50} of the *E. coli* endotoxin was 2,240 μg in untreated mice but only 77 μg in pertussis-treated mice. Likewise, the LD_{50} of the *S. typhosa* endotoxin was 2,120 μg in untreated mice but only 100 μg in pertussis-treated mice. Consequently, the susceptibility to the lethal effect of endotoxin in C3H/HeJ mice can be increased some 20- to 30-fold by pertussis treatment to a level similar to the natural susceptibility of A/HeJ mice. These

TABLE 4. *Mitogenic activity of endotoxin fractions on mouse spleen cells[a]*

Fraction	[³H]thymidine uptake (mean net cpm)		
	CBA/J	C3H/HeJ	"Nude"
LPS (aqueous phase)			
100 μg/ml	106,317 (22.0)[b]	5,476 (2.6)	40,570 (14.0)
50 μg/ml	107,678 (22.3)	4,268 (2.3)	33,252 (11.6)
10 μg/ml	99,534 (20.7)	2,704 (1.8)	25,804 (9.3)
Protein (phenol phase)			
100 μg/ml	192,671 (39.2)	102,389 (31.0)	105,219 (34.7)
50 μg/ml	194,936 (39.6)	108,762 (32.9)	104,056 (34.3)
10 μg/ml	190,634 (38.8)	90,060 (27.4)	83,220 (27.6)

[a] Data taken from Sultzer and Goodman (31). The starting endotoxin was extracted from *E. coli* O127:B8 by the trichloroacetic acid method.
[b] The numbers in parentheses are the stimulation index.

results suggest to us that the susceptibility to endotoxicosis of C3H/HeJ mice, although quantitatively different from that of most strains of mice, most likely is qualitatively similar to that of other inbred or random-bred strains.

Taken together, the results of the in vivo experiments we have described serve to emphasize that the genetic resistance and inflammatory leukocyte response to LPS exhibited by C3H/HeJ mice are the end result of complex phenomena. Although the relative unresponsiveness of the C3H/HeJ B lymphocyte to LPS, which we discuss below, raises the attractive hypothesis that endotoxin resistance in this strain may be due to cellular hyporeactivity (29), our in vivo experiments suggest that this idea may be somewhat simplistic. In any event, it is not surprising that the genetic control of the inflammatory response and endotoxin resistance appears to follow a pattern of multifactorial quantitative inheritance (29).

IN VITRO RESPONSES

Some time ago, in an attempt to gain more of an insight into the cellular reactions to endotoxin and at the same time simplify our model, we chose to culture cells from C3H/HeJ mice with the purpose of observing possible differences in macromolecular synthesis between cells from this strain and those from endotoxin-susceptible mice. Throughout our studies, we had used two types of endotoxin, i.e., both Boivin or trichloroacetic acid-extracted preparations containing 7 to 10% cell wall protein and aqueous phenol extracts of LPS containing less than 1% protein (36). It had been our experience that both types of endotoxins derived from either *E. coli* O127:B8 or *S. typhosa* O-901 produced similar results in C3H/HeJ mice and other strains. More often than not, however, the trichloroacetic acid preparations appeared somewhat more potent. Nevertheless, we accepted the long-standing conclusion that the protein component of the Boivin endotoxin was by and large superfluous and functioned as an inert carrier for LPS or at most an antigen, since removal of this protein by chemical or enzymatic means had little effect on the basic biological properties of LPS (37).

In our initial cell cultures we used a Boivin endotoxin that stimulated DNA synthesis in splenic lymphocytes from endotoxin-susceptible mice but activated DNA synthesis in C3H/HeJ lymphocytes to a much lesser extent (29). Subsequent experiments with essentially protein-free LPS revealed that splenic lymphocytes of C3H/HeJ mice were unresponsive or at the most low responders to the mitogenic effect of LPS.

TABLE 5. *Mitogenic activity of endotoxin protein on various C3H/HeJ cell types*[a]

Mitogen	Neonatal spleen cells	Pooled lymph node cells	Thymocytes	Cortisone-resistant thymocytes
Endotoxin protein				
500 μg/ml....	25,438 (24.0)	—	106 (1.2)	−226 (0.55)
100 μg/ml....	29,657 (27.8)	22,020 (96.3)	81 (1.1)	508 (1.84)
10 μg/ml....	32,184 (30.1)	16,934 (74.3)	−177 (0.67)	203 (1.33)
1 μg/ml....	26,019 (24.5)	4,410 (20.1)	—	—
Concanavalin A				
0.625 μg/ml....	—	—	21,089 (39.2)	51,213 (86.5)

[a] Results show [³H]thymidine uptake (see Table 4) with the stimulation index given in parentheses. Data taken from Sultzer and Goodman (31).

At about the same time, LPS had been shown to be a B-cell mitogen in a number of laboratories (1, 6). In addition, we found that purified protein derivative (PPD) was a nonspecific B-cell mitogen and could stimulate C3H/HeJ B cells to DNA synthesis and polyclonal antibody production (32). T-cell function and the response to thymus-dependent antigens as well were normal in C3H/HeJ mice (B. M. Sultzer, Abstr. Annu. Meet. Am. Soc. Microbiol. 1973, p. 85, M69). Furthermore, Rank had reported that the C3H/HeJ strain showed little if any immune response to lipid A (19). Therefore, we concluded that the unresponsiveness was in the B cells of C3H/HeJ mice and was restricted to LPS (lipid A). This conclusion was supported by the fact that more recently discovered B-cell mitogens such as dextran sulfate and polyinosinic-polycytidylic acid activated C3H/HeJ spleen cells (7, 20).

However, the fact that C3H/HeJ cells could be activated by Boivin endotoxin was puzzling. It occurred to us that the presumably inert protein might act as a carrier which would present the lipid A to the C3H/HeJ cell in a more advantageous way, thereby restoring responsiveness of their B cells. Since the hot phenol-water procedure can cleave the protein from the LPS moiety, we used this technique on Boivin endotoxins to recover the solubilized protein in the phenol phase and the LPS in the aqueous phase (37). Both extracts were precipitated from their respective phases by ethanol, extensively dialyzed, lyophilized, and tested for mitogenicity. According to our working hypothesis, neither the endotoxin protein (EP) nor LPS should activate C3H/HeJ lymphocytes. However, this was not the case (Table 4). EP is a potent mitogen for C3H/HeJ and athymic "nude" mouse spleen cells, whereas the LPS is active on all but the C3H/HeJ cells. Additional experiments suggest that EP is a B-cell mitogen since it does not activate thymocytes or cortisone-resistant thymocytes (Table 5). On

this basis, EP appears to activate the B cells in neonates and lymph nodes and, like other B-cell mitogens, can serve as a polyclonal activator (Tables 5 and 6).

Representative results of the chemical analysis of EP indicate that it contains approximately 81% protein, 12.5% nitrogen, 1.6% glucosamine, and less than 1% 2-keto-3-deoxyoctonate (KDO). That a residue of lipid A may be present in EP can be inferred from the small amount of glucosamine detected, which is a constitutent of lipid A. This content of glucosamine is consistent with that found by Wober and Alaupović, who reported 1.3% glucosamine in the "simple protein" they isolated from an *E. coli* Boivin endotoxin by aqueous phenol extraction (37). From the data already obtained it would appear that EP, the "simple protein" of Wober and Alaupović and a protein separated from butanol-extracted LPS by Morrison and co-workers (14), which activates C3H/HeJ lymphocytes, are one and the same. We believe EP is distinct from the murine-associated lipoprotein that activated

TABLE 6. *Polyclonal activation of C3H/HeJ lymphocytes by endotoxin protein*

Stimulant	No. of PFCs[a]/10⁶ viable cells (TNP-SRBC)[b]
Endotoxin protein	
50 μg	1,005
5.0 μg	343
0.5 μg	199
0.05 μg	29
Lipopolysaccharide	
50 μg	138
5.0 μg	48
0.5 μg	22
0.05 μg	30
Control	26

[a] Plaque-forming cells.
[b] TNP-SRBC: 2,4,6-trinitrophenyl conjugated to sheep red blood cells.

TABLE 7. *Effect of the addition of alkali-treated lipopolysaccharide (A-LPS) on the DNA synthesis stimulated by other B-cell mitogens*

Mouse strain	Mitogen[a]	Mean SI[b]	Change (%)
CBA/J	A-LPS	7.2	0
	EP	18.9	0
	PPD	11.7	0
	A-LPS + EP	13.8	−27
	A-LPS + PPD	17.8	+51
C3H/HeJ	A-LPS	1.2	0
	EP	29.8	0
	A-LPS + EP	22.2	−26

[a] All mitogens used at optimal concentrations. EP = endotoxin protein.
[b] Stimulation index of [³H]thymidine uptake.

C3H/HeJ lymphocytes, since the lipid component of this material is not lipid A (13). However, further work is needed before firm conclusions can be drawn.

Nevertheless, our results with EP serve to re-emphasize the specificity of the defect of C3H/HeJ B lymphocytes for LPS or lipid A and the usefulness of this genetic tool for detecting other molecular components of the cell walls of gram-negative bacteria which may be B-cell activators.

In view of the fact the C3H/HeJ B cells could respond to EP, we considered whether these EP-responding lymphocytes were those that could not respond to LPS or whether there existed separate subpopulations of B cells responding to LPS and EP, and C3H/HeJ mice simply lacked the appropriate LPS-responding sub-population. To examine this question, we chose to use alkali-treated LPS (A-LPS) prepared by the procedure of Neter et al. (15). A-LPS has a greater binding affinity for cell membranes than LPS, is more physically homogeneous, and in our hands was some 10 to 100 times more potent as a B-cell mitogen than LPS (G. W. Goodman and B. M. Sultzer, Fed. Proc. **35:** 653, 1976). In CBA/J high-responder cells, when A-LPS and EP were added together at optimal concentrations, no enhanced stimulation of DNA synthesis was obtained over that seen with EP alone (Table 7). Rather, there was a net loss in DNA synthesis of some 27%. If two subpopulations existed, a summation of stimulation or at the minimum a significant degree of enhancement should be obtained, as occurred with the combination of A-LPS and PPD. Evidence for the existence of LPS and PPD subpopulations has been previously reported (8), and in other experiments A-LPS in combination with LPS has been shown to produce results similar to those obtained here with EP (B. M. Sultzer,

B. S. Nilsson, and D. Kirschenbaum, submitted for publication). We interpret these results to indicate that probably there is a single population of B cells responding to both EP and A-LPS in CBA/J mice. On the other hand, A-LPS did not stimulate C3H/HeJ B cells, but again there was a partial suppression of EP stimulation when the two mitogens were added together (Table 7). These data carry the implication that those B cells in C3H/HeJ mice that respond to EP are the same cells that are incapable of responding to A-LPS or LPS. This defect in responsiveness would not appear to be due to primary nonspecific binding of LPS, since in this regard no differences have been found between high- and low-responding cells (30, 35; L. M. Glode and D. Rosenstreich, submitted for publication). Rather, a secondary signal receptor may exist that is specific for LPS (lipid A) and in some manner is incompetent in C3H/HeJ cells.

Genetic evidence suggesting this latter possibility has been obtained (30). Using C3H/HeJ mice for cross-breeding with high-responder CBA/J mice, our analysis suggests that two co-dominant alleles function to control the mitogenic responsiveness to LPS. Similar results have been reported by Coutinho et al. (4), who used B10.5M and C3H/TiF high-responder strains crossed with the C3H/HeJ strain. In addition, the results of breeding C3H/HeN and C3H/St mice with the C3H/HeJ strain are also consistent with autosomal co-dominant genetic control of LPS mitogenesis (L. M. Glode and D. L. Rosenstreich, submitted for publication). It is possible, therefore, that the phenotypic expression of low responsiveness in C3H/HeJ B lymphocytes may be determined by a gene product rather than by a lack of one due to a recessive genotype, as suggested by the results of Watson and Riblet (35). Possibly, the signal receptor we postulate may be this elusive gene product, but more definitive experiments are necessary to challenge this hypothesis. In any event, the C3H/HeJ model should continue to serve as an important analytical tool for gaining a clearer understanding of B-cell activation.

ACKNOWLEDGMENTS

We thank John Butke and Rosemary Tiernan for technical assistance and Maria Ferrara and Florence Schwartz for help in preparation of the manuscript.

This work was supported by Public Health Service grant AI-07816 from the National Institute of Allergy and Infectious Diseases.

LITERATURE CITED

1. **Anderson, J., G. Möller, and O. Sjöberg.** 1972. Selective induction of DNA synthesis in T and B lymphocytes. Cell. Immunol. **4:**381–393.

2. **Bergman, R. K., and J. Munoz.** 1968. Action of the histamine sensitizing factor from *Bordetella pertussis* on inbred and random bred strains of mice. Int. Arch. Allergy **34**:331–338.

3. **Coutinho, A., E. Gronowicz, and B. M. Sultzer.** 1975. Genetic control of B-cell responses. I. Selective unresponsiveness to lipopolysaccharide. Scand. J. Immunol. **4**:139–143.

4. **Coutinho, A., G. Möller, and E. Gronowicz.** 1975. Genetical control of B-cell responses. IV. Inheritance of unresponsiveness to lipopolysaccharides. J. Exp. Med. **142**:253–258.

5. **Füst, G., and G. Foris.** 1974. Role of complement system in the endotoxicity-enhancing and endotoxin-detoxifying effect of serum. Med. Microbiol. Immunol. **159**:141–150.

6. **Gery, I., G. S. Kruger, and S. Z. Spiesel.** 1972. Reactions of thymus-deprived mice and karyotypic analysis of dividing cells in mice bearing T_6 T_6 thymus grafts. J. Immunol. **108**:1088–1091.

7. **Gronowicz, E., and A. Coutinho.** 1974. Selective triggering of B cell subpopulations by mitogens. Eur. J. Immunol. **4**:771–776.

8. **Gronowicz, E., and A. Coutinho.** 1976. Heterogeneity of B cells. Direct evidence of selective triggering of distinct subpopulations by polyclonal activators. Scand. J. Immunol. **5**:55–69.

9. **Johnson, K. J., and P. A. Ward.** 1972. The requirement for serum complement in the detoxification of bacterial endotoxin. J. Immunol. **108**:611–616.

10. **Kind, L. S.** 1958. The altered reactivity of mice after inoculation with *Bordetella pertussis* vaccine. Bacteriol. Rev. **22**:173–182.

11. **Mainland, D., and I. M. Murray.** 1952. Tables for use in fourfold contingency tests. Science **116**:591–594.

12. **May, J. E., M. A. Kane, and M. M. Frank.** 1972. Host defense against bacterial endotoxemia. Contribution of the early and late components of complement to detoxification. J. Immunol. **109**:893–895.

13. **Melchers, F., V. Braun, and C. Galanos.** 1975. The lipoprotein of the outer membrane of *Escherichia coli*: a B-lymphocyte mitogen. J. Exp. Med. **142**:473–482.

14. **Morrison, D. C., S. J. Betz, and D. M. Jacobs.** 1976. Isolation of a lipid A bound polypeptide responsible for "LPS-initiated" mitogenesis of C3H/HeJ spleen cells. J. Exp. Med. **144**:840–846.

15. **Neter, E., O. Westphal, O. Lüderitz, E. A. Gorzynski, and E. Eichenberger.** 1956. Studies of enterobacterial lipopolysaccharides. Effects of heat and chemicals on erythrocyte-modifying, antigenic toxic and pyrogenic properties. J. Immunol. **76**:377–385.

16. **Nilsson, U. R., and H. J. Müller-Eberhard.** 1967. Deficiency of the fifth component of complement in mice with an inherited complement defect. J. Exp. Med. **125**:1–16.

17. **Pieroni, R. E., E. J. Broderick, A. Bundeally, and L. Levine.** 1970. A simple method for the quantitation of submicrogram amounts of bacterial endotoxin. Proc. Soc. Exp. Biol. Med. **130**:790–794.

18. **Pieroni, R. E., and L. Levine.** 1967. Properties of the immunogenic and sensitizing activities of *Bordetella pertussis* in mice. J. Allergy **39**:93–97.

19. **Rank, W. R., U. Flügge, and R. diPauli.** 1969. Inheritance of the lipid A-induced 19S plaque-forming cell response in mice. Evidence for three antigen recognition mechanisms. Behringwerk-Mitt. **49**:222–229.

20. **Scher, I., D. M. Strong, A. Shmed, R. C. Knudsen, and K. W. Sell.** 1973. Specific murine B-cell activation by synthetic single- and double-stranded polynucleotides. J. Exp. Med. **138**:1545–1563.

21. **Skarnes, R. C.** 1970. Host defense against bacterial endotoxemia: mechanisms in normal animals. J. Exp. Med. **132**:300–316.

22. **Skidmore, B. J., J. M. Chiller, W. O. Weigle, R. Riblet, and J. Watson.** 1976. Immunologic properties of bacterial lipopolysaccharide (LPS). III. Genetic linkage between the *in vitro* mitogenic and *in vivo* adjuvant properties of LPS. J. Exp. Med. **143**:143–150.

23. **Snyderman, R., J. K. Phillips, and S. E. Mergenhagen.** 1971. Biological activity of complement *in vivo*. Role of C5 in the accumulation of polymorphonuclear leukocytes in inflammatory enudates. J. Exp. Med. **134**:1131–1143.

24. **Snyderman, R., M. C. Pike, D. McCarley, and L. Lang.** 1975. Quantification of mouse macrophage chemotaxis in vitro: role of C5 for the production of chemotactic activity. Infect. Immun. **11**:488–492.

25. **Snyderman, R., H. S. Shin, and M. H. Hausman.** 1971. A chemotactic factor for mononuclear leukocytes. Proc. Soc. Exp. Biol. Med. **138**:387–390.

26. **Sultzer, B. M.** 1968. Endotoxin-induced resistance to a staphylococcal infection: cellular and humoral responses compared in two mouse strains. J. Infect. Dis. **118**:340–348.

27. **Sultzer, B. M.** 1968. Genetic control of leucocyte responses to endotoxin. Nature (London) **219**:1253–1254.

28. **Sultzer, B. M.** 1969. Genetic factors in leucocyte responses to endotoxin: further studies in mice. J. Immunol. **103**:32–38.

29. **Sultzer, B. M.** 1972. Genetic control of host responses to endotoxin. Infect. Immun. **5**:107–113.

30. **Sultzer, B. M.** 1976. Genetic analysis of lymphocyte activation by lipopolysaccharide endotoxin. Infect. Immun. **13**:1579–1584.

31. **Sultzer, B. M., and G. W. Goodman.** 1976. Endotoxin protein: a B-cell mitogen and polyclonal activator of C3H/HeJ lymphocytes. J. Exp. Med. **144**:821–827.

32. **Sultzer, B. M., and B. S. Nilsson.** 1972. PPD tuberculin—a B-cell mitogen. Nature (London) New Biol. **240**:198–200.

33. **Terry, W. D., T. Borsos, and H. J. Rapp.** 1964. Differences in serum complement activity among inbred strains of mice. J. Immunol. **92**:576–578.

34. **Vas, S. I., R. S. Roy, and H. G. Robson.** 1973. Endotoxin sensitivity of inbred mouse strains. Can. J. Microbiol. **19**:767–769.

35. **Watson, J., and R. Riblet.** 1974. Genetic control of responses to bacterial lipopolysaccharides in mice. I. Evidence for a single gene that influences mitogenic and immunogenic responses to lipopolysaccharides. J. Exp. Med. **140**:1147–1160.

36. **Westphal, O., O. Lüderitz, and F. Bister.** 1952. Uber die Extraktion von Bacterien mit Phenol-Wasser. Z. Naturforsch. Teil B **7b**:148.

37. **Wober, W., and P. Alaupovíc.** 1971. Studies on the protein moiety of endotoxin from gram-negative bacteria. Eur. J. Biochem. **19**:340–356.

B-Lymphocyte Subpopulations and Endotoxin Response in CBA/N Mice

IRWIN SCHER, NIEVES M. ZALDIVAR, AND DONALD E. MOSIER

Department of Clinical and Experimental Immunology, Division of Immunogenetics, Naval Medical Research Institute, and Laboratory of Immunology, National Institute of Allergy and Infectious Diseases, National Institutes of Health, Bethesda, Maryland 20014

In 1972, Amsbaugh and co-workers (3) reported that an inbred mouse strain, the CBA/N strain, had an inability to respond to pneumococcal polysaccharide (SIII). This trait was inherited in the X-linked manner. Subsequent studies (6, 8, 22) showed that CBA/N mice and F_1 male mice which were hemizygous for the CBA/N X chromosome were also unresponsive to the synthetic RNA polyriboinosinic-polyribocytidylic acid [poly(I·C)] and to dinitrophenyl derivatives of Ficoll (DNP-Ficoll). The thymus-independent nature of these three antigens suggested that the immune defect of CBA/N mice involved bone marrow-derived, thymus-independent (B) lymphocytes. This supposition was confirmed by direct reconstitution experiments with B cells from immunologically normal mice (22). Moreover, analysis of certain functional and surface membrane characteristics of B lymphocytes derived from CBA/N mice and immunologically abnormal F_1 mice revealed a number of abnormalities (1, 2, 4, 6, 7–9, 11, 12, 15–19, 21, 22; Fig. 1). By contrast, functional studies of CBA/N thymus-derived (T) lymphocytes were normal (17).

Studies in which the Fluorescence Activated Cell Sorter (FACS; Becton Dickinson Electronics, Mountain View, Calif.) and lactoperoxidase-catalyzed ^{125}I surface labeling were used indicated that adult CBA/N mice had a deficiency of B lymphocytes that was characterized by the density of their total surface immunoglobulin (Ig) and IgM and by the ratio of surface IgM to IgD (7, 19, 21). Since these B lymphocytes are found in large numbers in the spleens of normal adult mice and appear late in the development of normal neonatal mice (2 to 3 weeks), these cells have been considered to be a distinct mature B-lymphocyte subpopulation (20, 21, 23). Such late-developing B lymphocytes are also distinguished from less mature B cells by the presence of the minor lymphocyte-stimulating (M1s)-coded lympho-cyte-activating determinants (LADs) (2). Studies of CBA/N mice and immunologically abnormal (CBA/N ♀ × C3H/N ♂)F_1 male mice demonstrated that these mice did not express M1s-coded LADs, whereas the immunologically normal (CBA/N ♀ × C3H/N ♂)F_1 female mice stimulated M1s-distinct responder cells in mixed lymphocyte reactions (1, 16). These observations led to the hypothesis that the immune defect of CBA/N mice was secondary to a defect in the development of a late-appearing or mature subpopulation of B lymphocytes. This view was supported by findings that the nonexpression of the M1s-coded LADs and the unusual distribution of total Ig, IgM, and IgD on the surface of CBA/N B lymphocytes were, like the immune defect, transmitted in an X-linked manner.

In this communication, we describe experiments in which bacterial lipopolysaccharide (LPS) is used as a probe to analyze the functional properties of the B-lymphocyte population present in CBA/N mice. *Escherichia coli* O111: B4 LPS (Boivin preparation; Difco) was used either without any additional preparative steps (referred to as Boivin-LPS) or purified (to reduce the amount of protein from ~17 to ~5%) by hot phenol extraction (referred to as P-LPS; 14). Boivin-LPS or P-LPS specific antibody responses were measured by a modified microhemagglutination assay. Sheep red blood cells (SRBC) were coated with Boivin-LPS (LPS-SRBC) as previously described (13), washed, and made up to a 1.0% suspension (vol/vol) with 1% bovine serum albumin-0.9 M NaCl; 25 μl of LPS-SRBC (or SRBC, as a control) and 25 μl of mouse sera appropriately diluted with BSA-NaCl were mixed in microtiter wells and incubated at room temperature for 1 h. The titer at which agglutination occurred was noted ("direct" agglutination), the cells were washed, and 25 μl of a 1:1,000 dilution of a goat anti-mouse immunoglobulin (Meloy Laboratories Inc., Springfield, Va.) was added; the suspension was mixed, and the titer was read ("enhanced"

I. Abnormalities in immune function
   A. Absent responses to SIII, poly(I·C), and DNP-Ficoll (3, 18, 22)
   B. Reduced proliferative response to poly(I·C) and LPS (17)
   C. Diminished killing in antibody-dependent cell-mediated cytotoxicity (17)
II. CBA/N immune defect is X-linked (3, 18, 22) (CBA/N ♀ × DBA/2 ♂)F_1
   ♀ $X'X$ immunologically normal
   ♂ $X'Y$ immunologically abnormal
III. CBA/N T-lymphocyte function appears normal
   A. Graft rejection (17)
   B. T cell-mediated cytotoxicity (17)
   C. Response to phytohemagglutinin and concanavalin A (17)
   D. T-helper function (9)
IV. CBA/N immune defect associated with B-lymphocyte abnormalities
   A. Reduction of 30 to 40% in numbers of splenic B cells (17)
   B. B lymphocytes have a high density of surface immunoglobulin and IgM (19)
   C. B lymphocytes have a high ratio of surface IgM to IgD (7)
   D. B and not T lymphocytes from normal F_1 female mice reconstitute the poly(I·C) and DNP-Ficoll response in F_1 male mice (22)
V. Working hypothesis: CBA/N mice have an abnormality in the maturational development of B lymphocytes (1, 15, 21)

FIG. 1. *Characteristics of CBA/N defect.*

agglutination). The uncoated SRBC were not agglutinated by either control or high-titer LPS-SRBC agglutinating sera in either the direct or enhanced assays. Moreover, unimmunized control sera failed to agglutinate SRBC or LPS-SRBC in the direct or enhanced assays. Data are presented as the geometric mean ± the standard error of the reciprocal enhanced agglutination titer.

Excellent responses to 100 µg of Boivin LPS were observed in immunologically normal (CBA/N ♀ × DBA/2 ♂)F_1 female mice (heterozygous for the CBA/N X chromosome) at 10, 15, and 25 days, with mean titers of 1:237, 1:3,978, and 1:1,072, respectively (Fig. 2). The response of immunologically abnormal (CBA/N ♀ × DBA/2 ♂)F_1 male mice (hemizygous for the CBA/N X chromosome) was considerably different from that of their F_1 female littermates. Only one of 12 F_1 male mice responded to Boivin-LPS at 10 days. At 15 days, all F_1 male mice but one responded to Boivin-LPS with a mean titer of 1:7, and at 30 days the mean titer had increased to 1:317. Similar data were seen when 10 µg of Boivin-LPS was used as an immunogen (data not shown). Thus, the specific thymus-independent antibody response (4) of the F_1 male mice was considerably less

than that of the F_1 female mice, and the kinetics of their response was delayed compared with that of F_1 female mice. The responses of F_1 male spleen cells to the nonspecific in vitro proliferative and polyclonal effects of Boivin-LPS have also been shown to be different from the responses of F_1 female spleen cells. The amount of Boivin-LPS necessary to induce a response in F_1 male spleen cells was considerably more than required for F_1 female cells, although the maximal response at the highest concentration of Boivin-LPS was similar in the F_1 male and female cells (11, 17). These data support previous studies which indicated that the B-lymphocyte function of F_1 male mice was abnormal since both the specific antibody responses to LPS and the nonspecific polyclonal

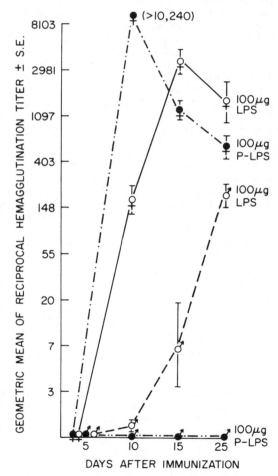

FIG. 2. *Mean reciprocal enhanced hemagglutination titers of (CBA/N ♀ × DBA/2 ♂)F_1 male and female mice to LPS (Boivin E. coli O111:B4) or hot phenol-extracted LPS (P-LPS) at different days after immunization.*

and proliferative stimulation induced by LPS have been shown to reflect thymus-independent B-cell responsiveness (4, 11, 17). It should be emphasized, however, that the initiation of both specific and nonspecific thymus-independent responses of any magnitude in F_1 male mice (spleen cells) with Boivin-LPS is in sharp contrast to the inability to induce specific responses with other thymus-independent antigens.

SIII, DNP-Ficoll, and poly(I·C) are all nonprotein thymus-independent antigens, whereas Boivin preparations of LPS are complex mixtures of LPS, protein, and lipoprotein (24). To determine whether the responses of F_1 male and female mice to Boivin-LPS would be altered by reducing the amount of protein and/or lipoprotein in these preparations, we prepared a hot phenol extract of Boivin-LPS and tested its immunogenicity in these mice. As shown in Fig. 2, the maximal F_1 female response with 100 μg of P-LPS was seen after 10 days (mean titer > 10,240), and excellent responses were seen on days 15 and 25. By contrast, F_1 male mice failed to make detectable responses to the P-LPS. The response characteristics of F_1 male B lymphocytes to P-LPS were further studied by testing the ability of this antigen to induce a polyclonal response in these mice. This was analyzed by measuring the number of cells which secreted antibody specific for trinitrophenyl (TNP) after immunization with P-LPS. F_1 male and female mice were given 10, 33, and 100 μg of P-LPS, and their polyclonal response was measured at day 3. As shown in Table 1, the polyclonal response to all doses of P-LPS was considerably greater in F_1 females than in F_1 males, with the maximal difference oc-

curring with 10 μg of P-LPS. F_1 male mice responded very poorly to 10 and 33 μg of P-LPS, and their response to 100 μg of P-LPS was only half the response of F_1 female mice to 10 μg of P-LPS. It should be emphasized, however, that F_1 male mice were stimulated to form TNP plaque-forming cells by P-LPS.

These results can be viewed in two general ways. It could be assumed that the polyclonal response induced by the P-LPS in F_1 males represents activation of a population of B lymphocytes which are unresponsive to the specific antigenic properties of P-LPS. This F_1 male P-LPS polyclonal-responsive B-lymphocyte population would necessarily be abnormal since the polyclonal response of F_1 male mice to P-LPS is both quantitatively and qualitatively different from that of F_1 female mice. Alternatively, the low polyclonal response of F_1 male mice to P-LPS could be attributed to contaminating antigens present in this preparation (P-LPS had approximately 5% protein by amino acid analysis) which were stimulatory for F_1 male B lymphocytes. If this assumption is correct, then further purification of the P-LPS would eliminate the polyclonal activation induced by this antigen in F_1 male mice.

Whichever view is correct, our data demonstrate that immunologically abnormal F_1 male mice are unresponsive to purified preparations of LPS used as an antigen and give very low polyclonal responses to these preparations. By contrast, Boivin-LPS induces easily measurable antibody responses in F_1 male mice and maximal polyclonal responses which are similar in F_1 male and female mice (11, 17). Thus, B lymphocytes of immune-defective CBA/N mice can respond to certain classes of thymus-independent antigens that are present in Boivin-LPS (10, 24), but are unable to respond to other classes of thymus-independent antigens (DNP-Ficoll, SIII, poly(I·C), and LPS). Since antigen-binding cells have been demonstrated in CBA/N mice for DNP-Ficoll and poly(I·C) (12, 18), the implication is that CBA/N B lymphocytes are able to interact with these antigens but are not triggered to form specific antibody by such interaction. The ability of Boivin-LPS to induce thymus-independent responses in immunologically abnormal F_1 male mice suggests that different subpopulations of B lymphocytes have different requirements for thymus-independent activation. It is possible that the differential ability of thymus-independent antigens to induce B-lymphocyte activation in immune-defective F_1 male mice is due to the structural characteristics of these antigens. These structural characteristics must be important in determining the avidity with which thymus-independent

TABLE 1. *Polyclonal TNP-antibody response to P-LPS in (CBA/N ♀ × DBA/2 ♂) male and female mice* [a]

Sex of F_1 mice	Amt (μg) of P-LPS	Mean[b] no. of TNP plaque-forming cells ± SE	
		Per spleen	Per 10^6 cells
Male	0	96 ± 66	1.2 ± 0.8
	10	158 ± 22	3.1 ± 0.3
	33	333 ± 98	5.0 ± 1.3
	100	1,367 ± 245	16.9 ± 3.1
Female	0	103 ± 49	1.7 ± 0.5
	10	2,567 ± 1133	28.7 ± 3.8
	33	7,117 ± 2679	60.9 ± 21.7
	100	7,517 ± 639	57.9 ± 4.3

[a] Number of TNP plaque-forming cells was determined on day 3.

[b] Mean number of TNP plaque-forming cells was calculated from the individual responses of three mice.

antigens bind to the surface of B lymphocytes. In this regard, it has been shown that the antibody responses of F_1 male mice to antigens to which they respond is characterized by a low average avidity (8, 11), which presumably reflects the avidity with which the F_1 male B-lymphocyte receptor interacts with antigen (5). Thus, it is possible that the inability of CBA/N B lymphocytes to respond to SIII, poly(I·C), DNP-Ficoll, and LPS is attributable to the presumed low avidity with which these B lymphocytes interact with such antigens.

ACKNOWLEDGMENTS

We thank Alice Berning for excellent technical assistance and Betty J. Sylvester for editorial assistance. The interesting and stimulating discussions with A. Ahmed, J. Mond, W. E. Paul, and I. Zitron are acknowledged and appreciated. The assistance of Lutz Kiesow in the preparation of the purified LPS is appreciated.

This work was supported by the Naval Medical Research and Development Command, Work Unit no. MR041.02.01.-0020 and MR041.02.01.0037.

LITERATURE CITED

1. **Ahmed, A., and I. Scher.** 1976. Studies on non-H-2 linked lymphocyte activating determinants. II. Nonexpression of Mls determinants in a mouse strain with an X-linked B-lymphocyte immune defect. J. Immunol. **117**:1922–1926.

2. **Ahmed, A., I. Scher, and K. W. Sell.** 1976. Functional studies of the ontogeny of the M-locus product: a surface antigen of murine B lymphocytes, p. 703–709. In V. P. Eijsvoogel, D. Roos, and W. P. Zeijlemaker (ed.), Leukocyte membrane determinants regulating immune reactivity. Academic Press Inc., New York.

3. **Amsbaugh, D. F., C. T. Hansen, B. Prescott, P. W. Stashak, D. R. Barthold, and P. J. Baker.** 1972. Genetic control of the antibody response to Type III pneumococcal polysaccharide in mice. I. Evidence that an X-linked gene plays a decisive role in determining responsiveness. J. Exp. Med. **136**:931–949.

4. **Andersson, B., and H. Blomgren.** 1971. Evidence for thymus-independent humoral antibody production in mice against polyvinylpyrrolidone and E. coli lipopolysaccharide. Cell. Immunol. **2**:411–424.

5. **Clafin, J. L., and J. M. Davie.** 1975. Specific isolation and characterization of antibody directed to binding site antigenic determinants. J. Immunol. **114**:70–75.

6. **Cohen, P. L., I. Scher, and D. E. Mosier.** 1976. In vitro studies of the genetically determined unresponsiveness to thymus-independent antigens in CBA/N mice. J. Immunol. **116**:301–304.

7. **Finkelman, F. D., A. H. Smith, I. Scher, and W. E. Paul.** 1975. Abnormal ratio of membrane immunoglobulin classes in mice with an X-linked B-lymphocyte defect. J. Exp. Med. **142**:1316–1321.

8. **Gershon, R. K., and K. Kondo.** 1976. Deficient production of a thymus-dependent high affinity antibody subset in mice (CBA/N) with an X-linked B-lymphocyte defect. J. Immunol. **117**:701–702.

9. **Janeway, C. A., Jr., and D. R. Barthold.** 1975. An analysis of the defective responses of CBA/N mice to T-dependent antigens. J. Immunol. **115**:898–900.

10. **Melchers, F., V. Braun, and C. Galanos.** 1975. The lipoprotein of the outer membrane of Escherichia coli: a B-lymphocyte mitogen. J. Exp. Med. **142**:473–482.

11. **Mosier, D. E., I. Scher, and W. E. Paul.** 1976. In vitro responses of CBA/N mice: spleen cells of mice with an X-linked defect that precludes immune responses to several thymus-independent antigens can respond to TNP-lipopolysaccharides. J. Immunol. **117**:1363–1369.

12. **Mosier, D. E., I. Scher, H. Ruhl, P. L. Cohen, I. Zitron, and W. E. Paul.** 1976. Activation of normal and defective B lymphocytes by thymus-independent antigens, p. 313–324. In J. J. Oppenheim and D. Rosenstreich (ed.), Role of mitogens in immunobiology. Academic Press Inc., New York.

13. **Rudbach, J. A.** 1971. Molecular immunogenicity of bacterial lipopolysaccharide antigens: establishing a quantitative system. J. Immunol. **106**:993–1001.

14. **Rudbach, J. A., I. Akiya, R. J. Elin, H. D. Hochstein, M. K. Luoma, E. C. B. Milner, K. C. Milner, and K. R. Thomas.** 1976. Preparation and properties of a national reference endotoxin. J. Clin. Microbiol. **3**:21–25.

15. **Scher, I., A. Ahmed, S. O. Sharrow, and W. E. Paul.** 1976. Maturation of murine B lymphocytes, p. 55–69. In M. D. Cooper and D. H. Dayton (ed.), The development of host defenses. Raven Press, New York.

16. **Scher, I., A. Ahmed, S. O. Sharrow, and K. W. Sell.** 1976. The murine minor lymphocyte stimulating locus defines a B-cell subclass whose expression is dependent on genes on the X chromosome. Transplant. Proc., in press.

17. **Scher, I., A. Ahmed, D. M. Strong, A. D. Steinberg, and W. E. Paul.** 1975. X-linked B-lymphocyte defect in CBA/N mice. I. Studies of the function and composition of spleen cells. J. Exp. Med. **141**:788–803.

18. **Scher, I., M. M. Frantz, and A. D. Steinberg.** 1973. The genetics of the immune response to a synthetic double-stranded RNA in a mutant CBA mouse strain. J. Immunol. **110**:1396–1401.

19. **Scher, I., S. O. Sharrow, and W. E. Paul.** 1976. X-linked B-lymphocyte defect in CBA/N mice. III. Abnormal development of B-lymphocyte populations defined by their density of surface immunoglobulin. J. Exp. Med. **144**:507–518.

20. **Scher, I., S. O. Sharrow, R. Wistar, Jr., A. Asofsky, and W. E. Paul.** 1976. B-lymphocyte heterogeneity: ontogenetic development and organ distribution of B-lymphocyte populations defined by their density of surface immunoglobulin. J. Exp. Med. **144**:494–506.

21. **Scher, I., S. O. Sharrow, R. Wistar, Jr., and W. E. Paul.** 1976. Density of surface Ig on B cells: ontogenetic studies of a population of splenic B cells in normal mice and mice with an X-linked B-lymphocyte immune defect, p. 189–195. In V. P. Eijsvoogel, D. Roos, and W. P. Zeijlemaker (ed.), Leukocyte membrane determinants regulating immune reactivity. Academic Press Inc., New York.

22. **Scher, I., A. D. Steinberg, A. K. Berning, and W. E. Paul.** 1975. X-linked B-lymphocyte defect in CBA/N mice. II. Studies of the mechanisms underlying the immune defect. J. Exp. Med. **142**:637–650.

23. **Vitetta, E. S., U. Melcher, M. McWilliams, M. E. Lamm, J. M. Phillips-Quagliata, and J. W. Uhr.** 1975. Cell surface immunoglobulin. XI. The appearance of an IgD-like molecule on murine lymphoid cells during ontogeny. J. Exp. Med. **141**:206–215.

24. **Westphal, O.** 1956. In G. F. Springer (ed.), Polysaccharides in biology, p. 115. Josiah Macy Jr. Foundation, New York.

Analysis of the Cellular Defects of Endotoxin-Unresponsive C3H/HeJ Mice

DAVID L. ROSENSTREICH, L. MICHAEL GLODE, LARRY M. WAHL, ANN L. SANDBERG, AND STEPHAN E. MERGENHAGEN

Laboratory of Microbiology and Immunology, National Institute of Dental Research, Bethesda, Maryland 20014

Endotoxin, the lipopolysaccharide (LPS) derived from the cell wall of gram-negative bacteria, is distinguished by its capacity to induce a great variety of biological effects in the susceptible host (15). These include immunostimulatory activities such as adjuvanticity and immunogenicity, and other properties not obviously related to the immune system such as the induction of abortion and lethality. However, despite over 80 years of study, the exact mechanism by which endotoxin mediates these numerous activities remains unexplained.

The relatively recent discovery of the endotoxin-unresponsive C3H/HeJ mouse strain (21) has furnished us with a potentially powerful tool for analyzing the mechanism of action of endotoxin. These mice appear to respond abnormally to all the effects of LPS thus far studied, including mitogenicity (22), immunogenicity (24), adjuvanticity (20), lethality (21), the extravascular accumulation of leukocytes (21), and the enhancement of nonspecific resistance to bacterial infection (3). Since the loss of some of these activities has been shown to be due to a single gene mutation (24), and since it is probable that the loss of all of these activities is due to the same mutation, it is extremely likely that all of the biological activities of endotoxin are initiated by some common mechanism that is defective in the C3H/HeJ mouse. Therefore, by identifying the underlying defect in these mice, it should be possible to uncover those processes that are essential for mediating specific biological activities of LPS.

The basic mechanisms by which endotoxin is thought to function are either those involving the activation of fluid-phase systems such as the complement (7), kinin (11), and coagulation (13) pathways, or those involving activation of cells such as fibroblasts (2), platelets (4), and the cells of the immune system. The immune system consists of three basic cell types: the bone marrow-derived (B) lymphocyte, the thymus-derived (T) lymphocyte, and the macrophage. Previous studies have demonstrated that

endotoxin exerts a direct effect on all three cell types (D. L. Rosenstreich, L. M. Glode, and S. E. Mergenhagen, J. Infect. Dis., in press).

We have chosen to analyze the interaction between endotoxin and various cell types in C3H/HeJ mice. In this report, we present evidence demonstrating that these mice possess a defect in both B-cell and macrophage responses to endotoxin. In addition, we show that there is a connection between these known defects of lymphoid cells and their resistance to a seemingly unrelated phenomenon, endotoxin-induced lethality.

NATURE OF THE C3H/HeJ B-CELL DEFECT

Our first set of studies were done to determine why C3H/HeJ mice did not respond to the mitogenic effects of endotoxin, and whether this was related to a defect intrinsic to their B cells. There were several other possible causes for this mitogenic unresponsiveness. These mice could have had a quantitative B-cell deficiency or a deficiency in some required helper cell, or they may have possessed an abnormal LPS-activated suppressor cell.

To answer these questions, it was necessary to utilize cells of various types from an endotoxin-sensitive mouse strain that was closely related to C3H/HeJ, so that the cell-mixing experiments in vitro could be performed without the added variable of mixed lymphocyte and cytotoxic reactions. For this, we chose the C3H/HeN strain, which shared a common ancestor with the C3H/HeJ mice. In a series of experiments, we determined that this strain was fully histocompatible with C3H/HeJ, since there was no mixed lymphocyte or graft-versus-host reaction between these two strains and since reciprocal skin grafts were never rejected (17). Utilizing this strain pair, we made the following observations about the absence of LPS-induced mitogenesis in the C3H/HeJ mouse (8).

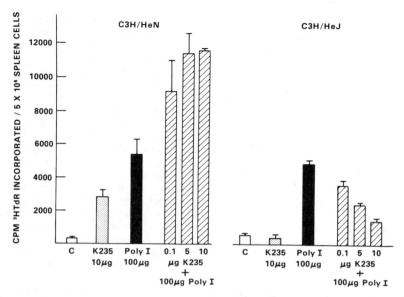

FIG. 1. *Suppression of C3H/HeJ B cell responsiveness by LPS. C3H/HeN or C3H/HeJ spleen cells cultured in plastic microtrays were stimulated with polyinosinic acid [poly(I)] either alone or in combination with increasing concentrations of E. coli K235 LPS (phenol extracted). Lymphocyte proliferation was determined after 48 h by measuring the incorporation of [³H]thymidine into new cell DNA. With C3H/HeN cells, poly(I) and LPS produce an additive or synergistic B-cell response. In contrast, K235 LPS suppresses the response of the C3H/HeJ B cells. From Glode et al. (8)*

First, we found that there was no quantitative B-cell defect in these mice. Second, we found that LPS unresponsiveness was not due to either a macrophage or T-cell suppressor since removal of either of these two cell types did not increase the C3H/HeJ LPS response. Furthermore, unresponsiveness was not due to a helper-cell deficiency since macrophages, T cells, and spleen cells from C3H/HeN mice were unable to restore the mitogenic response of C3H/HeJ spleen cells. Thus, on the basis of these studies, we concluded that the B cells of C3H/HeJ mice were intrinsically unresponsive to endotoxin.

There were several possible explanations for the intrinsic unresponsiveness of the C3H/HeJ B cell. One was that these cells might lack LPS receptors. However, this was found not to be the case since they bound LPS normally (10a, 25). Another possibility was that they recognized LPS, but instead of becoming activated, C3H/HeJ B cells were inactivated or "turned off" by LPS. Evidence that C3H/HeJ B cells are inactivated by LPS is given in Fig. 1. The B cells of C3H/HeJ mice respond normally to another non-LPS B-cell mitogen, polyinosinic acid [poly(I)]. When endotoxin (*Escherichia coli* K-235, phenol-water extracted) is added to responder (C3H/HeN) spleen cells in addition to poly(I), an enhanced mitogenic response (increased incorporation of [³H]-thymidine after 48 h of culture) is observed. However, when this LPS is added to poly(I)-stimulated C3H/HeJ spleen cells, the B-cell response is markedly decreased. Thus, these findings suggest that the primary interaction of endotoxin with C3H/HeJ B cells proceeds normally, but that this interaction results in an inactivation of these cells. The reasons for this inactivation remain to be elucidated.

EFFECT OF ENDOTOXIN ON MACROPHAGES

The next cell type investigated was the macrophage. LPS has been found to influence macrophages in a variety of ways. In vivo, endotoxin produces macrophage activation (14), and in vitro it produces macrophage activation (26) or cytotoxicity (19). However, it is not clear whether these are direct effects of endotoxin on macrophages or whether these phenomena are mediated through its effects on other cell types. In fact, whereas endotoxin effects such as the induction of macrophage collagenase production appear to be direct (23), others such as the enhancement of glucosamine incorporation by macrophages are mediated indirectly by LPS-activated B cells (26).

We therefore investigated whether the macro-

TABLE 1. *Resistance of C3H/HeJ macrophages to the cytotoxic effects of endotoxin in vitro*

Endotoxin	Macrophage cytotoxicity	
	C3H/HeN[b]	C3H/HeJ
None	1.5 ± 0.5	1.8 ± 0.25
E. coli K235 (phenol extracted)[c]	75.0 ± 10	17.0 ± 1
E. coli O128:B12	54.0 ± 0.8	6.5 ± 1.5

[a] Dead macrophages enumerated after staining with trypan blue dye.
[b] Macrophages were derived from thioglycolate-induced peritoneal exudate cells as described in the text.
[c] LPS concentration = 50 µg/ml.

phages of C3H/HeJ mice were LPS unresponsive and whether this was due to a defect in macrophages or merely due to their demonstrated B-cell defect. The only available information on this subject was that of Chedid et al., who reported that C3H/HeJ macrophages were not activated by endotoxin to kill tumor cells (3). The effect we chose to study was the cytotoxic effect of LPS on macrophages in vitro, since it seemed likely that this was mediated directly by LPS. Mice were injected intraperitoneally with 3 ml of thioglycolate, and after 6 days their peritoneal cells (>90% macrophages) were collected by peritoneal lavage. These cells were allowed to adhere to the surface of a plastic dish for 3 h at 37°C, and then the nonadherent cells were washed off. This monolayer (>95% macrophages) was cultured for 24 h in the presence or absence of different LPS preparations, and then the degree of cell death induced was measured by counting the percentage of cells stained with trypan blue dye.

Two endotoxin preparations were used for these studies: the phenol-water-extracted endotoxin derived from *E. coli* K235 by the method of McIntire (12), which is nonmitogenic for C3H/HeJ B cells, and a commercial Westphal LPS preparation of *E. coli* O128:B12 (Difco), which is weakly mitogenic in this strain. As can be seen in Table 1, at a concentration of 50 µg/ml, K235 killed 75% of the C3H/HeN macrophages while killing only 17% of the C3H/HeJ macrophages. The results with the O128:B12 LPS were similar; C3H/HeN macrophages were killed whereas C3H/HeJ macrophages were not. It thus appeared that C3H/HeJ macrophages were also insensitive to the effects of endotoxin.

A number of additional experiments were performed to clarify this phenomenon (data not

shown). We found that the killing was not due to residual phenol contamination. By allowing the cells to ingest latex beads before adding endotoxin, we determined that the dead cells were indeed phagocytic, and, by adding latex beads to already killed cultures, we ascertained that this was true macrophage death and not merely an increased permeability of these cells to the dye. Furthermore, we were able to prove that this was indeed a direct effect of LPS on macrophages. When macrophage-depleted C3H/HeN spleen cells were added to C3H/HeJ macrophages, the degree of killing was unchanged, demonstrating that this was not a lymphocyte-mediated phenomenon (Table 2). In addition, killing was unchanged when C3H/HeJ spleen cells were added to C3H/HeN macrophages, demonstrating that there was no abnormal cell in the C3H/HeJ that blocked the macrophage-killing phenomenon.

On the basis of these studies, we have concluded that the C3H/HeJ macrophage is also insensitive to endotoxin. Additional experiments utilizing other parameters of macrophage activation have produced similar results. Thus, C3H/HeJ macrophages do not develop enhanced metabolic activity in response to LPS as determined by glucose utilization, in contrast to C3H/HeN macrophages (J. Ryan, L. M. Glode, and D. L. Rosenstreich, in preparation). Furthermore, C3H/HeJ macrophages do not release the soluble mediator lymphocyte-activating factor (LAF; 6) in response to LPS, whereas LPS-activated C3H/HeN macrophages do release this factor (J. J. Oppenheim and D. L. Rosenstreich, in preparation). Finally, based on cell-mixing experiments similar to those already described (Table 2), we have determined that the latter activities are also mediated by a direct effect of LPS on macrophages.

TABLE 2. *Evidence that in vitro cytotoxicity is due to a direct effect of endotoxin on macrophages*

Cell population		Macrophage cytotoxicity[b] (% killed)
Macrophage	Spleen cell[a]	
HeN	None	69 ± 5
HeN	HeN	51 ± 5
HeN	HeJ	60 ± 2
HeJ	None	12 ± 3
HeJ	HeN	9 ± 1
HeJ	HeJ	7 ± 3

[a] Spleen cells were macrophage depleted by passage over a column containing G-10 Sephadex and were added to the macrophages at a concentration of 10%.
[b] LPS = 50 µg/ml, *E. coli* K235 LPS.

ACTION OF ENDOTOXIN ON T LYMPHOCYTES

The last cell type involved in the immune response is the T lymphocyte, and there is also evidence that LPS interacts with this cell type. Thus, the adjuvant effect of LPS in vivo (9) and in vitro (1) requires the presence of T cells, and in vitro LPS will enhance the activation of thymocytes by concanavalin A (5). However, interpretation of all these results is obscure since it is not clear whether these effects are really mediated by the action of LPS on macrophages. In fact, LPS-induced enhancement of the mixed lymphocyte reaction of thymocytes has been shown to be macrophage-dependent (16).

Despite these problems, we considered it important to determine whether there was an LPS-associated defect in the T cells of C3H/HeJ mice. For these experiments we analyzed the enhancement of the phytohemagglutinin (PHA) response of purified peripheral T cells. T cells were prepared by passing spleen cells over a nylon wool column (10). These T cells were then cultured in the presence or absence of PHA and LPS. We found that C3H/HeJ T-cell activation by suboptimal doses of PHA was enhanced by endotoxins that were mitogenic for the B cells of this strain, such as E. coli O111:B4 LPS (18) or by butanol-extracted K235 LPS, but that no enhancement was seen with the nonmitogenic LPS from K235. Furthermore, this phenomenon appeared to be a direct effect of LPS on T cells since it occurred in the presence of very few macrophages and since the readdition of fresh macrophages had no effect on the enhancement (Rosenstreich, Glode, and Mergenhagen, in press).

These findings suggested that C3H/HeJ T cells possessed a pattern of unresponsiveness similar to that of their B cells. However, further analysis revealed that the activation of C3H/HeN T cells by PHA was also enhanced by butanol-extracted K235 LPS, but only poorly by the phenol-extracted LPS, suggesting that the T cells of C3H/HeJ mice react to LPS similarly to the T cells of other mice. Thus, it seems that C3H/HeJ T cells either respond normally to LPS or possess a defect that is much less marked than that of their B cells or macrophages. Additional experiments to clarify this point are currently underway.

RELATIONSHIP BETWEEN LYMPHOID CELL ACTIVATION AND THE LETHAL EFFECTS OF LPS

It is clear from these studies, and from the work of others, that the defect in LPS-in-duced immunostimulation in C3H/HeJ mice can be directly related to defects in their lymphoid cells. However, the relationship between the lymphoid cell defect in these mice and their resistance to other, nonimmunological effects of LPS, such as the induction of lethality, is not clear. If we assume that the same gene mutation has produced loss of both types of activity, then there are two possibilities. Either there is some defect common to all the cells of this strain, and the toxic effects of LPS are due to its action on these nonlymphoid cell types, or LPS-induced activation of the immune system is involved in the initiation of endotoxicity.

We had previously shown that the adoptive transfer of C3H/HeN spleen cells into X-irradiated C3H/HeJ mice produced permanent chimeras whose spleen cells responded to the mitogenic effects of endotoxin (17). If lymphoid cells were related to lethality, then these chimeras would have also been sensitive to the lethal effects of endotoxin.

We therefore created two types of chimeras by adoptively transferring 30×10^6 spleen cells into X-irradiated recipients: (i) C3H/HeJ mice given C3H/HeN cells and (ii) C3H/HeN mice given C3H/HeJ cells. As controls, mice were X-irradiated and then given syngeneic spleen cells (C3H/HeJ given C3H/HeJ cells and C3H/HeN given C3H/HeN cells). These four groups of mice were then tested for sensitivity to the lethal effects of LPS (Table 3). C3H/HeJ chimeras containing responsive spleen cells were more than twice as sensitive to the lethal ef-

TABLE 3. Influence of lymphoid cell transfer on endotoxin-induced lethality in vivo and spleen cell mitogenesis in vitro

Recipient animal	Reconstituting spleen cells[a]	LD$_{50}$ after endotoxin challenge[b]	P	Maximal splenic proliferative response[c]
C3H/HeJ$_X$	C3H/HeJ	4.0 ± 0.12	<0.01	101 ± 9
	C3H/HeN	1.6 ± 0.26		19,843 ± 953
C3H/HeN$_X$	C3H/HeJ	0.46 ± 0.03	<0.01	1,545 ± 132
	C3H/HeN	0.18 ± 0.04		14,010 ± 1,252

[a] Recipient mice received 450 R of X-irradiation, followed by 30×10^6 spleen cells intravenously in the tail vein. All studies were performed 28 days or more after adoptive transfer.

[b] Results represent the arithmetic mean ± the standard error of the mean of three separate experiments. Each group of chimeric animals contained 20 to 30 mice. Statistical evaluation was performed as described (7a). Endotoxin = E. coli K235 LPS (phenol extracted).

[c] Expressed as Δcpm of [^{3}H]thymidine incorporated/8×10^5 cells. Results represent the mitogenic response to E. coli K235 LPS (20 μg/ml) of representative, untreated chimeric mice from each group. Data given are the arithmetic means ± the standard error of the mean of triplicate cultures.

fects of LPS as were control C3H/HeJ chimeras. Furthermore, C3H/HeN chimeras whose spleen cells responded poorly to LPS were more than twice as resistant to the lethal effects of LPS as their respective controls. Thus, these data demonstrate that the LPS sensitivity of the host lymphoid cells plays a significant role in determining sensitivity to LPS-mediated lethality.

There are several unresolved questions related to these findings, the most prominent being how lymphoid cells could possibly mediate endotoxicity. However, at this time, there are other problems with the interpretation of these results. One is that there exists a major discrepancy between the mitogenic reactivity in the spleen of chimeras and their sensitivity to the lethal effects of LPS. Thus, C3H/HeJ (+ C3H/HeN) chimeras are fully responsive to the mitogenic effects of LPS but are still relatively resistant to lethality. Conversely, C3H/HeN (+ C3H/HeJ) chimeras which are poorly responsive to LPS-induced mitogenesis are still relatively sensitive to lethality and are certainly much more sensitive to lethality than the C3H/HeJ (+ C3H/HeN) chimeras that are fully responsive to LPS-induced mitogenesis. These findings argue strongly that activation of the splenic B cell is not related to the induction of lethality, and that another cell type present in the transferred spleen cells is responsible for this effect. Furthermore, this cell should be relatively radioresistant since it seems to survive in the X-irradiated C3H/HeN mouse. The cell that best fits this description and is also endotoxin sensitive is the macrophage.

If macrophages are, in fact, responsible for some aspect of endotoxicity, then we should find that the presence of endotoxin-sensitive macrophages in chimeric animals is more closely related to sensitivity to LPS-induced lethality than the presence of LPS-sensitive B cells. We therefore took chimeric animals of all four types and tested their thioglycolate-induced macrophages for sensitivity to the cytotoxic effects of LPS in vitro. Preliminary experiments have revealed the above hypothesis to be true. We found (data not shown) that irradiated C3H/HeN recipients reconstituted with C3H/HeJ spleen cells contained almost as many LPS-sensitive macrophages as their respective control chimeras. C3H/HeJ recipients reconstituted with C3H/HeN spleen cells also contained LPS-sensitive macrophages, although not as many as the C3H/HeN (+ C3H/HeJ) chimeras. C3H/HeJ (+ C3H/HeJ) control chimeras contained the fewest LPS-responsive macrophages. Thus, there appears to be a correlation between the sensitivity of chimeric macrophages in vitro and the sensitivity of the chimeric group to lethality.

PROSTAGLANDIN SYNTHESIS BY ENDOTOXIN-ACTIVATED MACROPHAGES

If macrophage activation is truly related to the initiation of endotoxin-induced lethality, then it seems likely that the release of some toxic factor or factors by macrophages should be responsible for this effect. Of all the many molecules synthesized by macrophages, prostaglandins are likely to be involved for the following reasons (reviewed in 7a and Rosenstreich, Glode, and Mergenhagen, in press). First, prostaglandins are extremely potent vasoactive compounds, and can induce several endotoxin-like activities such as abortion. Second, elevated levels of prostaglandins can be measured in endotoxin-treated animals, and indomethacin, which inhibits prostaglandin synthesis, will protect animals against some toxic effects of endotoxin. Finally, macrophages are known to synthesize and release prostaglandins in vitro.

If macrophage release of prostaglandins is involved in mediating endotoxicity, then macrophages from endotoxin-sensitive mice would produce prostaglandins whereas macrophages from endotoxin-resistant mice would not. We therefore treated C3H/HeJ or C3H/HeN macrophages with endotoxin for 24 h and then measured prostaglandin levels in these supernatant fluids by use of a modified radioimmunoassay technique (27). As predicted, in response to K235 LPS, C3H/HeN macrophages produced large amounts of both PGE_2 and $PGF_{2\alpha}$, whereas C3H/HeJ macrophages did not secrete increased levels of prostaglandins (Table 4). The increase in secreted prostaglandins by C3H/HeN macrophages in response to K235 LPS was completely inhibitable by indomethacin, demonstrating that this was de novo synthesis of prostaglandin and not merely release of a preformed molecule.

TABLE 4. Endotoxin stimulation of prostaglandin synthesis by mouse macrophages

Source of macrophages[a]	Stimulant	Prostaglandin synthesized (pg/culture)	
		PGE_2	$PGE_{2\alpha}$
HeN	None	576	190
HeN	K235 LPS	42,240	8,218
HeJ	None	2,118	896
HeJ	K235 LPS	1,268	652

[a] Each 5-ml culture contained 20×10^6 macrophages. Supernatant fluids were harvested at 28 h and assayed for PGE_2 and $PGF_{2\alpha}$ by specific radioimmunoassay (Clinical Assays, Cambridge, Mass.).

CONCLUSIONS

Our results demonstrate that both the B lymphocytes and the macrophages of the C3H/HeJ mouse are unresponsive to endotoxin. In contrast, the difference in responsiveness between the T lymphocytes of this strain and other normal mouse strains is not as striking. Therefore, in dealing with lymphoid cell responses to LPS we can concern ourselves primarily with the B cell and macrophage.

The exact relationship of these two cell types to some of the in vivo immunological activities of LPS remains to be established. Although it seems likely that the potency of LPS as a thymic independent antigen is due to its direct B cell-activating effects, it is much more likely that its adjuvant effects are mediated via macrophages. Therefore, the absence of LPS-induced adjuvanticity in C3H/HeJ mice is probably due to their macrophage defect rather than to their B-cell defect, as has been postulated by others (20). Nevertheless, it seems likely that the exact cellular mediators of these phenomena will be relatively easy to clarify.

What is more intriguing is the relationship between LPS-induced immunological activation and the mechanism of endotoxicity. Our observations strongly suggest that LPS-induced activation of some splenic cell or cells either produces or significantly enhances LPS-mediated lethality. Preliminary observations also suggest that this cell may be the macrophage rather than the B cell. Finally, we have found that endotoxin-activated C3H/HeN macrophages release large quantities of prostaglandins in vitro, whereas this response is absent in macrophages from endotoxin-resistant mice. Since there is evidence linking endotoxicity with prostaglandins, this finding suggests a plausible link between the effects of endotoxin on lymphoid cells and its toxic properties.

Whether endotoxicity is mediated solely by the effect of LPS on lymphoid cells remains to be established. Although this would be intellectually quite satisfying in terms of having a common mechanism of action to explain so many LPS-induced events, it also seems unlikely to be that simple. Two types of evidence will be required to establish this relationship. The first would be to render a C3H/HeJ mouse completely sensitive to the lethal effects of endotoxin solely by the transfer of lymphoid cells. A population such as bone marrow which is richer in macrophage precursors than the spleen is a likely candidate. Second, characterization of the cellular defect of C3H/HeJ mice should be expanded to include other endotoxin-sensitive cell types such as platelets, fibroblasts, and endothelial cells.

It seems likely that a careful and comprehensive analysis of both the cellular and noncellular LPS-related defects in the C3H/HeJ mouse will be instrumental in uncovering the mechanisms of action of endotoxin.

LITERATURE CITED

1. **Armerding, D., and D. H. Katz.** 1974. Activation of T and B lymphocytes in vitro. I. Regulatory influence of bacterial lipopolysaccharide (LPS) on specific T-cell helper function. J. Exp. Med. 139:24–43.

2. **Buckingham, R. B., and C. W. Castor.** 1972. The effect of bacterial products on synovial fibroblast function: hypermetabolic changes induced by endotoxin. J. Clin. Invest. 51:1186–1194.

3. **Chedid, L., M. Parant, C. Damais, F. Parant, D. Juy, and A. Galelli.** 1975. Failure of endotoxin to increase nonspecific resistance to infection of lipopolysaccharide low-responder mice. Infect. Immun. 13:722–727.

4. **Des Prez, R. M., H. I. Horowitz, and E. W. Hook.** 1961. Effects of bacterial endotoxin on rabbit platelets. I. Platelet aggregation and release of platelet factors in vitro. J. Exp. Med. 114:857–873.

5. **Forbes, J. T., Y. Nakao, and R. T. Smith.** 1975. T mitogens trigger LPS responsiveness in mouse thymus cells. J. Immunol. 114:1004–1007.

6. **Gery, I., R. Gershon, and B. H. Waksman.** 1972. Potentiation of the T-lymphocyte response to mitogens. I. The responding cell. J. Exp. Med. 136:128–142.

7. **Gewurz, H., R. S. Snyderman, S. E. Mergenhagen, and H. S. Shin.** 1971. Effects of endotoxic lipopolysaccharides on the complement system, p. 127–149. In S. Kadis, G. Weinbaum, and S. Ajl (ed.), Microbial toxins, vol. 5. Academic Press Inc., New York.

7a. **Glode, L. M., S. E. Mergenhagen, and D. L. Rosenstreich.** 1976. Significant contribution of spleen cells in mediating the lethal effects of endotoxin in vivo. Infect. Immun. 14:626–630.

8. **Glode, L. M., I. Scher, B. Osborne, and D. L. Rosenstreich.** 1976. Cellular mechanism of endotoxin unresponsiveness in C3H/HeJ mice. J. Immunol. 116:454–461.

9. **Hamaoka, T., and D. H. Katz.** 1973. Cellular site of action of various adjuvants in antibody responses to hapten-carrier conjugates. J. Immunol. 111:1554–1563.

10. **Handwerger, B. S., and R. H. Schwartz.** 1974. Separation of murine lymphoid cells using nylon wool columns: recovery of the B cell-enriched population. Transplantation 18:544–548.

10a. **Kabir, S., and D. L. Rosenstreich.** 1977. Binding of bacterial endotoxin to murine spleen lymphocytes. Infect. Immun. 15:156–164.

11. **Kimball, H. R., K. L. Melmon, and S. M. Wolff.** 1972. Endotoxin-induced kinin production in man. Proc. Soc. Exp. Med. Biol. 139:1078–1082.

12. **McIntire, F. C., H. W. Sievert, G. H. Barlow, R. A. Finley, and A. Y. Lee.** 1967. Chemical, physical and biological properties of a lipopolysaccharide from Escherichia coli K-235. Biochemistry 6:2363–2372.

13. **McKay, D. G., and S. S. Shapiro.** 1958. Alterations in the blood coagulation system induced by bacterial endotoxin. J. Exp. Med. 107:353–367.

14. **Neter, I.** 1969. Endotoxins and the immune response. Curr. Top. Microbiol. Immunol. 47:82–124.

15. **Nowotny, A.** 1969. Molecular aspects of endotoxic reactions. Bacteriol. Rev. 33:72–98.

16. **Ritter, J., M. L. Lohmann-Matthes, H. G. Sonntag, and H. Fischer.** 1975. Requirement for macrophages in lipopolysaccharide-stimulated mixed thymocyte cultures. Cell. Immunol. 16:153–161.

17. **Rosenstreich, D. L., and L. M. Glode.** 1975. Difference in B cell mitogen responsiveness between closely related strains of mice. J. Immunol. **115:**777–780.

18. **Rosenstreich, D. L., and S. E. Mergenhagen.** 1975. Interaction of endotoxin with cells of the lymphoreticular system: cellular basis of adjuvanticity, p. 320–326. *In* D. Schlessinger (ed.), Microbiology—1975. American Society for Microbiology, Washington, D.C.

19. **Shands, J. W., D. L. Peavy, B. J. Gormus, and J. McGraw.** 1974. In vitro and in vivo effects of endotoxin on mouse peritoneal cells. Infect. Immun. **9:**106–112.

20. **Skidmore, B. J., J. M. Chiller, D. C. Morrison, and W. O. Weigle.** 1975. Immunologic properties of bacterial lipopolysaccharide (LPS): correlation between the mitogenic, adjuvant and immunogenic activities. J. Immunol. **114:**770–775.

21. **Sultzer, B. M.** 1968. Genetic control of leucocyte responses to endotoxin. Nature (London) **219:**1253–1254.

22. **Sultzer, B. M., and B. S. Nielson.** 1972. PPD tuberculin in a B-cell mitogen. Nature (London) New Biol. **240:**199–202.

23. **Wahl, L. M., S. M. Wahl, S. E. Mergenhagen, and G. R. Martin.** 1974. Collagenase production by endotoxin in activated macrophages. Proc. Natl. Acad. Sci. **71:**3598–3601.

24. **Watson, J., and R. Riblet.** 1974. Genetic control of responses to bacterial lipopolysaccharides in mice. I. Evidence for a single gene that influences mitogenic and immunogenic responses to lipopolysaccharide. J. Exp. Med. **140:**1147–1161.

25. **Watson, J., and R. Riblet.** 1975. Genetic control of responses to bacterial lipopolysaccharides in mice. II. A gene that influences a membrane component involved in the activation of bone marrow derived lymphocytes by lipopolysaccharides. J. Immunol. **114:**1462–1468.

26. **Wilton, J. M. A., D. L. Rosenstreich, and J. J. Oppenheim.** 1975. Requirement of bone-marrow derived lymphocytes for macrophage activation by bacterial lipopolysaccharide. J. Immunol. **114:**388–393.

27. **Zusman, R. M., B. V. Caldwell, L. Sperloff, and H. R. Behrman.** 1972. Radioimmunoassay of the A prostaglandins. Prostaglandins **2:**41–53.

Cellular Requirements for Enzyme Inhibition by Endotoxin in Mice

L. JOE BERRY, ROBERT N. MOORE, KENNETH J. GOODRUM, AND RAY E. COUCH, JR.

Department of Microbiology, The University of Texas, Austin, Texas 78712

Many of the biological effects of endotoxin are elicited by factors released into serum. They are protein in nature and have been named according to the response they cause in the host. The two recognized for the longest period of time are endogenous pyrogen (1) and interferon (10). More recently, leukocytic endogenous mediator (12) has been identified. It causes fever, lowers serum iron and zinc, and increases nonspecific resistance to infection (11). Colony-stimulating factor (5), tumor necrosis factor (TNF; 6), and glucocorticoid-antagonizing factor (GAF; 16) have also been identified. The last named, GAF, is the subject of this paper.

Glucocorticoid hormones, when given under appropriate conditions, suppress or diminish host responses to endotoxin (3). The nature of the protection has never been satisfactorily elucidated. This group of hormones stimulates gluconeogenesis, apparently through induced synthesis of several enzymes, including the rate-limiting one in this reaction sequence, phosphoenolpyruvate carboxykinase (PEPCK). Other enzymes appear to be important in protecting against endotoxemic stress even though specific roles have not been established in all instances.

Endotoxin blocks the glucocorticoid-induced synthesis of PEPCK (2), tryptophan oxygenase (3), glycogen synthase (15), fructose-1,6-diphosphatase (14), and glucose-6-phosphatase (14), all but the last two of short half-life. It has the reverse effect, however, on pyruvate kinase since the glucocorticoid-induced suppression of the enzyme is inhibited (18). The chemical structure of lipopolysaccharide (LPS), or lipid A, would not make it a compound likely to intervene in cells at the level of protein synthesis. Accordingly, a mediator has been assumed to exert the effect (3), and evidence for one has been found in serum of mice 2 h after an injection of 0.2 LD_{50} of endotoxin (15). Endotoxin-tolerant mice were injected with this serum, and the hormonal induction of PEPCK was inhibited, even though endotoxin itself does not inhibit induction of PEPCK in tolerant animals. The inhibitory substance responsible has been called GAF. The behavior of endotoxin-tolerant mice under these conditions suggests that they fail to respond normally to endotoxin, i.e., show an inhibition of hormonal induction of PEPCK, because they do not produce GAF. When GAF is provided from an exogenous source, they are able to respond normally in that the induction of PEPCK is suppressed.

Macrophages have been identified in two types of experiments as a likely source of GAF. First, rabbit antiserum against adherent mouse peritoneal exudate cells, when injected intravenously into mice, eliminated the ability of endotoxin to block PEPCK induction. Second, the supernatant fluid from mouse peritoneal exudate cells cultured overnight in the presence of endotoxin, when injected into endotoxin-tolerant mice, blocked the hormonal induction of PEPCK (16). In the first test, the antiserum is assumed to have prevented the formation of GAF in adequate amounts; in the second, GAF seems to have been present in the supernatant fluid. Both experiments point to macrophages as the source of GAF.

To determine whether other cells of the reticuloendothelial system are involved in the release of GAF, use was made of BALB/c athymic (nu/nu) mice and of their heterozygous (nu/+) littermates, made available to us by Jerry McGhee, University of Alabama Medical School. As Table 1 makes evident, the behavior of PEPCK in thymus-containing heterozygous littermates was the same as that seen in outbred conventional mice of the type used in previous studies. Cortisol, injected subcutaneously, induced the enzyme to a highly significant degree within 4 h, whereas a concurrent intraperitoneal (i.p.) injection of endotoxin (phenol-water-extracted LPS derived from *Salmonella typhimurium* strain SR-11) reduced the level of induction to a value no different, statistically, from that of the control. These results are shown in the first three lines of Table 1. PEPCK in athymic nude mice, however, responded to

TABLE 1. *Phosphoenolpyruvate carboxykinase (PEPCK) activity in BALB/c athymic mice (nu/nu) and in their heterozygous litter mates (nu/+) after injections of endotoxin and cortisol or sources of glucocorticoid-antagonizing factor and cortisol*

Treatment	PEPCK activity[a] in:	
	nu/nu mice	nu/+ mice
No injections	197 ± 20 (7)	157 ± 18 (6)
Cortisol (1 mg)	267 ± 20 (7)	234 ± 6 (7)
Cortisol (1 mg) + endotoxin (50 μg)	271 ± 11 (7)	179 ± 10 (8)
Cortisol (1 mg) + zymosan control serum (0.3 ml)	263 ± 12 (6)	
Cortisol (1 mg) + zymosan-endotoxin serum (0.3 ml)	157 ± 11 (6)	
Cortisol (1 mg) + peritoneal cells (7 × 10⁷) + endotoxin (20 μg)	151 ± 16 (4)	

[a] PEPCK activity was measured 4 h after treatment. Values represent micromoles of phosphoenolpyruvate formed per gram (dry weight) of liver per 6 min, expressed as the mean ± standard error of the mean for the number of mice (determinations) shown in parentheses.

cortisol by a significant elevation whether or not endotoxin was injected. Results with these animals are shown also in the first three lines of Table 1. The serum from zymosan-pretreated mice (0.5 mg of zymosan intravenously [i.v.]; 1.0 mg of zymosan i.p. 48 h later; mice exsanguinated 5 days after initial injection) failed to block cortisol induction of PEPCK in nude mice (line 4, Table 1). If, however, zymosan-pretreated mice were given 25 μg of Boivin *S. typhimurium* endotoxin 2 h prior to exsanguination, the resulting serum, when given with cortisol, blocked PEPCK induction in these animals. This is shown in the fifth line of Table 1.

The serum of zymosan-primed mice collected 2 h after an injection of 25 μg of endotoxin not only inhibited induction of PEPCK but also sensitized CFW mice to the lethal effect of LPS. This was observed when 0.2 ml of the serum was given i.v. at the same time as an i.p. injection of endotoxin. Under these conditions (data not tabulated), five of seven mice died when 50 μg of endotoxin was administered with the serum, and all of seven mice died when the dose of endotoxin was increased to 150 μg. No deaths occurred when these doses of endotoxin were given to mice also injected with serum derived from animals that had not

been primed with zymosan. Quite clearly, therefore, endotoxin lethality is enhanced by concurrent injection of the serum mediator (GAF).

Zymosan pretreatment was used in these studies because it was known to (i) increase the yield of tumor necrosis factor (6) and (ii) sensitize mice to the lethal effect of endotoxin (2). Presumably, the greater yield of mediator (GAF, TNF, and possibly others) in these animals comes from the proliferation of reticuloendothelial cells that follows an injection of zymosan.

The importance of reticuloendothelial cells in the formation of mediator is evidenced by the fact that 7 × 10⁷ peritoneal cells incubated with 20 μg of Boivin endotoxin for 15 min will, when injected (0.2 ml i.v. and 0.3 ml i.p.), block the cortisol induction of PEPCK in nude mice. This is shown in the last line of Table 1. Thus, according to the results contained in Table 1, athymic mice fail to release GAF in response to an injection of endotoxin, but nu/+ littermates do. The athymic mice respond to GAF whether it is administered via the serum of endotoxin-poisoned, zymosan-primed donor mice or is released in vivo by endotoxin-treated peritoneal exudate cells isolated from conventional outbred mice. One must assume from these observations either that thymocytes (T cells) are needed for GAF formation or that the macrophages of athymic mice are deficient in their ability to produce GAF.

T cells have been implicated in the formation of GAF in additional experiments in which conventional mice, pretreated with a reported T-cell suppressor, oxisuran (7), gave full hormonal induction in the presence of endotoxin (unpublished data). In pretreated animals, the interval between an injection of endotoxin and the onset of irreversible shock was greater than in control mice. A state of irreversible shock was identified as having been reached when an injection of cortisol no longer increased the percentage of surviving animals. These findings not only suggest, therefore, that T cells are required for GAF formation, but they afford important evidence indicating that GAF contributes to the host damage that results in irreversible shock.

C3H/HeJ mice are known to be unusually resistant to the lethal effect of endotoxin (21). In addition, their spleen cells fail to give a typical mitogenic response to endotoxin, a response characteristic of B lymphocytes (8). The lack of mitogenicity in these cells is observed when the LPS is extracted by a procedure in which phenol is employed. Trichloroacetic acid extracts of LPS are mitogenic for C3H/HeJ spleen cells (17).

This strain of mice was of interest to us as

a way of determining whether animals that are highly resistant to endotoxin lethality are also resistant to the inhibition of enzyme induction by LPS. In other words, the questions to be resolved are: do C3H/HeJ mice fail to produce GAF in response to the usual dose of endotoxin and/or do they fail to respond to GAF even though it is present? The data of Table 2, obtained with these animals, show that a phenol-water-derived LPS failed to inhibit the hormonal induction of PEPCK whereas a trichloroacetic acid extract did. Moreover, phenol-water LPS alone induced PEPCK, presumably because of the release of endogenous glucocorticoids from the adrenal gland, an effect not seen statistically, when a Boivin endotoxin was administered. These results suggest that GAF is released in these mice by LPS when it is prepared with trichloroacetic acid but not with phenol-water. Even with the trichloroacetic acid preparation there was significant hormonal induction of PEPCK above the control value (last line of the Table 2 compared with the first line), but it was less than that seen when phenol-water LPS was given (fourth line of Table 2). In results not presented in Table 2, an injection of 0.5 ml of serum from zymosan-primed endotoxin-poisoned CFW mice into C3H/HeJ mice was found to inhibit the cortisol induction of PEPCK, just as similar serum did in athymic mice (fifth line, Table 1). In addition, an intraperitoneal injection of 10^7 peritoneal

TABLE 3. *Time of death and protective effect of cortisol in control and zymosan-primed CFW mice*

Experimental treatment	Dose of LPS (μg)	No. of mice dying at:			No. dead/ total
		6–8 h	24 h	48 h	
LPS (i.v.)	200	0	5	8	13/16
	100	0	3	1	4/8
	50	0	1	0	1/8
LPS + cortisol (subcutaneous)	200	0	0	0	0/8
LPS + cortisol 24 h prechallenge	200	0	4	3	7/8
	100	0	0	0	0/8
Zymosan-primed + LPS	200	14	2	0	16/16
	100	6	2	0	8/8
	50	8	0	0	8/8
	25	6	1	0	7/8
	10	1	4	0	5/8
	1	3	6	0	9/16
Zymosan-primed + LPS + cortisol	200	14	0	2	16/16
	100	6	1	0	7/8
	50	2	10	0	12/16
	25	2	2	0	4/8
	10	3	0	0	3/7
Zymosan-primed + LPS + cortisol 24 h prechallenge	200	0	14	1	15/16
	100	0	4	0	4/8
	50	0	4	0	4/8
	25	0	4	1	5/8

TABLE 2. *Phosphoenolpyruvate carboxykinase (PEPCK) activity in C3H/HeJ mice after injections of cortisol and/or endotoxin prepared by either the phenol-water or trichloroacetic acid method*

Treatment	PEPCK activity[a]
No injections	52 ± 6 (7)
Cortisol (1 mg)	206 ± 11 (12)
Phenol-water LPS (50 μg)	95 ± 8 (5)
Cortisol (1 mg) + phenol-water LPS (50 μg)	199 ± 7 (5)
Trichloroacetic acid LPS (50 μg)	71 ± 11 (5)
Cortisol (1 mg) + trichloroacetic acid LPS (50 μg)	139 ± 8 (6)

[a] PEPCK activity was measured 4 h after treatment. Values represent micromoles of phosphoenolpyruvate formed per gram (dry weight) of liver per 6 min, expressed as the mean ± standard error of the mean for the number of mice (determinations) shown in parentheses.

exudate cells plus 50 μg of phenol-water-extracted LPS inhibited the cortisol induction of PEPCK. Thus, the deficiency in these animals seems to be in their ability to form GAF rather than a refractoriness to it. These findings also implicate B cells in the release or formation of GAF because LPS extracted with phenol-water elicited no change in the inducibility of PEPCK whereas Boivin LPS did. In previous studies, however, cyclophosphamide was used to suppress B-cell function, but without altering the ability of endotoxin in these animals to inhibit the induction of PEPCK (3).

Mediators contribute to the lethal response of mice to endotoxin as indicated above when serum of zymosan-primed, endotoxin-poisoned mice was used and as experiments by Glode et al. indicated (9). They found that sublethally X-irradiated C3H/HeJ mice, when reconstituted with spleen cells from an endotoxin-sensitive strain (C3H/HeN), became more susceptible to death from LPS than similarly irradiated mice reconstituted with homologous spleen cells. A similar effect was seen when irradiated sensitive mice, reconstituted with spleen cells from the resistant strain, were found to become more resistant to endotoxin than when reconstituted with homologous spleen cells.

A similar conclusion is supported by the data in Table 3. The time of endotoxin lethality in control CFW mice occurs prior to 24 and 48 h post-injection. This is seen with both the largest and the smallest doses that kill. These results are given in the top section of Table 3. The animals under these conditions die quietly and can be protected against a 200-μg dose by a concurrent injection of cortisol. When cortisol is given 24 h prior to endotoxin, it still protects against 100 μg (about the LD_{50}) but not against 200 μg. The times to death in the hormonally treated mice were similar to those in the controls. These observations are presented in the next two sections of Table 3. When zymosan-pretreated mice were injected with endotoxin, not only were they sensitized, but many deaths occurred prior to 8 h and none was seen after 24 h. The early deaths in these mice were convulsive. In zymosan-primed animals cortisol, when given concurrently, failed to provide any significant level of protection and it did not alter the time of death or the convulsive nature of death in those that died prior to 8 h. Treatment with cortisol 24 h before injecting endotoxin in zymosan-primed animals did not increase the number of survivors, but it postponed the time of death and eliminated convulsive deaths. These observations are shown in the last three sections of Table 3. The release (or formation) of GAF in mice given an injection of endotoxin seems to occur sooner and in larger amounts in zymosan-pretreated animals than in controls. In addition, the release of GAF is not antagonized by cortisol. If these conclusions are valid, then GAF (or some other serum mediator) must inhibit the induction of enzymes and, at the same time, result in changes that lead to death. There is no explanation as to why early deaths are convulsive and later deaths are not, but a number of possible experimental determinations should prove revealing.

Evidence as to the nature of GAF is at best fragmentary. Interferon may be involved since either infection with Sindbis virus (sublethal in adult mice) or an injection of polyinosinic-polycytidylic acid [poly(I)·poly(C)] inhibits the hormonal induction of PEPCK (unpublished data). The interval between initiation of the virus infection and the time when cortisol fails to induce PEPCK is longer (6 h) than that following administration of poly(I)·poly(C) (4 h). The interval required for full release of interferon in Sindbis virus infection is about 5 h (13), whereas the polynucleotide acts more rapidly (20), requiring a time similar to that required by endotoxin (19). In addition, nude mice have been found in our laboratory to produce levels of interferon, in response to an injection of endotoxin, about one-fourth that formed by their heterozygous littermates. No data are available for interferon production in C3H/HeJ mice.

There are reasons to question whether GAF and interferon are the same substance and whether they are identical to the other mediators of endotoxemic effects. For example, even though Sindbis virus infection or an injection of poly(I)·poly(C) inhibits induction of PEPCK (and other inducible enzymes), we have been unsuccessful in passively transferring this effect with serum from these animals. This was obtained when conventional or zymosan-primed mice were used as serum donors. These findings might mean that larger concentrations of GAF are present in serum of endotoxemic mice than in the serum of animals with a virus infection [or in those given an injection of poly(I)·poly(C)], but other interpretations are also possible. Until GAF is better characterized, no conclusions can be drawn.

The cellular origin of GAF must also await further experimentation. It is simplistic to assume that the unusual response of nude mice is due only to the absence of T cells. Their abnormality may well extend beyond the lack of thymus and hair. The same can be said for the C3H/HeJ mice. Although the B cells of these animals appear to lack receptors needed for the mitogenic response to phenol-water-derived LPS, cells such as macrophages may also behave in a manner different from those of other mice. Moreover, the antimacrophage serum cannot be assumed to possess antibody directed against no other cells of the reticuloendothelial system, despite efforts to the contrary, since a suspension of pure macrophages may not, with the most favorable procedures, be obtainable. Thus, the production of GAF can be reduced or eliminated in three ways: (i) by an injection of antimacrophage serum in conventional mice, (ii) by the use of nude mice, and (iii) by the injection of phenol-water-extracted LPS into C3H/HeJ mice. None of these observations identifies the cellular origin of the mediator, but other approaches may yield the answer.

ACKNOWLEDGMENTS

This work was supported by Public Health Service grant AI-10087 from the National Institute of Allergy and Infectious Diseases. K. J. Goodrum has been a recipient of a National Science Foundation Graduate Fellowship.

LITERATURE CITED

1. **Atkins, E.** 1960. Pathogenesis of fever. Physiol. Rev. **40**:580–646.

2. **Benacerraf, B., G. J. Thorbecke, and D. Jacoby.** 1959. Effect of Zymosan on endotoxin toxicity in mice. Proc. Soc. Exp. Biol. Med. **100**:796–799.

3. **Berry, L. J.** 1971. Metabolic effects of bacterial endotoxin, p. 165–208. *In* S. Kadis, G. Weinbaum, and S. J. Ajl (ed.), Microbial toxins, vol. 5. Academic Press Inc., New York.

4. **Berry, L. J., M. W. Laney, and R. N. Moore.** 1975. Effect of endotoxin on metabolism and the metabolic changes in bacterial shock, p. 271–277. *In* B. Urbasheck, R. Urbasheck, and E. Neter (ed.), Gramnegative bacterial infections and mode of endotoxin actions. Springer-Verlag, New York.

5. **Bradley, T. R., and D. Metcalf.** 1966. The growth of mouse bone marrow cells *in vitro*. Aust. J. Exp. Biol. Med. **44**:287–300.

6. **Carswell, E. A., L. J. Old, R. L. Kassel, S. Green, N. Fiore, and B. Williamson.** 1975. An endotoxin-induced serum factor that causes necrosis of tumors. Proc. Natl. Acad. Sci. U.S.A. **72**:3666–3670.

7. **Fox, A. E., D. L. Gawlak, D. L. Ballantyne, Jr., and H. H. Freedman.** 1973. Influence of oxisuran, a differential inhibitor of cell-mediated hypersensitivity, on allograft survival and humoral immunity. Transplantation **15**:389–394.

8. **Gery, I., J. Kruger, and S. Z. Spiessel.** 1972. Stimulation of B-lymphocytes by endotoxin. J. Immunol. **108**:1088–1091.

9. **Glode, L. M., S. E. Mergenhagen, and D. L. Rosenstreich.** 1976. Essential contribution of spleen cells in mediating the lethal effect of endotoxin in vivo. Infect. Immun. **14**:626–630.

10. **Isaacs, A.** 1963. Interferon. Adv. Virus Res. **10**:1–38.

11. **Kampschmidt, R. F., and L. A. Pulliam.** 1975. Stimulation of antimicrobial activity in the rat with leukocytic endogenous mediator. RES J. Reticuloendothel. Soc. **17**:162–169.

12. **Kampschmidt, R. F., L. A. Pulliam, and H. F. Upchurch.** 1973. Sources of leukocytic endogenous mediator. Proc. Soc. Exp. Biol. Med. **144**:882–886.

13. **Kono, Y., and M. Ho.** 1965. The role of the reticuloendothelial system in interferon formation in the rabbit. Virology **25**:162–166.

14. **McCallum, R. E., and L. J. Berry.** 1972. Mouse liver fructose-1,6-diphosphatase and glucose-6-phosphatase activities after endotoxin poisoning. Infect. Immun. **6**:883–885.

15. **McCallum, R. E., and L. J. Berry.** 1973. Effects of endotoxin on gluconeogenesis, glycogen synthesis, and liver glycogen synthase in mice. Infect. Immun. **7**:642–654.

16. **Moore, R. N., K. J. Goodrum, and L. J. Berry.** 1976. Mediation of endotoxin effects of macrophages. RES J. Reticuloendothel. Soc. **19**:187–197.

17. **Skidmore, B. J., D. C. Morrison, J. M. Chiller, and W. O. Weigle.** 1975. Immunologic properties of bacterial lipopolysaccharide (LPS). II. The unresponsiveness of C3H/HeJ mouse spleen cells to LPS-induced mitogenesis is dependent on the method used to extract LPS. J. Exp. Med. **142**:1488–1508.

18. **Snyder, I. S., M. Deters, and J. Ingle.** 1971. Effect of endotoxin on pyruvate kinase activity in mouse liver. Infect. Immun. **4**:138–142.

19. **Stinebring, W. R., and J. S. Youngner.** 1964. Patterns of interferon appearance in mice injected with bacteria or bacterial endotoxin. Nature (London) **204**:712.

20. **Straub, S. X., R. F. Garry, and W. E. Magee.** 1974. Interferon induction by poly(I):poly(C) enclosed in phospholipid particles. Infect. Immun. **10**:783–792.

21. **Sultzer, B. M.** 1969. Genetic factors in leukocyte responses to endotoxin: further studies in mice. J. Immunol. **103**:32–38.

Endotoxin Interaction with Phosphatides from Human Leukocytes and Platelets, and with Lymphoid Cells of Susceptible and Resistant Mice

GEORG F. SPRINGER AND JAMES C. ADYE; *work on mice in collaboration with*
STEPHAN E. MERGENHAGEN AND DAVID L. ROSENSTREICH

Department of Immunochemistry Research, Evanston Hospital, and Department of Microbiology-Immunology, Medical and Dental Schools, Northwestern University, Evanston, Illinois 60201; and Laboratory of Microbiology and Immunology, National Institute of Dental Research, Bethesda, Maryland 20014

Man is the mammal most highly sensitive to bacterial endotoxin (lipopolysaccharide [LPS]); LPS is thought to be responsible for the high mortality rate from systemic gram-negative infections, despite antibiotic treatment (7, 9, 21, 22), which may be of the order of 90,000 deaths annually in this country caused by endotoxic shock (9).

Before LPS can produce its noxious effect, it has to attach to tissue-bound or soluble receptors. Erythrocytes fix LPS of gram-negative bacteria to their surfaces in vitro (10) and under extreme conditions in vivo (1, 7, 16). They may transport LPS to reticuloendothelium-rich organs for detoxification.

We have isolated and extensively characterized physically, chemically, and biologically a homogeneous lipoglycoprotein (LPS receptor) from human erythrocyte membranes which reversibly bound LPS as well as bacterial protein-LPS complexes from all gram-negative bacteria but none of the other bacterial antigens tested (14–18). Only the protein component of this receptor was involved in LPS fixation (14). It is noteworthy in this respect that the erythrocytes from strains of relatively endotoxin-resistant mice were stated to have less affinity for LPS than erythrocytes from LPS-sensitive strain A mice (7). Using the coating inhibition assay with ^{32}P-labeled LPS (15), we established quantitatively that the receptor interacts with LPS and not with erythrocytes.

Other cellular blood elements and tissue components may play at least as important a role in LPS fixation as erythrocytes (2, 3). Leukocytes, on incubation with endotoxin in vitro, generate a procoagulant tissue factor which leads to intravascular coagulation; it was concluded that LPS has to interact with leukocyte membrane components before coagulation can be triggered (8, 11). Similarly, interaction of LPS with human platelets activates a so-called plasma membrane procoagulant factor, which induces intravascular clotting and shock (6, 11).

Observations by a number of laboratories that lymphocytes of certain mice are naturally relatively refractory to endotoxin have a profound bearing on the problem of susceptibility to the deleterious actions of endotoxin (4, 5, 19, 20). It was speculated that this resistance may be due to a cell membrane alteration.

We have recently studied binding sites for endotoxin on the surface of and within human leukocytes and platelets by using "cold" and ^{32}P-labeled LPS. We measured fixation of LPS to human erythrocytes as well as its inhibition by putative receptor-active substances by methods described earlier (14, 17). Most experiments were carried out with *Escherichia coli* O_{86} LPS from the smooth B:7 strain. We found that intact plasma-free granulocytes, lymphocytes, and platelets possessed high affinity for LPS. B and T lymphocytes had closely similar activities (13).

We extracted these cells and platelets with *n*-butanol–water (13–15) and subsequently extracted the butanol-soluble material with petroleum ether (G. F. Springer and J. C. Adye, in preparation). The endotoxin-binding materials always resided in the most lipophilic phase, with the exception of the moderately active sphingomyelin, which was soluble in butanol rather than petrol ether. No protein, carbohydrate, or nucleic acid was present in highly active material. The dry preparations retained full activity at 3°C for at least 3 months and in solution for 3 days. Autoclaving at pH 7.0 and 121°C for 20 min did not affect activity. Extracts were on the average 6 to 13 times as active (on a dry-weight basis) as the whole cells from which they originated.

(1) *Purified platelets or leukocytes*
│ Suspend 100 mg (dry wt) in 10 ml of petroleum ether (bp 35–60°C)
│ Shake mechanically, 16 h, 5°C
│ Centrifuge at 2,000 × g, 15 min, 4°C
(2) *Organic phase of (1), weight yield 5 to 7% for leukocytes and 16 to 18% for platelets*
│ *Five- to tenfold increase in inhibitory activity over intact cells*
│ Hi-Flosil column (1.1 cm by 30 cm)
│ Elute successively with chloroform-methanol mixtures (1:0, 4:1, 5:4, 1:9, 0:1)

(3)	(1:0)	(4:1)	(5:4)	(1:9)/(0:1)
Fraction I Triglycerides	Fraction II Cholesterol	Fraction III–V PE PS	Fraction VI–VIII PI PC	Fraction IX–X Sph

FIG. 1. *Isolation of lipid fractions (I–X) from a silicic acid column. Abbreviations: PE, phosphatidyl-ethanolamine; PS, phosphatidylserine; PI, phosphatidylinositol; PC, phosphatidylcholine; Sph, sphingo-myelin.*

Physical and chemical analyses of the extracts in the apolar solvents showed that they were lipids. Electrophoresis followed by appropriate staining excluded activity due to trace amounts of contaminating protein or peptide (13; Springer and Adye, in preparation). We therefore investigated the activities of commercial lipids as determined by inhibition of ^{32}P-labeled LPS fixation to human erythrocytes as well as by the agglutination assay described earlier (13). The most active compounds were glycerophosphatides. They had about 25% of the activity of the most active cell extracts; cholesterol and sphingomyelin had about 5%. Phosphatidic acids, ethanolamine, cholesteryl linoleate, glyceric acid, triolein, and most free fatty acids were inactive at the levels tested in spite of their fine dispersion. These findings indicated that the active inhibitory principle(s) of the leukocyte extracts is glycerophosphatide(s).

We separated the lipidic extracts from granulocytes, mononuclear white cells, and platelets on silicic acid columns as indicated in Fig. 1. All highly active lipids eluted from the silica gel column in the solvent mixture proportions shown in the boxed area of Fig. 1. Most of the active compounds listed were obtained from all three cell types in essentially pure form by preparative one- and two-dimensional thin-layer chromatography (Springer and Adye, in preparation). The active sites of the glycerophosphatides are likely to be hydrophobic acyl groups, since we have shown that "lipid A" of LPS is involved in attachment to host tissue and, more specifically, to some of its most apolar regions (G. F. Springer, J. C. Adye, and E. T. Rietschel, Fed. Proc. **34**:505, 1975; see below). In addition, the negative electric charge of LPS plays a role in tissue fixation. Since the human tissue

phospholipids also have a negative charge, bi- and trivalent cations in the environment may be involved in LPS binding.

The ability of the lipids from platelets, mononuclear leukocytes, and granulocytes to combine with LPS and thus to prevent the attachment of LPS to human erythrocytes was in the order: phosphatidylcholine > phosphatidylethanolamine, phosphatidylinositol > sphingomyelin > lysophosphatidylethanolamine > cholesterol. Triglycerides were inactive. All the compounds were found in the three cell species listed (13; Springer and Adye, in preparation).

Among the glycerophosphatides with saturated fatty acids, straight-chain acyl substituents with 14 carbon atoms were optimal for activity when $C_{8:0}$ through $C_{18:0}$ acyl substituents were compared. Free $C_{14:0}$ fatty acid possessed 2 to 5% of the activity of a synthetic glycerophosphatide containing only $C_{14:0}$ acyl groups (J. C. Adye and G. F. Springer, Fed. Proc. **36**: 3320, 1977).

Because of the lipidic nature of the inhibitory substances from leukocytes and platelets, we also tested the "lipid A" component of bacterial endotoxins and some of its derivatives, since there is strong evidence that it is the lipophilic area of LPS that interacts with cells and cell products (cf. 3, 21). Preincubation of "lipid A" and derivatives with any endotoxin tested prevented erythrocyte coating by such LPS. These lipid preparations were much less active, however, than the inhibitory leukocyte extracts. An exception was sodium methylate-treated "lipid A," which was completely and selectively de-O-acylated (obtained from E. Rietschel, Max-Planck-Institut für Immunbiologie, Freiburg, West Germany; Springer, Adye, and Rietschel, Fed. Proc. **34**:505, 1975) and contained, as the only fatty acid, amide-linked 3-D-hydroxymyristic acid; quite likely also some pyrophosphate bonds were split. Its LPS-inhibitory activity was about 20 times that of "lipid A" and approached that of our most active leukocyte preparations. De-O- and de-N-acylated "lipid A" was *inactive*. 3-D-Hydroxymyristic acid and the racemic 2-hydroxymyristic, 3-hydroxypalmitic, and 3-hydroxystearic acids possessed about 2% of the de-O-acylated lipid. Ordinary fatty acids as well as their methyl esters were inactive (Springer and Adye, in preparation).

We also compared spleen cells of the relatively endotoxin-resistant C3H/HeJ mouse strain with those of the closely related, fully histocompatible C3H/HeN strain, which has normal susceptibility to LPS, and have also included other LPS-susceptible mouse strains, namely, C3H/Bittner and C3HeB/FeJ. Spleen lymphoid cells were obtained from young adult mice and purportedly prepared concomitantly and in identical fashion as described by others (5, 18). The cells were freeze-dried and then sent from the National Institute of Dental Research to the Evanston laboratory. The gray powders were broken up, dried to constant weight as described (14), made 2% in 0.1 M aqueous NaCl plus 0.05 M phosphate, pH 7.4 (buffered saline), and sonicated in an ice bath for 4 min at 15-s intervals with a Bronwill Biosonik Probe at 20 kc/s. Two shipments of spleen cells were received; one contained uncoded and the other contained coded samples. After the code was revealed, virtually identical results were obtained with the corresponding samples of both shipments. In all instances, the HeJ preparations weighed more, and the cell sonicates from the C3H/HeJ mouse spleens could be clearly distinguished with the naked eye from the cells of the C3H/HeN and C3H/Bittner mice by the former's almost complete solubility in buffered saline, whereas the preparations from the latter mice gave turbid fine suspensions. In strictly quantitative ^{32}P-labeled LPS fixation inhibition assays, "solubilized" spleen cell preparations from C3H/HeJ mice gave only 10 to 20% of the inhibition given by cell suspensions from C3H/Bittner or C3H/HeN mice. Essentially the same results were obtained when "cold" LPS was used in serological coating inhibition assays (cf. 15).

This finding, in addition to the extraordinary solubility of the material originating from C3H/HeJ mice, prompted us not only to compare the dry weights of lymph cell material obtained from an equal number of spleens of each of the three different strains of mice but also to dialyze this material exhaustively and to determine yield and activity of the nondialyzable material. Much

to our surprise, an average of 85.35% of the material from the C3H/HeJ spleen preparations was dialyzable and extremely rich in NaCl as determined with $AgNO_3$, whereas on the average 20.3% of the spleen preparations from C3H/HeN and C3H/Bittner mice were dialyzable; i.e., the C3H/HeJ preparations contained more than four times as much dialyzable material as the others.

When the nondialyzable residues of the preparations from the three mouse strains were tested for their ability to inhibit fixation of LPS to red cells, there remained only a slightly higher inhibitory activity for the HeN and Bittner mouse-derived spleen lymphoid cells as compared with those from the C3H/HeJ cells, and no inhibitory activity was found in the crude, dialyzable material.

Two additional sets of preparations were therefore made by the National Institute for Dental Research; the isolated spleen cells were counted and then freeze-dried from equal volumes of distilled water rather than from uncontrolled volumes of phosphate-buffered saline as submitted previously. Inhibitory activity on a weight basis given by the C3H/HeJ cells was reproducibly less than that of control mice when the ^{32}P-labeled LPS uptake by red cells was measured in quadruplicate experiments at two different levels of spleen lymphoid cell concentrations. The difference was quite small, however, being on the average 7%. More experiments and tests on purified material will have to be carried out before it can be decided whether this difference is statistically significant. Experiments initiated and performed at the Evanston Laboratory on red blood cells of C3H/HeJ and C3HeB/FeJ mice showed no significant difference (± 1%) of *E. coli* O_{86} LPS uptake as measured quantitatively by ^{32}P-labeled LPS fixation.

These simple LPS uptake studies, even in a "three-component system" (putative inhibitor, LPS, and erythrocytes), without kinetic considerations may not reveal even substantial differences in affinity of "receptors" for endotoxin on whole cells.

ACKNOWLEDGMENTS

This work was supported by Public Health Service grant AI-11569 from the National Institute of Allergy and Infectious Diseases.

We thank Herta Tegtmeyer for excellent technical assistance.

LITERATURE CITED

1. **Buxton, A.** 1959. The *in vivo* sensitization of avian erythrocytes with *Salmonella gallinarum* polysaccharide. Immunology 2:203–210.
2. **Das, J., A. A. Schwartz, and J. Folkman.** 1973. Clearance of endotoxin by platelets: role in increasing the

accuracy of the Limulus gelation test and in combating experimental endotoxemia. Surgery **74**:235–240.

3. **Gimber, P. E., and G. W. Rafter.** 1969. The interaction of *Escherichia coli* endotoxin with leukocytes. Arch. Biochem. Biophys. **135**:14–20.

4. **Glode, L. M., S. Mergenhagen, and D. Rosenstreich.** 1976. Significant contribution of spleen cells in mediating the lethal effects of endotoxin in vivo. Infect. Immun. **14**:626–630.

5. **Glode, L. M., I. Scher, B. Osborne, and D. L. Rosenstreich.** 1975. Cellular mechanism of endotoxin unresponsiveness in C3H/HeJ mice. J. Immunol. **116**:454–461.

6. **Hawiger, J., A. Hawiger, and S. Timmons.** 1975. Endotoxin sensitive membrane component of human platelets. Nature (London) **256**:125–127.

7. **Hill, G. J., and D. W. Weiss.** 1964. Relationships between susceptibility of mice to heat-killed Salmonellae and endotoxin and the affinity of their red blood cells for killed organisms, p. 422–427. *In* M. Landy and W. Braun (ed.), Bacterial endotoxins. Rutgers University Press, New Brunswick, N.J.

8. **Horn, R. G., and R. D. Collins.** 1968. Studies on the pathogenesis of the generalized Shwartzman reaction. Lab. Invest. **18**:101–107.

9. **McCabe, W. R., A. Greely, T. DiGenio, and M. A. Johns.** 1973. Humoral immunity to type specific and cross-reactive antigens of gram-negative bacilli. J. Infect. Dis. **128**:S284–S289.

10. **Neter, E.** 1956. Bacterial hemagglutination and hemolysis. Bacteriol. Rev. **20**:166–188.

11. **Niemetz, J., and A. Marcus.** 1974. The stimulating effect of platelets and platelet membranes on the procoagulant activity of leukocytes. J. Clin. Invest. **54**:1437–1443.

12. **Peavy, D. L., J. W. Shands, W. Adler, and R. T. Smith.** 1973. Mitogenicity of bacterial endotoxins: characterization of mitogenic principle. J. Immunol. **111**:352–357.

13. **Springer, G. F., and J. C. Adye.** 1975. Endotoxin-binding substances from human leukocytes and platelets. Infect. Immun. **12**:978–986.

14. **Springer, G. F., J. C. Adye, A. Bezkorovainy, and B. Jirgensons.** 1974. Properties and activity of the lipopolysaccharide-receptor from human erythrocytes. Biochemistry **13**:1379–1389.

15. **Springer, G. F., J. C. Adye, A. Bezkorovainy, and J. R. Murthy.** 1973. Functional aspects and nature of the lipopolysaccharide-receptor of human erythrocytes. J. Infect. Dis. **128**:S202–S212.

16. **Springer, G. F., and R. E. Horton.** 1964. Erythrocyte sensitization by blood group-specific bacterial antigens. J. Gen. Physiol. **37**:1229–1250.

17. **Springer, G. F., S. V. Huprikar, and E. Neter.** 1970. Specific inhibition of endotoxin coating of red cells by a human erythrocyte membrane component. Infect. Immun. **1**:98–108.

18. **Springer, G. F., E. T. Wang, J. H. Nichols, and J. M. Shear.** 1966. Relations between bacterial lipopolysaccharide structures and those of human cells. Ann. N.Y. Acad. Sci. **133**:566–579.

19. **Sultzer, B. M.** 1969. Genetic factors in leucocyte responses to endotoxin: further studies in mice. J. Immunol. **103**:32–38.

20. **Watson, J., and R. Riblet.** 1975. Genetic control responses to bacterial lipopolysaccharides in mice. II. A gene that influences a membrane component involved in the activation of bone marrow-derived lymphocytes by lipopolysaccharides. J. Immunol. **114**:1462–1468.

21. **Westphal, O.** 1975. Bacterial endotoxins. The 2nd Carl Prausnitz Memorial Lecture. Int. Arch. Allergy Appl. Immunol. **49**:1–43.

22. **Ziegler, E. J., H. Douglas, and A. I. Braude.** 1973. Human antiserum for prevention of the local Shwartzman reaction and death from bacterial lipopolysaccharides. J. Clin. Invest. **52**:3236–3238.

Cell Wall Antigens of Gram-Positive Bacteria and Their Biological Activities

Position Paper

RICHARD M. KRAUSE

National Institute of Allergy and Infectious Diseases, Bethesda, Maryland 20014

It was my initial intent to place into perspective recent advances on the cell wall antigens of gram-positive bacteria. But in preparing the manuscript I came to realize that it would be presumptuous for me to do so. I therefore propose to review some of the work concerning the antigens of hemolytic streptococci—work with which I have been most closely associated.

The passage of time has forced a reassessment of some of our earlier assumptions about streptococcal antigens and cell wall structure. These assumptions were based, of course, on prior experiments, but subsequent studies by others and ourselves have altered our earlier views on the cell wall antigens. If I have any theme, it is that nature yields her secrets reluctantly, and none of us should be too confident that the knowledge we extract now will retain its luster.

In the first part of this presentation, I shall describe briefly the major features of the streptococcal cell wall and the properties of several of its antigens as we understood them in 1962; in the last part of the paper, I shall recast these concepts in the light of more recent discoveries.

In 1962, there was considerable evidence to support the notion that the group A streptococcus had a cross-sectional appearance similar to that illustrated in Fig. 1 (14). This diagram is familiar to many of you, and, I am embarrassed to say, it has been reproduced far more widely than it deserves.

The cell wall is clouded over with a hyaluronic acid slime, and on this fact there is still no controversy. M, T, and R antigens were identified as cell wall components (17), and much indirect evidence indicated that the carbohydrate domain was sandwiched between the outer protein component and the underlying peptidoglycan. This diagram, when it was originally prepared, portrayed a comfortable holiocentric view of the streptococcal universe and served to summarize a great deal of direct and indirect immunological and chemical evidence on structural organization.

Electron micrographs of various cell wall preparations are shown in Fig. 2 (20). Untreated cell walls are in the middle frame. They exhibit a somewhat granular topography. As can be seen in the bottom frame, the cell walls, after treatment by proteolytic enzymes to remove the surface proteins, were smooth in appearance. This suggests that the granular material on the surface of the cell walls is M protein, occupying a rather superficial position. Extraction of cell walls with hot formamide gave a peptidoglycan residue, depicted in the top frame.

Indirect immunological evidence suggested that the polysaccharide was superficial to the peptidoglycan. This notion was reinforced by experiments designed to identify the cell wall phage receptor which also indicated that the group C carbohydrate was freely accessible for phage attachment. For example, purified group C carbohydrate irreversibly inactivated the group C bacteriophage—an additional argument for the peripheral distribution of the carbohydrate (15). Similar inactivation of group A bacteriophage was not obtained with group A carbohydrate, presumably because of more complex receptor mechanisms.

It was my good fortune in the 1950s to work with McCarty on the immunochemical structure of the group A carbohydrate as well as the companion carbohydrates of the related group A-variant and group C streptococci (14, 18). The overall data were consistent with the diagram shown in Fig. 3 (16). The group A polysaccharide had a molecular weight of approximately 10,000, and for each mol of antigen there were 38 mol of rhamnose and 17 mol of N-acetylglucosamine. The evidence suggested that side chains consisted of disaccharides of rhamnose. The immunodominant determinants were terminal β N-acetylglucosaminide residues. Furthermore, it seemed probable that there were amino sugars buried within the

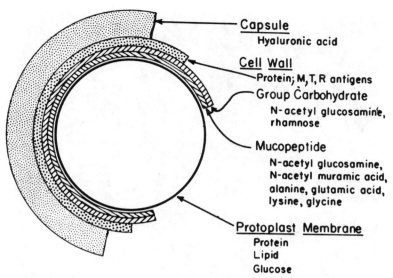

FIG. 1. *Schematic cross-section of group A hemolytic streptococci (14).*

antigen which were not accessible to enzymatic cleavage. Our view was that the group A-variant rhamnose moiety of the carbohydrate derived from the group A-variant organisms was similar to that of group A, but that the terminal amino sugars were lacking. This deficiency exposed serologically active disaccharides of rhamnose, the immunodominant determinants of the group A-variant antigen. In the case of group C polysaccharide, a similar rhamnose structure was envisioned with, however, terminal α-linked N-acetylgalactosaminide residues serving as the immunodominant determinants.

In the early 1960s, interest in streptococcal bacteriology abated, and many young investigators were reluctant to enter the field. Perhaps it seemed there was little prospect for additional discovery. As the President of the American Association of Immunologists, Lancefield gave her presidential address in which she summarized a lifetime of elegant work on the biology of the M protein (17). With so much already accomplished and the future opportunities uncertain, many scientists found excitement in other fields of bacteriology and immunology.

Fortunately, not all abandoned this apparently barren field, and a hardy, although diminished, band of microbiologists who continued the struggle were rewarded by the discovery of unexpected secrets of nature. Recent findings have now altered our prior notions on the structure and function of the cell wall antigens. Indeed, the streptococcus has re-emerged as a model system in which to study biological

phenomena as diverse as bacterial adherence, the genetics of the immune response, and the relationships between T and B cells.

To illustrate this renewed interest in streptococcal biology, I shall dwell briefly on three points. (i) M protein is more complex in structure and function than we had initially thought. (ii) Recent evidence has revised our prior views about the chemical structure of the group carbohydrate. This component, furthermore, appears to be functionally discontinuous so that patches of exposed peptidoglycan can interact with external events. (iii) Finally, I shall touch briefly on our discovery 11 years ago that rabbits immunized with streptococci produce large quantities of homogeneous antibodies to the group carbohydrate. In fact, the serum concentrations of such antibodies are comparable to the concentrations of myeloma proteins in patients with multiple myeloma. This latter observation has led to unexpected new pathways for studying antibody structure on the one hand and the biology and the genetics of the immune system on the other. I shall focus here on the idiotypic properties of these homogeneous antibodies.

Let me now turn briefly to a consideration of each of these three issues.

RECENT OBSERVATIONS ON M PROTEIN

Attention was initially focused on M proteins because these were serologically type-specific substances which induced type-specific resistance by stimulation of type-specific antibodies. M protein is a virulence factor, presumably because it impedes phagocytosis (17).

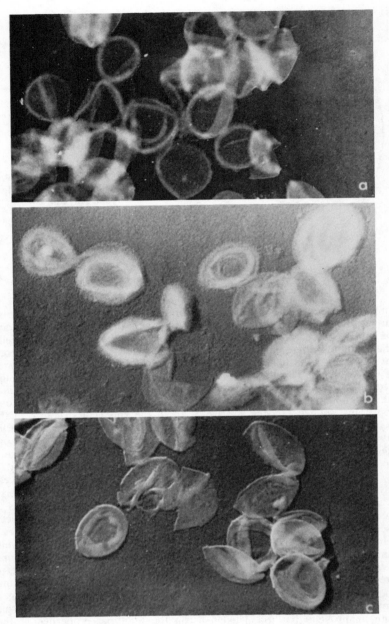

FIG. 2. *Chromium-shadowed preparations of isolated streptococcal cell walls. Magnification approximately ×10,000. (a) Walls extracted with hot formamide. This removes all components except the peptidoglycan. (b) Untreated cell walls. (c) Walls treated with proteolytic enzymes to remove surface proteins (18).*

In 1969, Swanson et al. (21) made an unexpected observation on M protein which is illustrated in the electron micrograph in Fig. 4. Streptococci rich in M protein possess hairlike fimbriae projecting from the surface, whereas the variants of streptococci which are lacking M protein are devoid of the fimbriae. By the use of ferritin-labeled antibody to M protein and high-resolution electron microscopy, the M protein was located on these fimbriae. Subsequent studies by Ellen and Gibbons (11) suggested that the fimbriae were organelles for bacterial attachment to the mucous membrane cell surfaces. Indirect evidence suggested that

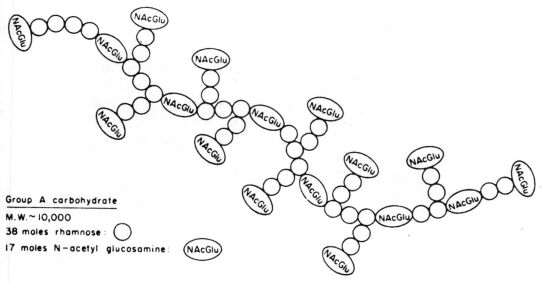

Group A carbohydrate

M.W.~ 10,000

38 moles rhamnose :

17 moles N-acetyl glucosamine : (NAcGlu)

FIG. 3. *Diagrammatic representation of the group A carbohydrate molecule (16).*

the M protein associated with the fimbriae was involved in this attachment.

The participation of M protein itself in attachment to cells has been contested by Beachey and Ofek (1), who were investigating the role of lipoteichoic acid in this process. In the electron micrograph in Fig. 5 (1), fimbriae were observed radiating from group A streptococci to the surface membrane of human oral epithelial cells. Chemical treatment, such as mild peptic digestion at pH 5.8, removed the serologically active M protein from these intact streptococci. This treatment had little visible effect on the fimbriae or on their capacity to adhere to human oral mucosal cell surfaces. Such evidence suggested that the fimbriae possess at least two components: M protein, which is involved in resistance to phagocytosis, and lipoteichoic acid, which is involved in epithelial cell binding.

In view of the important biological properties of M protein, it is not surprising that considerable attention has been given to its chemical properties. The problem has not yielded readily to attack despite the use of several extraction procedures and the latest in physical and chemical techniques for characterization. The exact nature of the M protein molecule(s) remains obscure. Nevertheless, the picture that is emerging is one of protein subunits held in covalent interaction to form larger macromolecules (13). It is perplexing that these larger M protein molecules can be separated into components with molecular weights as low as 5,000 which are type specific in reaction with

antibody, whereas the type-specific antiphagocytic moiety resides in the units of a larger molecular weight between 28,000 and 35,000 (13).

RECENT OBSERVATIONS ON GROUP-SPECIFIC CARBOHYDRATE

As stated earlier, indirect evidence indicated that the group-specific carbohydrate was external to the peptidoglycan matrix. Subsequent electron microscopic evidence obtained by Swanson et al. (21) reinforced this view. This is illustrated in Fig. 4. In the lower left-hand frame the two large arrows point to a pale electron-dense band within the cell wall which is exterior to an underlying electron-dense band. After the organisms were treated with weak nitrous acid, a procedure which completely removes the group-specific carbohydrate, the cell wall had a somewhat different appearance. This is shown in the lower right-hand frame. The outer pale band is absent, but the inner dense band is present. It was presumed that this residual component was the peptidoglycan. These experiments reinforced the impression that the peptidoglycan matrix was blanketed by a continuous layer of polysaccharide. Although this spatial topography is undoubtedly an accurate representation, there is reason to believe that, in a functional sense, patches of peptidoglycan are exposed to certain external events.

More recent studies on the interaction of bac-

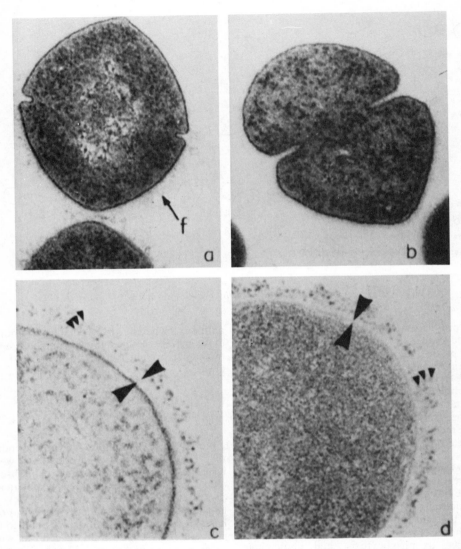

Fig. 4. *Electron micrographs of thin sections of streptococci. (a) M-positive strain, showing hairlike fimbriae of M protein (f). (b) M-negative strain lacking surface fimbriae. (c) Higher magnification of M-positive streptococcus tagged with ferritin-labeled antibody to M protein. Large arrows indicate thickness of homogeneous layer of cell wall. Small arrows indicate alignment of ferritin label along M-protein fimbriae. (d) Section similar to (c) after treatment of organisms with nitrous acid. Reduction in homogeneous outer zone of wall is correlated with removal of large part of group-specific carbohydrate, although M protein remains intact (ferritin-labeled M antibody). Large arrows indicate substantial reduction in thickness of wall associated with removal of carbohydrate. Note also that the dense line of the inner portion of the wall has been removed by nitrous acid treatment. Electron micrographs by John Swanson (18).*

teriophage and the streptococcal cell wall suggest that there are gaps in the carbohydrate moiety which expose patches of peptidoglycan matrix. As already stated, our earlier studies indicated that the group C carbohydrate was the receptor for the group C phage. This view must not be altered. Fischetti and Zabriskie (12) observed that group-specific carbohydrate ex-

tracted in such a way that it contained traces of peptidoglycan inactivated bacteriophage, whereas carbohydrate devoid of the peptidoglycan did not inactivate bacteriophage. In a major extension of these studies (P. P. Cleary et al., in press), attention is now focused on the peptidoglycan as a major element in the bacteriophage attachment site. It would appear

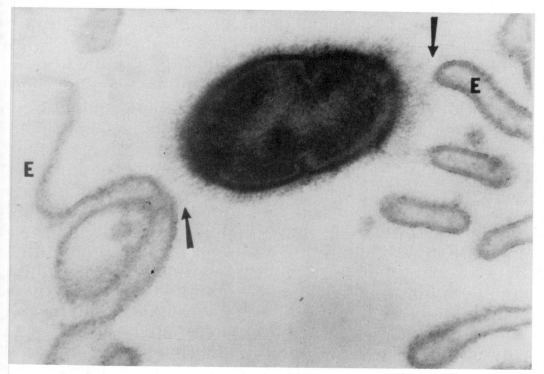

FIG. 5. *Fimbriae radiating from group A streptococcus to membrane (arrows) of human oral epithelial cells (E; 1).*

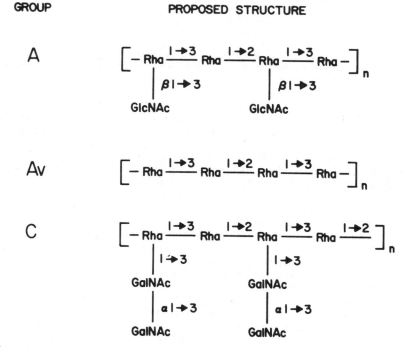

FIG. 6. *Schematic representation of the chemical structure of groups A, A-variant, and C streptococci (4).*

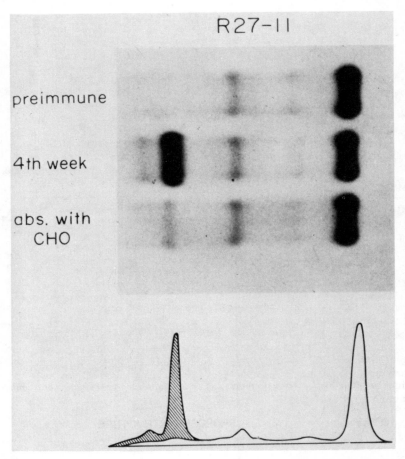

FIG. 7. *Demonstration of a monoclonal-like group C antibody response in a rabbit immunized with group C streptococci. Top frame: Upper electrophoretic pattern, pre-immune serum; middle pattern, immune serum; lower pattern, after absorption with group C carbohydrate. Bottom frame: Densitometric tracings of the unabsorbed and absorbed serum.*

that, if the carbohydrate is involved at all, it must be associated with the peptidoglycan moiety. The picture which emerges is that the bacteriophage tail structure seeks a path through the outer carbohydrate layer to those exposed underlying patches of peptidoglycan which are accessible to the external environment.

Current studies have led also to a revision of our prior concepts on the structure of the group-specific carbohydrates. In my laboratory in New York, Coligan et al. (4) reexamined the structure of the group-specific polysaccharides employing the most recent chemical techniques. After acid hydrolysis of the carbohydrate, the split products were isolated and the permethylation derivatives were examined in a mass spectrometer modified for chemical ionization. There were some surprises which we had not anticipated from our prior immuno-

chemical work. First of all, as shown in the middle frame of Fig. 6, the group A-variant carbohydrate consists of a linear rhamnose polymer in alternating 1–2, 1–3 linkage. There is very little branching. Work is now progressing to determine the anomeric linkages. A similar rhamnose polymer serves as the framework of the group A and group C carbohydrates. The group A immunodominant determinants consist of β N-acetylglucosaminide residues; there is no evidence for an appreciable number of rhamnose disaccharide side chains as previously thought. The group C determinants consist of a disaccharide of N-acetylgalactosamine. The terminal amino sugar is α-linked. In recent studies (J. E. Coligan, B. A. Fraser, and T. J. Kindt, in press), the disaccharide has been isolated and purified. The importance of these studies is that they pinpoint precisely the chemical structure of the antigenic determinants which react with the binding site of the homogeneous antibodies to streptococcal carbohydrates in immunized rabbits.

IDIOTYPIC PROPERTIES OF HOMOGENEOUS ANTIBODIES

Idiotype is a new term (3, 19). It refers to the antigenic marker on a homogeneous antibody that is associated with the antigen-binding site. These markers are detected serologically, and we need not go into that methodology here. Idiotypes have been used as markers to explore unknown domains of the immune system such as the genetics of the immune response, as well as the interactions between T and B cells.

Our studies on the inheritance of idiotypic markers were prompted by the occurrence of homogeneous antibodies to group-specific carbohydrates following immunization with groups A and C streptococci (8). One example of a homogeneous antibody response is given in Fig. 7. Illustrated here is the electrophoretic pattern of a group C antiserum which contains 40 mg of antibody per ml; the bulk of the antibody was monoclonal in nature.

An examination of the homogeneous antibodies which occurred in a large number of partially inbred rabbits indicated that idiotypic markers were inherited (8). Or, to put it more precisely, the studies suggested the inheritance of the genes which are responsible for the amino acid sequences associated with the antigen-binding sites of these homogeneous antibodies. The observations have now been extended to inbred mice (2, 7). In addition to streptococcal antigens, other antigen systems have been used by Nisonoff, Weigert, Cohn, Potter, and other investigators (19).

Eichmann et al. (10) were the first to show the Mendelian segregation of the idiotypic marker of the group A antibodies in inbred A/J mice immunized with group A streptococci. Furthermore, the expression of the idiotype was what one would expect in the F1 heterozygotes. Genetic studies have since progressed in the expected fashion with the observation of a recombination in the A/J heavy-chain linkage group. Since this initial observation, a number of other recombinant events have been observed with other idiotypic markers, and considerable progress has been made on idiotype genes and their chromosomal arrangement in mice. A tentative map has now been proposed, but this is still a matter of controversy (20).

A new dimension has recently been added to the significance of idiotypy by Eichmann (5). A

profound stimulation to immunity was seen with administration of anti-idiotype serum. Equally, or more intriguing, is the fact that immune *suppression* also occurred (6) under other experimental conditions with a different population of anti-idiotype antibodies. It is conceivable that the use of idiotypic antisera may provide a new therapeutic modality for specific immune suppression or immune enhancement.

Finally, it appears that idiotypes may serve as probes for identifying the elusive T-cell receptor (9). Experiments indicate that an anti-idiotype antibody reacts with the specific streptococcal antibody as well as the T cells from immunized mice. This suggests that there is a sharing of idiotypes between T-cell receptors and antibodies. Helper T cells may use, at least partially, the same antigen recognition system as B cells, namely, the product of the heavy-chain V-region gene.

Thomas speaks of the "lives of a cell" (22). Few cells have acquired more lives through scientific scrutiny than the streptococcus. Alert, agile, and vigorous, streptococci still retain the attention of taxonomists, pathologists, biochemists, and immunologists. Cunning and surreptitious, streptococci thrive on secretive behavior. We have still to penetrate the mysterious occurrence of rheumatic fever and acute nephritis following streptococcal infections. Streptococci will continue to fascinate scientists as long as this mystery remains.

LITERATURE CITED

1. **Beachey, E. H., and R. Ofek.** 1976. Epithelial cell binding of Group A streptococci by lipoteichoic acid on fimbriae denuded of M protein. J. Exp. Med. **143:** 759–771.
2. **Briles, D. E., and R. M. Krause.** 1974. Mouse strain-specific idiotypy and interstrain idiotypic cross-reactions. J. Immunol. **113:**522–530.
3. **Capra, J. D., and J. M. Kehoe.** 1975. Hypervariable regions, idiotypy and the antibody-combining site. Adv. Immunol. **20:**1–40.
4. **Coligan, J. E., W. C. Schnute, Jr., and T. J. Kindt.** 1975. Immunochemical and chemical studies on streptococcal group-specific carbohydrates. J. Immunol. **144:**1654–1658.
5. **Eichmann, K.** 1974. Idiotype suppression. I. Influence of the dose and of the effector functions of anti-idiotypic antibodies on the production of an idiotype. Eur. J. Immunol. **4:**296–302.
6. **Eichmann, K.** 1974. Idiotype suppression. I. Influence of the dose and of the effector functions of anti-idiotypic antibodies on the production of an idiotype. Eur. J. Immunol. **4:**296–302.
7. **Eichmann, K., and C. Berek.** 1973. Mendelian segregation of a mouse antibody idiotype. Eur. J. Immunol. **3:** 599–601.
8. **Eichmann, K., and T. J. Kindt.** 1971. The inheritance of individual antigenic specificities of rabbit antibodies to streptococcal carbohydrates. J. Exp. Med. **134:**532–552.
9. **Eichmann, K., and K. Rajewsky.** 1975. Induction of T and

B cell immunity by anti-idiotypic antibody. Eur. J. Immunol. **5**:661–666.

10. **Eichmann, K., A. S. Tung, and A. Nisonoff.** 1974. Linkage and rearrangement of genes encoding mouse immunoglobulin heavy chains. Nature (London) **250**:509–511.

11. **Ellen, R. P., and R. J. Gibbons.** 1972. M protein-associated adherence of *Streptococcus pyogenes* to epithelial surfaces: prerequisite for virulence. Infect. Immun. **5**:826–830.

12. **Fischetti, V. A., and J. B. Zabriskie.** 1968. Studies on streptococcal bacteriophages. II. Adsorption studies on Group A and Group C streptococcal bacteriophages. J. Exp. Med. **127**:489–505.

13. **Fischetti, V. A., E. C. Gotschlich, G. Siviglia, and J. B. Zabriskie.** 1976. Streptococcal M protein extracted by nonionic detergent. I. Properties of the antiphagocytic and type-specific molecules. J. Exp. Med. **144**:32–53.

14. **Krause, R. M.** 1963. Symposium on relationship of structure of microorganisms to their immunological properties. IV. Antigenic and biochemical composition of hemolytic streptococcal cell walls. Bacteriol. Rev. **27**:369–380.

15. **Krause, R. M.** 1957. Studies on the bacteriophages of hemolytic streptococci. I. Factors influencing the interaction of phage and susceptible host cell. J. Exp. Med. **106**:365–384.

16. **Krause, R. M.** 1970. The search for antibodies with molecular uniformity. Adv. Immunol. **12**:1–56.

17. **Lancefield, R. C.** 1962. Current knowledge of type-specific M antigens of Group A streptococci. J. Immunol. **89**:307–313.

18. **McCarty, M.** 1969–1970. The streptococcal cell wall. Harvey Lect. **65**:73–96.

19. **Nisonoff, A.** 1975. Idiotypic specificities of immunoglobulins, p. 444–496. *In* F. J. Dixon and H. G. Kunkel (ed.), The antibody molecule. Academic Press Inc., New York.

20. **Riblet, R., and B. Blomberg.** 1975. Genetics of mouse antibodies. I. Linkage of the dextran response locus, V_H-DEX, to allotype. Eur. J. Immunol. **5**:775–777.

21. **Swanson, J., K. C. Hsu, and E. C. Gotschlich.** 1969. Electron microscopic studies on streptococci. J. Exp. Med. **130**:1063–1091.

22. **Thomas, L.** 1974. The lives of a cell. Viking Press, New York.

Structure and Immunological Aspects of Peptidoglycans

K. H. SCHLEIFER AND H. P. SEIDL

Lehrstuhl für Mikrobiologie, Technische Universität München, 8 Munich 2, West Germany

Peptidoglycan is a characteristic component of the cell wall of almost all prokaryotes, not only of bacteria but also of blue-green algae. It is a heteropolymer built of polysaccharide chains which are cross-linked through short peptides (Fig. 1). The glycan moiety of peptidoglycan is relatively uniform and resembles chitin. Like chitin, it is made up of alternating β-(1,4)-glycosidically linked units of N-acetylglucosamine. But, in contrast to chitin, each alternate glucosamine residue is substituted by a D-lactic acid ether at C-3. This glucosamine derivative is called muramic acid. The carboxyl group of muramic acid is usually substituted by a peptide which is made up of alternating L- and D-amino acids. The presence of muramic acid and D-amino acids is a typical feature of peptidoglycan. The free amino group of the diamino acid forms a peptide linkage with the C-terminal D-alanine of an adjacent peptide subunit either directly or via an interpeptide bridge. This type of structure results in a tight network which, in fact, is a huge macromolecule encompassing the entire bacterial cell. It is beyond the scope of this paper to present a detailed account of the chemical structure of peptidoglycan (for a review, see 6). What we wish to discuss briefly are the main characteristics of the peptidoglycan structure.

1. The glycan strands are rather uniform. They exhibit only few variations, such as acetylation or phosphorylation of the muramyl 6-hydroxyl groups and the occasional absence of N-acyl or peptide substituents; among mycobacteria and some coryneform bacteria, muramic acid does not occur as the N-acetyl derivative but rather occurs as the N-glycolyl derivative.

2. Depending on the anchoring point of the cross-linkage of the peptide subunit, one can distinguish two main groups of peptidoglycans, named A and B. The cross-linkage of group A peptidoglycans extends, as shown in Fig. 1, from the distal amino group of the L-diamino acid to the carboxyl group of D-alanine in position 4 of an adjacent peptide subunit. The cross-linkage can occur either in a direct manner (e.g., all gram-negative bacteria) or via an interpeptide bridge. Interpeptide bridges consisting of L-monocarboxylic amino acids or glycine are very common among gram-positive bacteria. Typical examples are the peptidoglycans of Staphylococcus aureus (Fig. 1a) and of Streptococcus group A-variant (Fig. 1b). The interpeptide bridge of S. aureus peptidoglycan is a pentaglycine; that of the Streptococcus group A-variant is di- or tri-L-alanine. The peptidoglycan group B is much less common than group A and is found only among some coryneform bacteria. The cross-linkage in group B extends from the α-carboxyl group of D-glutamic acid to the carboxyl group of D-alanine in position 4 of an adjacent peptide subunit. Since two carboxyl groups are to be connected, a diamino acid must be present in the interpeptide bridge. An interesting correlation between the mode of linkage and the configuration of these diamino acids has been found. L-Diamino acids are always bound through their distal amino group to D-alanine, whereas D-diamino acids are linked via their α-amino group.

3. The number of amino acids occurring in the various peptidoglycans is rather restricted. From three to six chemically different amino acids can be found in a particular peptidoglycan. Branched, aromatic, and sulfur-containing amino acids, histidine, proline, and arginine have never been detected.

4. The tetrapeptide subunits display a sequence of alternating L- and D-amino acids. Even meso-diaminopimelic acid is integrated into this pattern, since it forms linkages with its L-asymmetric center.

5. The monocarboxylic, monoamino acids of the interpeptide bridges are usually present as L isomers. Dicarboxylic amino acids and diamino acids, on the other hand, can be found in both configurations in the interpeptide bridges.

6. Within the peptide subunit of different peptidoglycans, only a restricted variation is possible. L-Alanine in position 1 can be replaced in a few cases by glycine or L-serine. In some coryneform bacteria D-glutamic acid can be hydroxylated. The α-carboxyl group of glutamic acid is usually amidated or unsubstituted; in a few cases it is substituted by glycine, glycine amide, or D-alanine amide.

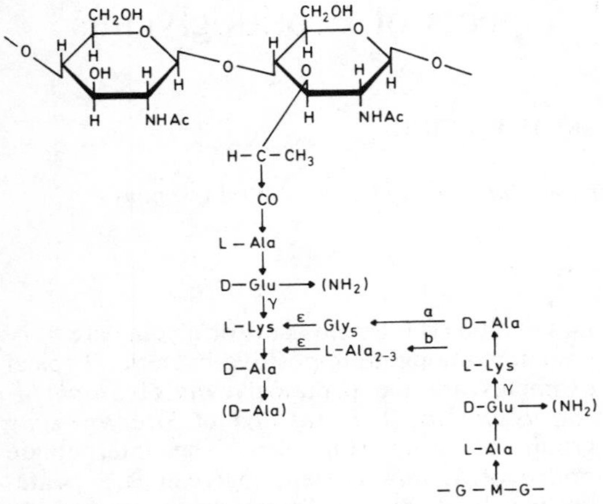

FIG. 1. *Fragment of the primary structure of the peptidoglycans of* Staphylococcus aureus *(a) and* Streptococcus *group A-variant (b). Abbreviations: Ac, acetyl; G, N-acetylglucosamine; M, N-acetylmuramic acid; γ, γ-carboxyl group of D-glutamic acid; ε, ε-amino group of L-lysine.*

Position 3 reveals the greatest variation. Nine different amino acids have been found in this position: *meso-* or LL-diaminopimelic acid, L-lysine, L-ornithine, *meso*-hydroxydiaminopimelic acid, L-diaminobutyric acid, L-hydroxylysine, L-homoserine, L-alanine, and L-glutamic acid. No variations are found at positions 4 and 5 under normal conditions (for exceptions, see 5). The pentapeptide subunit of the peptidoglycan precursor contains a D-alanyl-D-alanine at the COOH terminus. These pentapeptides can be preserved as a minor portion of the peptide subunits in peptidoglycans of cells lacking DD-carboxypeptidase.

In the second part of this paper, we shall consider three aspects of the antigenic properties of peptidoglycan: the antigenic properties of the glycan moiety, of the peptide subunit, and of the interpeptide bridges.

ANTIGENIC PROPERTIES OF THE GLYCAN STRAND

Streptococcal antisera, in particular group A-variant antisera, are rich in peptidoglycan antibodies (2). Most rabbit antisera had more antibodies specific for the peptide than for the glycan moiety, but some antisera had primarily antibodies specific for the glycan. Studies by Rolicka and Park (4) demonstrated that antibodies directed against the glycan chain recognize *N*-acetylglucosamine and not *N*-acetylmuramic acid as the immunodominant sugar. However, recent work by Wikler (10), employ-

ing antisera against *Micrococcus luteus* (former *M. lysodeikticus*), has indicated that *N*-acetylmuramic acid is the immunodominant sugar. To clarify this controversy, we investigated the precipitin reaction between peptidoglycan antisera and antigens such as chitin (structural analogue of the glycan strand) and *M. luteus* or *Bacillus subtilis* peptidoglycans. It is important to know that about 50% of the muramic acid residues of the *M. luteus* peptidoglycan are not substituted by peptide subunits, whereas the muramic acid residues of *B. subtilis* peptidoglycan are completely substituted. Thus, about half of the muramic acid residues of the *M. luteus* peptidoglycan exhibit an unsubstituted carboxyl group. The specificity of antibodies precipitable from the reaction of peptidoglycan antisera with the various antigens was then investigated by means of the quantitative precipitin inhibition reaction. As inhibitors we used various amino sugars and amino sugar derivatives: *N*-acetylglucosamine, *N*-acetylmuramic acid, *N*-acetylmuramic acid ethylamide, *N*-acetylchitobiose, *N*-acetylchitotriose, *N*-acetylchitotetraose, and disaccharides and tetrasaccharides from the glycan strand of peptidoglycan. The main results from these inhibition reactions are summarized in Table 1. The precipitin reactions between antisera of *Streptococcus* A-variant and the peptidoglycans of *Bacillus subtilis* and *Micrococcus luteus* and chitin were inhibited strongly by *N*-acetylglucosamine, whereas *N*-acetylmuramic acid exhibited no inhibitory capacity. Blocking the free carboxyl group of *N*-acetylmuramic acid re-

TABLE 1. *Inhibition of the agglutination of peptidoglycans of* Bacillus subtilis *and* Micrococcus luteus *with antisera to* Streptococcus *group A-variant or* M. luteus[a]

Antiserum	Antigen	Inhibition		
		GlcNAc	MurNAc	MurNAc ethylamide
Anti-(*Streptococcus* A-variant)-serum	Peptidoglycan of *B. subtilis*	+++	—	+
	Chitin	+++	—	+
	Peptidoglycan of *M. luteus*	+++	—	+
Anti-(*M. luteus*)-serum	Peptidoglycan of *B.subtilis*	+++	—	+
	Chitin	+++	—	+
	Peptidoglycan of *M. luteus*	—	+++	—

[a] GlcNAc = *N*-acetylglucosamine; MurNAc = *N*-acetylmuramic acid.

sulted in some inhibitory effect in comparison with that of unsubstituted *N*-acetylmuramic acid. In the case of *M. luteus* antisera, similar results were obtained if chitin or the peptidoglycan of *B. subtilis* was applied as antigen. The results were completely different, however, when peptidoglycan of *M. luteus* acted as the antigen. *N*-acetylglucosamine was not inhibitory, whereas *N*-acetylmuramic acid inhibited the precipitin reaction very well. It should be pointed out that in this case the carboxyl-protected muramic acid did not result in a more positive reaction.

The interpretation of these observations is as follows: (i) that all the antisera tested, including antisera to *M. luteus*, contain antibodies directed against *N*-acetylglucosamine and not against *N*-acetylmuramic acid as the determinant sugar; and (ii) that antisera to *M. luteus* contained additional antibodies with a high specificity for *N*-acetylmuramic acid and not for *N*-acetylglucosamine. The results of the reaction with *N*-acetylmuramic acid ethylamide clearly demonstrate that a free carboxyl group was absolutely necessary for the inhibitory capacity of *N*-acetylmuramic acid. This is in good agreement with the structural properties of the *M. luteus* peptidoglycan (see above).

ANTIGENIC PROPERTIES OF THE PEPTIDE SUBUNIT

The immunodominant determinant of the peptide subunit was determined by the quantitative precipitin inhibition test employing a series of peptides (L-Ala-γ-D-Glu-L-Lys-D-Ala-D-Ala) and not the predominantly occurring tetrapeptide (L-Ala-γ-D-Glu-L-Lys-D-Ala) as the antigenic determinant. The antibodies are directed against the COOH terminus of the pentapeptide, and D-alanyl-D-alanine is the immunodominant group. The contribution of the other amino acids to the antigenic site of the pentapeptide is of less importance (L-Lys, D-Glu) or insignificant (L-Ala).

To confirm these findings, we coupled synthetic pentapeptides (Gly-L-Ala-L-Ala-D-Ala-D-Ala) with their amino groups to a protein carrier and injected the conjugate into rabbits [8, 9]. The antisera of the synthetic immunogen resulted in a strong precipitin reaction with the homologous immunogen and with staphylococcal or streptococcal peptidoglycan. The reverse reaction between *Streptococcus* group A-variant antisera and the synthetic immunogen was also possible. Inhibition studies with various synthetic peptides demonstrated that the cross-reactions were due to the common COOH-terminal D-alanyl-D-alanine residues present

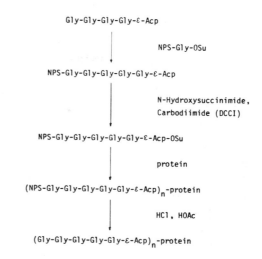

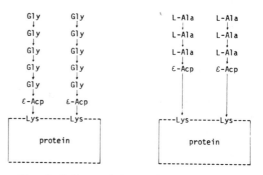

FIG. 2. *Scheme of the synthesis of pentaglycyl-ε-aminocaproyl-RNase and tri-L-alanyl-ε-aminocaproyl-RNase.*

in both the synthetic immunogen and the peptidoglycans employed.

ANTIGENIC PROPERTIES OF THE INTERPEPTIDE BRIDGE

Recent work by Helgeland et al. (1) and Ranu (3) has indicated that the D-alanyl-D-alanine-containing peptide subunit is not the only antigenic determinant of the peptide moiety of *S. aureus* peptidoglycan. To demonstrate that the interpeptide bridge contains an antigenic site, we synthesized the following immunogens. The carboxyl termini of synthetic peptides (pentaglycyl-ε-aminocaproic acid and tri-L-alanyl-ε-aminocaproic acid) were coupled to carrier proteins (Fig. 2). The conjugate bearing NH$_2$-terminal pentaglycine substituents resembles staphylococcal peptidoglycan in which

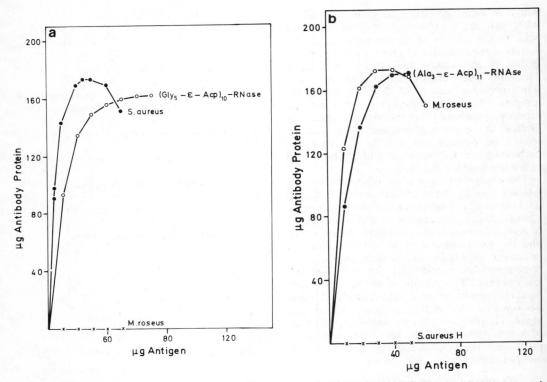

FIG. 3. *Quantitative precipitin reaction between antisera to pentaglycyl-ϵ-aminocaproyl-RNase (a) and tri-L-alanyl-ϵ-aminocaproyl-RNase (b) and their homologous antigens or peptidoglycans of* Staphylococcus aureus *and* Micrococcus roseus.

TABLE 2. *Agglutination reactions between antisera to pentaglycyl-ϵ-aminocaproyl-RNase (Gly$_5$-RNase) or tri-L-alanyl-ϵ-aminocaproyl-RNase (L-Ala$_3$-RNase) and peptidoglycans of different chemical composition*

Organism	Peptidoglycan type	Titer with antisera against	
		Gly$_5$-RNase	L-Ala$_3$-RNase
Staphylococcus aureus H	L-Lys-Gly$_5$	1:1,024	1:8
S. xylosus	L-Lys-Gly$_5$	1:1,024	1:4
Staphylococcus sp.	L-Lys-L-Ala-Gly$_4$	1:512	1:4
S. epidermidis	L-Lys-L-Ser$_{0.8}$, Gly$_4$	1:512	1:8
Streptococcus haemolyticus	L-Lys-L-Ser$_{1.4}$, Gly$_{3.5}$	1:256	1:4
Micrococcus roseus	L-Lys-L-Ala$_3$	0	1:1,024
M. varians	L-Lys-L-Ala$_3$	0	1:1,024
M. kristinae	L-Lys-L-Ala$_3$	0	1:1,024
Bacillus subtilis	m-Diaminopimelic acid-direct	0	0

a certain percentage of the interpeptide bridges are not cross-linked and exhibit NH$_2$-terminal glycine residues. Another conjugate with NH$_2$-terminal tri-L-alanine substituents is related to the peptidoglycans of many micrococci and streptococci containing di- or tri-L-alanine interpeptide bridges. Rabbit antisera to these synthetic immunogens reacted not only with the homologous conjugates but also with the corresponding peptidoglycans (Fig. 3a, b). Antisera of pentaglycyl-ϵ-aminocaproyl-RNase gave a strong precipitin reaction with the peptidoglycan of S. aureus but no reaction with M. roseus peptidoglycan, which lacks glycine peptides and in which tri-L-alanine peptides constitute the interpeptide bridge (Fig. 3a). Tri-L-alanyl-ϵ-aminocaproyl-RNase antisera, on the other hand, precipitated M. roseus peptidoglycan but not the peptidoglycan of S. aureus (Fig. 3b). The reverse reaction, with Streptococcus group A-variant antisera as the antibody source and the conjugates as antigens, was also possible. Since the peptidoglycan of the Streptococcus group A-variant contained di- or tri-L-alanine peptides as interpeptide bridges (Fig. 1b), it was self-evident that only tri-L-alanyl-conjugate and not pentaglycyl-conjugate would react with group A-variant antisera.

We conclude that there are at least three antigenic determinants in peptidoglycan:

1. The glycan strand N-acetylglucosamine is usually the immunodominant group, but in a few cases (e.g., *M. luteus*), in which the peptide substitution of the glycan strand is incomplete, N-acetylmuramic acid can also be an immunodominant group.

2. The non-cross-linked pentapeptide is the antigenic site of the peptide subunit, and the COOH-terminal D-alanyl-D-alanine is the immunodominant group.

3. The interpeptide bridges are also antigenic. Antibodies directed against these interpeptide bridges are very specific and can be employed for the serological differentiation of bacteria containing different peptidoglycan types (Table 2). Antisera to glycine peptides strongly agglutinate staphylococcal peptidoglycan, but no reaction takes place with peptidoglycans of micrococci or *B. subtilis*. On the contrary, antisera to tri-L-alanyl-RNase result in a very good agglutination with micrococcal peptidoglycans, but in almost no reaction with peptidoglycans of staphylococci. Since the different peptidoglycan types are a very valuable criterion for the differentiation of gram-positive bacteria, highly specific antisera for synthetic antigens cross-reacting with different interpeptide bridges may be a useful tool for the classification of many gram-positive bacteria.

LITERATURE CITED

1. **Helgeland, S., A. Grov, and K. H. Schleifer.** 1973. The immunochemistry of *Staphylococcus aureus* mucopeptide. I. Antigenic specificity of the peptide subunits. Acta Pathol. Microbiol. Scand. Sect. B **81:** 413–418.

2. **Karakawa, W. W., D. G. Braun, H. Lackland, and R. M. Krause.** 1968. Immunochemical studies on the cross-reactivity between streptococcal and staphylococcal peptidoglycan. J. Exp. Med. **128:**325–340.

3. **Ranu, R. S.** 1975. Studies on the immunochemistry of *Staphylococcus aureus* cell wall: antigenicity of pentaglycine bridges. Med. Microbiol. Immunol. **161:** 53–61.

4. **Rolicka, M., and J. T. Park.** 1969. Antimucopeptide antibodies and their specificity. J. Immunol. **103:**196–203.

5. **Schleifer, K. H., W. P. Hammes, and O. Kandler.** 1976. Effect of endogenous and exogenous factors on the primary structure of bacterial peptidoglycan. Adv. Microb. Physiol. **13:**245–292.

6. **Schleifer, K. H., and O. Kandler.** 1972. Peptidoglycan types of bacterial cell walls and their taxonomic implications. Bacteriol. Rev. **36:**407–477.

7. **Schleifer, K. H., and R. M. Krause.** 1971. The immunochemistry of peptidoglycan. I. The immunodominant site of the peptide subunit and the contribution of each of the amino acids to the binding properties of the peptides. J. Biol. Chem. **246:**986–993.

8. **Schleifer, K. H., and P. H. Seidl.** 1974. The immunochemistry of peptidoglycan. Antibodies against a synthetic immunogen cross-reacting with peptidoglycan. Eur. J. Biochem. **43:**509–519.

9. **Seidl, H. P., and K. H. Schleifer.** 1975. Immunochemical studies with synthetic immunogens chemically related to peptidoglycan. Z. Immunitaetsforsch. **149:**157–164.

10. **Wikler, M.** 1975. Isolation and characterization of homogenous rabbit antibodies to *Micrococcus lysodeikticus* with specificity to the peptidoglycan and to the glucose-N-acetyl-aminomannuronic acid polymer. Z. Immunitaetsforsch. **149:**193–200.

Biological Properties of Peptidoglycans

B. HEYMER AND E. TH. RIETSCHEL

Department of Pathology, University of Ulm, 7900 Ulm/Donau, Oberer Eselsberg, West Germany,
and Max-Planck-Institut für Immunbiologie, 78 Freiburg/Breisgau, West Germany

INTRODUCTION

To discuss the biological properties of peptidoglycan means to discuss a very complex and sometimes perplexing subject. Difficulties in dealing with this topic are primarily due to the diversity of the assay systems employed and to the hybrid nature of peptidoglycan, a substance which appears to possess both antigenic and toxic properties (46). Since several reviews on the biological activity of peptidoglycan have recently appeared (11, 12, 37), there is no need for extensive recapitulation of all the various aspects. Instead, a comprehensive survey will be presented of those peptidoglycan properties that have been substantiated. Then the activity of peptidoglycan and of cell walls will be compared, and the report will close with a brief discussion of the possible mechanisms of action involved.

SURVEY OF BIOLOGICAL PROPERTIES OF PEPTIDOGLYCAN

It has not been possible to find a common denominator for all the peptidoglycan properties that have been described thus far. However, a preliminary classification into four main groups is feasible: (i) immunological properties (immunogenicity, antigenicity), (ii) endotoxin-like activities (pyrogenicity, local Shwartzman reaction, nonspecific resistance to infection, complement activation), (iii) pathogenic effects not analogous to those of endotoxin (inflammatory skin reactions, lesions in internal organs, inhibition of macrophage migration, inhibition of phagocytosis of bacteria), and (iv) nonpathogenic phenomena with potential advantage to the host (adjuvant activity, antitumor activity, mitogenic activity).

Immunological Properties

The immunological aspects of peptidoglycan have already been discussed by Schleifer and Seidl (p. 339, this volume), so only a few additional findings will be mentioned here. When peptidoglycan is injected into rabbits as a component of the whole bacterial cell, in particular of the group A-variant *Streptococcus*, strong antibody formation is observed (13, 14, 21, 27, 47, 48). In contrast, when peptidoglycan is given in isolated form, there is only a weak immune response (1). Nevertheless, since the occurrence of peptidoglycan in nature is as widespread as that of bacteria, peptidoglycan antibodies are present in many normal sera of animals as well as of humans (17, 18, 36, 44, 51). The frequency of their detection depends primarily on the sensitivity of the methods employed (17, 18).

Endotoxin-Like Activities

Most of the endotoxin-like activities of peptidoglycan were first described by Rotta and his group (34, 37–41, 43). They also carefully studied fever induction by this polymer (42). We have recently compared the pyrogenicity of sonically solubilized streptococcal and staphylococcal peptidoglycans (15, 16) with that of lipid A complexed with bovine serum albumin (BSA; 35). When injected intravenously into rabbits, the smallest peptidoglycan dose required to provoke a fever response was found to be 50 μg/kg of body weight. In contrast, only 0.008 μg of lipid A-BSA per kg was needed to produce a similar effect. Peptidoglycan dosages above 100 μg/kg elicited a biphasic fever response with maxima at about 1.5 and 4 h after injection. The time course of the fever differed considerably from that induced by lipid A. It closely resembled the fever caused by double-stranded RNA (35). To exclude the possibility that the pyrogenic activity of the peptidoglycan samples employed was due to contamination by endotoxin, the preparations were subjected to a lipid A-specific cross-tolerance assay (35). As depicted in Fig. 1, rabbits injected with lipid A-BSA on day 0 and day 2 each time reacted with a significant fever response. In contrast, when they were pretreated with lipid A on day 0 followed by lipid A antiserum on day 1, they became highly resistant to a lipid A challenge on day 2 (Fig. 1).

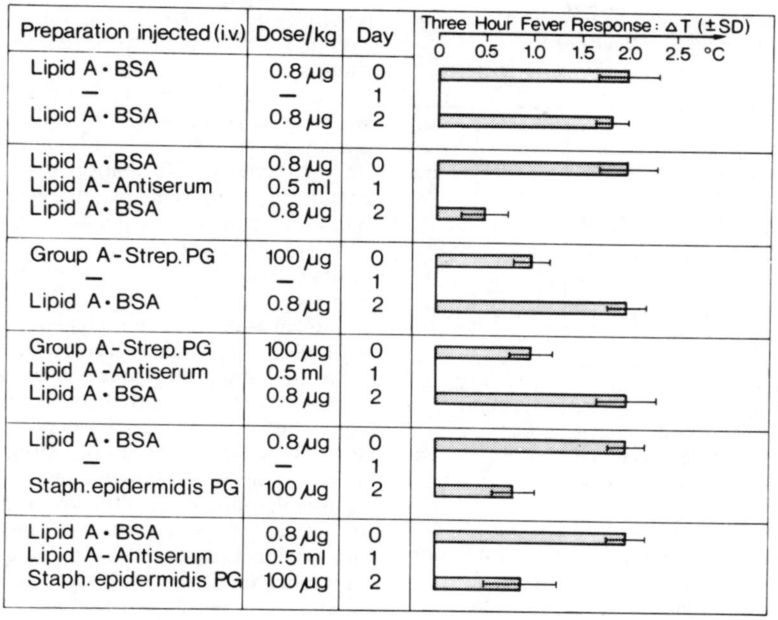

Preparation injected (i.v.)	Dose/kg	Day	Three Hour Fever Response: ΔT ($\pm$SD)
Lipid A · BSA	0.8 μg	0	
—	—	1	
Lipid A · BSA	0.8 μg	2	
Lipid A · BSA	0.8 μg	0	
Lipid A - Antiserum	0.5 ml	1	
Lipid A · BSA	0.8 μg	2	
Group A - Strep. PG	100 μg	0	
—	—	1	
Lipid A · BSA	0.8 μg	2	
Group A - Strep. PG	100 μg	0	
Lipid A - Antiserum	0.5 ml	1	
Lipid A · BSA	0.8 μg	2	
Lipid A · BSA	0.8 μg	0	
—	—	1	
Staph. epidermidis PG	100 μg	2	
Lipid A · BSA	0.8 μg	0	
Lipid A - Antiserum	0.5 ml	1	
Staph. epidermidis PG	100 μg	2	

FIG. 1. *Lipid A-specific fever tolerance cross-assay with peptidoglycan (PG) in rabbits.*

However, if group A streptococcal peptidoglycan was employed as pretreatment, no such tolerance was engendered. Also, rabbits made resistant to lipid A still remained sensitive to a challenge by staphylococcal peptidoglycan. Experiments without lipid A antiserum on day 1 served as controls (Fig. 1). From these studies we conclude that peptidoglycan possesses a characteristic pyrogenic activity distinct from that of endotoxin.

Although attempts to produce a generalized Shwartzman phenomenon have been unsuccessful (37), peptidoglycan readily elicits a local Shwartzman reaction in rabbits and guinea pigs (37–40). However, several hundred micrograms is necessary for the intradermal injection and about 2 mg for the intravenous injection (37). Endotoxin can be substituted for the preparative as well as the provocative dose (38–40). Another property that peptidoglycan shares with endotoxin is the ability to confer nonspecific resistance to bacterial infection (41). Thus, mice injected intraperitoneally with 250 μg of streptococcal peptidoglycan become resistant to a subsequent challenge by 10^4 virulent group A streptococci (37, 41). It has not yet been determined whether such protection covers infection by other bacteria.

The first indication that peptidoglycan may activate the complement system stems from the observation that it can cause lysis of platelets, provided that fresh plasma is present (34, 43). More direct evidence is derived from investiga-

tions by Mergenhagen (personal communication) and Bokisch (5). The latter found that 50 μg of peptidoglycan was able to consume about 70% of the hemolytic activity present in 1 ml of human serum. Although consumption of C_2 in normal human serum and consumption of C_3 in C_2-deficient serum indicates activation of both the classical and the alternate pathways, activation of the former appears much more efficient (5). We have recently studied the generation of chemotactic factors in human serum by peptidoglycan. When human granulocytes were placed in a modified Boyden chamber (22) and exposed to sonically solubilized peptidoglycan (15, 16) dissolved in fresh human serum, strong chemotactic attraction of cells occurred. As is evident from Table 1, peptidoglycans isolated from group A *Streptococcus*, *Staphylococcus aureus*, or *Bordetella pertussis* showed only slightly different capacities for the generation of chemotactic activity. Lack of chemotaxis of cells by peptidoglycan dissolved in heat-inactivated serum or in balanced salt solution (Table 1) demonstrates that peptidoglycan is not a chemotaxin but a chemotaxinogen. Identical results were obtained when the agarose technique (31) was employed.

Pathogenic Effects Not Analogous to Those of Endotoxin

As originally described by Abdulla and Schwab (2) and confirmed by others (16, 28, 49), the intradermal injection of 10 to 100 μg of

TABLE 1. *Generation of chemotactic activity in human serum by peptidoglycan*[a]

Peptidoglycan from:	Amt (μg/ml)	No. of cells[b]		
		Serum (active)	Serum (inactive)	Without serum
Streptococcus group A	100	306 ± 42	8 ± 4	0
	10	48 ± 10	5 ± 2	0
Staphylococcus epidermidis	500	358 ± 54	3 ± 1	0
	50	88 ± 16	7 ± 3	0
Bordetella pertussis	100	112 ± 11	6 ± 2	0
	10	32 ± 7	7 ± 2	0

[a] Single-filter (3-μm pore size) Boyden chamber technique with human granulocytes and peptidoglycan with or without 10% normal human serum.

[b] Mean number of cells counted (five experiments each) in four ×25 fields on the opposite surface of the filter.

sonically solubilized peptidoglycan into non-sensitized rabbits or even germfree rats (15) induces intense inflammatory skin reactions. These begin 4 to 6 h after injection, reach a maximum at about 24 h, and then rapidly disappear. Histologically, lesions are characterized by diffuse granulocytic infiltration of the epidermis and cutis (2, 15). The exact nature of these lesions is still unknown. To determine the relevance of such findings for humans, we performed corresponding studies in eight human volunteers. A summary of the results is depicted in Table 2. Within 20 min after the intradermal injection of 10 μg of sonically solubilized group A streptococcal or staphylococcal peptidoglycan (15, 16), a weal developed that was replaced after 3 to 6 h by an intense erythema, sometimes accompanied by slight induration of the skin. As is evident from Table 2, the intensity of the lesions varied considerably, indicating a differing reactivity in the subjects tested. Most

reactions increased during the first 24 h and, except for two patients suffering from allergic rhinitis, subsided within 48 h. As a general trend, responses to streptococcal peptidoglycan were more pronounced than those to staphylococcal peptidoglycan. Although these studies do not provide information on the underlying pathogenic mechanisms, they do show that peptidoglycan is pathogenic for humans.

There are several reports on the formation of cardiac lesions after intravenous injection of peptidoglycan into rabbits (37, 39). Although it is conceivable that peptidoglycan may possess such potency, confirmation by additional studies is needed since the induction of cardiac lesions appears to be a feature of poorly degradable cell walls rather than of peptidoglycan (6, 9, 10). Sonically solubilized streptococcal and staphylococcal peptidoglycans have been found to inhibit nonspecifically the random migration of rat or guinea pig macrophages (15, 16), to hinder the phagocytosis of bacteria by rabbit polymorphonuclear leukocytes (20), and to exhibit a weak but distinct cytotoxicity for various mammalian cells (20). All these effects have been extensively discussed elsewhere (11, 12).

Nonpathogenic Phenomena

When administered as a water-in-oil emulsion with unrelated antigens, peptidoglycans from almost all bacteria have been observed to display strong adjuvant activity (23, 24, 26, 29). They stimulate both antibody formation and induction of delayed hypersensitivity (3, 26, 30). The smallest peptidoglycan subunit still active appears to be a muramyl-dipeptide (4, 25). Probably related to immunopotentiation is the ability of peptidoglycan to enhance the mechanisms of defense against malignancies (50). However, this has only been studied by employing peptidoglycan prophylactically; therefore, the

TABLE 2. *Skin reactions to peptidoglycan (PG) in human subjects*[a]

Subjects tested			Group A *Streptococcus* PG[b]				*Staphylococcus epidermidis* PG[b]			
No.	Age	Diagnosis	20 min	6 h	24 h	48 h	20 min	6 h	24 h	48 h
1	37	Healthy volunteer	9/16	20	45	—	10/20	8	14	—
2	32	Healthy volunteer	7/16	19	30	—	7/16	21	20	—
3	39	Healthy volunteer	14/–	28	38	—	7/–	14	19	—
4	33	Healthy volunteer	4/–	36	42	—	8/–	16	21	—
5	27	Acne vulgaris	6/7	6	—		6/8	7	—	—
6	50	Dyshydrotic eczema	6/7	—	12		6/7	—	6	—
7	24	Allergic rhinitis	8/–	14	40	50	7/–	7	7	—
8	17	Allergic rhinitis	6/9	12	30	30	6/–	—	8	10

[a] Reactions elicited by intradermal injection of 10 μg of peptidoglycan.

[b] Grading of results: diameter of weal/erythema (mm) 20 min postinjection; diameter of erythema (mm) 6, 24, or 48 h postinjection.

question remains as to whether this effect is also present when it is therapeutically applied. Peptidoglycan is mitogenic for lymphocytes of various animal species (7). Since cells not only from rabbits and normal mice but also from nude mice are stimulated (7), peptidoglycan may be primarily a B-cell mitogen.

COMPARISON OF BIOLOGICAL PROPERTIES OF PEPTIDOGLYCAN AND CELL WALLS

Under natural conditions, the mammalian organism will not be exposed to isolated peptidoglycan but rather to whole bacterial cells or cell walls. Therefore, it is important to know whether and how the properties of these structures differ from those of peptidoglycan. Basically, cell walls possess biological activities similar to those of peptidoglycan (19). However, this does not hold true in every respect. To give just one example, whereas peptidoglycan injected intradermally induces acute inflammatory reactions which rapidly subside (2, 15), cell walls cause chronic inflammatory processes that may persist for weeks or even months (8, 32, 33). This difference does not appear to be due primarily to the activity of non-peptidoglycan components present in cell walls, but rather to the considerably different in vivo degradation rates of cell walls and peptidoglycan (10). Whereas the half-life of radiolabeled group A streptococcal cell walls after intradermal injection into rats is about 7 days, the half-life of group A-streptococcal peptidoglycan is only about 10 h (19; B. Heymer et al., Abstr. 6th Int. Symp. Streptococcus pyogenes, 28–31 October 1975, Prague, p. 37). Similar differences in degradation rates are observed when these preparations are exposed to human granulocytes in vitro (19). Although the autolytic enzymes of bacteria may constitute a significant mechanism of cell wall disposal in vivo (10), it is evident that the relative deficiency of the mammalian organism in enzymes capable of eliminating cell walls may result in a persistence of these structures and chronic inflammation (8, 33).

POSSIBLE MECHANISMS OF ACTION OF PEPTIDOGLYCAN

In considering the possible mechanisms of action of peptidoglycan, it is essential to keep in mind three facts: (i) most of the biological properties of peptidoglycan described in this review are not restricted to a particular peptidoglycan type but are shared by peptidoglycans from many different bacterial species (11, 12, 23,

49); (ii) the toxic activity of peptidoglycan in most, but not all, of the assay systems employed is 100 to 1,000 times less than that of endotoxin (7, 37, 42, 46); and (iii) some of the methods used for extracting peptidoglycan change the chemical characteristics of this polymer (45; B. Heymer, Abstr. 6th Int. Symp. Streptococcus pyogenes, 28–31 October 1975, Prague, p. 37). In view of the antigenic properties of peptidoglycan and the widespread occurrence of peptidoglycan antibodies, one might have the tendency to try to explain most of the phenomena on an immunological basis. However, although this may be true for complement activation and may be partially true for the skin reactions described, the finding that the activity of peptidoglycan is correlated with particle size (2, 16, 45) points in another direction. Treatment with lysozyme reduces or eliminates many of the biological activities of peptidoglycan (11, 12) without destroying its antigenic or at least its haptenic character (16). Therefore, one should remember that there exists a chemico-structural as well as a biologic-functional analogy between peptidoglycan and chitin (45). The latter substance, when parenterally applied, is well known to induce inflammation of the foreign-body type. This is not intended to imply that the in vivo phenomena elicited by peptidoglycan can be considered simply as reactions of this kind. Rather, it should indicate that a whole spectrum of factors, immunological and nonimmunological, may be involved in the mechanisms of action of peptidoglycan.

ACKNOWLEDGMENTS

We thank J. V. Mayenburg for performing most of the skin tests. The excellent technical assistance of A. Unz is gratefully acknowledged.

LITERATURE CITED

1. **Abdulla, E. M., and J. H. Schwab.** 1965. Immunological properties of bacterial cell wall mucopeptides. Proc. Soc. Exp. Biol. **118:**359–362.
2. **Abdulla, E. M., and J. H. Schwab.** 1966. Biological properties of streptococcal cell-wall particles. III. Dermonecrotic reaction to cell-wall mucopeptides. J. Bacteriol. **91:**374–383.
3. **Adam, A., R. Ciorbaru, F. Ellouz, J.-F. Petit, and E. Lederer.** 1974. Adjuvant activity of monomeric bacterial cell wall peptidoglycans. Biochem. Biophys. Res. Commun. **56:**561–567.
4. **Adam, A., F. Ellouz, R. Ciorbaru, J.-F. Petit, and E. Lederer.** 1975. Peptidoglycan adjuvants: minimal structure required for activity. Z. Immunitaetsforsch. **149:**341–348.
5. **Bokisch, V. A.** 1975. Interaction of peptidoglycans with anti-IgGs and with complement. Z. Immunitaetsforsch. **149:**320–330.
6. **Cromartie, W. J., and J. G. Craddock.** 1966. Rheumatic-like lesions in mice. Science **154:**285–287.

7. **Damais, C., C. Bona, L. Chedid, J. Fleck, C. Nauciel, and J. P. Martin.** 1975. Mitogenic effect of bacterial peptidoglycans possessing adjuvant activity. J. Immunol. **115:**268–271.

8. **Davies, P., R. C. Page, and A. C. Allison.** 1974. Changes in cellular enzyme levels and extracellular release of lysosomal acid hydrolases in macrophages exposed to group A streptococcal cell wall substance. J. Exp. Med. **139:**1262–1282.

9. **Ginsburg, I.** 1972. Mechanisms of cell and tissue injury induced by Group A Streptococci: relation to post-streptococcal sequelae. J. Infect. Dis. **126:**419–455.

10. **Ginsburg, I., and M. N. Sela.** 1976. The role of leukocytes and their hydrolases in the persistence, degradation and transport of bacterial constituents in tissues: relation to chronic inflammatory processes in staphylococcal, streptococcal and mycobacterial infections, and in chronic periodontal disease. Crit. Rev. Microbiol. **4:**249–332.

11. **Heymer, B.** 1975. Biological properties of the peptidoglycan. Z. Immunitaetsforsch. **149:**245–257.

12. **Heymer, B.** 1975. Biologische Aktivität bakterieller Peptidoglycane (Mureine). Klin. Wochenschr. **53:**49–57.

13. **Heymer, B., D. Bernstein, K. H. Schleifer, and R. M. Krause.** 1975. Measurement of peptidoglycan antibodies by a radioimmunoassay. Z. Immunitaetsforsch. **149:**168–178.

14. **Heymer, B., D. Bernstein, K. H. Schleifer, and R. M. Krause.** 1975. A radioactive hapten-binding assay for measuring antibodies to the pentapeptide determinant of peptidoglycan. J. Immunol. **114:**1191–1196.

15. **Heymer, B., B. Bültmann, and O. Haferkamp.** 1971. Toxicity of streptococcal mucopeptides in vivo and in vitro. J. Immunol. **106:**858–861.

16. **Heymer, B., B. Bültmann, W. Schachenmayr, R. Spanel, O. Haferkamp, and W. C. Schmidt.** 1973. Migration inhibition of rat peritoneal cells induced by streptococcal mucopeptides. Characteristics of the reaction and properties of the mucopeptide preparations. J. Immunol. **116:**1743–1754.

17. **Heymer, B., W. Schachenmayr, B. Bültmann, R. Spanel, O. Haferkamp, and W. C. Schmidt.** 1973. A latex agglutination test for measuring antibodies to streptococcal mucopeptides. J. Immunol. **111:**478–484.

18. **Heymer, B., K. H. Schleifer, S. Read, J. B. Zabriskie, and R. M. Krause.** 1976. Detection of antibodies to bacterial cell wall peptidoglycan in human sera. J. Immunol. **117:**23–26.

19. **Heymer, B., R. Spanel, and O. Haferkamp.** 1975. Biologische Aktivität bakterieller Zellwände. Immunität Infektion **3:**232–240.

20. **Jones, J. M., and J. H. Schwab.** 1970. Effects of streptococcal cell-wall fragments on phagocytosis and tissue culture cells. Infect. Immun. **1:**232–242.

21. **Karakawa, W. W., D. G. Braun, H. Lackland, and R. M. Krause.** 1968. Immunochemical studies on the cross-reactivity between streptococcal and staphylococcal mucopeptide. J. Exp. Med. **128:**325–329.

22. **Keller, H. U., M. W. Hess, and H. Cottier.** 1974. The in vitro assessment of leukocyte chemotaxis. Antibiot. Chemother. **19:**112–125.

23. **Kotani, S., et al.** 1975. Immunoadjuvant activities of cell-walls and their water-soluble fractions prepared from various gram-positive bacteria. Biken J. **18:**77–92.

24. **Kotani, S., et al.** 1975. Immunoadjuvant activities of peptidoglycan subunits from the cell-walls of Staphylococcus aureus and Lactobacillus plantarum. Biken J. **18:**93–103.

25. **Kotani, S., et al.** 1975. Immunoadjuvant activities of synthetic N-Acetyl-Muramyl-Peptides or-amino acids. Biken J. **18:**105–111.

26. **Kotani, S., et al.** 1975. Immunoadjuvant activities of cell-walls, their water-soluble factions and peptidoglycan subunits, prepared from various Gram-positive bacteria, and of synthetic N-Acetylmuramyl peptides. Z. Immunitaetsforsch. **149:**302–319.

27. **Krause, R. M.** 1975. Immunological activity of the peptidoglycan. Z. Immunitaetsforsch. **149:**136–150.

28. **Mageau, R. P., and B. S. Roberson.** 1969. Association of toxic capsule and cell-wall mucopeptide with virulence in Gaffkya tetragena. J. Bacteriol. **97:**16–22.

29. **Nauciel, C., and J. Fleck.** 1975. Adjuvant activity of bacterial peptidoglycans. Z. Immunitaetsforsch. **149:**349–353.

30. **Nauciel, C., J. Fleck, J.-P. Martin, M. Mock, and H. Nguyen-Huy.** 1974. Adjuvant activity of bacterial peptidoglycans on the production of delayed hypersensitivity and on antibody response. Eur. J. Immunol. **4:**352–356.

31. **Nelson, R. D., P. G. Quie, and R. L. Simmons.** 1975. Chemotaxis under agarose: a new and simple method for measuring chemotaxis and spontaneous migration of human polymorphonuclear leukocytes and monocytes. J. Immunol. **115:**1650–1656.

32. **Ohanian, S. H., and J. H. Schwab.** 1967. Persistence of Group A streptoccal cell-walls related to chronic inflammation of rabbit dermal connective tissue. J. Exp. Med. **125:**1137–1148.

33. **Page, R. C., P. Davies, and A. C. Allison.** 1974. Pathogenesis of the chronic inflammatory lesion induced by Group A streptococcal cell-walls. Lab. Invest. **30:**568–581.

34. **Rašková, H. Rýc, M., J. Rotta, and K. Mašek.** 1971. Release of 5-hydroxytryptamine and morphological changes in blood platelets induced by mucopeptide of streptococcal cell-walls. J. Infect. Dis. **123:**587–594.

35. **Rietschel, E. T., and O. Lüderitz.** 1975. Chemical structure of lipopolysaccharides and endotoxin immunity. Z. Immunitaetsforsch. **149:**201–213.

36. **Rolicka, M., and B. F. Massell.** 1973. Antipeptidoglycan in rheumatic fever: agreement with carditis. Proc. Soc. Exp. Biol. Med. **144:**892–895.

37. **Rotta, J.** 1975. Endotoxin-like properties of the peptidoglycan. Z. Immunitaetsforsch. **149:**230–244.

38. **Rotta, J.** 1968. Endotoxin properties of cell-wall mucopeptide of group A Streptococcus, p. 133–138. In R. Caravano (ed.), Current research on group A Streptococcus. Excerpta Medica Foundation, Amsterdam.

39. **Rotta, J.** 1968. Biological activity of cellular components of group A streptococci in vivo. Curr. Top. Microbiol. Immunol. **48:**64–101.

40. **Rotta, J., and B. Bednar.** 1969. Biological properties of cell-wall mucopeptide of hemolytic streptococci. J. Exp. Med. **130:**31–47.

41. **Rotta, J., T. J. Prendergast, W. W. Karakawa, C. K. Harmon, and R. M. Krause.** 1965. Enhanced resistance to streptococcal infection induced in mice by cell-wall mucopeptide. J. Exp. Med. **122:**877–890.

42. **Rotta, J., and K. H. Schleifer.** 1974. Pyrogenic activity of bacterial mucopeptides. J. Hyg. Epidemiol. Microbiol. Immunol. **18:**50–59.

43. **Rýc, M., and J. Rotta.** 1975. The thrombocytolytic activity of bacterial peptidoglycans. Z. Immunitaetsforsch. **149:**265–272.

44. **Schachenmayr, W., B. Heymer, and O. Haferkamp.** 1975. Antibodies to peptidoglycan in the sera from population surveys. Z. Immunitaetsforsch. **149:**179–186.

45. **Schleifer, K. H.** 1975. Chemical structure of the peptidoglycan, its modifiability and relation to the biological activity. Z. Immunitaetsforsch. **149:**104–117.

46. **Schleifer, K. H., and B. Heymer.** 1975. International

workshop on the immunological and biological properties of peptidoglycan and related bacterial cell-wall polymers. Z. Immunitaetsforsch. **149**:103–356.

47. **Schleifer, K. H., and R. M. Krause.** 1971. The immunochemistry of peptidoglycan separation and characterization of antibodies to the glycan and to the peptide subunit. Eur. J. Biochem. **19**:471–478.

48. **Schleifer, K. H., and R. M. Krause.** 1971. The immunochemistry of peptidoglycan: the immunodominant site of the peptide subunit and the contribution of each of the amino acids to the binding properties of the peptides. J. Biol. Chem. **246**:986–993.

49. **Schuster, G. S., J. A. Hayashi, and A. N. Bahn.** 1967. Toxic properties of the cell wall of gram-positive bacteria. J. Bacteriol. **93**:47–52.

50. **Werner, G. H., R. Moral, H. F. Floch, D. Migliore-Samour, and P. Jolles.** 1974. Activités biologiques des adjuvants hydrosolubles de faible poids moléculaire extraits de Mycobacterium tuberculosis var. hominis. C.R. Acad. Sci. Ser. D **278**:789–792.

51. **Zitnan, D., L. Cebecauer, and J. Rotta.** 1970. Precipitin reaction between mucopeptide of group A streptococci and human sera. J. Hyg. Epidemiol. Microbiol. Immunol. **14**:168–171.

Biological Aspects of Protein A

A. GROV

The Gade Institute, Department of Microbiology, University of Bergen, Bergen, Norway

During the past decade, considerable attention has been paid to staphylococcal protein A (pA) because of its unique property of interacting nonspecifically with immunoglobulins (7, 10, 11, 19, 20, 22, 30). Primarily, this property was thought to be a key to a wider understanding of some of the important intrinsic biological effects of staphylococcal infections. In addition, it has resulted in a widespread experimental application of pA, especially in the field of cellular immunology (1, 3, 14–16, 42).

Most *Staphylococcus aureus* strains produce pA, of which about one-third is released into the medium during cell growth (8). Dried cells of, e.g., strain Cowan I, which is a high producer of pA, contain 1.7% of the protein (39). There are also strains which release all the pA produced (35).

In the cell, pA is convalently linked to the peptidoglycan structure (39) and uniformly distributed in the whole cell wall (25). The exact attachment point of pA in the peptidoglycan has not yet been established.

The extraction of cells by heat or digestion of cell walls by pancreatic dornase results in preparations of pA with molecular weights of 12,000 to 15,000 (12, 17, 18, 43), whereas pA released by digestion of cells with enzymes acting on the peptidoglycan structure (lyso-staphin and lysozyme) shows a molecular weight of 42,000 (2). With regard to the chemical composition, the complete absence of trypto-phan and half-cystine is notable (12, 17).

About 10 years ago, Forsgren and Sjöquist showed that the interaction between pA and normal human immunoglobulin G (IgG; 10) and between pA and IgG from nonimmunized animals (7, 11) was a pseudo-immune reaction involving the Fc portion of the immunoglobulin. The interaction is very similar to an ordinary antigen-antibody reaction. A thermo-chemical study showed that the enthalpy of binding is strongly exothermic and highly temperature dependent (41). The binding site at the Fc region is not yet localized, but a linkage to the C_H2 homology region has been proposed (39). However, fragmentations of Fc from human IgG have indicated that one complete Fc chain is necessary for binding (5, 6). The Fc inter-action occurs with all subclasses of human IgG, except IgG_3 (31). Some human myeloma pro-teins or immunoglobulin from certain species, e.g., rabbits, do not precipitate with pA but form soluble complexes. Such interactions are demonstrated by co-precipitation or the "star" phenomenon (21, 32). These tests, in addition to immunoadsorbent columns, also showed that human IgM and IgA from sera and colostrum, respectively, reacted nonspecifically with pA (19, 20).

The biological effects of the pA-Fc inter-action are typical for regular antigen-antibody reactions. In vivo hypersensitivity reactions can be elicited by the injection of pA. Thus, local and systemic anaphylaxis were demon-strated in nonimmunized guinea pigs (38). The reaction could be prevented by modest doses of an antihistaminic drug. Similarly, the wheal and erythema reaction was shown in man (34). Rabbits developed an Arthus reaction after the injection of pA, after intravenous administra-tion of human IgG (38). Complexes of pA and Fc caused complement inactivation in a manner similar to that of antigen-antibody complexes (29, 40). Both the classical and alternative pathways were activated by pA (37). As a consequence of complement activation, pA is also chemotactic (24). In addition to positive in vitro tests for chemotaxis with human and guinea pig fresh serum, in vivo tests on rabbits were positive (Sveen and Grov, unpublished data). Although complement is activated by pA, increased opsonization is not observed. On the contrary, it has been demonstrated that pA blocks heat-labile (9) as well as heat-stable opsonins (4). This observation has been thought to be the result of a competition between pA and polymorphonuclear phagocytes for active sites on Fc regions of opsonizing IgG mole-cules. Similar competition between pA and polymorphonuclear leukocytes is suggested as the explanation for the observed inhibition of phagocytosis of *S. aureus* and *Escherichia coli* (4). In the presence of specific antibodies, however, pA is actively taken up by the rabbit peritoneal macrophages (27). This is most probably due to a Fab reaction, which leaves the Fc sites available for macrophage adherence. In vitro uptake of Fc-mediated pA-IgG complexes by human polymorphonuclear leukocytes is found to be dependent on several parameters (23).

Induction of histamine release from leukocytes by pA (36) is also explained by an Fc interaction between pA and IgG on the surface of the leukocytes. Protein A is also shown to stimulate human peripheral B lymphocytes, but not T lymphocytes (13). Furthermore, the observation that pA inhibits in vitro EA rosette formation (Matre and Grov, unpublished data) may indicate an in vivo inhibition of antibody-dependent cytotoxicity.

Independent of the Fc affinity, pA possesses true and distinct antigenic properties, as demonstrated by the Fab reactivity of immune sera (33) and by the induction of delayed hypersensitivity (26, 28). Delayed hypersensitivity to pA was induced in guinea pigs and rabbits by a single injection of 50 μg of pA in complete Freund adjuvant and was detected after 10 days. It could also be transferred from sensitive to normal animals by lymphoid cells but not by immune sera (26).

LITERATURE CITED

1. Biberfeld, P., V. Ghetie, and J. Sjöquist. 1975. Demonstration and assaying IgG antibodies in tissues and on cells by labeled staphylococcal protein A. J. Immunol. Methods 6:249–259.
2. Björk, I., B.-Å. Petersson, and J. Sjöquist. 1972. Some physicochemical properties of protein A from Staphylococcus aureus. Eur. J. Biochem. 29:579–584.
3. Dorval, G., K. I. Welsh, and H. Wigzell. 1974. Labeled staphylococcal protein A as an immunological probe in the analysis of cell surface markers. Scand. J. Immunol. 3:405–411.
4. Dosset, J. H., G. Kronvall, R. C. Williams, Jr., and P. G. Quie. 1969. Antiphagocytic effects of staphylococcal protein. A. J. Immunol. 103:1405–1410.
5. Endresen, C., and A. Grov. 1976. Further characterization of protein A reactive and non-reactive subfragments of Fc from human IgG. Acta Pathol. Microbiol. Scand. Sect. C 84:397–402.
6. Endresen, C., M. Heggeness, and A. Grov. 1974. Tryptic fragments of Fc from normal human IgG and their interaction with staphylococcal protein A. Scand. J. Immunol. 3:261–267.
7. Forsgren, A. 1968. Protein A from Staphylococcus aureus. VI. Reaction with subunits from guinea pig γ_1- and γ_2-globulin. J. Immunol. 100:927–930.
8. Forsgren, A. 1969. Protein A from Staphylococcus aureus. VIII. Production of protein A by bacterial and L-forms of Staphylococcus aureus. Acta Pathol. Microbiol. Scand. 75:481–490.
9. Forsgren, A., and P. G. Quie. 1974. Effects of staphylococcal protein A on heat labile opsonins. J. Immunol. 112:1177–1180.
10. Forsgren, A., and J. Sjöquist. 1966. Protein A from Staphylococcus aureus. I. Pseudoimmune reaction with human γ-globulin. J. Immunol. 97:822–827.
11. Forsgren, A., and J. Sjöquist. 1967. Protein A from Staphylococcus aureus. III. Reaction with rabbit γ-globulin. J. Immunol. 99: 19–24.
12. Forsgren, A., and J. Sjöquist. 1969. Protein A from Staphylococcus aureus. VII. Physicochemical and immunological characterization. Acta Pathol. Microbiol. Scand. 75:466–480.
13. Forsgren, A., A. Svedjelund, and H. Wigzell. 1976. Lymphocyte stimulation by protein A of Staphylococcus aureus. Eur. J. Immunol. 6:207–213.
14. Ghetie, V., H. Å. Fabricius, K. Nilsson, and J. Sjöquist. 1974. Movement of IgG receptors on the lymphocyte surface induced by protein A of Staphylococcus aureus. Immunology 26:1081–1091.
15. Ghetie, V., K. Nilsson, and J. Sjöquist. 1974. Identification on cell surface immunoglobulin markers by protein A-containing fluorescent staphylococci. Scand. J. Immunol. 3:397–403.
16. Ghetie, V., K. Nilsson, and J. Sjöquist. 1974. Detection and quantitation of IgG on the surface of human lymphoid cells by rosette formation with protein A-coated sheep red blood cells. Eur. J. Immunol. 4:500–505.
17. Grov, A. 1967. Studies on antigen preparations from Staphylococcus aureus. 3. On the homogeneity and structure of protein A. Acta Pathol. Microbiol. Scand. 69:567–575.
18. Grov, A. 1968. Studies on antigen preparations from Staphylococcus aureus. 4. Separation and purification of protein A and a related precipitinogen. Acta Pathol. Microbiol. Scand. 73:400–406.
19. Grov, A. 1975. Human IgM interacting with staphylococcal protein A. Acta Pathol. Microbiol. Scand. Sect. C 83:173–176.
20. Grov, A. 1976. Human colostral IgA interacting with staphylococcal protein A. Acta Pathol. Microbiol. Scand. Sect. C 84:71–72.
21. Grov, A., and C. Endresen. 1976. An examination of the "star-phenomenon," a three component immunoprecipitation involving staphylococcal protein A. Acta Pathol. Microbiol. Scand. Sect. C 84:333–336.
22. Grov, A., P. Oeding, B. Myklestad, and J. Aasen. 1970. Reactions of staphylococcal antigens with normal sera, γG-globulins and γG-globulin fragments of various species origin. Acta Pathol. Microbiol. Scand. Sect. B 78:106–111.
23. Hällgren, R., and G. Stålenheim. 1976. Quantification of phagocytosis by human neutrophils. The use of radiolabelled staphylococcal protein A-IgG complexes. Immunology 30:755–762.
24. Harvey, R. L., G. Kronvall, G. M. Troup, R. F. Anderson, and R. C. Williams, Jr. 1970. Chemotaxis of polymorphonuclear leukocytes by protein A of the Staphylococcus. Proc. Soc. Exp. Biol. Med. 135:453–456.
25. Haugen, Å., S. Helgeland, and A. Grov. 1975. Localization of antigens in thin sections of bacteria by the immuno-peroxidase technique. Acta Pathol. Microbiol. Scand. Sect. B 83:79–90.
26. Heczko, P. B., A. Grov, and P. Oeding. 1973. In vivo reactions of staphylococcal antigens. 1. Hypersensitivity to protein A. Acta Pathol. Microbiol. Scand. Sect. B 81:731–740.
27. Heczko, P. B., A. Grov, and P. Oeding. 1974. Uptake of staphylococcal protein A by peritoneal macrophages in vitro. Acta Pathol. Microbiol. Scand. Sect. B 82:283–286.
28. Helgeland, S. M., R. R. Næss, and A. Grov. 1975. Delayed hypersensitivity to staphylococcal protein A detected by leucocyte migration inhibition. Acta Pathol. Microbiol. Scand. Sect. C 83:15–18.
29. Kronvall, G., and H. Gewurz. 1970. Activation and inhibition of IgG mediated complement fixation by staphylococcal protein A. Clin. Exp. Immunol. 7:213–222.
30. Kronvall, G., U. S. Seal, J. Finstad, and R. C. Williams,

Jr. 1970. Phylogenetic insight into evolution of mammalian Fc fragments of γG globulin using staphylococcal protein A. J. Immunol. **104**:140–147.

31. **Kronvall, G., and R. C. Williams, Jr.** 1969. Differences in anti-protein A activity among IgG subgroups. J. Immunol. **103**:828–833.

32. **Kronvall, G., and R. C. Williams, Jr.** 1971. The star phenomenon, a three component immunoprecipitation involving protein A. Immunochemistry **8**:577–580.

33. **McDowell, G., A. Grov, and P. Oeding.** 1971. Reaction of staphylococcal protein A with rabbit immunoglobulins. Acta Pathol. Microbiol. Scand. Sect. B **79**:794–800.

34. **Martin, R. R., J. G. Crowder, and A. White.** 1967. Human reaction to staphylococcal antigens. A possible role of leukocyte lysosomal enzymes. J. Immunol. **99**:269–275.

35. **Movitz, J.** 1974. A study on the biosynthesis of protein A in *Staphylococcus aureus*. Eur. J. Biochem. **48**:131–136.

36. **Petersson, B.-Å.** 1975. Induction of histamine release and desensitization in human leukocytes. IgG-mediated histamine release. Scand. J. Immunol. **4**:777–784.

37. **Pryjma, J., K. Pryjma, A. Grov, and P. B. Heczko.** 1976. Immunological activity of staphylococcal cell wall antigens. Proc. 3rd Int. Symp. Staphylococci

and Staphylococcal Infections, September 1975, Warsaw. Zentralbl. Bakteriol. Parasitenk. Infektionskr. Hyg. Suppl. **5**:873–881.

38. **Sjöquist, J., A. Forsgren, G. T. Gustafson, and G. Stålenheim.** 1967. Biological importance of the Fc-region of γ-globulins. Cold Spring Harbor Symp. Quant. Biol. **32**:577–581.

39. **Sjöquist, J., J. Movitz, I.-B. Johansson, and H. Hjelm.** 1972. Localization of protein A in the bacteria. Eur. J. Biochem. **30**:190–194.

40. **Sjöquist, J., and G. Stålenheim.** 1969. Protein A from *Staphylococcus aureus*. IX. Complement-fixing activity of protein A-IgG complexes. J. Immunol. **103**:467–473.

41. **Sjöquist, J., and I. Wadsö.** 1971. A thermochemical study of the reaction between protein A from *S. aureus* and fragment Fc from immunoglobulin G. FEBS Lett. **14**:254–256.

42. **Welsh, K. I., G. Dorval, and H. Wigzell.** 1975. Rapid quantitation of membrane antigens. Nature (London) **254**:67–69.

43. **Yoshida, A., S. Mudd, and N. A. Lenhart.** 1963. The common protein agglutinogen of *Staphylococcus aureus*. II. Purification, chemical characterization, and serologic comparison with Jensen's antigen. J. Immunol. **91**:777–782.

Immunological Aspects of Protein A

A. FORSGREN

Department of Clinical Bacteriology, University of Lund, Malmö General Hospital, S-214 01 Malmö, Sweden

Protein A (SpA) is a protein present in the cell wall of most *Staphylococcus aureus* strains (2). SpA binds to human immunoglobulin G (IgG; 3) and also to IgG of several other mammalian species (4, 16). More recently, human IgM has also been demonstrated to react with SpA, with the primary SpA reactive site localized to the Fc region of the IgM molecules (13, 17).

SpA has recently been applied for analytical purposes in the field of cellular immunology. Sheep red cells coated with SpA have been used to assay membrane-bound IgG on lymphoid cell lines by the rosette-formation technique (8). In a human lymphoid cell line bearing membrane IgG, fluorescein-labeled SpA was shown to induce movement (patch and cap formation) of the IgG receptors on the membranes of the B lymphocytes (6). Also, normal human B lymphocytes can be stained with fluorescent SpA (7). It would thus seem clear that the Fc region of IgG to which SpA will bind is accessible on the IgG molecules present on the cell that produces them. However, SpA has been shown not to react with human lymphoid cell lines which bear IgM receptors (8, 19).

SpA has also been adapted to measure lymphoid surface antigens other than IgG (1, 8, 19). In these indirect techniques, radiolabeled SpA, fluorescent SpA-positive *S. aureus* Cowan I, or erythrocytes coated with fluorescent SpA have been used mainly to investigate human lymphocyte surface antigens after these antigens have been precoated with IgG antibodies. Separation methods based on the general reaction of SpA with the Fc region of IgG have also been developed for the isolation of lymphocytes according to their surface antigenic markers (9–11, 18).

Recently, we have found that SpA-positive *S. aureus* can be used as a selective mitogen for human peripheral blood B lymphocytes (5). Mitogens have found important applications in human research as functional markers of subpopulations of lymphocytes. Studies in which human peripheral blood was used as a source for lymphocytes have shown the existence of many substances, such as phytohemagglutinin (PHA) and concanavalin A, with seemingly selective capacity to trigger T lymphocytes into division (12, 14). Other substances have been reported to trigger both T and subsequently B lymphocytes into increased DNA synthesis, perhaps the most frequently reported structure in this regard being pokeweed mitogen (12, 14). However, purified B lymphocytes alone are not stimulated into mitosis by this mitogen (15). There is thus a need for a specific B-cell mitogen for human blood lymphocytes.

Table 1 shows the result of a typical experiment in which 1 million human lymphocytes were incubated with SpA-positive Cowan I staphylococci, soluble SpA, or PHA. B and T lymphocytes were separated by means of rosette formation and cell chromatography through an anti-IgG-coated column, respectively, and were used in the stimulation experiment. Maximal stimulation of lymphocytes was obtained with 20 bacteria per lymphocyte. With such a bacterial number, stimulation of almost the same extent as that induced by PHA was found for Ficoll-Isopaque-purified lymphocytes (B + T) when the cultures were terminated at day 3 of stimulation. Less uptake of thymidine was obtained with higher or lower numbers of staphylococci or longer incubation time. As can be seen in Table 1, the separated B-lymphocyte population showed a high degree of stimulation with Cowan I but essentially no stimulation with PHA. Exactly opposite results were obtained with PHA as mitogen. Separated T lymphocytes were not stimulated by Cowan I but showed high activity when incubated with PHA, a well-known T-lymphocyte mitogen. Thus, Cowan I staphylococci, in contrast to PHA, stimulated cell division of human B lymphocyte-enriched T lymphocyte-depleted populations.

A wide range of concentrations of purified SpA were tested in lymphocyte stimulation experiments, and maximal stimulation was obtained with the highest concentration of SpA, 100 μg/culture (Table 1). However, the degree of stimulation was always higher with whole Cowan I staphylococci or with soluble SpA covalently bound to an insoluble matrix. The interference of soluble SpA with the activation

TABLE 1. *Tritiated thymidine incorporation in human lymphocytes (10^6 cells/ml) stimulated with phytohemagglutinin (PHA), protein A (SpA), or SpA-positive* S. aureus *Cowan I*[a]

Treatment	[³H]thymidine uptake (cpm)		
	B + T lymphocytes	B lymphocytes	T lymphocytes
PHA, 1 µg/ml	28,784 ± 2,587	5,325 ± 229	26,553 ± 1,132
S. aureus Cowan I, 2 × 10⁷ colony-forming units	25,371 ± 2,689	37,033 ± 3,140	6,620 ± 29
SpA, 100 µg/ml	5,045 ± 199	4,231 ± 287	4,056 ± 411
Base line	2,652 ± 26	3,130 ± 213	1,604 ± 94

[a] B + T lymphocytes: Ficoll-Isopaque-purified lymphocytes with monocytes. T lymphocytes: prepared through removal over anti-Ig-coated glass-bead columns. B lymphocytes: separated through depletion of cells forming rosettes with sheep erythrocytes, containing monocytes. Removal of monocytes has a marginal effect on DNA synthesis. The lymphocytes were incubated in serum for medium.

TABLE 2. *Effect of protein A (SpA), mucopeptide, and teichoic acid on human lymphocyte response to phytohemagglutinin (PHA) and* S. aureus *Cowan I*[a]

Cells preincubated for 30 min at 37°C with:	Cells stimulated with:	
	PHA (1 µg/ml)	Cowan I[b]
SpA (100 µg/ml)..	28,426 ± 1,172	7,779 ± 187
SpA (10 µg/ml)..	29,400 ± 3,457	10,737 ± 386
Mucopeptide (100 µg/ml) ...	26,591 ± 1,253	14,609 ± 2,141
Teichoic acid (100 µg/ml) ...	29,018 ± 3,502	14,536 ± 287
Tissue culture medium	27,759 ± 1,221	15,457 ± 2,135

[a] The lymphocytes (10^6) were preincubated for 30 min at 37°C and then incubated with mitogens for 3 days. [³H]thymidine uptake (cpm) was then measured.
[b] *S. aureus* Cowan I (2 × 10⁷ colony-forming units/ml).

of lymphocytes by Cowan I but not by other mitogens is demonstrated in Table 2. When lymphocytes were preincubated with 100 µg of SpA for 30 min and then mixed with Cowan I, an uptake of only 6,000 cpm was obtained compared with 15,500 cpm for lymphocytes which had not been preincubated with SpA. In contrast, when purified mucopeptide or teichoic acid was preincubated with human lymphocytes, no significant inhibition of the lymphocyte response to the SpA-containing staphylococci was obtained. Neither SpA nor mucopeptide or teichoic acid could inhibit the PHA stimulation of lymphocytes. These experiments indicate that blocking of immunoglobulin on the lymphocyte

surface with purified SpA inhibits the stimulatory effect of staphylococci on human lymphocytes.

The relevance of SpA for stimulation of B lymphocytes is further shown in Table 3, which gives results of a typical experiment with SpA-positive *Staphylococcus* Cowan I and NG223, a protein A-negative mutant of Cowan I. The SpA-positive Cowan I activates lymphocytes much more effectively than the SpA-negative mutant NG223. The correlation of the degree of lymphocyte stimulation with content of SpA in bacteria used for stimulation was confirmed with SpA-negative and SpA-positive mutants of another *S. aureus* strain. The significance of SpA for lymphocyte stimulation is also indicated by the low degree of stimulation when the naturally occurring *S. aureus* strain Wood 46 with essentially no SpA was used (Table 3).

All experiments so far thus indicate SpA to be a most relevant structure in the triggering of human B lymphocyte-enriched populations into DNA synthesis. It should be realized, however, that, although the present system appears to be a most promising one for the studies of activated human B lymphocytes, several questions remain to be resolved at the theoretical level. First, we do not know whether the triggering is actually taking place via surface-bound IgG

TABLE 3. *Stimulatory effect on human lymphocytes of protein A-positive* S. aureus *Cowan I in comparison with protein A-negative Cowan I-derived NG223 and* S. aureus *Wood 46*

S. aureus strain	Protein A content	[³H]thymidine uptake (cpm)
Cowan I	+++	20,332 ± 686
Mutant NG223 ...	—	3,472 ± 97
Wood 46	—	3,888 ± 43
Base line	—	2,539 ± 104

molecules, be they intrinsically produced or absorbed by cytophilic means. Also, the very good response as measured by DNA synthesis with B cell-enriched populations may or may not be produced by the low number of actual IgG-producing B cells present at time zero of stimulation. Finally, we do not know as yet whether the proliferation will lead to increased immunoglobulin synthesis in the blast cells. Thus, several points remain to be established.

LITERATURE CITED

1. **Dorval, G., K. I. Welsh, and H. Wigzell.** 1974. Labeled staphylococcal protein A as an immunological probe in the analysis of cell surface markers. Scand. J. Immunol. **3:**405–411.
2. **Forsgren, A.** 1970. Significance of protein A production by staphylococci. Infect. Immun. **2:**672–673.
3. **Forsgren, A., and J. Sjöquist.** 1966. Protein A from S. aureus. I. Pseudoimmune reaction with human gammaglobulin. J. Immunol. **97:**822–827.
4. **Forsgren, A., and J. Sjöquist.** 1967. Protein A from Staphylococcus aureus. III. Reaction with rabbit gammaglobulin. J. Immunol. **99:**19–24.
5. **Forsgren, A., A. Svedjelund, and H. Wigzell.** 1976. Lymphocyte stimulation by protein A of Staphylococcus aureus. Eur. J. Immunol. **6:**207–213.
6. **Ghetie, V., H. Å. Fabricius, K. Nilsson, and J. Sjöquist.** 1974. Movement of IgG receptors on the lymphocyte surface induced by protein A of Staphylococcus aureus. Immunology **26:**1081–1091.
7. **Ghetie, V., K. Nilsson, and J. Sjöquist.** 1974. Identification of cell surface immunoglobulin markers by protein A-containing fluorescent staphylococci. Scand. J. Immunol. **3:**397–403.
8. **Ghetie, V., K. Nilsson, and J. Sjöquist.** 1974. Detection and quantitation of IgG on the surface of human lymphoid cells by rosette formation with protein A-coated sheep red blood cells. Eur. J. Immunol. **4:**500–505.
9. **Ghetie, V., K. Nilsson, and J. Sjöquist.** 1974. Density gradient separation of lymphoid cells adhering to protein-A-containing staphylococci. Proc. Natl. Acad. Sci. **71:**4831–4835.
10. **Ghetie, V., and J. Sjöquist.** 1975. Separation of lymphocytes by specific adherence to cellular monolayers containing protein A of Staphylococcus aureus. J. Immunol. **115:**659–664.
11. **Ghetie, V., G. Stålenheim, and J. Sjöquist.** 1975. Cell separation by staphylococcal protein A-coated erythrocytes. Scand. J. Immunol. **4:**471–477.
12. **Greaves, M. F., and G. Janossy.** 1972. Elicitation of selective T and B lymphocyte responses by cell surface binding ligands. Transplant. Rev. **11:**87–130.
13. **Grov, A.** 1975. Human IgM interacting with staphylococcal protein A. Acta Pathol. Microbiol. Scand. Sect. C **83:**173–176.
14. **Jondal, M.** 1974. Surface markers on human B and T lymphocytes. Scand. J. Immunol. **3:**739–747.
15. **Jondal, M., H. Wigzell, and F. Aiuti.** 1973. Human lymphocyte subpopulations: classification according to surface markers and/or functional characteristics. Transplant. Rev. **16:**163–195.
16. **Kronvall, G., U. S. Seal, J. Finstad, and R. C. Williams, Jr.** 1970. Phylogenic insight into evolution of mammalian Fc-fragment of gamma-G-globulin using staphylococcal protein A. J. Immunol. **104:**140–147.
17. **Lind, I., M. Harboe, and I. Føling.** 1975. Protein A reactivity of two distinct groups of human monoclonal IgG. Scand. J. Immunol. **4:**843–848.
18. **Nash, A. A.** 1976. Separation of lymphocyte subpopulations using antibodies attached to staphylococcal protein A-coated surfaces. J. Immunol. Methods **12:**149–161.
19. **Welsh, K. I., G. Dorval, and H. Wigzell.** 1975. Rapid quantitation of membrane antigens. Nature (London) **254:**67–69.

Immunochemistry of Lipoteichoic Acids

KENNETH W. KNOX AND ANTHONY J. WICKEN

Institute of Dental Research, United Dental Hospital, Sydney, New South Wales, 2010, and School of Microbiology, University of New South Wales, Kensington, New South Wales, 2033, Australia

INTRODUCTION

It seems probable that most if not all cell-surface membranes contain a carbohydrate-lipid complex as an integral part of the outer portion of the lipid bilayer, with the carbohydrate component bestowing specificity in cell-cell recognition and immunological properties.

Among the bacteria, the role of such components in serological reactions is best illustrated by the lipopolysaccharides of gram-negative bacteria, and studies in this area were considerably advanced before it was realized that gram-positive bacteria may also contain similarly reactive components. The slower developments with the gram-positive bacteria probably depended on the assumptions that surface antigens (other than capsular antigens) would be cell wall components and that it would be necessary to use procedures that would hydrolyze covalent linkages in the cell wall to get soluble antigens. Thus, although the presence of teichoic acids as cell components was well established by 1960 (2), a further 10 years were to elapse before the presence of teichoic acid-lipid complexes was established (22, 26). These complexes are derived from the cell membrane but can function as surface components; by analogy with lipopolysaccharides, they have been termed lipoteichoic acids (LTAs; 26). Subsequent detailed studies on organisms from a number of genera showed the teichoic acid component to be a glycerol teichoic acid, which is joined covalently to a glycolipid or phosphatidyl glycolipid (1, 14, 28). From the results of immunological studies, it may also be generalized that serological specificity depends on the teichoic acid component, though the lipid component does influence the immunogenicity and serological reactivity of the LTA as well as being important in defining biological properties (28; Wicken and Knox, p. 360, this volume).

OCCURRENCE OF LIPOTEICHOIC ACIDS

The evidence for LTA being a component of a wide variety of gram-positive bacteria comes from both chemical and serological studies (28). Its presence in the cytoplasmic fraction of cells led to its description as "intracellular" teichoic acid before its membrane location was realized. However, although a membrane component, LTA occurs to varying extents in cell wall preparations (4, 5, 28) and also extracellularly (9, 18). Its presence in wall preparations is not perhaps surprising in view of the difficulty in obtaining such preparations free from membrane; it is also consistent with its occurrence as a surface antigen. However, the cell wall location may not be just fortuitous and could relate to a specific function in the bacterial cell (Wicken and Knox, p. 360, this volume).

Extraction of LTA depends on using procedures that will disrupt cell membranes but not hydrolyze the labile teichoic acid-lipid linkage. Many of the methods used for extracting lipopolysaccharides have been shown to be applicable, particularly hot aqueous phenol (25). This method has proved a convenient way for surveying organisms for the occurrence of LTA, initially by the serological procedures described below and then by more detailed chemical methods. Such procedures led to the identification of LTA as a component of the gram-negative organism *Butyrivibrio fibrisolvens* (7). Similar studies have failed to detect LTA in extracts of *Actinomyces* strains, and, as yet, there does not appear to be any evidence for LTA in gram-positive filamentous organisms other than bifidobacteria (unpublished data).

Negative findings in such surveys do not, of course, rule out the occurrence of LTA. Unfortunately, LTAs do not contain a unique component that would provide chemical evidence for their presence, nor would the antiserum used necessarily react with all types of LTA. However, if the antiserum is specific for the common glycerol phosphate backbone, it is very likely that LTA will show a reaction provided that a sufficiently sensitive method is used.

SEROLOGICAL DETECTION PROCEDURES

The serological detection of a specified antigen depends on either injecting whole organisms

356

and detecting the antibodies reacting with the purified product or, less frequently, injecting the isolated product and then detecting the antigen in crude or purified extracts. Both procedures have been employed with LTA. In addition, certain properties enable it to be detected even in the presence of other antigens. First, its charge means that it can be readily distinguished from most other antigens by immunoelectrophoresis, as was shown by studies on *Streptococcus sanguis* (20). This procedure is unfortunately relatively insensitive, but sensitivity can be increased considerably by using the techniques of counterimmunoelectrophoresis and rocket immunoelectrophoresis (unpublished data). Further, LTA will sensitize normal erythrocytes, and this provides a very sensitive method for its detection (6) and for semiquantitative estimations of the amount of material in crude extracts (18). The hemagglutination procedure is the preferred method for detecting low concentrations of antibody as, for instance, in human sera (14, 17), and also for surveying organisms for the presence of LTA. By this means LTA was detected in phenol extracts from strains representing 10 of 14 species of bifidobacteria examined (unpublished data), whereas the qualitative precipitin method failed to detect a teichoic acid in acid extracts of any of the 11 strains from five species of bifidobacteria (21).

For immunochemical studies on an isolated LTA, the preferred procedure is the quantitative precipitin method, as it enables an accurate comparison to be made of reactions and cross-reactions and of the ability of various compounds to inhibit the reaction.

IMMUNODOMINANT COMPONENTS

The classical studies on lipopolysaccharides have defined the procedures for studying the serological reactivity of antigens and led to the introduction of the word "immunodominant" to describe the component that is the most effective inhibitor of the reaction (16). Compared with the complex O-antigenic determinants of lipopolysaccharides, LTAs have a very restricted array of components that could be immunodominant: (i) the glycerol phosphate sequence; (ii) the D-alanine substituents; and (iii) the carbohydrate substituents, generally glucose and/or galactose in mono-, di-, or trisaccharides.

Antibodies specific for the carbohydrate substituents provide the basis for the reactivity of the group-specific LTAs, as evidenced by the inhibition of the reaction by the appropriate carbohydrate. LTAs carrying group-specific

carbohydrate determinants have been isolated from lactobacilli of groups A (12) and F (10), streptococci of groups D (22) and N (29), and *S. mutans* serotype *a* (23); *S. sanguis* also contains a group-reactive LTA (20).

The glycerol phosphate backbone and the D-alanine substituents are common to all LTAs, and antibodies against these components would be expected to react with a variety of LTAs. Antibodies to the D-alanine substituents are apparently rare (14), but those against the glycerol phosphate backbone are formed more frequently and account for most of the observations on a common antigen of gram-positive bacteria (14).

The specificity of antibodies is generally determined by examining the ability of various components to inhibit the reaction. However, with teichoic acids it must be borne in mind that a charged component such as glucosamine HCl or D-alanine methylester HCl can cause nonspecific inhibition (15). The reaction of both ribitol teichoic acid (15) and LTA (Fig. 1) with antibodies is particularly sensitive to the ionic concentration of the reaction mixture. Teichoic acids have been implicated in the ion-binding properties of bacterial cells (8), and the serological results probably reflect this property.

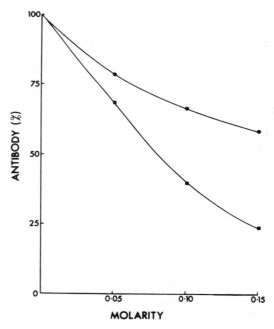

FIG. 1. *Inhibition of the precipitin reaction between* L. casei *lipoteichoic acid (20 μg) and homologous antiserum by increasing concentrations of sodium chloride (●) and magnesium chloride (■).*

CARBOHYDRATE-SPECIFIC ANTIBODIES

Studies on the specificity of antibodies reacting with polysaccharides led to the presumption that several sugar residues will occupy the antibody-combining site and be responsible for the specificity of the reaction. The more complex the sugar sequence, the less likely it is that cross-reactions will occur.

With LTAs, the maximal length for the carbohydrate chain is that found in the grouping antigen of some strains of *S. faecalis* where the trisaccharide kojitriose is present (24); other strains contain kojibiose (24). Both of these substituents are composed of D-glucose residues joined by α-1 → 2 linkages and react with the group-specific antiserum (3).

Disaccharides containing two different sugars occur in two serologically reactive LTAs. The first LTA to be described was the group F antigen of lactobacilli isolated from *Lactobacillus fermentum* NCTC 6991; 2-O-α-D-galactosyl-D-glucose and D-galactose were identified as the substituents, with α-D-galactosyl units being immunodominant (10). *S. mutans* AHT contains a partially characterized LTA in which a disaccharide of galactose and glucose occurs; galactose is the immunodominant component, and, as the methyl-β-D-galactoside is a more effective inhibitor of the precipitin reaction (22), it is probable that the disaccharide is β-D-galactosyl-D-glucose.

Two group-specific LTAs contain only monosaccharide substituents. That from the group N streptococcus *S. lactis* ATCC 9936 contains immunodominant α-D-galactosyl substituents (29), whereas lipoteichoic acid from the group A lactobacillus *L. helveticus* NCIB 8025 contains immunodominant α-D-glucosyl residues (12). *L. helveticus* provides the only known case where the wall glycerol teichoic acid and membrane LTA have the same glycosyl substituents; the degree of substitution with α-D-glucosyl

TABLE 1. *Reactivity of lipoteichoic acid grouping antigens with antiserum to* L. casei *lipoteichoic acid*

Genus and group	Strain	Substituents	Sugar-phosphorus ratio	Cross-reaction (%)
Lactobacillus				
F	6991	Gal-Glu	0.19:1	94
A	8025	Glu	0.45:1	92
Streptococcus				
N	9936	Gal	0.53:1	43
D	9790	Glu-Glu	0.71:1	81
	39	Glu-Glu	1.43:1	18
	8191	Glu-Glu-Glu	2.76:1	<5

residues is higher in the wall component, but it reacts less strongly with the grouping sera because of its lower molecular weight (12). With such simple carbohydrate substituents, it is not perhaps surprising that antibodies specific for the carbohydrate component of one LTA will cross-react with another LTA; for example, the cross-reaction between the group F lactobacillus antigen and the group N streptococcal antigen depends on their common α-D-galactosyl substituents (29).

Although it would be expected that an antibody-combining site would involve a number of glycerol phosphate residues in addition to the specific carbohydrate substituent, it has nevertheless been found that LTAs and other carbohydrate polymers may both react strongly with group-specific antisera. There are at least three instances of this occurring among the streptococci: in *S. mutans* strains of serotype *a* (19, 23), in *S. sanguis* strains of group H (B. Rosan and K. W. Knox, Abstr. Annu. Meet. Am. Soc. Microbiol. 1976, E49, p. 71), and in *S. lactis* strains of group N (29). In addition, dextrans will react with certain antisera to LTAs that are specific for their α-D-glucosyl substituents (13).

GLYCEROL PHOSPHATE-SPECIFIC ANTIBODIES

Although antibodies specific for the carbohydrate substituents account for some of the cross-reactions between LTAs, most of the known examples result from the presence of antibodies specific for the common glycerol phosphate backbone.

The formation of antibodies with such specificity accounts for many of the reports of "heterophile" or "common" antigens in gram-positive bacteria (14, 21, 28). They are readily formed against LTAs in which the teichoic acid component is devoid of carbohydrate substituents or has a very low carbohydrate content, for example, *L. casei* (27) and *S. mutans* BHT (5, 11). However, they may also be formed in some rabbits when the LTA contains a significant amount of carbohydrate, for example, *L. fermentum* group-specific LTA (10).

Evidence for the presence of antibodies specific for the glycerol phosphate "backbone" of LTA has been obtained in two ways. In the first, a strong reaction is obtained with a wide spectrum of LTAs carrying different substituents. This is illustrated in Table 1, where it is shown that each of the group-specific LTAs gives a reaction with antiserum to *L. casei* LTA except the one from group D with a very high degree of substitution; this LTA could, however, be detected by the hemagglutination method.

The second procedure for detecting antibodies specific for the glycerol phosphate "backbone" depends on the inhibition of the reaction with glycerol phosphate, as the monomer, trimer, or polymer. The trimer triglyceroldiphosphate prepared from cardiolipin is a very effective inhibitor and can be used to confirm the presence of LTA in a crude cell extract (18) or to show the presence of specific antibodies in, for example, human sera (17).

Sera that have been characterized as specific for the glycerol phosphate backbone can then be used for testing various cell fractions for the presence of LTA. This was the procedure followed for detecting LTA in strains of bifidobacteria representative of most of the known species (unpublished data), for quantitating the extracellular lipoteichoic acid formed by representative strains of lactobacilli and viridans streptococci (18), and for comparing the amounts of extracellular LTA present in cultures of *S. mutans* grown in a chemostat (unpublished data; Wicken and Knox, p. 360, this volume).

ACKNOWLEDGMENTS

Our work described in this article has been supported by the Australian National Health and Medical Research Council and by Public Health Service grants DE-04174 and DE-04175.

LITERATURE CITED

1. **Archibald, A. R.** 1974. The structure, biosynthesis and function of teichoic acid. Adv. Microb. Physiol. **11**:53–95.
2. **Archibald, A. R., J. J. Armstrong, J. Baddiley, and J. B. Hay.** 1961. Teichoic acids and the structure of bacterial walls. Nature (London) **191**:570–572.
3. **Burger, M. M.** 1966. Teichoic acids: antigenic determinants, chain separation and their location in the cell wall. Proc. Natl. Acad. Sci. U.S.A. **56**:910–917.
4. **Chiu, T. H., L. I. Emdur, and D. Platt.** 1974. Lipoteichoic acids from *Streptococcus sanguis*. J. Bacteriol. **118**:471–479.
5. **Chorpenning, F. W., H. R. Cooper, and S. Rosen.** 1975. Cross-reactions of *Streptococcus mutans* due to cell wall teichoic acid. Infect. Immun. **12**:586–591.
6. **Hewett, M. J., K. W. Knox, and A. J. Wicken.** 1970. Studies on the group F antigen of lactobacilli: detection of antibodies by haemagglutination. J. Gen. Microbiol. **6**:315–322.
7. **Hewett, M. J., A. J. Wicken, K. W. Knox, and M. E. Sharpe.** 1976. Isolation of lipoteichoic acids from *Butyrivibrio fibrisolvens*. J. Gen. Microbiol. **94**:126–130.
8. **Hughes, A. H., I. C. Hancock, and J. Baddiley.** 1973. The function of teichoic acids in cation control in bacterial membranes. Biochem. J. **132**:83–93.
9. **Joseph, R., and G. D. Shockman.** 1975. Synthesis and excretion of glycerol teichoic acid during growth of two streptococcal species. Infect. Immun. **12**:333–338.
10. **Knox, K. W., M. J. Hewett, and A. J. Wicken.** 1970. Studies on the group F antigen of lactobacilli: antigenicity and serological specificity of teichoic acid preparations. J. Gen. Microbiol. **60**:303–313.
11. **Knox, K. W., J. L. Markham, and A. J. Wicken.** 1976. Formation of cross-reacting antibodies against cellular and extracellular lipoteichoic acid of *Streptococcus mutans* BHT. Infect. Immun. **13**:647–652.
12. **Knox, K. W., and A. J. Wicken.** 1970. Serological properties of the wall and membrane teichoic acids from *Lactobacillus helveticus* NCIB 8025. J. Gen. Microbiol. **63**:237–248.
13. **Knox, K. W., and A. J. Wicken.** 1972. Reaction of dextrans with antisera to teichoic acids. Arch. Oral Biol. **17**:1491–1494.
14. **Knox, K. W., and A. J. Wicken.** 1973. Immunological properties of teichoic acids. Bacteriol. Rev. **37**:215–257.
15. **Knox, K. W., and A. J. Wicken.** 1973. Non-specific inhibition of the precipitin reaction between teichoic acids and antisera. Immunochemistry **10**:93–98.
16. **Lüderitz, O., A.-M. Staub, and O. Westphal.** 1966. Immunochemistry of O and R antigens of *Salmonella* and related *Enterobacteriaceae*. Bacteriol. Rev. **30**:192–255.
17. **Markham, J. L., K. W. Knox, R. G. Schamschula, and A. J. Wicken.** 1973. Antibodies to teichoic acids in humans. Arch. Oral Biol. **18**:313–318.
18. **Markham, J. L., K. W. Knox, A. J. Wicken, and M. J. Hewett.** 1975. Formation of extracellular lipoteichoic acid by oral streptococci and lactobacilli. Infect. Immun. **12**:378–386.
19. **Mukasa, H., and H. D. Slade.** 1973. Extraction, purification, and chemical and immunological properties of the *Streptococcus mutans* group "a" polysaccharide cell wall antigen. Infect. Immun. **8**:190–198.
20. **Rosan, B.** 1973. Antigens of *Streptococcus sanguis*. Infect. Immun. **7**:205–211.
21. **Sharpe, M. E., J. H. Brock, K. W. Knox, and A. J. Wicken.** 1973. Glycerol teichoic acid as a common antigenic factor in lactobacilli and some other Gram-positive organisms. J. Gen. Microbiol. **74**:119–126.
22. **Toon, P., P. E. Brown, and J. Baddiley.** 1972. The lipid-teichoic acid complex in the cytoplasmic membrane of *Streptococcus faecalis* NCIB 8191. Biochem. J. **127**:399–409.
23. **Van der Rijn, I., and A. S. Bleiweis.** 1973. Antigens of *Streptococcus mutans*. 1. Characterization of a serotype-specific determinant from *Streptococcus mutans*. Infect. Immun. **7**:795–804.
24. **Wicken, A. J., and J. Baddiley.** 1963. Structure of intracellular teichoic acid from group D streptococci. Biochem. J. **87**:54–62.
25. **Wicken, A. J., J. W. Gibbens, and K. W. Knox.** 1973. Comparative studies on the isolation of membrane lipoteichoic acid from *Lactobacillus fermenti* 6991. J. Bacteriol. **113**:365–372.
26. **Wicken, A. J., and K. W. Knox.** 1970. Studies on the group F antigen of lactobacilli: isolation of a teichoic acid-lipid complex from *Lactobacillus fermenti*. J. Gen. Microbiol. **60**:293–301.
27. **Wicken, A. J., and K. W. Knox.** 1971. A serological comparison of the membrane teichoic acids from lactobacilli of different serological groups. J. Gen. Microbiol. **67**:251–254.
28. **Wicken, A. J., and K. W. Knox.** 1974. Lipoteichoic acids—a new class of bacterial antigens. Science **187**:1161–1167.
29. **Wicken, A. J., and K. W. Knox.** 1975. Characterization of group N streptococcus lipoteichoic acid. Infect. Immun. **11**:973–981.

Biological Properties of Lipoteichoic Acids

ANTHONY J. WICKEN AND KENNETH W. KNOX

School of Microbiology, University of New South Wales, Kensington, New South Wales, 2033,
and Institute of Dental Research, United Dental Hospital, Sydney, New South Wales, 2010, Australia

INTRODUCTION

The amphipathicity of lipoteichoic acids (LTAs), in possessing a polar glycosylated glycerol teichoic acid moiety joined covalently to a membrane glycolipid, dictates not only their physicochemical properties but also their cellular location. Both of these latter parameters have a strong influence on the biological activity of macromolecules in general, and this is no less true in the case of LTAs.

LTAs have now been established as being located in two regions with respect to the bacterial cell (Fig. 1). Intracellular lipoteichoic acids (LTA$_i$) are normal plasma membrane components of most gram-positive bacteria (5, 9, 24, 34, 37, 38), the glycolipid moiety being embedded in the upper half of the phospholipid bilayer of the cell membrane. Extension of the polar glycerol teichoic acid portion of the molecule through the matrix of the cell wall can, in some organisms, result in the expression of this part of the molecule as a cell surface component (12, 35, 37). Extracellular lipoteichoic acids (LTA$_x$) are found in the external environment (22, 27) and result from either active excretion of LTA$_i$ or its loss from the cell during wall turnover in the normal processes of growth and cell division, or cell lysis. A transient existence of LTA$_i$ as a solely cell wall and surface component can also be postulated as a stage in the process LTA$_i$ → LTA$_x$. From both the intracellular and extracellular locations, LTA can be recovered in two physical forms, a high-molecular-weight micellar aggregate resulting from hydrophobic interaction of the glycolipid portions of the molecule and a lower-molecular-weight monomer resulting from deacylation of the still covalently attached glycolipid (8, 22, 27). The relative proportions of LTA$_i$ to LTA$_x$ and micellar form to deacylated monomer in both locations vary widely with the species of organism and its phase of growth (8, 22, 27). Whether or not deacylated monomer LTA$_i$ reflects a real situation within the intact cell or is an artifact of extraction procedures remains to be deter-

mined, but deacylated monomer LTA$_x$ has been isolated from the culture fluids of a number of organisms by physical procedures that do not deacylate micellar LTA (27). A further complication lies in the possibility that LTA$_x$ may not reflect the overall composition of LTA$_i$. Differences in the degree of glycosylation and in the fatty acid composition have been noted between the two forms of LTA from *Lactobacillus fermentum* (27).

The amphipathic nature of LTA provides the opportunity for both hydrophobic and hydrophilic interaction with other molecular species. Both hydrophobic and ionic forces are probably involved in the virtually irreversible binding of LTA to ion-exchange celluloses and dextrans (38). Crude extracts of LTA are often contaminated with protein and/or polysaccharide in the form of complexes which are difficult to separate without the use of detergents or prior deacylation of the LTA (38; unpublished data). Recently, we have found hydrophobic affinity chromatography to be useful in the separation of LTA from such contaminating polymers (unpublished data). LTA has also been shown to solubilize hydrophilic proteins and polysaccharides into alkyl alcohol solutions, and it has been speculated that a similar LTA binding of hydrophilic molecules in hydrophobic regions of the cell surface may have a biological role (13). Complex formation with LTA$_x$ may also explain the reported tenacious phosphorus contamination of extracellular glucans produced by oral streptococci (28), and the ready binding of LTA to hydroxyapatite (27), the chief component of dental enamel, is probably through the ionized phosphate groups of the polyglycerol phosphate portion of the molecule. Both phenomena have obvious possibilities with respect to the binding of glucans and bacteria to the tooth surface. Attachment of LTA to cell surfaces by a presumed intercalation of its glycolipid moiety into the lipid bilayer of the plasma membrane is well evidenced by the ready sensitization of erythrocytes with LTA and their use in hemagglutination assays of anti-LTA antibodies (24, 38; Knox and Wicken, p. 356, this volume). The binding of divalent cations, particularly Mg^{2+} ions, by LTA (and wall teichoic acids) has been well established and related to a role in maintaining high Mg^{2+} ion concentration in the vicinity of the bacterial plasma membrane (1, 21, 25). Location and the physicochemical properties of LTA are perhaps the keys to an understanding of its biological properties both in mammalian tissue and in the organisms that produce it.

BIOLOGICAL PROPERTIES OF LTA WITH RESPECT TO MAMMALIAN TISSUE

Comparisons between lipopolysaccharide (LPS) and LTA have inevitably been made (2, 24, 38). Both are high-molecular-weight amphipathic surface components, and many of the biological properties of LPS are shared by LTA (Table 1). The lack of pyrogenicity and lethality in mice of injected LTA (24, 38), in contrast to LPS, probably relates to the much simpler glycolipid substituents of LTA and the lack of hydroxyacyl esters characteristic of the more complex lipid A of LPS, lipid A having been shown to be responsible for these biological effects of LPS (31). The potential immunogenicity of LTA, both in isolation and as a surface immunogen in some bacterial species, has been well established in rabbits and mice (16, 24, 38; F. W. Chorpenning, R. W. Bolton, and G. T. Frederick, Fed. Proc. 33:2972, 1974; unpublished data). With respect to humoral response, both immunoglobulin M (IgM) and IgG antibodies have been regularly detected in both species (16, 38). Antibodies belonging to these classes and also IgA antibodies capable of reacting with LTA have been reported in humans (11, 26). Rats and guinea pigs have a low level of natural humoral and cellular immunity (as evidenced by macrophage migration inhibition) to LTA (3, 17; unpublished data). In rabbits humoral immunity to LTA is enhanced by association of the LTA with protein: the higher the protein content the higher the titer of the resultant antiserum (24, 38, 39). An interesting report of LTA causing repression of the humoral response to sheep erythrocytes (SRBC) in mice has recently been made (29). LTA appears to exert its maximal inhibiting effect when given in multiple doses and prior to the injection of SRBC. The nature of the immunosuppression appears to be in the afferent (antigen processing) limb of the immune system, since treatment with LTA after antigenic challenge had no immunosuppressive effect. In contrast to its effect on SRBC, LTA

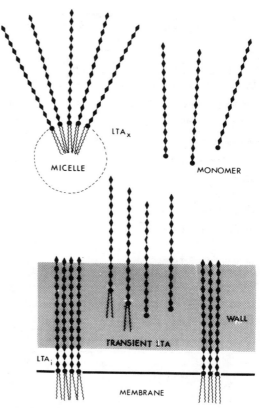

FIG. 1. *Diagrammatic representation of the relationship of extracellular lipoteichoic acid (LTA$_x$) and intracellular lipoteichoic acid (LTA$_i$) to the wall and membrane of a generalized gram-positive bacterial cell. LTA$_x$ is represented in a fully acylated micellar as well as deacylated monomer form. Transient LTA$_i$, both acylated and deacylated, is depicted as being in the process of excretion from the cell. The LTA structures shown are abridged, glycosyl and D-alanyl substituents being omitted, to emphasize the amphipathic nature of the fully acylated molecule. Chains of diamonds represent polyglycerol phosphate; solid circles attached to wavy lines represent glycolipid; solid circles alone represent deacylated glycolipid.*

has an enhancing effect on antibody production to LPS (29). This could be of some biological significance in situations, such as the oral cavity, where both LPS and LTA are likely to be present. We have also recently shown that LPS and LTA can readily form mixed micelles (unpublished data).

Unlike LPS, LTA is not mitogenic (38), but it will give a positive localized as well as a generalized Shwartzman reaction in rabbits, the latter reaction being accompanied by a bilateral necrosis of the kidneys characteristic of a LPS-induced reaction (24, 38). Hypersensitivity re-

TABLE 1. *Comparison of the biological properties of lipopolysaccharide (LPS) and lipoteichoic acid (LTA)*

Property	LPS	LTA	Reference
Pyrogenicity	+	−	24, 38
Lethality to mice	+	−	24, 38
Immunogenicity	+	+	16, 24, 38[a]
Mitogenicity	+	−	38
Shwartzman reaction	+	+	24, 38
Bilateral necrosis of kidneys	+	+	24, 38
Hypersensitivity	+	+	Unpublished
Stimulation of bone resorption	+	+	19
Stimulation of nonspecific immunity	+	+	24, 38
Carbon clearance in mice	+	+	29
Erythrocyte sensitization	+	+	24, 38[b]
Complement fixation	+	+	36

[a] See also Chorpenning, Bolton, and Frederick, Fed. Proc. **33**:2972, 1974.

[b] See also Knox and Wicken, p. 356, this volume.

actions to intradermal injection of LTA in immune rabbits have also been observed (unpublished data). LTA will also stimulate bone resorption in organ cultures, suggesting a pathogenic role for LTA in the alveolar bone loss associated with periodontitis (19). Although the amounts of LTA required are approximately 10-fold greater than for a similar LPS-induced response, the potential pool of LTA$_x$ in the oral cavity is significantly greater than that of LPS, given the predominance of gram-positive bacteria in this region. If LTA can penetrate oral tissue, as has been shown for LPS (32), it could stimulate the local production of antibody or react with nascent antibody and thereby, through localized inflammation, be a contributing factor in gingivitis. In common with LPS, LTA has also been shown to stimulate nonspecific immunity (24, 38) and enhance the clearance of carbon by the reticuloendothelial system in mice (29).

The ready attachment of LTA to erythrocytes, although it is a useful property in serological assays (24, 38; Knox and Wicken, p. 356, this volume), has implications in the pathogenesis of some streptococcal diseases. Streptococcal LTA can reversibly bind to erythrocytes and be transferred to uncoated erythrocytes and

to other tissue cells, including human heart tissue (24, 30). It has been suggested that this mechanism could play a role in the pathogenesis of rheumatic fever or glomerulonephritis (30). That these two sequelae of some group A streptococcal infections are autoimmune diseases in the sense of involving cross-reactive antigens is well established (42). LTA alone is unlikely to provide the observed species specificity in the etiology of these diseases but could act as a carrier for a complexed bacterial protein that provides the necessary immunological specificity (2, 24). Higher titers of anti-teichoic acid antibodies in the acute phase of rheumatic fever have been reported (23).

Rabbit antibodies to LTA are capable of fixing complement before hemolyzing sheep red blood cells sensitized with LTA (36). The frequent existence of humoral antibodies to LTA in humans (23, 24, 26, 38) raises the question of whether these antibodies can cross-react with human cell membrane constituents and subsequently participate in complement-mediated lysis and tissue damage. Cross-reaction and complement fixation between cardiolipin and rabbit antibodies to the glycerophosphate sequence of LTA have been clearly demonstrated (36), and the sugar moieties of eukaryotic membrane ceramides or glycoproteins are other possible candidates for similar reaction with LTA-induced antibodies specific for glycosyl groups. LTA$_x$ from *Streptococcus mutans* BHT has also been shown to protect SRBC from complement- and hemolysin-induced lysis if the erythrocytes are first coated with the LTA, and it has been suggested that in vivo LTA may similarly protect the bacterial membrane from the immune system (2).

The broad range of biological properties of LTA described above have one structural requirement in common. For any thus far observed biological effect, the glycolipid portion of the LTA molecule must be intact. Deacylated monomer LTA is entirely without effect as an immunogen, in attachment to cell membranes, or in eliciting any of the direct biological effects of LTA discussed above (2, 19, 24, 38; Knox and Wicken, p. 356, this volume).

BIOLOGICAL PROPERTIES OF LTA WITH RESPECT TO THE PRODUCING ORGANISM

Consideration of the ionic nature of both cell wall teichoic acids and membrane LTA led to early suggestions that both might function in cation-exchange reactions. There is now a considerable body of evidence (1, 21, 25) to support the hypothesis that an integrated array of charged groups provided by wall teichoic acids or wall acidic polysaccharides and membrane LTA forms a wall-membrane system which facilitates passage of cations, in particular Mg^{2+} ions, through the cell wall to the membrane, where they are known to be required for the stability of isolated cell membranes and for the activity of many membrane-bound enzymes. That LTA may be more significant in this role than the wall polymers is suggested (1) by the fact that (i) LTA is present in practically all gram-positive bacteria that have been examined, not all of which contain acidic wall polymers, and (ii) replacement of wall teichoic acid by acidic polysaccharides during growth under phosphate-limiting conditions does not cause a similar loss of LTA from the membrane.

A role of LTA_i as a lipid carrier for the biosynthesis of cell wall ribitol teichoic acid in *Staphylococcus aureus* has been established by Fiedler and Glaser (14, 15), chains of wall teichoic acids being assembled by the transfer of glycerol and ribitol phosphate units from the corresponding CDP derivatives directly to an LTA carrier. Concurrent assembly of teichoic acid with peptidoglycan synthesis is followed by attachment of teichoic acid to peptidoglycan at, or just after, the stage of peptide cross-linking (4, 10, 18, 41). Wong et al. (40) have also produced evidence to suggest that LTA_i, or a fraction of it, is the acceptor, in *S. aureus*, on which nascent peptidoglycan chains are synthesized. Addition of penicillin G to growing cultures led to a rapid secretion of polymeric peptidoglycan and LTA in the culture medium, as well as an intracellular accumulation of peptidoglycan fragments covalently linked to LTA; the complex did not contain any detectable ribitol teichoic acid. Pulse-chase experiments indicated a precursor-product relationship between the LTA-bound intracellular and extracellular LTA-free peptidoglycan. The mechanisms of each of these two suggested carrier roles for LTA_i and their universality among gram-positive organisms have yet to be established.

The importance of bacterial autolytic enzymes in cell division and the lytic action of penicillins and other wall-inhibitory antibiotics is well known (10). In *Streptococcus faecalis*, *Lactobacillus acidophilus*, and *Bacillus subtilis*, wall autolysis is inhibited by LTA from a variety of sources, and a physiological role for LTA in regulating autolysin activity has been suggested (7). In common with many other biological properties of LTA, an intact fully acylated glycolipid moiety is required for inhibitory activity (6, 7). *S. faecalis* ATCC 9790 LTA significantly inhibited autolysis of isolated walls

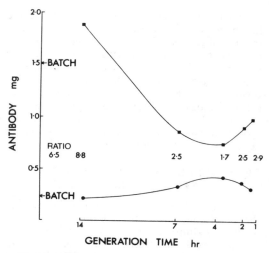

FIG. 2. *Production of extracellular lipoteichoic acid (LTA$_x$) and intracellular lipoteichoic acid (LTA$_i$) by chemostat-grown* Streptococcus mutans *BHT in dialyzed medium at pH 6 under glucose limitation (0.5%) and 5% CO$_2$ in N$_2$ at different generation times. LTA was estimated by the quantitative precipitin method (9) with the use of antisera specific to the polyglycerophosphate "back-bone" of LTA. Levels of LTA$_i$ (●) and LTA$_x$ (■) are expressed as the maximal amount of antibody protein precipitated by the LTA extracted from 1 mg of cells or contained in the volume of culture fluid from which 1 mg of cells was obtained. The levels of LTA$_i$ and LTA$_x$ in a stationary-phase 24-h culture of* S. mutans *BHT in the same medium are also shown (batch).*

from the same organism at concentrations (1.0 to 1.5 nmol of LTA per mg of wall) comparable to those found in intact cells (6). Monomer deacylated LTA failed to inhibit in the same concentration range. Phospholipids, particularly diphosphatidylglycerol, also inhibited wall autolysis (6), and both LTA and phospholipids were effective in inhibiting the lysis of intact cells of *S. faecalis* (8). The importance of the micellar form of LTA was illustrated by reversal of inhibition through addition of a low concentration of Triton X-100 (8). Preliminary data indicate that LTA binds to the autolysin rather than the cell wall, and this may reflect the ready binding of proteins by LTA referred to earlier. Reversal of inhibition by the action of a theoretical deacylase and subsequent excretion of the no longer required deacylated monomer LTA is an attractive model which would also explain the presence of deacylated monomer LTA in culture supernatant fluids (6). In *S. faecalis* ATCC 9790 it should be noted that the LTA$_x$ in the log phase of growth is almost entirely in the deacylated monomer form (22). Other carbohydrate polymers containing a lipid function, such as the lipomannan of *Micrococcus lysodeikticus* and the F antigen of *Diplococcus pneumoniae* did not act as inhibitors in the above autolytic systems (7). The F antigen of *D. pneumoniae* will, however, inhibit the autolysis of this organism (20) as well as exhibit a number of other biological effects (33). The chemical status of F antigen is still uncertain and, although it has been called an LTA, it would appear to be chemically unrelated to LTA.

EXTRACELLULAR LTA PRODUCTION IN RELATION TO GROWTH RATE

The existence of LTA_x in culture media in both the logarithmic and stationary phases of growth in batch culture has been well established by both chemical and serological criteria for a number of gram-positive bacteria (22, 27). From the known host-oriented properties of LTA, the potential secretion of large quantities of LTA_x into the external environment of, for example, the oral cavity has obvious implications on host-parasite relationships. That stationary-phase cultures of *S. mutans* BHT in rich medium produce an approximately 11-fold greater amount of LTA_x in the culture fluid than the LTA_i within the cells is a laboratory phenomenon (27). Recently, however, we have studied the behavior of the same organism in steady-state logarithmic growth under conditions of glucose limitation in a chemostat. Using quantitative serological detection procedures, we made a comparison between LTA_x and LTA_i at various dilution rates (Fig. 2). It is evident that at all dilution rates the cellular content of LTA_i remains fairly constant, but the excretion of LTA_x is markedly increased at both high and low dilution rates. Generation times of between 10 and 14 h have been estimated to reflect the likely growth rate of microorganisms in the nutritionally limited environment of the oral cavity. It is interesting to note that *S. mutans* BHT shows a high excretion of LTA_x in this range of generation times similar to the LTA_x produced in stationary phase in batch culture.

ACKNOWLEDGMENTS

Our work described in this article has been supported by the Australian National Health and Medical Research Council and by Public Health Service grants DE 04174 and DE 04175 from the National Institute of Dental Research.

LITERATURE CITED

1. **Archibald, A. R.** 1974. The structure, biosynthesis and function of teichoic acid. Adv. Microb. Physiol. **11**:53–95.
2. **Bleiweis, A. S., S. F. Hurst, R. A. Craig, and M. A. Morgenstern.** 1976. Lipoteichoic acid: an antigen of

cariogenic bacteria. Immunol. Abstr., Special Suppl. Immunological aspects of dental caries, p. 45–59.
3. **Bolton, R. W., and F. W. Chorpenning.** 1974. Naturally occurring cellular and humoral immunity to teichoic acids in rats. Immunology **27**:517–524.
4. **Bracha, R., and L. Glaser.** 1976. In vitro system for the synthesis of teichoic acid linked to peptidoglycan. J. Bacteriol. **125**:872–879.
5. **Button, D., and N. L. Hemmings.** 1976. Lipoteichoic acid from *Bacillus licheniformis* 6346MH-1. Comparative studies on the lipid portion of the lipoteichoic acid and the membrane glycolipid. Biochemistry **15**:989–995.
6. **Cleveland, R. F., L. Daneo-Moore, A. J. Wicken, and G. D. Shockman.** 1976. Effect of lipoteichoic acid and lipids on lysis of intact cells of *Streptococcus faecalis*. J. Bacteriol. **127**:1582–1584.
7. **Cleveland, R. F., J. V. Holtje, A. J. Wicken, A. Tomasz, L. Daneo-Moore, and G. D. Shockman.** 1975. Inhibition of bacterial wall lysins by lipoteichoic acids and related compounds. Biochem. Biophys. Res. Commun. **67**:1128–1135.
8. **Cleveland, R. F., A. J. Wicken, L. Daneo-Moore, and G. D. Shockman.** 1976. Inhibition of wall autolysis in *Streptococcus faecalis* by lipoteichoic acid and lipids. J. Bacteriol. **126**:192–197.
9. **Coley, J., M. Duckworth, and J. Baddeley.** 1975. Extraction and purification of lipoteichoic acids from Gram-positive bacteria. Carbohydr. Res. **40**:41–52.
10. **Daneo-Moore, L., and G. D. Shockman.** 1977. The bacterial cell surface in growth and division. *In* G. Poste and C. L. Nicolson (ed.), Cell surface reviews, vol. 4, Membrane assembly and turnover. ASP Biological and Medical Press, Amsterdam, in press.
11. **Daugherty, H. D., R. R. Martin, and A. White.** 1969. Reaction of sera and nasal secretions with staphylococcal antigens. J. Lab. Clin. Med. **73**:1011–1018.
12. **Dickson, M. R., and A. J. Wicken.** 1974. Ferritin labelling of thin sections by a "sandwich" technique. Int. Congr. Electron Microscopy, 8th, Canberra, vol. 2, p. 114–115.
13. **Doyle, R. J., A. N. Chatterjee, O. N. Streips, and F. E. Young.** 1975. Soluble macromolecular complexes involving bacterial teichoic acids. J. Bacteriol. **124**:341–347.
14. **Fiedler, F., and L. Glaser.** 1974. The attachment of poly (ribitol phosphate) to lipoteichoic acid carrier. Carbohydr. Res. **37**:37–46.
15. **Fiedler, F., J. Mauck, and L. Glaser.** 1974. Problems in cell wall assembly. Ann. N.Y. Acad. Sci. **235**:198–209.
16. **Frederick, G. T., and F. W. Chorpenning.** 1974. Characterization of antibodies specific for polyglycerolphosphate. J. Immunol. **113**:489–495.
17. **Frederick, G. T., R. A. Holmes, and F. W. Chorpenning.** 1972. Naturally occurring cell mediated immunity to purified glycerol teichoic acid antigens in guinea pigs. J. Immunol. **109**:1399–1401.
18. **Ghuysen, J. M.** 1976. Biosynthesis and assembly of bacterial cell walls. *In* G. Poste and G. L. Nicholson (ed.), Cell surface reviews, vol. 4, Membrane assembly and turnover. ASP Biological and Medical Press, Amsterdam, in press.
19. **Hausmann, E., O. Luderitz, K. Knox, A. J. Wicken, and N. Weinfeld.** 1975. Structural requirements for bone resorption by endotoxin and lipoteichoic acid. J. Dent. Res. **54**:B94–B99.
20. **Höltje, J. V., and A. Tomasz.** 1957. Lipoteichoic acid: a specific inhibitor of autolysin activity in Pneumococcus. Proc. Natl. Acad. Sci. U.S.A. **72**:1690–1694.
21. **Hughes, A. H., I. C. Hancock, and J. Baddiley.** 1973. The function of teichoic acids in cation control in bacterial membranes. Biochem. J. **132**:83–93.
22. **Joseph, R., and G. D. Shockman.** 1975. Synthesis and

excretion of glycerol teichoic acid during growth of two streptococcal species. Infect. Immun. **12**:333–338.

23. **Klesius, P. H., R. A. Zimmerman, J. H. Mathews, and A. H. Auernheimer.** 1974. Human antibody response to group A streptococcal teichoic acid. Can. J. Microbiol. **20**:853–859.

24. **Knox, K. W., and A. J. Wicken.** 1973. Immunological properties of teichoic acids. Bacteriol. Rev. **37**:215–257.

25. **Lambert, P. A., I. C. Hancock, and J. Baddiley.** 1975. The interaction of magnesium ions with teichoic acid. Biochem. J. **149**:519–524.

26. **Markham, J. L., K. W. Knox, R. G. Schamschula, and A. J. Wicken.** 1973. Antibodies to teichoic acids in humans. Arch. Oral Biol. **18**:313–318.

27. **Markham, J. L., K. W. Knox, A. J. Wicken, and M. J. Hewett.** 1975. Formation of extracellular lipoteichoic acid by oral streptococci and lactobacilli. Infect. Immun. **12**:378–386.

28. **Melvaer, K. L., K. Helgelard, and G. Rölla.** 1974. A charged component in purified polysaccharide preparations from *Streptococcus mutans* and *Streptococcus sanguis*. Arch. Oral Biol. **19**:589–595.

29. **Miller, G. A., J. Urban, and R. W. Jackson.** 1976. Effects of a streptococcal lipoteichoic acid on host responses in mice. Infect. Immun. **13**:1408–1417.

30. **Moskowitz, M.** 1966. Separation and properties of a red cell sensitizing substance from streptococci. J. Bacteriol. **91**:2200–2204.

31. **Rietschel, E. T., H. Gottert, O. Lüderitz, and O. Westphal.** 1972. Nature and linkage of the fatty acids present in the lipid A component of Salmonella lipopolysaccharide. Eur. J. Biochem. **28**:166–173.

32. **Schwartz, J., F. L. Stinson, and R. B. Parker.** 1972. The passage of tritiated bacterial endotoxin across intact gingival crevicula epithelium. J. Periodontol. **43**:270–276.

33. **Tomasz, A., M. Westphal, E. B. Briles, and P. Fletcher.** 1975. On the physiological functions of teichoic acids. J. Supramol. Struct. **3**:1–16.

34. **Toon, P., P. E. Brown, and J. Baddiley.** 1972. The lipid teichoic acid complex in the cytoplasmic membrane of *Streptococcus faecalis* NCIB8191 Biochem. J. **127**:399–409.

35. **van Driel, D., A. J. Wicken, M. R. Dickson, and K. W. Knox.** 1973. Cellular location of the lipoteichoic acids of *Lactobacillus fermenti* NCTC 6991 and *Lactobacillus casei* NCTC 6375. J. Ultrastruct. Res. **43**:483–497.

36. **Wicken, A. J., J. W. Gibbens, and K. W. Knox.** 1972. Antiteichoic acid antibodies and nontreponemal serological tests for syphilis. Infect. Immun. **5**:982–984.

37. **Wicken, A. J., and K. W. Knox.** 1970. Studies on the group F antigen of lactobacilli: isolation of a teichoic acid-lipid complex from *Lactobacillus fermenti*. J. Gen. Microbiol. **60**:293–301.

38. **Wicken, A. J., and K. W. Knox.** 1975. Lipoteichoic acids—a new class of bacterial antigens. Science **187**:1161–1167.

39. **Wicken, A. J., and K. W. Knox.** 1976. Immunogenicity of cell wall and plasma membrane components of some oral lactic acid bacteria. J. Dent. Res. **55**:C34–C41.

40. **Wong, W., F. E. Young, and A. N. Chatterjee.** 1976. Isolation of covalently linked lipoteichoic acid and peptidoglycan from penicillin treated *Staphylococcus aureus*. Proc. Natl. Acad. Sci. U.S.A., in press.

41. **Wyle, A. W., and J. B. Ward.** 1975. The synthesis of covalently-linked teichoic acid and peptidoglycan by cell-free preparations of *Bacillus licheniformis*. Biochem. Biophys. Res. Commun. **65**:877–885.

42. **Zabriskie, J. B.** 1967. Mimetic relationships between group A streptococci and mammalian tissues. Adv. Immunol. **7**:147–189.

Modulation of the Immune Response by Bacteria

Position Paper

JOHN H. SCHWAB

Department of Bacteriology and Immunology, University of North Carolina, Chapel Hill, North Carolina 27514

In this paper I try to develop a broad picture of bacteria influencing regulation of the specific immune system. Modulation of the immune response means any quantitative or qualitative modification, in either induction or expression, of cellular or humoral immunity. This includes effects on antigen-independent stages of maturation and distribution of lymphocytes or monocytes.

VARIOUS EXPRESSIONS OF IMMUNE MODULATION

General Remarks

Genetic control of the immune response has been shown to operate at several levels, including quantity of antibody produced (11, 18), affinity (65), restricted heterogeneity, and predominant immunoglobulin class (18, 67). Microbial products also have been shown to affect each of these facets of the immune response (21, 43, 57, 59, 63, 66, 73), and I shall review briefly each of these. The message for us is that bacterial agents can interact with the immune system at several control points and effectively change regulation.

Hyperimmunization achieved with bacterial adjuvants can be viewed as a deregulation of immunity. Thus, this topic includes consideration of the influence on immune response achieved with well-known adjuvants such as mycobacteria incorporated with antigen in a water-in-oil emulsion (Freund complete adjuvant), *Bordetella pertussis*, corynebacteria, and endotoxin (lipopolysaccharide, LPS) from gram-negative bacteria.

The capacity of bacterial adjuvants or crossreactive antigens (49) to circumvent tolerance against self-antigens can be viewed as further illustrations of the influence of bacterial products on immune regulation. As one recent example, Cunningham (19) showed that mice injected with LPS developed almost 100-fold more spleen cells producing antibody against bromelain-treated isologous erythrocytes. He suggests that there is a continuous balance between antigenic stimulation and suppression. Injection of LPS upsets this normal balance, allowing cells making antibody against self-antigens to increase in number. I shall mention later some properties of LPS which may help explain how this normal balance can be altered.

Quantitative Modulation

Quantitative changes, either enhancement or suppression, are the most obvious because they are the easiest to measure. The adjuvant factor from *B. pertussis* (36, 47), endotoxin (LPS) from gram-negative bacteria (29), and the watersoluble peptide from the peptidoglycan of cell walls (1) have now been well characterized, and, judging from the difference in structure, each must function by a different mechanism. The adjuvant activity of mycobacteria, corynebacteria, nocardia, and streptococci is due to the peptidoglycan of the cell wall (1, 7, 33). Although some of these products are B-cell mitogens (20), this property does not always correlate with adjuvant activity (6). Chedid and Audibert (p. 388, this volume) provides more information on this subject. Among the other bacterial products, *B. pertussis* will be discussed by Morse (p. 374), and endotoxin was considered in an earlier section. Our understanding of the cellular site of action can be summarized as follows. LPS, *B. pertussis*, and probably other bacterial adjuvants require T cells to function as adjuvants (2, 4, 21, 29). This action through T cells, however, may be indirect and mediated by a primary effect on macrophages (4, 64). In addition, LPS and cell wall peptidoglycan are selectively mitogenic for B cells, and there is evidence that this is also involved in the adjuvant effect (44). For LPS, we can conclude that the adjuvant effect involves stimulation of B-cell proliferation, but antigen-specific helper T-cell function must also be stimulated to influence B-cell differentiation into immunoglobulin-producing cells (4, 62). It should be noted that most agents utilized for their adjuvant properties can also function to depress an immune response, given appropriate manipulation of dose and timing of injection (59).

Products whose primary effect is to depress immune expression also have been highly purified. A good example is cholera enterotoxin, with which the molecular site of action has been precisely determined. This will be discussed by Henney and Witzke (p. 378, this volume). Many of these materials are active in very low concentrations. The suppressive factor obtained from the protoplasmic membrane of group A streptococci, which my laboratory has been studying, can suppress antibody formation in the mouse with as little as 3 ng of protein. Compare this with milligram doses of 6-mercaptopurine or cyclophosphamide required for comparable suppression in mice.

Qualitative Modulation

Affinity. Qualitative changes in immune response associated with microorganisms are less obvious but may be of considerable biological importance. Three examples of the effect on affinity have been reported (57, 63, 66). In one example, Saito and Nakano (57) showed that, in addition to an adjuvant effect involving both T and B cells, LPS increased the affinity of antibody against trinitrophenyl hapten. They concluded that LPS probably increases the efficiency of selection of high-affinity B cells. Mond et al. (45) demonstrated a similar, although less impressive, increase in affinity induced with either LPS or Freund complete adjuvant. It appears that the influence of LPS on regulation of quantity is exerted through a different mechanism than affinity of antibody production (4, 57).

Soothhill and Steward (63) showed that SWR/J and BIOD2 mice, which are prone to develop nephritis after neonatal lymphocytic choriomeningitis virus infection, produced antibody of low affinity to human serum albumin and transferrin. Strains resistant to nephritis (AJAX) produced high-affinity antibodies. However, if the protein antigens were incorporated with mycobacteria in Freund complete adjuvant, the higher-affinity antibody was produced by strains which produced only low-affinity antibody against antigen injected in saline. The affinity of antibody produced by the strain giving high affinity was not affected by the adjuvant.

A third example of a qualitative change in affinity is provided by a protozoan parasite. Steward and Voller (66) showed that mice infected with *Plasmodium berghei yoelii* produced antibody to human serum transferrin of significantly lower relative affinity ($K_R = 3.9 \times 10^5$) compared with uninfected controls ($K_R = 1.9 \times 10^6$). Mean antibody levels were not affected. These authors suggested that low-affinity antibody may contribute to poorer immune elimination of antigen and formation of soluble immune complexes associated with nephritis.

Immunoglobulin class and subclass. The suggestion that immunoglobulin class of antibody can be influenced by bacterial products comes from a recent report of Danneman and Michael (21). They showed that mice injected with egg albumin developed immunoglobulin E (IgE) as well as IgG_1 antibody if they also received LPS or gram-negative bacterial cells. No antibody was produced in the absence of adjuvant. This was not a unique property of bacteria since even greater IgE response was obtained with aluminum hydroxide gel. They also showed that the effect of LPS required the presence of T cells since LPS could not induce antibody in nu/nu mice.

Corynebacterium parvum is reported to selectively increase IgG_{2b} subclass in normal and tumor-bearing mice and to increase IgG_2 subclass in cancer patients (13).

Restricted heterogeneity. It is striking that the incidence of antibody of restricted heterogeneity is relatively high in mice and rabbits immunized with streptococcal vaccines (18, 37). Although this restricted response is under genetic control (18), some property of the bacterial cell other than antigen structure must contribute to this high incidence. This kind of monoclonal antibody response is most often associated with injection of bacteria. Thus, it is also observed in rabbits immunized with pneumococci and meningococci (37). Even the occasional monoclonal response against synthetic antigens occurs in animals immunized with hapten carrier emulsified in Freund complete adjuvant (51). Therefore, I suggest that this is another example of the qualitative influence of bacterial products on regulation of immune response. That is, during hyperimmunization with bacterial cells some component of the bacteria suppresses stimulation of the majority of high-affinity clones. This allows antigen stimulation of a very limited number of clones which are usually of low affinity. This is the opposite of the effect of LPS, a nonspecific polyclonal B-cell stimulator, which selectively stimulates higher-affinity antibody-forming cells (57).

ACTIVITIES WHICH HELP TO EXPLAIN MECHANISMS OF MODULATION

Other papers in this session present more precise information on mechanisms by which selected bacterial agents may affect regulation. I list below some biological activities of bacterial products which primarily affect antigen-independent maturation of the immune response.

Effects on Lymphocytes

Reaction of bacterial "mitogens" with the cytoplasmic membrane of B lymphocytes initiates several events, including blast cell formation, DNA synthesis, cell replication, and immunoglobulin production. LPS from gram-negative bacteria (62), purified protein derivative (PPD) from mycobacteria (50), *Mycoplasma pneumoniae* (10), *Listeria* cell wall fractions (14), pneumonococcal capsular polysaccharide (15), dextran (17), peptidoglycan from several gram-positive species (20), polymerized flagellin (POL) from *Salmonella* (16), levan from *Corynebacterium levaniformis* (16), *Klebsiella* capsular polysaccharide (48), and staphylococcal protein A (25) have been described as nonspecific polyclonal B-cell stimulators. The action of protein A can be explained as a reaction with an Fc structure in mammalian IgG on B lymphocytes (25). As Biberfield and Gronowicz (10) have pointed out, it is interesting that nearly all substances which are B-cell activators are derived from microorganisms. On the other hand, I am unaware of any bacterial products which have been proven to be T-cell mitogens (for exception see Morse, p. 374, this volume). I am impressed not only with the number but also with the variety of bacteria which can produce B-cell mitogens.

Reaction of lymphocytes with LPS (27) or lymphocytosis-promoting factor (LPF) from *B. pertussis* (5) has been shown to influence distribution and recirculation of immunocompetent cells.

Studies in my laboratory have revealed a different effect of a bacterial product on lymphocytes, namely, the ability of a component of bacterial cytoplasmic membranes to selectively block stimulation of a precursor B cell in bone marrow (Livesay and Schwab, Abstr. Annu. Meet. Am. Soc. Microbiol. 1976, E39, p. 70). This is probably the same factor that is such a potent immunosuppressant in mice (40).

Effects On Monocytes and Macrophages

Since monocytes and macrophages have a key role in both the affector and effector limbs of the immune response, any effect on their production, distribution, or function is potentially significant in expression of immune responses. Bacteria or bacterial products which have been shown to activate macrophages to increase production or secretion of lysosomal enzymes or cytotoxicity for target cells include endotoxin (3), *Corynebacterium (Propionibacterium) parvum* (61), group A streptococcal cell walls (22, 60), mycobacteria, and listeria (55).

Endotoxin has been shown to induce production both in vivo and in vitro of a factor, probably derived from macrophages, which stimulates bone marrow colony formation (colony-stimulating factor). This factor stimulates development of myelopoietic and lymphopoietic stem cells into mature granulocytes, macrophages, or lymphocytes (42, 56).

Listeria monocytogenes, which is also an adjuvant and a B-cell mitogen, produces a monocytosis-promoting activity (MPA) which is a membrane component (68).

Activation of Complement (C3)

Finally, the activation of complement by bacteria through the C3 bypass mechanism could also affect immune regulation. Activation has been demonstrated with LPS (38), cell wall peptidoglycan (12), cytoplasmic membranes (69), and cells of several species of bacteria including corynebacteria (39).

REGULATORY ROLE OF BACTERIAL FLORA

The important question for me is: What is the real meaning of these accumulated observations on bacterial modulation of the immune response? Do bacterial factors have a normal regulatory role? I want to present the following concept for your consideration.

The capacity of microorganisms to influence immune regulation is not confined to a few species or to contrived laboratory experiments. Rather, it is part of a natural process in which the microbial flora, both indigenous and transient, participates in regulation of numerous physiological processes, including the immune system. You will recognize that this is really a revival of an old concept first proposed by Pasteur about 1885. Dubos and co-workers have reinvestigated this in a long series of experiments on the influence of the indigenous flora of mice on rate of growth and resistance to endotoxin and other stress (23). More recently, Savage and Blumershine (58) and Freter and Abrams (28) have pursued studies on the importance of the microbial flora to the host. I am extending this concept to include regulation of the specific immune response.

Consider first the impressive list of bacterial products which affect B lymphocyte function, or monocyte maturation, or macrophage activation, or expression of the antigen-stimulated immune system. Most of the bacteria are either indigenous to, or frequently associated with, animals and humans. It seems reasonable to believe that we are continuously subjected to the influence of these materials. Consider further that some of the same changes induced by bacteria in contrived experiments occur naturally in the conventional animal with increasing age. The immunological dysfunctions associated with old age include depressed cellular and humoral immune responses, increased autoantibody formation, and restricted immunoglobulin heterogeneity. Each of these can be induced or exaggerated by bacterial products. This provides the rationale for speculating that bacterial factors contribute to immune expression and development. This influence, however, is subtle and at the physiological level compared with the effect achieved by sudden injection of high concentrations of bacteria or purified products. For this reason, the effect of the flora is difficult to demonstrate convincingly.

I shall present now some very preliminary data from an experiment we designed to gain direct information on this question of regulation by the bacterial flora. This work was based upon two observations: (i) there is a quantitative shift in the bacterial composition of the intestinal flora of mice and men with increasing age (54) and (ii) there is a quantitative decrease in antibody production with increasing age (32). We therefore tried to determine the influence of intestinal flora on antibody formation in mice by comparing the effects of flora from old and young animals.

Two approaches were used. In the first we tried to exchange the flora of old (109 weeks) and young (8 weeks) cohorts of CBA mice, which were identical in every genetic and environmental aspect except age. Following a well-established procedure (72), young and old conventional mice were bacteriologically decontaminated with a mixture of neomycin, streptomycin, bacitracin, and pimaricin in drinking water. They were treated for 4 weeks while kept in isolators. At this time, the young CBA cohorts were divided into three groups: one kept as a decontaminated control, a second recontaminated with flora from a young animal, and a third recontaminated with flora from an old donor. The young donors were selected for high antibody response to sheep erythrocytes (SRBC) and old donors were selected for low antibody response. The three recontaminated groups were kept for 5 weeks in isolators and then immunized with SRBC and bled 5 days later for serum titrations. Fecal specimens were cultured weekly to monitor decontamination and reestablishment of flora.

In a second experimental approach, middle-age (30 weeks) CBA germfree mice were divided into three groups: one kept germfree, a second contaminated with flora from old conventional CBA mice, and a third contaminated with flora from young CBA mice. These were maintained for 8 weeks in an isolator and then immunized with SRBC and bled 5 days later.

Figure 1 summarizes some of the results. It seems that these manipulations of the mice, which involve primarily changes in the bacterial flora, do affect antibody response. The method of measurement is relatively insensitive and the differences are small, but it is interesting that there are differences with a pattern emerging. We drew the following very tentative conclusions.

1. The antibody response of old conventional mice is lower than that of otherwise identical young conventional cohorts, confirming many previous studies.

2. The response of young and old conventional control mice maintained for 6 weeks in isolators decreases compared with identical cohorts maintained conventionally. The young-old ratio remains about the same. Relevant to this is the observation that the aerobic flora changes when conventional mice are maintained in isolators (54).

3. Young conventional mice decontaminated with antibiotics and maintained in isolators give a reduced response, comparable to cohorts only placed in isolators.

4. Recontamination of young decontaminated mice with flora from old conventional mice reduces the response even lower. Recontamination with flora from young mice did not have as great an effect.

5. Germfree mice produced the lowest antibody response. This was increased a little by contamination with flora from old mice. Contamination with flora from young mice increased the response to a slightly greater extent.

6. Old conventional mice, in isolators and decontaminated with antibiotics, all died within 7 days. This is a very intriguing observation which needs further study.

I emphasize that these are very preliminary data, but they lend support to the concept of a natural role for bacterial flora in immune regulation. The experiments are described because I am not aware of any other direct approaches to this question.

Information from Germfree Animals

Other evidence that the bacterial flora participates in regulation of host functions is indirect and is largely derived from studies of germfree or gnotobiotic animals (31). The fact that germfree animals can make immune responses is presented as evidence that the bacterial flora is

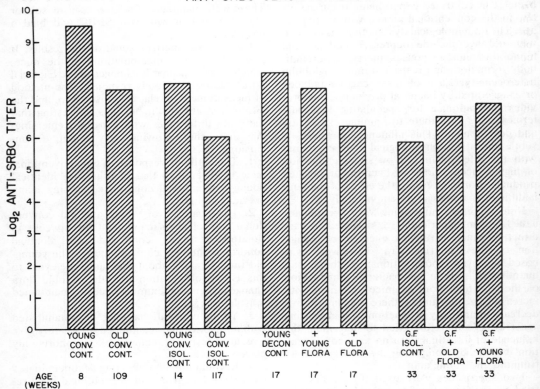

FIG. 1. *Effect of manipulation of the bacterial flora on the antibody response of CBA/Ry mice to sheep erythrocytes (SRBC). Abbreviations: conv., conventional; cont., control; isol., isolator; decon, decontaminated; G. F., germfree.*

not essential for function of this system. This is true, but the argument still remains that, if present, the flora does influence, qualitatively and quantitatively, the specific immune response as well as other physiological functions. Thus, upon closer examination we find that the immune system of germfree animals is different in many respects from that of otherwise identical conventional animals.

The lymphoid tissue is much less developed in germfree than in conventional animals (52). Spleen, lymph nodes, and Peyer's patches are much smaller. There are few if any germinal centers, blast cells, pyroninophilic cells, or plasma cells. There is less mitotic activity in the thymus and reduced numbers of both T and B thoracic-duct lymphocytes. These facts are well known and are ascribed to absence of immune stimulation by bacterial antigens, although, from what I have reviewed, this could as well be due to the absence of non-specific antigen-independent stimulation of lymphocyte and monocyte maturation. I do not

think this is a trivial observation. The point of importance to us is that, because bacteria are present, the lymphoid tissue in conventional animals responds differently to an antigenic stimulus.

As expected from the appearance of the lymphoid tissue, serum levels of immuno-globulins are low in germfree animals. In an attempt to determine the contribution of in-dividual bacterial species to development of the immune system, Balish et al. (8) monocon-taminated germfree Sprague-Dawley rats with several species and measured antibodies and changes in serum proteins. It is interesting that there was a variation in the capacity of different bacterial species to stimulate globulin production. After 4 weeks of contamination, immunoglobulin production was induced only by *Clostridium perfringens*, *Staphylococcus aureus*, *Pseudomonas aeruginosa*, *Klebsiella pneumoniae*, and *Enterobacter aerogenes* . In contrast, *Lactobacillus acidophilus*, *Strepto-coccus faecalis*, *Candida albicans*, *Bacteroides fragilis, Proteus vulgaris,* and *Citrobacter freundi* could not. In addition, 4 weeks of monoassociation with *S. faecalis* or *C. albicans* did not stimulate agglutinating antibodies. These observations suggested to the authors that "The composition of an animal's microbial flora could play a key role in the development of both humoral and cellular immunity."

The antibody response of germfree mice to injected antigens has given variable results (26, 34, 71). Generally, germfree mice show a slower primary response but ultimately often a greater and more sustained antibody level. A different response was observed by Frederick and Chorpenning (26). They found that the "natural" antibody response to bacterial teichoic acid was detectable much earlier in germfree guinea pigs than in conventional animals. The explanation given for this difference is less antigenic competition from bacterial antigen in germfree animals. I have also observed that germfree female (but not male) CBA mice have a higher incidence of autoantibody against bromelain-treated syngeneic erythrocytes compared with control animals. The higher incidence of antinuclear autoantibody in germfree NZB mice compared with conventional animals was also reported by Unni et al. (71). Olson and Wostmann (53) suggested that the sluggish immune response of germfree mice to *Salmonella* or human gamma globulin antigens could be attributed to decreased macrophage "processing" of antigen.

There have also been reports that cell-mediated immunity (CMI) is reduced in germfree animals. Ueda et al. (70) reported that germfree mice immunized with *Mycobacterium tuberculosis* in oil developed delayed hypersensitivity much more slowly than conventional mice. This was measured in vivo by footpad swelling and in vitro by macrophage migration inhibition. They concluded that the hyporeactivity to PPD in germfree mice reflected a defect in the induction rather than expression of CMI.

Finally, studies on graft-versus-host (GvH) disease may be interpreted as suggesting a role of the bacterial flora in immune regulation. van Bekkum et al. (9), Jones et al. (35), and Heit et al. (30) have all shown that fatal GvH or secondary disease in mouse radiation chimeras is very much reduced or absent in germfree or antibiotic-decontaminated animals. The role of the microflora in fatal GvH disease is more profound than mere infection through an injured intestinal wall, since germfree mice do not develop fatal disease even if contaminated 30 days after transplantation (9). At this time interval, control conventional

mice are developing the disease. I suggest that these results are an example of the involvement of bacterial products from the normal microbial flora in effector cell functions.

Mechanisms

How can we envision the bacterial flora exerting this hypothetical influence on the immune system? Is it possible that sufficient amounts of bacterial agents can gain access to appropriate host tissue to react with cells of the immune system or activate humoral components such as complement? There is no evidence on this, but the fact that antibody production against a large number of bacterial antigens is considered normal shows that entrance of some bacterial substances is achieved. A more indirect effect can also be proposed. As an example, Mertin and Hunt (41) have demonstrated the influence of polyunsaturated fatty acids on the immune response. Thus, linoleic acid given subcutaneously or orally prolongs the survival of skin allografts in mice. Diets low in polyunsaturated fatty acids produce relative immunopotentiation. This is relevant to this topic because it has also been reported recently that several bacterial species isolated from the intestinal microflora can hydrogenate linoleic acid into the saturated octadecenoic acid (46). Eyssen et al. (24) have also demonstrated that intestinal bacteria can hydrogenate oleic and linoleic acid. They state: "Intestinal bacteria transform lipids, neutral sterols, steroid hormones and bile acids into a variety of metabolites, some of which might have important pharmacological activities."

CONCLUSION

There are four aspects of this topic which are of special interest and warrant pursuit:

1. Application of bacterial agents in treatment of disease. Immunotherapy with *C. parvum* or BCG is one example of potential usefulness.

2. Utilization as tools for dissecting the immune response. LPS and cholera enterotoxin are good examples.

3. The role of such agents in infection. There is, as yet, no evidence that such agents contribute to the pathogenesis of an infection through their influence on the immune response. There is some evidence that these agents can influence infection by unrelated microorganisms (59).

4. Most speculative, but in my view most interesting, is a revival of the concept that agents derived from the indigenous flora contribute to regulation of normal physiological functions of the host.

ACKNOWLEDGMENTS

Part of this study was conducted as a Macy Faculty Scholar, Josiah Macy, Jr., Foundation. I am grateful for the support of the staff of the TNO Institute for Experimental Gerontology and the Radiobiological Institute, Rijswijk, The Netherlands. The assistance of Peter Heidt and the Bacteriology Laboratory of the Institute is gratefully acknowledged. This work was supported by National Cancer Institute contract CB-43929-31.

LITERATURE CITED

1. **Adam, A., R. Ciorbru, F. Ellouz, J.-F. Petit, and E. Lederer.** 1974. Adjuvant activity of monomeric bacterial cell wall peptidoglycans. Biochem. Biophys. Res. Commun. **56**:561–567.

2. **Allison, A. C., and A. J. S. Davies.** 1971. Requirements of thymus-dependent lymphocytes for potentiation by adjuvants of antibody formation. Nature (London) **233**:330–332.

3. **Allison, A. C., P. Davies, and R. C. Page.** 1973. Effects of endotoxin on macrophages and other lymphoreticular cells. J. Infect. Dis. **128**:5212–5219.

4. **Armerding, D., and D. H. Katz.** 1974. Activation of T and B lymphocytes in vitro. I. Regulatory influence of bacterial lipopolysacchoride (LPS) on specific T cell helper function. J. Exp. Med. **139**:24–43.

5. **Athanassiades, T. J., and S. I. Morse.** 1973. Lymphocytes induced in mice by supernatant fluids of *Bordetella pertussis* cultures: a histopathological study. Blood **42**:611–621.

6. **Azuma, I., K. Sugimura, T. Taniyama, M. Yamawaki, Y. Yamamura, S. Kusumoto, S. Okada, and T. Shiba.** 1976. Adjuvant activity of mycobacterial fractions: adjuvant activity of synthetic N-acetyl-muramyl-dipeptide and the related compounds. Infect. Immun. **14**:18–27.

7. **Azuma, I., F. Kanetsuna, T. Taniyama, Y. Yamamura, H. Hori, and Y. Tanaka.** 1975. Adjuvant activity of mycobacterial fractions. I. Purification and in vivo adjuvant activity of cell wall skeletons of *Mycobacterium bovis* BCG, *Nocardia asteroides* 131 and *Corynebacterium diphtheriae* PW8. Biken J. **18**:1–13.

8. **Balish, E., C. E. Yale, and R. Hong.** 1973. Influence of a defined flora on the serum proteins of gnotobiotic rats, p. 485–491. In J. B. Heneghan (ed.), Germfree research. Academic Press Inc., New York.

9. **Bekkum, D. W. van, J. Roodenburg, P. J. Heidt, and D. van der Waaij.** 1974. Mitigation of secondary disease of allogeneic mouse radiation chimeras by modification of the intestinal microflora. J. Natl. Cancer Inst. **52**:401–404.

10. **Biberfield, G., and E. Gronowicz.** 1976. *Mycoplasma pneumoniae* is a polyclonal B-cell activator. Nature (London) **261**:238–239.

11. **Biozzi, G., C. Stiffel, D. Morton, Y. Bouthillier, and C. Decreusefond.** 1968. Selection artificielle pour la production d'anticorps chez la souris. Ann. Inst. Pasteur Paris **115**:965–971.

12. **Bokish, V.** 1975. Interaction of peptidoglycans with anti-IgGs and with complement. Z. Immunitaetsforsch. **149**:320–330.

13. **Clunie, J. K., and C. J. A. Woodruff.** 1975. The effect of *C. parvum* therapy on Ig class and IgG subclass levels in cancer patients. Br. J. Cancer **32**:310–322.

14. **Cohen, J. J., G. E. Rodriquez, P. D. Kind, and P. A. Campbell.** 1975. Listeria cell wall fraction: a B-cell mitogen. J. Immunol. **114**:1132–1134.

15. **Coutinho, A., and G. Moller.** 1973. Mitogenic properties of the thymus-independent antigen pneumococcal polysaccharide III. Eur. J. Immunol. **3**:608–613.

16. **Coutinho, A., and G. B. Moller.** 1973. B cell mitogenic properties of thymus-independent antigens. Nature (London) **245**:15–24.

17. **Coutinho, A., G. Moller, and W. Richter.** 1974. Molecular basis of B-cell activation. I. Mitogenicity of native and substituted dextrans. Scand. J. Immunol. **3**:321–338.

18. **Cramer, M., and D. G. Braun.** 1975. Genetics of restricted antibodies to streptococcal group polysaccharides in mice. II. The Ir-A-CHO gene determines antibody levels, and regulatory genes influence the restriction of the response. Eur. J. Immunol. **5**:823–830.

19. **Cunningham, A. J.** 1975. Active suppressor mechanisms maintaining tolerance to non-self components. Nature (London) **254**:143–144.

20. **Damais, C., C. Bona, L. Chedid, J. Fleck, C. Nauciel, and J. P. Martin.** 1975. Mitogenic effect of bacterial peptidoglycans possessing adjuvant activity. J. Immunol. **115**:268–271.

21. **Danneman, P., and J. G. Michael.** 1976. Adjuvant and immunogenic properties of bacterial LPS in IgE and IgG₁ antibody formation in mice. Cell. Immunol. **22**:128–129.

22. **Davies, P., R. C. Page, and A. C. Allison.** 1974. Changes in cellular enzyme levels and extracellular release of lysosomal acid hydrolases in macrophages exposed to group A streptoccocal cell wall substance. J. Exp. Med. **139**:1262–1273.

23. **Dubos, R., R. Schaedler, R. Costello, and P. Hoet.** 1965. Indigenous, normal and autochthonous flora of the gastrointestinal tract. J. Exp. Med. **122**:67–75.

24. **Eyssen, H., G. De Pauw, and P. De Somer.** 1973. Biohydrogenation of long-chain fatty acids by intestinal microorganisms, p. 277–283. In J. B. Heneghan (ed.), Germfree research. Academic Press Inc., New York.

25. **Forsgren, A., A. Svedjelund, and H. Wigzell.** 1976. Lymphocyte stimulation by protein A of *Staphylococcus aureus*. Eur. J. Immunol. **6**:207–213.

26. **Frederick, G. T., and F. W. Chorpenning.** 1973. Comparison of natural and immune antibodies to teichoic acids in germfree and conventional guinea pigs, p. 493–499. In J. B. Heneghan (ed.), Germfree research. Academic Press Inc., New York.

27. **Freitas, A. A., and M. de Sousa.** 1976. Control mechanisms of lymphocyte traffic. Altered distribution of ⁵¹Cr-labeled mouse lymph node cells pretreated in vitro with lipopolysaccharide. Eur. J. Immunol. **6**:269–273.

28. **Freter, R., and G. D. Abrams.** 1972. Function of various intestinal bacteria in converting germfree mice to the normal state. Infect. Immun. **6**:119–126.

29. **Hamaoka, T., and D. Katz.** 1973. Cellular site of action of various adjuvants in antibody responses to hapten carrier conjugates. J. Immunol. **111**:1554–1563.

30. **Heit, H., R. Wilson, T. M. Fliedner, and E. Kohne.** 1973. Mortality of secondary disease in antibiotic-treated mouse radiation chimeras, p. 477–483. In J. B. Heneghan (ed.), Germfree research. Academic Press Inc., New York.

31. **Heneghan, J. B. (ed.).** 1973. Germfree research. Academic Press Inc., New York.

32. **Hijmans, W., and C. F. Hollander.** 1976. The pathogenic role of age-related immune dysfunctions. In T. Makinodan and E. Yunis (ed.), Immunology and aging. Plenum Publishing Co., New York.

33. **Holton, J., and J. H. Schwab.** 1966. Adjuvant properties of bacterial cell wall mucopeptides. J. Immunol. **96**:134–138.

34. **Horowitz, R. E., H. Bauer, F. Poronetto, G. D. Abrama, K. C. Watkins, and H. Popper.** 1964. The response of the lymphatic tissue to bacterial antigen. Studies in germfree mice. Am. J. Pathol. **44**:747–761.

35. **Jones, J. M., R. Wilson, and P. Bealmer.** 1971. Mortality and gross pathology of secondary disease in germfree mouse radiation chimeras. Radiat. Res. **45**:577–588.

36. **Kong, A. H., and S. I. Morse.** 1976. The effect of *Bordetella pertussis* on the antibody response in mice to type III pneumococcal polysaccharide. J. Immunol. **116:**989–993.

37. **Krause, R.** 1970. The search for antibodies with molecular uniformity. Adv. Immunol. **12:**1–53.

38. **Loos, M., D. Bitter-Suermann, and M. Dierich.** 1974. Interaction of the first (C1), the second (C2) and fourth (C4) component of complement with different preparations of bacterial lipopolysacchorides and with lipid A. J. Immunol. **112:**935–940.

39. **McBride, W., D. M. Weir, A. B. Kay, D. Pearce, and J. R. Caldwell.** 1975. Activation of the classical and alternate pathways of complement by *Corynebacterium parvum*. Clin. Exp. Immunol. **19:**143–147.

40. **Malakian, A. H., and J. H. Schwab.** 1971. Biological characterization of an immunosuppressant from group A streptococci. J. Exp. Med. **134:**1253–1265.

41. **Mertin, J., and R. Hunt.** 1976. Influence of polyunsaturated fatty acids on survival of skin allografts and tumor incidence in mice. Proc. Natl. Acad. Sci. U.S.A. **73:**928–931.

42. **Metcalf, D.** 1976. Role of mercaptoethanol and endotoxin in stimulating B lymphocyte colony formation *in vitro*. J. Immunol. **116:**635–638.

43. **Miller, G. A., and R. W. Jackson.** 1973. The effects of *Streptococcus pyogenes* teichoic acid on the immune response of mice. J. Immunol. **110:**148–156.

44. **Moller, G.** 1975. One non-specific signal triggers B lymphocytes. Transplant. Rev. **23:**126–137.

45. **Mond, J., Y. K. Kim, and G. W. Siskind.** 1974. Studies on the control of antibody synthesis. V. Effect of nonspecific modification of the magnitude of the immune response on the affinity of the antibody synthesized. J. Immunol. **112:**1255–1263.

46. **Morotomi, M., Y. Kawai, and M. Mutai.** 1976. Intestinal microflora in rats: isolation and characterization of strictly anaerobic bacteria requiring long-chain fatty acids. Appl. Environ. Microbiol. **31:**475–480.

47. **Murgo, A. J., and T. J. Athanassiades.** 1975. Studies on the adjuvant effect of *Bordetella pertussis* vaccine to sheep erythrocytes in the mouse. I. *In vitro* enhancement of antibody formation with normal spleen cells. J. Immunol. **115:**928–931.

48. **Nakashima, I., and N. Kato.** 1974. Non-specific stimulation of immunoglobulin synthesis in mice by capsular polysaccharide of *Klebsiella pneumoniae*. Immunology **27:**179–193.

49. **Neter, E., and F. Milgrom.** 1975. The immune system and infectious diseases. 4th Int. Convoc. Immunol., Buffalo, N.Y., 1974. Karger, Basel.

50. **Nilsson, B. S., B. M. Sultzer, and W. W. Bullock.** 1973. Purified protein derivative of tuberculin induces immunoglobulin production in normal mouse spleen cells. J. Exp. Med. **137:**127–136.

51. **Nisonoff, A., S. Zappacosta, and R. Jureziz.** 1967. Properties of crystallized rabbit anti-p-azobenzoate antibody. Cold Spring Harbor Symp. Quant. Biol. **32:**89–93.

52. **Olson, G. B., and B. S. Wostmann.** 1966. Lymphocytopoietin, plasmacytopoietin and cellular proliferation in non antigenically stimulated germfree mice. J. Immunol. **97:**267–274.

53. **Olson, G. B., and B. S. Wostmann.** 1966. Cellular and humoral immune response of germfree mice stimulated with 7S HGG or *Salmonella typhimurium*. J. Immunol. **97:**275–286.

54. **Pesti, L., and H. A. Gordon.** 1973. Effects of age and isolation on the intestinal flora of mice. Gerontologia **19:**153–161.

55. **Petit, J.-C., and E. R. Uanue.** 1974. Effects of bacterial products on lymphocytes and macrophages: their possible role in natural resistance to listeria infection in mice. J. Immunol. **113:**984–992.

56. **Quessenberg, P., A. Morley, F. Stohlman, Jr., K. Richard, D. Howard, and M. Smith.** 1972. Effect of endotoxin on granulopoiesis and colony-stimulating factor. N. Engl. J. Med. **286:**227–229.

57. **Saito, T., and M. Nakano.** 1975. Effect of bacterial lipopolysaccharides on anti-trinitrophenyl antibody producing cells. Non-specific modification of the affinity at the cellular level. Jpn. J. Microbiol. **19:**419–425.

58. **Savage, D. C., and R. V. H. Blumershine.** 1974. Surface-surface associations of microbial communities populating epithelial habitats in the murine gastrointestinal ecosystem: scanning electron microscopy. Infect. Immun. **10:**240–250.

59. **Schwab, J. H.** 1975. Suppression of immune response by microorganisms. Bacteriol. Rev. **39:**121–143.

60. **Schwab, J. H., and R. Smialowicz.** 1975. Interaction of bacterial cell wall polymers and rat macrophages. Z. Immunitaetsforsch. **149:**283–288.

61. **Scott, M. T.** 1972. Biological effects of the adjuvant *Corynebacterium parvum*. II. Evidence for macrophage T-cell interactions. Cell. Immunol. **5:**469–479.

62. **Shinohara, N., and M. Kern.** 1976. Differentiation of lymphoid cells: B cell as a direct target and T cell as a regulator in lipopolysaccharide-enhanced induction of immunoglobulin production. J. Immunol. **116:**1607–1612.

63. **Soothill, J. F., and M. W. Steward.** 1971. The immunopathological significance of the heterogeneity of antibody affinity. Clin. Exp. Immunol. **9:**193–199.

64. **Spitznagel, J. D., and A. C. Allison.** 1970. Mode of action of adjuvants: effects on antibody responses to macrophage-associated bovine serum albumin. J. Immunol. **104:**128–139.

65. **Steward, M. W., and R. E. Petty.** 1976. Evidence for the genetic control of antibody affinity from breeding studies with inbred mouse strains producing high and low affinity antibody. Immunology **30:**789–797.

66. **Steward, M. W., and A. Voller.** 1973. The effect of malaria on the relative affinity of mouse anti-protein antibody. Br. J. Exp. Pathol. **54:**198–202.

67. **Strosberg, A. D., C. Hamers-Casterman, W. v.d. Loo, and R. Hamers.** 1974. A rabbit with the allotypic phenotype: ala2a3b4b5b6. J. Immunol. **113:**1313–1318.

68. **Tadayon, R. A., K. K. Carroll, and R. G. E. Murray.** 1970. Purification and properties of biologically active factors in lipid extracts of *Listeria monocytogenes*. Can. J. Microbiol. **16:**535–544.

69. **Tauber, J. W., M. J. Polley, and J. B. Zabriskie.** 1976. Nonspecific complement activation by streptococcal structures. II. Properdin-independent initiation of the alternate pathway. J. Exp. Med. **143:**1352–1366.

70. **Ueda, K., S. Yamayaki, and S. Someya.** 1975. Hyporeactivity to tuberculin in germ-free mice. RES J. Reticuloendothel. Soc. **18:**107–117.

71. **Unni, K. K., K. E. Holley, F. C. McDuffie, and J. L. Titus.** 1975. Comparative study of NZB mice under germfree and conventional conditions. J. Rheumatol. **2:**36–44.

72. **Waaij, D. van der, and C. A. Sturm.** 1968. Antibiotic decontamination of the digestive tract of mice. Technical procedures. Lab. Animal Care **18:**1–10.

73. **Wolstenholme, G. E. W., and J. Knight.** 1973. Immunopotentiation. Elsevier, Amsterdam.

Components of *Bordetella pertussis* That Modulate the Immune Response

STEPHEN I. MORSE

State University of New York, Downstate Medical Center, Brooklyn, New York 11203

INTRODUCTION

During recent years, there has been an increasing interest in *Bordetella pertussis*. The interest has not centered on the pathogenetic features of the organism, even though it is clear that we are virtually completely ignorant of these, and even though the vaccine in current use, although effective in preventing disease in infants, is exceedingly crude and by no means free from side effects. Rather, most experimental studies have been concerned with the manifold biological effects which are produced in experimental animals by phase I *B. pertussis* cells, extracts, or supernatant fluids from liquid cultures. Some of these effects are listed in Fig. 1, and information pertaining to many of them can be found in several recent reviews (9, 10; S. I. Morse, Adv. Appl. Microbiol., in press). The main interest in our laboratory has been the nature of the lymphocytosis-promoting factor (LPF), the mechanism by which it causes lymphocytosis, and the relationship of LPF to other phenomena produced by the organism.

HEMATOLOGICAL EFFECTS OF LPF

In addition to the characteristic clinical manifestations of paroxysmal coughing punctuated by an inspiratory "whoop," elevation of the lymphocyte count is a striking feature in many patients with clinical whooping cough. This phenomenon was first noted by Frölich in 1897 (2), but until comparatively recently the dynamics of this change in the circulation have not been clearly understood. It should be noted that the cells appearing in the blood of patients with pertussis possess normal morphology, and immature or atypical lymphocytes are not present. The hematological changes are therefore markedly different from those found in infectious mononucleosis.

Lymphocytosis can be produced with killed *B. pertussis* cells or products of *B. pertussis* in a variety of experimental animals including mice, rats, rabbits, guinea pigs, horses, cows, and sheep. In our studies, we have utilized the mouse as the experimental animal, and in earlier experiments we induced lymphocytosis in these animals with intact phase I cells. More recently, we have used culture supernatant fluids, and this material has served as a starting point for purification of active LPF.

When *B. pertussis* cells are injected intravenously into mice, lymphocytosis appears as early as several hours after inoculation, but peak values are not reached until 3 to 5 days later (4). At the height of the reaction, the total white blood cell count may exceed 200,000 cells per mm^3, and 60 to 70% of the cells are mature-appearing small lymphocytes. Over the course of the next 2 weeks, the leukocyte count gradually falls to normal. A polymorphonuclear leukocytosis also occurs, and studies in which purified LPF was used have indicated that this phenomenon is indeed a property of LPF and not of another product such as endotoxin.

In recent years, the pertussis syndrome with lymphocytosis has been ascribed to virus infection in a number of patients from whom *B. pertussis* could not be isolated. It has therefore been suggested that *B. pertussis* may activate certain viral agents and that it is these latter which are responsible for the disease. However, the results in experimental animals would seem to indicate that, although other agents may produce the events seen in whooping cough, in some instances *B. pertussis* itself can induce lymphocytosis.

MECHANISM OF THE LYMPHOCYTOSIS

Our earlier studies suggested that the lymphocytosis was due to a redistribution of lymphocytes from lymphoid organs into the blood rather than to a sudden increase in proliferation resulting in enlargement of the total pool of lymphocytes. Several lines of evidence support the redistribution hypothesis. (i) Histological examination of tissues from animals undergoing pertussis-induced lymphocytosis revealed depletion of lymphoid elements from the lymphoid organs. Moreover, there was no histological evidence of proliferative changes (4). (ii) When

374

mice were injected with tritiated thymidine during the course of pertussis-induced lymphocytosis, the extent of labeling of cells in the blood of these animals was essentially the same as that found in normal animals injected with tritiated thymidine according to the same schedule (8). (iii) Despite the fact that there was a 10-fold or greater increase in the number of circulating lymphocytes in the experimental animals, the outflow from the thoracic duct, which one would expect to be high if the recirculating pathway of lymphocytes was normal, was in fact considerably diminished with respect to cell concentration and total output of lymphocytes over 24 h (7). Taken together, these data suggested that the lymphocytosis was related to the inability of circulating lymphocytes to "home" from the blood into lymphoid tissues at a normal rate. The question of the rate and routes of egress of cells from the lymphoid tissue into blood has not been completely resolved, although Rai and his associates (13) have shown a marked outpouring of lymphocytes from the spleen shortly after the injection of supernatant fluids from *B. pertussis* cultures.

The reduced capacity of lymphocytes in pertussis-treated animals to "home" was also shown by cross-transfusion experiments of lymphocytes labeled with tritiated uridine (5). In addition, lymphocytes incubated with crude preparations of LPF showed a reduced ability to exit from the blood after tranfusion (15).

However, there still remain questions as to whether the primary effect of LPF is on the lymphocyte itself. Thus, it has been shown that LPF will bind to a variety of cells and tissues and, more importantly, that it readily elutes spontaneously with maintenance of biological activity (1).

Another unanswered question is whether the lymphocytes in pertussis-treated animals maintain their functional capacity for such reactions as graft-versus-host and delayed skin sensitivity, although preliminary observations would suggest that at least some of these functional capabilities may be retained (12).

ISOLATION AND PROPERTIES OF LPF

LPF has been isolated in a highly purified state from culture supernatant fluids of phase I *B. pertussis* (6). LPF migrates as a single band in 5% acrylamide gels at pH 4.5. After dissociation by sodium dodecyl sulfate and 2-mercaptoethanol, four polypeptides are detected with molecular weights of 13,400, 17,400, 19,300, and 23,500. The molecular weight of LPF as determined by this procedure and by its behavior in molecular sieving is approximately

In Vivo

1. Clinical whooping cough
2. Sensitization to the lethal effects of histamine, serotonin, and nonspecific stresses
3. Hypoglycemia and unresponsiveness to the hyperglycemic effect of epinephrine
4. Leukocytosis with a predominating lymphocytosis
5. Adjuvanticity
   a. Humoral antibody formation including reaginic antibody
   b. Cell-mediated immunity
6. Acute toxicity
   a. Heat-labile toxin
   b. Endotoxin

In Vitro

1. Inhibition of the cyclic AMP response of human lymphocytes to isoproterenol and prostaglandin E_1
2. Proliferation of murine T cells and human peripheral blood lymphocytes

FIG. 1. *Partial list of the effects of phase I* Bordetella pertussis *cells and products*.

73,000. When high-resolution electron microscopic techniques are used with negatively stained preparations, LPF appears as round particles which are usually ring-shaped and which have a diameter of 7.5 to 8.0 nm. There appear to be four to five round subunits measuring 2.8 nm in diameter in each ring.

The kinetics of the changes in the leukocyte counts of mice injected with purified LPF are quite similar to those obtained with partially purified preparations. In particular, polymorphonuclear leukocytosis was noted as well as lymphocytosis, indicating that this phenomenon is indeed a property of the LPF itself.

With the use of purified LPF, it was also possible to show clearly that there is an increase in both circulating T and B cells although the T cells predominate. In addition, LPF causes a lymphocytosis in "nude" mice which lack mature T cells.

RELATIONSHIP OF LPF TO OTHER BIOLOGICAL EFFECTS OF *B. PERTUSSIS*

The ability of *B. pertussis* to sensitize mice and other rodents to the lethal effects of histamine has been known for some 30 years. This phenomenon has been attributed to the histamine-sensitizing factor (HSF), but HSF has not been obtained in pure form. Our studies indicate that purified LPF is identical to HSF, and in the case of CF-1 mice as little as 0.01 µg will sensitize 50% of mice to the lethal effect of 1 mg of histamine (6). Normal CF-1 mice are resistant to 10 mg of the amine.

Another of the striking effects of *B. pertussis* is the production of hypoglycemia and unresponsiveness to the hyperglycemic effect of epinephrine. This effect of *B. pertussis* has been attributed to a beta adrenergic blockade which in turn is thought to be mediated by inhibition of cyclic AMP formation. Indeed, Parker and Morse, using partially purified LPF, showed that the increment in cyclic AMP which normally occurs in human lymphocytes after incubation with beta adrenergic agonists such as isoproterenol or with prostaglandin E_1 is inhibited (11). In mice it has been found that fasting hypoglycemia can be induced by as little as 0.02 μg of LPF and that unresponsiveness to epinephrine-induced hyperglycemia also occurs (6).

The peak times of lymphocytosis, histamine sensitization, and epinephrine unresponsiveness all occur some 3 to 5 days after inoculation of LPF. All effects can be produced by material eluted from the single band on polyacrylamide electrophoresis, and all can be blocked by a monospecific antiserum to LPF. Thus, these three markedly disparate reactions are all induced by a single substance.

It has been suggested by others that LPF is also responsible for the enhanced production of reaginic antibody which occurs after injection of *B. pertussis* or its products (3). Tada and co-workers have hypothesized that the lymphocytosis is responsible for this phenomenon by virtue of preventing suppressor cells from exerting their effects on the production of reaginic antibody (14). We have not thus far tested purified LPF for this property.

IN VITRO EFFECTS OF LPF ON MURINE LYMPHOCYTES: MITOGENICITY AND PRODUCTION OF CYTOTOXIC LYMPHOCYTES

In association with A. S. Kong, I have examined the in vitro effects of LPF on murine lymphocytes (A. S. Kong and S. I. Morse, J. Exp. Med., in press). We found that LPF is markedly mitogenic for spleen and lymph node cells. The extent of the reaction is greater than that achieved with optimal doses of phytohemagglutinin (PHA) and approaches or equals that induced by concanavalin A (ConA). Normal thymocytes do not proliferate in response to LPF but cortisone-resistant thymocytes do. Bone marrow cells, however, are unresponsive.

Pretreatment of lymph node or spleen cell cultures with Thy-1 (theta) antiserum abrogates the mitogenic effect of LPF. Moreover, Thy-1 antiserum in the presence of complement destroys the blast cells. In addition, the electron microscopic appearance of the stimulated cells is characteristic of T-cell blasts, and, in contrast to B-cell blasts, dilated rough endoplasmic reticulum is not seen. Thus, the evidence clearly indicates that LPF is a T-cell mitogen. The inability to stimulate normal thymocytes differentiates LPF activity from that of ConA, and the responsiveness of DBA/2J spleen cells to LPF but not to PHA differentiates these two mitogens. In addition, the receptors for LPF appear to be different from those for PHA and ConA.

Although LPF is clearly a T-cell mitogen, an accessory cell is required for the mitogenic effects. Thus, murine spleen cell populations enriched for T cells by removing aherent cells through passage over a nylon-wool column respond poorly. Addition of the adherent cell population to the nonadherent cell population results in restoration of full mitogen response. The nature of the accessory cell is not fully defined. However, it cannot be substituted for by peritoneal macrophages, or by 2-mercaptoethanol. In addition, removal of phagocytic cells from spleen cell suspensions does not diminish the mitogenic response. The accessory cell is also not an adherent T cell. It remains to be determined whether the accessory cell is a B cell or is a thus far unrecognized or null cell.

It is unlikely that the mitogenic effect of LPF is dependent upon the presence of lymphocytes previously sensitized to components or products of *B. pertussis* or to antigens cross-reactive with LPF. The magnitude of response is far greater than that generally seen with sensitized T cells stimulated by antigen. In addition, lymphoid cells from a variety of different mouse strains react to approximately the same extent. Furthermore, spleen cells from germfree mice are fully reactive, and, although it is still possible that such animals were sensitized to cross-reactive antigens in food or by viral components which were cross-reactive, such could not be demonstrated by serological methods with the use of high-titer LPF antiserum. Human lymphocytes have been shown to be stimulated by LPF in vitro, and the extent of stimulation is the same irrespective of a past history of immunization against whooping cough or occurrence of a natural disease (J. H. Morse et al., in preparation). More importantly, cord blood lymphocytes proliferated to the same extent as did lymphocytes from adults.

In the basic system utilized to test for the production of cytotoxic lymphocytes in response to LPF, a chromium release assay was used with CBA spleen cells as effector cells and P815 mastocytoma cells as target cells. The major histocompatibility antigen for CBA mice is H-2k, whereas the mastocytoma target cells are derived from DBA/2(H-2d) mice. When CBA spleen cells had been incubated for 72 h in the presence of LPF, there was 78% specific lysis at an effector-to-target-cell ratio of 30:1. Under the same conditions but with the mitogen not present in the assay system, spleen cells incubated with ConA exhibited only 23% specific lysis and those incubated with PHA showed less than 10% specific lysis of the P815 cells. In all cases the amount of mitogen utilized gave a maximal proliferative response. However, in the case of LPF, time-course studies indicated that the maturation of cytotoxic cells did not parallel the proliferative response. Thus, after 48 h of incubation of CBA spleen cells in the presence of LPF, proliferation was readily observed. However, cytotoxicity could not be detected in 48-h cultures but was first present at 72 h. It was of note that LPF antiserum added at the beginning of the period of assay for cytotoxic cells nullified the activity of the killer cells, whereas there was no effect of normal rabbit serum. LPF antiserum did not affect the efficacy of killer cells generated in a mixed lymphocyte interaction.

Not only did LPF cause the production in vitro of lymphocytes cytotoxic for allogeneic cells, but the same was true with respect to syngeneic cells. Thus, cytotoxic spleen cells were generated both from BALB/c(H-2d) spleen cells, which carry an H-2 antigen identical to that of P815 mastocytoma cells although there is an M-locus difference, and from syngeneic DBA/2 spleen cells.

RELATIONSHIP BETWEEN IN VITRO AND IN VIVO EFFECTS OF LPF

As noted above, there is no evidence of lymphocyte proliferation when lymphocytosis is induced in vivo by LPF, whereas proliferation is evident in vitro. The most reasonable explanation for this discrepancy relates to the dosage of LPF required. Thus, the optimal dose for production of lymphocytosis in vivo is between 0.5 and 1.5 μg per mouse; at doses greater than 2 μg toxicity may be seen. In contrast, the optimal dose for in vitro proliferation of 5 $\times$ 10^5 lymphocytes is 0.5 μg of LPF. Considering the blood volume of the mouse and the fact that LPF binds to a variety of tissues and cells, it is likely that the effective dose normally employed for lymphocytosis is too small to induce proliferation. The same, of course, is true with respect to the generation of cytotoxic lymphocytes. However, it is possible that, under certain circumstances in natural infection, local production and concentration of

LPF might occur and cause alterations in lymphocyte function.

It is most likely true that a single fundamental effect of LPF is responsible for the diverse in vitro and in vivo reactions which occur, but the nature of this activity, which may relate to cyclic nucleotides, remains to be elucidated.

ACKNOWLEDGMENT

These studies were supported by Public Health Service grant AI-09683 from the National Institute of Allergy and Infectious Diseases.

LITERATURE CITED

1. **Adler, A., and S. I. Morse.** 1973. Interaction of lymphoid and nonlymphoid cells with the lymphocytosis-promoting factor of *Bordetella pertussis*. Infect. Immun. 7:461–467.
2. **Frölich, J.** 1897. Beitrag zue Pathologie des Keuchustens. J. Kinderkrankh. 44:53–58.
3. **Lehrer, S. B., E. M. Tan, and J. H. Vaughan.** 1974. Extraction and partial purification of the histamine-sensitizing factor of *Bordetella pertussis*. J. Immunol. 113:18–26.
4. **Morse, S. I.** 1965. Studies on the lymphocytosis induced in mice by *Bordetella pertussis*. J. Exp. Med. 121:49–68.
5. **Morse, S. I., and B. A. Barron.** 1970. Studies on the leukocytosis and lymphocytosis induced by *Bordetella pertussis*. III. The distribution of transfused lymphocytes in pertussis-treated and normal mice. J. Exp. Med. 132:663–672.
6. **Morse, S. I., and J. H. Morse.** 1976. Isolation and properties of the leukocytosis- and lymphocytosis-promoting factor of *Bordetella pertussis*. J. Exp. Med. 143:1483–1502.
7. **Morse, S. I., and S. K. Riester.** 1967. Studies on the leukocytosis and lymphocytosis induced by *Bordetella pertussis*. II. The effects of pertussis vaccine on the thoracic duct lymph and lymphocytes of mice. J. Exp. Med. 125:619–628.
8. **Morse, S. I., and S. K. Riester.** 1967. Studies on the leukocytosis and lymphocytosis induced by *Bordetella pertussis*. I. Radioautographic analysis of the circulating cells in mice undergoing pertussis-induced hyperleukocytosis. J. Exp. Med. 125:401–408.
9. **Munoz, J.** 1971. Protein toxins from *Bordetella pertussis*, p. 271–300. *In* S. Kadis, T. C. Montie, and S. J. Ajl (ed.), Microbial toxins, vol. 2A. Academic Press Inc., New York.
10. **Olson, L. C.** 1975. Pertussis. Medicine 54:427–469.
11. **Parker, C. W., and S. I. Morse.** 1973. The effect of *Bordetella pertussis* on lymphocyte cyclic AMP metabolism. J. Exp. Med. 137:1078–1090.
12. **Phanuphak, P., J. W. Moorhead, and H. N. Claman.** 1972. Immunologic activities of pertussis-treated lymphocytes. Int. Arch. Allergy Appl. Immunol. 43:305–316.
13. **Rai, K. R., A. D. Chanana, E. P. Cronkite, D. D. Joel, and J. B. Stevens.** 1971. Studies on lymphocytes. XVIII. Mechanism of lymphocytosis induced by supernatant fluids of *Bordetella pertussis*. Blood 38:49–59.
14. **Tada, T. K., T. Okumura, T. Ochiai, and S. Isasa.** 1972. Effect of lymphocytosis-promoting factor of *Bordetella pertussis* on the immune response. II. Adjuvant effect for the production of reaginic antibody in the rat. Int. Arch. Allergy Appl. Immunol. 43:207–216.
15. **Taub, R. N., W. Rosett, A. Adler, and S. I. Morse.** 1972. Distribution of labelled lymph node cells in mice during the lymphocytosis induced by *Bordetella pertussis*. J. Exp. Med. 136:1581–1593.

Cholera Enterotoxin-Induced Suppression of Effector T-Cell Function In Vivo and In Vitro[1]

CHRISTOPHER S. HENNEY AND FREDRICA M. WITZKE

Department of Medicine, Johns Hopkins University School of Medicine, and O'Neill Memorial Research Laboratories, Good Samaritan Hospital, Baltimore, Maryland 21239

The enterotoxin of *Vibrio cholerae* causes augmentation of cyclic $3',5'$-adenosine monophosphate (cAMP) levels in a wide variety of cell types (1, 14, 17, 18), including gut mucosa, where this action is thought to be the pathogenic basis of cholera (10). In lymphoid cell populations, elevation of cAMP levels by cholera toxin (CT) is characterized by: (i) a delayed onset— cAMP levels do not rise significantly until 1 to 2 h after addition of the enterotoxin (13); (ii) a protracted time course—increased cAMP levels are maintained for many hours (7); and (iii) specific antagonism by antitoxin serum and by a choleragenoid preparation which lacks the biological activity of the parent compound (13). The first two of these parameters distinguish the effects of CT on lymphocyte cyclic nucleotide levels from changes induced by other "cAMP-active" drugs such as isoproterenol, which initiate only rapid (1 to 3 min) and transient (10 to 20 min) changes in cAMP levels (5).

Because lymphocyte cAMP levels stay elevated for prolonged periods after CT treatment, we considered the toxin to be a useful reagent to probe the role of cyclic nucleotides in antigen-induced T-cell differentiation and in the efferent arm of the cell-mediated immune response. Our particular interest centered on the production and function of cytolytically active T lymphocytes, cells which are thought to be centrally involved in allograft rejection and which may aid in the destruction of neoplastic tissue (2).

Our initial investigations focused on the fully differentiated effector cell and the mechanism by which this cell exerts its lytic function (5, 6). It is a common working hypothesis that killer T cells effect cytolysis by secreting a lytic mediator (6). We reasoned that modulation of cyclic nucleotide levels might interfere with the secretory processes of T cells, as it does in many other cell types, and thus affect cytolysis.

When isoproterenol, theophylline, or the prostaglandins E1 and E2 were added to cultures containing killer and target cells, cytolysis was suppressed (2, 5, 11). The inhibition observed was linearly related to drug dose. There was, furthermore, an excellent inverse correlation between augmented cAMP levels in the lymphoid cells and inhibition of lysis; when cAMP levels returned to base line, the lytic activity of the effector cells was fully restored. (See 5 and 12 for detailed review of these findings.)

The principal weakness of these studies from a mechanistic standpoint was that the continued presence of drug was required for lysis to be suppressed. Thus, it was impossible to determine whether the suppression was due to inhibited effector cell function or to a cAMP-induced "resistance" of the target cell to lytic attack. The relative irreversibility of action of cholera enterotoxin enabled this issue to be resolved. Target cells treated with CT showed elevated cAMP levels but were as susceptible to lysis as untreated controls. In contrast, effector cell populations treated with CT were unable to lyse target cells (13). As effector T-cell populations ceased to lyse target cells during that period when their cAMP levels were raised, we asked whether administration of CT might be capable of compromising effector cell function in vivo.

EFFECT OF CT ON THE IMMUNE RESPONSE TO ALLOGENEIC TUMOR CELLS

Cholera enterotoxin (1 μg) was administered intraperitoneally (i.p.) to adult C57BL/6 mice, within 1 h of administration of 10^7 DBA/2 mastocytoma cells to the same site. Other groups of mice were given the same dose of antigen but were given CT only 4, 7, or 10 days later. Pooled spleen cell suspensions were made from each group (six mice/group) 11 days after alloantigenic stimulation, and the cytolytic activity of these populations towards ^{51}Cr-labeled DBA/2 mastocytoma cells was assessed (4). Typical results are shown in Fig. 1. Cholera enterotoxin administration at the time of immun-

[1] Communication no. 260 from the O'Neill Memorial Research Laboratories.

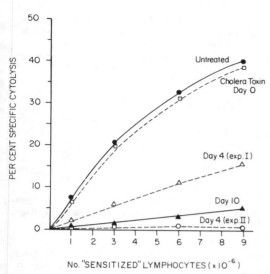

FIG. 1. *Effect of in vivo administration of cholera enterotoxin on the cell-mediated immune response to allogeneic cells. The lytic activity of spleen cell suspensions from adult C57BL/6 mice 11 days after antigenic challenge with 10^7 DBA/2 mastocytoma cells i.p. is shown. Animals received either antigen (untreated) or a dose (1 μg) of cholera toxin. Choleragen was given on the day of antigenic challenge (day 0), on day 4, or on day 10. The assay employed a 4-h incubation of various numbers of immune spleen cells with 10^5 ^{51}Cr-labeled mastocytoma cells.*

ization with DBA/2 mastocytoma cells had no effect on the subsequent development of cytolytically active cells in the spleen. When choleragen was given 4 days after antigen, however, a marked suppression of cytolytic activity was observed, ranging between 70 and 100% suppression in four experiments. Cholera toxin administration on day 7, 8, or 9 after antigen challenge invariably resulted in a complete inhibition of cytolytic activity as assessed in vitro on day 11.

The suppression of cytolytic activity by CT treatment 7 to 10 days after alloantigen would seem to be directly related to elevated cAMP levels in the differentiated effector cell population. This implies that, under these conditions, effector cell differentiation occurs normally but the functioning of these cells is inhibited.

Suppression by administration of choleragen on day 4 (Fig. 1), however, may be due to inhibition of antigen-induced clonal proliferation, for several investigations have recently shown that mitogen-induced lymphocyte transformation is inhibited by agents that elevate cAMP levels (8, 16). Alternatively, or additionally, it may be that increased cAMP levels 4 and 5 days after antigenic stimulation, a time

of rapid cellular proliferation, cause lysis of newly differentiated cells, a phenomenon recently described with cultured lymphoma cells by Daniel et al. (3).

Varying the i.p. dose of cholera enterotoxin given on day 10 demonstrated that a partial (30 to 40%) suppression of cytolytic activity, measured in vitro 24 h later, could be accomplished with as little as 0.01 μg of toxin.

Administration of cholera toxin i.p. in quantities up to 1 μg had no effect either on lymphoid cell numbers (spleen or axillary nodes) or on cell viability as assessed by vital dye exclusion tests. When larger doses (4 μg) of CT were employed, however, evidence of cellular depletion, particularly in the splenic lymphoid cell pool, was observed.

Although CT has been established as an immunogen (15), none of the regimens which we employed led to detectable antibody formation, despite the fact that the antibody assay system used (reversal of the toxin-induced inhibition of histamine release) was capable of detecting antitoxin antibody in nanogram amounts (13).

As cholera enterotoxin caused a profound suppression of the immune response to allogeneic cell suspensions, similar studies were made employing skin allografts as antigen.

EFFECT OF CT ON THE REJECTION OF SKIN ALLOGRAFTS

Because of the marked suppression of the immune response to allogeneic cell suspensions, similar studies were carried out with DBA/2 skin allografts as antigen. Cholera enterotoxin (1 μg) was given i.p. on the day of grafting or

TABLE 1. *Effect of cholera toxin on immune responses in C57BL/6 mice to DBA/2 allografts*

Cholera toxin (days after allografting)[a]	Cytolytic activity[b]		Graft rejection[c] (day)
	Spleen	Draining nodes	
None	12.7	22.0	8–9
0	<2	<2	8–10
2	<2	Not tested	8
4	<2	4.0	7–8

[a] The dose was 1 μg intraperitoneally. Day 0 was the day of the graft.

[b] Percent specific cytolysis of 10^5 DBA/2 mastocytoma cells in 4 h at 37°C by 5.0×10^6 lymphoid cells. Pooled cell suspensions (four animals) were used; values given are means of triplicate assays. Replicate assays varied less than ±5% of value shown.

[c] Range of time for skin allograft rejection. The values given represent at least 20 animals for each suppressive regimen employed. The normal values represent >50 grafts.

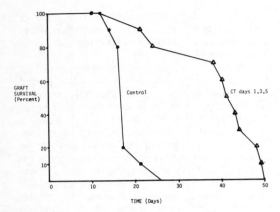

FIG. 2. *Effect of cholera toxin (CT) on skin graft rejection across the H-7 barrier. B10C(47N)Sn ♀ mice were grafted with C57BL/10J ♀ skin. Groups of 20 mice were either untreated (control) or given 0.1 μg of CT intravenously on days 1, 3, and 5. Graft survival was then followed.*

TABLE 2. *Effect of various cholera enterotoxin dose regimens on skin allograft survival [B10C(47N)Sn ♀ skin grafted on C57BL/10J ♀ mice][a]*

Cholera toxin given on day:	Mean graft survival time ± SD (days)
None	18 ± 2
−1	30 ± 12
0	30 ± 14
+1	28 ± 11
+1+3	28 ± 12
+1+3+5	40 ± 8
+1+3+5+7	33 ± 15

[a] The dose of cholera toxin was 0.1 μg intravenously. Each group represents 10 animals. Day 0 was the day of the graft.

on day 1, 2, or 4 thereafter. Spleens, and in some experiments draining lymph nodes, were obtained on day 11, and the cytolytic activity of these populations was assessed against ^{51}Cr-labeled DBA/2 mastocytoma cells.

Marked to complete suppression of the cell-mediated immune response was observed in treated animals (Table 1). Graft prolongation was not, however, consistently observed. Larger (5 to 10 μg) doses of cholera toxin given intra-peritoneally on the day of grafting also failed to cause significant prolongation of skin allograft survival and were often toxic, profoundly depressing circulating leukocyte counts for several days. No leukopenia was observed following the 1-μg doses of CT.

In further attempts to demonstrate prolongation of skin allograft survival after CT administration, we sought strains of mice which differed only at minor histocompatibility loci. We chose to graft B10C(47N)Sn ♀ skin onto C57BL/10J ♀ mice, a strain combination which is identical at the H-2 locus but differs at H-7. One set of 20 mice received 0.1 μg of CT intravenously on days 1, 3, and 5 after grafting. In a control series 20 grafted animals were left untreated. Graft survival was then followed. As can be seen (Fig. 2), graft survival in CT-treated mice was significantly longer than in the un-treated series. Indeed, by day 21 after grafting, 18 of 20 (90%) of the control series had rejected their grafts, whereas among the CT-treated animals only 2 of 20 (10%) showed rejection. The mean graft survival time for the CT-treated animals (43 days) was more than twice that of untreated animals (17 days). We have also observed significant prolongation of

B10C(47N)Sn skin grafts on C57BL/10J mice using other CT administration regimens (Table 2). None of these CT doses caused any overt toxicity, nor did they affect circulating leukocyte levels.

Although we found that CT caused significant prolongation of primary graft survival, re-grafted animals showed second-set rejections. Animals, who had received an initial graft and then CT treatment 1, 3, and 5 days later, and who had shown a mean graft survival time of 43 days, were regrafted on day 75. The mean survival time of secondary grafts was 11 ± 1 days. Untreated control animals in whom the primary grafts had survived 17 days, and who

TABLE 3. *Effect of cAMP-active drugs on antigen-induced differentiation of memory to killer cells (C57BL/6 anti-DBA/2)[a]*

Drug in culture[b]	Cytolytic index after 48 h with antigen[c]
None	0.9
	(no antigen)
None	21.4
PGE$_1$	1.2
PGF1α	19.9
Dibutyryl cAMP	2.8
Cholera toxin	0.8

[a] C57BL/6 mice were immunized with 10^7 P815 cells intraperitoneally, and spleens were collected 61 days later. These cells had no demonstrable lytic activity towards homologous (^{51}Cr-labeled P815) cells.

[b] Spleen cells were cultured in the presence of mitomycin C-treated P815 cells and one of the following drugs: 10^{-5} M PGE$_1$, 10^{-5} M PGF1α; 10^{-4} M dibutyryl cAMP, or 100 ng of cholera toxin. The cytolytic activity of the cultures was assessed 48 h later.

[c] The values given are a relative index of the amount of cytolytic activity present in the cultures. See reference 9 for further details of this index.

were also regrafted on day 75, rejected secondary grafts in 12 ± 1 days. We have not yet investigated whether the second-set rejections can be inhibited by renewed CT administration.

Although these studies suggested that T-cell memory was not impaired in CT-treated animals, other investigations showed that the antigen-induced differentiation of memory cells into killer cells could be suppressed by CT.

EFFECT OF CT ON MEMORY CELL DIFFERENTIATION IN VITRO

Spleen cells obtained later than 30 days after alloimmunization showed little or no cytolytic activity towards homologous target cells (9). Within 48 h of exposure to alloantigen in vitro, however, marked cytolytic activity was demonstrable (9). Antigen induction of killer cells under these conditions was independent of cell proliferation (9). We investigated the possibility that CT and a number of other "cAMP-active" drugs might be able to modulate differentiation. Typical results are shown in Table 3. As can be seen, a number of drugs inhibited the "conversion" of memory to killer cells. The spectrum of drugs found capable of preventing differentiation suggested that inhibition was due to elevated cAMP levels in the memory cell population. Thus, inhibition was noted with dibutyryl cAMP, with CT, and with prostaglandin E_1 (PGE$_1$), all of which have adenylate cyclase stimulatory activities (13), but not with a prostaglandin congener, PGF1α, which does not stimulate adenylate cyclase.

It would thus appear that cholera enterotoxin can effect "immunosuppression" by inhibiting the antigen-induced proliferation and differentiation of T-cell populations as well as by interfering with the activity of fully differentiated effector T cells. In all cases, suppression appears to be due to the capacity of CT to stimulate membrane-associated adenylate cyclase. Although the evidence for this assertion is indirect, and will continue to be so until such time as homogeneous effector and memory cell populations can be isolated, the specificity of the drugs used and the excellent temporal relationship between elevated cAMP levels and compromised functions make it extremely likely. The molecular nature of the linkage between augmented cAMP levels and the inhibited functions is at present unclear.

ACKNOWLEDGMENTS

Richard Finkelstein, Southwestern Medical School, Dallas, Tex., kindly provided the cholera enterotoxin and toxoid samples used in this study.

This work was supported by Public Health Service grants AI 10280 and AI 11334 from the National Institute of Allergy and Infectious Diseases. C.S.H. is recipient of Research Career Development Award AI 70393 from the National Institute of Allergy and Infectious Diseases.

LITERATURE CITED

1. **Bourne, H. R., R. I. Lehrer, L. M. Lichtenstein, G. Weissmann, and R. Zurier.** 1973. Effects of cholera enterotoxin on adenosine 3',5'-monophosphate and neutrophil function. Comparison with other compounds which stimulate leukocyte adenyl cyclase. J. Clin. Invest. **52:**698–708.

2. **Cerottini, J.-C., and K. T. Brunner.** 1974. Cell-mediated cytotoxicity, allograft rejection, and tumor immunity. Adv. Immunol. **18:**67–132.

3. **Daniel, V., G. Litwack, and G. M. Tompkins.** 1973. Induction of cytolysis of cultured lymphoma cells by adenosine 3',5'-cyclic monophosphate and the isolation of resistant variants. Proc. Natl. Acad. Sci. U.S.A. **70:**76–79.

4. **Henney, C. S.** 1971. Quantitation of the cell-mediated immune response. I. The number of cytolytically active mouse lymphoid cells induced by immunization with allogeneic mastocytoma cells. J. Immunol. **107:**1558–1566.

5. **Henney, C. S., H. R. Bourne, and L. M. Lichtenstein.** 1972. The role of cyclic 3',5'-adenosine monophosphate in the cytolytic activity of lymphocytes. J. Immunol. **108:**1526–1534.

6. **Henney, C. S., and J. E. Bubbers.** 1973. Antigen-T lymphocyte interactions: inhibition by cytochalasin B. J. Immunol. **111:**85–90.

7. **Henney, C. S., L. M. Lichtenstein, E. Gillespie, and R. T. Rolley.** 1973. In vivo suppression of the immune response to alloantigen by cholera enterotoxin. J. Clin. Invest. **52:**2853–2857.

8. **Hirschorn, R., J. Grossman, and G. Weissman.** 1970. Effect of cyclic 3',5'-adenosine monophosphate and theophylline on lymphocyte transformation. Proc. Soc. Exp. Biol. Med. **133:**1361–1365.

9. **Kamat, R., and C. S. Henney.** 1976. Studies on T cell clonal expansion. II. The in vitro differentiation of pre-killer and memory T cells. J. Immunol. **116:**1490–1495.

10. **Kimberg, D. V., M. Field, J. Johnson, A. Henderson, and E. Gershon.** 1971. Stimulation of intestinal mucosal adenyl cyclase by cholera enterotoxin and prostaglandins. J. Clin. Invest. **50:**1218–1230.

11. **Lichtenstein, L. M., E. Gillespie, H. R. Bourne, and C. S. Henney.** 1972. The effects of a series of prostaglandins on in vitro models of the allergic response and cellular immunity. Prostaglandins **2:**519–528.

12. **Lichtenstein, L. M., and C. S. Henney.** 1974. Adenylate cyclase-linked hormone receptors: an important mechanism for the immunoregulation of leukocytes. Prog. Immunol. **2:**73–83.

13. **Lichtenstein, L. M., C. S. Henney, H. R. Bourne, and W. B. Greenough III.** 1973. The effect of cholera enterotoxin on in vitro models of immediate and delayed hypersensitivity: further evidence for the role of cAMP. J. Clin. Invest. **52:**691–697.

14. **Pierce, N. F., W. B. Greenough III, and C. C. J. Carpenter, Jr.** 1971. Vibrio cholerae enterotoxin and its mode of action. Bacteriol. Rev. **35:**1–13.

15. **Pierce, N. F., E. A. Kaniecki, and R. S. Northrop.** 1972. Protection against experimental cholera by antitoxin. J. Infect. Dis. **126:**606–616.

16. **Smith, J. W., A. L. Steiner, and C. W. Parker.** 1971. Human lymphocyte metabolism. Effects on cyclic and non-cyclic nucleotides on stimulation by phytohemagglutinin. J. Clin. Invest. **50:**442–448.

17. **Vaughn, M., N. F. Pierce, and W. B. Greenough III.** 1970. Stimulation of glycerol production in fat cells by cholera toxin. Nature (London) **226:**658–659.

18. **Zieve, P. D., N. F. Pierce, and W. B. Greenough III.** 1971. Stimulation of glycogenolysis by purified cholera enterotoxin in disrupted cells. Johns Hopkins Med. J. **129:**299–303.

Depression of Cell-Mediated Immunity by Pretreatment with Adjuvants

G. L. ASHERSON

Clinical Research Centre, Division of Immunology, Harrow, Middlesex HA1 3UJ, England

INTRODUCTION

Lumsden (22) in 1949 in England and the Svet-Moldavskys (26) in 1958 in Russia found that guinea pigs injected with inert material in Freund complete adjuvant (FCA) failed to develop allergic encephalomyelitis when they were later injected with brain in FCA. This was the first of several descriptions of the ability of pretreatment with adjuvants to depress cell-mediated immunity.

The original workers suggested that the phenomenon might be due to damage to lymph nodes caused by pretreatment with adjuvant or to a form of "competition of antigen" due to the double exposure to tubercle bacillus in the FCA. Later workers noted that two factors were responsible for the depression of cell-mediated immunity: a reduction in the activity of effector T cells and an anti-inflammatory effect of FCA which limited skin reactions.

Recently, the discovery of several different suppressor or modulator cells which arise during normal immunization with contact sensitizing agents and antigen in FCA has suggested that pretreatment with FCA may depress cell-mediated immunity indirectly by acting as an adjuvant for modulator cells. Finally, work on the low-molecular-weight analogues of bacterial adjuvants has raised the possibility that macrophages or lymphocytes may have specific receptors for adjuvant and that the response of these cells may depend upon whether they first meet adjuvant alone or adjuvant together with antigen.

DEPRESSION OF AUTOIMMUNE DISEASE AND OF DELAYED AND CONTACT SENSITIVITY BY ADJUVANT

Kies and Alvord (19) in 1958 formally showed that pretreatment with FCA prevented the allergic encephalomyelitis which normally follows immunization with antigen in FCA. Janko-

vic (16) found a similar effect on autoimmune thyroiditis. He also showed that pretreatment with FCA limited the delayed hypersensitivity reactions normally produced by immunization with bovine gamma globulin and human serum albumin in FCA (17).

This phenomenon can be demonstrated in guinea pigs, rats, and mice (3), and with antigens such as serum albumin and globulin, azobenzenearsonate-N-acetyltyrosine (an antigen which is said not to elicit antibody formation [3]), and picryl chloride in FCA. Several different adjuvants can be used, including Freund-type (water-in-oil emulsion) adjuvant made with *Mycobacterium tuberculosis* or *Corynebacterium parvum* (3), and *C. parvum*, *C. granulosum* (27), and *Brucella abortus* (28). The phenomenon occurs shortly after the first injection of the adjuvant and can be demonstrated when the antigen in FCA is given 10 days later in the guinea pig and 6 days later in the rat (3).

DEPRESSION OF TUMOR AND GRAFT REJECTION AND OTHER ASPECTS OF CELL-MEDIATED IMMUNITY BY PRETREATMENT WITH ADJUVANTS

The use of BCG in the treatment of human tumors has led to considerable interest in the ability of bacterial adjuvants to depress tumor immunity. Pretreatment with BCG increases or depresses tumor resistance depending upon the precise timing of the injection and other factors. However, pretreatment with FCA has a more uniform effect in reducing tumor immunity (11, 23, 37, 38). The effect is produced only when FCA is given before the tumor, and it is associated with depressed skin reactions. This is not due to an anti-inflammatory effect, as the reaction to turpentine and local passive transfer is normal. It is probably due to an inhibition of the production of T effector cells, for the effect can be reversed by the injection of peritoneal exudate cells from immune guinea pigs (23). In mice the depression is associated with diminished lymph node cytotoxic activity (38).

BCG given intravenously facilitates rejection across a weak transplantation barrier when given 21 days beforehand but prolongs survival when two injections are given (39).

Resistance to experimental *Salmonella typhimurium* infection in mice is attributed to cell-mediated immunity. Injection of FCA followed by a vaccine increased the mortality on challenge as compared with no treatment, and it was suggested that this was due to depression of cell-mediated immunity (12).

SYNERGY BETWEEN THE DEPRESSION OF DELAYED HYPERSENSITIVITY CAUSED BY PRETREATMENT WITH ADJUVANT AND THE DEPRESSION CAUSED BY PRETREATMENT WITH ANTIGEN

There is an interesting synergy between the ability of antigen and adjuvant to depress delayed hypersensitivity. Pretreatment with antigen in the adult guinea pig depresses the delayed hypersensitivity which otherwise follows immunization with antigen in FCA. This is true whether the antigen is dissolved in saline (5, 14), precipitated with alum (14), or in Freund incomplete adjuvant (21). When alum-precipitated antigen is used, there is a selective depression of delayed hypersensitivity and gamma$_2$ hemolytic and cytophilic antibody, with normal or raised levels of total antibody and the antibody responsible for passive cutaneous anaphylaxis (5, 13). This selective depression of certain immune responses with retention of others is sometimes called immune deviation. Pretreatment with FCA also depresses delayed hypersensitivity. When guinea pigs are given separate injections of adjuvant and antigen before immunization with the same antigen in FCA, there is a synergic effect. For instance, in a particular experiment (3) antigen alone caused a depression of the mean diameter of the 24-h skin reaction to bovine gamma globulin of 25%; adjuvant alone caused a depression of 21%. However, the depression caused by both pretreatments was 76%. In contrast, the adjuvant had no effect on the depression of cytophilic or hemolytic antibody production caused by the pretreatment with antigen.

This phenomenon is of theoretical interest and raises the question whether pretreatment with FCA depresses delayed hypersensitivity by acting as an adjuvant for suppressor or modulator cells. According to this hypothesis, pretreatment with antigen as well as adjuvant should immunize the animal to develop modulator cells

which limit cell-mediated immunity (see below). The phenomenon may also be of practical importance, as nontoxic analogues of bacterial adjuvants are now available and might act synergically with antigen in depressing cell-mediated immunity.

MECHANISM OF DEPRESSION OF CELL-MEDIATED IMMUNITY BY ADJUVANT: ANTI-INFLAMMATORY EFFECT

It is useful to distinguish two different mechanisms for the depression of delayed hypersensitivity by pretreatment with adjuvant: (i) an anti-inflammatory effect which limits skin reactions, and (ii) a depression of the production of effector cells for delayed hypersensitivity.

There is good evidence that FCA can reduce certain skin reactions by acting on the inflammatory aspect of the response. For instance, the injection of FCA into guinea pigs depresses the passive local Arthus reaction. This is produced by injecting guinea pig serum intravenously and challenging locally (1). It is normally attributed to complement activation, chemotaxis of polymorphs, and the release of polymorph enzymes. Some of these enzymes are proteases which are inhibited by the various serum inhibitors of proteolytic enzymes, and it would be interesting to know which stage of this sequence was affected in recipients injected with FCA.

The injection of FCA into recipients also depresses passively transferred delayed hypersensitivity reactions. This is true in both guinea pigs and inbred rats. However, interpretation is complicated by the fact that the cells used for passive transfer were produced in animals immunized with bovine gamma globulin in FCA (and therefore sensitive to the tubercle bacillus) and were then injected into recipients given FCA.

There is some suggestion in the literature, by analogy with other agents, that FCA may have an anti-inflammatory effect because of its ability to cause local inflammation. For instance, a number of agents, such as carrageenan (9) and vitamin A (29), which affect macrophages and cause inflammation also block the delayed hypersensitivity reaction when given at the time of skin testing, and it has been suggested that agents of this type act in the rat by causing the production of a macrofetoprotein (30). Other workers have shown that the serum of animals bearing sponges depresses the tuberculin reaction when given at the time of skin testing (15). It is known that inflammation causes a rise in the serum inhibitors of proteolytic enzymes, and it would be interesting to know whether the serum factor acts in this way.

MECHANISM OF DEPRESSION OF CELL-MEDIATED IMMUNITY BY ADJUVANTS: LIMITATION OF THE PRODUCTION OF EFFECTOR CELLS

Passive transfer studies show that the peritoneal exudate cells of guinea pigs and rats pretreated with FCA have a reduced ability to transfer delayed hypersensitivity. In tumor systems there is evidence that these animals produce fewer cytotoxic cells (38) and that their defect can be reversed by immune peritoneal exudate cells (23). These findings indicate that pretreatment with FCA limits the production of effector cells for cell-mediated immunity. An alternative view is that effector cells are produced but their action is masked by the presence of suppressor cells. The rest of this discussion will consider the mechanisms which may be responsible for the limited production of effector cells.

Role of Damage Caused by Adjuvant

There are several possible explanations of the ability of pretreatment with FCA to depress the production of effector cells. Some workers have suggested that the depression is related to the antigen being injected with FCA. This is probably not a general explanation, as the phenomenon can be elicited in tumor systems (11, 23, 38). It seems unlikely that the phenomenon is due to gross morphological damage to the lymphoid system caused by pretreatment with adjuvant, because pretreatment with FCA (3) or *C. parvum* either has no effect or increases the antibody response to subsequent immunization (32).

Role of Lymphocyte Trapping

Another possibility is that pretreatment with FCA depresses the production of effector cells because recirculating lymphocytes are trapped in the nodes affected by the first injection of FCA and are unavailable to move to the nodes draining the site of injection with antigen in FCA. In fact, the arrival of ^{51}Cr-labeled lymphocytes in the lymph nodes draining the site of injection of antigen in FCA is depressed in mice previously injected with FCA on the other site. However, the effect is small and probably unimportant (2).

Role of Receptor Site for Adjuvant

Another possibility is that pretreatment with adjuvant makes the subset of T cells responsible for cell-mediated immunity unresponsive. This concept may be introduced by summarizing the evidence that T cells (or macrophages) have a receptor for bacterial cell wall adjuvants. This is suggested by the finding that N-acetylmuramyl-L-alanine-D-isoglutamine, which is a synthetic analogue of the basic unit of the bacterial cell wall, is an adjuvant for antibody production when injected in saline and for delayed hypersensitivity when mixed with antigen and injected in a water-in-oil emulsion (Freund incomplete adjuvant) (8). Replacement of the L-alanine by D-alanine gives rise to an analogue which inhibits the action of the active material, and this suggests that there is a special receptor for the basic molecular configuration (personal communication). Bretscher and Cohn (10) and others (31) have suggested that the condition for immunization is that the lymphocyte should be presented with both the relevant antigenic determinants and a nonspecific or specific second signal and that exposure to antigen alone provides the signal for unresponsiveness or perhaps for the production of suppressor cells. A modification of this hypothesis suggests that antigen together with adjuvant causes delayed hypersensitivity, whereas exposure to adjuvant alone causes unresponsiveness. Another view is that pretreatment with adjuvant blocks the receptor site so that the animal cannot respond to antigen presented together with adjuvant. This is unlikely to be a general explanation, as FCA depresses the response to tumor grafts.

Role of FCA as an Adjuvant for the Production of Modulator (Suppressor) Cells

Several modulator (suppressor) cells influence the response to contact sensitizing agents in mice and occur after routine immunization by painting of the skin. These modulator cells are best discussed by considering separately the different changes that occur after painting the skin.

Induction phase. The induction phase of contact sensitivity can be analyzed by painting mice with contact sensitizing agents and injecting their regional lymph node cells 1 to 4 days later into the footpads of normal recipients. Evidence summarized elsewhere shows that the recipients develop contact sensitivity as a result of an active immunization process by antigen associated with T cells and macrophages (4, 7a) and that the active form of the antigen is probably contact sensitizing agent linked to H-2 antigens. Painting mice with contact sensitizing agents in the standard way for producing contact sensitivity gives rise to B cells which depress this induction process when injected into the donors of the cells used for the footpad transfer (Asherson,

Zembala, and Mayhew, submitted for publication). One phrasing of this phenomenon is that immune B cells limit the persistence of antigen on T cells and macrophages in a form which is able to immunize.

Cell proliferation. After painting with contact sensitizing agent, there is a wave of DNA synthesis in the regional lymph nodes which reaches a peak on day 3. When regional lymph node cells are taken from mice 5 days after immunization and then injected into normal mice which are subsequently immunized, there is a mainly specific depression of DNA synthesis. This depression is due to a special class of T cells which are unaffected by adult thymectomy but are sensitive to 300 mg of cyclophosphamide per kg given before immunization (6, 7).

Cytotoxicity. Workers in my laboratory have described a T cell which is also sensitive to cyclophosphamide and which depresses the production of cytotoxic cells. Briefly, the regional lymph node cells of mice painted with contact sensitizing agents show little or no cytotoxicity against haptene-treated syngeneic cells. However, high levels of T-cell cytotoxic activity against these target cells are found in mice treated with cyclophosphamide before skin painting. This effect of cyclophosphamide is reversed by the injection of normal or immune T cells (V. Taggart, Transplantation, in press).

Manifestation of contact sensitivity. There is also a B cell which inhibits the manifestation of contact sensitivity and is demonstrated by its ability to depress contact sensitivity (35). Its precursor is sensitive to cyclophosphamide (34). It is responsible for the curious phenomenon that spleen cells taken 8 days after immunization with contact sensitizing agents fail to transfer contact sensitivity but contain both T effector cells able to transfer and B suppressor cells which block their action. B cells which are probably similar occur in guinea pigs immunized with antigen in FCA (18).

Suppressor T cells in unresponsive mice. In addition to these modulator cells found in mice after routine immunization for contact sensitivity, there are suppressor T cells in mice injected with di- or trinitrobenzenesulfonic acid—agents which cause specific unresponsiveness (25, 33; see also 24). The cells in mice injected with trinitrobenzenesulfonic acid block the passive transfer of contact sensitivity. They differ from the T cells which affect DNA synthesis in the resistance of their precursors to cyclophosphamide, their sensitivity to adult thymectomy (7b), and their failure to influence DNA synthesis. Suppressor T cells which may be similar are found in mice rendered tolerant to transplantation antigen by the injection of *B. pertussis*, antilymphocyte serum, and antigen (20).

Against this background the analysis of the depression of cell-mediated immunity caused by pretreatment with adjuvant needs to answer the following questions. Does pretreatment with FCA act as an adjuvant for the production of B suppressor cells which limit the persistence of antigen in a form which is able to immunize and for the B cells which depress the manifestation of delayed hypersensitivity? Does it also act as an adjuvant for the T cells which limit DNA synthesis and cytotoxicity and for the distinct T suppressor cell found in unresponsive mice?

Role of macrophages. It is worthwhile considering whether pretreatment with FCA may act directly on macrophages and only secondarily on effector or modulator cells. This is suggested by the finding that pretreatment of guinea pigs with FCA does not depress the delayed hypersensitivity caused by immunization with antigen on peritoneal exudate cells (a possible limitation of these experiments is that the skin tests were undertaken at 7 days, a time at which in our hands the classical depression caused by pretreatment with FCA is not well shown [3]). The concept of the macrophage as a site at which the decision of antibody versus cell-mediated immunity is taken is suggested by the finding that cytophilic antibody increases the ability of antigen on macrophages to stimulate cell-mediated immunity and depresses their ability to cause antibody production (36). There is also evidence that one bacterial adjuvant, *C. parvum*, alters the handling of antigen by macrophages and causes more antigen to persist on the macrophage surface (32).

Biological significance. Mammals have a range of immune responses which presumably have been selected by evolutionary pressures to enable them to handle a range of infectious agents. This gives rise to the problem of how animals find the immune responses appropriate to a particular invading microorganism. It is possible that the animal might use the widespread presence of bacterial adjuvants, i.e., bacterial cell wall components, as an indication that strong cell-mediated immune responses might lead to undue tissue damage. Evolutionary pressure may have led to a special mechanism whereby widespread bacterial cell wall material limits cell-mediated immunity. In the further investigation of these mechanisms, the availability of synthetic adjuvants which are nonimmunogenic and cause little tissue reaction should be very helpful.

ACKNOWLEDGMENTS

I thank Geoffrey Allwood and Jack Colover for helpful discussion.

LITERATURE CITED

1. **Allwood, G. G., and G. L. Asherson.** 1971. Depression of delayed hypersensitivity by pretreatment with Freund-type adjuvants. II. Mechanism of the phenomenon. Clin. Exp. Immunol. 9:259–266.

2. **Allwood, G. G., and G. L. Asherson.** 1972. Depression of delayed hypersensitivity by pretreatment with Freund-type adjuvants. Clin. Exp. Immunol. 11:579–584.

3. **Asherson, G. L., and G. G. Allwood.** 1971. Depression of delayed hypersensitivity by pretreatment with Freund-type adjuvants. I. Description of the phenomenon. Clin. Exp. Immunol. 9:249–258.

4. **Asherson, G. L., and B. Mayhew.** 1976. Induction of cell-mediated immunity in the mouse: circumstantial evidence for highly immunogenic antigens in the regional lymph nodes following skin painting with contact sensitizing agents. Isr. J. Med. Sci. 12:454–467.

5. **Asherson, G. L., and S. H. Stone.** 1965. Selective and specific inhibition of 24 hour skin reactions in the guinea pig. I. Immune deviation: description of the phenomenon and the effect of splenectomy. Immunology 9:205–217.

6. **Asherson, G. L., P. J. Wood, and B. Mayhew.** 1975. Control of the immune response. I. Depression of DNA synthesis by immune lymph node cells. Immunology 29:1057–1065.

7. **Asherson, G. L., and M. Zembala.** 1976. Suppressor T cells in cell-mediated immunity. Br. Med. Bull. 32:158–164.

7a. **Asherson, G. L., M. Zembala, and B. Mayhew.** 1977. Analysis of the induction phase of contact sensitivity by footpad transfer of regional lymph node cells: macrophages and radioresistant T lymphocytes to induce immunity. Immunology 32:81–88.

7b. **Asherson, G. L., M. Zembala, B. Mayhew, and A. Goldstein.** 1976. Adult thymectomy prevention of the appearance of suppressor T cells which depress contact sensitivity to picryl chloride and reversal of adult thymectomy effect by thymus extract. Eur. J. Immunol. 6:699–703.

8. **Audibert, F., and L. Chedid.** 1976. Distinctive adjuvanticity of synthetic analogs of myobacterial water-soluble components. Cell. Immunol. 21:243–249.

9. **Bice, D., H. J. Schwartz, W. W. Lake, and J. Salvaggio.** 1971. The effect of carrageenan on the establishment of delayed hypersensitivity. Int. Arch. Allergy 41:628–636.

10. **Bretscher, P., and H. Cohn.** 1970. A theory of self-nonself discrimination. Science 169:1042–1049.

11. **Byfield, P. E., J. Z. Finklestein, K. I. Tittle, C. Hsi, and D. T. Imagowa.** 1975. The role of serum factors in the acceleration by Freund's complete adjuvant on the growth of transplanted murine leukaemic cells. Cancer Res. 35:409–414.

12. **Cranley-Dillon, S.** 1974. The effect of preadministration of Corynebacterium parvum on the protection afforded by heat-killed and acetone killed vaccines against experimental mouse typhoid. J. Hyg. 72:13–18.

13. **Davey, M. J., G. L. Asherson, and S. H. Stone.** 1971. Selective and specific inhibition of 24 hour skin reactions in the guinea pig. III. Depression of cytophilic and haemolytic antibodies by pretreatment with antigen and the effect of irradiation. Immunology 20:513–522.

14. **Dvorak, H. F., and M. H. Flax.** 1966. Immunologic unresponsiveness in the adult guinea-pig. II. The kinetics of unresponsiveness. J. Immunol. 96:546–553.

15. **Gaugas, J. M., M. E. J. Billingham, and R. J. W. Rees.** 1971. Suppressive effect of homologous and heterologous inflammatory exudate on tuberculin sensitivity in the guinea pig. Am. Rev. Respir. Dis. 101:432–434.

16. **Jankovic, B. D.** 1962. Suppression of experimental allergic thyroiditis, delayed hypersensitivity and antibody production to homologous thyroglobulin in guinea pigs by prior injection of adjuvant. Int. Arch. Allergy 21:207–220.

17. **Jankovic, B. D.** 1962. Impairment of immunological reactivity in guinea pigs by prior injection of adjuvant. Nature (London) 193:789–790.

18. **Katz, S. I., D. Parker, and J. L. Turk.** 1974. B cell suppresion of delayed hypersensitivity reactions. Nature (London) 251:550–551.

19. **Kies, M. W., and E. C. Alvord.** 1958. Prevention of allergic encephalomyelitis by prior injection of adjuvant. Nature (London) 182:1106.

20. **Kilshaw, P. J., L. Brent, and M. Pinto.** 1975. Suppressor T cells in mice made unresponsive to skin allografts. Nature (London) 255:489–491.

21. **Loewi, G., E. J. Holborow, and A. Temple.** 1966. Inhibition of delayed hypersensitivity by preimmunization without complete adjuvant. Immunology 10:339–347.

22. **Lumsden, C. E.** 1949. Experimental 'allergic' encephalomyelitis. II. On the nature of the encephalitogenic agent. Brain 72:517–537.

23. **Meltzer, M. S., and E. Leonard.** 1973. Enhanced tumour growth in animals pretreated with complete Freund's adjuvant. J. Natl. Cancer Inst. 50:209–218.

24. **Moorhead, J. W.** 1976. Tolerance and contact sensitivity to DNFB in mice. VI. Inhibition of afferent sensitivity by suppressor T cells in adoptive tolerance. J. Immunol. 117:802–806.

25. **Phanuphak, P., J. W. Moorhead, and H. N. Claman.** 1974. Tolerance and contact sensitivity to DNFB in mice. III. Transfer of tolerance with "suppressor T cells." J. Immunol. 113:1230–1236.

26. **Svet-Moldavskaya, I. A., and G. J. Svet-Moldavsky.** 1938. Acquired resistence to experimental allergic encephalomyelitis. Nature (London) 181:1536.

27. **Toujas, L., L. Dazord, A. Martin, and J. Guelfi.** 1973. Stimultaneous stimulation of plaque forming cells and depression of cellular immunity to sheep red cells after adjuvant treatment. Biomedicine 19:503–505.

28. **Toujas, L., D. Sabolovic, L. Dazord, Y. Le Garree, J. P. Toujas, J. Guelfi, and C. Pilet.** 1972. The mechanism of immunostimulation induced by inactivated Brucella abortus. Rev. Eur. Etud. Clin. Biol. 17:267–273.

29. **Uhr, J. W., G. Weissmann, and L. Thomas.** 1963. Acute hypervitaminosis A in guinea pigs. II. Effects on delayed hypersensitivity. Proc. Soc. Exp. Biol. Med. 112:287–291.

30. **Vacher, J., R. Deraedt, and J. Benzoni.** 1974. Anti-inflammatory effect mediated by a change in the activity of the reticuloendothelial system (RES) in the rat: its relationship to α-macrofetoprotein induction. RES J. Reticuloendothel. Soc. 16:48–55.

31. **Waldmann, H., and A. Munro.** 1975. The inter-relationship of antigenic structure, thymus-independence and adjuvanticity. IV. A general model for B-cell induction. Immunology 28:509–522.

32. **Wiener, E., and A. Bandieri.** 1975. Modifications in the handling in vitro of I^{125}-labelled keyhole limpet haemocyanin by pretreated macrophages from mice pretreated with the adjuvant Corynebacterium parvum. Immunology 29:265–274.

33. **Zembala, M., and G. L. Asherson.** 1973. Depression of the T cell phenomenon of contact sensitivity by T cells from unresponsive mice. Nature (London) 244:227–228.

34. **Zembala, M., and G. L. Asherson.** 1976. The effect of

cyclophosphamide and irradiation on cells which suppress contact sensitivity in the mouse. Clin. Exp. Immunol. 23:554–561.

35. Zembala, M., G. L. Asherson, J. Noworolski, and B. Mayhew. 1976. Contact sensitivity to picryl chloride: the occurrence of B suppressor cells in the lymph nodes and spleen of immunized mice. Cell. Immunol. 25:266–278.

36. Zembala, M., W. Ptak, and M. Hanczakowska. 1974. The induction of delayed hypersensitivity by macrophage associated antigen. The role of macrophage cytophilic antibody. Immunology 26:465–476.

37. Zola, H. 1972. Modulation of the immune response to transplantation antigens. I. The effect of immunization using adjuvants on the immune response of mice to a tumour allograft. Clin. Exp. Immunol. 11:585–593.

38. Zola, H. 1974. Modulation of the immune response to transplantation antigens. III. Further studies on the effect of Freund's complete adjuvant on the immune response of mice to allogeneic tumour antigen. Clin. Exp. Immunol. 16:469–479.

39. Zschiesche, W. W., and H. Heinecke. 1973. Effects of variable bacillus Calmette Guerin regimens on skin graft rejection. Transplantation 15:172–173.

Recent Advances in the Use of the Synthetic Immunoadjuvants Muramyl Dipeptide and Analogues[1]

LOUIS CHEDID AND FRANÇOISE AUDIBERT

Groupe de Recherche no. 31 du C.N.R.S., Immunothérapie Expérimentale, Institut Pasteur,
75015 Paris, France

Mycobacteria have been extensively used by several investigators because of their multiple effects on the immune response. The specific capacity to immunize against tuberculous infection is restricted to certain strains, whereas nonspecific resistance to infections and enhancement of tumor immunity has been elicited by a large variety of mycobacteria. These organisms are also capable, when administered with an antigen in a water-in-oil emulsion, of producing delayed hypersensitivity and of markedly increasing humoral antibody levels (20). Besides these responses, administration of mycobacterial cells can stimulate the reticuloendothelial system and elicit several other biological reactions, many of which are considered "side effects," such as lymphoid hyperplasia and granuloma formation, increased susceptibility to endotoxic shock, tuberculin sensitization, and adjuvant polyarthritis. Moreover, because immune modulation can be unruly after administration of BCG cells (for instance, tumor "enhancement" instead of rejection), their utilization has often been restricted to experimental systems. Clinical applications have also been greatly limited by the presence of nonmetabolizable oil in Freund complete adjuvant (FCA).

ADJUVANT ACTIVITY OF VARIOUS MYCOBACTERIAL PREPARATIONS ADMINISTERED IN FREUND INCOMPLETE ADJUVANT

The adjuvant-active materials which exist in mycobacteria are found in the cell wall (see reviews by Lederer [27, 28]). Early investigators showed that the whole organisms could be replaced by liposoluble wax D (43, 44) or by purified cell walls (1, 6) and, recently, by water-soluble fractions (1, 2, 32, 40). Thus, a preparation containing arabinogalactan linked to peptidoglycan was obtained after lysozyme treatment by Adam et al. (1, 2) and was shown to substitute for whole mycobacterial cells in FCA. This fraction was called water-soluble adjuvant (WSA). More recently, it was demonstrated that synthetic N-acetylmuramyl-L-alanyl-D-isoglutamine, hereafter referred to as MDP (for muramyl dipeptide), had the minimal structure required for adjuvant activity since neither muramyl amino acids nor the di- and tetrapeptide moieties alone were active (3, 8, 18, 24, 31).

In contrast to whole cells or to mycobacterial crude cell walls, WSA did not induce the following "side effects": splenomegaly, increased susceptibility to endotoxins, and sensitization to tuberculin (14). Moreover, WSA was not arthritogenic (14, 35), although this adjuvant could enhance delayed hypersensitivity and even autoimmune encephalomyelitis (26) and orchitis (41). A surprising observation was that, under conditions which allowed enhancement of the immune response, WSA did not stimulate the reticuloendothelial system (RES) as measured by carbon clearance (35). The same biological profile was observed with MDP: strong adjuvant activity and absence of side effects. Moreover, guinea pigs sensitized by FCA or even by MDP in Freund incomplete adjuvant (FIA) had negative skin tests against MDP (5). As will be seen later, several analogues of this molecule were also synthesized, and many of them were adjuvant active. The formula of WSA is shown in Fig. 1, which represents the mycobacterial cell wall skeleton and the wax D structure according to Lederer (27), and the structure of MDP is shown in Fig. 2.

ADJUVANT ACTIVITY OF VARIOUS BACTERIAL PREPARATIONS ADMINISTERED IN SALINE

Although WSA had a marked adjuvant activity when administered to guinea pigs in FIA, it did not increase the immune response when

[1] This review is dedicated to Jacques Monod. Much of the work contained was rendered possible and achieved because of his unfailing interest, his vigorous support, and his friendly counseling.

388

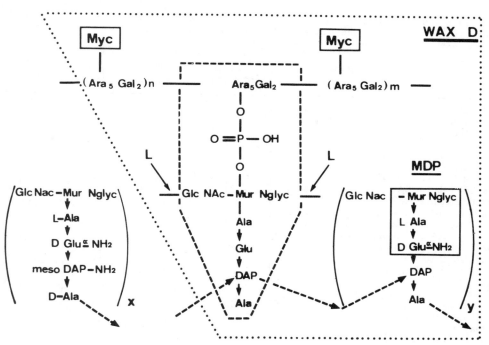

FIG. 1. *Simplified scheme of the mycobacterial cell wall and its adjuvant-active derivatives wax D, water-soluble adjuvant (WSA), and N-acetylmuramyl-L-alanyl-D-isoglutamine (MDP). The WSA unit shown here has a molecular weight of about 2,000. Myc = mycolic acid. L = lysozyme.*

administered with an antigen in an aqueous medium to mice. Under certain experimental conditions, the antibody response was even inhibited (12). Gram-negative lipopolysaccharides (LPS) administered in saline are, however, strong adjuvants of the humoral antibody response (19, 22). They can also elicit a wide range of pharmacological and immunological effects. Since most of the studied activities can be produced by lipid A, which represents the toxic moiety of LPS, and since in most cases the preparations used were highly pyrogenic, toxicity has generally been assumed to be a prerequisite of all the biological effects of LPS (30, 34, 42). Therefore, their remarkable activity in saline could not be taken advantage of because of their pyrogenicity in humans.

Schenck et al. reported, however, that derivatives of LPS detoxified by succinylation (SuLPS) maintained their adjuvant activity (37). We have confirmed these findings and have shown in addition that, although sodium phthalate LPS (SPLPS) was even less toxic than SuLPS, it had retained its mitogenic activity (11) and could even stimulate spleen lymphocytes of C3H/HeJ mice, which are LPS low responders (13).

These derivatives of LPS markedly enhanced the humoral antibody response to various antigens after administration to mice, rabbits, and guinea pigs. We have also shown that acylation of WSA enables this molecule to acquire adjuvant activity in an aqueous medium (4). More important was the finding that, in contrast to the native WSA, MDP and several low-molecular-weight synthetic analogues were also active in water.

$$CH_2OH$$

$$CH_3-C-CO-NH-CH-CO-NH-CH-CONH_2$$

H;OH

HO

NH Ac

H

CH_3

(CH_2)_2

COOH

M DP

FIG. 2. *Muramyl dipeptide formula.*

TABLE 1. *Activity in saline or in water-in-oil emulsion of various bacterial adjuvants and derivatives and of synthetic glycopeptides or amino acids*

Preparation	Water-in-oil			Saline	
	Activity[a]		References	Activity[a] (Ab)	References
	Ab	DTH			
Lipopolysaccharide (LPS)	+	−	11	+	19, 22
LPS detoxified by succinylation	NT	NT		+	1, 37
Sodium phthalate LPS	+	−	11	+	11
Mycobacterial cells	+	+	20	Insoluble	
Wax D	+	+	43, 44	Insoluble	
Purified cell wall	+	+	1, 6	Insoluble	
Water-soluble adjuvant (WSA)	+	+	1, 21, 32, 40	−↓	4, 12
Sodium phthalate WSA	+	+	—[b]	+	4
Synthetic preparations					
Glc-NAc-Mur-NAc-L-Ala 1	−	−	3, 18	NT	
Mur-NAc-L-Ala-D-iso-Gln-L-Lys-D-Ala .. 2	+	+	8, 24	+	—[c]
Mur-NAc-L-Ala-D-iso-Gln-L-Lys 3	+	+	24	+	—[b]
Mur-NAc-L-Ala-D-iso-Gln = MDP 4	+	+	3, 8, 18, 24	+	5
Mur-NAc-L-Ala 5	−	−	8, 24, 31	NT	
Mur-NAc-D-iso-Gln 6	−	−	14	NT	
Mur-NAc-D-Ala 7	−	−	14	NT	
Mur-NAc 8	−	−	14	NT	
L-Ala-D-iso-Gln-L-Lys-D-Ala 9	−	−	7, 8, 18, 24	NT	
L-Ala-D-iso-Gln-L-Lys 10	−	−	7, 8	NT	
L-Ala-D-iso-Gln 11	−	−	7, 8, 12, 18, 24	−	12
Mur-NAc-L-Ala-L-iso-Gln 12	−	−	2a, 12, 24	−	12
Mur-NAc-L-Ala-D-Glu = MDPA 13	±	−	2a, 5	+	5
Mur-NAc-L-Ala-L-Glu 14	−	−	12, 24	−	12
Mur-NAc-D-Ala-D-iso-Gln 15	−↓	−	2a, 12, 24	−↓	12
Mur-NAc-D-Ala-L-iso-Gln 16	−	−	12	−	12
Mur-NAc-L-Ala-D-Gln 17	−	−	24	NT	
Mur-NAc-L-Ala-L-Gln 18	−	−	24	NT	
Mur-NAc-L-Ser-D-iso-Gln 19	+	+	2a	+	12
Mur-NAc-Gly-D-iso-Gln 20	±	±	2a	±	12
Mur-NAc-L-Ala-γ-Abu 21	−	−	—[c]	−	—[c]
Mur-NAc-L-Ala-Nleu 22	−	−	—[c]	−	—[c]
Mur-NAc-L-Ala-D-iso-Asn 23	−	−	24[c]	−	—[c]
Mur-NAc-L-Ala-D-Ala 24	−	−	24	NT	
Mur-NAc-L-Ala-D-α-Glu-Gly 25	−	−	—[c]	−	—[c]
Mur-NAc-L-Ala-D-Glu(NH$_2$)NH$_2$ 26	+	+	—[c]	+	—[c]
Mur-NAc-L-Ala-D-Glu(OCH$_3$)NH$_2$ 27	+	+	2a, 12	+	12
Mur-NAc-L-Ala-D-Glu(OCH$_3$)OCH$_3$ 28	+	+	2a, 12	+	12
Mur-NAc-L-Ala-D-Glu-NHCH$_3$ 29	+	+	12	+	12
Mur-NAc-L-Ala-D-Glu(NHCH$_3$)NHCH$_3$ ... 30	−	−	—[c]	−	—[c]
Mur-NAc-L-Ala-D-Glu(NHCH$_3$)NH$_2$ 31	−	−	—[c]	−	—[c]
Muramicitol-L-Ala-D-iso-Gln 32	−	−	2a	NT	
Lactyl-L-Ala-D-iso-Gln-L-Lys-D-Ala 33	−	−	7	NT	
Lactyl-L-Ala-D-iso-Gln 34	−	−	2a, 7	NT	
Nor-Mur-NAc-L-Ala-D-iso-Gln 35	−	−	2a	NT	
6 O-Stearoyl-Mur-NAc-L-Ala-D-iso-Gln ... 36	±	±	7	NT	

[a] AB = humoral antibody response; DHT = delayed-type hypersensitivity; NT = not tested.

[b] Unpublished data.

[c] F. Audibert et al., Ann. Immunol., in press.

The results presented in Table 1 compare the adjuvant activity of these various preparations. In most cases they were administered to guinea pigs in a single injection in FIA with ovalbumin or ABA-tyrosine and to mice in saline, generally with bovine serum albumin (BSA), followed by a recall 4 weeks later of BSA only. (In separate experiments MDP was also

shown to enhance the immune response both in vivo and in vitro, when administered with other antigens such as thymus-independent dinitrophenyl-Ficoll dissolved in phosphate-buffered saline [7].)

The data contained in Table 1 can be summarized as follows:

1. LPS and its acylated derivatives induced

no delayed hypersensitivity when administered in FIA to guinea pigs. In contrast, under the same conditions, mycobacterial cells and cell walls, wax D, WSA, and sodium phthalate WSA (SPWSA) had a very marked adjuvant activity as measured both by skin tests and by humoral antibody titers. Similarly MDP and several analogues were also found to have adjuvant activity in water-in-oil emulsion.

2. LPS and its phthalylated derivatives administered with BSA in an aqueous medium increased the humoral immune response. Whereas WSA was inactive in saline, a strong enhancement was observed after phthalylation. Indeed, these derivatives produced antibody levels which were equal to or even greater than those obtained with LPS. It has therefore been assumed tentatively that a certain conformation of the WSA molecule which could be masked by acylation hinders the full expression of its adjuvant activity in saline.

MDP and several analogues were also active when administered in saline. In most cases these analogues, like MDP and SPWSA, were active both in saline and in a water-in-oil emulsion. However, MDPA (13 in Table 1) increased humoral antibodies but did not induce delayed hypersensitivity when administered in FIA (5). Still, the possibility that such lack of activity could be related to the hydrophilic or hydrophobic nature of its chemical groups should not be ruled out.

3. If smaller dosages of BSA are administered to mice, an immune response can be observed in the absence of adjuvants. Under these conditions, mice treated with WSA and with a stereoisomer of MDP, Mur-NAc-D-Ala-D-iso-Gln (15 in Table 1), administered in water had low or negative titers of antibodies (12). Similar results were obtained when this stereoisomer was administered with FIA or with MDP in FIA (2a).

4. As can be seen, many of the chemical modifications of MDP concern the D-glutamyl residue. The results show that both carboxyl functions were required for adjuvant activity and that they should be at an appropriate distance. Several structural prerequisites of activity could be observed and have been discussed in previous reports (2a, 12; F. Audibert et al., Ann. Immunol., in press).

INFLUENCE OF VARIOUS ROUTES OF ADMINISTRATION ON ADJUVANT ACTIVITY OF MDP AND ANALOGUES

The data summarized in Fig. 3 make it evident that it is not necessary to administer the antigen and MDP by the same route to observe an increase of the humoral immune response and that MDP was active even after oral administration (12).

It has tentatively been assumed that the amazing activity of MDP and other analogues by this route was related to their small size (molecular weight smaller than 500) and to the presence of D-isoglutamine, which could render them resistant to biological degradation.

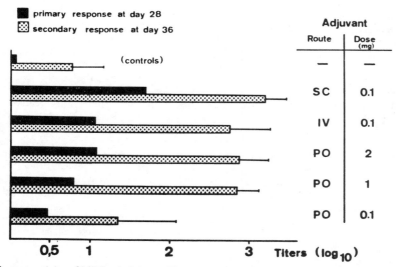

FIG. 3. *Adjuvant activity of MDP administered by various routes including the oral route. Mice (10 per group) received subcutaneously 500 μg of BSA with or without adjuvant and 30 days later a recall of 100 μg of antigen alone. Antibody titers are estimated by passive hemagglutination of BSA-sensitized sheep red blood cells. In the four first experimental groups titers are highly significantly elevated* (P < 0.01) *as compared with the controls by Student's* t *test.*

TARGET CELLS FOR THE ACTIVITY OF WSA OR MDP

In contrast to other peptidoglycan preparations and to a *Nocardia* water-soluble extract (9, 15, 16), WSA had no mitogenic activity and has even been shown to inhibit blast transformation by phytohemagglutinin (38). All these previous investigations had been performed, however, in the presence of fetal calf serum. More recently, experiments were undertaken with the use of media to which mercaptoethanol had been added. Under these conditions, WSA was mitogenic for spleen cells of normal or of nude mice, whereas no activity was observed with MDP in the presence of either fetal calf serum or mercaptoethanol (C. Damais, unpublished data). Absence of mitogenic activity of various synthetic peptides has also been reported by Azuma et al. (7).

Comparison with WSA in various test systems has shown that the native cell wall adjuvant appears to possess a greater affinity than MDP for the phagocytizing cell. After incubation with MDP, peritoneal macrophages became capable of inhibiting the growth of tumor target cells, but MDP did not activate macrophages in vivo, in contrast to what was observed with WSA (23). Moreover, also in contrast to WSA, MDP incubated with peritoneal macrophages did not increase their capacity to phagocytize sheep erythrocytes (SRBC; I. Löwy, unpublished data).

Other in vitro experiments of Modolell et al. (33) have shown that WSA can enhance the immune response towards a T-independent antigen and that the adjuvant acts at the level of the macrophage. However, WSA has been shown to be active in a mixed lymphocyte reaction (10) and to be capable of restoring the immune response in rosette-forming-cell-depleted mice (29). These results argue in favor of a thymus-derived cell mediation.

Recent experiments have established that MDP increased the primary response to SRBC in irradiated recipients reconstituted with syngeneic thymocytes and bone marrow cells. Cooperation between T and B lymphocytes was required for the expression of this adjuvant activity. This adjuvant effect of MDP was abolished if, prior to their injection into irradiated hosts, the donor cells were incubated with anti-θ serum, but was not affected by the depletion of the donor spleen cells of the phagocytic adherent cell fraction. MDP and SRBC-pretreated macrophages showed no increase in ability to induce an anti-SRBC immune response in normal mice. These results demonstrate the importance of T lymphocytes for the adjuvant activity of MDP although they do not exclude totally a possible role of splenic macrophages (I. Löwy, Cell. Immunol., in press).

Adjuvant activity of MDP on the primary response to SRBC was also demonstrated during in vitro immunization by the method of Marbrook (7; Specter, personal communication).

OTHER BIOLOGICAL ACTIVITIES OF WSA AND MDP

Under certain conditions, WSA was shown capable of increasing nonspecific resistance of mice challenged by a fungus (*Candida albicans*), a gram-negative bacterium (*Klebsiella pneumoniae*), or a gram-positive bacterium (*Streptoccus pneumoniae*). This effect was not related to some possible contamination by endotoxin-like materials since WSA was shown to be apyrogenic and limulus negative (17). Kotani et al. demonstrated, however, that administration of MDP to rabbits elicited a febrile response. In their study 14 different *N*-acetylmuramyl peptides or amino acids were tested, and all adjuvant-active compounds assayed were found to be pyrogenic (25).

CONCLUSIONS

The chemistry of adjuvant fractions of mycobacteria has been investigated for many years, but it is only recently that the relevant structures have been identified (18, 31). The data briefly reviewed here and the availability of synthetic adjuvants render various hypotheses accessible to experimental verification. Some of the possibilities which are currently being investigated can be summarized as follows:

1. The peptidoglycan structure that can duplicate the activity of mycobacteria in FCA is very widely distributed in bacterial species and has been demonstrated not only in acid-fast but also in gram-negative and gram-positive organisms. The observation that small synthetic molecules with a configuration inherent to bacterial cell wall peptidoglycan were endowed with strong immunological activity suggests the possibility of certain structural analogies with mammalian mediators.

2. A rewarding observation was that, in opposition to what is observed with most adjuvants, MDP not only was devoid of toxicity, immunogenicity, and mitogenicity, but apparently had no effect on the RES as measured by increased phagocytosis. Therefore, such "functionally pure" preparations, which are now available, should provide distinctive means for definitive studies of mechanisms.

3. Such well-defined agents should also enable immunogenetic studies of adjuvant activity which until now have necessarily always been undertaken with very complex adjuvant materials.

4. All known bacterial adjuvants (such as LPS, BCG, or *Haemophilus pertussis*, for example) have a great antigenic heterogeneity. Since enhancement of the immune response can now be observed with nonantigenic molecules, one is tempted to speculate whether adjuvant activity could be elicited in the absence of simultaneous administration of another antigen. In other words, is there still a detectable immune response when an agent such as MDP is administered alone?

5. As was very well stated in Schwab's recent review (36), modulation of the immune response by various bacterial preparations is rather baffling. Thus, most immunostimulants also have strong immunodepressive activity according to the moment of their injection and other experimental parameters. Analogues which have been shown to inhibit the immune response could contribute to the clarification of certain paradoxical aspects of immunostimulation.

6. It is noteworthy that the extraordinary effectiveness of FCA in amplifying immune responses has been extensively documented during the past quarter century, but its utilization other than in experimental procedures has been restricted by the toxic reactivity of mycobacteria and the use of the nonmetabolizable oil component. Synthetic adjuvants devoid of toxicity and immunogenicity have been shown to be very effective in the absence of mineral oil even if administered by the oral route (5, 12). They should, therefore, constitute useful tools for clinical application. Several investigators are actively studying enhancement of the immune response, not only in view of protection against bacterial, viral, or protozoal infections, but also for various other purposes such as fertility control (39). Neutralization by antibodies of harmful endogenous peptides in various pathological situations is also being very seriously considered. In all such cases enhancement of the immune response should be desirable since the appropriate modified antigens with limited cross-reactivity which are required will probably be weak immunogens.

LITERATURE CITED

1. Adam, A., R. Ciorbaru, J. F. Petit, and E. Lederer. 1972. Isolation and properties of a macromolecular, water soluble, immuno-adjuvant fraction from the cell wall of *Mycobacterium smegmatis*. Proc. Natl. Acad. Sci. U.S.A. **69**:851–854.

2. Adam, A., R. Ciorbaru, J. F. Petit, E. Lederer, L. Chedid, A. Lamensans, F. Parant, M. Parant, J. P. Rosselet, and F. M. Berger. 1973. Preparation and biological properties of water-soluble adjuvant fractions from delipidated cells of *Mycobacterium smegmatis* and *Nocardia opaca*. Infect. Immun. **7**:855–861.

2a. Adam, A., M. Devys, V. Souvannavong, P. Lefrancier, J. Choay, and E. Lederer. 1976. Correlation of structure and adjuvant activity of N-acetylmuramyl-L-alanyl-D-isoglutamyl (MDP), its derivatives and analogues. Anti-adjuvant and competition properties of some stereoisomers. Biochem. Biophys. Res. Commun. **72**:339–346.

3. Adam, A., F. Ellouz, R. Ciorbaru, J. F. Petit, and E. Lederer. 1975. Peptidoglycan adjuvants: minimal structure required for activity. Z. Immunitaetsforsch. **149S**:341–348.

4. Audibert, F., and L. Chedid. 1976. Activity in saline of phthalylated or succinylated derivatives of mycobacterial water-soluble adjuvant. Infect. Immun. **14**:1263–1268.

5. Audibert, F., L. Chedid, P. Lefrancier, and J. Choay. 1976. Distinctive adjuvanticity of synthetic analogs of mycobacterial water soluble components. Cell. Immunol. **21**:243–249.

6. Azuma, I., S. Kishimoto, Y. Yamamura, and J. F. Petit. 1971. Adjuvanticity of mycobacterial cell walls. Jpn. J. Microbiol. **15**:193–197.

7. Azuma, I., K. Sugimura, T. Taniyama, M. Yamawaki, Y. Yamamura, S. Kusumoto, S. Okada, and T. Shiba. 1976. Adjuvant activity of mycobacterial fractions. Adjuvant activity of synthetic N-acetylmuramyl-dipeptide and the related compounds. Infect. Immun. **14**:18–27.

8. Azuma, I., K. Sugimura, Y. Yamamura, S. Kusumoto, Y. Tarumi, and T. Shiba. 1976. Adjuvant activity of synthetic cell wall peptidoglycan subunits on monoarobenzene arsonate-N-acetyl-L-tyrosine and bacterial α-amylase in guinea pigs. Jpn. J. Microbiol. **20**:63–66.

9. Bona, C., C. Damais, A. Dimitriu, L. Chedid, R. Ciorbaru, A. Adam, J. F. Petit, E. Lederer, and J. P. Rosselet. 1974. Mitogenic effect of a water soluble extract of *Nocardia opaca*. A comparative study with some bacterial adjuvants on spleen and peripheral lymphocytes of four mammalian species. J. Immunol. **112**:2028–2035.

10. Bona, C., C. Heuclin, and L. Chedid. 1974. Enhancement of human mixed lymphocyte cultures by a water soluble adjuvant. Recent Results Cancer Res. **47**:197–200.

11. Chedid, L., F. Audibert, C. Bona, C. Damais, F. Parant, and M. Parant. 1975. Biological activities of endotoxins detoxified by alkylation. Infect. Immun. **12**:714–721.

12. Chedid, L., F. Audibert, P. Lefrancier, J. Choay, and E. Lederer. 1976. Modulation of the immune response by a synthetic adjuvant and analogs. Proc. Natl. Acad. Sci. U.S.A. **73**:2472–2475.

13. Chedid, L., M. Parant, C. Damais, F. Parant, D. Juy, and A. Galelli. 1976. Failure of endotoxin to increase nonspecific resistance to infection of lipopolysaccharide low-responder mice. Infect. Immun. **13**:722–727.

14. Chedid, L., M. Parant, F. Parant, R. H. Gustafson, and F. M. Berger. 1972. Biological study of a non-toxic, water soluble immuno-adjuvant from mycobacterial cell walls. Proc. Natl. Acad. Sci. U.S.A. **69**:855–858.

15. Ciorbaru, R., J. F. Petit, E. Lederer, E. Zissmann, C. Bona, and L. Chedid. 1976. Presence and subcellular localization of two distinct mitogenic fractions in the cells of *Nocardia rubra* and *Nocardia opaca*: prepara-

tion of soluble mitogenic peptidoglycan fractions. Infect. Immun. **13**:1084–1090.

16. **Damais, C., C. Bona, L. Chedid, J. Fleck, C. Nauciel, and J. P. Martin.** 1975. Mitogenic effect of bacterial peptidoglycans possessing adjuvant activity. J. Immunol. **115**:268–271.

17. **Elin, R. J., S. M. Wolff, and L. Chedid.** 1976. Nonspecific resistance to infection in mice induced by a water soluble adjuvant derived from *Mycobacterium smegmatis*. J. Infect. Dis. **133**:500–505.

18. **Ellouz, F., A. Adam, R. Ciorbaru, and E. Lederer.** 1974. Minimal structural requirements for adjuvant activity of bacterial peptidoglycan derivatives. Biochem. Biophys. Res. Commun. **59**:1317–1325.

19. **Franzl, R. E., and P. D. McMaster.** 1968. The primary immune response in mice. I. The enhancement and suppression of hemolysin production by a bacterial endotoxin. J. Exp. Med. **127**:1087–1107.

20. **Freund, J.** 1956. The mode of action of immunologic adjuvants. Adv. Tuberc. Res. **7**:130–148.

21. **Hiu, I. J.** 1972. Water soluble and lipid-free fraction from BCG with adjuvant and antitumor activity. Nature (London) New Biol. **238**:241–242.

22. **Johnson, A. G., S. Gaines, and M. Landy.** 1956. Studies on the O antigen of *Salmonella typhosa*. V. Enhancement of antibody response to protein antigens by the purified lipopolysaccharide. J. Exp. Med. **103**:225–246.

23. **Juy, D., and L. Chedid.** 1975. Comparison between macrophage activation and enhancement of non-specific resistance to tumors by mycobacterial immunoadjuvant. Proc. Natl. Acad. Sci. U.S.A. **72**:4105–4109.

24. **Kotani, S., Y. Watanabe, F. Kinoshita, T. Shimono, I. Morisaki, T. Shiba, S. Kusumoto, Y. Tarumi, and K. Ikenaka.** 1975. Immunoadjuvant activities of synthetic N-acetyl muramyl-peptides or -aminoacids. Biken J. **18**:105–111.

25. **Kotani, S., Y. Watanabe, T. Shimono, K. Haruda, T. Shiba, S. Kusumoto, K. Yokogawa, and M. Taniguchi.** 1976. Correlation between immunoadjuvant activities and pyrogenicities of synthetic N-acetyl muramylpeptides or -aminoacids. Biken J. **19**:9–13.

26. **Lebar, R., and G. A. Voisin.** 1974. Production d'une encéphalomyélite allergique expérimentale auto-immune (EAE) chez le cobaye à l'aide d'un adjuvant hydrosoluble extrait de *Mycobacterium smegmatis*. Ann. Immunol. **125C**:911–916.

27. **Lederer, E.** 1977. Natural and synthetic immunostimulants related to the mycobacterial cell wall. Proceedings of the 5th International Symposium on Medicinal Chemistry. Elsevier Scientific, Amsterdam.

28. **Lederer, E., A. Adam, R. Ciorbaru, J. F. Petit, and J. Wietzerbin.** 1975. Cell walls of mycobacteria and related organisms: chemistry and immunostimulant properties. Mol. Cell. Biochem. **7**:87–104.

29. **Liacopoulos, P., J. L. Birrien, C. Bleux, and J. Couderc.** 1974. Early recovery of the immune response of a specifically depleted cell population under the influence of water soluble adjuvant. Recent Results Cancer Res. **47**:201–206.

30. **Lüderitz, O., C. Galanos, V. Lehmann, M. Nurminen, E. T. Rietschel, G. Rosenfelder, M. Simon, and O. Westphal.** 1973. Lipid A, chemical structure and biological activity. J. Infect. Dis. **128S**:17–29.

31. **Merser, C., P. Sinaÿ, and A. Adam.** 1975. Total synthesis and adjuvant activity of bacterial peptidoglycan derivatives. Biochem. Biophys. Res. Commun. **66**:1316–1322.

32. **Migliore-Samour, D., and P. Jollès.** 1972. A hydrosoluble, adjuvant-active mycobacterial "polysaccharide-peptidoglycan." Preparation by a single extraction technique of the bacterial cells (strain peurois). FEBS Lett. **25**:301–304.

33. **Modolell, M., G. A. Luckenbach, M. Parant, and P. G. Munder.** 1974. The adjuvant activity of a mycobacterial water soluble adjuvant (WSA) *in vitro*. I. The requirement for macrophages. J. Immunol. **113**:395–403.

34. **Nowotny, A., K. R. Cundy, N. L. Neale, A. M. Nowotny, R. Radvany, S. P. Thomas, and D. J. Tripodi.** 1966. Relation of structure to function in bacterial O antigens. IV. Fractionation of the components. Ann. N.Y. Acad. Sci. **133**:586–603.

35. **Parant, M., and L. Chedid.** 1974. Biological properties of non-toxic water soluble immunoadjuvants from mycobacterial cells. Recent Results Cancer Res. **47**:189–195.

36. **Schwab, J. H.** 1975. Immunosuppression by bacteria, p. 64–75. *In* E. Neter and F. Milgrom (ed.), The immune system and infectious diseases. Karger, Basel.

37. **Schenck, J. R., M. P. Hargie, M. S. Brown, D. S. Ebert, A. L. Yoo, and F. C. McIntyre.** 1969. The enhancement of antibody formation by *Escherichia coli* lipopolysaccharide and detoxified derivative. J. Immunol. **102**:1411–1422.

38. **Sharma, B., O. Kohashi, M. R. Mickey, and P. I. Terasaki.** 1975. Effect of water soluble adjuvants on *in vitro* lymphocyte immunization. Cancer Res. **35**:666–669.

39. **Stevens, V. C.** 1975. Female contraception by immunization with HCG. Prospects and status, p. 217–231. *In* E. Neschlag (ed.), Immunization with hormones in reproduction research. North-Holland Publishing Co., Amsterdam.

40. **Stewart-Tull, D. E. S., T. Shimono, S. Kotani, M. Kato, Y. Ogawa, Y. Yamamura, T. Koga, and C. M. Pearson.** 1975. Adjuvant activity of a non-toxic, water soluble glycopeptide present in large quantities in the culture filtrate of *Mycobacterium tuberculosis* strain OT. Immunology **29**:1–15.

41. **Toullet, F., F. Audibert, L. Chedid, and G. A. Voisin.** 1974. Production d'une orchiépididymite aspermatogénétique auto-immune (OAAI) chez le cobaye à l'aide d'un adjuvant hydrosoluble extrait de *Mycobacterium smegmatis*. Ann. Immunol. **125C**:901–910.

42. **Westphal, O.** 1960. Récentes recherches sur la chimie et la biologie des endotoxines des bactéries à gram-négatif. Ann. Inst. Pasteur Paris **98**:789–813.

43. **White, R. G., L. Bernstock, R. G. S. Johns, and E. Lederer.** 1958. The influence of components of *M. tuberculosis* and other mycobacteria upon antibody production to ovalbumin. Immunology **1**:54–66.

44. **White, R. G., P. Jollès, D. Samour, and E. Lederer.** 1964. Correlation of adjuvant activity and chemical structure of wax D fractions of mycobacteria. Immunology **7**:158–171.

Adherence of Bacteria to Host Tissue

Position Paper

R. J. GIBBONS

Forsyth Dental Center, Boston, Massachusetts 02115

INTRODUCTION

Bacteria in a variety of natural environments have a predilection for colonizing surfaces. For example, almost any solid immersed in seawater or freshwater quickly becomes colonized by adherent microorganisms (14, 31, 108). Bacteria have also been observed to colonize the surfaces of sand grains (76), colloidal soil particles (72), living algae (14), plant tissues (22, 68), and other bacteria (59). The skin and particularly the mucous membranes of humans and animals are also heavily colonized by adherent indigenous bacteria (8, 50, 85). Moreover, the first step in the development of an infectious disease entails colonization of the host by the infecting organism, and with most pathogenic bacteria this occurs initially on a mucosal or skin surface (89). In fact, a variety of pathogenic bacteria, including beta-hemolytic streptococci (26), gonococci (105), *Salmonella* (100), *Shigella* (62), enteropathogenic *Escherichia coli* strains (90, 92), *Vibrio cholerae* (33), *Clostridium* species (5), *Corynebacterium diphtheriae* (7), etc., have been observed to be attached to mucosal surfaces of their host during natural or experimentally induced infections. Similarly, dental pathogens such as *Streptococcus mutans* and *Actinomyces* species adhere to and colonize the surfaces of teeth (50).

Although surface colonization appears to be widespread in nature, remarkably little is known about its ecological significance or the mechanisms by which bacteria attach to surfaces. In the past few years, studies of the adherence of bacteria to host tissues have attracted considerable interest, for they have indicated that bacteria attach with a high degree of specificity, and this appears to be one of the dominating factors which determine whether or not they may colonize (50). Thus, the adherent interactions between host and parasite appear to form a basis for understanding the innate resistance or susceptibilities of hosts and tissues to bacterial infection. The following discussion focuses upon some of the general ecological principles which have evolved from studies of the adherence of bacteria to host tissues. More detailed information concerning the adherence of specific organisms will be presented by other participants.

SELECTIVE NATURE OF BACTERIAL ATTACHMENT TO SOLID SURFACES

The adsorption of bacteria to inorganic solids has been known to be selective for many years. In early studies of the attachment of marine bacteria to glass, ZoBell (108) noted that, of 96 isolates from sea water, 29 strains adhered markedly, 20 strains adhered variably, and 47 strains did not attach at all. The selectivity of bacterial adsorption to glass has also been noted by others (63, 74), including Zvyagintsev (109). The latter investigator further demonstrated that considerable variation in adsorption could be exhibited by strains within the same genus. Bacteria also adsorb selectively to anion and cation exchange resins, cellulose fibers, charcoal, kaolin, bentonite, sand, and a variety of other adsorbents (reviewed by Daniels [19]). Evidence that at least some bacteria attach selectively to certain mammalian cells has also been available for some time. For example, piliated bacteria attach to and induce the agglutination of erythrocytes of certain mammalian and avian species, whereas nonpiliated strains generally do not (13). Virulent strains of certain enteric pathogens were also observed to associate with intestinal mucosa, whereas avirulent mutants did not (10, 24, 90).

It was also recognized for many years that bacteria colonize different hosts and tissues in a highly selective manner. Lactobacilli, for example, colonize the surface of nonsecreting keratinized epithelial cells in the stomach of rats and mice, but not the surface of secreting stomach epithelium (86). Furthermore, lactobacilli, fusobacteria, streptococci, yeasts, coliforms, and other organisms selectively colonize different surfaces within the gastrointestinal canal of rodents (20, 78, 84). Similarly, streptococci and other bacteria indigenous in the human mouth have been shown to selectively colonize the tongue, cheek, or tooth surfaces (45, 50, 61). Many pathogenic organisms also are known to display a sharply restricted range of hosts or tissues which they infect under natural conditions. In fact, this has hindered studies of the factors which influence their natural colonization, for many human pathogens do not colonize the mucosal surfaces of experimental animals when administered by natural routes. Thus, ample evidence has existed in the literature which indicated that both the adsorption of bacteria to surfaces and the bacterial colonization of host tissues were selective processes. It seems all the more remarkable, therefore, that it has been realized only in the past few years that the selectivity of bacterial attachment appears to be the major underlying basis which accounts for the tissue, organ, and host tropisms of a variety of bacteria (42, 50).

Evidence which first convincingly linked bacterial adherence with natural colonization was derived from studies of the ecology of indigenous bacteria in the human mouth (for reviews, see 42, 50). The mouth contains a variety of surfaces, including those of the teeth, tongue, buccal mucosa, palate, and gingiva, which are available for bacterial colonization, and it has been well established that certain oral species selectively colonize these sites. *Streptococcus salivarius*, for example, comprises about half of the streptococcal populations present on the dorsal surface of the tongue, yet it is found in only low or undetectable proportions on teeth (45, 61). In contrast, *S. mutans* can comprise a significant proportion of the bacteria which colonize teeth, but its proportions on oral mucosal surfaces are almost always low (50). Several other organisms, including *S. miteor*, *S. sanguis*, *Veillonella* and *Haemophilus* species, vibrios, *Bacteroides melaninogenicus*, fusobacteria, and spirochetes have also been shown to colonize preferentially specific sites within the mouth (50).

By use of several in vitro and in vivo approaches, it has been shown that indigenous streptococci and other bacteria adsorb in a highly selective manner to various surfaces of the mouth, and the experimentally determined affinity of these organisms has been found to correlate directly with their natural intraoral colonization (49, 50, 54, 64, 101, 102). These studies therefore indicate that the bacterial cell surface contains a highly developed recognition system capable of specifically interacting with distinct host tissues. In addition, the high degree of correlation found between adherence and natural colonization very strongly implies that adherence is an important determinant of colonization for bacteria in the mouth (42, 50).

ECOLOGICAL CONSIDERATIONS OF SELECTIVE BACTERIAL ATTACHMENT TO HOST SURFACES

Early studies by Bloomfield (11, 12) demonstrated that organisms such as *Escherichia coli*, *Staphylococcus albus*, and *Klebsiella pneumoniae* were rapidly eliminated following their introduction onto the tongue, the nasal septum, or tonsil crypts. He concluded that this was primarily due to mechanical cleansing forces, since these organisms were found to grow in saliva, and their rate of elimination was similar to that of clay particles. Appleton and co-workers (4) introduced strains of *Serratia marcescens* into the mouth and came to a similar conclusion; in fact, they drew analogies between the mouth and a flowing stream. Thus, it has long been known that the human mouth contains potent mechanisms for removing bacteria and other particles. Essentially similar experiments have been performed in the intestinal canal of animals. Dixon (23) introduced cells of *Serratia marcescens* and ^{51}Cr-labeled erythrocytes into the small intestine of dogs and found that both were removed rapidly and at similar rates. He concluded that peristaltic movements and the flow of secretions were the major reasons which accounted for the sparse bacterial populations usually found in this site.

In view of the cleansing mechanisms present, it seems likely that the colonization of the mouth, nasopharyngeal area, small intestine, or other environments which contain surfaces exposed to a fluid flow, such as the eye, bladder, heart, etc., requires that bacteria either become firmly attached to a surface or else find a protected niche to avoid being washed way. If organisms were to remain free in the bathing secretions, their rates of multiplication would have to exceed the washout rate caused by the fluid flow. However, experimentally derived estimates have suggested that the bacterial biomass in the intestinal canal of mice, hamsters, and guinea pigs (44), and in the bovine rumen (27), doubles only two to four times each day; similar estimates have been calculated for the overall turnover of bacteria in the mouth (41). This relatively slow rate of growth appears to be characteristic of a number of natural environments, for bacteria present in seawater also appear to double only a few times each day (15). Since humans secrete 1 to 1.5 liters of saliva each day and swallow every few minutes during their waking moments, it is apparent that bacteria cannot maintain themselves free in oral secretions solely by their rates of proliferation. Because of the generally rapid rate of removal of free bacteria from nasal passages, tonsular areas, and the small intestine, a similar situation probably exists in these sites. The attachment of an organism to a host tissue therefore appears to be the first essential step for persistent colonization. It follows that the extent to which a species can attach to a surface would influence the extent to which it can colonize.

In addition to their adsorption affinity, the number of cells of a bacterial species which adsorb to a surface is related to the number of cells available. This has been shown for the attachment of oral streptococci to buccal epithelial cells and to saliva-coated hydroxyapatite surfaces which mimic teeth (9). It has also been noted for the attachment of *S. faecalis* to urothelial cells (70), for lactobacilli to rodent stomach epithelial cells (95), and for *Vibrio cholerae* cells to isolated brush borders of rabbit intestinal mucosa (56). In an in vivo situation, van Houte and Green (103) have shown that the number of cells of *S. mutans* or *S. sanguis* which can be recovered from tooth surfaces a few hours after careful cleaning is related to their concentrations naturally present in saliva. Approximately 10^3 to 10^4 cells of *S. sanguis* must be present per ml of saliva before it becomes statistically probable that one cell will become associated with a cleaned tooth surface. Tenfold-higher salivary concentrations of *S. mutans* are required to attain this because of its innately lower adsorption affinity for teeth.

That only a small percentage of available bacteria attach to epithelial surfaces under conditions of equilibrium has been noted in several in vitro models. Depending upon their adsorption affinities, generally 10% or less of the available cells of *S. salivarius*, *S. miteor*, *S. pyogenes*, *Veillonella*, *Actinomyces*, and other bacteria become associated with human buccal epithelial cells at equilibrium in reaction mixtures containing 10^5 epithelial cells and 10^8 bacteria per ml (49). Likewise, only a fraction of the available cells of *S. faecalis* (70) and of *V. cholerae* (56) attach to human urothelial cells or to rabbit brush borders, respectively, when tested under generally comparable conditions. Similar observations have been made for the attachment of piliated gonococci to tissue-cultured cells (96) and for the attachment of *Treponema pallidum* to cultured rabbit testicular cells (29). Under such conditions, only a fraction of the total surface area of the epithelial cells becomes occupied by adsorbed organisms.

In the case of cleaned teeth, it has been calculated that about 1% of their surface area becomes occupied by bacteria after exposure to saliva containing about 10^8 organisms per ml (50).

The adsorption of a bacterial cell to a tooth or to an epithelial cell surface does not necessarily imply that the organism will become sufficiently firmly bound to resist removal by the cleansing actions present and thus colonize. Rather, a variety of observations indicate that most bacterial cells which initially associate with a host surface become desorbed. For example, when streptomycin-labeled strains of indigenous bacteria are introduced into the mouth, their numbers recoverable from oral surfaces decrease over time (50). In vitro models have also shown the adsorption of cells of *S. mutans* (W. F. Clark and R. J. Gibbons, unpublished data) and of *S. miteor* (46) to untreated and to saliva-coated hydroxyapatite to be reversible. Furthermore, certain strains of *S. mutans* have been reported to associate reversibly with the teeth of rodents maintained on glucose-containing diets (104). In the case of intestinal surfaces, Jones and co-workers observed that maximal adsorption of *V. cholerae* cells to isolated brush borders occurred within 15 min; however, the number of attached vibrios decreased sharply thereafter, and few remained attached after 45 min. The adsorption of *V. cholerae* cells to the intestinal mucosa of live animals exhibits similar phases, but has a different time course. Nelson and co-workers (80) noted that it took 1 h for large numbers of vibrios to become attached to the intestinal villi, but relatively few organisms remained attached 12 h after challenge.

On the basis of the observations described above, it seems clear that the majority of bacterial cells which initially associate with a host tissue become desorbed. Evidently, only a small fraction of initially adherent organisms become sufficiently firmly bound over time to promote long-term colonization.

INFLUENCE OF DESQUAMATION

Persistent colonization of a rock in a flowing stream, or of a tooth in the oral cavity, could conceivably be initiated by a single bacterial cell becoming firmly attached and subsequently proliferating. However, a greater adherence-selective pressure probably exists on mucosal surfaces because of desquamation (50). Desquamation continuously exposes new epithelial cells which must also be colonized by a species if its populations are to remain in that environment. This recolonization conceivably could occur by contiguous growth of bacteria from one epithelial cell to another on very densely populated surfaces. However, the number of indigenous bacteria found on epithelial cells in the mouth ranges from 10 to 15 per buccal epithelial cell to 100 or so per tongue epithelial cell (49). Microscopic observations give the impression that densities of this order are probably not sufficient to make direct spread of bacteria an event of high frequency. Rather, newly exposed epithelial cells probably more commonly become recolonized by free bacteria transiently present in the secretions. Under such conditions, colonization of a bacterial species on a mucosal surface would require not only that at least one cell become sufficiently firmly attached to resist removal, but, in addition, that a certain percentage of progeny of the organism must be desorbed and available to reattach to newly exposed surfaces. Persistent colonization would therefore entail a cycle of events consisting of cell attachment, proliferation, dislodgment of progeny, and the reattachment of some progeny to new surfaces.

Several observations suggest that bacterial colonization of at least some oral and intestinal surfaces takes place in this manner. For example, the large numbers of bacteria continuously found in saliva (up to 10^9/ml) represent organisms which are dislodged or desorbed from oral surfaces; the tongue and teeth have been shown to be major contributors (45, 50, 61). That cells of a bacterial species transiently present in saliva play an important role in colonization is suggested by studies of the ecology of *S. sanguis*. This organism comprises about 40% of the streptococcal populations of teeth and about 15% of the steptococci on the tongue dorsum; its numbers in saliva approach 10^8/ml (50). However, its ability to colonize the tongue is dependent upon its colonization of the teeth, for it does not colonize the mouths of infants prior to tooth eruption, and it can no longer be detected in the mouths of adults following extraction of all teeth (17). Evidently, cells of *S. sanguis* derived from the teeth are essential for continued maintenance of this species on the tongue; this argues that *S. sanguis* cells do not spread with sufficiently high frequency from one epithelial cell to another on the relatively densely populated tongue dorsum by contiguous growth.

A similar situation probably exists in the intestinal canal, for the ability of enteric pathogens to attach to the lining of the small intestine has been shown to promote their colonization, and during infections a significant fraction of the bacterial populations present are found free in the lumen (10, 58, 90). Such observations suggest that a balance between bacterial desorption and attachment is probably important for persistent colonization on many desquamating surfaces. It may even be theorized that if too high a percentage of the progeny of an organism become firmly attached to an epithelial surface this would be disadvantageous for the species because the entire microcolony could be lost by desquamation.

The rate of epithelial cell desquamation appears to be related to the microbial burden imposed upon the tissue. Thus, epithelial cell turnover is slower in the intestinal canal of germfree rodents than in conventional animals (1). Sloughing of the intestinal lining during certain acute enteric infections appears to be analogous; larger numbers of sloughed epithelial cells are also associated with urinary tract infections. In the human mouth, the highest rates of epithelial cell turnover occur in the gingiva proximate to the large bacterial accumulations which develop on teeth (88). The responsiveness of desquamation to bacterial colonization suggests that it serves as a host defense mechanism which contributes to the cleansing action operative on mucosal surfaces. It limits the mass of bacteria which can accumulate. Teeth lack this important characteristic, and, consequently, large quantities of colonizing bacteria accumulate. That dental caries and periodontal diseases are the most prevalent bacterial infections afflicting humans suggests the vulnerability of such a nondesquamating tissue to microbial attack.

EFFECTS OF MUSCULAR MOVEMENTS

Muscular movements also appear to augment the cleansing action operative on mucosal surfaces and, in this manner, influence bacterial colonization. Peristaltic motility is thought to be important in preventing the buildup of large bacterial populations in the small intestine. That peristalsis can affect bacterial colonization is suggested by several observations. *Salmonella enteriditis* or strains of *Shigella flexneri* generally do not colonize the small intestine of rodents and guinea pigs when given orally. However, these organisms will colonize if peristaltic motility is retarded by morphine or opium administration (32, 77). Similarly, Abrams and Bishop (2) noted that *Salmonella typhimurium* colonized the small intestine of germfree mice to a greater extent than in conventional animals, but they were unable to demonstrate that the indigenous flora of the conventional animals exerted antibacterial effects against this organism. They noted that the rate of peristalsis was lower in germfree than in conventional animals (2, 3) and suggested that this accounted for the differences in colonization.

The contribution of cilial beating to the cleansing activities of respiratory passages is well known. Moreover, the presence of calculi in the urinary tract which impair the normal cleansing action is generally believed to predispose to bladder or renal infections. In the mouth, mastication and muscular movements of the tongue and cheek, as well as those involved in the swallowing reflex, probably play a comparable role, but data regarding their potential effects upon bacterial colonization are lacking. Different degrees of cleansing action do appear to be imposed upon various microenvironments contained in the oral cavity which affect colonization (50). Thus, organisms with a comparatively low adsorption affinity for teeth, such as lactobacilli and *S. mutans*, mainly colonize protected tooth sites such as the deep fissures on occlusal surfaces and contact points between teeth; these organisms are also regularly found in carious lesions.

ADHERENCE AS A DETERMINANT OF THE COLONIZATION OF OTHER BACTERIA

Within the past year or two, data have become available which suggest that selective adherence also plays an important role in the tropisms and colonization of bacteria in addition to indigenous oral organisms. The selective attachment of pathogenic bacteria to different mucosal surfaces is illustrated by the observation that when mixed suspensions of *S. pyogenes* and *E. coli* are applied to the tongue and bladder mucosa of rats, larger numbers of *S. pyogenes* adsorb to the tongue dorsum, whereas larger numbers of *E. coli* attach to bladder mucosa (26). Strains of *S. pyogenes* have also been shown to attach well to human buccal and pharyngeal cells, whereas indigenous and enteropathogenic strains of *E. coli* adhere feebly.

Streptococcus agalactiae and *Staphylococcus aureus* are the most common pathogens involved in mammary gland infections of cows. Strains of both species isolated from animals with subclinical mastitis have been found to adhere far better to udder ductular epithelial cells in vitro than other bacteria commonly found in the cow's environment (35); these include strains of *Corynebacterium bovis*, *Streptococcus faecalis*, and *E. coli*. When washed suspensions of these organisms were infused into the udder of living animals, similar adherence selectivity was observed, although the numbers of bacteria which attached per epithelial cell were lower than in vitro.

The adherence of indigenous human vaginal bacteria, and of organisms associated with genital tract infections, to vaginal epithelial cells has been studied by Mardh and Westrom (71). They observed that freshly isolated gonococci, group B streptococci, and *Corynebacterium vaginalis* attached in higher numbers to such cells than did strains of *E. coli*, *Aerobacter aerogenes*, *Bacteroides melaninogenicus*, fusobacteria, and *Lactobacillus acidophilus*. They concluded that the experimentally observed adherence of these organisms generally correlated with current opinion of their relative virulence in genital tract infections.

The adherence of bacteria isolated from the urine of patients with persistent bacteriuria to epithelial cells contained in freshly voided urine has also been studied by Mardh and his colleagues (70). Freshly isolated strains of *Staphylococcus saprophiticus* attached better than those of *S. epidermidis*, and the former species is more commonly associated with acute cystourethritis in young women. They also found that the adherence of strains of *E. coli* to epithelial cells collected from the same individual on different occasions, and to exfoliated cells from males and females, was similar.

Since attachment of bacteria seems to be a prerequisite for colonization of several host tissues, it should be noted that adherence has proven to be a virulence factor for a variety of pathogenic organisms. These include strains of *Shigella flexneri* (62), enteropathogenic *E. coli* (10, 24, 58, 90), gonococci (82, 96), *Vibrio cholerae* (52), *S. mutans* (50), and *S. pyogenes* (25). Adherence is also related to the virulence of organisms which infect plants, including *Agrobacterium tumefaciens* (68) and *Rhizobium* species (22). It seems apparent that adherence will prove to be essential for the natural colonization and hence virulence of a variety of other pathogenic organisms.

SELECTIVE ADHERENCE AND THE HOST TROPISMS OF BACTERIA

The selectivity of bacterial attachment to tissues is surprisingly high, and data are available which suggest that this may account for the host tropisms displayed by a variety of bacteria. In the case of indigenous oral organisms, *S. salivarius* and *S. sanguis* are regularly found on the human tongue dorsum, but they are not indigenous on the tongues of rats. However, strains of *S. faecalis* and serumrequiring diphtheroids are prominent on the tongues of rats, but they are not commonly detected on human tongues. When mixtures of labeled strains of these organisms were introduced into the mouths of humans and rats, much higher proportions of *S. salivarius* and *S. sanguis* adsorbed to the human tongues, whereas *S. faecalis* and the diphtheroids adsorbed far better to the tongues of rats (48). Furthermore, when germfree rats were infected with mixtures of *S. salivarius* and *S. faecalis*, colonization of the tongue dorsum paralleled the adherence selectivities of these organisms.

The adherence of lactobacilli to crop epithelium of chickens and to stomach epithelium of rodents has also been shown to exhibit a striking host specificity. Fuller and co-workers (36, 38) observed that strains of several *Lactobacillus* species isolated from the crop walls of chickens, quail, pheasants, pigeons, and ducks attached to crop epithelial cells of chickens, whereas lactobacilli derived from mammals including humans, pigs, horses, dogs, rats, mice, gerbils, guinea pigs, rabbits, and cows did not. Suegara and his colleagues (95) reported similar findings. They showed that strains of *L. salivarius*, *L. fermentii*, and *L. acidophilus* derived from rats generally attached well to keratinized stomach epithelial cells of conventional rats and mice and to those of germfree rats; however, these strains did not adhere to chicken crop epithelial cells. In contrast, lactobacilli isolated from chickens did not adhere to rat stomach epithelium, and *L. fermentii* and *L. acidophilus* strains isolated from swine did not attach to either rodent stomach epithelium or the crop epithelium of chickens.

There are examples of adherence determining bacterial host selectivity which do not involve mammals or fowl. The symbiotic host-parasite relationship in leguminous plants that results in nitrogen fixation is characterized by a high bacterium-host specificity. Strains of *Rhizobium* capable of inducing symbiotic infections in clover roots adsorb to the root hairs of their host, whereas noninfective *Rhizobium* strains do not (22). Other examples include the high degree of host specificity involved in phage-bacterium interactions (67) and in the predatory interactions between the *Bdellovibrio bacteriovorus* and its microbial hosts (93).

ADSORPTION OF BACTERIA TO SURFACES

The adsorption of bacteria to surfaces has been mainly studied by marine and soil microbiologists. ZoBell (108) and several subsequent investigators (19, 31, 73) noted that marine bacteria initially became loosely associated with a surface and that firm attachment occurred over time and was frequently associated with the synthesis of mucilaginous or holdfast material. Marshall and co-workers (73) distinguished two phases in the adsorption of bacteria to glass surfaces. They considered the initial phase of adsorption to be reversible and theorized that organisms in this phase were in a state of equilibrium, being attracted by van der Waals forces and repelled by the electric double-layer energies on the bacterial and adsorbent surface, respectively. The attachment of the organisms was observed to become more firm or "irreversible" over time, and they suggested that this was a result of the synthesis of extracellular polymeric material which could form a more stable bonding with the surface. As discussed previously, several observations suggest that the association of bacteria with mammalian surfaces is also reversible, at least in the early stages.

Daniels (19), Marshall (72), and Hattori and Hattori (53) have reviewed some of the factors which influence the adsorption of bacteria to solid adsorbents. The adsorption of bacteria to clay used in water purification has been reported to follow the kinetics of a Langmuir isotherm. Similarly, the adsorption of cells of *S. miteor* and *S. mutans* to untreated and to saliva-coated hydroxyapatite has also been found to be of the Langmuir type (46; Clark and Gibbons, unpublished data), but, to date, isotherms for the adsorption of bacteria to epithelial surfaces do not appear to have been studied.

Important variables recognized to influence the sorptive behavior of marine or soil bacteria include the species tested, the culture medium used for propagation, the culture age, and the bacterial cell concentration used (19). Important parameters of the sorption environment include the hydrogen ion concentration, the ionic strength, the incubation time and temperature, and the degree of agitation (19).

Only fragmented observations are available concerning the influence of these and other variables on the adsorption of bacteria to host tissues. Clearly, the character of the microorganism is important with regard to its species and its past history. Several investigators have noted that strains maintained by laboratory culture frequently, though not invariably, no longer attach well to a host surface. Thus, strains of *S. sanguis*, *S. mitis*, and *S. salivarius* unpredictably lose the ability to adsorb in high numbers to human buccal epithelial cells or to interact with mucinous glycoproteins (107). Laboratory-maintained strains of lactobacilli (95) and gonococci (70) have also been reported to adhere less well to epithelial cells than freshly isolated strains. In addition, Mardh and co-workers (70) noted that *E. coli* strains isolated from urine and transferred only twice attached in significantly fewer numbers to urothelial cells than did organisms originally present in urine. The decrease in ability of bacterial strains to attach to host tissues after laboratory culture is of interest, since many pathogenic organisms are known to lose virulence under similar conditions. However, this presents a serious problem in studies of bacterial attachment. Caution must clearly be used in attempting to extrapolate observations made with well-characterized, laboratory-maintained strains to the in vivo situation, and important observations should be confirmed with several freshly isolated strains.

The stage of growth has also been found to influence the adsorption of bacteria to epithelial surfaces in some instances. Thus, cells of three strains of *S. pyogenes* harvested from early stationary-phase cultures attached in higher numbers to human buccal epithelial cells than did streptococci prepared from exponential-phase cultures (26). However, *Lactobacillus* strains tended to adhere better to rat stomach epithelial cells when in logarithmic growth (95), whereas cells of *V. cholerae* had adhesive properties in both log and stationary growth phases (56); thus, generalizations cannot be made from one organism to another. That cultural conditions may significantly affect bacterial attachment to mammalian surfaces is indicated by the observation that *V. cholerae* cells grown in Trypticase soy broth attach to brush borders isolated from rabbit intestinal mucosa, whereas vibrios harvested from Trypticase soy agar do not (56).

Environmental variables may affect the attachment of different bacteria in various ways. For example, the adsorption of strains of *S. salivarius* and *S. pyogenes* (26) to human buccal cells, of *E. coli* to urothelial cells (70), and of lactobacilli to rat stomach epithelium (95) or to chicken crop (37) does not differ significantly between pH 5 and 8. However, the adsorption of *S. miteor* to saliva-coated hydroxyapatite shows a sharp pH maximum at pH 6 (66), and the adherence of gonococci to urothelial cells increases with increasing acidity (70). It is evident that the optimal conditions must be delineated for each bacterium-host tissue interaction, and knowledge of the in vivo conditions is essential when attempting extrapolations from laboratory observations.

The nature of the surface clearly has a pronounced effect upon bacterial attachment; the presence of adsorbed molecules can also exert significant influences. Thus, oral bacteria adsorb differently to hydroxyapatite containing a film of adsorbed salivary components than to un-treated hydroxyapatite (46, 54, 66); the number of cells of some species which attach is increased by the salivary coating, whereas the adherence of other organisms is decreased. Similarly, Meadows (75) observed that glass treated with gelatin or casein adsorbed more cells of *Pseudomonas liquefaciens*, *E. coli*, and *Flavobacterium* species, whereas treatment with salmine or albumin resulted in fewer adsorbed organisms. Exposure of polystyrene to various proteins also alters its adsorptive properties for bacteria (30).

BACTERIAL HEMAGGLUTINATION

Some bacteria, particularly those with pili, attach to and agglutinate erythrocytes of certain host species (13). Because of its simplicity, direct bacterial hemagglutination can be a useful tool for studying adherent interactions between bacteria and host tissues. However, it seems essential to determine that the bacterial and host cell surface components involved in the hemagglutination reaction are similar to those involved in attachment of the organism to the host tissue of interest. Kondo and co-workers (60) presented evidence that the hemagglutinating activities of *Leptotrichia buccalis* entailed molecular interactions similar to those involved in their adherence to saliva-coated enamel powder and their interactions with salivary glycoproteins. On the other hand, *V. cholerae*-induced hemagglutination has different characteristics than adhesion of the organism to isolated brush borders prepared from rabbit intestine, and this, in turn, differs from vibrio associations with slices of rabbit intestinal mucosa (34, 50, 57). It should also be noted that several bacteria attach well to specific epithelial cell surfaces and yet do not agglutinate erythrocytes (47).

BACTERIAL POLYMERS PROMOTING FIRM ATTACHMENT

Relatively little is known about the polymers possessed by various bacteria which may interact with host tissue components so as to increase the strength of the adsorption bonds and promote more firm attachment. Cells of *S. salivarius* (51), *S. miteor* (65), and *S. pyogenes* (25) possess a "fuzzy coat" consisting of thin, densely distributed surface fibrils which are morphologically distinct from pili. Electron micrographs suggest that these fibrils interact with surface components of epithelial cells (25, 51). Trypsin treatment removes these fibrils and markedly reduces the number of streptococci which attach to epithelial cells; this indicates that the fibrils increase the strength of the adsorption bonds involved (25, 51). The fuzzy surface coating of *S. pyogenes* cells is known to contain the trypsin-sensitive, type-specific M antigen associated with virulence of the organism (97). That the M antigen may in some way be associated with attachment of *S. pyogenes* is also suggested by the observations that M-negative mutants attach feebly and that specific anti-M antibodies inhibit attachment (25). The involvement of a proteinaceous component is also consistent with the observations that heat treatment markedly impairs the attachment of *S. pyogenes* (26) and *S. salivarius* (51). On the other hand, Beachey (9), and Ofek and co-workers (81) showed that lipoteichoic acid extracted from heat-treated group A streptococci will bind to epithelial cell surfaces and also block the adsorption of intact cells of the organism. The well-recognized ability of lipoteichoic acids to bind to cell membranes makes them attractive molecules for mediating bacterial adherent interactions. However, it is not yet known whether the lipoteichoic acids of *S. pyogenes* possess the same binding specificities as intact streptococci. Moreover, the relative heat stability and trypsin resistance of lipoteichoic acid suggest that it is not the sole polymer involved in the adherence of *S. pyogenes* to epithelial surfaces.

In contrast to these observations with streptococci, the attachment of lactobacilli to chicken crop epithelium is not affected by heat or trypsin treatment (37). Ruthinium-stained transmission electron photomicrographs suggest the involvement of polysaccharide components. Other evidence supporting this possibility is that adhesive strains of lactobacilli agglutinate with polyvalent concanavalin A and that treatment of such strains with monovalent concanavalin inhibits attachment.

It is reasonable to believe that the chances for perpetuation of a bacterial species in nature would be increased if the organism could have adapted to colonize many tissues and hosts during the course of evolution. However, in view of the sharply defined host and tissue tropisms of many indigenous and pathogenic bacteria, it is apparent that this has not occurred. This suggests that multiple surface components may be required for bacterial colonization of a host tissue, rather than a single component which would be more readily altered by mutation. The limited data available in fact suggest that at least some bacteria possess multiple recognition and binding components which mediate their adherent interactions. Thus, cells of *S. mutans* specifically interact with high-molecular-weight mucinous glycoproteins found in whole saliva (47) and in parotid secretion (28). These salivary substances adsorb selectively to hydroxyapatite (28), and the attachment of this organism to teeth appears to entail interactions with such constituents (50). *S. mutans* also synthesizes extracellular glucans specifically from sucrose, and this is associated with its ability to accumulate in large masses on hard surfaces (50). The organism possesses a specific glucan-binding protein (69) which attaches glucan molecules to its cell surface; this results in streptococcal aggregation (43). *S. mutans* cells also adsorb in high numbers to glucan-treated surfaces. In addition to these binding properties, the glucosyl transferases elaborated by *S. mutans* which are involved in glucan synthesis also bind to glucan molecules, and evidence is available which suggests that aggregates of enzyme bound to glucan molecules on the streptococcal surface can serve as additional glucan-binding receptors (39). Thus, *S. mutans* cells appear to have at least three and probably more recognition molecules which are involved in its overall adherence and colonization.

V. cholerae cells also appear to possess multiple recognition systems which are separately associated with its attachment to erythrocytes, to isolated brush borders, and to slices of rabbit intestinal mucosa, respectively (34, 56, 57). Guentzel and Berry (52) demonstrated that nonmotile mutants of *V. cholerae* were both less virulent and less adhesive to the intestinal lining of mice than motile forms. They suggested that active motility might increase the chance for the vibrios to become associated with the intestinal mucosa, and perhaps also to penetrate the mucous lining. However, Jones and Freter (57) have shown that vibrios lacking flagella do not attach to isolated brush border membranes prepared from rabbit intestines or induce hemagglutination, even when their concentrations are elevated to increase the chance of contact. They suggested that the flagellum carries or is associated with an adhesive recognition component(s) in these models.

Pili have been associated with the adherence of gonococci (82, 96, 105), *Proteus* (87), and *E. coli* (13, 79) strains to epithelial surfaces. Pili are also associated with gonococcal virulence (82, 96); they further mediate attachment of this organism to sperm cells (55) and to erythrocytes (16). However, the interaction of gonococci with leukocytes appears to be involved in a different recognition component (98, 99). The K88 antigen is a proteinaceous pilus-like surface component possessed by certain *E. coli* strains which are enteropathogenic for piglets, and it has been shown to be required for adherence and virulence (58). This component is determined by a plasmid (94), and antibodies to it are protective (58, 84). Preparations of K88 antigen agglutinate guinea pig erythrocytes at 4°C, but not at 37°C, whereas this antigen adheres to piglet intestinal cells at both temperatures (43); this suggests that the receptors on the two types of mammalian cells are not identical. Other strains of *E. coli* do not possess K88 antigen, yet they adhere well to intestinal epithelium and are enteropathogenic for pigs (79). In the case of these strains, it has been suggested that the polysaccharide K antigens and/or pili contribute to their adhesive and colonizing abilities.

Surface components of certain plant pathogens are also receiving attention regarding their role in adherence and colonization. Lipopolysaccharides isolated from *Agrobacterium tumefaciens* block attachment of the organism to pinto bean leaves, thereby preventing tumor initiation (71). Lipopolysaccharides of avirulent *Agrobacterium* strains do not bind to leaves and are ineffective; this illustrates the high degree of specificity involved. The attachment of *Rhizobium trifolii* strains to clover root hairs, which leads to infection, represents a particularly interesting model. Infective strains interact specifically with a lectin produced by the plant, whereas noninfective strains do not (6). Such infective *Rhizobium* strains possess a surface polysaccharide antigen which is serologically cross-reactive with a component on the root hairs, and it has been suggested that polyvalent lectin links the organism to the root hairs via these cross-reactive components (21). In view of the lectin-like properties of bacterial pili, the glucan-binding protein of *S. mutans*, and the components of oral streptococci involved in binding mucinous glycoproteins, it is possible that related mechanisms may prove to be involved in adherence specificities of these and other bacteria.

RECEPTORS FOR BACTERIA ON HOST TISSUES

The nature of the receptors on host tissues with which bacteria interact have not been well characterized. Incomplete evidence suggests that cell surface glycoproteins or glycolipids serve as receptors for some bacterial species. Thus, certain sugar constituents of mammalian glycoproteins specifically inhibit hemagglutination reactions by some piliated organisms (13). Attachment of strains of *S. mitis*, *S. sanguis*, and *S. salivarius* to human buccal epithelial cells is also associated with surface glycoproteins, for antibodies to specific blood group antigens, or concanavalin A, mask the receptors on epithelial cells required for their attachment (107). In addition, blood group-reactive salivary glycoproteins are known to comprise part of the acquired pellicle on human teeth (91) to which indigenous oral organisms attach, and oral streptococci selectively bind these components (47). Kondo and co-workers (60) have shown that the same sugars which inhibit hemagglutination of human erythrocytes by *Leptotrichia buccalis* cells also inhibit adsorption of the organism to saliva-coated enamel powder; this suggests that molecules possessing similar binding determinants are involved in these adherent interactions.

Mucinous glycoproteins of secretions frequently inhibit the attachment of bacteria to host tissues, and this also suggests that cell surface glycoproteins, including those with blood group antigen reactivity, may serve as bacterial receptors. Thus, glycoproteins isolated from swine intestine inhibit hemagglutination induced by K88 antigen preparations derived from pathogenic strains of *E. coli* (40). Blood group-reactive salivary mucins have also been shown to inhibit the attachment of oral streptococci to buccal epithelial cells (107).

The possession of determinants of blood group antigens by both mucins and surface components of epithelial cells suggests that the mucinous glycoproteins of host secretions mimic the surfaces they bathe and, in this manner, competitively inhibit bacterial adsorption. Such a hypothesis can explain how mucins augment the cleansing action of secretions, and it provides a teleological basis for understanding why these components exhibit microheterogeneity in their carbohydrate structures and why they possess blood group substance reactivity (107). Blood group-reactive glycoproteins and glycolipids are thought to form the basis of the recognition systems by which mammalian cells adhere to one another (83). They are recognized to differ in their distribution on various cell types within a mammalian host; they also differ between different mammalian species. If they prove to be associated with receptors involved in the attachment of a wide range of bacteria, they could provide a basis for understanding the remarkable specificities involved in bacterial attachment and colonization of different organs, tissues, and mammalian hosts. The oligosaccharide chains of mucins, glycoproteins, and glycolipids are not synthesized by a template mechanism; rather, the appropriate genes which code for each type of molecule result in the formation of a specific complex of glycosyl transferases which stepwise and selectively add monosaccharides to the ends of growing oligosaccharide chains (83). Thus, mucins and cell surface glycoproteins, more than many other molecules, are subject to considerable environmental modification. It is therefore intriguing to speculate that factors known to influence host resistance or susceptibility to infectious agents, such as stress, age, malnutrition, hormonal influences, etc., conceivably could be expressed by an alteration in glycoprotein synthesis which affects bacterial colonization.

LITERATURE CITED

1. **Abrams, G. D., H. Bauer, and H. Spring.** 1963. Influence of the normal flora on mucosal morphology and cellular renewal in the ileum. A comparison of germfree and conventional mice. Lab. Invest. **12:**355–364.
2. **Abrams, G. D., and J. E. Bishop.** 1966. Effect of the normal microbial flora on the resistance of the small intestine to infection. J. Bacteriol. **92:**1604–1608.
3. **Abrams, G. D., and J. E. Bishop.** 1967. Effect of the normal microbial flora on gastrointestinal motility. Proc. Soc. Exp. Biol. Med. **126:**201–304.
4. **Appleton, J. L. T., H. Klein, and C. E. Palmer.** 1938. A method for measuring the rate of elimination of bacteria from the human mouth. Am. J. Hyg. **28:**213–231.
5. **Arbuckle, J. B. R.** 1972. The attachment of *Clostridium welchii* (Cl perfringens) type C to intestinal villi of pigs. J. Pathol. **106:**65–72.
6. **Bahlool, B. B., and E. L. Schmidt.** 1974. Lectins: a possible basis for specificity in the rhizobium-legume root nodule symbiosis. Science **185:**269–271.
7. **Barksdale, L.** 1970. *Corynebacterium diphtheriae* and its relatives. Bacteriol. Rev. **34:**378–422.
8. **Bauchop, T., R. T. J. Clarke, and J. C. Newhook.** 1975. Scanning electron microscope study of bacteria associated with the rumen epithelium of sheep. Appl. Microbiol. **30:**668–675.
9. **Beachey, E. H.** 1975. Binding of group A streptococci to human oral mucosal cells by lipoteichoic acid. Trans. Assoc. Am. Physicians **88:**285–292.
10. **Bertschinger, H. V., H. W. Moon, and S. C. Whipp.** 1972. Association of *Escherichia coli* with the small intestinal epithelium. I. Comparison of enteropathogenic and non-enteropathogenic porcine strains in pigs. Infect. Immun. **5:**595–605.
11. **Bloomfield, A. L.** 1920. The fate of bacteria introduced into the upper air passages. V. The Friedlander bacilli. Johns Hopkins Hosp. Bull. **31:**203–206.
12. **Bloomfield, A. L.** 1920. The fate of bacteria introduced into the upper air passages. II. *B. coli* and *Staphylococcus albus*. Johns Hopkins Hosp. Bull. **13:**14–19.
13. **Brinton, C. C.** 1967. Contributions of pili to the specificity of the bacterial surface, p. 37–70. *In* B. D. Davis and L. Warren (ed.), The specificity of cell surfaces. Prentice Hall, N.J.
14. **Brock, T. D.** 1966. Principles of microbial ecology. Prentice Hall, Englewood Cliffs, N.J.
15. **Brock, T. D.** 1967. Bacterial growth rate in the sea: direct analysis by thymidine autoradiography. Science **155:**81–83.
16. **Buchanan, T. M., and W. A. Pearce.** 1976. Pili as a mediator of the attachment of gonococci to human erythrocytes. Infect. Immun. **13:**1483–1489.
17. **Carlsson, J., G. Soderholm, and J. Almfeldt.** 1969. Prevalence of *S. sanguis* and *S. mutans* in the mouth of persons wearing full dentures. Arch. Oral Biol. **14:**243–249.
18. **Corpe, W. A.** 1970. Attachment of marine bacteria to solid surfaces, p. 73–87. *In* R. S. Manly (ed.), Adhesion in biological systems. Academic Press Inc., New York.
19. **Daniels, S. L.** 1972. The adsorption of microorganisms onto solid surfaces: a review. Dev. Ind. Microbiol. **13:**211–253.
20. **Davis, C. P., J. S. McAllister, and D. C. Savage.** 1973. Microbial colonization of the intestinal epithelium in suckling mice. Infect. Immun. **7:**666–672.
21. **Dazzo, F. B., and D. H. Hubbell.** 1975. Cross-reactive antigens and lectin as determinants of symbiotic specificity in the *Rhizobium*-clover association. Appl. Microbiol. **30:**1017–1033.
22. **Dazzo, F. B., C. A. Napoli, and D. H. Hubbell.** 1976. Adsorption of bacteria to roots as related to host specificity in the *Rhizobium*-clover symbiosis. Appl. Environ. Microbiol. **32:**166–171.
23. **Dixon, J. M. S.** 1960. The fate of bacteria in the small intestine. J. Pathol. Bacteriol. **79:**131–140.
24. **Drucker, M. M., R. Yeivin, and T. G. Sacks.** 1967. Pathogenesis of *Escherichia coli* enteritis in the ligated rabbit gut. Isr. J. Med. Sci. **3:**445–452.
25. **Ellen, R. P., and R. J. Gibbons.** 1972. M-protein associated adherence of *Streptococcus pyogenes* to epithelial surfaces: a prerequisite for virulence. Infect. Immun. **5:**826–830.
26. **Ellen, R. P., and R. J. Gibbons.** 1974. Parameters affecting the adherence and tissue tropisms of *Streptococcus pyogenes*. Infect. Immun. **9:**85–91.
27. **El-Shazly, K., and R. E. Hungate.** 1965. Fermentation capacity as a measure of net growth of rumen microorganisms. Appl. Microbiol. **13:**62–69.
28. **Ericson, T., and J. Magnusson.** 1976. Affinity for hydroxyapatite of salivary substances inducing aggregation of oral streptococci. Caries Res. **10:**8–18.
29. **Fitzgerald, T. J., J. N. Miller, and J. A. Sykes.** 1975. *Treponema pallidum* (Nichols strain) in tissue cultures: cellular attachment, entry, and survival. Infect. Immun. **11:**1133–1140.
30. **Fletcher, M.** 1976. The effects of proteins on bacterial attachment to polystyrene. J. Gen. Microbiol. **94:**400–404.
31. **Floodgate, G. D.** 1972. The mechanism of bacterial attachment to detritus in aquatic systems. Mem. Ist. Ital. Idrobiol. **29**(Suppl.)**:**309–323.
32. **Formal, S. B., G. D. Abrams, H. Schneider, and H. Spring.** 1963. Experimental *Shigella* infections. VI. Role of the small intestine in an experimental infection in guinea pigs. J. Bacteriol. **85:**119–125.
33. **Freter, R.** 1972. Parameters affecting the association of vibrios with the intestinal surface in experimental cholera. Infect. Immun. **6:**134–141.
34. **Freter, R., and G. W. Jones.** 1976. Adhesive properties of *Vibrio cholerae*: nature of the interaction with intact mucosal surfaces. Infect. Immun. **14:**246–256.
35. **Frost, A. J.** 1975. Selective adhesion of microorganisms to the ductular epithelium of the bovine mammary gland. Infect. Immun. **12:**1154–1156.
36. **Fuller, R.** 1973. Ecological studies on the lactobacillus flora associated with the crop epithelium of the fowl. J. Appl. Bacteriol. **36:**131–139.
37. **Fuller, R.** 1975. Nature of the determinant responsible for the adhesion of lactobacilli to chicken crop epithelial cells. J. Gen. Microbiol. **87:**245–250.
38. **Fuller, R., and B. E. Brooker.** 1974. Lactobacilli which attach to the crop epithelium of the fowl. Am. J. Clin. Nutr. **27:**1305–1312.
39. **Germaine, G. R., and C. F. Schachtele.** 1976. *Streptococcus mutans* dextransucrase: mode of interaction with high-molecular-weight dextran and role in cellular aggregation. Infect. Immun. **13:**365–372.
40. **Gibbons, R. A., G. W. Jones, and R. Sellwood.** 1975. An attempt to identify the intestinal receptor for the K88

adhesion by means of a haemagglutination test using glycoproteins and fractions from sow colostrum. J. Gen. Microbiol. **86**:228–240.

41. **Gibbons, R. J.** 1964. The bacteriology of dental caries. J. Dent. Res. **43**:1021–1028.

42. **Gibbons, R. J.** 1973. Bacterial adherence in infection and immunity, p. 115–131. *In* J. B. Robbins, R. E. Horton, and R. M. Krause (ed.), New approaches for inducing natural immunity to pyrogenic organisms. DHEW publication no. (NIH) 74–553.

43. **Gibbons, R. J., and R. J. Fitzgerald.** 1969. Dextran-induced agglutination of *Streptococcus mutans* and its potential role in the formation of microbial dental plaque. J. Bacteriol. **98**:341–346.

44. **Gibbons, R. J., and B. Kapsimalis.** 1967. Estimates of the overall rate of growth of the intestinal microflora of hamsters, guinea pigs, and mice. J. Bacteriol. **93**:510–512.

45. **Gibbons, R. J., B. Kapsimalis, and S. S. Socransky.** 1964. The source of salivary bacteria. Arch. Oral Biol. **9**:101–103.

46. **Gibbons, R. J., E. C. Moreno, and D. M. Spinell.** 1976. Model delineating the effects of a salivary pellicle on the adsorption of *Streptococcus miteor* onto hydroxyapatite. Infect. Immun. **14**:1109–1112.

47. **Gibbons, R. J., and V. Qureshi.** 1976. Interactions of *Streptococcus mutans* and other oral bacteria with blood group reactive substances, p. 163–181. *In* W. J. Loesche and H. M. Stiles (ed.), Microbial aspects of dental caries. Information Retrieval Inc., Washington, D.C.

48. **Gibbons, R. J., D. M. Spinell, and Z. Skobe.** 1976. Selective adherence as a determinant of the host tropisms of certain indigenous and pathogenic bacteria. Infect. Immun. **13**:238–246.

49. **Gibbons, R. J., and J. van Houte.** 1971. Selective bacterial adherence to oral epithelial surfaces and its role as an ecological determinant. Infect. Immun. **3**:567–573.

50. **Gibbons, R. J., and J. van Houte.** 1975. Bacterial adherence in oral microbial ecology. Annu. Rev. Microbiol. **29**:19–44.

51. **Gibbons, R. J., J. van Houte, and W. F. Liljemark.** 1972. Some parameters affecting the adherence of *S. salivarius* to oral epithelial surfaces. J. Dent. Res. **51**:424–435.

52. **Guentzel, M. N., and L. J. Berry.** 1975. Motility as a virulence factor for *Vibrio cholerae*. Infect. Immun. **11**:890–897.

53. **Hattori, T., and R. Hattori.** 1976. The physical environment in soil microbiology: an attempt to extend principles of microbiology to soil microorganisms. Crit. Rev. Microbiol. **4**:423–461.

54. **Hillman, J. D., J. van Houte, and R. J. Gibbons.** 1970. Sorption of bacteria to human enamel powder. Arch. Oral Biol. **15**:899–903.

55. **James-Holmquest, A. N., J. Swanson, T. M. Buchanan, R. D. Wende, and R. P. Williams.** 1974. Differential attachment by piliated and nonpiliated *Neisseria gonorrhoeae* to human sperm. Infect. Immun. **9**:897–902.

56. **Jones, G. W., G. D. Abrams, and R. Freter.** 1976. Adhesive properties of *Vibrio cholerae*: adhesion to isolated rabbit brush border membranes and hemagglutinating activity. Infect. Immun. **14**:232–239.

57. **Jones, G. W., and R. Freter.** 1976. Adhesive properties of *Vibrio cholerae*. Nature of the interaction with isolated rabbit brush-border membranes and human erythrocytes. Infect. Immun. **14**:240–245.

58. **Jones, G. W., and J. M. Rutter.** 1972. Role of the K88 antigen in the pathogenesis of neonatal diarrhea caused by *Escherichia coli* in piglets. Infect. Immun. **6**:918–927.

59. **Jones, S. J.** 1972. A special relationship between spher-

ical and filamentous microorganisms in mature human dental plaque. Arch. Oral Biol. **17**:613–616.

60. **Kondo, W., M. Sato, and H. Ozawa.** 1976. Haemagglutinating activity of *Leptotrichia buccalis* cells and their adherence to saliva-coated enamel powder. Arch. Oral Biol. **21**:363–369.

61. **Krasse, B.** 1954. The proportional distribution of *Streptococcus salivarius* and other streptococci in various parts of the mouth. Odontol. Revy **5**:203–211.

62. **Labrec, E. H., H. Schneider, T. J. Magnani, and S. B. Formal.** 1964. Epithelial cell penetration as an essential step in the pathogenesis of bacillary dysentery. J. Bacteriol. **88**:1503–1518.

63. **Larsen, D. H., and R. L. Dimmick.** 1964. Attachment and growth of bacteria on surfaces of continuous culture vessels. J. Bacteriol. **88**:1380–1387.

64. **Liljemark, W. F., and R. J. Gibbons.** 1971. Ability of *Veillonella* and *Neisseria* species to attach to oral surfaces and their proportions present indigenously. Infect. Immun. **4**:264–268.

65. **Liljemark, W. F., and R. J. Gibbons.** 1972. The proportional distribution and relative adherence of *Streptococcus miteor* (*mitis*) in the human oral cavity. Infect. Immun. **6**:852–859.

66. **Liljemark, W. F., and S. V. Schauer.** 1975. Studies on the bacterial components which bind *Streptococcus sanguis* and *Streptococcus mutans* to hydroxyapatite. Arch. Oral Biol. **20**:609–615.

67. **Lindberg, A. A.** 1973. Bacteriophage receptors. Annu. Rev. Microbiol. **27**:205–241.

68. **Lippincott, B. B., and J. A. Lippincott.** 1969. Bacterial attachment to a specific wound site as an essential stage of tumor initiation by *Agrobacterium tumefaciens*. J. Bacteriol. **97**:620–628.

69. **McCabe, M. M., and E. E. Smith.** 1976. Carbohydrate receptors of oral streptococci, p. 111–119. *In* W. H. Bowen, R. J. Genco, and T. C. O'Brien (ed.), Immunologic aspects of dental caries. Information Retrieval Inc., Washington, D.C.

70. **Mardh, P. A., S. Colleen, and B. Hovelius.** 1977. Attachment of bacteria to exfoliated cells from the urogenital tract. J. Infect. Dis., in press.

71. **Mardh, P. A., and L. Westrom.** 1976. Adherence of bacteria to vaginal epithelial cells. Infect. Immun. **13**:661–666.

72. **Marshall, K. C.** 1971. Sorptive interactions between soil particles and microorganisms. Soil Biochem. **2**:409–445.

73. **Marshall, K. C., M. Stout, and R. Mitchell.** 1971. Mechanism of the initial events in the sorption of marine bacteria to surfaces. J. Gen. Microbiol. **68**:337–348.

74. **Marshall, K. C., R. Stout, and R. Mitchell.** 1971. Selective sorption of bacteria from seawater. Can. J. Microbiol. **17**:1413–1416.

75. **Meadows, P. S.** 1971. The attachment of bacteria to solid surfaces. Arch. Mikrobiol. **75**:374–381.

76. **Meadows, P. S., and J. G. Anderson.** 1968. Microorganisms attached to marine sand grains. J. Mar. Biol. Assoc. U.K. **48**:161–175.

77. **Miller, C. P., and M. Bohnhoff.** 1962. A study of experimental *Salmonella* infection in the mouse. J. Infect. Dis. **111**:107–116.

78. **Morotomi, M., T. Watanabe, N. Suegara, Y. Kawai, and M. Mutai.** 1975. Distribution of indigenous bacteria in the digestive tract of conventional and gnotobiotic rats. Infect. Immun. **11**:962–968.

79. **Nagy, B., H. W. Moon, and R. E. Isaacson.** 1976. Colonization of porcine small intestine by *E. coli*: ileal colonization and adhesion by pig enteropathogens that lack K88 antigen and by some acapsular mutants. Infect. Immun. **13**:1214–1220.

80. **Nelson, E. T., J. D. Clements, and R. A. Finkelstein.** 1976. *Vibrio cholerae* adherence and colonization in

experimental cholera: electron microscopic studies. Infect. Immun. **14**:527–547.

81. **Ofek, I., E. H. Beachey, W. Jefferson, and G. L. Campbell.** 1975. Cell membrane binding properties of group A streptococcal lipoteichoic acid. J. Exp. Med. **141**:990–1003.

82. **Punsalang, A. P., Jr., and W. D. Sawyer.** 1973. Role of pili in the virulence of *Neisseria gonorrhoeae*. Infect. Immun. **8**:255–263.

83. **Rosemon, S.** 1970. The synthesis of complex carbohydrates by multiglucosyltransferase systems and their potential function in intercellular adhesion. Chem. Phys. Lipids **5**:270–297.

84. **Rutter, J. M., and J. C. Anderson.** 1972. Experimental neonatal diarrhaea caused by an enteropathogenic strain of *Escherichia coli* in piglets: a study of the disease and the effect of vaccinating the dam. J. Med. Microbiol. **5**:197–210.

85. **Savage, D. C.** 1972. Survival on mucosal epithelia, epithelial penetration and growth in tissues of pathogenic bacteria. Soc. Gen. Microbiol. **22**:25–28.

86. **Savage, D. C.** 1969. Microbial interference between indigenous yeast and lactobacilli in the rodent stomach. J. Bacteriol. **98**:1278–1283.

87. **Silverblatt, F.** 1974. Host-parasite interaction in the rat pelvis; a possible role for pili in the pathogenesis of pyelonephritis. J. Exp. Med. **140**:1696–1711.

88. **Skougaard, M.** 1970. Cell renewal, with special reference to the gingival epithelium. Adv. Oral Biol. **4**:261–288.

89. **Smith, H.** 1972. The little-known determinants of microbial pathogenicity. Soc. Gen. Microbiol. **22**:1–24.

90. **Smith, H. W., and S. Halls.** 1968. The production of oedema disease and diarrhaea in weaned pigs by the oral administration of *Escherichia coli*: factors that influence the course of the experimental disease. J. Med. Microbiol. **1**:45–59.

91. **Sonju, T., T. B. Christensen, L. Kornstad, and G. Rolla.** 1974. Electron microscopy, carbohydrate analyses, and biological activities of the proteins adsorbed in two hours to tooth surfaces. Caries Res. **8**:113–122.

92. **Staley, T. E., E. W. Jones, and L. D. Corley.** 1969. Attachment and penetration of *Escherichia coli* into intestinal epithelium of the ileum in new born pigs. Am. J. Pathol. **56**:371–392.

93. **Starr, M. P., and N. L. Baigent.** 1966. Parasitic interaction of *Bdellovibrio bacteriovorus* with other bacteria. J. Bacteriol. **91**:2006–2017.

94. **Stirm, S., F. Orskow, I. Orskow, and A. Birch-Anderson.** 1968. Episome carried surface antigen K88 of *Escherichia coli*. III. Morphology. J. Bacteriol. **93**:740–748.

95. **Suegara, N., M. Morotomi, T. Watanabe, Y. Kawai, and M. Mutai.** 1975. Behavior of microflora in the rat stomach: adhesion of lactobacilli to the keratinized epithelial cells of the rat stomach in vitro. Infect. Immun. **12**:173–179.

96. **Swanson, J.** 1973. Studies on gonococcus infection. IV. Pili: their role in attachment of gonococci to tissue culture cells. J. Exp. Med. **137**:571–589.

97. **Swanson, J., K. C. Hsu, and E. C. Gotschlich.** 1969. Electron microscopic studies on streptococci. I. M antigen. J. Exp. Med. **130**:1063–1091.

98. **Swanson, J., G. King, and B. Zeligs.** 1975. Studies on gonococcus infection. VII. In vitro killing of gonococci by human leukocytes. Infect. Immun. **11**:65–68.

99. **Swanson, J., E. Sparks, B. Zeligs, M. A. Siam, and C. Parrott.** 1974. Studies on gonococcus infection. V. Observations on in vitro interactions of gonococci and human neutrophils. Infect. Immun. **10**:633–644.

100. **Takeuchi, A.** 1967. Electron microscopic studies of experimental *Salmonella* infection. I. Penetration into the intestinal epithelium by *Salmonella typhimurium*. Am. J. Pathol. **50**:109–117.

101. **van Houte, J., R. J. Gibbons, and S. B. Banghart.** 1970. Adherence as a determinant of the presence of *S. salivarius* and *S. sanguis* on the human tooth surface. Arch. Oral Biol. **15**:1025–1034.

102. **van Houte, J., R. J. Gibbons, and A. J. Pulkkinen.** 1971. Adherence as an ecological determinant for streptococci in the human mouth. Arch. Oral Biol. **16**:1131–1142.

103. **van Houte, J., and D. B. Green.** 1974. Relationship between the concentration of bacteria in saliva and the colonization of teeth in humans. Infect. Immun. **9**:624–630.

104. **van Houte, J., and V. N. Upeslacis.** 1976. Studies of the mechanism of sucrose-associated colonization of *Streptococcus mutans* on teeth of conventional rats. J. Dent. Res. **55**:216–222.

105. **Ward, M. E., and P. J. Watt.** 1972. Adherence of *Neisseria gonorrhaeae* to urethral mucosal cells: an electron-microscopic study of human gonorrhea. J. Infect. Dis. **126**:601–605.

106. **Whatley, M. H., J. S. Bodwin, B. B. Lippincott, and J. A. Lippincott.** 1976. Role for *Agrobacterium* cell envelope lipopolysaccharide in infection site attachment. Infect. Immun. **13**:1080–1083.

107. **Williams, R. C., and R. J. Gibbons.** 1975. Inhibition of streptococcal attachment to receptors on human buccal epithelial cells by antigenically similar salivary glycoproteins. Infect. Immun. **11**:711–718.

108. **ZoBell, C. E.** 1943. The effect of solid surfaces upon bacterial activity. J. Bacteriol. **46**:39–59.

109. **Zvyagintsev, D.** 1973. Interaction between microorganisms and solid surfaces. Moscow University Press, Moscow.

Attachment of Marine Bacteria to Surfaces

MADILYN FLETCHER

*Marine Science Laboratories, University College of North Wales, Menai Bridge,
Gwynedd LL59 5EH, United Kingdom*

SIGNIFICANCE OF MARINE BACTERIAL ATTACHMENT TO SOLID SURFACES

In aquatic habitats, most of the resident bacterial population is found on solid surfaces, e.g., sediments, particulate detritus, man-made structures (6, 35). One important aspect of microbial attachment and growth on surfaces is that the formation of such microbial films may "condition" these surfaces and make them more suitable as settlement sites for larger organisms (R. Mitchell and L. Young, unpublished data). Many marine macroorganisms, e.g., invertebrate larvae, go through a sessile stage in their life cycle and require attachment to a solid surface for subsequent development. This attachment may be influenced by the nature of the microbial films existing on available surfaces (9, 25, 37; Mitchell and Young, unpublished data), which suggests that by controlling microbial film formation we may be able to encourage settlement and development of economically important food crops, e.g., oysters (Mitchell and Young, unpublished data), or to minimize costly attachment of fouling macroorganisms to man-made structures, e.g., ship hulls (37).

A second important aspect of marine bacterial attachment concerns the relative importance of sessile and free-living bacteria in biodegradative processes. The bacterial breakdown of particulate detritus is probably carried out by attached microorganisms (13). Moreover, in low-nutrient conditions, metabolic activity of attached bacteria may exceed that of free-living forms (14–16, 19, 33, 36, 39).

Attached bacterial populations are also important from an ecological standpoint. The relationship between epiphytic (30) and epizoic bacteria and their hosts and the possible survival advantage of attached bacteria (1) are just two factors contributing to the overall stability of the marine ecosystem.

MECHANISM OF MARINE BACTERIAL ATTACHMENT

Several different forms of marine bacterial attachment have been described (6, 17). How-ever, most marine bacteria probably attach to solid surfaces through nonspecific interactions, and extracellular polymeric adhesives appear to be involved (5–8, 12, 21–23).

An important question regarding the initial attachment of a bacterium to a surface is whether attachment is time-dependent, requiring physiological activity, e.g., extracellular polymer production (23, 38), or whether it is a spontaneous process, dependent upon the physico-chemical compatibility of the bacterial and attachment surfaces, i.e., an adsorption process. There is evidence for time-dependent attachment (21–23, 38); two successive stages have been described as (i) reversible attachment, in which bacteria are weakly held at the attachment surface by a balancing of electrical double-layer repulsion forces and van der Waals attractive energies, followed by (ii) irreversible attachment, which may be the result of extracellular polymer production (21, 23). However, other bacteria can attach rapidly and firmly to certain substrata (Fletcher, Proc. Soc. Gen. Microbiol. **3:**44, 1975; 11a, 12a), indicating that the speed of attachment may be largely determined by the affinity between bacterial and attachment surfaces (12a); i.e., the bacterial surface polymer may be an efficient adhesive on certain surfaces, whereas on others production of additional or alternative polymers is required for firm attachment (22, 23).

IMPORTANCE OF SUBSTRATUM PROPERTIES

Bacteria can vary markedly in their ability to attach to various substrata (10, 22, 28, 29, 32, 38, 40), and this may be influenced further by chemotaxic attraction or repulsion (4, 26; S. Fogel, I. Chet, and R. Mitchell, unpublished data). The importance of substratum properties was stressed in investigations of the attachment properties of a marine pseudomonad (NCMB 2021), a motile bacterium which attaches to surfaces by means of an extracellular polymer (12). Various materials were tested as attachment

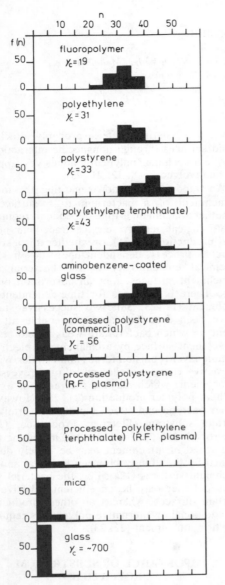

FIG. 1. *Histograms indicating numbers of attached bacteria on test substrata. The symbol n = number of attached bacteria (at intervals of 5) per 100-μm² field; f(n) = number of fields counted containing n bacteria. Where known, the critical surface tensions (γc) are given in dyne/cm and indicate the relative surface-free energies of the substrata. Processed polystyrene (commercial) refers to polystyrene tissue culture dishes, whereas processed polystyrene (R.F. plasma) and processed poly(ethylene terphthalate) (R.F. plasma) were prepared by treating the plastics in a radio-frequency plasma cleaning device (Harrick Scientific Corp.) for 10 min at maximal power at 250 × 10⁻³ Torr residual air pressure. Both tissue culture dishes and R.F. plasma processed plastics have higher surface charge densities and surface-free energies than untreated plastics. (From reference 12a)*

substrata (12a), and bacteria attached in large numbers and in an evenly distributed film to surfaces composed of fluoropolymer, polyethylene, polystyrene, poly(ethylene terphthalate), and amino benzene-coated (18) glass (Fig. 1). By contrast, attachment was sparse and erratic with mica, glass, and plastics which had been treated to increase their negative surface charge densities and surface-free energies (12a). Both factors can be important in attachment processes; surface charge density is important in electrostatic interactions between cell and attachment surfaces (20, 21, 23), whereas surface-free energy effects (also discussed in terms of wettability; 2, 3) may predominate over electrostatic interactions (2, 3, 20). It is not yet clear which of these two factors, if not both, is responsible for differences in attachment to various substrata. Moreover, the situation in a given experiment is further complicated, since surface charges (20) and surface-free energies (2) can be influenced through adsorption of medium components.

The importance of adsorbed organic components was shown in investigations into the influence of dissolved proteins on the attachment of the marine pseudomonad (NCMB 2021) to polystyrene (11). Bovine serum albumin, fibrinogen, gelatin or pepsin could inhibit attachment by modification of the substratum through adsorption (Fig. 2). Bovine serum albumin could also reduce attachment through action on the bacteria, but this effect is not understood. Other workers have shown that attachment of bacteria (23, 24) and of a marine *Chlorella* (34) can be affected by dissolved organic substances, although it was not clear whether this was through action on the cells or substratum. In the sea, adsorption of dissolved organic components occurs rapidly on newly immersed surfaces (27) and, hence, this may be an important factor in situ, as well as in the laboratory.

OTHER FACTORS AFFECTING ATTACHMENT

A variety of environmental (23, 31, 32) and physiological (24) factors can affect bacterial adhesion. Numbers of attached cells have been shown to be proportional to culture concentration and the time allowed for attachment (11a). Both factors would influence the number of bacterial collisions with the attachment surface, and hence opportunity for attachment. Also important is medium composition (e.g., cation concentration; 23) and temperature (11a), which may influence attachment directly through physicochemical effects or indirectly by affecting cell physiology. Bacterial activity and viability (24) must be extremely important in attachment processes; ad-

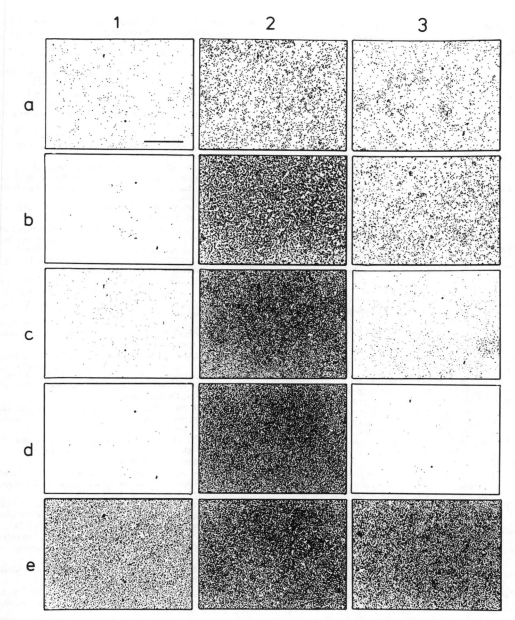

FIG. 2. *Effects of protein treatment on the number of bacteria attached to polystyrene petri dishes. (1) Bacteria which attached when protein solution was added directly to actively attaching culture; both bacteria and attachment surface were exposed to protein. (2) Bacteria which attached after incubation in protein solution; attachment surface was not exposed to protein. (3) Bacteria which attached to protein-coated polystyrene. Dissolved protein was adsorbed onto the polystyrene and the excess was washed away before addition of bacterial cultures; the bacteria were not exposed directly to protein solutions. The proteins were (a) bovine serum albumin, (b) gelatin, (c) fibrinogen, (d) pepsin, and (e) protamine sulfate. Note the correlation between treatments 1 and 3, indicating that dissolved protein inhibits bacterial attachment through modification of the attachment surface. All magnifications are the same; the bar in 1a = 50 μm.*

hesion has been shown to depend on culture age (11a, 23) and, in some cases, the capacity of the cells to synthesize protein (21).

LITERATURE CITED

1. **Atkinson, B., and H. W. Fowler.** 1974. The significance of microbial film in fermenters. Adv. Biochem. Eng. **3:**221–277.
2. **Baier, R. E.** 1970. Surface properties influencing biological adhesion, p. 15–48. In R. S. Manly (ed.), Adhesion in biological systems. Academic Press Inc., New York.
3. **Carter, S. B.** 1967. Haptotaxis and the mechanism of cell motility. Nature (London) **213:**256–260.
4. **Chet, I., P. Asketh, and R. Mitchell.** 1975. Repulsion of bacteria from marine surfaces. Appl. Microbiol. **30:**1043–1045.
5. **Corpe, W. A.** 1970. An acid polysaccharide produced by a primary film-forming marine bacterium. Dev. Ind. Microbiol. **2:**402–412.
6. **Corpe, W. A.** 1970. Attachment of marine bacteria to solid surfaces, p. 73–87. In R. S. Manly (ed.), Adhesion in biological systems. Academic Press Inc., New York.
7. **Corpe, W. A.** 1972. Microfouling: the role of primary film forming bacteria, p. 598–609. In Proc. 3rd Int. Congr. Marine Corrosion and Fouling. National Bureau of Standards, Gaithersburg, Md.
8. **Corpe, W. A., L. Matsuuchi, and B. Armbruster.** 1976. In J. M. Sharpley and A. M. Kaplan (ed.), Proc. 3rd Int. Biodegradation Symp., p. 433–442. Applied Science Publishers Ltd., London.
9. **Crisp, D. J., and J. S. Ryland.** 1960. Influence of filming and of surface texture on the settlement of marine organisms. Nature (London) **185:**119.
10. **Dexter, S. C., J. D. Sullivan, Jr., J. Williams III, and S. W. Watson.** 1975. Influence of substrate wettability on the attachment of marine bacteria to various surfaces. Appl. Microbiol. **30:**298–308.
11. **Fletcher, M.** 1976. The effects of proteins on bacterial attachment to polystyrene. J. Gen. Microbiol. **94:**400–404.
11a. **Fletcher, M.** 1977. The effects of culture concentration and age, time and temperature on bacterial attachment to polystyrene. Can. J. Microbiol. **23:**1–6.
12. **Fletcher, M., and G. D. Floodgate.** 1973. An electron-microscopic demonstration of an acidic polysaccharide involved in the adhesion of a marine bacterium to solid surfaces. J. Gen. Microbiol. **74:**325–334.
12a. **Fletcher, M., and G. I. Loeb.** 1976. The influence of substratum surface properties on the attachment of a marine bacterium, p. 459–469. In M. Kerker (ed.), Colloid and interface surface, vol. 3. Academic Press Inc., New York.
13. **Floodgate, G. D.** 1973. Where there's muck there's energy. New Sci. **59:**19–20.
14. **Hattori, T., and C. Furusaka.** 1960. Chemical activities of E. coli adsorbed on a resin. J. Biochem. (Tokyo) **48:**831–837.
15. **Hendricks, C. W.** 1974. Sorption of heterotrophic and enteric bacteria to glass surfaces in the continuous culture of river water. Appl. Microbiol. **28:**572–578.
16. **Heukelekian, H., and A. Heller.** 1940. Relation between food concentration and surface for bacterial growth. J. Bacteriol. **40:**547–558.
17. **Hirsch, P., and S. H. Pankratz.** 1970. Study of bacterial populations in natural environments by use of submerged electron microscope grids. Z. Allg. Mikrobiol. **10:**589–605.
18. **Kennedy, J. F., S. A. Barker, and C. A. White.** 1974. The selective adsorption of polysaccharides on poly-aromatic surfaces. Carbohydr. Res. **38:**13–23.
19. **Lloyd, B.** 1937. Bacteria in stored sea water. J. R. Tech. Coll. Glasgow **4:**173–177.
20. **Maroudas, N. G.** 1975. Adhesion and spreading of cells on charged surfaces. J. Theor. Biol. **49:**417–424.
21. **Marshall, K. C.** 1972. Mechanism of adhesion of marine bacteria to surfaces, p. 625–632. In Proc. 3rd Int. Congr. Marine Corrosion and Fouling. National Bureau of Standards, Gaithersburg, Md.
22. **Marshall, K. C., R. Stout, and R. Mitchell.** 1971. Selective sorption of bacteria from seawater. Can. J. Microbiol. **17:**1413–1416.
23. **Marshall, K. C., R. Stout, and R. Mitchell.** 1971. Mechanism of the initial events in the sorption of marine bacteria to surfaces. J. Gen. Microbiol. **68:**337–348.
24. **Meadows, P. S.** 1971. The attachment of bacteria to solid surfaces. Arch. Mikrobiol. **75:**374–381.
25. **Meadows, P. S., and G. B. Williams.** 1963. Settlement of Spirorbis borealis Daudin larvae on surfaces bearing films of microorganisms. Nature (London) **198:**610.
26. **Mitchell, R.** 1972. Bacterial chemotaxis, marine fouling, and pollution. Nav. Res. Rev. **25:**1–6.
27. **Neihof, R., and G. Loeb.** 1972. Molecular fouling of surfaces in seawater, p. 710–718. In Proc. 3rd Int. Congr. Marine Corrosion and Fouling. National Bureau of Standards, Gaithersburg, Md.
28. **O'Neill, T. B., and G. L. Wilcox.** 1971. The formation of a 'primary film' on materials submerged in the sea at Port Hueneme, California. Pac. Sci. **25:**1–12.
29. **Sechler, G. E., and K. Gundersen.** 1972. Role of surface chemical composition on the microbial contribution to primary films, p. 610–616. In Proc. 3rd Int. Congr. Marine Corrosion and Fouling. National Bureau of Standards, Gaithersburg, Md.
30. **Sieburth, J. McN.** 1968. The influence of algal antibiosis on the ecology of marine microorganisms. Adv. Microbiol. Sea **1:**63–94.
31. **Skerman, T. M.** 1956. The nature and development of primary films on surfaces submerged in the sea. N.Z. Sci. Technol. Ser. B **38:**44–57.
32. **Sládečková, A.** 1966. The significance of the periphyton in reservoirs for theoretical and applied limnology. Verh. Int. Ver. Limnol. **16:**753–758.
33. **Stotzky, G., and L. T. Rem.** 1966. Influence of clay minerals on microorganisms. I. Montmorillonite and kaolinite on bacteria. Can. J. Microbiol. **12:**547–563.
34. **Tosteson, T. R., and W. A. Corpe.** 1975. Enhancement of adhesion of the marine Chlorella vulgaris to glass. Can. J. Microbiol. **21:**1025–1031.
35. **Wood, E. J. F.** 1965. Marine microbial ecology. Chapman and Hall, London.
36. **ZoBell, C. E.** 1937. The influence of solid surface upon the physiological activities of bacteria in sea water. J. Bacteriol. **33:**86.
37. **ZoBell, C. E.** 1939. The biological approach to the preparation of anti-fouling paints. Cric. 588, Sci. Sec. Natl. Paint, Varnish and Lacquer Assoc., San Francisco, Calif.
38. **ZoBell, C. E.** 1943. The effect of solid surfaces upon bacterial activity. J. Bacteriol. **46:**39–56.
39. **ZoBell, C. E., and D. Q. Anderson.** 1936. Observations on the multiplication of bacteria in different volumes of stored seawater and the influence of oxygen tension and solid surfaces. Biol. Bull. **71:**324–342.
40. **Zvyagintsev, D. G.** 1959. Adsorption of microorganisms by glass surfaces. Microbiology (USSR) **28:**104–108.

Cell Surface Antigenic Polymers of *Streptococcus mutans* and Their Role in Adherence of the Microorganism In Vitro

HUTTON D. SLADE

Department of Microbiology-Immunology, Northwestern University Medical and Dental Schools, Chicago, Illinois 60611

Streptococcus mutans is known to form plaque on the smooth surfaces of human teeth and to produce extensive tooth decay in monoinfected germfree animals on a sucrose diet. Several reviews have summarized the literature on this subject (14, 36, 49). The conversion of sucrose to glucan by glucosyltransferase (dextran sucrase) enzymes from growing cells of *S. mutans* during adherence to glass and wire surfaces has been reported from many laboratories (11, 17, 22, 39, 43).

S. mutans strains have been shown to synthesize fructan as well as glucan by means of extracellular enzymes. The ratio varies from 1:1 to 1:4.8 (8, 39, 48). The extracellular glucosyltransferases (GTases) from a limited number of strains synthesize 60 to 100% water-insoluble glucan (4). Strains which produce good in vitro adherence are those which usually synthesize significant quantities of the insoluble polymer (26, 39). Strains possessing a weak adherence synthesize mostly fructan (8, 44). Glucan from *S. mutans* is composed of a backbone of α,1–3 glucose units and short side chains of α,1–6 units (1, 8, 15, 27). It has been suggested that the backbone structure may be primarily responsible for water insolubility and the side chains for adherence (8).

Glucan is synthesized by GTases which are both cell free and cell associated (13, 16, 51). It seems likely that a mixture of several enzymes is needed for the synthesis of the water-insoluble polymer because of the complexity of such a branched-chain structure (6a, 39). The purified extracellular enzyme(s) contains a glucose carbohydrate polymer (5, 41, 46) and can be considered a glycoprotein. The activity of these preparations is increased by the addition of dextran. The GTase enzyme has been isolated in aggregated forms of various sizes (10, 26, 41). A low-molecular-weight preparation was shown to synthesize water-soluble glucan and a high-molecular-weight preparation was shown to synthesize insoluble glucan (41).

The enzyme is synthesized during growth on glucose although the quantity of enzyme is increased markedly when sucrose is added (51). Cell-free enzyme is synthesized in glucose (51) or fructose (10) media and also in a glucose-synthetic medium (47). Fructose yields four times as much enzyme as does glucose. The enzyme is primer dependent, whereas that from glucose-grown cultures shows a weak primer-dependent activity (10).

Various types of surfaces have been used to assay the in vitro adherence of *S. mutans* (for a review, see reference 49a). The glass surface has been frequently used to obtain data on the mechanism of the adherence process. Both growing cells (44) and cell suspensions of labeled (48) and nonlabeled cells (39) have been used.

S. mutans strains have been classified into seven types on an immunological basis (2, 3, 45). The genetic homology of types *a*, *b*, *c*, and *d* studied so far agree with this classification (7). Cell suspensions of strains belonging to types *a*, *d*, and *g* adhere strongly to a glass surface when cell-free enzyme and sucrose are added, whereas strains of types *c*, *e*, and *f* are less effective, and *b* strains adhere poorly (Hamada and Slade, unpublished data).

The type-specific antigens of *S. mutans* occur in the cell wall and are carbohydrate in nature. Types *a* (38), *d* (31), and *g* (21) are composed of glucose and galactose; *c* (29, 55), *e* (19), and *f* (18), of rhamnose and glucose; and *b* (37), of rhamnose and galactose. They do not contain teichoic acid. The *a*, *b*, *c*, and *d* purified antigens have been shown by comparative immunoelectrophoresis to be identical to those present in the extracts of whole cells used in the original studies upon which the classification is based (29). The *e* and *f* antigens have not as yet been examined in the same manner.

The *f* antigen is unusual in that it reacts with antibodies to *S. mutans* glucan, most likely because of the presence of $\alpha,1$–6 glucose linkages in the *f* polymer (18). This polymer primes a highly purified GTase (Slade and Schachtele, unpublished data). The presence of 5% or less protein in these purified polysaccharides indicates that they are associated with protein in the cell wall (38). They may be considered as glycoproteins. The possible function of these cell surface type-specific polysaccharide antigens in the adherence process is discussed below.

A cross-reaction between the *a* and *d* serotypes was noted during studies on the specificity of the type polysaccharides (3). This cross-reaction is due to a second antibody combining site which is present in both the *a* and *d* polysaccharides (30, 38). The cross-reaction between group E (50) and type *e* of *S. mutans* has also been found to be due to the presence of these two specificities on a single polysaccharide molecule (20). Some strains, however, do not contain the *e* specificity, whereas others possess both E and *e*. Cross-reactions between *c* and *e* strains have also been recorded (3). The remaining cross-reactions which are seen in various antigen extracts of *S. mutans* are due to the polyglycerophosphate structure of teichoic acids present in all *S. mutans* strains examined to date (6, 20a, 24).

Much of the information on the mechanism of the in vitro adherence of *S. mutans* has been obtained in my laboratory, and a summary of these studies follows. Initial experiments showed that viable nongrowing cell suspensions of *S. mutans* produced adherence to a glass surface in the presence of sucrose (39). This activity is due to cell-associated GTase. To obtain cells for adherence studies which do not contain cell-associated enzyme, the cells were held at 65°C for two 1-h periods, or at 100°C for 20 min. To demonstrate adherence these cells require the addition of cell-free GTase and sucrose (39). The addition to these cells of soluble dextran or glucan synthesized by *S. mutans* did not result in adherence. The binding of enzyme by these cells is indicated by the exposure of the cells to enzyme, removal of the free enzyme by washing, and addition of sucrose to the cells. Upon incubation of cells and sucrose, adherence results (39). Antibody against the enzyme prevents insoluble glucan synthesis. Antibody against the heat-treated whole *S. mutans* cell (strain HS6, type *a*) inhibits adherence (39). This serum did not contain polyglycerophosphate, glucan, or GTase antibodies (19). Normal rabbit serum is inactive (39).

Information on the nature of the GTase binding site on the surface of *S. mutans* heat-treated type *a* and *e* cells has been obtained (19, 40). Antiserum specific for the *a-d* site on the *a* polysaccharide antigen was found to inhibit the binding of the enzyme and adherence. Anti-*a*-specific globulin at similar levels did not inhibit binding of GTase, and adherence did occur. A fivefold increase in the *a* antibody is required to inhibit adherence. The *a* and *a-d* antisera used in these experiments did not contain polyglycerophosphate or glucan/dextran antibodies, and the glucan antiserum did not contain polyglycerophosphate or GTase antibodies. Anti-glucan antibodies also inhibit the binding of GTase and adherence.

Antibody specific for the type *e* *S. mutans* polysaccharide antigen likewise demonstrated an inhibition of adherence of cell suspensions (19). Adsorption of this serum with group A streptococcal cells for the removal of PGP and dextran antibodies did not affect the inhibitor activity. In all these experiments the cells were exposed to antibody and washed; then GTase and sucrose were added. Subagglutinating dilutions (32×10^3 or 128×10^3) of *e* serum still inhibited adherence. The adsorption of the GTase occurs within 1 min and is maximal between pH 5 and 8 (40).

The immunological specificity of the *S. mutans* GTase has been checked in several laboratories. Antibodies against a purified GTase preparation from type *a* which synthesized only water-insoluble glucan (41) inhibits both glucan synthesis and adherence by crude GTases from strains of types *a*, *b*, *c*, and *d* (32). Antibodies against a crude GTase preparation from type *e* inhibit the homologous enzyme but not a crude type *a* GTase (19). Antiserum against strain 6715 (type *g*) inhibits the synthesis of glucan and adherence by growing 6715 cells, whereas cells from strains of serotypes *b*, *c*, and *e* are not inhibited in polysaccharide synthesis or adherence. Antiserum to serotype *a* (strain E49) cells inhibits adherence but not glucan synthesis. The results are semiquantitative in that they are expressed as more or less than a 10% change (9). It is clear from these results that additional experiments with purified GTases from each serotype used as antigens are necessary before it can be concluded that they possess a common antigenic determinant.

Serotype *a* cells, free from cell-associated GTase, after treatment with dextranase, show an inhibition of 53% in their ability to bind GTase and a 64% inhibition of adherence to a glass surface. Treatment with trypsin produced a 75% and a 94% inhibition, respectively. Pepsin is also a strong inhibitor (40). Similar results have been obtained with type *e* cells (19).

The function of dextran or a dextran-like

polymer as a binding site for GTase is supported by the use of dextran-coated hydroxylapatite (28). A threefold increase in adherence to this hydroxylapatite is obtained with a type *g* strain. Trypsin and Pronase treatment of these cells reduces the adherence to both saliva-coated and dextran-coated hydroxylapatite eightfold. Dextranase treatment of the cells results in a 95% reduction.

These results indicated, with adherence to glass or hydroxylapatite, that glucan is the binding site for extracellular GTase on the surface of the *S. mutans* cell. Cell-associated GTase would provide the glucan. The ability of glucan to function as a binding site is to be expected in view of the presence of a glucose polymer in preparations of GTase and the priming effect of dextran on the enzyme. On this basis, glucan would be expected to possess a greater specificity in enzyme binding than the type-specific carbohydrate antigen polymers. However, the likelihood that α and β glucose units have a terminal location on the side chains of the type-specific *a*, *c*, *d*, *e*, *f*, and *g* polysaccharides (18, 19, 21, 29, 31, 38, 55) may also confer on these polysaccharides the ability to bind GTase. A location of the glucan adjacent to the polysaccharide on the cell surface may explain the inhibitory activity of both the glucan and polysaccharide antisera. No formation of a complex between GTase and the type *a* polysaccharide could be demonstrated by electrophoresis (41). The present data thus do not allow a conclusion as to which of these two polymers is the specific binding site for GTase but, on the contrary, indicate that both may function. Although the type-specific polysaccharides (except *f*) do not prime GTase (Slade and Schachtele, unpublished data), there may be a stereochemical structure in these polymers which has an affinity for the enzyme.

The role of protein in the binding of the GTase is not clear. The antigen polysaccharide and glucan may be complexed with cell wall protein so that the hydrolytic action of trypsin releases the enzyme. The binding of glycoprotein (GTase) to the glycoprotein of the cell wall site would be expected to produce similar results.

A number of gram-positive and -negative bacteria, including *S. mutans*, have been examined for adherence to a glass surface (Hamada and Slade, unpublished data). Two methods of assay used in earlier studies have been used (39). In the first, heated cells, GTase, and sucrose are mixed together at the same time and then incubated for 17 h to allow adherence to develop. In the second procedure, the cells and enzyme are mixed and incubated, the cells are removed by centrifugation and washed, sucrose is added to the cells, and the suspension is then incubated to allow adherence to develop. In the first procedure, all the strains examined produced a relative adherence ranging from 48 to 106%, with *S. mutans* (strain HS6) as 100%. Only *Lactobacillus plantarum* and *S. pyogenes* showed essentially no adherence. In contrast, when these same strains were tested by the second procedure, the only strains showing adherence were those of *S. mutans*. The relative adherence ranged from 75 to 114%. Strains from each of the seven serotypes were tested. Strain FA1 (b) showed only 4% adherence, whereas in the first method it showed 76%. These results indicate clearly that the *S. mutans* cells bind GTase and that glucan synthesis on the cell surface is required for adherence to occur. These results agree with our earlier conclusions (19, 39, 40).

A quantitative examination of the binding of GTase and subsequent synthesis of cell-surface glucan from [^{14}C]sucrose by nontreated and heat-treated *S. mutans* cells has shown that the same quantity of glucan is synthesized in each case. About one-third of the total synthesis in the nontreated cells is due to cell-associated GTase. It is likely that the heat-inactivated GTase is able to bind approximately the same amount of active extracellular GTase so that both cells synthesize the same quantity of glucan. In each case the cells are fully saturated with enzyme. The results indicate that the heat treatment at 65 or 100°C to inactivate cell-associated GTase does not generate additional binding sites for the enzyme.

The residual GTase remaining after the uptake of GTase by the *S. mutans* cells in the latter experiments has been determined. Under the conditions employed, 50 to 75% of the GTase is removed from solution by either heat-treated or nontreated cells. Only 10 to 20% is removed by other gram-positive or gram-negative species, and as such these cells are not able to adhere upon incubation in sucrose.

These results strongly indicate, in agreement with our earlier conclusions, that *S. mutans* has the ability to bind GTase, to convert sucrose to glucan upon its cell surface, and to produce adherence. Other oral bacteria are not able to bind sufficient GTase and to synthesize sufficient glucan to produce adherence. The presence of a variety of bacteria in dental plaque can be explained by these results. The gradual synthesis of glucan by *S. mutans*, leading to the increase in the size of the plaque accompanied by the attachment and/or trapping of other oral species, is quite possibly a significant aspect of plaque development. In vivo studies on plaque development indicate that a weak association of the cells with the tooth surface is followed by a more stable attachment as new glucan synthesis proceeds (54). These in vivo studies are in agreement with our results.

Adherence, equal to only 20% of the adherence discussed above, may also occur by the attachment of heat-treated *S. mutans* cells to a preformed glucan layer (25). The binding of the cells to GTase in the glucan layer is indicated by a 50% inhibition of the adherence by GTase antibody (19). Evidence that GTase does not function as a binding agent in this type of adherence has been cited (35: data not given).

The adherence of *S. mutans* to preformed glucan layers does not appear to play a significant role in plaque development. In vivo studies indicated that active glucan synthesis is necessary for *S. mutans* to achieve a firm attachment to tooth surfaces (54).

A process which may relate to adherence is that of whole-cell agglutination. Agglutination of *S. mutans* occurs upon the addition of high-molecular-weight (2×10^6) dextran to viable cell suspensions or when sucrose is converted to glucan by cells possessing cell-associated GTase. A number of strains of *S. mutans* (except GS-5, type *c*) agglutinate in this manner, whereas other gram-positive and -negative bacteria do not. The dextran-synthesizing species *S. bovis*, *S. sanguis*, and *L. mesenteroides* do not agglutinate. Cells heated at 100°C for 10 min do not agglutinate (12). The oral species *Actinomyces viscosus* is also agglutinated by glucans and by dextran. This is a heat-sensitive reaction (33). This species however, does not synthesize glucan.

It is postulated that the binding site for dextran in agglutination is GTase (12). However, neither anti-GTase nor competitive inhibition experiments support this possibility (23, 44). The participation of cell-surface glucan as the glucan/dextran binding site in agglutination of *S. mutans*

(Wu-Yuan and Slade, unpublished data) and *A. viscosus* (33) is indicated by a loss of ability of dextranase-treated cells to agglutinate. This glucan, however, does not preferentially bind to the type-specific polysaccharide (20b). A mutant strain of type *g* (6715) cells bound twofold more glucan/dextran than the wild-type cells. Anti-type *g* immunoglobulin G inhibited the binding 28%, whereas one-half the antibody showed only a 3% inhibition. The direct binding of dextran did not occur. The participation of a cell wall protein in agglutination (as well as adherence), however, is indicated in work from three laboratories (10, 23, 51). Divalent ions are also required (23, 34).

Several investigations support the possibility that adherence and agglutination are separate processes (10, 23, 39, 42, 52, 53). Another report claims that they involve the same glucan receptor site (34, 35). If a relationship exists, it would appear to be in regard to the protein which is associated with the type-specific polysaccharide and glucan which act as the GTase binding site in adherence, and the protein which appears to function as a binding site for dextran/glucan in agglutination (23, 34; Wu-Yuan and Slade, unpublished data). Heat lability of the agglutination protein as compared with the heat stability of the adherence protein is a strong indication of a difference between the two. The ability of *S. mutans* cells grown on a synthetic medium to adhere but not to agglutinate also indicates a separation of the two processes (Wu-Yuan and Slade, unpublished data).

A model depicting the essential features of adherence and agglutination is presented in Fig. 1. Adherence is represented as requiring the association of GTase with a glucan molecule on the cell surface which in turn is associated with a cell wall protein. This concept is also supported by other workers (10, 54). Agglutination is represented as requiring a glucan acceptor associated with a heat-sensitive cell wall protein. A model which also includes a glucan receptor for glucan/dextran agglutination, and which includes in addition the cross-linking of cell-attached dextran by GTase, has been presented (10).

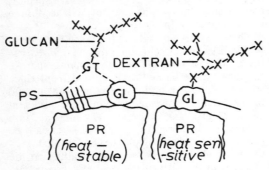

FIG. 1. *Binding sites for glucosyltransferase and dextran on the cell wall surface of* Streptococcus mutans. *PR = protein; PS = type-specific polysaccharide; GL = glucan; GT = glucosyltransferase.*

ACKNOWLEDGMENTS

The work reported herein from my laboratory was supported by Public Health Service research grants HE-03709-19 from the National Heart and Lung Institute and DE-03615-04 from the National Institute of Dental Research and by grants from the Grainger Fund, the Pioneer Fund, and the Hemac Fund. H.D.S. is the recipient of Public Health Service research career award K6-GM-16284 from the National Institute of General Medical Sciences.

LITERATURE CITED

1. **Baird, J. K., V. M. C. Longyear, and D. C. Ellwood.** 1973. Water insoluble and soluble glucans produced by extracellular glycosyltransferases from *Streptococcus mutans*. Microbios 8:143–150.

2. **Bratthall, D.** 1969. Immunodiffusion studies on the serological specificity of streptococci resembling *Streptococcus mutans*. Odontol. Revy 20:231–244.

3. **Bratthall, D.** 1970. Demonstration of five serological groups of streptococcal strains resembling *Streptococcus mutans*. Odontol. Revv 21:143–152.

4. **Chassy, B. M., J. R. Beall, R. M. Bielawski, E. V. Porter, and J. A. Donkersloot.** 1976. Occurrence and distribution of sucrose-metabolizing enzymes in oral streptococci. Infect. Immun. 14:408–415.

5. **Chludzinski, A. M., G. R. Germaine, and C. F. Schachtele.** 1974. Purification and properties of dextransucrase from *Streptococcus mutans*. J. Bacteriol. 118:1–7.

6. **Chorpenning, F. W., H. R. Cooper, and S. Rosen.** 1975. Cross-reactions of *Streptococcus mutans* due to cell wall teichoic acid. Infect. Immun. 12:586–591.

6a. **Ciardi, J. E.** 1976. Glucosyltransferases of *Staphylococcus mutans*, p. 101–110. *In* W. H. Bowen, R. J. Genco, and J. C. O'Brien (ed.), Immunologic aspects of dental caries (special supplement to Immunology Abstracts). Information Retrieval, Inc., Washington, D.C.

7. **Coykendall, A. L.** 1974. Four types of *Streptococcus mutans* based on their genetic, antigenic and biochemical characteristics. J. Gen. Microbiol. 83:327–338.

8. **Ebisu, S., K. Kato, S. Kotani, and A. Misaki.** 1975. Structural differences in fructans elaborated by *S. mutans* and *S. salivarius*. J. Biochem. (Tokyo) 78:879–887.

9. **Genco, R., R. Evans, and M. Taubman.** 1974. Specificity of antibodies to *S. mutans*; significance of inhibition of adherence, p. 327–336. *In* J. Mestecky and A. R. Lawton III (ed.), The immunoglobulin A system. Plenum Press, New York.

10. **Germaine, G. R., and C. F. Schachtele.** 1976. *Streptococcus mutans* dextransucrase: mode of interaction with high-molecular-weight dextran and role in cellular aggregation. Infect. Immun. 13:365–372.

11. **Gibbons, R. J., and S. B. Banghart.** 1967. Synthesis of extracellular dextran by cariogenic bacteria and its presence in human dental plaque. Arch. Oral Biol. 12:11–24.

12. **Gibbons, R. J., and R. J. Fitzgerald.** 1969. Dextran-induced agglutination of *Streptococcus mutans*, and its potential role in the formation of microbial dental plaque. J. Bacteriol. 98:341–346.

13. **Gibbons, R. J., and M. Nygaard.** 1968. Synthesis of insoluble dextran and its significance in the formation of gelatinous deposits by plaque-forming streptococci. Arch. Oral Biol. 13:1249–1262.

14. **Gibbons, R. J., and J. van Houte.** 1975. Bacterial adherence in oral microbial ecology. Annu. Rev. Microbiol 29:19–44.

15. **Guggenheim, B.** 1970. Enzymatic hydrolysis and structure of water-insoluble glucan produced by glucosyltransferases from a strain of *Streptococcus mutans*. Helv. Odontol. Acta 14:89–108.

16. **Guggenheim, B.** 1970. Extracellular polysaccharides and microbial plaque. Int. Dent. J. 20:657–678.

17. **Guggenheim, B., and E. Newbrun.** 1969. Extracellular glucosyltransferase activity of an HS strain of *Streptococcus mutans*. Helv. Odontol. Acta 13:84–97.

18. **Hamada, S., K. Gill, and H. D. Slade.** 1976. Chemical and immunological properties of type *f* polysaccharide antigen of *Streptococcus mutans*. Infect. Immun. 14:203–211.

19. **Hamada, S., and H. D. Slade.** 1976. The adherence of serotype *e Streptococcus mutans* and the inhibitory effect of Lancefield group E and *S. mutans e* antiserum. J. Dent. Res. 55:C65–C74.

20. **Hamada, S., and H. D. Slade.** 1976. Purification and immunochemical characterization of type *e* polysaccharide antigen of *Streptococcus mutans*. Infect. Immun. 14:68–76.

20a. **Hamada, S., S. Tai, and H. D. Slade.** 1976. Selective adsorption of heterophile polyglycerophosphate antigen from antigen extracts of *Streptococcus mutans* and other gram-positive bacteria. Infect. Immun. 14:903–910.

20b. **Iacono, V. J., et al.** 1976. *In* W. H. Bowen, R. J. Genco, and J. C. O'Brien (ed.), Immunologic aspects of dental caries (special supplement to Immunology Abstracts), p. 75–90. Information Retrieval, Inc., Washington, D.C.

21. **Iacono, V. J., M. A. Taubman, D. J. Smith, and M. J. Levine.** 1975. Isolation and immunochemical characterization of the group-specific antigen of *Streptococcus mutans* 6715. Infect. Immun. 11:117–128.

22. **Jordan, H. V., and P. H. Keyes.** 1966. *In vitro* methods for the study of plaque formation and carious lesions. Arch. Oral Biol. 11:793–801.

23. **Kelstrup, J., and T. D. Funder-Nielsen.** 1974. Adhesion of dextran to *S. mutans*. J. Gen. Microbiol. 81:485–489.

24. **Knox, K. W., J. L. Markham, and A. J. Wicken.** 1976. Formation of cross-reacting antibodies against cellular and extracellular lipoteichoic acid of *Streptococcus mutans* BHT. Infect. Immun. 13:647–652.

25. **Kuramitsu, H.** 1974. Adherence of *Streptococcus mutans* to dextran synthesized in the presence of extracellular dextransucrase. Infect. Immun. 9:764–765.

26. **Kuramitsu, H.** 1975. Characterization of extracellular glycosyltransferase activity of *Streptococcus mutans*. Infect. Immun. 12:738–749.

27. **Lewicki, W. J., L. W. Long, and J. R. Edwards.** 1971. Determination of the structure of a broth dextran produced by a cariogenic streptococcus. Carbohydr. Res. 17:175–182.

28. **Liljemark, W. F., and S. V. Schauer.** 1975. Studies on the bacterial components which bind *Streptococcus sanguis* and *Streptococcus mutans* to hydroxyapatite. Arch. Oral Biol. 20:609–615.

29. **Linzer, R., K. Gill, and H. D. Slade.** 1976. Chemical composition of *Streptococcus mutans* type *c* antigen: comparison to type *a*, *b* and *d* antigens. J. Dent. Res. 55:A109–A115.

30. **Linzer, R., H. Mukasa, and H. D. Slade.** 1975. Serological purification of polysaccharide antigens from *Streptococcus mutans* serotypes *a* and *d*: characterization of multiple antigenic determinants. Infect. Immun. 12:791–798.

31. **Linzer, R., and H. D. Slade.** 1974. Purification and characterization of *Streptococcus mutans* group *d* cell wall polysaccharide antigen. Infect. Immun. 10:361–368.

32. **Linzer, R., and H. D. Slade.** 1976. Characterization of an anti-glucosyltransferase serum specific for insoluble glucan synthesis by *S. mutans*. Infect. Immun. 13:494–500.

33. **McBride, B. C., and G. Bourgeau.** 1975. Dextran-induced aggregation of *Actinomyces viscosus*. Arch. Oral Biol. 20:837–841.

34. **McCabe, M. M., and E. E. Smith.** 1975. Relationship between cell-bound dextransucrase and the agglutination of *Streptococcus mutans*. Infect. Immun. 12:512–520.

35. **McCabe, M. M.** 1976. Comments on adherence of *S. mutans*. J. Dent. Res. 55:C226–C228.

36. **Makinen, K. K.** 1972. The role of sucrose and other sugars in the development of dental caries: a review. Int. Dent. J. **22:**362–386.

37. **Mukasa, H., and H. D. Slade.** 1973. Structure and immunological specificity of the *Streptococcus mutans* group *b* cell wall antigen. Infect. Immun. **7:**578–585.

38. **Mukasa, H., and H. D. Slade.** 1973. Extraction, purification, and chemical and immunological properties of the *Streptococcus mutans* group *a* polysaccharide cell wall antigen. Infect. Immun. **8:**190–198.

39. **Mukasa, H., and H. D. Slade.** 1973. Mechanism of adherence of *Streptococcus mutans* to smooth surfaces. I. Roles of insoluble dextran-levan synthetase enzyme and cell wall polysaccharide antigen in plaque formation. Infect. Immun. **8:**555–562.

40. **Mukasa, H., and H. D. Slade.** 1974. Mechanism of adherence of *Streptococcus mutans* to smooth surfaces. II. Nature of the binding site and adsorption of dextran-levan synthetase enzyme on the cell wall surface of streptococcus. Infect. Immun. **9:**419–429.

41. **Mukasa, H., and H. D. Slade.** 1974. Mechanism of the adherence of *Streptococcus mutans* to smooth surfaces. III. Purification and properties of the enzyme complex responsible for adherence. Infect. Immun. **10:**1135–1145.

42. **Nalbandian, J., M. Freedman, J. Tanzer, and S. Lovelace.** 1974. Ultrastructure of mutants of *Streptococcus mutans* with reference to agglutination, adhesion, and extracellular polysaccharide. Infect. Immun. **10:**1170–1179.

43. **Newbrun, E.** 1972. Extracellular polysaccharide synthesized by glucosyltransferases of oral streptococci. Caries Res. **6:**132–147.

44. **Olson, G., A. Bleiweis, and P. Small.** 1972. Adherence inhibition of *Streptococcus mutans*: an assay reflecting a possible role of antibody in dental caries prophylaxis. Infect. Immun. **5:**419–427.

45. **Perch, B., E. Kjems, and T. Ravn.** 1974. Biochemical and serological properties of *Streptococcus mutans* from various human and animal sources. Acta Pathol. Microbiol. Scand. Sect. B **82:**357–370.

46. **Schachtele, C. F., G. R. Germaine, and S. K. Harlander.** 1975. Production of elevated levels of dextransucrase by a mutant of *Streptococcus mutans*. Infect. Immun. **12:**934–937.

47. **Schachtele, C. F., S. K. Harlander, and G. R. Germaine.** 1976. *Streptococcus mutans* dextransucrase: availability of disaggregated enzyme after growth in a chemically defined medium. Infect. Immun. **13:**1522–1524.

48. **Schachtele, C. F., A. E. Laken, and M. K. Schmitt.** 1972. Use of specifically labeled sucrose for comparison of extracellular glucan and fructan metabolism by oral streptococci. Infect. Immun. **5:**91–97.

49. **Scherp, H.** 1971. Dental caries: prospects for prevention. Science **173:**1199–1205.

49a. **Slade, H. D.** 1976. *In* W. H. Bowen, R. J. Genco, and J. C. O'Brien (ed.), Immunologic aspects of dental caries (special supplement to Immunology Abstracts), p. 21–38. Information Retrieval, Inc., Washington, D.C.

50. **Soprey, P., and H. D. Slade.** 1971. Chemical structure and immunological specificity of the streptococcal group E cell wall polysaccharide antigen. Infect. Immun. **3:**653–658.

51. **Spinell, D. M., and R. J. Gibbons.** 1974. Influence of culture medium on the glucosyltransferase and dextran-binding capacity of *Streptococcus mutans* 6715 cells. Infect. Immun. **10:**1448–1451.

52. **Tanzer, J., M. Freedman, R. Fitzgerald, and R. Larson.** 1974. Diminished virulence of glucan synthesis-defective mutants of *Streptococcus mutans*. Infect. Immun. **10:**197–203.

53. **Tanzer, J. M., and R. M. McCabe.** 1968. Selection of plaque-forming streptococci by the serial passage of wires through sucrose-containing broth. Arch. Oral Biol. **13:**139–143.

54. **Van Houte, J., and V. N. Upeslacis.** 1976. Studies on the mechanism of sucrose-associated colonization of *S. mutans* on teeth of conventional rats. J. Dent. Res. **55:**216–222.

55. **Wetherell, J. R., Jr., and A. S. Bleiweis.** 1975. Antigens of *Streptococcus mutans*: characterization of a polysaccharide antigen from walls of strain GS5. Infect. Immun. **12:**1341–1348.

Possible Role of *Streptococcus salivarius* Glucosyltransferase in Adherence of *Veillonella* to Smooth Surfaces

CHARLES L. WITTENBERGER, ALFRED J. BEAMAN, LINDA N. LEE,
ROBERT M. McCABE, AND JACOB A. DONKERSLOOT

*Microbiology Section, Laboratory of Microbiology and Immunology, National Institute of
Dental Research, Bethesda, Maryland 20014*

INTRODUCTION

Among the many intriguing and as yet unresolved problems in oral microbiology is the precise means by which various members of the indigenous microbial flora attach to and colonize oral tissues. Gibbons and van Houte (4, 5) have recently reviewed this subject in detail and summarized data which show that certain members of the microflora exhibit distinct tropisms for attachment to various oral surfaces. *Streptococcus salivarius*, for example, is present in high numbers on the dorsum of the tongue but is only a minor component of the microbial flora found on teeth. In contrast, *S. mutans* is found mainly on teeth and is present in very low numbers on oral mucosal surfaces (4). In the case of streptococci which attach primarily to the tooth surface, their ability to synthesize high-molecular-weight carbohydrate polymers from sucrose is thought to play a major role in the colonization process. As Gibbons and van Houte (4, 5) have pointed out, however, polymer synthesis is not the only factor involved in microbial colonization of oral tissues and indeed may not even be the major one. Interbacterial aggregation (3) is probably another important factor. Cell-cell interactions between various members of the oral flora appear to be involved in the in vitro formation of adherent microbial deposits on smooth surfaces. For example, in vitro "plaque" formation on wires by certain pairs of oral microorganisms has been shown to be greater than that observed with either organism alone (10, 11). It has also been demonstrated that several strains of *Veillonella*, which have no primary ability to attach to smooth surfaces, can, nevertheless, form secondary deposits on nichrome wires initially colonized by *Actinomyces* species (1).

Another factor that might be important in colonization is the acquisition of extracellular bacterial products and/or salivary components by certain members of the indigenous microflora which may impart to them the ability to attach to oral tissues. In this communication, we report that several strains of *Veillonella* can form a complex with an extracellular glucosyltransferase produced by *S. salivarius*. The *Veillonella* cells so endowed are subsequently able to synthesize water-insoluble carbohydrate polymers and adhere to a smooth surface in vitro in the presence of sucrose.

PREPARATION OF CELLS AND CRUDE GLUCOSYLTRANSFERASE

V. parvula ATCC 17744 (strain KON) was inoculated into 125 ml of a complex medium described previously (9) except that 0.9% DL-sodium lactate served as the major energy source. The cells were harvested after 18 h of incubation at 37°C, washed twice with 20 mM potassium phosphate buffer, pH 6.5, containing 0.85% (wt/vol) NaCl (PBS), and resuspended in 10 ml of PBS.

Crude glucosyltransferase preparations were obtained from *S. salivarius* ATCC 25975. Cells were inoculated into 100 ml of the same medium used for growing *V. parvula* except that 0.2% glucose replaced lactate. After incubation at 37°C for 15 h, the cells were removed by centrifugation. The culture fluid was then adjusted to pH 6.5, passed through a 0.45-μm filter (Millipore Corp.), and dialyzed overnight at 4°C against distilled water. The pH of the dialyzed fluid was again adjusted to 6.5, and it was then filtered as before. This preparation was stored at 4°C and served as a source of crude glucosyltransferase (CGTase).

Glucosyltransferase was assayed by measuring the incorporation of [U-*glucosyl*-^{14}C]-sucrose into water-insoluble polysaccharide polymer essentially as previously described (12). One unit is defined here as the amount of enzyme that incorporates 1 μmol of the glucosyl moiety of sucrose into water-insoluble polymer per h at 37°C. Fructosyltransferase was assayed in the same way except that [U-*fructosyl*-^{14}C]sucrose served as substrate and the product analyzed for radioactivity was polymer insoluble in 75% ethanol. One unit of fructosyltransferase is the amount of enzyme that incorporates 1 μmol of the fructose moiety of sucrose into 75% ethanol-insoluble polymer per h at 37°C.

ABILITY OF *VEILLONELLA* TO COLONIZE SMOOTH SURFACES

McCabe and Donkersloot observed that when various species of *Veillonella* were incubated with the spent culture medium from *S. salivarius* (ATCC 25975) and then washed to remove loosely associated media or other extracellular bacterial components, the organisms subsequently formed adherent deposits on nichrome wires (8) in the presence of sucrose (Fig. 1 and unpublished data). The fact that the adherence phenomenon was specifically sucrose dependent and did not occur when cells were preincubated with uninoculated *S. salivarius* growth medium

suggested that the extracellular enzyme glucosyltransferase, which is known to be elaborated by several of the oral streptococci, was intimately involved with the acquired adherence capability. Indeed, when the spent *S. salivarius* growth medium was assayed for glucosyltransferase, this activity was found at levels of about 6.8 units per ml. Fructosyltransferase activity was also present, but at a lower level of approximately 1.8 units per ml. It was of interest, therefore, to determine directly whether *Veillonella* cells could bind the glucosyltransferase produced by *S. salivarius*.

BINDING OF *S. SALIVARIUS* GLUCOSYLTRANSFERASE BY *VEILLONELLA* CELLS

The ability of *Veillonella* cells to form complexes with *S. salivarius* glucosyltransferase was assessed in the following way. A 1-ml amount of a *V. parvula* cell suspension prepared as described above was incubated with 5 ml of CGTase at room temperature for 3 h with gentle shaking. Controls consisted of cells

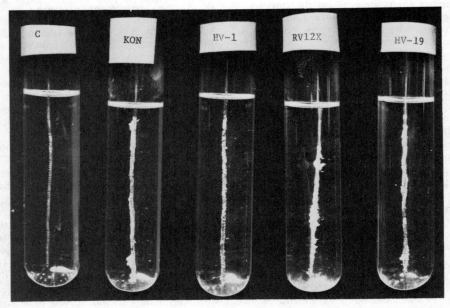

FIG. 1. *Colonization of nichrome wires by various* Veillonella *species after preincubation of cells in spent* Streptococcus salivarius *growth medium. Various strains of* Veillonella *were grown overnight in brain heart infusion broth (BHI) containing 5% (wt/vol) sucrose. All subsequent steps were carried out aseptically. Cells were harvested, washed with PBS, and preincubated with spent* S. salivarius *(ATCC 25975) growth medium for 3 h at room temperature. The cells were again washed with PBS (pH 6.5) and inoculated into tubes of BHI (adjusted to pH 6.5) containing 5% (wt/vol) sucrose and fitted with nichrome wires (8). Tubes were incubated for 24 h at 37°C and then observed for the formation of adherent microbial deposits on the wires. From left to right: (C) control cells preincubated with uninoculated BHI; (KON)* V. parvula *ATCC 17744; (HV-1)* V. alcalescens *ATCC 17747; (RV12X)* V. alcalescens *ATCC 17746; (HV-19)* V. parvula *ATCC 17743. No colonization of the wires was observed when sucrose was omitted from the growth medium (data not shown).*

incubated in the same way with uninoculated *S. salivarius* growth medium. Cells were then removed by centrifugation, washed twice with PBS, and resuspended in 5 ml of PBS. The optical density at 660 nm of a 1:2 dilution of such suspensions ranged between 1.3 and 1.7, and the undiluted suspensions contained about 5 mg (dry weight) of cells per ml. A 1-ml amount of the undiluted cell suspension was then added to a reaction mixture containing 50 mM potassium phosphate buffer, pH 6.5, and 10 mM [U-*glucosyl*-^{14}C]sucrose (120,000 cpm). The mixture was incubated at 37°C for 1 h, and the incorporation of the glucosyl moiety of sucrose into water-insoluble polymer was determined as previously described.

By use of this procedure, it was found that *V. parvula* cells do bind the *S. salivarius* glucosyltransferase and that the amount of enzyme bound is roughly proportional to the concentration of cells present in the CGTase preincubation mixture (Fig. 2). Cell-associated fructosyltransferase activity could not be detected under these conditions, and no glucosyltransferase activity was found associated with control cells which were preincubated in uninoculated *S. salivarius* growth medium.

pH OPTIMUM

The ability of *V. parvula* to bind the *S. salivarius* glucosyltransferase is influenced somewhat by pH. Within the pH range of 6.2 to 8.2, optimal binding occurred at about pH 7.5. The optimum was not sharp, however, and the amount of enzyme bound at pH 6.2 and 8.2 was about 71 and 80%, respectively, of that bound at pH 7.5. In these experiments, as in all others reported here, the assay for cell-associated glucosyltransferase was carried out at pH 6.5, which is near the optimum for enzyme activity. Thus, the pH optimum for binding is more alkaline than the pH optimum for catalytic activity. Control studies established that incubating the enzyme (CGTase) for 3 h at pH values between 6.2 and 8.2 did not significantly affect its activity when subsequently assayed at pH 6.5.

Stability of the Cell-Associated Glucosyltransferase Complex

The complex between *Veillonella* cells and the glucosyltransferase appears to be quite stable. Attempts to elute the bound enzyme by washing the cells with 1.0 M NaCl or with 1.0 M LiCl were unsuccessful. These experiments are difficult to interpret on an absolute quantitative basis because high salt concentrations

tended to inhibit glucosyltransferase activity. On a qualitative basis, however, we have not been able to remove completely the cell-associated enzyme by these techniques. It appears, therefore, that the cell-enzyme complex is a rather stable one and that the enzyme, once bound, is not easily dissociated from the cell.

EFFECT OF VARIOUS PRETREATMENT CONDITIONS ON THE ABILITY OF *V. PARVULA* CELLS TO BIND GLUOCOSYLTRANSFERASE

In an attempt to gain some insight into the nature of the glucosyltransferase binding, *V. parvula* cells were subjected to various treatments prior to their incubation with CGTase (Table 1). It was found that cells heated at 100°C for 20 min, incubated at pH 2.0 for 1 h at 37°C, or washed extensively with 100 mM EDTA and then incubated for 1 h at 37°C with EDTA were unaffected in their subsequent ability to bind the *S. salivarius* glucosyltransferase. Similarly, pretreatment of cells with Pronase, trypsin, or neuraminidase at 37°C for 1 h did not reduce their capability to bind the enzyme. Trypsin-treated cells, in fact, exhibited a three- to fourfold enhancement in their binding ability. This suggests that cell surface proteins are not likely involved in binding the enzyme and, moreover, that if specific surface components are involved in the phenomenon they may be more available after the cells have been subjected to mild

TABLE 1. *Effect of pretreating* Veillonella parvula *cells in various ways on their subsequent ability to bind* S. salivarius *glucosyltransferase*

Treatment of *V. parvula* cells[a]	*S. salivarius* glucosyltransferase bound (units/mg [dry wt] of cells)
None	0.173
100°C for 20 min	0.169
pH 2.0	0.364
EDTA (100 mM)	0.190
Trypsin (5 mg/ml)	0.672
Pronase (130 µg/ml)	0.210
Neuraminidase (1.0 mg, 1.71 units/ml)	0.190

[a] A 1-ml amount of a *V. parvula* ATCC 17744 cell suspension, prepared as described in the text, was incubated for 1 h at 37°C under the various conditions noted above. Cells from each incubation mixture were removed by centrifugation, washed twice with PBS, pH 6.5, and resuspended in 1 ml of the same buffer. Each cell suspension was then preincubated with 55.6 units of crude glucosyltransferase, washed with PBS, and subsequently assayed for cell-associated glucosyltransferase as described in the text.

proteolytic digestion. The results with EDTA further suggest that metal ions are not obligatorily involved in the binding.

SPECIFICITY

It was also of interest to determine whether *Veillonella* species were the only organisms capable of binding the *S. salivarius* glucosyltransferase. Slade (13) has tested a variety of gram-positive and gram-negative bacteria for their ability to adhere to glass surfaces in the presence of sucrose after preincubating the organisms with glucosyltransferases produced by various strains of *S. mutans*. When the organisms were thoroughly washed after the preincubation, none (except *S. mutans*) had acquired the ability to adhere to glass in the presence of sucrose. We have tested three different organisms for their ability to bind the *S. salivarius* glucosyltransferase under the conditions described for *V. parvula* and found that *Streptococcus faecalis* (ATCC 27792),

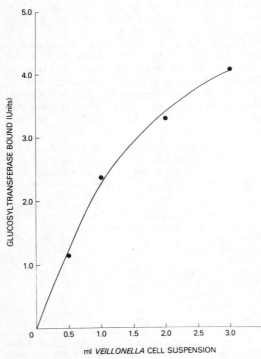

FIG. 2. *Relationship between* V. parvula *cell concentration and the amount of* S. salivarius *glucosyltransferase bound. The indicated volumes of a* V. parvula *ATCC 17744 cell suspension were preincubated with* S. salivarius *crude glucosyltransferase (250 units), washed with PBS, and then assayed for cell-associated glucosyltransferase as described in the text.*

Escherichia coli (ATCC 11775), and *Lactobacillus casei* (ATCC 393) were all capable of binding the enzyme to a certain extent. Again, quantitation is difficult in these experiments because it appears that binding of the enzyme leads to its partial inactivation (Wittenberger, unpublished data). Consistent with Slade's (13) observations, however, is the fact that *L. casei* (the only one of the three organisms tested) was unable to adhere to wires in the presence of sucrose after preincubation of cells with *S. salivarius* CGTase. This suggests that the ability of an organism to bind glucosyltransferase and produce glucans from sucrose may not by itself be sufficient to confer in vitro adherence capability to that organism. What might be required to complete the process is some mechanism for adherent interactions between cells, either direct or perhaps mediated by the glucan product of the *S. salivarius* glucosyltransferase. An extension of this reasoning leads to the prediction that such a mechanism(s) exists for *Veillonella* species but not for *L. casei*. It is perhaps pertinent to point out in this regard that high-molecular-weight dextrans have been shown to aggregate strains of *S. mutans* but not *L. casei*, *E. coli*, or *S. faecalis* (2). In any case, these preliminary data suggest that, when dealing with organisms other than *S. mutans*, adherence assays may not always detect cellular binding of glucosyltransferases, and direct assays for cell-associated glucosyltransferase may not necessarily reflect cellular adherence capabilities.

CONCLUSIONS

V. parvula can form a relatively stable complex with the extracellular glucosyltransferase produced by *S. salivarius*. The *Veillonella* cells are then able to produce water-insoluble polymers from sucrose and adhere to a smooth surface in vitro. It is uncertain at present whether binding of the enzyme involves specific receptor sites on the cell surface or whether the association is nonspecific in nature. It is well known that the glucosyltransferase produced by strains of *S. mutans* is a glycoprotein with inherent "sticky" properties. If the *S. salivarius* enzyme is similar in nature, its association with *Veillonella* might involve a simple nonspecific adsorption to the cells, possibly mediated by the carbohydrate moiety of the enzyme. Another possibility is that *Veillonella* species possess cell surface components that have an avidity for glycoproteins in general. Obviously, additional studies are required to resolve these questions.

Quite aside from the mechanistic considerations is the question of the possible ecological significance of the phenomenon. Clearly, no direct extrapolation from these preliminary in vitro studies to the situation in the oral environment is possible. *Veillonella* species, however, are known to be a persistent constituent of plaque and have been reported to represent between 1 and 6% of the total cultivable microbial flora (4, 6, 7). Inasmuch as this group of gram-negative organisms have no known innate ability to colonize smooth surfaces, it is tempting to speculate that their acquisition of the *S. salivarius* glucosyltransferase and the accompanying potential to synthesize high-molecular-weight polymers from sucrose may somehow be involved in their association with plaque.

LITERATURE CITED

1. **Bladen, H., G. Hageage, F. Pollock, and R. Harr.** 1970. Plaque formation *in vitro* on wires by Gram-negative oral microorganisms (*Veillonella*). Arch. Oral Biol. **15:**127–133.
2. **Gibbons, R. J., and R. J. Fitzgerald.** 1969. Dextran-induced agglutination of *Streptococcus mutans*, and its potential role in the formation of microbial dental plaques. J. Bacteriol. **98:**341–346.
3. **Gibbons, R. J., and M. Nygaard.** 1970. Interbacterial aggregation of plaque bacteria. Arch. Oral Biol. **15:**1397–1400.
4. **Gibbons, R. J., and J. van Houte.** 1973. On the formation of dental plaques. J. Periodontol. **44:**347–360.
5. **Gibbons, R. J., and J. van Houte.** 1975. Bacterial adherence in oral microbial ecology. Annu. Rev. Microbiol. **29:**19–44.
6. **Hardie, J. M., and G. H. Bowden.** 1974. The normal microbial flora of the mouth, p. 47–74. *In* F. A. Skinner and J. G. Carr (ed.), The normal microbial flora of man. Academic Press Inc., New York.
7. **Liljemark, W. F., and R. J. Gibbons.** 1971. Ability of *Veillonella* and *Neisseria* species to attach to oral surfaces and their proportions present indigenously. Infect. Immun. **4:**264–268.
8. **McCabe, R. M., P. H. Keyes, and A. Howell, Jr.** 1967. An *in vitro* method for assessing the plaque forming ability of oral bacteria. Arch. Oral Biol. **12:**1653–1656.
9. **Maryanski, J. H., and C. L. Wittenberger.** 1975. Mannitol transport in *Streptococcus mutans*. J. Bacteriol. **124:**1475–1481.
10. **Miller, C. H., and J. L. Kleinman.** 1974. Effect of microbial interactions on *in vitro* plaque formation by *Streptococcus mutans*. J. Dent. Res. **53:**427–434.
11. **Parsons, J. C., Jr., and C. H. Miller.** 1974. Plaque formation by mixed cultures of nonprimary plaque-forming microorganisms. J. Dent. Res. **53:**825–831.
12. **Robrish, S. A., W. Reid, and M. I. Krichevsky.** 1972. Distribution of enzymes forming polysaccharides from sucrose and the composition of extracellular polysaccharide synthesized by *Streptococcus mutans*. Appl. Microbiol. **24:**184–190.
13. **Slade, H. D.** 1976. *In vitro* models for the study of adherence of oral streptococci, p. 21–38. *In* W. H. Bowen, R. J. Genco, and J. C. O'Brien (ed.), Immunologic aspects of dental caries (a special supplement to Immunology Abstracts). Information Retrieval, Inc., Washington, D.C.

Electron Microscopy of Bacteria Adherent to Epithelia in the Murine Intestinal Canal

DWAYNE C. SAVAGE

Department of Microbiology and School of Basic Medical Sciences, University of Illinois, Urbana, Illinois 61801

INTRODUCTION

Numerous bacterial types are known to associate with epithelial surfaces in the gastrointestinal tracts of mice and rats (12). In most of these microbe-epithelium associations, the microorganisms adhere physically to the epithelium. In this paper, I shall review some recently published findings from work with electron microscopy, both transmission and scanning, on the mechanisms involved in these microbial associations with epithelial surfaces in the murine gastrointestinal tract. In addition, I shall present some new findings on the mechanisms by which certain oxygen-intolerant anaerobic bacteria associate with the mucosal epithelium in the large bowels of mice.

In so doing, I wish to take note of recent concern expressed (3) that many micrographs obtained by scanning electron microscopy have been published unaccompanied by definition of widely accepted criteria for assessing their scientific merit. Four suggestions were made which were intended to "reduce the prevalence of published artifacts and their misinterpretation by authors and readers" (3). Paraphrased somewhat, the suggestions were as follows:

1. All structures observed in scanning electron micrographs should be verified with photographs at equivalent magnifications of the same or comparable specimens prepared by conventional transmission techniques—light or electron microscopic or both.

2. Scanning photomicrographs that do not present data necessary to the argument of the paper should not appear in the work.

3. Incidental artifacts on the micrographs presented, which the author realizes are artifacts, should be identified as such in the figure legends.

4. Detailed descriptions, or references to such descriptions, should be given for all sampling and preparation techniques employed for the scanning electron microscopy.

I share the concerns expressed and accept the suggestions as a means of minimizing misinterpretation of published micrographs derived from scanning electron microscopy. Accordingly, whenever discussing a particular microbial type associating with an epithelium, I shall note where possible by what microscopic means, other than scanning electron microscopy, the microbe has been observed in its habitat in a naturally colonized animal. In addition, I shall note whether or not the microbial type has been isolated in pure culture from the natural habitat and then shown microscopically to colonize in the same way the same habitat in a gnotobiotic animal. Finally, I shall omit unnecessary micrographs, identify artifacts on the micrographs included, and cite references in which detailed methods are given.

THE STOMACH

Lactobacilli are known to associate with the keratinizing stratified squamous epithelium in the nonsecreting portion of the stomachs of both mice (12, 13) and rats (11). Such bacteria have been isolated from their naturally colonized hosts and shown to colonize the same habitat in monoassociated gnotobiotic models (11, 16, 18). They have been visualized in their habitats in both the gnotobiotic models and naturally colonized animals by the techniques of frozen-section histology and conventional light microscopy (16, 18). They have been visualized in naturally colonized animals by the procedures of both scanning (13) and transmission electron microscopy (A. Takeuchi and D. C. Savage, Abstr. Annu. Meet. Am. Soc. Microbiol. 1973, M254, p. 115).

As observed primarily in scanning electron micrographs (4, 13), but also in micrographs taken by conventional light microscopy of frozen-section preparation (16, 18), the lactobacilli attach to the epithelium either end-on or sideways. As suggested by findings made with ultramicroscopic histochemistry, their attachment to the epithelium may be mediated by acidic mucopolysaccharides on their surfaces

(Takeuchi and Savage, see above). Similar histochemical findings suggest that polysaccharides mediate attachment of lactobacilli to the stratified squamous epithelium in the crops of chickens (1). Biochemical evidence from experiments performed by examining lactobacilli attaching to crop cells in vitro tends to support the electron microscopic findings (1).

A biochemical study also has been made of the mechanisms of attachment in vitro of indigenous lactobacilli to squamous epithelial cells obtained from rat stomachs (15). Findings from this study support the evidence from electron microscopy that surface structures on the bacteria mediate their attachment to epithelial cells. The surface structures behave as polysaccharides only in some experiments, however, and behave as proteins or protein-like substances in others. These conflicting findings require further investigation.

THE SMALL BOWEL

In the small intestines of both mice (6, 13) and rats (2, 6), segmented, filamentous microbes with the ultrastructure of gram-positive bacteria have been found attached to the epithelium. They have been seen in frozen-section preparations examined by conventional light microscopy (6, 13) and in appropriate preparations viewed by both scanning (2, 6, 13) and transmission (2, 6) electron microscopy. They have been found on the epithelium in all areas of the small bowel. Usually, however, their populations are most dense in the ileum (6). Unfortunately, they have not yet been isolated in pure culture in vitro. Accordingly, no gnotobiotic model has yet been developed.

In all cases reported (2, 6, 13), the microbes, consisting of from one to many segments, have been observed to attach to the brush-border membranes of the absorptive epithelial cells on the villi of the intestinal mucosa. In rats, they may tend to cluster in more dense populations on the epithelium covering Peyer's patches (G. D. Abrams, Am. J. Clin. Nutr., in press). At the site of attachment, an apparently specialized segment of the microbe, approximately $0.7\ \mu m$ in diameter, inserts into the brush-border membrane on the apical region of the epithelial cell (2, 6). In transmission electron micrographs, the membrane of the epithelial cell appears to be intact around the bacterial segment (2, 6). The wall of the bacterial segment in contact with the epithelial cell membrane is composed of two layers. By contrast, the wall of segments not in contact with the epithelial cell is made up of four layers (2, 6). The epithelial cell cytoplasm is strongly electron

dense in a layer adjacent to the membrane in contact with the bacterial segment (2, 6). Cytoplasm surrounding this dense layer is also somewhat more electron dense than is cytoplasm more remote from the site. In scanning electron micrographs, the site appears as a dark hole into which the bacterial segment is inserted (2, 6, 13).

Similar observations have been made with preparations of the intestinal mucosa of rats and mice given penicillin for a few hours (7). In these preparations examined by scanning electron microscopy, putative attachment sites also appear as dark holes in the epithelial cells. However, the microbes may be missing from the holes. Neither the bacteria nor the holes can be seen after 7 h or more of treatment of the animals with penicillin (7). Normal mechanisms of membrane turnover apparently remove the attachment sites once the microbes are killed.

As revealed in the preparations examined by transmission electron microscopy, the microbe forms inside some of its segments intracellular bodies with the ultrastructure of bacterial endospores (2, 6, 7). More frequently observed in the segments, however, are intracellular bodies with prokaryotic ultrastructure similar morphologically to the specialized segment of the organism that attaches to the epithelial cell (2, 6). The discovery of these latter intracellular bodies has stimulated speculation that the microbe may have a complex life cycle in which the intracellular body, released from the mother cell to the epithelium, induces the attachment site and then grows out segmentally to become a mature filament (2, 6). Evidence for this hypothesis is derived only from work with preparations examined by microscopic techniques. Its confirmation must await success of efforts to isolate the microbe and study its properties in pure culture.

THE LARGE BOWEL

Fusiform and spiral-shaped microbes can be observed in layers on the epithelium of the cecum and especially the proximal colon of mice and rats (12). The microbes have been seen on the epithelia in frozen histological sections viewed by conventional light and fluorescence microscopy (14) and in appropriate preparations examined in scanning (4, 13) and transmission electron microscopes (14). Spirochetes have also been detected by conventional light and transmission electron microscopy in the crypts and intracellularly in macrophages in the cecal mucosa in rats (5, 8–10). Also in rats, a rod-shaped microbe has been seen attached end-on to colonic epithelial cells viewed by

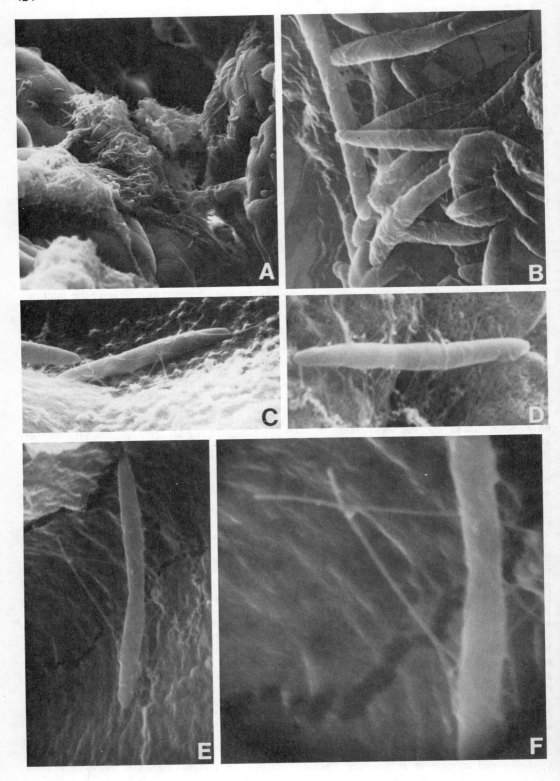

transmission electron microscopy (17). In this case, as with the segmented, filamentous microbe populating the epithelium of the small bowel, one end of the rod appears to be modified to form a mechanism for attaching to the epithelial cell (17).

Unidentified microbes with spiraling filaments running the full length of their cells and tufts of flagella on their ends have been observed by transmission electron microscopy in washings of the epithelium of the ceca of mice from certain colonies (14). Organisms believed to be similar, if not identical, have been observed in preparations of rat small bowel (S. L. Erlandsen, personal communication) and mouse colons (Savage, unpublished data) viewed by scanning electron microscopy.

None of the spirochetes, spirochete-like microbes, or spiral-shaped bacteria has been isolated and sustained in pure culture. However, a fusiform bacterium has been isolated from the mouse colonic epithelium, maintained in pure culture, and shown to be a *Clostridium* sp. (16). This microbe will colonize the colonic, and to lesser extent the cecal, epithelium in gnotobiotic mice previously associated with a *Lactobacillus* and a *Bacteroides* sp. (16; Fig. 1A).

In highly magnified scanning electron micrographs, the organism can be seen to have a generally smooth surface criss-crossed with thin lines that may be ridges (Fig. 1B). A similar surface can be seen on one of the three types of fusiform bacteria commonly seen in layers on the colonic epithelium in natively colonized mice (13). In preparations from such natively colonized mice, filaments can be observed by scanning electron microscopy extending from the fusiform bacterium to the epithelium (13). The filaments often appear to extend from the lines on the bacterial surface. In preparations of colon from the triassociated gnotobiotes, similar filaments can be seen extending from the lines on the surface of the clostridial cells to the epithelium (Fig. 1C–F).

The filaments may anchor the bacteria to the epithelium. Alternatively, they may have nothing to do with the attachment and may even be artifacts of the preparation. Recent transmission electron micrographs have revealed no obvious filaments extending from the microbes to the epithelium (M. J. R. Gilchrist and D. C. Savage, unpublished data). At this time, therefore, the mechanism by which these microbes adhere to the epithelium is unknown.

ACKNOWLEDGMENTS

My experimental work reported herein has been supported by the National Institute of Allergy and Infectious Diseases and by the National Dairy Council. I am indebted to Ruth V. H. Blumershine for assistance with the electron microscopy and to the staff of the Electron Microscope Laboratory of the University of Illinois for allowing us to use their equipment.

LITERATURE CITED

1. **Brooker, B. E., and R. Fuller.** 1975. Adhesion of lactobacilli to the chicken crop epithelium. J. Ultrastruct. Res. **52:**21–31.
2. **Chase, D. G., and S. L. Erlandsen.** 1976. Evidence for a complex life cycle and endospore formation in the attached, filamentous segmented bacterium from murine ileum. J. Bacteriol. **127:**572–583.
3. **Clark, J. M., and S. Glagov.** 1976. Evaluation and publication of scanning electron micrographs. Science **192:**1360–1361.
4. **Davis, C. P.** 1976. Preservation of gastrointestinal bacteria and their microenvironmental associations in rats by freezing. Appl. Environ. Microbiol. **31:**304–312.
5. **Davis, C. P., D. Mulcahy, A. Takeuchi, and D. C. Savage.** 1972. Location and description of spiral-shaped microorganisms in the normal rat cecum. Infect. Immun. **6:**184–192.
6. **Davis, C. P., and D. C. Savage.** 1974. Habitat, succession, attachment, and morphology of segmented, filamentous microbes indigenous to the murine gastrointestinal tract. Infect. Immun. **10:**948–956.
7. **Davis, C. P., and D. C. Savage.** 1976. Effect of penicillin on the succession, attachment, and morphology of segmented, filamentous microbes in the murine small bowel. Infect. Immun. **13:**180–188.
8. **Gustafsson, B. E., and A. B. Maunsbach.** 1971. Ultrastructure of the enlarged cecum in germfree rats. Z. Zellforsch. Mikrosk. Anat. **120:**555–578.
9. **Henrikson, R. C.** 1973. Ultrastructural aspects of mouse

FIG. 1. *Fusiform* Clostridium *sp. on the surface of the columnar epithelium of the colonic mucosa in gnotobiotic CD-1 mice (Charles River, Wilmington, Mass.) triassociated with the* Clostridium *sp., a* Bacteroides *sp., and a* Lactobacillus *sp. (16). The micrographs were take of preparations viewed in a Cambridge Mark II Stereoscan scanning electron microscope. For details of all procedures see reference 13. (A) Overview of the epithelium at low magnification showing microcolonies and individual cells of the bacterium on the epithelial surface.* ×1,105. *(B) A microcolony showing individual bacterial cells. Note the thin lines criss-crossing the bacterial surfaces.* ×13,600. *(C) Individual bacterial cell lying on the epithelium. Note filaments extending from the lines (ridges?) on the bacterium to the epithelial surface.* ×12,750. *(D) Another individual bacterial cell on the epithelial surface. Again, filaments extend from the bacterial to the epithelial surface.* ×16,575. *(E) Individual bacterial cell on epithelium. Long, straight filaments extend from bacterium to epithelium. The bacterium may have been dividing. Dark jagged cracks in the epithelium (upper left corner and in center extending from right to left under bacterial cell) are undoubtedly artifacts due to drying of the preparation.* ×11,050. *(F) Enlargement of central area of E.* ×22,100.

cecal epithelium. Z. Zellforsch. Mikrosk. Anat. **140:** 445–449.

10. **Leach, W. D., A. Lee, and R. P. Stubbs.** 1973. Localization of bacteria in the gastrointestinal tract: a possible explanation of intestinal spirochaetosis. Infect. Immun. **7:**961–972.

11. **Morotomi, M., T. Watanabe, N. Suegara, Y. Kawai, and M. Mutai.** 1975. Distribution of indigenous bacteria in the digestive tract of conventional and gnotobiotic rats. Infect. Immun. **11:**962–968.

12. **Savage, D. C.** 1975. Indigenous microorganisms associating with mucosal epithelia in the gastrointestinal ecosystem, p. 120–123. *In* D. Schlessinger (ed.), Microbiology—1975. American Society for Microbiology, Washington, D.C.

13. **Savage, D. C., and R. V. H. Blumershine.** 1974. Surface-surface associations in microbial communities populating epithelial habitats in the murine gastrointestinal ecosystem: scanning electron microscopy. Infect. Immun. **10:**240–250.

14. **Savage, D. C., J. S. McAllister, and C. P. Davis.** 1971. Anaerobic bacteria on the mucosal epithelium of the murine large bowel. Infect. Immun. **4:**492–502.

15. **Suegara, N., M. Morotomi, T. Watanabe, Y. Kawai, and M. Mutai.** 1975. Behavior or microflora in the rat stomach: adhesion of lactobacilli to the keratinized epithelial cells of the rat stomach in vitro. Infect. Immun. **12:**173–179.

16. **Tannock, G. W., and D. C. Savage.** 1976. Indigenous microorganisms prevent reduction in cecal size induced by *Salmonella typhimurium* in vaccinated gnotobiotic mice. Infect. Immun. **13:**172–179.

17. **Wagner, R. C., and R. J. Barrnett.** 1974. The fine structure of prokaryotic-eukaryotic cell junctions. J. Ultrastruct. Res. **48:**404–413.

18. **Yolton, D. P., and D. C. Savage.** 1976. Influence of certain indigenous gastrointestinal microorganisms on duodenal alkaline phosphatase in mice. Appl. Environment. Microbiol. **31:**880–888.

Adherence of Gonococci

JOHN SWANSON

Departments of Pathology and Microbiology, University of Utah College of Medicine,
Salt Lake City, Utah 84132

My understanding of the interactions between *Neisseria gonorrhoeae* and eukaryotic cells was reviewed at a similar conference held about a year and a half ago (13) and is summarized in Table 1. It should be noted that there seems to be agreement that pili assist, promote, or actually effect attachment of gonococci to epithelial or epithelium-derived cells (9, 11, 12, 22). Pili also appear to enhance attachment of gonococci to human sperm (3) and erythrocytes (6, 21). Interactions of isolated gonococcal pili with several kinds of eukaryotic cells, in vitro, have recently been studied and appear to agree with findings based on the use of intact piliated (P+) or nonpilated (P−) gonococci (T. M. Buchanan, Prog. Abstr. Intersci. Conf. Antimicrob. Agents Chemother., 16th, Chicago, Ill., 1976). Pili also have an effect on interactions of gonococci with mouse peritoneal macrophages, and in this system P+ organisms are less readily associated with the macrophages than are the P− bacteria of the same strain (1). The gonococcus-macrophage system is not influenced by the LA+ or LA− characteristics of the bacteria, as discussed below.

Less agreement can be found on the topic of interactions between gonococci and human peripheral blood neutrophils. Studies from my laboratory suggest that a nonpilus surface component ("leukocyte-association factor" or LA) is the primary determiner of gonococcus-polymorphonuclear leukocyte (PMN) association and that pili may play a minor, negative role in such interactions (14, 17, 18). Accordingly, high-level (LA+) or low-level (LA−) associations with PMN can be demonstrated for either P+ or P− gonococci. These phenomena have been found also in another laboratory (J. Sadoff, personal communication). Several other groups are of the opinion that pili strongly inhibit interactions between gonococci and human leukocytes (2, 10, 19, 20). One of these groups has recently found an additional antiphagocytic factor that is susceptible to removal or modification by EDTA treatment (W. D. Sawyer et al., Abstr. Annu. Meet. Am. Soc. Microbiol. 1975, B11, p. 13). This last-mentioned phenomenon has been corroborated in my laboratory by

Gretchen King, who has found conversion of low-level to high-level association for P− gonococci with human PMN after treatment of the organisms with EDTA. This treatment does not modify protein components as far as we can tell nor does it remove the protein associated with LA+ activity, as described below.

LA+ gonococci have been shown to differ from LA− organisms of the same strains by the presence of an additional protein moiety in the former, as resolved by sodium dodecyl sulfate (SDS)-polyacrylamide gel electrophoresis (G. J. King and J. Swanson, Abstr. Annu. Meet. Am. Soc. Microbiol. 1976, D28, p. 56). In this work, done by King, LA+ organisms have a protein which can be labeled by ^{125}I in the lactoperoxidase-catalyzed reaction carried out on intact organisms. The molecular weight of this LA-associated band varies in different strains (approximately 29,000 for strains MS11 and F62, and approximately 28,000 for strain C109, a recent isolate).

Quite recently, John James in my laboratory has demonstrated capsules on gonococci by numerous morphological methods (manuscript in preparation). Capsules of various sizes are found both on recently isolated gonococci and on organisms that have been passaged several hundred times. Although the recent isolates seem to have somewhat larger capsules, all colony forms (after Kellogg) can be shown to be encapsulated by a variety of techniques. The capsular material is resistant to removal by trypsin, chymotrypsin, glucosidase, or neuraminidase, but is easily lost by subjecting the bacteria to mild shearing forces. Similar findings have been obtained by Jerry Sadoff (personal communication to James). We have no information as to the possible function or the chemical composition of the gonococcal capsule.

My own recent work has focused on colonial "coloration" variations in gonococci and will be briefly summarized. (A portion of this work was described at a recent symposium on "Current Status and Prospects for Improved and New Bacterial Vaccines" held at the National Institutes of Health, March 1976.)

Colonies of either P+ or P− gonococci from

TABLE 1. *Gonococcus-host cell interactions*

Interaction	Pili	LA factor[a]
Gonococcus attachment to tissue culture cells, Fallopian tubal cells, and buccal mucosal cells	+(↑)	−
Gonococcus attachment to sperm, erythrocytes (human)	+(↑)	−(?)
Gonococcus association with human or mouse PMNs	±(↓)	+(↑)
Gonococcus association with mouse peritoneal macrophages	+(↓)	−

[a] Leukocyte-association factor.

virtually all strains may exhibit any of several hues when examined with a dissecting, stereomicroscope utilizing transmitted light reflected from a diffusing surface. Careful selection and passage yields homogeneous preparations of any desired colony coloration. The spectrum of colors seen ranges from dark brown-black to nearly colorless. Through use of light trans-

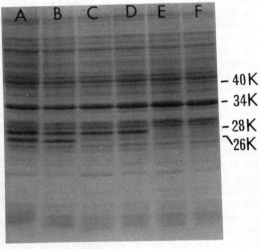

FIG. 1. *Derivatives of strain F62 were solubilized in 1% SDS with β-mercaptoethanol and subjected to polyacrylamide electrophoresis as described by Laemmli (7). The derivatives that are to be compared are as follows: A = P+ Op; B = P− Op; C = P+ OP/Bl; D = P− Op/Bl; E = P+ Bl; and F = P− Bl. The approximate, apparent molecular weights are given. Note the identical patterns for Coomassie blue staining bands for all preparations over 40,000 molecular weight. The Op (opaque) colony forms exhibit bands of 26,000 molecular weight that are absent from both the Op/Bl and Bl (blue) forms and also have a 28,000-molecular-weight band that is present in the Op/Bl but not in the Bl organisms.*

mitted from a plane-polished mirror surface and the same microscope, differences in colonial color are seen as variations in opalescence and extend along a spectrum from opaque to blue, similar to the differences noted by McCarty for streptococci (8). The very dark colonies appear opaque and the lightest ones are blue by this method of examination. In the subsequent discussion the terms opaque (Op) and blue (Bl) will be used rather than dark, light, etc.

Examination of colonies with conventional light microscopy (objectives of ×25 to ×40) reveals tightly clumped organisms comprising the edges of Op colonies, whereas those gonococci at the peripheries of Bl colonies show little evidence of intercellular aggregation or connection. Twitching motility is readily observed in P+ Bl colonies examined by this microscopic technique, is always absent in P− colonies regardless of coloration or aggregation type, and may be seen infrequently in P+ Op colonies. Gonococci from Op colonies tend to clump in liquid medium or buffer, whereas those from Bl colonies ae usually smooth in liquid suspension. Electron microscopic examination of thin-sectioned organisms shows abundant zones of adherence, which have been previously described (15) and appear between adjacent portions of cell wall exteriors of Op gonococci. Such zones are not seen between organisms from Bl colonies. These differences in interbacterial adhesion are somewhat similar to those demonstrated for opaque and blue variants of streptococci (16). For the reasons noted above, I shall refer to these Op and Bl colonies as aggregation variants.

Gonococci comprising Op colonies appear to be more sensitive to killing by trypsin than are Bl gonococci of the same strain. This can be demonstrated either on agar with trypsin-impregnated disks or after addition of trypsin to liquid cultures. The trypsin effect appears to correlate with the susceptibilities of proteins on the different aggregation variants to the enzyme, as discussed later.

The proteins comprising the outer membrane of aggregation variants have been studied by SDS-polyacrylamide gel electrophoresis carried out on organisms from several strains and after preparation by a variety of techniques. For the strains F62 and MS11, which have been most extensively studied, the protein patterns for the various aggregation variants are depicted in Fig. 1 and 2. Those proteins which are labeled by the lactoperoxidase-^{125}I method are similar in molecular weight to those found in isolated gonococcal envelopes by Johnston and Gotschlich (4). By both autoradiography of radiolabeled organisms and simple Coomassie

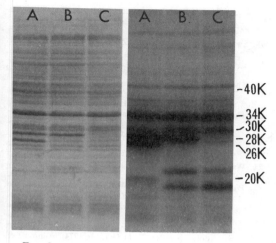

FIG. 2. *Derivatives of strain MS11* ^{125}I *labeled by the lactoperoxidase-H_2O_2-catalyzed reaction were subjected to polyacrylamide-SDS electrophoresis (7) and were stained with Coomassie blue (left); the dried gel was then used for autoradiography (right). Note that the 26,000- to 28,000-molecular-weight components mentioned in Fig. 1 are iodine labeled. Also note the differences in autoradiograms of the banding patterns of moieties with molecular weights less than 20,000. A = P+ Op; B = P+ Op/Bl; C = P+ Bl.*

blue staining of gels, gonococci of all strains and colony forms have identical protein patterns for components having molecular weights greater than 40,000. Striking differences among aggregation variants are seen in Coomassie blue-stained gels in the molecular weight region from 25,000 to 30,000, and additional differences are found in comparative autoradiograms in the 18,000-to-22,000 area. These differences are summarized in Fig. 2.

Striking differences among aggregation variant protein patterns are also seen after incubation of the organisms with trypsin prior to their solubilization for electrophoresis. Blue colony gonococci appear to undergo little change in protein banding as a consequence of exposure to trypsin. After incubation under identical conditions, opaque variants show loss of several cell wall protein bands. This difference appears to correlate with the differing susceptibilities of Op and Bl organisms to killing by trypsin.

Extraction of aggregation variants with chaotropic salt solutions has been undertaken by the method utilized by Johnston et al. (5). Column chromatography of the extracts reveals primarily outer membrane proteins in the eluate comprising the void volume. Differences in the positions of minor cell wall proteins are seen in extracts of Op and Bl variants, whereas their major proteins are

identical. This may serve to complicate the serotyping scheme that has been proposed (5) and which is based on the combination of major and minor protein molecular weights of material found in the void volume of material chromatographed on Sepharose 6B.

Do the aggregation variants have any relevance to pathogenicity of gonococci? To date, no differences have been noted in the production of either nonspecific, trypsin-like protease or immunoglobulin A-specific protease by the Op and Bl colony variants. John James has studied the occurrence of these variants in clinical isolates from males and females and has found a preponderance of Op forms in specimens from male urethrae, whereas Bl forms are more frequently found in isolates from female cervices. This might mean that Bl colony forms are selected in the female genital tract because of their relative resistance to trypsin or chymotrypsin-like enzymes that are abundant in this locale. Alternatively, the greater clumping ability of Op variants may provide them an advantage for survival in the male urethra. These are only some of several possible mechanisms in which the Op/Bl colony differences might be important for virulence or pathogenicity of gonococci, but at present these are only speculations.

LITERATURE CITED

1. **Blake, M., and J. Swanson.** 1975. Studies on gonococcus infection. IX. In vitro decreased association of pilated gonococci with mouse peritoneal macrophages. Infect. Immun. **11:**1402–1403.
2. **Dilworth, J. A., J. O. Hendley, and G. L. Mandell.** 1975. Attachment and ingestion of gonococci by human neutrophils. Infect. Immun. **11:**512–516.
3. **James-Holmquest, A. N., J. Swanson, T. M. Buchanan, R. D. Wende, and R. P. Williams.** 1974. Differential attachment by piliated and nonpiliated *Neisseria gonorrhoeae* to human sperm. Infect. Immun. **9:**897–902.
4. **Johnston, K. H., and E. C. Gotschlich.** 1974. Isolation and characterization of the outer membrane of *Neisseria gonorrhoeae*. J. Bacteriol. **119:**250–257.
5. **Johnston, K. H., K. K. Holmes, and E. C. Gotschlich.** 1976. The serological classification of *Neisseria gonorrhoeae*. I. Isolation of the outer membrane complex responsible for serotypic specificity. J. Exp. Med. **143:** 741–757.
6. **Koransky, J. R., R. W. Scales, and S. J. Kraus.** 1975. Bacterial hemagglutination by *Neisseria gonorrhoeae*. Infect. Immun. **12:**495–498.
7. **Laemmli, U. K.** 1970. Cleavage of structural proteins during the assembly of the head of bacteriophage T4. Nature (London) **227:**680.
8. **McCarty, M.** 1966. The nature of the opaque colony variation in group A streptococcus. J. Hyg. **64:**185–188.
9. **Mardh, P.-A., and L. Westrom.** 1976. Adherence of bacteria to vaginal epithelial cells. Infect. Immun. **13:** 661–666.
10. **Ofek, I., E. H. Beachey, and A. L. Bisno.** 1974. Resistance of *Neisseria gonorrhoeae* to phagocytosis: relationship to colonial morphology and surface pili. J. Infect. Dis. **129:**310–316.

11. **Punsalang, A. P., Jr., and W. D. Sawyer.** 1973. Role of pili in the virulence of *Neisseria gonorrhoeae*. Infect. Immun. **8:**255–263.

12. **Swanson, J.** 1973. Studies on gonococcus infection. IV. Pili: their role in attachment of gonococci to tissue culture cells. J. Exp. Med. **137:**571–589.

13. **Swanson, J.** 1975. Role of pili in interactions between *Neisseria gonorrhoeae* and eukaryotic cells in vitro, p. 124–126. *In* D. Schlessinger (ed.), Microbiology— 1975. American Society for Microbiology, Washington, D.C.

14. **Swanson, J., G. King, and B. Zeligs.** 1975. Studies on gonococcus infection. VIII. ^{125}Iodine labeling of gonococci and studies on their in vitro interactions with eukaryotic cells. Infect. Immun. **11:**453–459.

15. **Swanson, J., S. J. Kraus, and E. C. Gotschlich.** 1971. Studies on gonococcus infection. I. Pili and zones of adhesion; their relation to gonococcal growth patterns. J. Exp. Med. **134:**886–905.

16. **Swanson, J., and M. McCarty.** 1969. Electron microscopic studies on opaque colony variants of group A streptococci. J. Bacteriol. **100:**505–511.

17. **Swanson, J., E. Sparks, D. Young, and G. King.** 1975. Studies on gonococcus infection. X. Pili and leukocyte association factor as mediators of interactions between gonococci and eukaryotic cells in vitro. Infect. Immun. **11:**1352–1361.

18. **Swanson, J., E. Sparks, B. Zeligs, M. A. Siam, and C. Parrott.** 1974. Studies on gonococcus infection. V. Observations on in vitro interactions of gonococci and human neutrophils. Infect. Immun. **10:**633–644.

19. **Thomas, D. W., J. C. Hill, and F. J. Tyervar, Jr.** 1973. Interactions of gonococci with phagocytic leukocytes from men and mice. Infect. Immun. **8:**98–104.

20. **Thongthai, C., and W. D. Sawyer.** 1973. Studies on the virulence of *Neisseria gonorrhoeae*. I. Relation of colonial morphology and resistance to phagocytosis by polymorphonuclear leukocytes. Infect. Immun. **7:** 373–379.

21. **Waitkins, S. A.** 1974. Fimbrial haemagglutination by *Neisseria gonorrhoeae*. Br. J. Vener. Dis. **50:**272–278.

22. **Ward, M. E., and P. J. Watt.** 1975. Studies on the cell biology of gonorrhea, p. 229–241. *In* D. Danielsson, L. Juhlin, and P.-A. Mardh (ed.), Proceedings of the symposium on genital infections and their complications (A Wellcome Foundation Symposium held in Stockholm, Sweden, 9–11 October 1974). Almqvist & Wiksell International, Stockholm.

V. PERSISTENT VIRAL INFECTIONS

Introduction

JULIUS S. YOUNGNER

Department of Microbiology, School of Medicine, University of Pittsburgh, Pittsburgh, Pennsylvania 15261

The ASM conference on Persistent Viral Infections was held on 13–16 June 1976 in Dearborn, Michigan, and was attended by 172 participants. The conference was particularly timely since there is an increasing body of evidence concerning the biochemical and genetic aspects of persistently infected virus-carrier cultures and the possible usefulness of these model systems for understanding disease states in humans and other animals. The conference considered the mechanisms of establishment and maintenance of persistent viral infections, the problems of viral persistence in animals, including immunological modulation of viral persistence, and the possible role of persistent viral infections in diseases of humans. A portion of the meeting was devoted to a consideration of the strategies and problems of the development and use of live virus vaccines in humans.

I wish to thank Wolfgang K. Joklik and Neal Nathanson, members of the Organizing Committee, for their invaluable help in making the Conference a success.

Mechanisms of Establishment and Maintenance of Persistent Infections

Summary of Mechanisms Involved in Persistent Viral Infections

WOLFGANG K. JOKLIK

Department of Microbiology and Immunology, Duke University Medical Center, Durham, North Carolina 27710

Many animal viruses, even some that are considered to be highly cytocidal, can establish infections of cell cultures that result in the long-term multiplication of the virus while the cells continue to divide and grow.

PERSISTENT VIRAL INFECTIONS IN CULTURED CELLS

Persistent infections of cultured cells can be grouped into several classes on the basis of criteria such as the following (15, 16):

(i) Must antibody or other antiviral factors be supplied in the culture medium to maintain equilibrium in the infected culture?

(ii) Can the cultures be freed of virus (cured) by serial cultivation in a medium containing antiviral antibody, and can virus-free clones readily be obtained by cloning under antibody?

(iii) Is the culture resistant to superinfection by the carrier virus; is it resistant to challenge by other viruses?

(iv) What fraction of cell population is infected under the conditions in which the persistent state is most stable?

(v) Do infected cells divide and grow into infected clones?

(vi) Can interfering factors be demonstrated in the persistently infected cultures?

The class of persistent viral infections at one end of the spectrum is persistent noncytocidal infections transmitted through cell division. This type of persistent infection is characterized by the following properties:

(i) The cells are permissive.

(ii) All cells in the culture are infected.

(iii) All or most infected cells divide and grow into infected clones, most of which are infected.

(iv) The cells are resistant to superinfection by the infecting virus but are not resistant to unrelated viruses.

(v) Antibody or other antiviral factors play no role in the mechanism of persistence, and the culture is not cured by the addition of antiserum.

Numerous viruses, all of them enveloped budding viruses, are capable of establishing this type of persistently infected cell culture; among them are a variety of paramyxoviruses (mumps, measles, parainfluenza viruses 1 and 3, Sendai, and simian virus 5); rubella; rabies; lymphocytic choriomeningitis virus; lactic dehydrogenase elevating virus (LDH virus); and the RNA tumor viruses and visna virus. These types of infected cell cultures contain the viral genome in *all* cells; the viral genome expresses itself to at least some extent in all cells, and in most cases infectious virus is liberated by all cells. The extent to which the viral genome expresses itself can often be influenced markedly by altering growth conditions; thus, human conjunctiva cells persistently infected with mumps virus have been described in which only about 2% of the cells liberate viral progeny, but this proportion can be increased to 100% by preventing cell multiplication. By the same token, the amount of virus per cell can be drastically reduced and sometimes even eliminated by a variety of techniques such as raising the incubation temperature to 38°C and adding antibody to the medium to protect the uninfected cells that then arise.

The type of persistent infection at the other end of the spectrum is that in which the cells are semipermissive or nonpermissive, and a variety of factors that interfere with virus multiplication operate: thus, antiviral antibody is present, and interferon and defective interfering viral progeny are produced. In such cultures only a small proportion of cells are infected, and the two principal mechanisms of persistence are (i) the yield of virus progeny is small, and (ii) external factors in the medium minimize the number of cells that this limited amount of progeny can infect productively. The following are the basic characteristics of this type of persistent infection:

(i) The cells are rather nonpermissive; virus yields are small.

(ii) Only a small fraction of the cell population is infected. The viral multiplication cycle is a normal one, and the cells are destroyed; they do not divide.

(iii) Interferon and interfering virus are present in the medium.

(iv) Antiviral antibody in small amounts perpetuates persistent infection; in large amounts, it cures persistent infection.

(v) Clones of uninfected cells are easily obtained by cloning cells in an antibody-containing medium.

Two classical examples of infections of this kind are coxsackievirus A9 infection of HeLa cells, described by Takemoto and Habel in 1959 (13), and poliovirus infection of HeLa cells, described by Pacsa in 1961 (10).

Walker defined two further classes of persistent infections, which are subclasses of the type just described. The first is those infections of this type in which the protection of uninfected cells is mediated largely by antiviral factors in the *medium*, primarily antiserum; interferon and interfering virus play no role. The best examples of this type of infection are various cell lines persistently infected with herpes simplex virus and HeLa cells persistently infected with adenovirus types 3 and 4 (2).

The second subclass of such persistent infections consists of those in which the protection of uninfected cells is mediated *intracellularly* by interferon and interfering virus particles rather than by antibody-mediated neutralization of virus in the medium; the virus yield, already low by virtue of the cells' nonpermissiveness, is reduced even further by the largely abortive infection of those cells that become infected. The cells are resistant to superinfection not only by homologous but also by heterologous virus (because of the presence of interferon). Although antibody itself plays no role in the maintenance of this type of persistent infection, cell cultures are cured if antiviral antibody is added to the medium.

PERSISTENT INFECTIONS IN ANIMALS

The factors that appear to be involved in the persistence of viral infections in animals are the following (8):

(i) Persistent viruses tend to have low or zero pathogenicity. However, even viruses that are commonly cytopathic may persist for long periods of time provided that this occurs on a small scale and is limited by immunological means, by interference or by interferon.

(ii) There may be an ineffective antibody response. Among the reasons for such an ineffective response may be tolerance, autoimmunosuppression, the production of non-neutralizing or blocking antibodies, insufficient viral antigen on the surface of the infected target

cell, and the fact that virus may spread directly from cell to cell.

(iii) There may be an ineffective cell-mediated immune response, and immune cells may be prevented from reaching the infected target cells.

(iv) There may be a defective interferon response. Thus, mice persistently infected with LCM or leukemia virus do not produce detectable interferon, although mice infected with these viruses give normal interferon responses on infection with other viruses; the defect is thus specifically related to a particular virus.

(v) Lymphocytes and macrophages are often infected in persistent viral infections, and such infection may cause an alteration of the immune response.

ROLE OF CELLULAR PERMISSIVENESS

The mechanisms involved in permissiveness and nonpermissiveness are not well known. It is an area that is very difficult to study since what one would really like to compare is a cell type in which a given virus multiplies very well, to high titer, and a cell line in which the virus multiplies poorly. Ideally, one would like two cell strains that differ in a single genetic locus, so as to have a handle on some host protein with an essential or almost essential function during viral infection. Good systems of this type are very rare. Further, elucidation of the function of this polypeptide would by no means be an easy task. It may well be that the sensitive step, or the step that does not occur efficiently in nonpermissive cells, is some step after adsorption and before the uncoated viral genome begins to express itself; once the viral genome begins to express itself, it probably does so efficiently, with production of progeny genomes. In other words, the mechanism of nonpermissiveness probably does not involve a lack of compatible initiation or termination factors for either nucleic acid or protein synthesis. Rather, it is likely to involve that much more difficult to investigate portion of the multiplication cycle following adsorption of the virus, when, by some almost completely unknown mechanisms, invading viral particles or genomes are transported to that location within the cell where viral genome expression begins.

ROLE OF CYTOPATHOGENICITY

Irrespective of the permissiveness or nonpermissiveness of a given cell, the virus that initiates persistent infection of the *first* type that was discussed above must be noncytocidal. Few hard data are available concerning the nature of the factors that operate in the establishment of cytopathogenicity. There is not even unanimity as to whether cytopathic effects (CPE) are caused by virion components introduced into the cell along with or as part of parental viral particles, or whether they are caused by viral gene products that are formed after the cell has been infected. In the case of vaccinia virus, there is evidence that the former is the case; nucleases introduced into the cell as components of parental virus particles are postulated to be responsible for the breakdown of nascent host DNA, and this could in turn lead to the development of CPE (9). On the other hand, we have found in the case of reovirus that the agent causing CPE is unlikely to be a component of parental virus particles, since empty virus particles, which in the case of reovirus are indistinguishable in structure and polypeptide constitution from complete virions, have no effect whatever on host cells, even at very high multiplicities (6). Numerous other workers have tested a variety of conditions under which early and late viral gene expression is either permitted or inhibited in order to determine what viral component triggers CPE, but no clear and unequivocal answers have resulted. Since almost all viruses cause CPE, the effect is unlikely to be highly specific. In the final instance, the mechanism that causes CPE is most likely to be mediated through inhibition of host-cell gene expression and failure to maintain the integrity of host membranes, both lysosomal membranes, damage to which would cause leakage into the interior of the cell of the potent hydrolytic enzymes that they contain, and damage to the plasma membrane, which would lead to failure to maintain the appropriate intracellular ionic milieu. However, this model clearly leaves unanswered the questions as to why certain viruses interfere with the host-cell gene expression under some conditions but not others. Numerous examples are known of persistently infected cells supporting vigorous virus multiplication without apparent interference with the functioning of their own genome. Once again, elucidation of this problem will come only as the result of comparing pairs of cell lines infected with the same virus, one destined for complete destruction and the other unaffected. No doubt such studies will be carried out as soon as adequate systems are available for sophisticated biochemical and molecular experimentation.

ROLE OF DEFECTIVE INTERFERING VIRUS PARTICLES

Another factor in the initiation and maintenance of persistent viral infections is the presence of defective interfering (DI) virus particles. The first DI particles to be discovered were those of influenza virus (14). DI-like particles have now been discovered in almost every animal virus group.

The basic properties of DI virus particles are as follows:

(i) They contain the normal structural capsid proteins.

(ii) They contain only a part of the viral genome.

(iii) They can reproduce only in cells infected with homologous virions, which act as helpers.

(iv) Although unable to reproduce on their own, they can nevertheless express a variety of functions in the absence of helper, such as inhibition of host biosynthesis, synthesis of viral proteins, and transformation of cells.

(v) They specifically interfere with the multiplication of homologous virus.

(vi) As a result they tend to replace standard virus in virus yields.

(vii) The optimal conditions for their formation tend to be repeated passage of virus at high multiplicity.

Some of these properties will now be examined in more detail.

Defectiveness

Defectiveness implies that there is a lesion in some necessary gene. For all DI particles studied so far, this lesion appears to be deletion of genetic material, which in some cases can be quite extensive; some DIs of papovaviruses and vesicular stomatitis virus (VSV) contain less than 30% of the total information found in standard genomes. The mechanism of deleting genetic material to form DI nucleic acid is not well understood, but appears to depend on the genetic organization of the specific virus system (5). There may be terminal as well as internal deletions, and segmented genomes may become deleted by losing specific segments as well as by deletion of portions of a segment.

Ability to Interfere with the Multiplication of Homologous Standard Virus

Five properties distinguish this type of homologous interference caused by DI particles from other interference phenomena: (i) interference by DI particles is homologous; (ii) interferon plays no role in this interference, although DI particles may, by themselves, induce interferon synthesis; (iii) prior UV irradiation of DI particles destroys their ability to interfere; (iv) the interference by DI particles occurs during an intracellular step of the viral multiplication cycle; and (v) the ability of different host cells to support interference by DI particles varies considerably. The host functions that control these variations are unknown.

Interference and Enrichment

Consideration of the molecular mechanisms that operate in the interference of DI particles with the multiplication of standard virus is linked to consideration of the mechanisms that lead to the enrichment of DI particles in viral yields. Most models for enrichment involve the preferential replication of DI nucleic acid or the preferential encapsidation of DI nucleic acid. The former is likely to be the more important. It seems that interference operates at the site where DI particle nucleic acid competes with standard virus nucleic acid for whatever factor limits the rate of viral nucleic acid replication, probably the initiation of replication (5).

Role of DI Particles in the Initiation and Maintenance of Persistent Viral Infections

As long ago as 1951, von Magnus demonstrated that when undiluted passage influenza virus (which contained DI particles) was inoculated into mice the surviving mice developed long-term resistance to the acute paralytic disease caused by standard preparations of influenza virus (14). However, the essential significance of DI particles in initiating and maintaining persistent infections has become fully appreciated only recently, as a result of the work of several investigators: Huang and Baltimore (4), who codified the properties of DI particles and postulated a significant role for them in acute and persistent viral disease; McLaren and Holland (7), who showed that vaccine strains of poliovirus contained a high proportion of DI particles and that the standard virus from vaccine strains generated DI particles with a much higher frequency than does virulent poliovirus; and, finally, Holland and Villarreal (3), who harvested VSV from mouse brains and demonstrated that the viral yields contained DI particles identical with those formed in continuous cell cultures, which showed that DI particles were produced in animals under conditions of natural persistent infection.

ROLE OF TEMPERATURE-SENSITIVE VIRAL VARIANTS

The third and most recently recognized factor in persistent viral infections is provided by temperature-sensitive (ts) virus mutants. A role for such mutants was suggested by Fields (1) on the basis of his studies on the response of mice to certain ts mutants of reovirus and by Preble and Youngner (11), who isolated ts virus from L cells persistently infected with Newcastle disease virus. Holland and Villarreal (3) demonstrated that persistent infection can be established by inoculating standard virus together with an excess of DI particles; Youngner and his colleagues (17) found that persistent VSV infections in L cells could also be established by very low multiplicities of ts mutants of VSV, in the complete absence of DI particles. These workers also found that when persistent infection of L cells is initiated by infection with low multiplicities of standard VSV in the presence of large numbers of DI particles, ts variants of VSV are rapidly selected. The reasons that ts mutants are selected under conditions of persistent infection are probably as follows. First, Youngner and Quagliana (18) have shown that ts mutants of VSV interfere strongly with the multiplication of wild-type virus at both permissive and nonpermissive temperatures, the interference occurring prior to or at the level of RNA transcription. Second, ts mutants are rescued by wild-type virus at nonpermissive temperatures; ts mutants thus act as DI virus at nonpermissive temperatures. As a result, the replication of ts virus tends to be dominant at nonpermissive or almost nonpermissive temperatures, thereby explaining why ts mutants are selected. Since also under these conditions ts mutants tend to be noncytocidal and the replication of cytocidal wild-type virus is suppressed, these observations provide an explanation of both why ts variants tend to be selected and why this selection leads to the maintenance of persistent infections.

POSSIBLE ROLE OF INTEGRATED VIRAL GENOMES

The final mechanism that may operate in persistent viral infections is integration of the viral genome into that of the host cell, which in the case of RNA-containing viruses would require the mediation of an RNA-dependent DNA polymerase. There have been several reports of this mechanism operating in cells persistently infected with respiratory syncytial virus (12), simian virus 5, measles virus, Sindbis virus, tick-borne encephalitis virus (19), and possibly also influenza virus.

The existence of this mechanism raises a whole host of questions, such as the source of the RNA-dependent DNA polymerase that initially transcribes the RNA of the infecting virus into provirus, the nature of the DNA integration systems, and the regulatory mechanisms and conditions that repress and derepress the expression of the integrated provirus. The question of the mechanisms that limit the use of this mechanism, if it occurs, also arises. In other words, why are not all viral genomes, both RNA and DNA, present in all cells as proviruses; what limits this type of persistent infection? What are the mechanisms that ensure that such proviruses are not carried in germ cells?

If this is a mechanism for establishing persistent viral infection, it is peculiarly adapted for RNA-containing viruses, for persistent infection is then maintained simply by transcription of the provirus. Parenthetically, it would acutally be an awkward mechanism for minus RNA strand-containing viruses, since in this case *both* strands of the provirus would have to be transcribed (unless only plus-stranded RNA [messenger RNA] is transcribed from the integrated viral genome; this would then have to code for the transcriptase, and the minus strands [virion strands] would be transcribed separately elsewhere in the cell). This mechanism would not be a satisfactory one for maintaining persistent infection of DNA-containing viruses, since in that case the expression of persistent infection would require the continuous excision of proviral DNA, which is extremely unlikely.

LITERATURE CITED

1. **Fields, B. N.** 1972. Genetic manipulation of reovirus— a model for modification of disease. N. Engl. J. Med. **287**:1026–1033.

2. **Ginsberg, H. S.** 1958. A consideration of the role of serum inhibitors in latency and analysis of persistent adenovirus infection of mammalian cells, p. 157–168. *In* D. Walker, R. Hanson, and A. Evans (ed.), Symposium: latency and masking in viral and rickettsial infections. Burgess Publishing Co., Minneapolis.

3. **Holland, J. J., and L. P. Villarreal.** 1974. Persistent noncytocidal vesicular stomatitis virus infections mediated by defective T particles that suppress virion transcriptase. Proc. Natl. Acad. Sci. U.S.A. **71**:2956–2960.

4. **Huang, A. S., and D. Baltimore.** 1970. Defective viral particles and viral disease processes. Nature (London) **226**:325–327.

5. **Huang, A. S., and D. Baltimore.** 1977. Defective interfering animal viruses. *In* H. Fraenkel-Conrat and R. R. Wagner (ed.), Comprehensive virology, vol. 8. Plenum Press, New York, in press.

6. **Lai, M. T., J. J. Wérenne, and W. K. Joklik.** 1973. The preparation of reovirus top component and its effect on host DNA and protein synthesis. Virology **54**:237–244.

7. **McLaren, L. C., and J. J. Holland.** 1974. Defective interfering particles from poliovirus vaccine and vaccine reference strains. Virology **60**:579–583.

8. **Mims, C. A.** 1974. Factors in the mechanism of persistence of viral infections. Prog. Med. Virol. **18**:1–14.

9. **Olgiati, D., B. G. T. Pogo, and S. Dales.** 1976. Biogenesis of vaccinia virus: specific inhibition of rapidly labeled host DNA in vaccinia inoculated cells. Virology **71**:325–335.

10. **Pacsa, S.** 1961. Poliovirus-carrying lines of HeLa cells: their establishment and sensitivity to viruses. Acta Microbiol. **8**:329–332.

11. **Preble, O. T., and J. S. Youngner.** Temperature-sensitive mutants isolated from L cells persistently infected with Newcastle disease virus. J. Virol. **9**:200–206.

12. **Simpson, R. W., and M. Iinuma.** 1975. Recovery of infectious proviral DNA from mammalian cells infected with respiratory syncytial virus. Proc. Natl. Acad. Sci. U.S.A. **72**:3230–3234.

13. **Takemoto, K. K., and K. Habel.** 1959. Virus-cell relationships in a carrier culture of HeLa cells and Coxsackie A9. Virology **7**:28–44.

14. **von Magnus, P.** 1951. Propagation of PR-8 strain of influenza A virus in chick embryos. III. Properties of the incomplete virus produced in serial passages of undiluted virus. Acta Pathol. Microbiol. Scand. **29**:157–181.

15. **Walker, D. L.** 1964. The viral carrier state in animal cell cultures. Prog. Med. Virol. **6**:111–148.

16. **Walker, D. L.** 1968. Persistent viral infection in cell cultures, p. 99–110. *In* M. Sanders and E. H. Lennette (ed.), Medical and applied virology (Proc. 2nd Int. Symp.). Warren H. Green, Inc., St. Louis.

17. **Youngner, J. S., E. J. Dubovi, D. O. Quagliana, M. Kelly, and O. T. Preble.** 1976. Role of temperature-sensitive mutants in persistent infection initiated with vesicular stomatitis virus. J. Virol. **19**:90–101.

18. **Youngner, J. S., and D. O. Quagliana.** 1976. Temperature-sensitive mutants of vesicular stomatitis virus are conditionally defective particles which interfere with and are rescued by wild-type virus. J. Virol. **19**:102–107.

19. **Zhdanov, V. M.** 1975. Integration of viral genomes. Nature (London) **256**:471–473.

Defective Interfering Particles of Vesicular Stomatitis Virus

M. E. REICHMANN AND W. M. SCHNITZLEIN

Department of Microbiology, University of Illinois, Urbana, Illinois 61801

INTRODUCTION

Certain deletion mutants, which are generated spontaneously during undiluted passages of animal viruses in cell tissue culture, interfere with the replication of their homologous virus (8, 31). These mutants were named defective interfering (DI) particles (8) and were defined as having the following general properties (7): (i) structurally, they are composed of normal viral proteins and a deleted viral genome; (ii) functionally, they are unable to reproduce in the absence of their nondefective helper virus; (iii) as a consequence of this dependence, they interfere specifically with the intracellular replication of the helper virus. The importance of interference in the establishment and maintenance of some persistent infections has been proposed (8) and recently demonstrated (5); it is discussed in more detail by Graham in the next article.

DI particles of vesicular stomatitis virus (VSV) are bullet-shaped, are shorter than the standard virus, and can be easily separated from the latter by rate zonal centrifugation (3, 9). Thus, they were characterized with respect to their biological, physical, and chemical properties (4, 11, 12, 23, 33). In addition, the isolation, from cells infected with temperature-sensitive (ts) mutants of VSV, of a great variety of DI particles with RNA molecules containing from 8 to 50% of the viral genome (22) provided the opportunity to make certain generalizations about the origin of these particles and about their possible mode of action. The rationale for these investigations was based on early reports, which demonstrated that the biologically active component of these DI particles was their RNA and not their proteins (11). Rapid characterization of the nucleotide sequences conserved in the various DI particles became possible in this system, because five unique complementary mRNA species are produced by VSV (14, 24, 26). Annealing of DI-particle RNAs with various mRNA species provided a convenient method for determining the cistronic origin of DI-particle RNAs and thus allowed the construction of a map of the viral genome (14, 29).

HOMOTYPIC AND HETEROTYPIC INTERFERENCE

DI particles of VSV generally interfere most with virions of homologous serotype (homotypic interference; 2, 11, 27). The degree of interference reflects the degree of serological relatedness (2). Weak heterotypic interference of DI particles from the Indiana serotype of VSV with the distantly related New Jersey serotype has been reported (2, 27). The extent of this interference, although always very weak, seems to be host dependent (27). A similar host dependence, suggesting the involvement of a host cell factor, has also been observed in homotypic interference (8, 17).

One DI particle, isolated from an infection with a heat-resistant (HR) mutant of the Indiana serotype, was exceptional with respect to its ability to interfere heterotypically. Quantitative measurements have shown that this particle can interfere equally well with infections by Indiana and New Jersey serotype virions, regardless of host cell lines (19, 20, 27).

RNA OF DI PARTICLES

Inactivation of interfering ability of DI particles by UV irradiation suggested a requirement for a functional RNA (11). However, the size of this RNA, which is reflected in the size of the DI particle, seems to vary between 1,000 and 6,000 nucleotides, whereas the interfering ability at similar particle concentrations remains approximately the same (Table 1). Generally, each isolate of the Indiana serotype produces predominantly one characteristic DI particle that contains one major RNA species (14, 27). However, exceptions have been observed, particularly in early undiluted passages (6). In contrast, New Jersey isolates generate a heterogeneous population of DI particles and corresponding RNAs, although in most isolates only two or three major DI-particle RNA species are present (4, 17). Indiana wild-type isolates generate DI particles with approximately one-third to one-fourth of the viral genome (12),

TABLE 1. *Relative homotypic interfering ability of Indiana DI particles*

DI particle[a]	Dilution of DI particle[b]	Log$_{10}$ reduction of infectivity[c] (PFU/ml)	Approx mol wt of DI-particle RNA
Gla	Undiluted	1.64	1.1×10^6 [d]
	1:10	1.18	
	1:100	0.37	
How	Undiluted	1.40	1.4×10^6 [e]
	1:10	0.80	
	1:100	0.35	
Hu	Undiluted	1.65	1.1×10^6 [e]
	1:10	0.91	
	1:100	0.39	
MS	Undiluted	1.30	9.0×10^5 [e]
	1:10	0.72	
	1:100	0.23	
ts G11	Undiluted	1.12	1.8×10^6 [d]
	1:10	0.72	
	1:100	0.14	
ts G22	Undiluted	1.58	1.8×10^6 [d]
	1:10	1.00	
	1:100	0.64	
ts G31	Undiluted	0.81	4.5×10^5 [e]
	1:10	0.58	
	1:100	0.22	

[a] Nomenclature of DI particles was described previously (27).

[b] Concentrations were normalized to be equal with respect to the number of DI particles per milliliter. This was based on protein analyses and on the assumption that relative particle molecular weights were equal for their relative RNA molecular weights. The undiluted solutions contained approximately 3,000 particles per cell.

[c] Interference measurements were performed as described previously (27).

[d] Reference 27.

[e] Reference 14.

although there is some variation around this value from isolate to isolate (14, 21, 27). The HR DI-particle RNA is considerably larger and approaches one-half the size of the viral genome (14, 19, 21, 27). However, the size of this particle RNA is not the cause of heterotypic interference, as postulated previously (20). Since then, at least three DI particles with an RNA of comparable size have been isolated and lack the ability for heterotypic interference (27). Two of these were generated by mutants ts G11 and ts G22 (22), and the third was isolated from a persistently infected cell line (5, 27).

CISTRONIC ORIGIN OF DI-PARTICLE RNAs

In order to determine the nature of the genomic content of DI-particle RNAs, the latter were an-

nealed with virus-induced mRNA species. These experiments showed that all DI-particle RNAs (except HR) consisted of nucleotide sequences complementary to a portion of the viral 30S mRNA (27). Earlier reports of some complementarity to the 13S to 18S mRNA's by two of these DI-particle RNAs (14, 21, 29) were probably due to contamination, since careful purification procedures completely eliminated annealing with these mRNA species (27). Competition annealing with mixtures of DI-particle RNAs in various combinations indicated that the nucleotide sequences of the shorter particle RNAs were always contained in the nucleotide sequences of the longer DI-particle RNAs (14, 27). This suggested that DI-particle RNAs either originated from or terminated at a constant site. The conserved sequences appeared to correspond to a site at or very near the 5' terminus of the viral genome. The evidence in favor of this conclusion was based on the following considerations. (i) Early in vitro transcription of the viral genome generated, after 10 min, nucleotide sequences complementary to the HR DI-particle RNA but not to the wild-type and ts mutant DI-particle RNAs. After 30 min, the first transcripts, annealable to the latter RNAs, were detectable, and their relative concentrations increased up to 60 min (20a). This suggested that the nucleotide sequences of the characteristic DI-particle RNAs are near the 5' end of the viral genome. (ii) The location of the 13S to 18S mRNA cistrons based on inactivation by UV light in a coupled in vitro transcription-translation system was near the 3' end of the viral genome in the order shown in Fig. 1 (1), with the 30S mRNA cistron at the 5' end. (iii) Annealing experiments with fragmented 30S mRNA showed that one wild-type-generated DI-particle RNA annealed to the 3' end fragments of this message, which would correspond to the 5' end of the complementary genomic cistron (29). Based on these considerations, a proposed map of DI-particle RNAs is shown in Fig. 1. This map also shows that the HR DI-particle RNA, which is exceptional in its ability to interfere heterotypically with infections by the New Jersey serotype virion, is also exceptional in that its RNA annealed to all 13S to 18S mRNA's and had no or few nucleotide sequences complementary to the 30S mRNA.

Several of the DI-particle RNAs, shown in Fig. 1, exhibited a high degree of self-annealing. In at least one case, this was shown to be attributable to the presence of the complementary RNA strand in the preparations (25). However, more recently, some DI-particle RNAs have been found to contain complementary nucleotide sequences that were covalently linked to the DI-particle negative RNA strand. In at least one case, the particle RNA exhibited properties consistent with a hairpin-like structure (13, 16). The mechanism by which these RNA species might have been generated is not known. Although these findings do not affect the general map outlined in Fig. 1, it is possible that the length of genomic nucleotide sequences may be, in some cases, shorter than surmised from the molecular weights of the RNAs. In any case, the relative lengths of DI-particle RNAs, shown in Fig. 1, were based on annealing experiments, which were a direct measure of unique virus-like sequences and were also consistent with the molecular weights of these RNAs (27).

ESTIMATE OF THE SIZE OF SPECIFIC NUCLEOTIDE SEQUENCES REQUIRED FOR INTERFERENCE

Recent investigations of DI particles of the New Jersey serotype in our laboratories have indicated that the specific nucleotide sequences, which may be required for interference, were considerably shorter than the 1,000 nucleotides present in the shortest available Indiana DI-particle RNA. Several isolates of the New Jersey serotype virion showed very limited homologies among their RNA. An example of this is illustrated in Table 2, where annealing data between Ogden viral mRNA species and Glasgow New Jersey virion RNA are shown. Whereas the homologous Ogden virion RNA annealed to 96% of its mRNA's, the Glasgow New Jersey virion RNA annealed to not more than 26% of the Ogden mRNA's. Similarly, two Glasgow DI-particle RNAs showed only 3.5 and 7% homology to the $30S$ mRNA of the Ogden isolate (Table 2, last column).

Since the $30S$ mRNA corresponds to about 6,000 nucleotides, this homology is equivalent to 200 and 600 nucleotides, respectively. Yet, even the smaller of the DI particles fully interfered with either Glasgow or Ogden virions (W. M. Schnitzlein and M. E. Reichmann, Virology, in press). If a conserved nucleotide sequence is required for interference, these data suggested that it would not exceed 200 nucleotides.

Similar conclusions can be drawn from the homologies between the HR DI-particle RNA and New Jersey virion RNA (Prevec's isolate; Table 3). As mentioned before, this exceptional particle interfered with infections by this virion. For the sake of comparision, Table 3 also shows the lack of homologies between other Indiana serotype particle RNAs and the New Jersey (Prevec's) mRNA's. From these data, the estimated length of the nucleotide sequence which the HR DI-particle RNA could

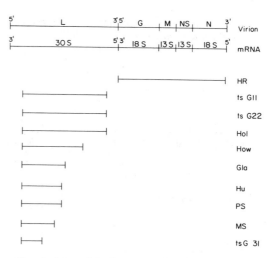

FIG. 1. *Map of the location of DI-particle RNAs in relation to viral cistrons. The order of the 13 S and 18 S mRNA's relative to the 3' end of the viral RNA is based on published data (1). The position of the 30 S mRNA is based on the results discussed in the text. The letters referring to VSV proteins follow the accepted nomenclature (32). The 5' end of DI-particle RNAs (except HR) is displaced in relation to the 5' end of the viral RNA in order to indicate the possibility of an altered sequence at this end (see text). This displacement is exaggerated, thus giving an erroneous impression that ts G11, ts G22, and Hol DI-particle RNAs are considerably shorter than HR DI-particle RNA.*

have in common with the New Jersey virion RNA does not exceed 300 bases.

DISCUSSION

Interference by VSV DI particles has been shown to occur during an early intracellular event of viral infection (30). Primary transcription of the viral genome is unaffected by the presence of DI particles (10, 18). Recent work with ts mutants has provided some evidence that interference might be taking place on the level of RNA replication (15). This is also consistent with the observed predominant synthesis of DI-particle RNA (7), which is probably a result of an advantage over viral RNA synthesis. This advantage cannot be explained on the basis of a faster turnover rate of the shorter DI-particle RNA. Such a hypothesis is inconsistent with various observations: (i) the preferential generation by a given mutant of a certain DI-particle RNA which is often longer than the DI-particle RNA of the wild type (22); (ii) the frequent occurrence of selection in infections with mixed DI-particle species in which the final preference does not always favor the shortest RNA (6); (iii) the apparent same-

TABLE 2. *Annealing of Ogden (N.J.) viral mRNA's with various virion and DI-particle RNAs*

RNA		Counts after RNase treatment[a]	
		Ogden mRNA	
Type	Amt (μg)	13S – 18S	30S
Ogden (N.J.) virus	0.05	867	651
	0.10	1,057	781
	0.20	1,041	860
	0.50	1,088	834
Glasgow (N.J.) virus	0.05	210	33
	0.10	363	120
	0.20	303	112
	0.50	296	141
Glasgow short DI	0.05	0	6
	0.10	0	32
	0.20	0	22
	0.50	5	32
Glasgow long DI	0.05	—	40
	0.10	—	43
	0.20	—	67
	0.50	—	65
BHK rRNA	0.05	0	0
	0.10	0	0
	0.20	0	0
	0.50	0	0
mRNA cpm used		1,129	910

[a] Annealing and digestion procedures were as described previously (27).

ness of the specific interference by shorter and longer DI particles (Table 1). The advantage of DI RNA replication over that of viral RNA must be based on different principles. Huang suggested that interference is a consequence of competition for some limiting viral protein, most likely the RNA replicase (7, 30). The replicative step involves at least two stages: transcription of the complete negative (viral) strand and the utilization of the transcript as template for generation of more negative (viral) strands (28). Interference could take place with either one or both of these stages. The conservation of the 5'-terminal sequences in all DI particles (except HR) suggests that interference probably takes place at the level of the second step, where the conserved 5' terminus becomes the 3' end of the complementary strand and serves as an attachment site of the replicase. Huang's hypothesis of increased affinity for the replicase would require that this site of the DI-particle RNAs not be quite identical to the equivalent viral site.

An alternate hypothesis, based on the observation that DI particles are unable to transcribe their genome into complementary mRNA's (10, 18), has been proposed (27). Although most of the viral RNA template is engaged in transcription during the infectious cycle, all DI-particle RNA templates are available for replication and bind the majority of the enzyme molecules. This hypothesis obviates the requirement for an altered nucleotide sequence at the 5' end. Moreover, it explains the necessity for a deletion of the 3' end in DI-particle RNA, since this terminus is likely to be the recognition site for transcription and must be absent in the latter.

The unique HR DI-particle RNA, whose genome corresponds to the other half of the viral genome, may interfere by a distinct mechanism of its own. The conservation of the 3' terminus suggests that interference in this case might be taking place in the first replicative step—transcription of the negative (virus-like) strand. It is possible that the 3' termini of the

TABLE 3. *Annealing of Prevec's (N.J.) mRNA's with various virion and DI-particle RNAs*

RNA		Counts after RNase treatment[a]	
		Ogden mRNA	
Type	Amt (μg)	13S – 18S	30S
Prevec's (N.J.) virus	0.25	6,150	6,718
	0.50	8,888	7,598
	1.00	9,733	7,576
	1.75	10,177	8,348
	2.50	10,203	8,561
Glasgow (Ind.) virus	0.25	170	35
	0.50	226	145
	1.00	329	113
	1.75	275	99
	2.50	290	158
MS (Ind.) DI	0.25	13	52
	0.50	13	36
	1.00	14	61
	2.50	0	81
HR (Ind.) DI	0.25	130	91
	0.50	364	68
	1.00	314	62
	2.50	423	64
BHK rRNA	0.25	0	32
	0.50	0	39
	1.00	0	7
	2.50	0	44
mRNA cpm used		10,775	9,232

[a] Annealing and digestion procedure were as described previously (27).

New Jersey and Indiana serotypes are more similar than the 5' termini; this could explain the ability of the HR DI particle to interfere heterotypically with the New Jersey serotype.

Alternately, the deletion resulting in the HR DI-particle RNA may have exposed a 5' nucleotide sequence similar to both the equivalent Indiana and New Jersey sequences. In that case, the mechanism of interference by the HR DI particle would be similar to that proposed for all other DI particles.

The inability of the HR DI-particle RNA to be transcribed into mRNA's (23) is puzzling. This RNA carries the genetic information for all except the 30S mRNA species. Moreover, its origin from the 3' end of the viral genome suggests that it may contain the promoter region for the transcribing enzyme. It is, of course, possible that a deletion of part or all of the promoter region has taken place. However, since the RNA must be transcribed into a complete complementary strand as a preamble to replication, the site for this event must be intact and different from the promoter for mRNA transcription. It is obvious that the answer to these important questions requires partial nucleotide sequence determinations of DI and viral RNAs at these sites. Work along these lines is in progress in our laboratory.

ACKNOWLEDGMENTS

P. Bay and L. Erickson's excellent technical assistance was appreciated.

This work was supported by Public Health Service grant AI 12070 from the National Institute of Allergy and Infectious Diseases and National Science Foundation grant GB 34171. W. S. was the recipient of a Public Health Service Predoctoral Traineeship from Microbiology Training grant GM 00510 from the National Institute of General Medical Sciences.

LITERATURE CITED

1. **Ball, L. A., and C. N. White.** 1976. Order of transcription of genes of vesicular stomatitis virus. Proc. Natl. Acad. Sci. U.S.A. **73:**442–446.
2. **Crick, J., and F. Brown.** 1973. Interference as a measurement of cross-relationship in the vesicular stomatitis virus group of rhabdoviruses. J. Gen. Virol. **18:**79–82.
3. **Hackett, A. J., F. L. Schaffer, and S. H. Madin.** 1967. The separation of infectious and autointerfering particles in vesicular stomatitis virus preparations. Virology **31:**114–119.
4. **Hartford, S. L., J. A. Lesnaw, W. H. Flygare, R. MacLeod, and M. E. Reichmann.** 1975. Physical properties of New Jersey serotype of vesicular stomatitis virus and its defective particles. Proc. Natl. Acad. Sci. U.S.A. **72:**1202–1205.
5. **Holland, J. J., and L. P. Villarreal.** 1974. Persistent noncytocidal vesicular stomatitis virus infections mediated by defective T particles that suppress virion transcriptase. Proc. Natl. Acad. Sci. U.S.A. **71:** 2956–2960.
6. **Holland, J. J., L. P. Villarreal, and M. Breindl.** 1976. Factors involved in the generation and replication of rhabdovirus defective T particles. J. Virol. **17:**805–815.

7. **Huang, A. S.** 1973. Defective interfering viruses. Annu. Rev. Microbiol. **27:**101–117.
8. **Huang, A. S., and D. Baltimore.** 1970. Defective viral particles and viral disease processes. Nature (London) **226:**325–327.
9. **Huang, A. S., J. W. Greenawalt, and R. R. Wagner.** 1966. Defective T particles of vesicular stomatitis virus. I. Preparation, morphology, and some biologic properties. Virology **30:**161–172.
10. **Huang, A. S., and E. K. Manders.** 1972. Ribonucleic acid synthesis of vesicular stomatitis virus. IV. Transcription by standard virus in the presence of defective interfering particles. J. Virol. **9:**909–916.
11. **Huang, A. S., and R. R. Wagner.** 1966. Defective T particles of vesicular stomatitis virus. II. Biologic role in homologous interference. Virology **30:**173–181.
12. **Huang, A. S., and R. R. Wagner.** 1966. Comparative sedimentation coefficients of RNA extracted from plaque-forming and defective particles of vesicular stomatitis virus. J. Mol. Biol. **22:**381–384.
13. **Lazzarini, R. A., G. H. Weber, L. D. Johnson, and G. M. Stamminger.** 1975. Covalently linked message and antimessage (genomic) RNA from a defective vesicular stomatitis virus particle. J. Mol. Biol. **97:**289–307.
14. **Leamnson, R. N., and M. E. Reichmann.** 1974. The RNA of defective vesicular stomatitis virus particles in relation to viral cistrons. J. Mol. Biol. **85:**551–568.
15. **Palma, E. L., S. M. Perlman, and A. S. Huang.** 1974. Ribonucleic acid synthesis of vesicular stomatitis virus. VI. Correlation of defective particle RNA synthesis with standard RNA replication. J. Mol. Biol. **85:**127–136.
16. **Perrault, J.** 1976. Cross-linked double stranded RNA from a defective vesicular stomatitis virus particle. Virology **70:**360–371.
17. **Perrault, J., and J. J. Holland.** 1972. Variability of vesicular stomatitis autointerference with different host cells and virus serotypes. Virology **50:**148–158.
18. **Perrault, J., and J. J. Holland.** 1972. Absence of transcriptase activity or transcription inhibiting ability in defective interfering particles of vesicular stomatitis virus. Virology **50:**159–170.
19. **Petric, M., and L. Prevec.** 1970. Vesicular stomatitis virus—a new interfering particle, intracellular structures and specific RNA. Virology **41:**615–630.
20. **Prevec, L., and C. Y. Kang.** 1970. Homotypic and heterotypic interference by defective particles of vesicular stomatitis virus. Nature (London) **228:**25–27.
20a. **Reddy, D. V. R., W. M. Schnitzlein, and M. E. Reichmann.** 1977. Use of defective interfering particle RNA probes in the determination of the order of in vitro transcription of vesicular stomatitis virus genes. J. Virol. **21:**432–434.
21. **Reichmann, M. E., and R. N. Leamnson.** 1974. Temperature sensitive mutants of vesicular stomatitis virus and interference, p. 101–105. In W. S. Robinson and C. F. Fox (ed.), Mechanisms of viral disease. W. A. Benjamin, Inc., Menlo Park, Calif.
22. **Reichmann, M. E., C. R. Pringle, and E. A. C. Follett.** 1971. Defective particles in BHK cells infected with temperature-sensitive mutants of vesicular stomatitis virus. J. Virol. **8:**154–160.
23. **Reichmann, M. E., L. P. Villarreal, D. Kohne, J. A. Lesnaw, and J. J. Holland.** 1974. RNA polymerase activity and poly(A) synthesizing activity in defective T particles of vesicular stomatitis virus. Virology **58:** 240–249.
24. **Rose, J. K., and D. Knipe.** 1975. Nucleotide sequence complexities, molecular weights, and poly(A) content of the vesicular stomatitis virus mRNA species. J. Virol. **15:**994–1003.
25. **Roy, P., P. Repik, E. Hefti, and D. H. L. Bishop.** 1973. Complementary RNA species isolated from vesicular stomatitis (HR strain) defective virions. J. Virol. **11:** 915–925.

26. **Schaffer, F. L., A. J. Hackett, and M. E. Soergel.** 1968. Vesicular stomatitis virus RNA: complementarity between infected cell RNA and RNA's from infectious and autointerfering viral fractions. Biochem. Biophys. Res. Commun. **31:**685–692.

27. **Schnitzlein, W. M., and M. E. Reichmann.** 1976. The size and the cistronic origin of defective vesicular stomatitis virus particle RNAs in relation to homotypic and heterotypic interference. J. Mol. Biol. **101:**307–325.

28. **Soria, M., S. P. Little, and A. S. Huang.** 1974. Characterization of vesicular stomatitis virus nucleocapsids. I. Complementary 40S RNA molecules in nucleocapsids. Virology **61:**270–280.

29. **Stamminger, G. M., and R. A. Lazzarini.** 1974. Analysis of RNA of defective VSV particles. Cell **3:**85–93.

30. **Stampfer, M., D. Baltimore, and A. S. Huang.** 1969. Ribonucleic acid synthesis of vesicular stomatitis virus. I. Species of ribonucleic acid found in Chinese hamster ovary cells infected with plaque-forming and defective particles. J. Virol. **4:**154–161.

31. **Von Magnus, P.** 1951. Propagation of the PR-8 strain of influenza A virus in chick embryos. III. Properties of the incomplete virus produced in serial passages of undiluted virus. Acta Pathol. Microbiol. Scand. **29:**157–181.

32. **Wagner, R. R., L. Prevec, F. Brown, D. F. Summers, F. Sokol, and R. MacLeod.** 1972. Classification of rhabdovirus proteins: a proposal. J. Virol. **10:** 1228–1230.

33. **Ware, B. R., T. Raj, W. H. Flygare, J. A. Lesnaw, and M. E. Reichmann.** 1973. Molecular weights of vesicular stomatitis virus and its defective particles by laser light-scattering spectroscopy. J. Virol. **11:**141–145.

Possible Role of Defective Virus in Persistent Infection

A. F. GRAHAM

Department of Biochemistry, McGill University Medical School, Montreal, Quebec, Canada

The line of thought in this paper is based on the following proposition: Apparent complete recovery from an acute viral infection may be followed months or years later by chronic degenerative effects in one or another organ or tissue of the body. Sometimes virus can be found in the tissue, more often not. It is widely speculated that some chronic disorders of unknown etiology may in fact have a viral origin. We know very little about the mechanisms involved in the evolution of such chronic diseases, but they are undoubtedly highly complex and may vary from one virus infection to another (10). In this general context the question posed here can be simply stated. Does defective virus play a role in the initiation and maintenance of these chronic viral diseases? My remarks will be directed specifically to three aspects of a reovirus model: the nature of defective reovirus, persistent infection in cell culture, and persistent infection in rats.

NATURE OF DEFECTIVE VIRUS

As is well known, defective virus is more or less readily generated by high-multiplicity serial passage of infectious virus in cell culture. Defective virions are essentially deletion mutants. More or less of the nucleic acid genome is missing, and the defective virus can multiply only in the presence of infectious virus, which supplies the deleted function. As far as reovirus is concerned, the genome consists of 10 discrete segments of double-stranded RNA (dsRNA) with a total molecular weight of 16×10^6 (8). Genetic (2, 4) and biochemical data (9, 20) are consistent in defining each segment as a single gene. Seven different classes of temperature-sensitive (ts) mutants are known (termed classes A to G), and therefore 7 of the 10 segments are genetically marked. Defective reovirions have one or more complete segments of the genome deleted.

Defective virions and standard (infectious) reovirions are similar in physical properties, and it has not been possible to separate them from each other by direct means. The presence of defective virus in a population can, however, be determined in the following way. The viral population is labeled with [³H]uridine during growth in L-cell cultures and is purified. Such virus, whether defective or not, bands at 1.37 g/ml when subjected to isopycnic centrifugation in CsCl. The purified virus is then subjected to digestion with chymotrypsin, which removes the outer capsomeres, some 50% of the total viral protein, leaving core particles that still contain the dsRNA of the virus. The cores are banded in a CsCl gradient and have a buoyant density of 1.43 g/ml if derived from standard virions. If defective virus is present in the population, its cores band at lighter densities and can thus be readily recognized. To assist in the analysis, ¹⁴C-labeled virus from a freshly cloned stock, and thus free from defective virus, is added before chymotrypsin digestion. The resulting ¹⁴C-labeled cores act as density markers in the succeeding CsCl centrifugation.

A variety of defective reovirions can be readily generated by serial passage in cell culture of wild-type virus or various classes of ts mutants (12, 15). The most common deletion is the largest or L_1 segment of the viral genome, and such virions are called L_1 defectives. Cores from L_1 defectives band in CsCl at 1.415 g/ml, and if multiple deletions have occurred the cores band at still lighter densities. Analysis of dsRNA from cores of different densities indicate which segments are missing. Populations of L_1 defective virions have been obtained practically free from infectious virus and other defectives (16), but as yet we have not been able to get a pure population of any other single type of defective virion.

DEFECTIVE VIRUS AND PERSISTENT INFECTION IN CELL CULTURE

Our work during the past year (R. Ahmed, unpublished data) will be briefly summarized. Persistent infection can be started readily in L cells with any class of ts mutants of type 3 reovirus provided homologous defective virus is present. Persistent infection can rarely be initiated if defectives are not present in the parental virus. It is difficult to initiate a persistent infection with wild-type 3 reovirus even in the presence of defectives. We have studied the evolution of the viral populations over a period of months in these carrier cultures and have observed a cyclic shift in the type of defective particles in the cells which can be correlated with the periodic "crises" in the cells. Virtually all the cells are still producers of infectious virus after several months, but the virus is changed in character. In persistent infections initiated with ts mutants, a small-plaque mutant with a ts^+ phenotype is rapidly selected and then persists. This small-plaque mutant will not start a persistent infection by itself, but it will if it is associated with its homologous defective virus.

Thus, defective reovirus seems to play a key role in initiating and maintaining the persistent infection. There is a complex evolution of both the infectious virus and the defectives during the infection, and generally similar observations have been made with vesicular stomatitis virus (VSV; 6). All defective particles interfere to a greater or lesser extent with the growth of infectious virus, and presumably it is this interfering effect along with the genetic interactions of the various particles (17) that maintain the carrier state. In themselves, however, these results tell us little about the chronic state in vivo. The selection pressures on viral replication in the body are totally different and far more complex than they are in cell culture, and to get any insight into the role of defectives in vivo we have to go to an animal model.

DEFECTIVE REOVIRUS AND CHRONIC INFECTION IN RATS

There is an extensive literature on in vivo infections with reovirus in various animal models (5, 18, 19). The experiments of most concern here, though, are the ones Fields and Raine started several years ago (3, 13, 14). They infected newborn rats by the intracerebral route with wild-type reovirus, with a C-class ts mutant and with a B-class ts mutant. Most of the rats infected with wild virus died of acute encephalitis within 2 weeks. Most of those infected with the C mutant recovered from the infection and grew normally. Many of those infected with the B mutant recovered from the acute infection but became runted. During the succeeding 2 or 3 months, virus gradually disappeared from the brains of these runted rats, but nevertheless they went on to develop a brain degeneration resembling communicating hydrocephalus. Thus, single gene differences in this virus have resulted in quite different disease states, one of them being a chronic degenerative disorder of the nervous system. In the work described below, we used the rat model of Fields and Raine and the same ts mutants they employed.

In our first experiment, 2-day-old rats were inoculated intracerebrally with 10^7 PFU of wild-type reovirus. As far as we could tell, this virus was free from defectives. Under these conditions, all rats died within 12 to 14 days. [^{3}H]uridine was injected into the brain to label the multiplying virus, and 8 days after infection brains were taken from moribund rats. The virus was extracted from the brains, partially purified, and analyzed for defective virus. It was found that defective virus accumulated rapidly during this acute infection and contained exclusively L_1 defectives. Holland and Villarreal (7) found that defective particles of VSV are generated in mouse brains under generally similar conditions. Such results are not at all unexpected. In this kind of experiment, the brain is used essentially as an in vivo cell culture; the virus multiplies to high titer, and it is hardly surprising that defective particles form in large amounts. Moreover, all the animals die, so we cannot study a chronic infection. Because of these considerations, we decided to use a different route of inoculation, the subcutaneous route, the idea being that this is a more natural means of infection. The parental virus would be exposed to the defense mechanisms of the animal, and, moreover, any small amount of defective virus present in the inoculum would be screened out. In the remainder of the experiments, we will assume the subcutaneous route of inoculation into 2-day-old rats of about 10^7 PFU of virus.

During the first 10 days postinfection, there is a rapid rise in virus in brain (up to 5×10^8 PFU/g of tissue), liver, and blood, and then a rapid drop over the succeeding few days. Up to 10% of these animals die with acute encephalitis. About half the surviving animals recover rapidly and completely, and no virus can be found in them after 1 month. The remaining 50% of survivors are the interesting ones because they are runted. It is easy to determine a few days after infection which animals are going to be runted and to select them for further study. Virus persists in the brains of the runted animals for at least 60 days after infection and can no longer be found after 80 days. These animals would likely have gone on to develop the hydrocephalus described by Raine and Fields if we had observed them long enough. Thus, we can distinguish two phases of infection in this animal model: an acute phase during the first 10 days after infection when virus multiplies in the brain to its maximal titer and a chronic or persistent phase in the runted animals, which constitute a large fraction of the population. The course of infection is similar with wild-type reovirus and its B- and C-class ts mutants. Moreover, virus isolated from the brains of chronically infected

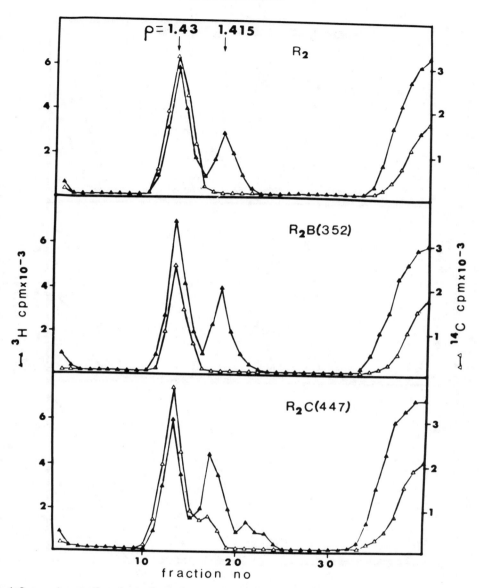

FIG. 1. *Isopycnic centrifugation in CsCl of amplified virus obtained from the brains of rats at the acute stage of infection after subcutaneous inoculation of 2-day-old rats. Virus was isolated from the brains of rats, concentrated, and then amplified by a single passage in L cells, during which the progeny was labeled with [³H]uridine. Purified marker virus labeled with ¹⁴C was added to the L-cell lysate; the virus was concentrated, digested with chymotrypsin, and centrifuged in a CsCl gradient. Top panel: Animals infected with wild-type virus and virus isolated from the brain 9 days postinfection. Middle panel: Animals infected with R_2B (352) mutant and virus isolated from the brain at 10 days postinfection. Bottom panel: Animals infected with R_2C (447) mutant and virus isolated from the brain 11 days postinfection. (▲) ³H-labeled virus from rat brain; (△) ¹⁴C-labeled marker virus. Cores from marker virus and infectious ³H-labeled virus from brain band together at 1.43 g/ml. The ³H-labeled virus at the lighter densities is defective.*

animals retains the genetic character of the inoculated virus with one or two exceptions. That is, if the virus inoculated is ts, the virus isolated from the chronically infected brain is ts.

We then examined the brains of these animals in the acute and chronic phases of infection for the presence of defective virus. Virus did not grow to high enough titers in the brain to allow

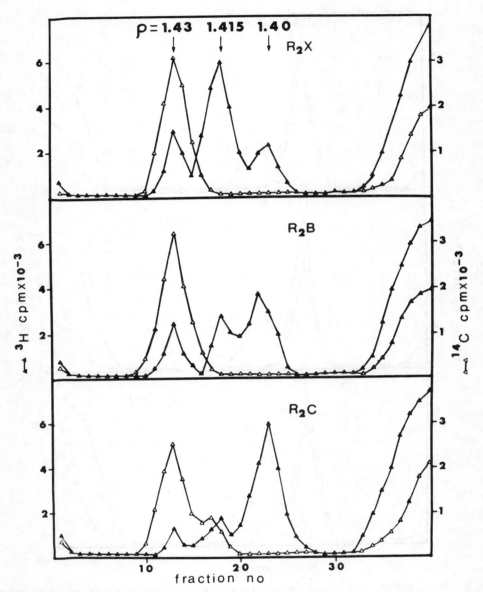

FIG. 2. *Isopycnic centrifugation in CsCl of amplified virus obtained from the brains of rats persistently infected 30 days after subcutaneous inoculation. Procedure was similar to that described in the legend to Fig. 1. Top panel: Animals infected with wild-type virus. Middle panel: Animals infected with R_2B (352) mutant. Bottom panel: Animals infected with R_2C (447) mutant. (▲) ^3H-labeled virus obtained from rat brain; (△) ^{14}C-labeled marker virus.*

us to label it directly, so we used an amplification technique (7). Virus is isolated from the brain, concentrated by centrifugation, and then used to infect a monolayer of cells at high multiplicity. The virus grows in the cell cultures and so too does any defective virus, and

it can be labeled with [^3H]uridine. The virus from these cells is then partially purified, digested with chymotrypsin, and examined on a CsCl density gradient. The technique is highly sensitive for picking up defective virus.

Figure 1 shows amplified virus from the brains

of acutely infected rats infected with wild type, B mutant, and C mutant. In all three cases, defective virus was generated by 8 days after subcutaneous inoculation. The defectives formed are lacking the L_1 genomic segment.

In Fig. 2 is shown the amplified viral population from chronically infected rats 60 days after infection. Defective virus is again present, but the nature of the defective population has changed. In addition to defectives missing the L_1 segments, other defectives with multiple gene deletions are being formed, particularly with the C-class mutant.

Thus, defective virus is formed in the brains of these animals during both the acute and the chronic phase of infection, and there is a shift in the type of defectives as the disease progresses. We have other evidence that these defectives can interfere more or less markedly with the growth of infectious virus in cell culture. It is thus easy to make the argument that initiation and maintenance of the chronic phase of infection is controlled by the generation of a defective viral population. On the other hand, there is only one piece of evidence I know to support this argument, and that arises from the following experiment.

We carried out an experiment in which newborn rats were inoculated intracerebrally with wild-type virus and a large excess of L_1 defective virions. Only 6 of 23 rats died, whereas all of them died in the absence of defectives. Doyle and Holland (1) have observed a similar protective effect of VSV defectives. In our experiment, 15 of the 23 animals became runted and showed the usual signs of a chronic infection. Virus was isolated from the brains and examined for defective virus. The results in the top panel of Fig. 3 show clearly that defective virus was being formed in the brain during the acute phase of infection. The bottom panel of Fig. 3 shows the result obtained 30 days after infection during the chronic phase. A new population of defectives has arisen in addition to the L_1 defectives, and these have multiple deletions, just as was found for persistently infected animals inoculated by the subcutaneous route.

Thus, the evidence is good that defective virus can modify the course of an infection with reovirus and may well be involved in setting up the chronic state in vivo. This may be true also for some chronic infections with VSV. To this extent, I have answered the question I posed at the beginning. I do not know of any such evidence for other in vivo systems, so we cannot yet extend the argument to any kind of generality. Obviously a variety of factors contribute to chronic infections and to the long-

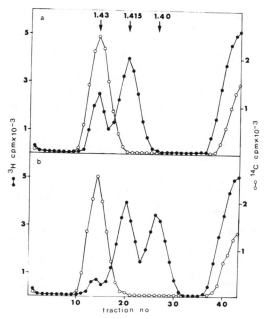

FIG. 3. *Isopycnic centrifugation in CsCl of amplified virus obtained from the brains of rats inoculated intracerebrally at 2 days of age with wild-type virus (10^4 PFU/rat) and L_1 defective virus (10^7 particles/rat). Procedure was the same as that described in the legend to Fig. 1.* (○) *Cores derived from purified, ^{14}C-labeled R_2 marker virus;* (●) *cores from [^3H]uridine-labeled virus derived by amplification in L-cell monolayers. Top panel: Virus obtained from the brain of a moribund rat 8 days postinfection. Bottom panel: Virus obtained from the brain of a persistently infected, runted rat 30 days postinfection.*

term degenerative effects that might ensue. Our results suggest that defective virus should be considered as one of the possible contributing factors.

ACKNOWLEDGMENTS

This work was supported by grants from the Medical Research Council of Canada and the National Cancer Institute of Canada.

LITERATURE CITED

1. **Doyle, M., and J. J. Holland.** 1973. Prophylaxis and immunization in mice by use of virus-free defective T particles to protect against intracerebral infection by vesicular stomatitis virus. Proc. Natl. Acad. Sci. U.S.A. **70:**2105–2108.

2. **Fields, B. N.** 1971. Temperature-sensitive mutants of reovirus type 3: features of genetic recombination. Virology **46:**132–148.

3. **Fields, B. N.** 1972. Genetic manipulation of reovirus. A model for modification of disease. N. Engl. J. Med. **287:**1026–1033.

4. **Fields, B. N., and W. K. Joklik.** 1969. Isolation and preliminary genetic and biochemical characterization of temperature-sensitive mutants of reovirus. Virology **37:** 335–342.

5. **Gonatas, N. K., G. Margolis, and L. Kilham.** 1971. Reovirus type III encephalitis: observations of virus-cell interactions in neural tissues. II. Electron microscopic studies. Lab. Invest. **24:**101–109.

6. **Holland, J. J., and L. P. Villarreal.** 1974. Persistent noncytocidal vesicular stomatitis virus infections mediated by defective T particles that suppress virion transcriptase. Proc. Natl. Acad. Sci. U.S.A. **71:**2956–2960.

7. **Holland, J. J., and L. P. Villarreal.** 1975. Purification of defective interfering T particles of vesicular stomatitis and rabies viruses generated *in vivo* in brains of newborn mice. Virology **67:**438–439.

8. **Joklik, W. K.** 1974. Reproduction of reoviridae, p. 231–334. *In* H. Fraenkel-Conrat and R. R. Wagner (ed.), Comprehensive virology, vol. 2. Plenum Press, New York.

9. **Millward, S., and M. Nonoyama.** 1970. Segmented structure of the reovirus genome. Cold Spring Harbor Symp. Quant. Biol. **35:**773–779.

10. **Mims, C. A.** 1974. Factors in the mechanism of persistence of viral infections. Prog. Med. Virol. **18:**1–14.

11. **Nonoyama, M., and A. F. Graham.** 1970. Appearance of defective virions in clones of reovirus. J. Virol. **6:**693–694.

12. **Nonoyama, M., Y. Watanabe, and A. F. Graham.** 1970. Defective virions of reovirus. J. Virol. **6:**226–236.

13. **Raine, C. S., and B. N. Fields.** 1973. Reovirus type III encephalitis. A virologic and ultrastructural study. J. Neuropathol. Exp. Neurol. **32:**19–33.

14. **Raine, C. S., and B. N. Fields.** 1974. Neurotropic virus. Host relationship alterations due to variation in viral genome as studied by electron microscopy. Am. J. Pathol. **75:**119–138.

15. **Schuerch, A. R., T. Matsuhisa, and W. K. Joklik.** 1974. Temperature-sensitive mutants of reovirus. VI. Mutants *ts* 447 and *ts* 556 particles that lack one or two L genome RNA segments. Intervirology **3:**36–46.

16. **Spandidos, D. A., and A. F. Graham.** 1975. Complementation of defective reovirus by ts mutants. J. Virol. **15:**954–963.

17. **Spandidos, D. A., and A. F. Graham.** 1975. Complementation between temperature-sensitive and deletion mutants of reovirus. J. Virol. **16:**1444–1452.

18. **Stanley, N. F.** 1974. The reovirus murine models. Prog. Med. Virol. **18:**257–272.

19. **Stanley, N. F., and R. A. Joske.** 1975. Animal model of human disease: active chronic hepatitis. Animal model: chronic murine hepatitis induced by reovirus type 3. Am. J. Pathol. **79:**181–184.

20. **Zweerink, H. J., M. J. McDowell, and W. K. Joklik.** 1971. Essential and nonessential noncapsid reovirus proteins. Virology **45:** 716–723.

Role of Temperature-Sensitive Mutants in Persistent Infection

Department of Microbiology, School of Medicine, University of Pittsburgh, Pittsburgh, Pennsylvania 15261

In the presentation that follows, evidence will be summarized suggesting that the selection of temperature-sensitive (ts) mutants plays an important role in the establishment and maintenance of a number of persistent viral infections (6). In addition, a mechanism will be proposed to explain the role of ts mutants in both the establishment and the maintenance of the persistently infected state. This presentation will concentrate on two viruses with which we have worked: the paramyxovirus Newcastle disease virus (NDV) and the rhabdovirus vesicular stomatitis virus (VSV).

PERSISTENT INFECTIONS WITH NDV

Our original observations were made while studying the abortive infection of mouse L cells with NDV. We soon found that the abortive infection quickly led to a persistent infection of L cells (8, 9). Culture fluid from the persistently infected L cells (L_{NDV} cells) always contained about 10^4 to 10^5 PFU of NDV per ml and 10 to 20 U of interferon per ml. L_{NDV} cells were completely resistant to challenge with VSV, a heterologous virus, whereas control L cells were completely susceptible.

L_{NDV} cells have now been maintained in continuous culture for more than 7 years. The properties of the virus (referred to as "NDV_{pi}") recovered from the persistently infected cells differed markedly from the properties of the wild-type Herts strain (referred to as "NDV_0") used to initiate the infection (3). Most important to the present paper was the difference in replication of the two viruses in permissive chick embryo cells incubated at 37°C and 43°C. Whereas NDV_0 replicated with almost equal efficiency at both temperatures, the replication of NDV_{pi} was effectively inhibited at the higher temperature.

Biochemical characterization of the NDV_{pi} ts mutants showed that all NDV_{pi} clones isolated from the persistent infection failed to synthesize virus-specific RNA at the nonpermissive temperature, and all clones studied appeared to have defects associated with RNA polymerase activity (4). Alterations in the virion-associated polymerase of virus mutants isolated from L_{NDV}

cells have also been reported by Furman and Hallum (1).

We found that the selection of ts mutants by persistent infection of L cells was not a peculiarity of the Herts strain of NDV, but was also true for two other strains, Texas-GB and Kansas-Man (5). When L cells were infected with low multiplicities of these two strains, the infection became persistent and the cells had the characteristics of L_{NDV} cells, described previously. In addition, the virus present was temperature sensitive, and isolated mutant clones exhibited RNA^- phenotypes.

When cell lines of hamster or canine origin were used to initiate persistent infections with Herts NDV_0, the evidence obtained confirmed that again ts mutants with an RNA^- phenotype were spontaneously selected (11).

The findings that have been described illustrate several important points regarding persistent infection of cell lines with NDV.

First, selection of ts mutants occurs in mouse, hamster, and canine cell lines infected at low multiplicities with several strains of NDV.

Second, all the ts mutants of NDV that were isolated from persistently infected mouse, hamster, and canine cell lines were RNA^-, that is, defective in RNA synthesis at the nonpermissive temperature. This evidence points to the possible importance of a viral transcriptional defect in the establishment of persistent infections with NDV.

Third, in contrast to L_{NDV} cells, BHK and MDCK cells persistently infected with NDV made no interferon and were completely susceptible to VSV. This suggests that in the case of NDV, interferon mediation is not essential for the establishment or maintenance of the persistently infected state.

PERSISTENT INFECTIONS WITH VSV

The remainder of this paper deals with the establishment of persistent infections of mouse L cells with VSV (10). The role of defective interfering (DI) particles in establishment and maintenance of the carrier state will be considered, as well as the selection and characteristics of

451

TABLE 1. *Properties of L cells persistently infected with VSV (L$_{VSV}$ cells)*

Property	Result
VSV production (PFU per cell per day) . .	<1
DI particle production (by interference assay)	<1 DI/PFU
Proportion of cells yielding infectious centers	1–25%
Proportion of cells with VSV antigens in cytoplasm and cell membrane	100%
Susceptible to wild-type VSV	No
Susceptible to pseudorabies virus	No
Interferon produced	No

TABLE 2. *Properties of VSV (VSV$_{pi}$) isolated from persistently infected L cells 12 weeks after initiation of infection*

Property	VSV$_0$	VSV$_{pi}$
Plaque size (32°C, 3 days) . .	2–3 mm	<1–1.5 mm
Efficiency of plating (39.5°C/32°C)	0.35	6.1×10^{-5}
RNA phenotype (39.5°C) . . .	RNA+	RNA−
Complementation group	—	Group I
LD$_{50}$ for adult mice (intracerebral route)	3 PFU	$>10^7$ PFU

ts mutants in the persistent infection. In addition, the altered properties of the persistently infected L cells will be described.

To begin with, our attempts to establish persistent infections in L cells with wild-type VSV essentially free from DI particles were unsuccessful; at multiplicities of infection (MOI) from 10^{-1} to 10^{-5}, all cells were destroyed within 1 or 2 days. These results with L cells were similar to those reported with BHK-21 cells by Holland and Villarreal (2). However, when we followed their successful technique, that is, when we infected L cells with wild-type infectious B particles in the presence of large numbers of DI particles, under these conditions persistent infections were readily established. To obtain a suitable mixture of B and DI particles, we used the third undiluted passage of a large-plaque strain of VSV$_{IND}$. Monolayer cultures of L cells were infected with this third undiluted passage to give input MOI of 1,000 DI and <1 B particles per cell. In the succeeding weeks, there were frequent crises of cell destruction, followed by regrowth of cells. After many medium changes and cell passages during the next month, the persistently infected cell line stabilized and was maintained in 16-ounce (about 480-ml) bottles.

When the persistently infected line had stabilized 6 weeks after the infection was initiated, the properties of the L$_{VSV}$ cells were determined, (Table 1). The properties of the virus (VSV$_{pi}$) isolated from persistently infected L$_{VSV}$ cells 12 weeks after the infection was initiated are listed in Table 2.

A prospective study was undertaken to determine more precisely the early events in the establishment of persistent infection by VSV. The study was designed particularly to determine the rate at which ts mutants appeared. This prospective study was started by infecting L cells with the third undiluted passage of wild-type VSV in BHK cells, as described earlier in this paper.

Clonal analysis revealed that the frequency of spontaneous ts mutants in the inoculum used to initiate the persistent infection was 4.4%. This is shown in the top line of Table 3. By 10 days after initiation of the persistent infection, there was a statistically significant increase in the frequency (17.8%) of ts mutants in the fluids harvested from L$_{VSV}$ cells. The frequency of ts mutants increased dramatically in fluids harvested at 11 and 17 days. By 63 days, all 29 clones isolated at 32°C from the L$_{VSV}$ cells were temperature sensitive. This persistently infected cell line has now been maintained for 10 months without the appearance of revertants in the virus population. The rapid rate of selection of ts mutants by the conditions established in the persistent infection is dramatically illustrated by the prospective study summarized in Table 3.

We next examined the ability of a cloned ts mutant derived from L$_{VSV}$ cells to establish persistent infection in the absence of significant numbers of DI particles. To this end, we used clone ts pi 364, which was isolated from the 7-day fluid of the persistent infection established in connection with the prospective study described earlier. The original plaque isolate grown at 32°C was used to initiate the infection; this plaque isolate contained 8.4×10^7 PFU/ml and showed a 39.5/32°C yield efficiency of $<1.1 \times 10^{-6}$. Under the conditions used, that is, a plaque isolate passed at low multiplicity, few DI particles would be present in the virus pool.

L-cell monolayers were infected with 10-fold dilutions of ts pi 364 to give input MOI ranging from 10^{-1} to 10^{-5}. These low MOI and the nature of the original plaque isolate would preclude a role for DI particles in the initiation of the carrier state. By 4 days after infection at the different multiplicities, the cultures infected at the three highest MOI showed complete cell destruction, and virus yields were considerable, although the progeny were still clearly ts. The two persistently infected L$_{VSV}$ lines established by use of low MOI of ts virus (10^{-4} or 10^{-5}) were passed at 4- to 6-day intervals. These lines have now been maintained for 30 cell passages over a period of 4 months. Only occasional foci of cell damage have been seen, and the infectivity of the medium ranges from 10^3 to 10^5 PFU/ml at 32°C. The 39.5/32°C efficiency of plating (EOP) ratio has not exceeded 2×10^{-4}, indicating the persistence of a ts population in the carrier cultures. The cultures are completely resistant to wild-type VSV and to pseudorabies virus, and no interferon is produced.

The ts mutant used to initiate the persistent infection was tested for its ability to replicate at 32, 37, and 39.5°C. It was found that there was a marked decrease in the ability of ts pi 364 to replicate at 37°C compared with its replication at 32°C. At 39.5°C the conditions were nonpermissive, providing a 39.5/32°C ratio of 1.4×10^{-5}. This "leakiness" of ts pi 364 at 37°C is an important aspect of the mechanism for establishment and maintenance of persistent infection by ts mutants which will be proposed below.

PROPOSED MECHANISMS FOR ESTABLISHMENT AND MAINTENANCE OF PERSISTENT INFECTIONS BY ts MUTANTS

The results that have been presented thus far demonstrate the important role played by ts virus in the establishment and maintenance of persistent infections of L cells with VSV. For clarity, it is desirable to separate this process into two components, establishment and maintenance, and to examine what is known about each.

The establishment of persistent infections with VSV at 37°C in L cells clearly depends on the characteristics of the virus used. For example, when wild-type infectious B particles are employed, it is necessary to co-infect the cells with large numbers of DI particles in order to establish the carrier state. Even at extremely low MOI, B particles alone replicate and completely destroy the host cells. These findings agree with those of Holland and Villarreal, who used VSV_{IND} and BHK-21 cells. However, the requirement for large numbers of DI particles to establish persistent VSV infection in L cells can be eliminated by initiating the infection with very low MOI of a ts mutant. Under conditions of low MOI (that is, 10^{-4} or 10^{-5}), conditions under which the persistent infection is initiated with ts virus propagated and diluted to exclude significant numbers of DI particles, it is apparent that the establishment of persistent infection may occur without a requirement for mediation by DI particles.

The ability of ts virus at low MOI to establish the carrier state may depend on the decreased efficiency of this virus to replicate in L cells at 37°C. In effect, replication of ts virus at this temperature may be "leaky," leading to an altered virus-host cell interaction.

On the other hand, when wild-type virus or large amounts of ts virus are used to initiate infection at 37°C, DI particles are essential to reduce the initial virus replication and cell destruction which follows. Only by the intercession of DI particles can the destructive effects of the virus be modulated sufficiently for persistence to follow under these conditions.

There are two major questions which remain

TABLE 3. *Prospective study: appearance of ts mutants in L cells persistently infected with VSV*

Cell passage	Days after initiation	Assay temp (°C)	PFU/ml in medium	EOP (39.5/32°C)	No. of clones isolated	No. ts	Percent ts
Inoculum		32	3.0×10^5	0.27	90	4	4.4
		39.5	8.0×10^4				
P-1	7	32	1.1×10^3	0.55	59	5	8.4
		39.5	6.1×10^2				
P-1	10	32	3.9×10^3	0.46	56	10	17.8
		39.5	1.8×10^3				
P-2	11	32	3.7×10^5	0.18	56	41	73.2
		39.5	6.9×10^4				
P-2	17	32	2.5×10^4	0.088	61	52	85.2
		39.5	2.2×10^3				
P-8	63	32	2.2×10^5	0.001	29	29	100
		39.5	2.2×10^2				

unanswered by the data provided so far in this paper: (i) "How are ts mutants able to establish and maintain persistent infections?" and (ii) "Why don't revertants replace the ts population at 37°C, a temperature not optimal for the ts mutants?"

As a basis for designing experiments to answer these questions, the following hypothesis was offered: ts mutants of VSV interfere with wild-type replication, and, further, the ts mutants are "rescued" by wild-type virus.

The basis for this hypothesis rested on experiments reported by Preble and Youngner (4) with NDV and by Stollar and his colleagues, who worked with Sindbis virus (7). In both these instances it was reported that in cells co-infected with ts mutants and wild-type viruses at permissive temperatures, interference with wild-type virus replication was observed quite consistently.

To test the hypothesis, mixed infections of BHK-21 cells with wild-type VSV and ts mutants were carried out in BHK-21 cells as described in detail elsewhere (12). BHK-21 cell monolayers were singly or mixedly infected with a wild-type VSV cloned population and a group I mutant (ts G11). The analysis of progeny viruses produced by single and mixed infections with the two viruses at 32, 37, and 39.5°C is shown in Table 4.

It is clear that at all three temperatures the replication of the wild-type virus was significantly reduced by co-infection with ts G11. The ability of ts G11 to inhibit wild-type virus replication was not affected by the reduced ability of the ts mutant to replicate at 37 and 39.5°C. In confirmation of our hypothesis, at 37 and 39.5°C the progeny of mixed infections contained 44- and 7,100-fold higher concentrations of small-plaque ts virus than did the progeny of single infections with the ts virus alone. At 32°C, the number of ts mutant progeny was not different in single or mixed infections.

Mixed infections (Table 4) were also carried out with other ts mutants belonging to complementation groups I, II, and IV. In every case, mixed infection resulted in a significant *decrease* in wild-type progeny and a significant *rescue* of the ts mutant. This rescue of the ts mutant by the wild-type virus was significant at 37°C and dramatic at 39.5°C as a result of the decreased background of the ts mutant at the two higher temperatures.

These observations concerning the "dominance" of the replication of ts virus over that of the wild type at 37°C must be considered a rationale for the spontaneous selection and maintenance of ts mutants in persistently infected cell lines. The ability of the ts mutants to interfere with the replication of wild-type virus at 37°C would provide an answer to the question, "Why don't revertants replace the ts population at 37°C, a temperature not optimal for the ts mutants?" Since the ts mutants present in a persistent infection can inhibit the replication of wild-type virus, revertants would be prevented from providing a significant portion of the virus population. In this way, a ts virus population selected during a persistent infection could maintain its mutant character. In addition, it has been noted that strong homologous interference to challenge with wild-type virus is established in persistently infected L cells carrying ts VSV mutants.

The mechanism by which the ts mutants are able to establish themselves in persistent infections is still not clear. The role of DI particles of VSV in the initiation of persistent infections with wild-type virus is well documented (2, 10). The ability of DI particles to modulate the replication of the infective B particles may be crucial at the outset to prevent

TABLE 4. *Analysis of progeny viruses produced by mixed infection of BHK-21 cells with WT$_0$3 and ts G11 at 32, 37, and 39.5°C*

| Temp of replication in BHK-21 cells (°C) | Plaque size at 32°C (mm) | PFU/ml | | Mixed infection (WT$_0$3 × ts G11) | Ratio: mixed infection/ single infection |
| | | Single infection | | | |
		WT$_0$3 (MOI = 0.1)	ts G11 (MOI = 1.0)		
32	2.5–3.0	7.6 × 10^8	0	3.0 × 10^7	0.03
	1.0–1.5	0	4.9 × 10^8	4.7 × 10^8	0.95
37	2.5–3.0	8.2 × 10^8	0	2.0 × 10^7	0.02
	1.0–1.5	0	2.7 × 10^6	1.2 × 10^8	44.4
39.5	2.5–3.0	2.4 × 10^8	0	6.0 × 10^6	0.02
	1.0–1.5	0	1.4 × 10^3	1.0 × 10^7	7.1 × 10^3

total cell destruction. Once this danger has passed, there may be a rapid selection of ts mutants by some intervening mechanism that is not evident. The dramatic rapidity of the selection of ts mutants during the early phases of the establishment of VSV persistence in mouse L cells has been documented earlier in this paper.

Also recalled should be the experiments described in which persistent infection of L cells at 37°C was initiated in the absence of significant numbers of DI particles by employing low input multiplicities of a plaque-purified RNA⁻ group I mutant. In this instance, two conditions from the outset favored the continued maintenance of the ts mutant in the persistently infected cells. First, less than optimal replication of the ts mutant at 37°C did not result in the destruction of the infected cells. Second, the dominance of the ts mutant replication over that of the wild-type virus provided conditions for exclusion of revertant viruses. Continued efforts are being made to provide more detailed insight into the mechanisms involved in these phenomena.

ACKNOWLEDGMENTS

I wish to acknowledge participation in different aspects of this work by Olivia T. Preble, Edward J. Dubovi, Harshad R. Thacore, Diane O. Quagliana, and Marion Kelly.

This investigation was supported by Public Health Service Research grant AI-06264 from the National Institute of Allergy and Infectious Diseases.

LITERATURE CITED

1. **Furman, P. A., and J. V. Hallum.** 1973. RNA-dependent DNA polymerase activity in preparations of a mutant of Newcastle disease virus arising from persistently infected L cells. J. Virol. **12:**548–555.

2. **Holland, J. J., and L. P. Villarreal.** 1974. Persistent noncytocidal vesicular stomatitis virus infections mediated by defective T particles that suppress virion transcriptase. Proc. Natl. Acad. Sci. U.S.A. **71:**2956–2960.

3. **Preble, O. T., and J. S. Youngner.** 1972. Temperature-sensitive mutants isolated from L cells persistently infected with Newcastle disease virus. J. Virol. **9:**200–206.

4. **Preble, O. T., and J. S. Youngner.** 1973. Temperature-sensitive defect of mutants isolated from L cells persistently infected with Newcastle disease virus. J. Virol. **12:**473–480.

5. **Preble, O. T., and J. S. Youngner.** 1973. Selection of temperature-sensitive mutants during persistent infection: role in maintenance of persistent Newcastle disease virus infections of L cells. J. Virol. **12:**481–491.

6. **Preble, O. T., and J. S. Youngner.** 1975. Temperature-sensitive viruses and the etiology of chronic and inapparent infections. J. Infect. Dis. **131:**467–473.

7. **Stollar, V., J. Peleg, and T. E. Shenk.** 1974. Temperature sensitivity of a Sindbis virus mutant isolated from persistently infected *Aedes aegypti* cell culture. Intervirology **2:**337–344.

8. **Thacore, H. R., and J. S. Youngner.** 1969. Cells persistently infected with Newcastle disease virus. I. Properties of mutants isolated from persistently infected L cells. J. Virol. **4:**244–251.

9. **Thacore, H. R., and J. S. Youngner.** 1970. Cells persistently infected with Newcastle disease virus. II. Ribonucleic acid and protein synthesis in cells infected with mutants isolated from persistently infected L cells. J. Virol. **6:**42–48.

10. **Youngner, J. S., E. J. Dubovi, D. O. Quagliana, M. Kelly, and O. T. Preble.** 1976. Role of temperature-sensitive mutants in persistent infections initiated with vesicular stomatitis virus. J. Virol. **19:**90–101.

11. **Youngner, J. S., and D. O. Quagliana.** 1975. Temperature-sensitive mutants isolated from hamster and canine cell lines persistently infected with Newcastle disease virus. J. Virol. **16:**1332–1336.

12. **Youngner, J. S., and D. O. Quagliana.** 1976. Temperature-sensitive mutants of vesicular stomatitis virus are conditionally defective particles that interfere with and are rescued by wild-type virus. J. Virol. **19:**102–107.

Properties of *Aedes albopictus* Cell Cultures Persistently Infected with Sindbis Virus

VICTOR STOLLAR, AKIRA IGARASHI,[1] AND ROSE KOO

Department of Microbiology, Rutgers Medical School, College of Medicine and Dentistry of New Jersey, Piscataway, New Jersey 08854

When cultures of mosquito cells (*Aedes albopictus* or *Aedes aegypti*) are infected with alphaviruses, no cytopathic effect is observed even though high yields of progeny virus are obtained and the majority, if not all, of the cells are infected (1, 4, 6, 7). These observations contrast sharply with the typical outcome of a productive virus infection in chick or hamster cells, in which case virtually all cells are rapidly killed. Since the mosquito cells are not killed and virus production continues indefinitely, the outcome is a persistently infected culture. We have studied in some detail a system in which *A. albopictus* cell cultures are infected with Sindbis virus. From the results of our experiments carried out over the past few years and from the results of other workers, it appears that there are a number of properties usually associated with such cultures once they reach a "stable" state or a state of equilibrium.

(1) Both with respect to morphology (as observed by light microscopy) and rate of growth, cell cultures of *A. albopictus* cells persistently infected with Sindbis virus (*A. albo*$_{PI-SV}$) cannot be distinguished from normal or uninfected cells (7).

(2) The virus population obtained from these cultures is composed predominantly or even exclusively of readily recognized genotypic variants which (i) produce much smaller plaques than the standard Sindbis virus (SV$_{STD}$), 2 mm in diameter versus 8 mm (9), and (ii) are temperature sensitive (5, 8).

(3) Whereas in *A. albopictus* cells acutely infected with SV$_{STD}$ the principal viral double-stranded RNA (dsRNA) species sediments at 22S, in *A. albo*$_{PI-SV}$ a 12S dsRNA is also seen, and may even be more prominent than the 22S species (9). (From our studies with Sindbis virus defective interfering [DI] particles in chick embryo and hamster cells [2], the finding of smaller than normal viral RNAs, i.e., 12S dsRNA, constitutes strong evidence for the presence of

Sindbis virus DI particles or genomes in the persistently infected mosquito cell cultures.)

(4) *A. albopictus* cell cultures persistently infected with Sindbis virus are completely resistant to superinfection with SV$_{STD}$ but do permit the replication of other alphaviruses, e.g., Eastern equine encephalitis virus (9).

EVOLUTION OF PERSISTENTLY INFECTED CULTURES WITH TIME

To follow more carefully the progression from the acute infection to the stage of a stable persistent infection, replicate cultures of *A. albopictus* cells were infected with Sindbis virus, subcultured at approximately weekly intervals (1:20 split), and assayed for infective virus, usually 3 days after each subculture.

Figure 1 shows the history of a typical culture. During the first week the level of infective virus (assayed at 34°C) remained very high (10^8 to 10^9 PFU/ml), but thereafter gradually dropped and by 8 to 10 weeks stabilized at a level about 10^{-4} to 10^{-3} of the peak levels. This titer of infective virus ($\sim 10^6$ PFU/ml) has been maintained now for 17 months, as long as this particular culture has been carried.

During the first 8 weeks, there was relatively little difference in the infectivity titers as measured at 34 and 39.5°C. However, at 12 weeks when measured at 39.5°C, the viral titer was only 10^{-2} of the titer assayed at 34°C. At later times, virus from the persistently infected culture produced no plaques and yielded no detectable progeny virus at the higher temperature.

An examination of plaque morphology revealed some small-plaque variants as early as 4 to 6 weeks after the primary infection, but by 10 to 12 weeks these variants had clearly become the predominant population.

When the patterns of viral dsRNA were examined at regular intervals after infection (these results were obtained with an independently infected culture), only the 22S species was found during the first 8 to 9 weeks (Fig. 2). At about 10 weeks, a well-defined 12 to 14S species could

---

[1] Present address: Research Institute for Microbial Disease, Osaka University, Suita, Osaka, Japan 565.

456

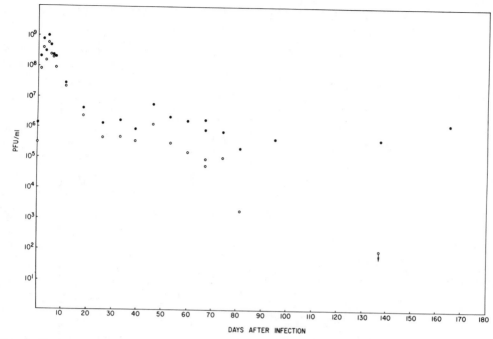

FIG. 1. *Evolution of a persistently infected culture. A.* albopictus *cells were infected with* SV$_{STD}$ *at an approximate input multiplicity of 2 PFU/cell. Cultures were subdivided thereafter (1:20) at weekly intervals. Samples of medium for plaque assay were taken daily during the first week, and after that once a week 3 days after each subculture. Plaque assays were carried out on monolayers of chicken embryo fibroblasts at 34°C (●) and 39.5°C (○).*

also be seen, and was thereafter consistently present in these cultures. Thus, with respect to each of the properties described in the preceding section, the *A. albo*$_{PI-SV}$ cultures appear to reach a stable state by 12 weeks after infection.

All replicate cultures evolved in a similar fashion. Minor variations could be seen, however, from culture to culture with respect to (i) the absolute level of virus found, (ii) the size of the plaques (which might vary from pinpoint or barely discernible to those not much smaller than the plaques produced by SV$_{STD}$), and (iii) the time of appearance of temperature-sensitive virus.

Establishment of Persistently Infected Cultures

Since Sindbis virus does not kill mosquito cells, there is basically no obstacle to the establishment of persistently infected cultures. We should point out, however, that even in cases where infection with togaviruses leads to massive syncytium formation and cell destruction, the cultures generally recover after several weeks, thereafter appear relatively normal, and continue to shed virus for long periods of time. We have made such observations in the case of

A. albopictus cells infected with CFA (cell-fusing agent), a togavirus that is neither an alphavirus nor a flavivirus (12), and others have made similar observations for mosquito cells infected with any of a variety of flaviviruses (3, 14).

MAINTENANCE OF PERSISTENTLY INFECTED CULTURES

It is clear that infection of cultured mosquito cells with Sindbis virus may persist for months and probably years. This implies the maintenance under such conditions of complete functional genomes, which retain all the information for making infectious virus. It also implies, once a stable or steady state is reached, that the rate of viral replication keeps pace with the rate of cell division so that the virus is not finally diluted out.

Turning to how the persistent infection is maintained, we can visualize two possibilities: (i) vertical transmission, in which viral genomes are transmitted from parent cell to daughter cell each time an infected cell divides, and (ii) horizontal transmission, in which the persistently infected culture is maintained by a continual

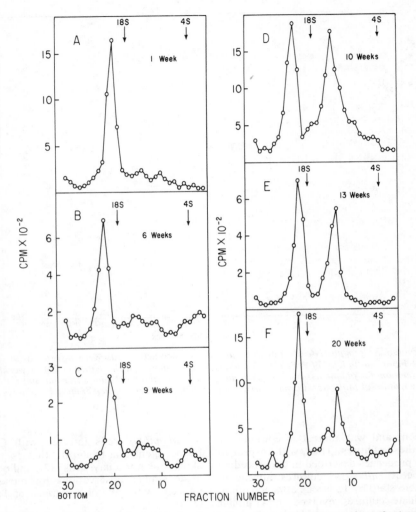

FIG. 2. *Double-stranded RNA synthesized in* A. albopictus *cells at various times after infection with Sindbis virus. A culture of* A. albopictus *was infected with Sindbis virus and maintained by weekly subcultures in a manner similar to that described in the legend to Fig. 1. Three days after each subculture, cells (about 3×10^6 cells/60-mm petri plate) were labeled with [³H]uridine for 5 h in the presence of actinomycin D. RNA was extracted, and the dsRNA was analyzed by sucrose gradient centrifugation (2, 11).*

reinfection of those cells in the culture which are not infected (perhaps because they have undergone spontaneous curing). Evidence pointing to horizontal transmission will be presented below.

MODULATION OR CONTROL OF THE VIRAL INFECTION

Although Sindbis virus infection does not kill mosquito cells, it seems clear that viral replication is not allowed to go unchecked in these cultures. Two types of observations point to some type of control mechanism, which serves to limit viral replication.

(1) When persistently infected cultures that had reached a stable state were subdivided and then followed daily by monitoring both cell number and "viral activity," there appeared to be a disassociation between cell multiplication and viral replication. In such an experiment, whereas the cell number continued to increase for 6 days, the level of infective virus rose rapidly for the first 2 days and then stabilized and declined (Fig. 3). The rate of synthesis of viral RNA (specifically viral dsRNA) also rose and fell in a parallel fashion (not shown), as did the level of intracellular viral antigen (measured by the fluorescent-antibody technique).

(2) Modulation during the course of the acute

infection (i.e., during the first 24 to 40 h after infection) can also be recognized. After the exponential rise in virus titer, we see a leveling off, sometimes followed by a decline (10). As in the stable-state persistently infected culture, the leveling off in the viral titer has been shown to correlate well with a sharp decrease in the rate of viral RNA synthesis (M. W. Davey, Ph.D. thesis, Australia National Univ., Canberra, 1973). We must obviously address ourselves to these mechanisms of regulation and learn how they function, both in the acute infection and in the stable-state infection.

It is here that we must examine the role of host factors, temperature-sensitive mutants, and DI particles, how they influence the maintenance of infection in this system, and also, of course, how they contribute singly or together to the resistance to superinfection with homologous virus. In the process, it will, of course, be necessary to know whether, in these cultures, viral replicative processes are regulated (i) by controlling the proportion of infected cells, (ii) by controlling the amount of viral synthesis in individual cells, or (iii) by both mechanisms simultaneously.

This is also a convenient point at which to recall that infection of mosquito cell cultures with alphaviruses appears to reflect what is observed after infection of the intact mosquito. The infected mosquito appears to suffer no ill effects as a consequence of infection with these viruses, but remains infected for the rest of its life. At the level of the whole organism, the absence of certain defense mechanisms ("classical" immune system, interferon) in insects undoubtedly contributes to the persistence of virus. It seems clear, however, from our experiments with cultured cells that persistence must also be explained at the level of the individual cell.

CLONING EXPERIMENTS AND CURING WITH ANTISERUM

In order to understand the dynamics of persistently infected cultures, including the proportion of cells which are infected, stable-state persistently infected cultures (A. albo$_{PI-SV}$) were cloned in the presence of anti-Sindbis virus serum. Clones were grown to larger populations and then examined to see whether they were virus positive or virus negative. Clones were recognized as virus positive when they (i) produced infectious virus, (ii) contained intracellular viral antigen, and (iii) were nonpermissive with respect to the replication of superinfecting Sindbis virus. (The endogenously produced virus, SV$_{PI}$, could easily be distinguished from the superinfecting virus on the basis of plaque size.) Virus-negative clones differed from the positive

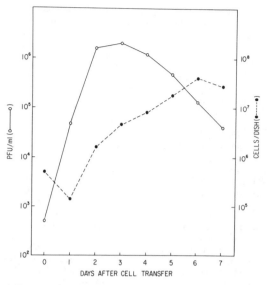

FIG. 3. *Viral replication in* A. albopictus *cells persistently infected with Sindbis virus. Replicate cultures (0.5 × 10⁶ per 60-mm petri plate) were prepared from* A. albo$_{PI-SV}$ *(see Fig. 1) 8 months after the initial infection and were maintained at 28°C. Each day thereafter, samples of medium were harvested for plaque assay (34°C), and the number of cells per plate was counted.*

clones in each of these three characteristics. We have not yet found clones positive for only one or two of these properties. In several experiments of this kind (Table 1), between 30 and 80% of the clones from persistently infected cultures were virus positive. These results were obtained both with populations that had not been previously cloned (lines 1, 2, 8) and with populations derived from virus-positive clones (lines 4, 5, 6, 7). Thus, in this respect, these cultures resemble what Walker termed "regulated infections of cultured cells" in which "all or a large fraction of the cells are infected when the culture is stable" (13). These results suggest that, in the stable-state persistently infected culture, at any given time we are dealing with a mixture of cells, some of which are infected and some of which at least transiently are uninfected. Although the virus-negative clones may possibly have arisen because of curing during the cloning process itself, we consider this unlikely because of the time required for curing (see below). In addition, experiments in which fluorescent-antibody techniques were used show that the proportion of cells containing viral antigen agrees well with the results of cloning experiments. The question may be posed as to why, if in the persistently infected culture about 50% of the cells were uninfected, such cultures as a

TABLE 1. *Clonal analysis of* A. albopictus *cells persistently infected with Sindbis virus* [a]

Cells cloned	No. of clones tested	No. of virus-positive clones	No. of virus-negative clones
A. albo$_{PI-SV}$(A)	38	16	22
A. albo$_{PI-SV}$(CA)	38	31	7
A. albo$_{PI-SV}$(AA)	33	0	33
A. albo$_{PI-SV}$(A-12)	10	6	4
A. albo$_{PI-SV}$(A-14)	14	8	6
A. albo$_{PI-SV}$(A-19)	7	3	4
A. albo$_{PI-SV}$(A-35)	16	12	4
A. albo$_{PI-SV}$(E)	24	14	10
A. albo normal	48	—	48

[a] *A. albo$_{SV-PI}$(A) is the same culture shown in Fig. 1. Cells (A, CA, and AA) were taken for cloning at the times indicated in Fig. 4. (A) represents cells taken from cultures that had not been treated previously with antiserum, whereas (CA) and (AA) refer to cultures that had been treated with antiserum for 4 to 10 weeks, respectively. (A-12), (A-14), (A-19), and (A-35) indicate cells grown from virus-positive clones obtained when (A) was cloned (line 1). A. albo$_{PI-SV}$(E) is a different persistently infected culture, which was initially infected at the same time as (A). Cells were cloned in the presence of 1% anti-Sindbis virus serum. Clones were generally harvested after 12 to 14 days, and the cloning efficiency was about 30%.*

whole did not permit replication of superinfecting Sindbis virus. The answer to this question, however, may well depend on precisely how such resistance to superinfection is mediated, i.e.,

through temperature-sensitive mutants, through DI particles, or through viral products already present in infected cells.

To distinguish between the two proposed mechanisms (vertical and horizontal transmission) for the maintenance of the persistent viral infection, we attempted to cure stable-state persistently infected cultures with antiviral serum. The presence of antiviral serum in the medium should neutralize extracellular virus and prevent reinfection of any uninfected cells. If horizontal transmission were necessary to maintain persistent infection, curing would ultimately result. On the other hand, if virus could be transmitted indefinitely from cell to cell at the time of cell division, antiserum would be unlikely to cure. Persistently infected cultures were grown in the presence of 10% immune rabbit serum (50% plaque-reduction titer = 1:10,000); at various times (Fig. 4) the immune serum was removed, and the cultures were tested at regular intervals for signs of viral infection. In two experiments with different persistently infected cultures, 4 weeks of treatment failed to cure (Fig. 4); after 24 weeks of treatment, however, the cultures appeared completely and permanently cured (Fig. 4); that is, the culture medium was free from virus, cells contained no intracellular viral antigen, and the cultures were permissive for the replication of "superinfecting" Sindbis virus. The curing of these cultures with antiserum marks one important difference from the "regulated infections" described by Walker (13). Our results indicate, in the case of A.

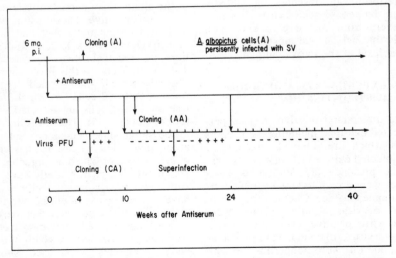

FIG. 4. *Time sequence of cloning experiments and antiserum treatment of a culture of* A. albopictus *cells persistently infected with Sindbis virus. These cells were derived from the culture shown in Fig. 1. Cloning experiments were performed in the presence of 1% anti-Sindbis virus serum. When curing of mass cultures was attempted, 10% antiviral serum was used. These experiments were begun with cultures which had been infected 6 months previously.*

albopictus cells persistently infected with Sindbis virus, that even though persistence may be maintained for some time through the division of infected cells (vertical transmission), in order to maintain a long-term persistent infection, extracellular infectious virus and continual reinfection (horizontal transmission) are necessary. By means of RNA-DNA hybridization and infectious DNA experiments, we have looked for evidence of Sindbis virus sequences or information in host-cell DNA, but no evidence for such DNA sequences was obtained.

SUMMARY

In looking at the stable-state persistently infected cultures, we have seen that a large proportion (30 to 80%), but not all, of the cells are infected. We suggest that a significant fraction of cells are constantly being cured by unknown host mechanisms. Such cells should be immediately susceptible to reinfection by extracellular virus (which by the *stable-state* period is temperature sensitive), subject, however, to interference by extracellular DI particles (not proven but suggested by the finding of intracellular 12*S* dsRNA). The inclusion, however, in the culture medium of antiviral serum would prevent the reinfection of "*cured*" cells. If at the same time the host cells are able to continue their regulatory or modulatory functions and eliminate the "*foreign*" viral material, eventually all the cells and thus the culture should become cured.

The continued study of persistently infected mosquito cells should be instructive, not only with respect to how alphaviruses are maintained in nature, but also for the study of certain types of "regulated" persistent viral infections in mammalian cell cultures.

ACKNOWLEDGMENTS

This investigation was supported by grant BMS-73-06883 from the National Science Foundation, by Public Health Science grant AI-11290 from the National Institute of Allergy and Infectious Diseases, and by the United States-Japan Cooperative Medical Science Program through Public Health Service grant AI-05920 from the same Institute.

LITERATURE CITED

1. **Davey, M. W., D. P. Dennet, and L. Dalgarno.** 1973. The growth of two togaviruses in cultured mosquito and vertebrate cells. J. Gen. Virol. **20:**225–232.
2. **Guild, G. M., and V. Stollar.** 1975. Defective interfering particles of Sindbis virus. III. Intracellular viral RNA species in chick embryo cell cultures. Virology **67:**24–41.
3. **Paul, S. D., K. R. P. Singh, and U. K. M. Bhat.** 1969. A study on the cytopathic effect of arboviruses on cultures from Aedes albopictus cell line. Indian J. Med. Res. **57:**339–348.
4. **Peleg, J.** 1968. Growth of arboviruses in monolayers from subcultured mosquito embryo cells. Virology **35:**617–619.
5. **Shenk, T. E., K. A. Koshelnyk, and V. Stollar.** 1974. Temperature-sensitive virus from *Aedes albopictus* cells chronically infected with Sindbis virus. J. Virol. **13:**439–447.
6. **Singh, K. R. P., and S. D. Paul.** 1968. Susceptibility of Aedes albopictus and Aedes aegypti cell lines to infection by arbo and other viruses. Indian J. Med. Res. **56:**815–820.
7. **Stevens, T. M.** 1970. Arbovirus replication in mosquito cell lines (Singh) grown in monolayer or suspension culture. Proc. Soc. Exp. Biol. Med. **134:**356–361.
8. **Stollar, V., J. Peleg, and T. E. Shenk.** 1974. Temperature sensitivity of a Sindbis virus mutant isolated from persistently infected Aedes aegypti cell culture. Intervirology **2:**337–344.
9. **Stollar, V., and T. E. Shenk.** 1973. Homologous viral interference in *Aedes albopictus* cultures chronically infected with Sindbis virus. J. Virol. **11:**592–595.
10. **Stollar, V., T. E. Shenk, R. Koo, A. Igarashi, and R. W. Schlesinger.** 1975. Observation on Aedes albopictus cell cultures persistently infected with Sindbis virus. Ann. N.Y. Acad. Sci. **266:**214–231.
11. **Stollar, V., T. E. Shenk, and B. D. Stollar.** 1972. Double-stranded RNA in hamster chick and mosquito cells infected with Sindbis virus. Virology **47:**122–132.
12. **Stollar, V., and V. L. Thomas.** 1975. An agent in the Aedes aegypti cell line (Peleg) which causes fusion of Aedes albopictus cells. Virology **64:**367–377.
13. **Walker, D. L.** 1964. The viral carrier state in animal cell cultures. Prog. Med. Virol. **6:**111–148.
14. **Yunker, C. E., and J. Cory.** 1975. Plaque production by arboviruses in Singh's *Aedes albopictus* cells. Appl. Microbiol. **29:**81–89.

Genetics of Measles Virus and Reovirus—Aspects Related to the Analysis of Persistent Viral Infections

BERNARD N. FIELDS, ANNE HAMBURGER, C. S. RAINE, AND R. F. RAMIG

Department of Microbiology and Molecular Genetics, Harvard Medical School, and Department of Medicine, Peter Bent Brigham Hospital, Boston, Massachusetts 02115; and Department of Neuropathology, Albert Einstein College of Medicine, Bronx, New York 10461

INTRODUCTION

Although ordinarily associated with an acute self-limiting illness, measles virus has occasionally been implicated in unusual disease processes. The isolation of a virus closely related to measles from cultured brain cells of patients with subacute sclerosing panencephalitis (SSPE) has been of particular interest (1, 12, 17). SSPE is a subacute degenerative disease usually occurring several years after a primary measles infection. This indolent infection strongly suggests that conventional "fast" RNA viruses, such as measles, may occasionally be associated with chronic neurological illness and viral persistence. The mechanism(s) of latency and neurovirulence are, however, poorly understood.

Naturally selected temperature-sensitive (ts) mutants may be involved in chronic disease states in vivo (18). Alternatively, ts mutants selected under laboratory conditions may result in attenuation of neurovirulence (3, 5, 9–11). Based on our prior experience with reovirus ts mutants, we initiated a genetic analysis of measles virus.

Three other laboratories have also isolated ts mutants of measles virus. Selected data from these laboratories will be cited.

ISOLATION OF MUTANTS AND GROWTH PROPERTIES (Hamburger and Fields, unpublished data)

After mutagenesis with N-methyl-N'-nitro-N-nitrosoguanidine (NTG) or 5-fluorouracil (5-FU), 10 ts mutants were isolated (Table 1). The efficiency of plating (39°C/33°C) ranged from 10^{-2} to 10^{-5}. The overall frequency of isolation of genetically useful stocks was 2.1% after 5-FU and 0.6% after NTG.

Yields of the wild-type parent were comparable at 39°C (48 h) and 33°C (72 h). The yields of ts mutants at 39°C, however, were between 1 and 0.01% that of 33°C infection.

CLASSIFICATION OF MUTANTS BY COMPLEMENTATION TESTS (Hamburger and Fields, unpublished data)

Complementation tests were carried out to determine whether the 10 mutants contained mutations in the same or different cistrons. Data from complementation tests involving mutant tsCl and the tsA3 indicated that neither the yield at 39°C nor the complementation level varied significantly when input multiplicities of 2 or 10 PFU/cell for each mutant were used. Therefore, a multiplicity of 2 PFU/cell for each mutant was chosen in all subsequent complementation experiments to reduce possible multiplicity-dependent leak. In addition, virus yields from monolayers infected with a single mutant at 30°C did not differ significantly when input multiplicities of 2 or 4 were used (Hamburger, unpublished data). Therefore, self-crosses were eliminated in most subsequent experiments. All possible pairwise complementation tests were carried out with the 10 mutants (Table 2). Complementation indices of 5 or greater were considered significant. On the basis of these data, mutants have been assigned to four complementation groups (A through D). Group A consists of four mutants, group B includes two, group C has three, and group D contains a single mutant.

Complementation levels ranged from 6 to 250. Five replicate experiments gave complementation levels similar to these.

MUTANT PROPERTIES (Hamburger and Fields, in preparation)

Heat Stability of the Virions

The heat stability of the mutants was examined to determine whether the temperature sensitivity of the mutants resulted from an alteration in a structural protein associated with viral infectivity. Inactivation of the ts mutants at 50°C was compared with the inactivation of wild-type

462

measles virus at the same temperature. The results (Table 3) indicate that mutants in complementation groups C and D possessed heat lability at 50°C similar to that of wild type. Mutants of group A (tsA1-4) were more heat stable during the first 30 min of heating, yielding a decrease of 3 $\log_{10}$ in virus titer as compared with a decrease of 5 $\log_{10}$ in titer for the wild type. Mutants of group B (tsB1 and -2) showed increased rates of heat inactivation. After 5 min at 50°C, there was a greater than 4-$\log_{10}$ decrease in virus titer as compared with a decrease in titer of 1.5 $\log_{10}$ for wild type.

Hemadsorption Capacity of ts Mutant-Infected Monolayers

The ability of measles virus-infected cells to absorb monkey erythrocytes is presumably the result of insertion into the cell membrane of virus-specific proteins (15). Adsorption of monkey erythrocytes to wild-type measles virus-infected cells was not demonstrable before 24 h

TABLE 1. *Titer of ts mutants assayed at permissive and nonpermissive temperatures*

Strain	Designation[a]	PFU/ml assayed at: 33°C	PFU/ml assayed at: 39°C	EOP (39°C/33°C)
Wild	ts+	6.0×10^6	5.0×10^6	0.8
9	C1	1.5×10^7	3.0×10^4	2.0×10^{-3}
11	C2	5.0×10^7	7.0×10^4	1.4×10^{-3}
16	D1	2.0×10^6	5.0×10^4	2.1×10^{-2}
21[b]	A1	3.0×10^7	6.0×10^4	2.0×10^{-3}
47	A2	1.5×10^7	2.5×10^4	1.4×10^{-3}
65	B1	3.0×10^7	3.0×10^5	1.0×10^{-2}
123	A3	1.8×10^7	5.0×10^2	2.6×10^{-5}
131	B2	1.3×10^6	5.0×10^4	3.8×10^{-2}
216	A4	3.0×10^7	4.0×10^4	1.3×10^{-3}
230	C3	8.0×10^6	1.0×10^3	1.3×10^{-4}

[a] For purposes of clarity, mutants have been named according to complementation groups (Table 3) followed by sequential numbers.

[b] All mutants except ts21 were isolated after mutagenesis with 5-FU; ts21 was derived from a stock mutagenized with NTG.

TABLE 2. *Complementation between measles ts mutants*

Group	ts mutant	Single yield[a] (PFU/ml)	Yields (PFU/ml from mixed infection at 39°C)[a] A1	A2	A3	A4	B1	B2	C1	C2	C3
ts+	—	1.0×10^7									
A	A1	1.0×10^4									
	A2	1.0×10^4	1.0×10^4 (neg)								
	A3	5.0×10^4	3.0×10^4 (neg)	3.0×10^3 (neg)							
	A4	3.0×10^3	6.0×10^4 (neg)	9.0×10^4 (3)	2.0×10^4 (neg)						
B	B1	2.0×10^3	8.0×10^5 (80)	6.0×10^4 (6)	1.0×10^6 (20)	1.0×10^6 (200)					
	B2	3.0×10^4	4.0×10^6 (100)	4.2×10^5 (10)	1.0×10^6 (12)	9.0×10^6 (100)	2.0×10^4 (neg)				
C	C1	5.0×10^4	4.5×10^6 (75)	2.5×10^5 (11)	1.0×10^7 (100)	2.5×10^5 (50)	1.5×10^6 (30)	3.0×10^6 (37)			
	C2	1.0×10^4	8.0×10^5 (40)	1.0×10^5 (10)	1.0×10^6 (22)	2.5×10^6 (250)	2.0×10^5 (20)	9.0×10^5 (12)	3.0×10^3 (neg)		
	C3	5.0×10^3	3.0×10^5 (30)	2.0×10^6 (280)	6.0×10^5 (12)	1.0×10^5 (25)	2.0×10^5 (28)	5.0×10^5 (17)	8.0×10^4 (neg)	4.0×10^2 (neg)	
D	D1	3.0×10^4	$10. \times 10^6$ (20)	6.0×10^5 (11)	4.0×10^5 (5)	8.0×10^5 (80)	2.0×10^5 (18)	8.0×10^5 (18)	7.8×10^5 (8)	5.0×10^5 (12)	2.0×10^6 (65)

[a] The complementation index is given in parentheses. After infection at 39°C, the following formula was used:

$$\text{Complementation index} = \frac{\text{yield (A} \times \text{B) at 33°C} - \text{yield (A} \times \text{B) at 39°C}}{\text{yield (A) at 33°C} + \text{yield (B) at 33°C}}$$

TABLE 3. *Properties of measles ts mutant groups*

Complementation group	Mutant	Hemadsorption (39°C)	Heat stability (50°C)	Time of defect
A	21	++++	++++	Early
	47	++++	++++	
	123	++++	++++	
	216	++++	++++	
B	65	0	—	Late
	131	0	—	
C	9	++++	+++	Early
	11	++++	+++	
	230	++++	+++	
D	16	++++	+++	Early
	Wild type	++++	++++	

postinfection at either 33 or 39°C (Table 4). At 24 h after wild-type infection, about 75% of cells at 39°C and 5% of cells at 33°C showed positive hemadsorption. By 72 h postinfection, 100% of cells were positive for hemadsorption at both temperatures. The greatest numbers of adsorbed erythrocytes were seen on viral syncytia, although they were occasionally observed on single cells with normal morphology.

There were no significant differences in either the rate of appearance or the final number of cells positive for hemadsorption for wild-type or mutant infections at 33°C, although 100% of cells did not always show positive hemadsorption. At the nonpermissive temperature, mutant viruses of groups A and C induced hemadsorption at a slower rate than wild-type virus, although the final number of hemadsorption-positive cells was essentially the same for mutant and wild-type infections at 72 h. Cell cultures infected with mutants of group B contained fewer hemadsorption-positive cells than wild-type virus at all time points at 39°C (Table 4). Varying the multiplicity of infection did not significantly alter this pattern.

Temperature-Shift Experiments

The yield of cells infected with ts mutants ts47, ts65, ts230, and ts16 at 39°C and subsequently transferred to 33°C at 5, 10, or 20 h postinfection is shown in Fig. 1. The final yields of virus were similar whether infected cells had been maintained at 33°C throughout or were shifted from 39°C to 33°C before 20 h. However, the high yield of virus at 48 h from cells infected with ts65 (B) at 39°C and switched to 33°C at 50 or 12 h postinfection suggests a shortening of the latent period at the nonpermissive temperature, where viral replication

proceeds more rapidly than at 33°C. Therefore, the defect in replication of tsB65 is probably late in the infectious cycle. The results for ts16, ts230, and ts47 indicate a slight lag in virus production at 48 h of cells preincubated at the nonpermissive temperature as compared with cells incubated at only 33°C, suggesting that replication is blocked at an early time in the growth cycles of these mutants.

Growth of the ts mutants when the infected cells were first incubated at 33°C and then shifted to 39°C is shown in Fig. 2. Cells infected with ts mutants 16, 230, and 47 show a generally progressive increase in yield, with temperature shifts at 5, 12, and 34 h postinfection. This indicates an early or midstage block in virus replication that is progressively overcome by incubation at the lower temperature. Production of tsB65, however, declined under these conditions. This result is similar to the temperature shift-down experiments and again suggests that the defect in viral replication of tsB65 at 39°C is late in the infectious cycle.

Viral Antigen Formation as Determined by Fluorescent Antibody

The pattern of antigen formation in cells infected with measles virus has been well described (for example, see 13, 19). At 33°C, all ts mutants and the wild-type virus induced identical patterns of antigen formation. When CV-1 cells were inoculated with mutant or wild-type virus, no fluorescence was detected at 33°C until 48 h after infection. At this time, about

TABLE 4. *Production of hemadsorption by mutants at 33 °C and 39 °C at different times after injection*

Virus	Percentage of cells positive for hemadsorption (39°C/33°C)			
	1 h[a]	6 h	24 h	72 h
ts+	0/0[b]	0/0	75/5	100/100
A1	0/0	0/0	0/6	100/100
A2	0/0	0/0	5/1	95/85
A3	0/0	0/0	0/0	70/85
A4	0/0	0/0	0/0	100/85
B1	0/0	0/0	2/8	30/100
B2	0/0	0/0	0/15	20/75
C2	0/0	0/0	22/25	50/60
C3	0/0	0/0	10/8	85/80
D1	0/0	0/0	80/75	70/10

[a] Hours postinfection.
[b] Fraction refers to 39°C/33°C based on counting ~200 cells.

25% of the cells showed bright perinuclear fluorescence. Occasional discrete particles were seen in cytoplasmic processes. Patches of membrane fluorescence were seen in about 30% of the cells in unfixed preparations. The infected cells in both fixed and unfixed preparations tended to cluster, forming small foci scattered in the cell sheet. At 72 h postinfection, diffuse cytoplasmic fluorescence was observed in about 70% of the cells. Specific fluorescence was evenly distributed in the cytoplasm of syncytia. The intensity of fluorescence reached a maximum at this time. Occasional dotlike nuclear inclusions were seen at this time, but their appearance followed no specific pattern. At 72 h, a ring of continuous fluorescence was seen around the membrane of unfixed cells.

Wild-type measles virus induced virtually the same pattern of cytoplasmic fluorescence at 39°C as at 33°C. However, each morphological stage appeared about 24 h earlier than at 33°C. The pattern of immunofluorescence induced by all mutants at 30°C was indistinguishable from that of wild type.

Ultrastructural Studies of ts Mutant-Infected Cells
(Raine, Hamburger, and Fields, in preparation)

The morphogenesis of wild-type and all 10 mutant viruses was essentially identical and similar to that previously described for the

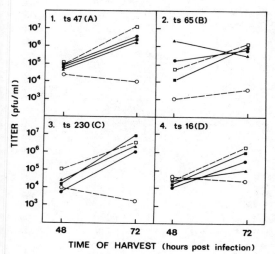

FIG. 1. *Temperature-shift experiments: shift-down. At 5 (▲), 12 (●), or 24 (■) h postinfection, monkey CV-1 cells infected with (1) ts47(A), (2) ts65(B), (3) ts230(C), or (4) ts16(D) were transferred from 39 to 33°C. Additional monolayers were maintained at 33°C (□) or 39°C (○). Virus yields at 48 or 72 h were determined by plaque assay at 33°C.*

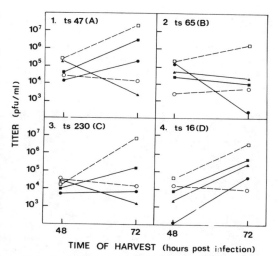

FIG. 2. *Temperature-shift experiment: shift-up. Identical to Fig. 1 except that infected cells were transferred from 33 to 39°C.*

Edmonston strain virus in monkey cell lines (7, 13, 14, 16). The three main structural changes encountered were (i) occasional smooth intranuclear tubular inclusions, (ii) intracytoplasmic coiled "fuzzy" nucleocapsids, and (iii) budding of particles at the cytoplasmic membrane. At 33°C, no ultrastructural changes were seen until 48 h postinfection. At this time, intracytoplasmic complexes of "fuzzy" nucleocapsids were seen dispersed throughout the cytoplasm. Coincident with the appearance of the cytoplasmic inclusions, a dense inner lining of the cell membrane was seen budding to form complete virus particles. Occasional smooth nucleocapsids were also seen dispersed or forming small aggregates in the nuclei of random cells. However, this was a variable finding in three separate trials. Nuclear inclusions were seen in occasional cells infected with both wild-type and all mutant viruses.

At 39°C, the kinetics of maturation of wild-type virus was more rapid than at 33°C, but ultrastructural development was qualitatively normal. Normal-appearing cytoplasmic and nuclear inclusions were seen in cells infected with all mutants. However, budding virions were either absent or infrequently observed at the nonpermissive temperature with all four mutant groups (Fig. 3). Low yields of virus were obtained from these cells.

Resume of Lesions of Measles Mutants

Although the precise lesion(s) responsible for each ts mutation is not defined, certain facts emerge concerning the properties of the four groups of mutants isolated in our laboratory (Table 3):

(1) Each mutant within a complementation group behaves in a consistent fashion.

(2) The group A mutants are more heat stable than the wild type and have an early lesion as defined by temperature shift. The group B mutants are thermolabile, have a late lesion, and have reduced ability to induce hemadsorption. The defect is possibly in the hemagglutinin glycoprotein. The C and D mutants have early, as yet undefined lesions.

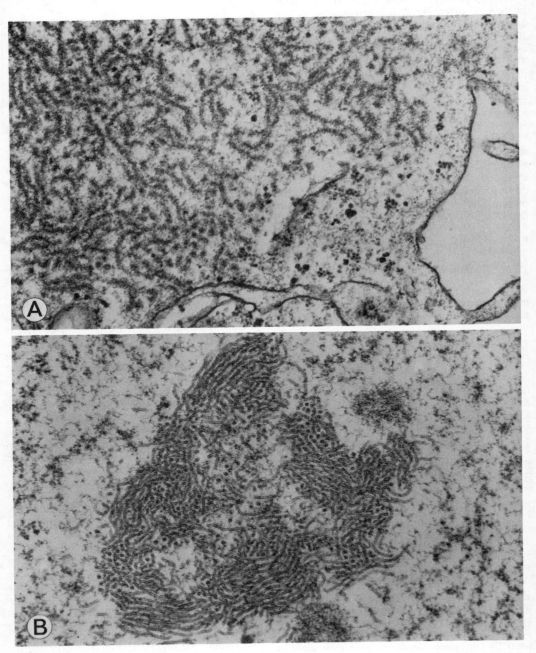

FIG. 3. *Electron micrograph of monkey CV-1 cells infected with measles mutant ts65B; 48 h at 39°C. (A) Cytoplasm showing abundant intracytoplasmic nucleocapsid inclusion without surface budding (×40,000). (B) A collection of smooth intranuclear nucleocapsids (×70,000).*

(3) Electron microscopic analysis of cells infected with all four mutant groups revealed an accumulation of nucleocapsids without detectable cell surface structures. In addition, a similar accumulation of cytoplasmic antigen as detected by fluorescent antibody was seen after wild-type or mutant infection.

RELATIONSHIP OF ts MUTANT PHENOTYPE TO THE PROBLEM OF VIRAL PERSISTENCE

The typical finding in brain cells from patients with SSPE is an accumulation of "fuzzy" viral nucleocapsids with little or no cytoplasmic membrane assembly (15). In addition, there is often an accumulation of "smooth" intranuclear nucleocapsids. The finding that four genetically discrete classes of ts mutants result in a similar phenotype suggests that defects in several viral genes (perhaps in all viral genes that do not fully block viral mRNA synthesis) result in a similar phenotype. Since the mutant infections tended to be somewhat less destructive than wild-type virus, infected cells were present for a longer period of time before falling off the monolayer. This was associated with the occasional appearance, with all mutants, of intranuclear inclusions. This raises a second point, namely that no single class of mutants of measles virus yet identified has a lesion that is associated with a selective accumulation of nuclear viral nucleocapsids. Both of these sets of data suggest that abortive infections due to any of a number of viral mutations or nonpermissive cells can all lead to a similar phenotype. Since a similar phenotype has been observed following infection of cells with defective interfering (DI) particles, it is clear that this phenotype should not be interpreted as a marker for such particles.

ANALYSIS OF ts MUTANTS OF MEASLES VIRUS FROM OTHER LABORATORIES

Rapp and colleagues isolated 24 ts mutants of the Schwarz vaccine strain following mutagenesis (8). The mutants fell into three complementation groups. Two groups were defective in viral RNA synthesis, producing no detectable antigen. One group exhibited wild-type RNA synthesis and was defective in hemolysis antigen synthesis and fusion from within. One ts mutant (tsG) produced hydrocephalus in suckling hamsters at high efficiency (11). The parental strain, at appropriate doses, possessed a similar capability (3, 9).

Payne and colleagues isolated nine ts mutants from the nonattenuated Edmonston strain (2). These mutants fell into three complementation groups. One group (A) produced no detectable antigen; a second group (B) generally was similar to A (although one isolate produced antigen); and the third group (C) produced viral antigen but was restricted in syncytia formation and hemadsorption. All mutants were attenuated for neurovirulence.

A third set of mutants (Black and colleagues) exists that present a variable phenotype and have not been amenable to unambiguous complementation analysis (20).

INITIATION AND MAINTENANCE OF PERSISTENCE

The ability of the available ts mutants to establish persistence either alone or in conjunction with DI particles has not been established. Such experiments are a major goal in the genetic analysis of measles and are currently underway. Data are available, although still limited, bearing on the isolation of ts mutants from persistent lines of measles. For example, Gould (6) reported that a line persistently infected with Edmonston measles released virus that produced foci of syncytia which, unlike the parent strain, was temperature sensitive. This finding has not yet been confirmed for other persistent lines, and, of considerable importance, it is not known whether these ts clones belong to a single complementation group or to several. The availability of different mutant families should allow this question to be resolved.

DEFINITION OF THE ts PHENOTYPE

As the genetic analyses of animal viruses progress, it becomes fundamental to define the mechanisms whereby ts mutants are generated to result in the ts phenotype (18) or revert from a ts phenotype to one resembling the ts$^+$ parent in persistent cells (Ahmed and Graham, personal communication). Recent studies in our laboratory with reovirus ts mutants and ts$^+$ revertants derived from such mutants suggest a previously undetected general mechanism whereby the ts$^-$ phenotype may be altered (Ramig, White, and Fields, in preparation). Revertants may be true revertants (in the gene causing the original ts mutation) or may represent the acquisition of second, suppressor mutations. Such extragenic mutations could mimic the wild-type phenotype while possessing two or more ts mutations. To examine this possibility, ts$^+$ revertants were isolated from the reovirus group A mutant ts201. One revertant clone (101) was selected for detailed examination. A backcross to wild type was performed. Since both clones behaved as ts$^+$ by plaque assay at permissive and nonpermissive temperatures, the appearance of ts$^-$ progeny should indicate the presence of a suppressed ts$^-$ gene in clone 101. Progeny plaques were picked from plates grown at the permissive

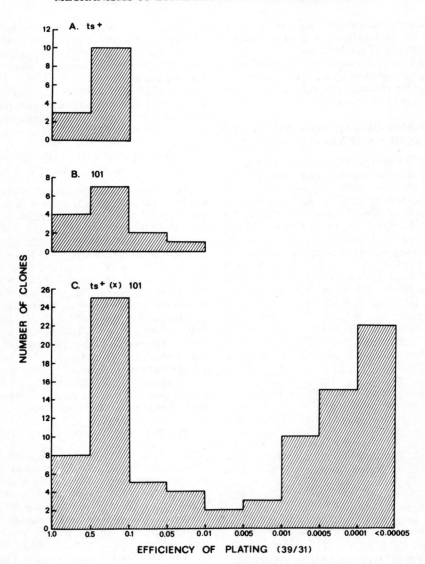

FIG. 4. *Distribution of EOP of progeny and control clones. Suspension culture mouse L cells (10⁷) were mixedly infected with a multiplicity of infection of 10 each with freshly cloned clone 101 and wild type. Two hours postinfection, unadsorbed virus was removed by pelleting the infected cells and resuspending them in fresh medium. Forty-eight hours postinfection, the cells were sonically treated to release cell-associated virus and disrupt viral aggregates. Appropriate dilutions were plated on L-cell monolayers and incubated for 13 days at 31°C. The plates were overlaid with neutral red agar, and after overnight incubation plaques were picked. The plaques were passaged twice on L-cell monolayers at 31°C. Second-passage virus titer and efficiency of plating were determined by plating on L-cell monolayers at 39°C and 31°C. Plates at 39°C were overlaid and counted on day 5; 31°C plates were overlaid and counted on day 13 postinfection. Wild-type and clone 101 controls were the same except that for single infection a multiplicity of infection of 20 was used. EOP = titer at 39°C/titer at 31°C. (A) EOP of wild-type control clones. (B) EOP of clone 101 control clones. (C) EOP of clone 101 – wild-type progeny clones.*

temperature and were titered after two passages at permissive temperature. The temperature phenotypes of the progeny clones and control clones are shown in Fig. 4.

The distribution of temperature phenotypes

clearly shows two populations among the progeny of the cross, one with a wild-type efficiency of plating (EOP) and the other with an EOP that is temperature sensitive. Genetic studies have shown that almost all of the progeny ts clones are identical to the group A ts mutant (201). Thus, virus clones with a ts$^+$ phenotype may in fact contain genes (and gene products) that are intrinsically temperature sensitive. The genotype is thus actually ts$^-$.

As animal virus mutants become more widely used for in vitro and in vivo studies, the genotype and phenotype will have to be carefully distinguished. Temperature sensitivity per se is a phenotypic property that can be generated by mutations in several sites on the genome. Reversion from temperature sensitivity can occur in the same gene or elsewhere. Data on the genotype must be available for proper interpretation of the role of the ts gene and its gene product (Table 5).

DISCUSSION AND PERSPECTIVES

Temperature-sensitive mutants have gained increasing significance in a variety of studies involving animal viruses and the cells (and hosts) they infect. They are not only important in basic studies on genetics and biochemistry, but may play a role in vivo in diseases and viral persistence. As such strains are isolated and identified under conditions where the investigator has not experimentally produced the ts lesion, but rather where the cell or host has been actively involved, it becomes imperative to analyze fully the viral *genotype*. It is important to know, for example, whether the viral mutant contains a single or multiple mutation(s) (both appearing as ts$^-$). It is equally important in analyzing putative "ts$^+$ revertants" to realize that ts genes may exist in suppressed forms (appearing as ts$^+$). The biological significance of this phenomenon is currently unexplored.

TABLE 5. *Distinction between phenotype and genotype*

Phenotype	Genotype	Examples
ts$^+$	+	Wild-type parent
	−	101 revertant
ts$^-$	−	ts mutants
	—	Backcross clone

LITERATURE CITED

1. **Barbanti-Brodano, G., S. Oyanagi, M. Katz, and H. Koprowski.** 1970. Presence of two different viral agents in brain cells of patients with subacute sclerosing panencephalitis. Proc. Soc. Exp. Biol. Med. **143:**230–236.

2. **Bergholz, C. M., M. P. Kiley, and F. E. Payne.** 1975. Isolation and characterization of temperature-sensitive mutants of measles virus. J. Virol. **16:**192–202.

3. **Breschkin, A. M., M. V. Haspel, and F. Rapp.** 1976. Neurovirulence and induction of hydrocephalus with parental, mutant, and revertant strains of measles virus. J. Virol. **18:**809–811.

4. **Carter, C., A. Schluederberg, and F. Black.** 1973. Viral RNA synthesis in measles virus infected cells. Virology **53:**379–383.

5. **Fields, B. N.** 1972. Genetic manipulation of reovirus—a model for modification of disease? N. Engl. J. Med. **287:**1026–1033.

6. **Gould, E.** 1974. Variants of measles virus. Med. Microbiol. Immunol. **160:**211–219.

7. **Hamilton, R., L. Barbosa, and M. Dubois.** 1973. Subacute sclerosing panencephalitis measles virus: a study of biological markers. J. Virol. **12:**632–642.

8. **Haspel, M. V., R. Duff, and F. Rapp.** 1975. Isolation and preliminary characterization of temperature-sensitive mutants of measles virus. J. Virol. **16:**1000–1007.

9. **Haspel, M. V., R. Duff, and F. Rapp.** 1975. Experimental measles encephalitis: a genetic analysis. Infect. Immun. **12:**785–790.

10. **Haspel, M. V., P. R. Knight, R. G. Duff, and F. Rapp.** 1973. Activation of a latent measles virus infection in hamster cells. J. Virol. **12:**690–695.

11. **Haspel, M. V., and F. Rapp.** 1974. Measles virus—an unwanted variant causing hydrocephalus. Science **187:**450–451.

12. **Horta-Barbosa, L., D. A. Fucillo, J. L. Sever, and W. Zeman.** 1969. SSPE: isolation of measles virus from a brain biopsy. Nature (London) **221:**974.

13. **Matsomoto, N.** 1966. Studies on the measles virus in tissue culture. I. Morphological changes and development of virus antigen examined by the fluorescent antibody technique. Bull. Yamaguchi Med. Sch. **13:**49–59.

14. **Nakai, M., and D. Imagawa.** 1969. Electron microscopy of measles virus replication. J. Virol. **3:**187–192.

15. **Norrby, E.** 1972. Intracellular accumulation of measles virus nucleocapsids and envelope antigens. Microbios **5:**31–40.

16. **Oyanagi, S., V. terMeulen, M. Katz, and H. Koprowski.** 1971. Comparison of subacute sclerosing panencephalitis and measles virus: an electron microscope study. J. Virol. **7:**176–187.

17. **Payne, F. E., J. V. Baublis, and H. H. Itabashi.** 1969. Isolation of measles virus from cell cultures of brain from a patient with subacute sclerosing panencephalitis. N. Engl. J. Med. **281:**585–589.

18. **Preble, O. T., and J. T. Youngner.** 1975. Temperature-sensitive viruses and the etiology of chronic and inapparent infections. J. Infect. Dis. **131:**467–473.

19. **Rapp, F., F. Gordon, and R. Baker.** 1960. Observations of measles virus infections of cultured human cells. I. A study of development and spread of virus antigen by means of immunofluorescence. J. Biophys. Biochem. Cytol. **7:**43–49.

20. **Yamazi, Y., F. L. Black, H. Honda, Y. Todome, M. Suganuma, M. Watari, H. Iwaguchi, and M. Nagashima.** 1975. Characterization of temperature-sensitive mutants of measles virus: temperature-shift experiments. Jpn. J. Med. Sci. Biol. **28:**223–229.

Mechanisms of Synthesis and Persistence of Virus-Specific DNA in Cells Infected by RNA Tumor Viruses

HAROLD E. VARMUS, PETER R. SHANK, HSING-JIEN KUNG, RAMAREDDY GUNTAKA,
OLIVER C. RICHARDS, AND J. MICHAEL BISHOP

Department of Microbiology, University of California Medical School, San Francisco, California 94143

INTRODUCTION

After infection of either permissive or non-permissive cells by RNA tumor viruses, viral genetic information appears to persist indefinitely in the form of virus-specific, double-stranded DNA integrated covalently into the host chromosome (3). In this report, we summarize our progress in deciphering the sequence of molecular events that culminates in the integration of viral DNA into the DNA of avian cells infected by avian sarcoma virus (ASV), and we offer our current view of the mechanisms involved.

METHODS

The experiments reported here utilized either Peking duck embryo fibroblasts or quail tumor cells (QT-6 cells, derived from a methyl-cholanthrene-induced fibrosarcoma in Japanese quail) as permissive hosts for infection by high-titer stocks of B77 strain of ASV; these stocks also contain high titers of transformation-defective deletion mutants of ASV. Because the amount of viral DNA synthesized in infected cells is small (generally from 1 to 20 copies per cell), analyses require the high sensitivity provided by annealing of labeled virus-specific reagents to unlabeled viral DNA present in cell extracts; labeled viral RNA [(+) strand] is employed to test for (−) strand DNA, and labeled DNA complementary to the viral genome [cDNA, (−) strand], synthesized in vitro from a template of viral RNA, is used to test for (+) strand DNA. Hybridization is assessed by resistance of the labeled reagents to digestion by single-strand-specific nucleases.

CYTOPLASMIC SYNTHESIS OF VIRAL DNA

During the first 5 to 8 h after infection of avian cells by ASV, viral DNA is synthesized exclusively in the cytoplasm, as demonstrated by analysis of fractionated cells or by infection of enucleated cells (4). Studies with conditional mutants of ASV have documented that viral DNA synthesis is catalyzed by the RNA-directed DNA polymerase associated with virus particles (8). The principal form of viral DNA in the cytoplasm is a linear duplex with (−) strands the length of a subunit of the viral genome (3×10^6 daltons) and segmented (+) strands of 0.1×10^6 to 1.0×10^6 daltons; shorter duplexes are also observed and may be either precursors to the full-length forms or abortive products. Viral DNA can be purified from the cytoplasm of infected cells by labeling both strands with 5-bromodeoxyuridine (BUdR) and selecting DNA that bands appropriately in cesium chloride density gradients and in rate zonal gradients of sucrose. When observed in an electron microscope, these molecules appear to be linear duplexes of about 5×10^6 to 6×10^6 daltons; however, if the spreading is performed in the presence of 0.5 M salt, a significant portion of the molecules form circles, suggesting that the linear DNA contains complementary tails ("sticky ends") capable of converting linear duplexes into noncovalently closed circles.

FORM I DNA IN THE NUCLEUS

After synthesis in the cytoplasm, viral DNA appears in the nucleus, where a portion (up to 50%) is converted to covalently closed circular (form I) duplexes (1, 2). The claim that the cytoplasmic DNA is a precursor to form I DNA is supported by experiments in which the cytoplasmic linear forms were labeled with BUdR and then converted into nuclear form I DNA during a "chase" with thymidine. Presumably, the conversion is facilitated by the presence of "sticky ends" on the linear duplexes, as noted above. A variety of physicochemical procedures have been employed to purify form I DNA from the nuclei of infected QT-6 cells (2). When the size of form I DNA was analyzed by electron microscopy or by electrophoresis in agarose gels, three size classes of circular viral DNA were observed: DNA of about 6.6×10^6 daltons, presumed to be synthesized from a subunit of the ASV genome; DNA of about 5.6×10^6 daltons, presumed to be synthesized from a subunit of the genome of transformation-defective deletion mutants known to be present in the infecting stocks; and DNA of about 2×10^6 to 4×10^6 daltons, presumed to represent highly defective molecules generated by errors during DNA synthesis. As expected, these small circles are not infectious under conditions that allow successful transfection by the two larger species. The genetic composition of the small circles, however, is not known, and it is not known whether they can replicate independently or integrate into the host cell genome.

STEPS IN SYNTHESIS OF VIRAL DNA

Based upon these observations and upon studies of the behavior of viral DNA polymerase in vitro in this laboratory and others, it is possible to propose five sequential steps in the synthesis of viral DNA: (i) initiation of (−) strand synthesis, using the tRNA^{trp} that is bound to the RNA genome near the 5′ end as primer and viral genome as template; (ii) a "transcriptional leap," promoted by an unknown mechanism, which allows transcription to proceed beyond the 5′ end, at which it is presumably stopped, to the 3′ end of the same or a different subunit; (iii) initiation of (+) strand synthesis, using viral RNA partially digested by RNase H activity as primer and (−) strand DNA as template; (iv) completion of the DNA strands, presumably by continuous synthesis of the (−) strand and multiple initiations of the segmented (+) strands; and (v) circularization of the linear duplex, by virtue of "sticky ends," and ligation of all ends to form a covalently closed circle of duplex DNA (form I). All of these steps, save the ligation, are likely to occur in the cytoplasm of infected cells and may require no other enzymes than the viral DNA polymerase with its associated RNase H activity. There are, of course, several unexplained events: the mechanism of the "transcriptional leap" is still obscure; the "blocked" (inverted) guanidylate residue at the 5′ terminus and the polyadenylate sequence at the 3′ end of the genome are probably not transcribed to DNA, but the "avoidance mechanism" is not known; preservation of the primer binding site in the viral genome presents theoretical difficulties not yet resolved; the cellular enzyme presumably responsible for ligation has not yet been identified.

INTEGRATION OF VIRAL DNA

Circumstantial evidence (1), intuition, and the analogy with other animal and bacterial viruses suggest that the form I viral DNA is the form that integrates into the host chromosome. Covalent integration has been documented with several techniques (5, 7), and it is logical to assume that, at least in permissive cells, the integrated provirus is colinear with the RNA genome. However, the number and nature of sites in the host genome at which integration may occur are unknown, as is the mechanism of integration.

NATURE OF UNINTEGRATED DNA

Generally, we find two to eight copies of viral DNA integrated into the genome of permissive (avian) cells (3), but not all of the viral DNA synthesized early after infection is integrated (5). The failure to integrate could be due to limitation of integration sites or to some defect in the synthesized DNA. In addition to this early species of unintegrated DNA, however, we have observed recently synthesized, unintegrated viral DNA in chronically infected cells. In ASV-infected duck embryo fibroblasts, viral DNA is synthesized in the cytoplasm several weeks after the initial infection (6). The structure of the DNA [linear duplexes of subunit-length (−) strand and segmented (+) strands] and the mode of incorporation of density label into the DNA suggest that it is made by viral reverse transcriptase, perhaps in nascent virus particles in the cytoplasm of these virus-producing cells. In ASV-infected QT-6 cells, on the other hand, we find form I viral DNA persisting in the nucleus in an unintegrated state up to 600 h after infection (2). The mode of persistence of unintegrated viral DNA in this case is not known, and it is possible that the form I DNA replicates autonomously. Although the forms and location of free viral DNA may differ, it is apparent that all cells chronically infected with RNA tumor viruses are liable to contain unintegrated as well as integrated DNA. (For example, we have recently observed unintegrated viral DNA in rat hepatoma cells chronically infected with murine mammary tumor virus [G. M. Ringold, K. R. Yamamoto, P. R. Shank, and H. E. Varmus, Cell, in press].) There is, however, as yet no evidence that unintegrated DNA serves as template for synthesis of viral RNA or that it serves any other function in the virus life cycle.

ACKNOWLEDGMENTS

The work was supported by grants from the American Cancer Society and the National Cancer Institute. H.E.V. is a recipient of a Career Development Award from the U.S. Public Health Service.

LITERATURE CITED

1. **Guntaka, R. V., B. Mahy, J. M. Bishop, and H. E. Varmus.** 1975. Ethidium bromide inhibits the appearance of closed circular viral DNA and integration of virus-specific DNA in duck cells infected by avian sarcoma virus. Nature (London) **253:**507–511.

2. **Guntaka, R. V., O. C. Richards, P. R. Shank, H. J. Kung, N. Davidson, E. Fritsch, J. M. Bishop, and H. E. Varmus.** 1976. Covalently closed circular DNA of avian sarcoma virus: purification from nuclei of infected quail tumor cells and measurement by electron microscopy and gel electrophoresis. J. Mol. Biol. **106:**337–357.

3. **Varmus, H. E., R. V. Guntaka, C. T. Deng, and J. M. Bishop.** 1975. Synthesis, structure, and function of avian sarcoma virus-specific DNA in permissive and non-permissive cells. Cold Spring Harbor Symp. Quant. Biol. **39:**987–996.

4. **Varmus, H. E., R. V. Guntaka, W. Fan, S. Heasley, and J. M. Bishop.** 1974. Synthesis of viral DNA in the cytoplasm of duck embryo fibroblasts and in enucleated cells after infection by avian sarcoma virus. Proc. Natl. Acad. Sci. U.S.A. **71:**3874–3878.

5. **Varmus, H. E., S. Heasley, J. Linn, and K. Wheeler.** 1976. Use of alkaline sucrose gradients in a zonal rotor to detect integrated and unintegrated avian sarcoma virus-specific DNA in cells. J. Virol. **18:**574–585.

6. **Varmus, H. E., and P. R. Shank.** 1976. Unintegrated viral DNA is synthesized in the cytoplasm of avian sarcoma virus-transformed duck cells by viral DNA polymerase. J. Virol. **18:**567–573.

7. **Varmus, H. E., P. K. Vogt, and J. M. Bishop.** 1973. Integration of Rous sarcoma virus specific DNA following infection of permissive and nonpermissive hosts. Proc. Natl. Acad. Sci. U.S.A. **70:**3067–3071.

8. **Verma, I. M., H. E. Varmus, and E. Hunter.** 1976. Characterization of "early" temperature-sensitive mutants of avian sarcoma viruses: biological properties, thermolability of reverse transcriptase *in vitro*, and synthesis of viral DNA in infected cells. Virology **74:**16–29.

Transfection with DNA Copies of RNA Tumor Viruses

MIROSLAV HILL

Department of Cellular and Molecular Biology and Equipe de Recherche no. 148 du C.N.R.S.,
Institute of Cancerology and Immunogenetics, Villejuif, France

For a virus to form a persistent and stable relationship with its host cell, the viral information must both remain intact and be transmitted to the daughter cells during cell replication. Hence, it is not surprising to find that many viruses capable of maintaining a chronic or latent infection in a host, by a mechanism other than continued virus production and reinfection, have both a DNA intermediate in their life cycle and often a mechanism of integrating this DNA into the host cell chromosome. To detect such viral DNA sequences, there are essentially two techniques: hybridization and transfection. The former only detects sequences complementary to a single-stranded nucleic acid probe and has a habit of giving contradictory or ambiguous results. Transfection, because it tests for the biological function of such sequences, can give almost definitive evidence that a cell contains a complete DNA copy of the viral genome. In this paper the transfection technique is discussed with relation to the type C tumor viruses.

SYNTHESIS OF ROUS SARCOMA VIRUS DNA

Disrupted virions of RNA tumor viruses catalyze an endogenous RNA-directed DNA synthesis (1, 31). The DNA product was shown to be composed mostly (though not exclusively; 20, 24) of short polynucleotide chains (for references, see 30) and was uninfectious in transfection assays when either whole nucleic acids or 60 to 70S RNA-DNA hybrids recovered from endogenous enzymatic reaction in vitro were used (R. Mariage, unpublished data). A reaction mixture composed of purified reverse transcriptase (Boehringer) and the viral RNA, as well as the endogenous reaction products generated in the presence of actinomycin D, either alone or together with high concentrations of all four deoxynucleoside triphosphates, in order to get more representative (6) and more continuous (24) DNA copies of the viral RNA, were shown to be uninfectious. Similarly, no biological activity of the in vitro-synthesized structures could be detected when either the crude reaction product or 60 to 70S

RNA-DNA hybrid was assayed in both helper virus-infected and uninfected chicken cells. These results eliminated the possibility that partial RNA → DNA transcripts synthesized in vitro can infect chicken cells and suggest that no full-size (infectious) viral DNA is synthesized.

Efforts were made to prepare Rous sarcoma virus (RSV) DNA in vivo. In preliminary experiments infectious material was isolated from chicken cells 6 h after infection at high multiplicity (about 10 focus-forming units per cell) of the virus. However, the number of infectious units in these preparations was rather low, about 1 per 10 to 20 million infected cells. In experiments using Hirt's fractionation (19), the infectious material was found at the same time interval in both the supernatant fluid and the pellet. This seems to indicate that the full-length (i.e., infectious) DNA copies of RSV RNA are available, if at all, only for a very short time before being integrated or destroyed by cellular nucleases. There are hints that integration takes place during cellular DNA synthesis, for infectious DNA has been found in the Hirt's supernatant fluid, but not in the pellet, when the cells were subjected to gamma rays prior to RSV infection (R. Mariage, N. Stedman, and M. Marx, unpublished data).

Unlike chicken cells, mouse cells infected with a murine leukemia virus can be shown to contain a fairly high amount of infectious unintegrated viral DNA. In the presence of ethidium bromide, this DNA bands at the position of both supercoiled circular and relaxed circular or linear molecules (28). According to the contour length, the DNA circles had a molecular weight of about 5.5×10^6, i.e., the size of approximately one RNA subunit of the virion RNA (7).

INFECTIOUS DNA ENTIRELY SPECIFIES THE PROGENY VIRUS

In the case of RSV, the subgroup specificity, the temperature sensitivity of the transforming function, and the reverse transcriptase of the parent virus are all recovered in the DNA progeny following transfection (for references, see 12). This provides evidence that the infectious DNA molecules code for the *env*, *sarc*, and *pol* genes of the virus, and that recombination with cellular genes such as endogenous virogenes is not required. Concerning the fourth viral gene termed *gag* (2), only circumstantial evidence is available. For instance, it has been shown that the DNA from RSV-transformed chicken cells is able to give rise to RSV in duck, pheasant (3), and turkey (N. Stedman, unpublished data) cells, i.e., in cells lacking RSV-specific nucelotide sequences which could be suspected to provide *gag* genetic material of the recovered virus. The strongest evidence that the transfecting DNA codes for all functions of the progeny virus is provided by the DNA of mammalian RNA tumor viruses. These transfections were also carried out in cells lacking nucleotide sequences specific for the recovered virus, e.g., feline endogenous RD114 virus in human and dog cells (23), feline leukemia and gibbon ape leukemia viruses in human cells (23), visna virus in sheep choroid plexus cells (10), and HL23V virus (for isolation of this virus from cultured human leukemic cells, see 5) in bat lung cells (J. Hillova, unpublished data).

INTEGRATED STATE OF THE VIRAL DNA IN THE CELLULAR GENOME

Further experiments have been concerned with the structure, size, and intracellular location of the infectious DNA in virus-infected and virus-transformed cells. At present we know that the DNA in question is double stranded because of its behavior on hydroxylapatite chromatography (13) and its resistance to S1 single-strand-specific nuclease (17; G. Goubin, Doctorate Thesis, Université Pierre et Marie Curie, Paris, 1976). Transfections after thermal (G. Goubin, unpublished data) or alkali (3, 15) denaturation, and sedimentation in alkaline glycerol gradients (13, 16) or banding in alkaline CsCl (13), clearly show that single (S1 susceptible [10, 17; Goubin, Doctorate Thesis, 1976]) strands of this DNA are also able to initiate infections in permissive cells. It seems, however, that under more stringent denaturation conditions the biological activity of the DNA is lost, for instance, when the DNA is treated with alkali at 37°C (10, 15) or heated at 100°C for 10 min (10) but not for 3 min (G. Goubin, unpublished data).

Evidence that in infected cells the viral DNA is covalently bound to the host cell chromosome has been obtained by means of Hirt's (19)

fractionation of the cellular DNA (22, 23) and, more convincingly, both by co-sedimentation of viral DNA with the chromosomal DNA in alkaline glycerol gradients (16) and by the ability of the viral DNA to reassociate into the network structure (10). The possibility that some unintegrated DNA does occur late after infection has not yet been properly eliminated (12).

The size of infectious DNA molecules has also been determined by shearing the DNA samples (3, 10, 13) with subsequent fractionation in sucrose gradients (Goubin, Doctorate Thesis, 1976). Infectivity is lost at the size below 6×10^6 daltons. Transfection kinetics so far available have been interpreted to reveal either a single-hit mechanism for transfections with unintegrated murine leukemia virus DNA (28) and integrated RSV DNA (3), or, in contrast, a double-hit mechanism with integrated visna virus DNA (10). There is general agreement, however, over the transfection efficiency, which is estimated to be betweeen 10^{-5} and 10^{-6}, i.e., amounting to one transfection event per 10^5 to 10^6 viral DNA copies administered (3, 10, 12, 13, 23). This estimate favors the hypothesis of single-hit transfections. Double-hit transfections would require two independent DNA pieces to be expressed, each with a probability as high as 10^{-3}, i.e., much higher than that operating, for instance, in infections with simian virus 40 DNA (12).

ISOLATION OF VIRAL DNA

Molecular biologists hope to have available viral DNA of RNA tumor viruses in large enough quantities to be able to undertake physical mapping of the DNA form of the viral genome. There are two approaches which promise to make this possible in the near future. On the one hand, unintegrated DNA can be isolated from cells 9 h after infection with a murine leukemia virus. Digestion with *Eco*RI restriction endonuclease, which lacks cleavage sites in viral but not cellular (including mitochondrial) DNA, can be used to concentrate the supercoiled viral DNA molecules, which are then separated from the rest of the digest by banding in an ethidium bromide-CsCl gradient (7).

In another approach, the DNA is extracted from cells several cell passages after infection with the virus and is digested with a restriction enzyme(s) which specifically cleaves cellular but not viral DNA. The fragments that contain integrated viral DNA with adjacent cellular sequences can then be subjected to electrophoretic migration in agarose gels and identified by hybridization techniques. The experiments carried out so far have screened for suitable enzymes. Table 1 shows that out of eight restriction endonucleases tested only one, *Ava* I, was found to be unable to abolish infectivity of the DNA of RSV-transformed cells. Electrophoretic migration of the digest demonstrated cleavage of the cellular DNA, in which the fragments occurring with maximal abundance had a molecular weight larger than 20×10^6 (21). The size of the fragment(s) containing the viral DNA has not yet been determined. Probably, however, further restriction endonucleases must be found that together with *Ava* I will generate fragments approaching the size of the full-length viral genome.

TRANSFORMATION OF CHICKEN CELLS WITH INCOMPLETE RSV DNA

Recently, we have provided strong evidence that an incomplete RSV DNA can transform cells (12). In one transfection assay, we observed that the DNA from Prague strain RSV-transformed cells gave rise to a focus of transformed chicken cells which, surprisingly, did not release sarcoma virus. That this transformation was due to the expression of RSV DNA was suggested by the fact that an infectious sarcoma virus pseudotype was rescued upon superinfection of these cells with a helper virus. We have concluded that in this particular case the RSV DNA lacked a portion of the viral genome required for the synthesis of infectious virions. Accordingly, the rescued virus (designated as *Vi*718PR) belongs to the category of nonconditional replication-defective mutants.

This experiment also suggests that defective viral DNAs are capable of forming a stable relationship with the recipient cell and of being conserved during cell replication.

SEARCH FOR THE INFECTIOUS DNA IN UNINFECTED CELLS

Uninfected cells of different animal species contain virus-specific DNA and are able either spontaneously or upon induction to synthesize type C viral particles (for references, see 8, 12, 18). Occurrence of infectious virions in these cells provides evidence that the cell possesses a complete viral genome. This is supported by transfection assays which have shown that both murine BALB/c cells and cat CCC cells harbor infectious DNA which in heterologous recipients gives rise to murine and feline endogenous viruses, respectively (25). In contrast, no infectious DNA could be detected in chicken cells, though such a DNA was readily found if the same cells were experimentally infected with the endogenous chick virus (4). To explain

TABLE 1. *Effect of different restriction endonucleases on the infectivity of RSV DNA*[a]

Restriction endonuclease[b]	No. of infected/ total no. of DNA-treated cultures[c]	Infectivity of RSV DNA
None	14/15	Conserved
*Hin*dII	0/3	Lost
*Hin*dIII	0/3	Lost
Hae III	0/3	Lost
Hpa I	0/3	Lost
Hpa II	0/3	Lost
*Eco*RI	0/3	Lost
Ava I	12/21	Conserved
Ava II	0/3	Lost

[a] DNA was extracted from RSV-transformed chicken cells and digested with different restriction endonucleases as described (21). The transfection assay of the digest in chicken cells was carried out using either the DEAE-dextran (14) or the calcium phosphate (17) technique. See reference 21 for further details.

[b] For the nomenclature of bacterial restriction endonucleases see reference 27. *Ava* I and *Ava* II were isolated from *Anabaena variabilis* (K. Murray et al., in preparation).

[c] Each culture received 5 μg of undigested or digested DNA.

this, Cooper and Temin (4) suggested that a "*cis*-acting control element" interferes with the expression of the endogenous provirus, both in cells from which the DNA is extracted and in those which upon transfection receive this DNA. If this is true, shearing (or cleaving with a suitable restriction enzyme) could break the linkage between the hypothetical element and the provirus and render the DNA infectious. This remains to be shown.

Alternatively, the endogenous provirus in cells containing no infectious DNA may be composed of more than one genetic element. Upon induction, type C particles encapsidating a complete set of these elements (see reference 9 for a possible mechanism) would be able to generate an infectious provirus by using the mechanism which supposedly operates in the formation of recombinant viruses from heterozygotes (11, 32). According to this possibility, digestion of the cellular DNA with restriction endonucleases lacking cleavage sites in viral DNA will yield separate portions instead of full-sized proviruses. At least one replication cycle of the virus will be required in order to obtain infectious viral DNA from an uninfectious provirus.

In this context, it is worth mentioning the case of human leukemic cells. The occurrence of intracellular and extracellular particles in these cells has been reported from several laboratories (for references, see 8); however, in only one case (5, 29) were these particles found to be infectious. Recently, we have shown (Fig. 1) that in this infection the secondary cells harbored infectious DNA (J. Hillova, unpublished data). One wonders whether such infectious DNA resides in freshly withdrawn leukemic cells or, alternatively, whether it is formed after the assemblage of viral genetic elements during the first cycle of viral infection.

INFECTIOUS DNA OF RNA VIRUSES

Recent experimental work, which has not yet been confirmed, on transfections carried out with the DNA of animal cells infected with RNA viruses such as respiratory syncytial virus (26) or tick-borne encephalitis virus (33) has shown, unexpectedly, that DNA copies of viral RNA are synthesized even when the virus lacks reverse transcriptase. Simpson and Iinuma (26) claimed that a DNA polymerase was found in clones of the respiratory syncytial virus originating from the DNA transfections. These results suggest that recombination between an RNA virus and the gene(s) of a type C virus

endogenously carried in host cells may be a pathway for establishment of persistent infections. The formation of such recombinants might explain why infectious DNA in chronically infected cell cultures could be found in such abundance.

ACKNOWLEDGMENTS

I am grateful to my colleagues G. Goubin, J. Hillova, R. Mariage, M. Marx, and N. Stedman, who forwarded unpublished data of their work carried out in this laboratory. Uninfected and HL23V-infected bat lung 88 cells were kindly provided by R. C. Gallo. Electron microscopy of HL23V DNA-infected bat cells performed by S. Fakan, Lausanne, is acknowledged with pleasure.

The unpublished work cited is supported by C.N.R.S. contract no. 2120.

LITERATURE CITED

1. **Baltimore, D.** 1970. RNA-dependent DNA polymerase in virions of RNA tumour viruses. Nature (London) **226:**1209–1211.
2. **Baltimore, D.** 1974. Tumor viruses: 1974. Cold Spring Harbor Symp. Quant. Biol. **39:**1187–1200.
3. **Cooper, G. M., and H. M. Temin.** 1974. Infectious Rous sarcoma virus and reticuloendotheliosis virus DNAs. J. Virol. **14:**1132–1141.
4. **Cooper, G. M., and H. M. Temin.** 1976. Lack of

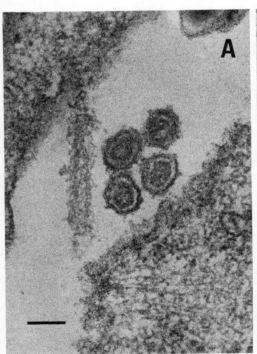 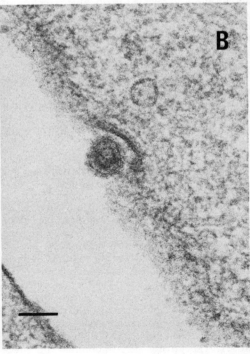

FIG. 1. *Type C particles in bat lung 88 cells after HL23V virus infection (A) and transfection (B). The transfection assay in B was carried out with DNA extracted from the HL23V-infected bat cells shown in A. Both A and B cultures were positive for reverse transcriptase in the culture medium. Electron microscopy was performed by S. Fakan. Bar represents 0.1 μm.*

infectivity of the endogenous avian leukosis virus-related genes in the DNA of uninfected chicken cells. J. Virol. **17**:422–430.

5. **Gallagher, R. E., and R. C. Gallo.** 1975. Type C RNA tumor virus isolated from cultured human acute myelogenous leukemia cells. Science **187**:350–353.

6. **Garapin, A. C., H. E. Varmus, A. J. Faras, W. E. Lewinson, and J. M. Bishop.** 1973. RNA-directed DNA synthesis by virions of Rous sarcoma virus: further characterization of the templates and the extent of their transcription. Virology **52**:264–274.

7. **Gianni, A. M., J. R. Hutton, D. Smotkin, and R. A. Weinberg.** 1976. Proviral DNA of Moloney leukemia virus: purification and visualization. Science **191**: 569–571.

8. **Gillespie, D., W. C. Saxinger, and R. C. Gallo.** 1975. Information transfer in cells infected by RNA tumor viruses and extension to human neoplasia. Prog. Nucleic Acid Res. Mol. Biol. **15**:1–108.

9. **Goldberg, R. J., R. Levin, W. P. Parks, and E. M. Scolnick.** 1976. Quantitative analysis of the rescue of RNA sequences by mammalian type C viruses. J. Virol. **17**:43–50.

10. **Haase, A. T., B. L. Traynor, P. E. Ventura, and D. W. Alling.** 1976. Infectivity of visna virus DNA. Virology **70**:65–79.

11. **Hayward, W. S., and H. Hanafusa.** 1975. Recombination between endogenous and exogenous RNA tumor virus genes as analyzed by nucleic acid hybridization. J. Virol. **15**:1367–1377.

12. **Hill, M., and J. Hillova.** 1976. Genetic transformation of animal cells with viral DNA of RNA tumor viruses. Adv. Cancer Res. **23**:237–297.

13. **Hill, M., J. Hillova, D. Dantchev, R. Mariage, and G. Goubin.** 1974. Infectious viral DNA in Rous sarcoma virus-transformed nonproducer and producer animal cells. Cold Spring Harbor Symp. Quant. Biol. **39**:1015–1025.

14. **Hillova, J., D. Dantchev, R. Mariage, M.-P. Plichon, and M. Hill.** 1974. Sarcoma and transformation-defective viruses produced with infectious DNA(s) from Rous sarcoma virus (RSV)-transformed chicken cells. Virology **62**:197–208.

15. **Hillova, J., G. Goubin, and M. Hill.** 1972. Transfection des fibroblastes de Poule par l'acide désoxyribonucléique dénaturé de cellules transformées de Rous. C. R. Acad. Sci. **274**:1970–1973.

16. **Hillova, J., G. Goubin, D. Coulaud, and M. Hill.** 1974. Nuclear localization and covalent linkage of infective virus DNA to chromosomal DNA of nonproducer Rous sarcoma cells. J. Gen. Virol. **23**:237–245.

17. **Hillova, J., M. Hill, G. Goubin, and D. Dantchev.** 1975. Infectivity of Rous sarcoma cell DNA: comparison of two techniques of transfection assay. Intervirology **5**:367–374.

18. **Hirsch, M. S., and P. H. Black.** 1974. Activation of mammalian leukemia viruses. Adv. Virus Res. **19**: 265–313.

19. **Hirt, B.** 1967. Selective extraction of polyoma DNA from infected mouse cell cultures. J. Mol. Biol. **26**:365–369.

20. **Junghans, R. P., P. H. Duesberg, and C. A. Knight.** 1975. In vitro synthesis of full-length DNA transcripts of Rous sarcoma virus RNA by viral DNA polymerase. Proc. Natl. Acad. Sci. U.S.A. **72**:4895–4899.

21. **Kopecka, H., J. Hillova, and M. Hill.** 1976. Effect of restriction endonucleases on infectivity of Rous sarcoma virus DNA. Nature (London) **262**:72–74.

22. **Montagnier, L., and P. Vigier.** 1972. Un intermédiaire ADN infectieux et transformant du virus du sarcome de Rous dans les cellules de Poule transformées par ce virus. C. R. Acad. Sci. **274**:1977–1980.

23. **Nicolson, M. O., F. Hariri, H. M. Krempin, R. M. McAllister, and R. V. Gilden.** 1976. Infectious proviral DNA in human cells infected with transformation-defective type C viruses. Virology **70**:301–312.

24. **Rothenberg, E., and D. Baltimore.** 1976. Synthesis of long, representative DNA copies of the murine RNA tumor virus genome. J. Virol. **17**:168–174.

25. **Scolnick, E. M., and S. J. Bumgarner.** 1975. Isolation of infectious xenotropic mouse type C virus by transfection of a heterologous cell with DNA from a transformed mouse cell. J. Virol. **15**:1293–1296.

26. **Simpson, R. W., and M. Iinuma.** 1975. Recovery of infectious proviral DNA from mammalian cells infected with respiratory syncytial virus. Proc. Natl. Acad. Sci. U.S.A. **72**:3230–3234.

27. **Smith, H. O., and D. Nathans.** 1973. A suggested nomenclature for bacterial host modification and restriction systems and their enzymes. J. Mol. Biol. **81**:419–423.

28. **Smotkin, D., A. M. Gianni, S. Rozenblatt, and R. A. Weinberg.** 1975. Infectious viral DNA of murine leukemia virus. Proc. Natl. Acad. Sci. U.S.A. **72**: 4910–4913.

29. **Teich, N. M., R. A. Weiss, S. Z. Salahuddin, R. E. Gallagher, D. H. Gillespie, and R. C. Gallo.** 1975. Infective transmission and characterisation of a C-type virus released by cultured human leukaemia cells. Nature (London) **256**:551–555.

30. **Temin, H. M., and D. Baltimore.** 1972. RNA-directed DNA synthesis and RNA tumor viruses. Adv. Virus Res. **17**:129–186.

31. **Temin, H. M., and S. Mizutani.** 1970. RNA-dependent DNA polymerase in virions of Rous sarcoma virus. Nature (London) **226**:1211–1213.

32. **Weiss, R. A., W. S. Mason, and P. K. Vogt.** 1973. Genetic recombinants and heterozygotes derived from endogenous and exogenous avian RNA tumor viruses. Virology **52**:535–552.

33. **Zhdanov, V. M.** 1975. Integration of viral genomes. Nature (London) **256**:471–473.

Role of DNA Intermediates in Persistent Infections Caused by RNA Viruses

A. T. HAASE, L. STOWRING, P. VENTURA, B. TRAYNOR, K. JOHNSON, P. SWOVELAND,
M. SMITH, M. BRITTEN-DARNALL, A. FARAS, AND O. NARAYAN

*Veterans Administration Hospital, San Francisco, California 94121; Department of Microbiology,
University of Minnesota, Minneapolis, Minnesota 55455; and Departments of Neurology and
Animal Medicine, Johns Hopkins University, Baltimore, Maryland 21218*

INTRODUCTION

The concerted action of interferon, cellular and humoral immunity, and the reticuloendothelial system generally terminates viral infection. Thus, it is axiomatic that persistent infections must reflect a virus-host interaction that allows a virus to elude these defensive measures (3, 12). In many persistent infections this is a consequence of inaccessibility; some aspect of virus replication in vivo results in a prolonged residence of virus inside the host cell where the usual clearance mechanisms are inoperative. Proviruses represent one of the stable and the most subtle of the intracellular modes of existence for a virus, and provide an attractive explanation for viral persistence. Formation of a DNA intermediate conserves viral genetic information; if genetic expression is restricted, the infected cell escapes detection by immune surveillance. This is a restatement of the conditions of lysogeny, save for the scale; here, lysogeny refers to an infected animal rather than the bacterial cell (7).

The discovery of reverse transcription provided a plausible mechanism for the formation of DNA intermediates and a logical basis to suggest that proviruses might play a role in persistent infections caused by RNA C-type viruses (18). In this paper, we summarize evidence that lysogeny may be involved in the persistent infection caused by one RNA C-type virus, visna, and we report results that argue against DNA intermediates as a universal phenomenon in cells chronically infected with riboviruses that lack a DNA polymerase system.

VISNA

Description of Infection

Visna is an inflammatory demyelinating disease of the central nervous system of sheep, and a prototype of slow and persistent infections caused by viruses (7). The major events in infection under controlled experimental conditions are depicted in Fig. 1. Virus introduced intracranially replicates in sheep choroid plexus (SCP) and ependymal cells lining the lateral ventricles, and there provokes an inflammatory response. Subsequent viremia leads to infection of secondary sites, principally lung and organs of the reticuloendothelial system, and an immune response, responsible for a decrease in extracellular virus. However, neutralizing antibody and the host inflammatory response generally fail to eliminate infection, and low titers of virus persist in numerous tissue sites for years. In the pulmonary and neurological systems inflammatory foci develop, and associated tissue destruction leads to dysfunction and death of the animal (7).

Visna Virus

The causative agent of visna resembles RNA C-type viruses in structure and in replication (7). Common features include morphology, morphogenesis, a major structural polypeptide of 30,000 molecular weight that co-migrates in gel electrophoresis with the major structural component and group-specific antigen of RNA tumor viruses, and a segmented single-stranded RNA genome, comprised of subunits of about 3×10^6 molecular weight. The distinctive initial event in replication, formation of a DNA intermediate by reverse transcription, is also similar. In permissive cells a complete transfer of genetic information from RNA to DNA takes place during the viral eclipse period, and some of the viral DNA is covalently integrated into host DNA (10, 11, 19).

Visna virus can be distinguished from other RNA C-type agents by its antigenic makeup, by its lytic interaction with cells in vitro, where it causes cell degeneration and formation of multinucleated cells, and by its pattern of DNA synthesis in vitro (B. Traynor and A. Haase, in preparation). Visna virus is representative of

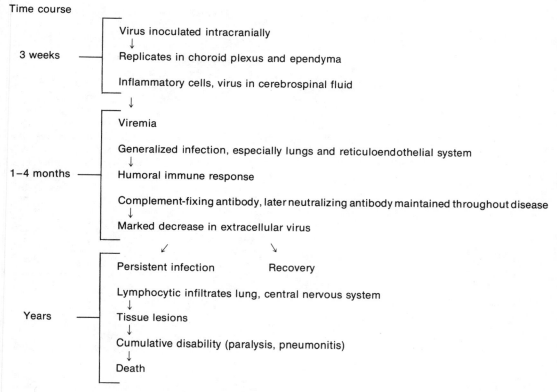

FIG. 1. *Major events in visna virus infection.*

exogenous RNA C-type viruses; proviral DNA is added to the genetic complement of a cell that previously lacked nucleotide sequences homologous to the virus. Net synthesis of visna DNA takes place during the life cycle to reach levels of about 200 copies/cell; synthesis proceeds independent of cell DNA synthesis, and most, if not all, of the viral DNA is found at all times in the nucleus of the host cell. The autonomous replication of visna DNA, and the occurrence of both extrachromosomal and integrated forms of viral DNA, are analogous to episomes in bacterial cells and to Epstein-Barr virus DNA in eukaryotic cells (1, 2, 17).

EXPERIMENTAL TEST OF THE LYSOGENY HYPOTHESIS IN VIVO

Predictions and Overview of Strategy and Methods

In permissively infected tissue culture cells, the later orderly sequence of provirus activation, transcription of viral RNA for translation and for encapsidation, and assembly appear, to date, to take place in much the same way in the life cycle of visna virus as for any other RNA C-type

virus. Clearly, if lysogeny is the explanation for persistence of visna virus in the infected animal, a different temperate relationship of virus and host cell must prevail; i.e., events that follow provirus formation in the viral life cycle must be blocked in vivo. Phrased in this way, the lysogeny argument makes two explicit predictions: (i) in an infected animal, cells should harbor viral DNA, but (ii) few cells if any should synthesize viral proteins or progeny. Examination of these predictions in vivo requires appropriate methodology for identification and quantitation of cells in infected tissues that contain viral DNA and for determining the proportion of such cells that also have synthesized viral gene products. The experimental strategy we have employed is to assay viral DNA in tissues by in situ hybridization (6, 9); the proportion of cells in tissue sections that also contain the major virion structural polypeptide can then be determined by immunofluorescence.

Animal Model

Our studies were conducted in an experimental system congruent in many respects with natural infections and with the postulated restriction

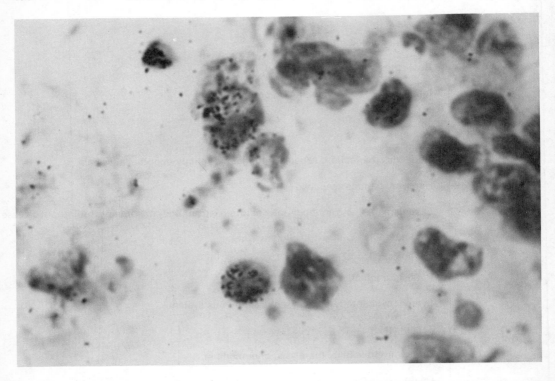

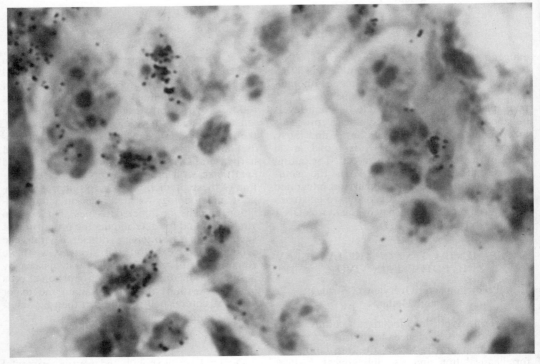

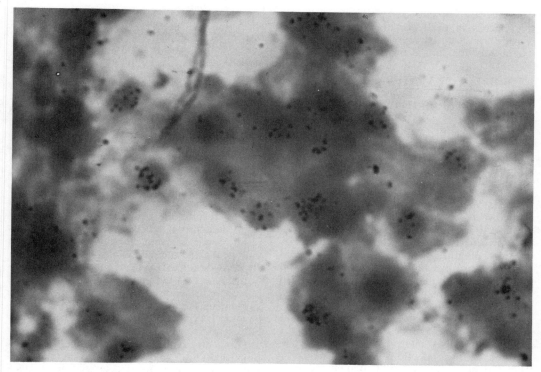

FIG. 2. *Demonstration of visna DNA in infected tissues by in situ hybridization. Sections of SCP were cut from frozen infected tissues, fixed, and treated with RNase and HCl to remove RNA and proteins. The DNA was denatured and annealed to ³H-labeled virus-specific probe, containing sequences complementary to virion DNA. Unreacted probe was subsequently removed by washing and digestion with S1 single-strand-specific nuclease. After radioautographic exposures of 14 weeks, the slides were developed and stained (6, 9).*

in completion of the viral life cycle in vivo. Visna virus causes a persistent infection in American lambs in which little, if any, virus can be recovered directly from tissues and in which viral particles are not observed in tissues (13). Explant cultures, however, nearly uniformly produce virus; cloning experiments indicate that about 15% of the cells can be induced to synthesize virus in vitro (O. Narayan et al., in preparation). These observations are in accord with the notion that viral replication is blocked at some step in the infected animal and that this constraint is relieved under conditions of in vitro cultivation.

In Situ Hybridization, Immunofluorescence

To determine the step at which replication is inhibited, we assayed infected SCP tissues for viral DNA and proteins. SCP was chosen for study since it reflects the in vivo restriction, is the most frequent site for viral isolation, and

is sufficiently small to be examined at the level of the individual cell in multiple-tissue sections.

Viral DNA was readily detected in radioautographs (Fig. 2) of infected tissues that had been hybridized to a ³H-labeled virus-specific probe (9). Cells were observed that had a large number of silver grains over their nuclei. These cells were found in foci; in other areas cells had no more than background levels of 1 to 2 grains/ nucleus. Collectively, the cells containing viral DNA comprised an average of 18% of the cells in the tissue section, in good agreement with the number expected to carry the viral genome from cloning experiments.

By contrast, only rare cells in these foci also could be stained by fluorescent antibody specific for the principal structural virion polypeptide, p30. Quantitatively, only about 1/1,000 of the cells containing viral DNA also had p30. Moreover, sera largely directed against virion envelope components failed to stain any of the cells in these foci (9). These experiments thus demonstrate directly that restricted viral genetic expression occurs in the infected animal, and they provide an attractive explanation for the persistent infection caused by visna virus.

ROLE OF DNA INTERMEDIATES IN CHRONIC INFECTIONS CAUSED BY OTHER RIBOVIRUSES

Recent results have pointed to the possibility that DNA intermediates might be universally involved in chronic infections by riboviruses, even those that ordinarily lack a DNA polymerase system. DNA extracted from a bovine culture latently infected with a temperature-sensitive (ts) mutant of respiratory syncytial virus elicited virus synthesis from uninfected cells, and the infectivity of DNA was lost with prior exposure to deoxyribonuclease. Infectious DNA was also obtained from a chronically infected HEp-2 culture that had survived an initial lytic growth cycle with respiratory syncytial virus; in this cell line small amounts of extracellular virus were synthesized (16).

Other riboviruses in taxonomic groups as diverse as paramyxoviruses and arboviruses may replicate via DNA intermediates under conditions of chronic infection. Reports emanating from Zhdanov's laboratory (20) demonstrate that cultures persistently infected with measles,

TABLE 1. *Assay for DNA intermediates in chronic infections by riboviruses*[a]

| Source of DNA | Infectivity of DNA | | Hybridization of virion RNA |
	Production of virus	Production of viral antigen	
Hamster cells infected with SSPE agent	Negative	Negative	Negative
Lu106 cells infected with measles virus	Negative	Negative	Negative
L cells infected with Sindbis virus	Negative	Not tested	Negative

[a] DNA extracted from cultures of hamster cells persistently infected with SSPE virus (Cremer, personal communication), from Lu106 cells infected with measles virus (14), or from L cells infected with Sindbis virus (Darnall et al., personal communication) was tested for infectivity by the calcium technique (10). To detect partial genome expression, indicator cells were also fixed and assayed for viral antigens by immunofluorescence employing antisera to envelope, hemagglutinin, and hemolytic components of measles virus (15). DNA was also hybridized in vast excess as previously described (11) to ^{32}P-labeled virion RNA isolated from purified virus preparations (8). The designation "Negative" denotes less than 1 to 2% resistance to RNase after hybridization to C_0t values in excess of 10^5. In these experiments the specific activity of the RNA ranged from 3×10^6 to 6×10^6 cpm/μg; in a reaction with 0.3 ng of RNA and 1 mg of DNA, as little as 0.1 copy/cell could have been detected.

Sindbis, or tick-borne encephalitis virus contain DNA that is infectious and will hybridize to the respective viral RNAs; in addition, DNA extracted from the tissues of a patient with systemic lupus erythematosis hybridized to measles virus RNA.

What is surprising about these findings is that these riboviruses ordinarily lack a DNA polymerase system and, by implication, must have acquired one. This could be a consequence of a new class of virus-virus interaction in which resident C-type viruses, latently infecting the carrier cultures, provide the "reverse transcriptase." More intriguing from the standpoint of genetic exchange in eukaryotic cells is the allusion to reverse transcriptase-like activity in the respiratory syncytial virus recovered from the cultures infected with DNA (16). This result could indicate recombination between viral genes and normal cellular genes coding for an RNA-directed DNA polymerase. This situation may not be without precedent; there is yet one unconfirmed report (5) of a mutant of Newcastle disease virus recovered from persistently infected L cells that had an RNA-directed DNA polymerase not present in wild-type virus.

These observations raise a number of questions, such as the explicit mechanism of acquisition of reverse transcriptase and how DNA synthesis would be primed by the diverse RNAs of riboviruses that do not have the unusual structural feature of C-type virus RNA, where primer and template RNA are specifically associated in the virion (4). Moreover, no independent confirmation of these results has yet appeared.

These considerations prompted us to examine a number of chronically infected cultures for evidence of DNA intermediates as an alternate pathway in the genetic reproduction of riboviruses. DNA was extracted from three cell lines: Lu106, a human cell line that contains measles virus antigen in virtually every cell after many generations of serial transfer; a hamster culture persistently infected with the measles virus variant that causes subacute sclerosing panencephalitis; and L cells that survived the initial cytocidal infection with Sindbis virus. DNA from these cultures did not induce virus production or viral antigens in uninfected cells and did not hybridize to the respective virion RNAs (Table 1). Under the conditions employed, vast DNA excess and RNA labeled to high specific activity, we would have been able to detect as little as 0.1 copy of viral DNA/cell. It therefore seems unlikely that the transfer of genetic information from RNA to DNA is a necessary characteristic of chronic infections by riboviruses.

CONCLUSIONS

There is firm evidence that RNA C-type viruses like visna that cause slow and persistent infections replicate via a DNA intermediate and that in the infected animal later steps in the viral growth cycle appear to be blocked. The temperate relationship of virus and host cell in vivo may provide the mechanism for persistence of the virus in the face of the immune and inflammatory attack mounted by the infected animal. How general a mechanism this is in chronic infections is by no means clear. DNA intermediates have been reported to be present in cells chronically infected with riboviruses that lack a DNA polymerase system. Evidence presented indicates that this phenomenon is certainly not a universal one in chronic infections.

ACKNOWLEDGMENTS

We thank Joan Clearwater for preparation of this manuscript.

This work was supported by grants from the American Cancer Society (VC120B) and the U.S. Public Health Service (NS11782). This is Project MRIS 3367 within the Veterans Administration.

LITERATURE CITED

1. **Adams, A., and T. Lindahl.** 1975. Epstein-Barr virus genome with properties of circular DNA molecules in carrier cells. Proc. Natl. Acad. Sci. U.S.A. **72:**1477–1481.
2. **Adams, A., T. Lindahl, and G. Klein.** 1973. Linear association between cellular DNA and Epstein-Barr virus DNA in a human lymphoblastoid cell line. Proc. Natl. Acad. Sci. U.S.A. **70:**2888–2892.
3. **Andrews, C. H.** 1965. The troubles of a virus. J. Gen. Microbiol. **40:**140–156.
4. **Bishop, J. M., C. Tsan-Deng, A. J. Faras, H. M. Goodman, W. E. Levinson, J. M. Taylor, and H. E. Varmus.** 1973. Transcription of the Rous sarcoma virus genome by RNA-directed DNA polymerase, p. 15–31. In F. C. Fox (ed.), Virus research. Academic Press Inc., New York.
5. **Furman, P. A., and J. V. Hallum.** 1973. RNA-dependent DNA polymerase activity in preparations of a mutant of Newcastle disease virus arising from persistently infected L cells. J. Virol. **12:**548–555.
6. **Gall, J. G., and M. L. Pardue.** 1969. Nucleic acid hybridization in cytological preparations. Methods Enzymol. **21:**470–480.
7. **Haase, A. T.** 1975. The slow infection caused by visna virus. Curr. Top. Microbiol. **72:**101–156.
8. **Haase, A. T., A. C. Garapin, A. J. Faras, J. M. Taylor, and J. M. Bishop.** 1974. A comparison of the high molecular weight RNAs of visna virus and Rous sarcoma virus. Virology **57:**259–270.
9. **Haase, A. T., L. Stowring, O. Narayan, D. Griffin, and D. Price.** 1976. The slow persistent infection caused by visna virus: the role of host restriction. Science, in press.
10. **Haase, A. T., B. L. Traynor, and P. E. Ventura.** 1976. Infectivity of visna virus DNA. Virology **70:**65–79.
11. **Haase, A. T., and H. E. Varmus.** 1973. Demonstration of a DNA provirus in the lytic growth of visna virus. Nature (London) New Biol. **245:**237–239.
12. **Mims, C. A.** 1974. Factors in the mechanism of persistence of viral infections. Prog. Med. Virol. **18:**1–14.
13. **Narayan, O., A. M. Silverstein, D. Price, and R. T. Johnson.** 1974. Visna virus infection of American lambs. Science **183:**1202–1203.
14. **Norrby, E.** 1967. A carrier cell line of measles virus Lu 106 cells. Arch. Gesamte Virusforsch. **20:**215–224.
15. **Norrby, E., and Y. Gollmar.** 1975. Identification of measles virus-specific hemolysis-inhibiting antibodies separate from hemagglutination-inhibiting antibodies. Infect. Immun. **11:**231–240.
16. **Simpson, R. W., and M. Iinuma.** 1975. Recovery of infectious proviral DNA from mammalian cells infected with respiratory syncytial virus. Proc. Natl. Acad. Sci. U.S.A. **72:**3230–3234.
17. **Tanaka, A., and M. Nonoyama.** 1974. Latent DNA of Epstein-Barr virus: separation from high-molecular-weight cell DNA in a neutral glycerol gradient. Proc. Natl. Acad. Sci. U.S.A. **71:**4658–4661.
18. **Temin, H. M.** 1971. Mechanism of cell transformation by RNA tumor viruses. Annu. Rev. Microbiol. **25:**609–648.
19. **Weiss, M. J., S. C. Gulati, D. H. Harter, R. W. Sweet, S. Spiegelman, and C. Lopez.** 1975. Unique virus-related DNA sequences in sheep progressive pneumonia lung. J. Gen. Virol. **29:**335–339.
20. **Zhdanov, V. W.** 1975. Integration of viral genomes. Nature (London) **256:**471–473.

Animal and Human Models of Persistent Viral Infections

Modulation of Viral Infection by Cell-Mediated Immunity

PETER C. DOHERTY AND ROLF M. ZINKERNAGEL

The Wistar Institute of Anatomy and Biology, Philadelphia, Pennsylvania 19104, and Scripps Clinic and Research Foundation, La Jolla, California 92037

INTRODUCTION

The role of cell-mediated immunity (CMI) in virus infection has, until recently, not been well understood. The reason for this is that (unlike antibody) suitable in vitro and in vivo assay systems were simply not available. This situation has changed extremely rapidly, at least as far as mouse models are concerned, as a result of the exploitation of two basic experimental protocols. These are (i) adoptive transfer of effector function into immunologically naive recipients and (ii) lymphocyte-mediated lysis of virus-infected, ^{51}Cr-labeled target cells in vitro. Observations made in these two systems have, to date, shown an extremely close correlation (6, 11). We are thus now able to make some useful generalizations concerning the role of CMI in virus diseases, even though the first definitive analytical article was published as recently as 1971 (1).

BASIC CONCEPTS

It is necessary to make a restrictive definition for CMI. Obviously, all immunity is mediated at one level or another by cells, whether these be antibody-secreting cells, macrophages, or recirculating lymphocytes. The following operational statement accommodates present concepts: CMI is a property of specifically sensitized thymus-derived lymphocytes (T cells), effector function depending on membrane-to-membrane contact between immune T cell and (in the present context) virally modified target cell.

Phenomena attributed to CMI do not generally, however, depend solely on T cell-mediated processes. Elimination of virus from tissue sites also requires participation of macrophages (Fig. 1). The immune system must, to be of benefit to the host, function to prevent further dissemination of virus throughout the organ (2). Direct T cell-mediated lysis of, say, virally modified liver cells will only be protective if the lytic event occurs before infectious virus is formed. Otherwise, the net effect will be to hasten both virus spread and, perhaps, onset of immunopathological process due to premature loss of

somatic cells which may still be functional. The other essential consequence of the T cell-target cell interaction is thus the secretion of mediators (4), which operate to recruit and activate macrophages. Infectious virus is then eliminated by those activated macrophages.

IMMUNOLOGICAL SURVEILLANCE AGAINST VIRALLY MODIFIED CELLS

The obvious prelude to T cell-mediated elimination of virus is that lymphocytes bearing the relevant receptor must see antigen, that considerable clonal expansion occurs with concurrent differentiation to functional status, and that effector T cells migrate to (and localize in) organ sites of virus growth. Our understanding of these processes is, to say the least, somewhat incomplete. Even so a general statement may, though it is certain to be at least partly wrong, prove useful as a framework for experiments and ideas.

Experiments in which the in vitro cytotoxic assay was used (7, 16) revealed the somewhat surprising fact that virus-immune effector T cells exhibit two orders of specificity. The first of these is, as would be expected, for virus. The second, which was completely unexpected, is for targets expressing major transplantation (H-2) antigens present in the mouse in which the T cell was sensitized (6, 15). The virus-immune T cell apparently sees something of self (H-2) and something of non-self (virus). Current debate is concerned with establishing whether this reflects recognition of a neoantigen ("interaction antigen"), which is coded for partly by H-2 genes and partly by the viral genome (3, 6), or whether two distinct recognition events (the one for self, the other for virus) are operating (6a). The latter could reflect operation of two separate receptors on the T cell or associative recognition of "altered self" by a single receptor with two components (Fig. 2).

The host genes involved in CMI to viruses map in the H-2K and H-2D regions of the mouse major histocompatibility complex, and are probably the same genes that code for transplantation

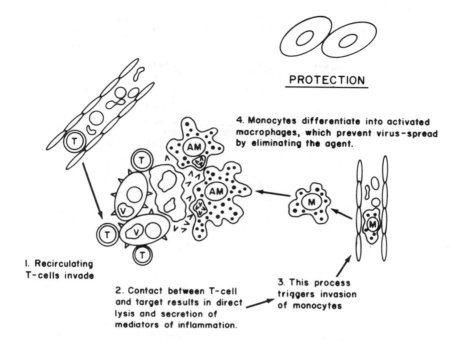

PROTECTION

4. Monocytes differentiate into activated macrophages, which prevent virus-spread by eliminating the agent.

I. Recirculating T-cells invade

2. Contact between T-cell and target results in direct lysis and secretion of mediators of inflammation.

3. This process triggers invasion of monocytes

IMMUNOPATHOLOGY

FIG. 1. *Virus elimination from solid tissues depends on interaction between specifically sensitized thymus-derived lymphocytes (T cells) and activated macrophages.*

antigens recognized during graft rejection (Fig. 2). Different "clones" of virus-immune effector T cells are associated with each locus. However, helper T cell function, required for maximal production of immunoglobulin G class antibody, is apparently associated with the I region (Fig. 2) of the H-2 gene complex (10). The same is true for delayed-type hypersensitivity (DTH) to some, but not to all, soluble antigens (13). This could indicate that different functions are associated with distinct genetic regions: H-2K or H-2D for cytotoxicity, H-2I for T cell help. Alternatively, processing of soluble antigens may be a property of the I region, whereas viruses associate with K or D. We need to know whether T cell help in virus infections also maps in the I region.

Surveillance (cytotoxic) and helper T cell functions (Fig. 2) are thus mediated by functionally, and serologically (5), distinct classes of thymus-derived lymphocytes. This is, teleologically at least, a logical division of labor. Recirculating T cells may be thought to monitor cell surface via transient recognition of structures coded for within the H-2 gene complex. Antigens specified at H-2K or H-2D are present on all cell types throughout the organism,

though concentration may vary from tissue to tissue (12). Virus-immune effector T cells could, therefore, potentially operate in any organ supporting growth of the pathogen. However, antigens coded for in the I region (Ia) are found principally on B cells and macrophages. Macrophages are probably involved in processing antigen for presentation to B cells. Thus, helper T cells, recognizing I-region determinants, need only monitor cells with which functional interaction is possible (8).

T CELL SURVEILLANCE AND VIRUS PERSISTENCE

Virus persistence could, from the CMI aspect, result from defects either in surveillance or in effector function. Some tissues, such as the brain and the anterior chamber of the eye, may not be subject to surveillance by thymus-derived lymphocytes. This could, at least insofar as the brain is concerned, reflect either that T cells do not recirculate through nervous tissue or that there is no lymphatic drainage to regional lymph nodes. It may be that surveillance function is concerned essentially with monitoring of lymphoid tissue, whereas effector T cells can operate

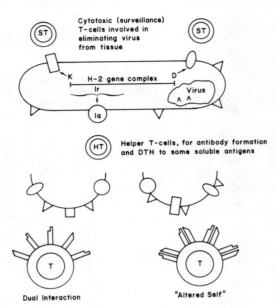

FIG. 2. *Recognition by surveillance T cells of phenotypic products of genes coding for strong transplantation antigens. Recirculating T cells may monitor antigens coded for within the major histocompatibility (H-2) complex. Surveillance (ST, cytotoxic) T cells are associated with H-2K and H-2D, whereas helper T cells (HT, involved in antibody production) are in some way involved with Ir gene function. Specific CMI may reflect operation of a dual interaction mechanism or associative recognition of "altered self" by a single receptor with two components.*

in all organ sites. Viruses which multiply only in nervous tissue and do not cause viremia may thus "sneak through." Rabies may be a case in point.

Some viruses may not cause changes in cell membrane that are recognized by surveillance T cells. Evidence of cytotoxic T cell function in herpesvirus infections has, despite considerable effort, been conspicuously lacking to date.

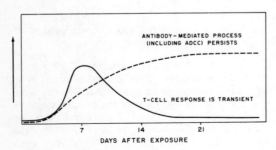

FIG. 3. *Cytotoxic T cells may only be found for a relatively short time during primary infection, whereas antibody-mediated processes may persist throughout the life of the host.*

However, antibody-dependent cell-mediated toxicity (ADCC), which is independent of effector T cells, is readily demonstrated for this group of viruses (14). This may simply reflect technical problems in the T cell assay system. Even so, T cell-mediated lysis has been shown for all other viruses that have been thoroughly investigated in mouse models (Zinkernagel and Doherty, in press).

Virus persistence may also reflect failure of the effector arm of the CMI process. Cytotoxic T cell activity tends to be a rather transient phenomenon in all virus infections studied so far, though antibody production may continue throughout the life of the host (Fig. 3). Unless, therefore, the virus is eliminated rather rapidly, persistence may follow modulation of the T cell response. The extremely high levels of antibody found in some chronic infections (9) may represent an attempt to compensate for defective CMI, persistent presence of antigen acting as a potent stimulus for continued immunoglobulin synthesis. The classical example may be subacute sclerosing panencephalitis. A variety of mechanisms may be invoked, from the virological aspect, to explain escape during the relatively brief interval during which CMI is effective. Such processes will, no doubt, be considered by other papers in this volume.

LITERATURE CITED

1. **Blanden, R. V.** 1971. Mechanisms of recovery from a generalized viral infection: mousepox. III. Regression of infection foci. J. Exp. Med. **133:**1090–1104.

2. **Blanden, R. V.** 1974. T cell response to viral and bacterial infection. Transplant. Rev. **19:**56–88.

3. **Blanden, R. V., A. J. Hapel, and D. C. Jackson.** 1976. Mode of action of Ir genes and the nature of T cell receptors for antigen. Immunochemistry **13:**179–191.

4. **Bloom, B. R.** 1971. *In vitro* approaches to the mechanism of cell-mediated immune reactions. Adv. Immunol. **13:**102–208.

5. **Cantor, H., and E. A. Boyse.** 1975. Functional subclasses of T lymphocytes bearing different Ly antigens. II. Co-operations between subclasses of Ly$^+$ cells in the generation of killer activity. J. Exp. Med. **141:**1390–1399.

6. **Doherty, P. C., R. V. Blanden, and R. M. Zinkernagel.** 1976. Specificity of virus-immune effector T cells for H-2K or H-2D compatible interactions: implications for H antigen diversity. Transplant. Rev. **29:**89–124.

6a. **Doherty, P. C., D. Götze, G. Trinchieri, and R. M. Zinkernagel.** 1976. Models for recognition of virally-modified cells by immune thymus-derived lymphocytes. Immunogenetics **3:**517–524.

7. **Doherty, P. C., and R. M. Zinkernagel.** 1974. T-cell-mediated immunopathology in viral infection. Transplant. Rev. **19:**89–120.

8. **Doherty, P. C., and R. M. Zinkernagel.** 1975. A biological role for the major histocompatibility antigens. Lancet **i:**1406–1408.

9. **Hotchin, J.** 1971. Persistence and slow virus infections. Monogr. Virol. **3:**1–211.

10. **Katz, D. H., and B. Benacerraf.** 1975. The function and interrelationship of T cell receptors, Ir genes and other histocompatibility gene products. Transplant. Rev. **22:**175–195.

11. **Kees, U., and R. V. Blanden.** 1976. A single genetic element in H-2K affects mouse T cell anti-viral function in poxvirus infection. J. Exp. Med. **143:**450–455.

12. **Klein, J.** 1975. Biology of the mouse histocompatibility-2 complex. Springer-Verlag, New York.

13. **Miller, J. F. A. P., M. A. Vadas, A. Whitelaw, and J. Gamble.** 1975. H-2 gene complex restricts transfer of delayed-type hypersensitivity in mice. Proc. Natl. Acad. Sci. U.S.A. **72:**5095–5098.

14. **Ramshaw, I. A.** 1975. Lysis of herpesvirus-infected target cells by immune spleen cells. Infect. Immun. **11:**767–769.

15. **Zinkernagel, R. M.** 1976. Specific T cell-mediated cytotoxicity across the H-2 barrier to virus-altered allo-antigen. Nature (London) **248:**701–703.

16. **Zinkernagel, R. M., and P. C. Doherty.** 1974. Restriction of *in vitro* T cell-mediated cytotoxicity in lymphocytic choriomeningitis virus within a syngeneic or semial-logeneic system. Nature (London) **248:**701–702.

Persistent Enterovirus Infections in Agammaglobulinemia

CATHERINE M. WILFERT, REBECCA BUCKLEY, FRED S. ROSEN, JOHN WHISNANT,
MICHAEL N. OXMAN, JOHN F. GRIFFITH, SAMUEL L. KATZ, AND MARCIE MOORE

*Department of Pediatrics and Microbiology, Duke University Medical Center, Durham, North
Carolina 27706; and Department of Medicine, Children's Hospital Medical Center, and
Department of Pediatrics, Harvard Medical School, Boston, Massachusetts 02115*

This presentation is a summary of evidence which is accumulating to suggest that patients with agammaglobulinemia may have "persistent" enteroviral infections. Over the past 5 to 10 years, it has become apparent that these individuals seem to be at increased risk of acquiring paralytic poliomyelitis. During the past 8 years, we have seen four patients with agammaglobulinemia who have demonstrated the prolonged presence of an echovirus in their central nervous system associated with progressive symptomatic illness. In this paper, we review the relevant literature, discuss in some detail the patients we have observed, and describe initial prospective evaluations of immunodeficient patients at Duke University Medical Center (DUMC).

LITERATURE REVIEW PERTAINING TO POLIOMYELITIS IN IMMUNO-COMPROMISED PATIENTS

The literature contains reference to seven patients classified as "hypogammaglobulinemics" who have developed paralytic poliomyelitis (1, 3, 4, 14, 16; Karzon and Wright, in preparation). These patients are listed in Table 1. The patients range in age from 6 months to 31 years. Five of these patients were oral polio vaccine recipients. Poliovirus isolated from three of these five patients was characterized as vaccine-like. The virus isolated from the fourth vaccine recipient was characterized as intermediate by antigenic markers. These cases were described between 1962 and 1975. At the present time, the total number of recognized cases of paralytic poliomyelitis in the United States is fewer than 10 per year.

Six patients with cellular deficits or combined immunodeficiency have been reported with paralytic poliomyelitis between 1968 and 1975 (2, 5, 11–13). These patients are listed in Table 2. Five of these children developed their disease prior to the age of 1 year. Unfortunately, their immunological compromise may not be recognized during the first several months of life

so that a standard immunization schedule is initiated and they may receive trivalent oral polio vaccine (TOPV) as early as 2 months of age. Several of the children probably acquired virus by contact with an immunized sibling. All of these patients succumbed to their infection. The polioviruses isolated from these children have been characterized as vaccine-like in three instances and nonvaccine-like in two instances; virus from the last infant has not yet been characterized. Poliovirus was excreted in the stools of the fourth child for 4 months. The isolation of virus from the cerebrospinal fluid (CSF) and the lung of case 6 is an indication of the inability of the host to limit poliovirus infection.

In summary, the literature provides evidence that patients with an isolated humoral or cellular deficit, as well as those with combined deficiency, are at significant risk of developing paralytic poliovirus infections.

ECHOVIRUS INFECTIONS IN AGAMMAGLOBULINEMICS

Case 1

In 1968, the first of four patients came to our attention because of an obscure central nervous system illness. The diagnosis of agammaglobulinemia was made in 1952. He received replacement immune serum globulin (ISG) each 3 to 4 weeks from 1952 until 1968. At the age of 22 years, he was admitted to Children's Hospital Medical Center in Boston (CHMC) after a gran mal seizure, at which time the results of the lumbar puncture, skull X ray, and an electroencephalogram (EEG) were normal. Two years later he developed a dermatomyositis-like syndrome and was treated with prednisone. The onset of dizziness, headache, and epigastric discomfort precipitated his final hospitalization. The patient was extremely weak and appeared chronically ill. His temperature was 40°C. He had findings consistent with dermatomyositis, including symmetrical muscle weakness, edema of all extremities, and atrophic skin with flexion

TABLE 1. *Paralytic poliomyelitis in immunocompromised patients—hypogammaglobulinemics*

Age of patient and year of illness[a]	Reference	Poliovirus isolates	Antigenic characterization
7 years, 1962 (OPV recipient)	16	Throat, polio I Stool, polio I	Vaccine-like
11 years, 1962 (OPV recipient)	16	None	
31 years, 1967 (no contact)	1	Throat, polio II Stool, polio II	Nonvaccine-like
21 years, 1967 (no contact)	1	None	
4 years, 1968 (OPV recipient and contact)[b]	3	Throat, polio II	Vaccine-like
10 months, 1972 (OPV 5 and 2½ months before illness)	4; Center for Disease Control, unpublished data	Stool, polio I Brain, polio I	Intermediate
6 months, 1975 (OPV recipient)[c]	Karzon and Wright, in preparation	Throat, polio II	Vaccine-like

[a] OPV = oral polio vaccine.
[b] Later report refutes agammaglobulinemia but gives no laboratory support.
[c] A report of paralytic disease due to polio II but patient with adequate immunoglobulin levels.

contractures of the elbows and knees. No localizing neurological signs were evident. He developed pneumonia and anicteric hepatitis. Steady deterioration occurred, and progression of his pulmonary disease necessitated assisted ventilation. He became hypotensive and died 7 weeks after admission. Blood, urine, and CSF cultures were consistently negative for bacteria and fungi.

Postmortem examination revealed findings typical of agammaglobulinemia, with absence of plasma cells and diminution of all lymphoid tissue with depletion of subcapsular and medullary areas of lymph nodes. There was perivascular round cell infiltration in all major viscera, including the brain.

Echovirus type 9 was isolated from four samples of CSF obtained during the 7-week period of his terminal hospitalization (Table 3). The same agent was also isolated from premortem leukocytes and urine as well as postmortem lung, intestine, brain, spleen, and kidney.

Case 2

The diagnosis of agammaglobulinemia was made in this first-born female child of normal parents at the age of 15 months. There were no detectable surface immunoglobulin-bearing B lymphocytes in the peripheral blood, and she had normal cell-mediated immunity. Replacement ISG therapy was initiated for the next 23 months. The patient developed anicteric hepatitis (hepatitis B surface antigen [Hb$_s$ Ag] negative) at the age of 3 years, 2 months. The hepatitis persisted for 4 months, and she suddenly developed behavioral changes with petit mal seizures. She was admitted to the hospital with fever (40.1°C), bidirectional lateral nystagmus, ataxia, and opisthotonus. She was found to have an extremely high serum dilantin level, and these symptoms subsided when this therapy was discontinued. CSF examinations showed minimal pleocytosis and elevation of protein (Table 3). All bacterial, fungal, and mycobacterial stains and cultures of the CSF were negative. She was discharged on the 7th hospital day, alert, active, and ambulatory.

Her subsequent course over the next 2.5 years has been one of exacerbation of central nervous symptoms alternating with periods when she is neurologically normal. She has experienced seizures and a left-sided hemiparesis with associated EEG asymmetry on one occasion. She has been symptom-free for the past 4 months on phenobarbital therapy. The CSF findings are summarized in Table 3. Echovirus 30 was isolated from the CSF of this patient on eight occasions over a 6-month period of observation. Four consecutive spinal fluid cultures obtained from 7 to 21 months after the onset of this illness failed to yield virus, although elevation of the CSF protein persisted.

TABLE 2. *Paralytic poliomyelitis in immunocompromised patients—cellular and combined deficiency*

Diagnosis, age, year[a]	References	Poliovirus isolates	Antigenic characterization
Combined immunodeficiency, 8 months, 1968 (sibling TOPV)	2, 11, 12	Throat, polio III Stool, polio III Brain, polio III Cord, polio III	Vaccine-like
Combined immunodeficiency, 6½ years, 1969 (TOPV 5 and 7 months) PTA	5	Stool, polio II	Vaccine-like
Cartilage hair hypoplasia, combined immunodeficiency, 8 months, 1974 (TOPV × 3)	13	Stool, polio II Throat, polio II Spinal cord, polio II Brain stem, polio II Basal ganglia, polio II	Nonvaccine-like Vaccine-like
Severe combined immunodeficiency, 8 months, 1973 (TOPV × 2)	Center for Disease Control, unpublished data	Throat⎫ Polio I, II, III for Rectal⎭ 1 month Rectal, polio II for 4 months	Nonvaccine-like
Severe combined immunodeficiency, 9 months, 1973	Center for Disease Control, unpublished data	Brain, polio II	Nonvaccine-like
Severe combined immunodeficiency, 7 months, 1975 (TOPV)	Horwitz, personal communication	Stool, polio II Spinal fluid, polio II Lumbar spinal cord, polio II Medulla, polio II Midbrain, polio II Lung, polio II	?

[a] TOPV = trivalent oral polio vaccine.

With exacerbation of her illness, virus was again isolated from her spinal fluid 2 years after onset of her illness. Cultures of throat, urine, and peripheral blood repeatedly failed to yield virus. No virus was detected in family members at any time.

Case 3

The third patient was identified as an agammaglobulinemic at the age of 3.5 years. He has no surface immunoglobulin-bearing B lymphocytes, and cell-mediated immune functions are normal. He received replacement ISG therapy. He developed a dermatomyositis-like syndrome at the age of 12 years. Deterioration in his clinical condition prompted hospitalization at the age of 15.5 years for evaluation. Skin and muscle biopsies showed interstitial inflammation and focal calcification with perivascular lymphocytic infiltration. Fungal and bacterial cultures of CSF were negative. Echovirus 30 was isolated from the CSF on two occasions over a 15-month period (Table 3). In addition, echovirus 19 was also isolated on the first occasion.

Case 4

This boy was admitted for his fifth DUMC admission at the age of 7.5 years because of increased intracranial pressure. The patient is a known agammaglobulinemic with no surface immunoglobulin-bearing B lymphocytes who was diagnosed at the age of 3 years, 10 months. He received paternal plasma infusions for 3.5 years and subsequently has been receiving intramuscular ISG therapy. The illness prompting this hospitalization was characterized by headaches of increasing severity over the month prior to admission. His physician observed papilledema 3 weeks after the onset of his symptoms. His father had experienced an illness characterized by rash, jaundice, and gastrointestinal symptoms in the month prior to recognition of the patient's headaches. This illness was not associated with detection of Hb_s Ag at any time. The patient did not receive plasma from his father during the several weeks preceding the onset of that illness.

The patient was afebrile and, except for the papilledema, the physical examination was unremarkable. Skull films and brain scan were normal. Three lumbar punctures were done in 12 days. The pressure was markedly elevated, and the characteristics of the fluids are listed in Table 3. Fungal and bacterial cultures of all CSF specimens were negative. The patient has now been followed for 6 months with decreasing frequency of headaches and diminution of his papilledema.

The four CSF specimens from this patient obtained over a 6-month interval were submitted for viral culture. The second and fourth specimens received over this interval were positive for echovirus 9. The nasopharyngeal and stool cultures have been negative for virus on five occasions.

There are an additional five patients with hypogammaglobulinemia and central nervous system viral infections reported in the literature (6, 7, 15, 17). Three of these patients had echovirus infections varying in duration from 2 weeks to 3 years. The data accumulated from our four patients and those cited in the literature suggest that patients with agammaglobulinemia are not able to limit the central nervous system replication of enteroviruses.

ENTEROVIRUS EXCRETION BY IMMUNO-DEFICIENT PATIENTS

Patients with agammaglobulinemia are deficient in local secretory antibody in sites such as the respiratory and gastrointestinal tract. If antibody is important in limiting virus replication locally, these patients should demonstrate prolonged excretion of agents such as the enteroviruses. McCallum reported in 1964 (9) that agammaglobulinemic patients could excrete poliovirus for a prolonged period of time after immunization. These observations were reported at the time when the diagnosis of immunological deficiency disease had not achieved its present level of sophistication. Therefore, this group of patients is probably heterogeneous. Two children excreted virus of the same serotype as the monovalent vaccine for 29 and 21 months, respectively. These viruses were tested by the in vitro markers and found to be stable with regard to their characterization as vaccine-like. However, when they were injected into monkeys, a tendency for increased neurovirulence was demonstrated (10). In addition, two other patients with agammaglobulinemia and paralytic poliomyelitis have had virus excretion documented from the pharynx or stool for several months (16; Center for Disease Control, unpublished data).

A single report contains additional experience

TABLE 3. *Agammaglobulinemics with echovirus central nervous system infections*

Patient and date	CSF findings		
	Leukocytes/ mm^3	Protein	Virus isolation
Case #1			
3-22-68	244	162	Echo 9
3-30-68	444	632	Echo 9
4-8-68	1,163	216	Echo 9
4-15-68	325	315	Echo 9[a]
Case #2			
12-6-73	50	40	Echo 30
12-12-73	95	30	Echo 30
1-2-74	10	90	Echo 30
1-21-74	60		Echo 30
2-11-74	45	70	Echo 30
3-6-74	120		Echo 30
4-17-74	110	100	Echo 30
5-29-74	80	115	Echo 30
7-31-74	25	75	Negative
10-2-74	0	35	Negative
5-12-75	30	65	Negative
9-26-75	45	132	Negative
11-5-75	450	179	Echo 30
Case #3			
3-14-73	26	115	Echo 30, echo 19
6-28-74	220	182	Echo 30
Case #4			
10-18-75	9	35	Negative
10-23-75	26	43	Echo 9
10-30-75	37	44	Negative
12-12-75	28	39	Echo 9

[a] $10^{6.5}$ TCID$_{50}$/ml.

with virus excretion by several patients with severe combined immunodeficiency (8). Virus was continually excreted until they had received immunocompetent cells. It is not possible to ascertain which type of immunocompetent cells (T or B) curtailed the excretion of virus.

In view of the preceding observations, a prospective surveillance of our immunocompromised patients followed at DUMC was initiated. For a 2-year period, nasopharyngeal and stool cultures from these patients were submitted for viral culture at the time of their visit to the clinic or admission to the hospital. Materials from 31 patients with a variety of diagnoses have been processed. Since the agammaglobulinemic patients usually return for replacement globulin therapy, they are seen more frequently; 16 of the 31 patients fall into this category. Of the 181 cultures obtained to date, 23 have been positive for viruses. This includes the CSF specimens of the four patients described in detail in this report. The viral isolates have been obtained from seven patients (Table 4). Of particular interest is the observation that six of these seven patients are agammaglobulinemics with no surface immunoglobulin-bearing B lymphocytes. One of these patients has had a total of eight consecutive stool specimens obtained at random visits over the past 2 years which are all positive for an enterovirus. Two of these are echovirus type 3. The remaining six isolates have not yet been serotyped. There is also one patient who received TOPV and who has transiently excreted vaccine-like virus in his stool.

DISCUSSION

Patients with agammaglobulinemia who are characterized by the absence of surface immunoglobulin-bearing B lymphocytes are at increased risk of central nervous system infection with enteroviruses. The four patients presented here have been studied extensively and do not have a defined cellular immune deficit. All identified agammaglobulinemic patients receive replacement globulin therapy. It seems likely that the passive transfer of viral antibodies is capable of protecting these individuals from viremia and distant visceral infection with homologous serotypes of agents. The inability to limit replication of enteroviruses in such sites as the gastrointestinal tract could enhance the possibility of invasion in an individual with no humoral antibodies.

The spectrum of illness observed in these patients with prolonged central nervous system infection is somewhat at variance with that observed in the normal host. The patients may experience fever, but acute meningeal symptoms are conspicuously absent. This raises the question of what role antibody may play in the symptomatology of viral meningitis in normal individuals. In addition, the clinical illness is one of chronicity with clinical remissions and exacerbations. Each of the four described patients has had virus present in the CSF for weeks to years. In one of these patients, virus was not detectable for an interval of several months.

We know less about the specific viruses isolated from the central nervous system of these patients. In the case of poliomyelitis infections, the available genetic marker characterizations have not demonstrated a reversion to wild-type virus as determined by RCT (reproductive capacity at supraoptimal temperatures) or antigenic (intratypic sero-differentiation) markers in the agammaglobulinemics. However, the known disparity between neurovirulence and these markers leaves the question unanswered. At the present time, neurovirulence testing (the only in vivo assessment of wild versus vaccine-derived virus) is not available except as part of the safety testing procedures of vaccine production. McCallum's observations hint that prolonged human carriage may allow virus to develop increased neurovirulence.

The prominence of echovirus 30 and echovirus 9 in the agammaglobulinemic patients is intriguing. Echovirus type 9 is a common serotype and is frequently recognized as a causative agent of large outbreaks of enterovirus infection in the general population. Its prevalence might partially explain its occurrence in two of these patients. On the other hand, echovirus type 30 is a rather infrequently observed cause of enterovirus infection. We evaluated the first and sixth isolates of echovirus type 30 from patient 2. The viruses are indistinguishable from each other and from the standard Metcalf strain in several cell culture systems. Cross-neutralization studies performed with antisera produced in rabbits could detect no immunological differences between these two strains or the standard strain. Preliminary kinetic neutralization studies have also failed to demonstrate an antigenic difference in the two isolates obtained over a 6-month interval.

These cases and a review of the literature have been presented to call attention to a syn-

TABLE 4. *Duke 1974–1976 prospective evaluation of virus excretion in immunodeficient patients*

No. of patients	Virus isolated	Site[a]	No. of cultures
1	Adenovirus 2	N/P	1
1	Enterovirus	Stool	
	Echovirus 3		2
	Not yet serotyped		6
1	Herpes simplex virus	N/P	1
1	Poliovirus 2 (vaccine-like)	Stool	1
1	Echovirus 30	CSF	9
1	Echovirus 9	CSF	2
1	Enterovirus[b]	Stool	1
7			23

[a] N/P = nasopharynx; CSF = cerebrospinal fluid.
[b] All patients with virus isolation were agammaglobulinemic with no surface immunoglobulin-bearing B lymphocytes except this patient, who is immunoglobulin A deficient.

drome of enteroviral encephalitis in agamma-globulinemic patients. Thus far, this persistent infection seems to be confined to those patients who lack peripheral blood surface immuno-globulin-bearing B lymphocytes. Further study may show it to occur in other varieties of agammaglobulinemia as well. These observations should also emphasize the potential hazards of administration of any live virus vaccine including poliomyelitis to hosts with alterations of either humoral or cellular immunity.

ACKNOWLEDGMENTS

This investigation was supported by Public Health Service grants TOL-HD-000132, AI-05877, FR-128, AI-0192, and General Clinical Research Centers RR-30.

LITERATURE CITED

1. **Annual Poliomyelitis Summary.** 1967. National Communicable Disease Center, Neurotropic Viral Diseases Surveillance, U.S. Department of Health, Education and Welfare, Public Health Service, p. 17, 20 June 1968.
2. **Annual Poliomyelitis Summary.** 1968. Neurotropic Viral Diseases Surveillance, 1 June 1969.
3. **Annual Poliomyelitis Summary.** 1969. National Communicable Disease Center, Neutrotropic Viral Diseases Surveillance, U.S. Department of Health, Education and Welfare, Public Health Service, p. 19, 15 June 1970.
4. **Cesario, T. C., J. H. Nakano, G. G. Caldwell, and R. A. Youmans.** 1969. Paralytic poliomyelitis in an unimmunized child. Apparent result of vaccine-derived polio virus. Am. J. Dis. Child. **118:**895–898.
5. **Feigin, R. D., M. A. Guggenheim, and S. G. Johnsen.** 1971. Vaccine related paralytic poliomyelitis in an immunodeficient child. J. Pediatr. **79:**642–647.
6. **Hanissian, A. S., J. T. Jabbour, S. D. DeLamerens, J. H. Garcia, and L. Horta-Barbosa.** 1972. Subacute encephalitis in hypogammaglobulinemia. Am. J. Dis. Child. **123:**151–155.
7. **Linnemann, C. C., D. B. May, W. K. Schubert, C. T. Caraway, and G. M. Schieff.** 1973. Fatal viral encephalitis in children with x-linked hypogamma-globulinemia. Am. J. Dis. Child. **126:**100–103.
8. **Lopez, C., W. D. Biggar, B. H. Park, and R. A. Good.** 1974. Non-paralytic poliovirus infections in patients with severe combined immunodeficiency disease. J. Pediatr. **84:**497–502.
9. **McCallum, F. O.** 1964. Observations and the feeding of attenuated live polioviruses (Sabin) to children with hypogammaglobulinemia. Proc. Eur. Assoc. of Poliomyelitis and Allied Diseases 56 IX (9th symposium), p. 226–228, p. 240–244.
10. **Magrath, D. I., L. R. Boulger, and E. G. Hartley.** 1966. Strains of polio virus from individuals fed Sabin vaccines studied by *in vitro* markers in the monkey neurovirulence tests. Proc. Eur. Assoc. of Poliomyelitis and Allied Diseases 56 IX (10th symposium), p. 334–345.
11. **Morbidity and Mortality Weekly Report.** 1968. Poliomyelitis in a patient with thymic displasia and dysgammaglobulinemia. **17:**14–16.
12. **Riker, J. B., C. D. Brandt, R. Chandra, J. O. Arrobio, and J. H. Nakano.** 1971. Vaccine associated poliomyelitis in a child with thymic abnormality. Pediatrics **48:**923–929.
13. **Saulsburg, F. T., J. A. Winkelstein, L. E. Davis, S. H. Hsu, B. J. D'Souza, G. R. Gutcher, and I. J. Butler.** 1975. Combined immunodeficiency and vaccine-related poliomyelitis in a child with cartilage-hair hypoplasia. J. Pediatr. **86:**868–872.
14. **Stolley, P. D., J. M. Joseph, J. C. Allen, G. Deane, and J. H. Janney.** 1968. Poliomyelitis associated with Type 2 polio virus vaccine strain. Possible transmission from an immunized child to a non-immunized child. Lancet i:661–662.
15. **Webster, A. D. B.** 1974. Workshop in Immunodeficiency Diseases, p. 361–365. *In* L. Brent and J. Holborrow (ed.), Progress in immunology II, vol. 5, Clinical aspects. American Elsevier, New York.
16. **Wen Chang, T. E., L. Weinstein, and H. E. MacMahon.** 1966. Paralytic poliomyelitis in a child with hypogammaglobulinemia: probable implication of Type I vaccine strain. Pediatrics **37:**630–636.
17. **Ziegler, J. B., and R. Penny.** 1975. Fatal Echo 30 virus infection in amyloidosis in x-linked hypogammaglobulinemia. Clin. Immunol. **3:**347–352.

Lymphocytic Choriomeningitis Virus Infection of Mice

GERALD A. COLE

*Department of Epidemiology, The Johns Hopkins University School of Hygiene and Public Health,
Baltimore, Maryland 21205*

An understanding of the biology of natural and experimentally produced lymphocytic chorio-meningitis (LCM) virus infections came first from early studies of Traub (11–13), followed by those of Rowe (10) and Hotchin (6). Collectively, these studies defined most of the conditions under which the administration of virus to mice could lead to either a lifelong carrier state, an abortive immunizing infection, or an acutely fatal disease.

Most strains of LCM virus replicate inefficiently in adult mouse parenchymal tissues and produce an abortive immunizing infection when administered peripherally, yet they uniformly kill when given by the intracerebral route.

The inoculation of neonatal mice, by any route, with all common strains of LCM virus usually results in the survival of a high proportion of animals that subsequently develop permanent noncytopathic carrier infections. At any time during their lifespan, virus is readily demonstrable in blood and many parenchymal tissues of carrier mice, and the infection is naturally perpetuated by congenital transmission to their progeny.

Mice deprived of T cells as adults by thymectomy, followed by lethal irradiation and reconstitution with bone marrow (AT × BM mice), or mice which are congenitally athymic, will also develop persistent infections in essentially the same manner as neonatal mice (8). Thus, the absence of functional T cells or an immaturity of the T cell compartment clearly seems to be an important factor in the initiation of the LCM virus carrier state.

However, immunocompetent adult mice treated with the immunosuppressive drug cyclophosphamide shortly after intracerebral LCM virus inoculation also develop persistent carrier infections (1), and these animals, as well as carriers inoculated at birth, eventually gain normal immunological responsiveness to other T cell-dependent antigens such as sheep erythrocytes or allogeneic tumor cells (G. A. Cole, unpublished data). Therefore, the mechanism by which the carrier state is maintained appears to be a continued selective lack of functional virus-reactive T cells rather than a generalized T cell deficiency.

For many years, the LCM virus carrier state was considered to be the paradigm of specific immunological tolerance since, by conventional means, no virus-specific antibodies could be detected in carrier mouse sera. This notion became untenable, however, when Oldstone and Dixon, using specific fluorescein-conjugated antisera to stain sections of kidneys from carrier mice, were able to demonstrate the presence of glomerular deposits containing viral antigens, immunoglobulin G, and complement (9). In addition, immunoglobulin G eluted from carrier mouse kidneys contained virus-specific complement-fixing (CF) antibody. These observations established that LCM virus carrier infections are accompanied by a continuous humoral response directed against one or more viral determinants, which in some mouse strains results eventually in chronic immune complex disease.

However, two recent findings tend to reinstate this notion in a qualified way. First is the evidence presented by Zinkernagel and Doherty (14) suggesting that LCM virus-specific cytotoxic T cells do not recognize viral antigens alone (as do antiviral antibodies) but rather in combination with certain major histocompatibility (H-2) antigens on the surfaces of the infected host's cells. Second is the finding by Lehmann-Grube and co-workers (personal communication) that the specificity of LCM virus-induced CF antibody (which is non-neutralizing) is directed against a viral component that is expressed neither on the surface of the virion nor on that of the infected cell; yet high concentrations of this component are found within infected cells.

Since carrier mice apparently retain the ability to produce virus-specific CF antibody throughout their lives, viral persistence is obviously not the result of paralysis of all virus-reactive B cells or collaborative T helper cells. However, the induction of paralysis which is limited to clones of T cells with receptor specificities for a complex of self-determinants and virus is not difficult to envision since, on theoretical grounds, paralysis followed by tolerance to cell-surface antigens comprised of self-determinants should be relatively easy to achieve.

We have found that when approximately 10^8 unprimed syngeneic lymphocytes are adoptively transferred to a carrier mouse, they have virtually no effect on existing levels of virus in blood and tissues; yet these same lymphocytes, when transferred to an AT × BM mouse (which conventionally would develop a carrier infection when given LCM virus), enable the animal to make a primary immune response to virus. The simplest interpretation of this observation is that in the carrier these transferred unprimed cells are made tolerant.

However, when adoptive transfers of immune lymphocytes are performed with neonatally inoculated carrier mice as the recipients, the levels of virus in their blood and parenchymal tissues begin to fall gradually—sometimes to barely detectable levels (3, 5). We have observed that in the brains of these animals there is a concomitant dramatic decrease in the numbers of neural cells containing immunofluorescent viral antigen. It should be emphasized that if T cells are depleted from the donor population prior to transfer, by treatment with anti-θ serum and complement, viral clearance does not occur, although the remaining primed B cells produce an impressive CF antibody response. This finding constitutes fairly strong evidence that maintenance of the carrier state depends on the absence of virus-reactive T cells, and it also indicates that the respective specificities of LCM virus-induced T cells and B cells are different. What has always been a puzzling observation associated with this immune-mediated viral clearance phenomenon is how virus or virus-induced antigens can literally disappear from a static population of neural cells in the absence of any discrete neuronal pathology. This observation raises several questions which bear on the virological status of the immunofluorescent antigen-positive cells in the central nervous system. Are these cells inaccessible to immune T cells or are they simply nonsusceptible? Inaccessibility is not likely since, under other experimental conditions, immune T cells can produce massive destructive lesions of the neuroparenchyma (1).

A number of observations on the replication of LCM virus in murine cell cultures would, collectively, tend to support the alternative possibility. First, productive infections are more easily initiated and maintained in actively proliferating cells (Cole, unpublished data). Second, infected cultures, particularly those that are contact-inhibited, gradually cease producing infectious virus and become temporarily refractory to reinfection (7). Third, well after the time when infected cells begin to produce little or no infectious virus, they continue to show striking intracytoplasmic concentrations of immunofluorescent viral antigen but little or none on their surfaces (4). Fourth, the presence of defective particles in LCM virus inocula or those produced during active replication have been shown to markedly interfere with, or modify, the subsequent course of infection (7). Finally, only productively infected cells which display virus-induced surface antigens appear to be susceptible to lysis by virus-specific cytotoxic T cells (4). Therefore, a speculative construction of the events which lead to the disappearance of antigen-positive cells in the central nervous sytem of the adoptively immunized carrier would consist of the following: first, there is elimination of the relatively small percentage of productively infected cells in the total antigen-positive population throughout the body of the carrier. The productively infected cells are likely to be concentrated in, or arise from, tissues with high proliferative or turnover rates such as the lymphoreticular system. Eliminating the foci of virus production precludes the maintenance of infection in the central nervous system and other parenchymal organs where most cells have already been rendered nonproducing or refractory as a result of previous infection and defective virus production. These are the antigen-positive cells which would then gradually become negative. It should be noted that, even in the brains of unmanipulated neonatally inoculated carrier mice, the total number of fluorescing antigen-positive cells decreases markedly during the first two months of life, indicating a marked loss in their ability to maintain virus replication (5). This decrease is not accompanied by a proportional decrease in the level of circulating virus.

Thus, to summarize briefly the dynamics of the LCM virus carrier state:

Initiation is best achieved in the neonate because this animal is immunologically immature and also because the immediate postnatal period is one during which there is active cell proliferation occurring in all organ systems. Infection, therefore, is readily established at a time when tolerance to virus complexed with self-determinants is most easily induced.

Maintenance of the carrier state depends on a continued source of productively infected cells, probably arising in the lymphoreticular system or in other organs in which there is sustained cell proliferation or turnover. These productively infected cells supply a constant tolerogenic signal to clones of T lymphocytes reactive to a complex of virus plus self-determinants as they are generated. An antibody response is eventually induced to immunogenic viral structural proteins which are not present on the surfaces of virions or infected cells but which are continuously released by the latter during cell turnover. Under these conditions, immune complexes are formed and chronic renal disease may follow.

The most convincing evidence for the immunopathological basis of choriomeningitis is its prevention by immunosuppression. Since Rowe's observation that irradiation prior to infection prevented or delayed the onset of disease (10), a number of investigators have shown that other immunosuppressive procedures are also effective to a greater or lesser degree.

One of the most efficient ways to convert a potentially lethal cerebral infection to a carrier state is by the use of cyclophosphamide. A single immunosuppressive dose of this drug given within 2 to 3 days after intracerebral inoculation of adult mice with the neurotropic Armstrong strain of LCM virus prevents the development of immune-mediated choriomeningitis and results in the development of a chronic asymptomatic carrier infection (1). This simple manipulation, combined with the use of adoptive immunization, provided the means to determine which of the immune-response components generated during acute infection is responsible for the elicitation of, and also recovery from, disease.

As first shown by studies from our laboratory, splenic lymphocytes obtained from mice immunized by intraperitoneal injection with Armstrong virus, when adoptively transferred to syngeneic cyclophosphamide-induced virus carrier mice, regularly produce an acute lethal central nervous system disease which, clinically and histologically, is typical of classical LCM (1, 3, 5). The administration of serum with high virus-specific CF activity is without effect. Furthermore, central nervous system disease mediated by exogenous immune lymphoid cells requires the participation of T lymphocytes. Depletion of this population with anti-θ serum and complement completely abrogates the ability of the transferred cells to elicit LCM, although their capacity to produce virus-specific CF antibody is retained (3). These findings, together with the fact that neutralizing antibody is not detected during acute infections, constitute a strong argument against any significant role of antibody in mediating acute disease.

Only carrier mice produced by intracerebral virus inoculation, followed by immunosuppression with cyclophosphamide, are uniformly susceptible to the development of fatal choriomeningitis elicited by immune lymphocyte transfer, and this susceptibility is limited to a 6-week period following carrier state initiation (3). As mentioned previously, adoptive immunization of mice with carrier states initiated at birth results in virus clearance, but this occurs in the total absence of choriomeningitis. These contrasting outcomes can be accommodated by again considering the dynamics of the infection within the central nervous system. Replication of virus in the intracerebrally inoculated adult mouse is initially confined to the neural membranes— namely, the leptomeninges, the ependyma, and the choroid plexus (1). Cells comprising these membranes and whose surfaces have been altered by virus serve as the primary targets of immune attack. Superimposing an immunosuppressive dose of cyclophosphamide permanently prevents this attack and also allows the infection to spread to susceptible cells in the neural parenchyma as well as those in other tissues. However, productive infection in the neural membranes can continue only for a limited period of time for reasons already discussed. These membranes, in both the cyclophosphamide-induced carrier and the neonatally inoculated carrier, eventually become insusceptible to immune-mediated damage because they no longer display the appropriate viral antigens.

Virus-specific cytotoxic T lymphocytes appear in the spleens of adult mice about 5 days after either intraperitoneal or intracerebral infection with the Armstrong strain of LCM virus. The response peaks between 8 and 10 days (when intracerebrally inoculated animals die), and in intraperitoneally inoculated animals it declines rapidly at about the time infectious virus is cleared from the spleen, becoming undetectable by 30 days (8).

The temporal relationship of the appearance of cytotoxic T cells, the disappearance of infectious virus in spleen, and the development of choriomeningitis suggests that both recovery from infection and fatal disease resulting from cerebral infection are mediated by cytotoxic T cells. That such is the case is illustrated by experimental evidence presented in detail elsewhere (8).

ACKNOWLEDGMENTS

This work was supported by Public Health Service grants NS11286 and RCDA 46242.

LITERATURE CITED

1. Cole, G. A., D. H. Gilden, A. A. Monjan, and N. Nathanson. 1971. Lymphocytic choriomeningitis virus. Pathogenesis of acute central nervous system disease. Fed. Proc. **30:**1831–1841.
2. Cole, G. A., and N. Nathanson. 1974. Lymphocytic choriomeningitis. Pathogenesis. Prog. Med. Virol. **18:** 95–110.
3. Cole, G. A., N. Nathanson, and R. A. Prendergast. 1972. Requirement for θ-bearing cells in lymphocytic choriomengitis virus-induced central nervous system disease. Nature (London) **238:**335–337.

4. **Cole, G. A., R. A. Prendergast, and C. S. Henney.** 1973. In vitro correlates of LCM virus-induced immune response, p. 61–71. *In* F. Lehmann-Grube (ed.), Lymphocytic choriomeningitis virus and other arenaviruses. Springer, Vienna.

5. **Gilden, D. H., G. A. Cole, and N. Nathanson.** 1972. Immunopathogenesis of acute central nervous system disease produced by lymphocytic choriomeningitis virus. II. Adoptive immunization of virus carriers. J. Exp. Med. **135:**874–889.

6. **Hotchin, J.** 1971. Virus, cell surface and self: lymphocytic choriomeningitis of mice. Am. J. Clin. Pathol. **56:**333–349.

7. **Hotchin, J.** 1974. The role of transient infection in arenavirus persistence. Prog. Med. Virol. **18:**81–93.

8. **Johnson, E. D., and G. A. Cole.** 1975. Functional heterogeneity of lymphocytic choriomeningitis virus-specific T lymphocytes. I. Identification of effector and memory subsets. J. Exp. Med. **141:**866–881.

9. **Oldstone, M. B. A., and F. J. Dixon.** 1971. Immune complex disease in chronic viral infections. J. Exp. Med. **134:**32s–40s.

10. **Rowe, W. P.** 1954. Studies on pathogenesis and immunity in lymphocytic choriomeningitis infection in the mouse. Research report NM 005 048.14.01. Naval Medical Research Institute, Bethesda, Md.

11. **Traub, E.** 1936. An epidemic in a mouse colony due to the virus of acute lymphocytic choriomeningitis. J. Exp. Med. **63:**533–546.

12. **Traub, E.** 1936. Persistence of lymphocytic choriomeningitis virus in immune animals and its relation to immunity. J. Exp. Med. **63:**847–861.

13. **Traub, E.** 1936. The epidemiology of lymphocytic choriomeningitis in white mice. J. Exp. Med. **64:**183–200.

14. **Zinkernagel, R. M., and P. C. Doherty.** 1974. Immunological surveillance against altered self components by sensitized T lymphocytes in lymphocytic choriomeningitis. Nature (London) **251:**547–548.

Persistent Infection of Wild Mice with Murine Leukemia Virus

MURRAY B. GARDNER

Department of Pathology, University of Southern California School of Medicine, Los Angeles, California 90033

INTRODUCTION

This paper describes a recently discovered naturally occurring population of wild mice (*Mus musculus*) persistently infected with indigenous murine leukemia virus (MuLV). We will summarize the host-virus relationship of this persistent infection and the pathogenesis of its associated diseases.

EPIDEMIOLOGY AND VIRUS EXPRESSION

Wild mice from most of the trapping areas in southern California, upon aging in the laboratory, are cancer resistant, are completely free from motor neuron disease, and show throughout life only a low level of indigenous MuLV activity (5, 7). By contrast, wild mice from one particular trapping area, a squab farm near Lake Casitas (LC) in rural southwest Ventura County, show, at time of trapping and throughout life, a high level of indigenous MuLV activity and a proneness to develop spontaneous lymphoma, other tumors (hepatoma, breast carcinoma, lung adenoma), and a neurogenic lower-limb paralytic disease (4–6).

In LC mice both spontaneous lymphoma and paralysis have an onset at about 10 to 12 months of age; thereafter, lymphoma occurs in 2% of the surviving mice per month until all are dead after 35 months, whereas paralysis occurs in about 2% of the surviving mice until 18 months of age, after which it no longer develops. The increased incidence of breast carcinoma, hepatoma, and lung adenoma in LC mice is not apparent until even later in life (5). Thus, among a starting population of 2,000 newly trapped LC mice, about 16% eventually develop lymphoma, 12% develop paralysis, and 4% develop other tumors. Lymphoma is twice as common in LC females as in males, but paralysis has an equal sex distribution. LC mice with paralysis have a 12-fold increased risk of developing lymphoma compared with LC mice without paralysis.

After several weeks of age, most (85 to 90%) LC mice have in their liver, spleen, and genital organs high titers ($\geq$1:4) of MuLV group-specific (gs) (p30) antigen by complement fixation (CF), numerous type C particles by electron microscopy, and high titers (10^3 to 10^5 fluorescent focus-forming units [FFFU] per gram of tissue) of infectious virus (10). They also have infectious virus in their tail clips and serum filtrates (average $10^{3.5}$ FFFU/ml; 15). Virus is concentrated in B lymphocyte areas of normal spleens and hepatocytes of normal livers.

Those LC mice destined to develop paralysis generally have at time of trapping a significantly higher serum MuLV p30 titer (>100 ng/ml) compared with those mice later developing lymphoma or remaining free from these diseases (10). Mice dying with lymphoma have only a slightly higher serum p30 titer at trapping compared with mice that do not develop lymphoma. At death, markedly elevated serum p30 titers (>200 ng/ml) and spleen CF p30 antigen are found in almost all (~90%) LC mice regardless of diagnosis. Virus is detected in the central nervous system mainly in those LC mice with lymphoma or paralysis (6).

EXPERIMENTAL TRANSMISSION

Both lymphoma and paralysis are transmissible with virus preparations from LC wild mice, including those never housed in the laboratory. Disease-producing isolates have been obtained from embryo extracts (ether-bathed before extract preparation to remove external contamination from maternal virus), cultured embryo cells in primary or secondary passage or after 4 years of passage in vitro, spleen extracts of normal young mice, or spleen and central nervous system extracts from mice with lymphoma or paralysis (6, 16). The in vivo host range for induction of both lymphoma and paralysis includes Fv-1^{NN} strains of laboratory mice and also cancer-resistant wild mice. The LC isolates induce serial transmission of lymphoma and paralysis in rats, and serial transmission from rats back to mice has produced both lymphoma and paralysis. Other rodents, e.g., peromyscus, rabbits, hamsters, and guinea pigs, are resistant to experimental infection.

The paralytic disease is strikingly age and dose dependent, being transmissible mainly within the first few days of life (6, 16). After inoculation of concentrated virus from tissue culture fluids into newborns by intraperitoneal, intracranial, or intravenous routes, virtually 100% of the survivors develop paralysis, usually without lymphoma, within 6 to 12 weeks. With less potent virus inocula or with slightly older recipients, the frequency of paralysis is reduced and the frequency of lymphoma is 10 to 30% after 4 to 12 months. The experimentally induced lymphoma and paralysis are pathologically and virologically very similar to the natural diseases (6, 16). Both experimentally induced paralysis and lymphoma are preventable by in vitro neutralization of virus inocula with type-specific antisera (13).

NATURAL VIRUS TRANSMISSION

The isolation of MuLV from LC embryo cultures in primary or early passage (10), the transmission of lymphoma with LC embryo extracts (ether-bathed to remove external virus), and the demonstration of numerous virus particles and infectious virus in maternal breast tissue, milk (19), endometrium, ovary, salivary gland (18), and amniotic fluid, and in male genital organs (10, 18), document the potential for vertical epigenetic (nongenetic) virus spread in LC mice. Furthermore, reciprocal crosses and foster nursing experiments leave no doubt that epigenetic spread of LC virus, transplacentally and via milk, is of singular importance in causing increased infectious virus expression early in life. There is , however, no evidence of MuLV spread to or from the birds or other wild rodents cohabiting this ranch.

VIRUS PROPERTIES IN VITRO

The virus population in LC and other wild mice consists of a mixed population of two MuLV classes: (i) mouse-tropic or ecotropic virions and (ii) a new class of MuLV with a broad in vitro host range (3, 12). The latter are called "amphotropic" (17) because they exhibit the in vitro host range of both mouse-tropic and xenotropic (replicate only in heterologous species) classes of MuLV. The amphotropic virus strains are also a distinct MuLV class based upon interference and neutralization criteria (12). Only the mouse-tropic virus produces a positive XC cell test. These amphotropic viruses of wild mice may represent "wild-type" or ancestral virus from which the ecotropic and xenotropic viruses of laboratory mice were derived. As yet, we have not isolated a purely xenotropic virus strain from wild mice. In vivo transmission experiments with cloned viruses suggest that the mouse (eco)-tropic strains in-

duce both the paralytic disease and lymphoma whereas the amphotropic strains induce only lymphoma.

IMMUNE RESPONSIVENESS

In adult LC mice, free virus-specific antibodies (>1:10) to indigenous MuLV detectable by virus neutralization or immunofluorescence are completely absent (15), nor can free antibody be detected by a sensitive radioimmunoprecipitation assay except in a few uniquely virus-negative LC mice. However, even these virus-negative LC mice have no detectable neutralizing or immunofluorescent antibody. LC mice do not respond with a measurable rise in neutralizing antibody to immunization with their indigenous MuLV given as formalinized vaccine or as MSV pseudotype (15). By contrast, LC mice show a normal humoral immune response to an unrelated antigen (sheep red blood cells), and their overall longevity and normal histopathological response to other pathogens attest to a generally vigorous immune responsiveness. Ia and Ir typings give no evidence of an abnormality of these H-2-linked traits in LC mice (14).

There is no histopathological or immunofluorescent evidence in LC mice of immune complex glomerulonephritis or arteritis. Viral p30 (core) and gp70 (envelope) antigens are not detected by fluorescent microscopy in glomeruli or Kupfer cells of the liver. In preliminary experiments, the virus titer in LC mouse sera is not reduced by anti-mouse gamma globulin antiserum (15). It thus appears that LC mice have at least a partial immunological tolerance to their indigenous MuLV associated with pre- and perinatal epigenetic infection with this virus. An important role for cellular immunity in curtailing latent MuLV infection in LC wild mice is shown by the effect of antithymocyte serum (ATS) treatment, which increases the incidence of lymphoma and paralysis as well as activating latent cytomegalovirus (11).

PATHOLOGY

The pathogenic features of the paralytic disease in LC wild mice are found primarily in the anterior lateral horn of the lumbosacral spinal cord (1, 6). They consist of spongiosis, gliosis, and vacuolar neuronal degeneration without inflammation. Numerous type C particles are seen by electron microscopy in the extracellular spaces of the neuropil and budding from glia and endothelia. Aberrant intracytoplasmic type C particles are seen within some anterior horn neurons, whereas only severely vacuolated and degenerative neurons are apparently free from virus particles. Budding from neuronal plasma membranes is only rarely seen. The affected musculature shows neurogenic atrophy. In LC mice the lymphomas are usually generalized with early spleen involvement and leukemia; they are mostly poorly differentiated lymphocytic type and of B or null cell origin (2).

GENETIC AND IMMUNOLOGICAL CONTROL OF INDIGENOUS MuLV

Cross-breeding of LC wild mice with C57 B10 Sn (B10) inbred mice has resulted in a near total suppression of LC virus expression early in life (9) and in a dramatic reduction in lymphoma and paralysis occurrence in the F1 and B10 back-cross progeny (8). A dominant homozygous Fv-1^b gene of B10 mice is a major factor responsible for this suppressive effect. Repeated passive immunization of laboratory-bred newborn LC mice with anti-virus goat immunoglobulin has led to a dramatic suppression of infectious MuLV at 5 to 7 weeks of age.

SUMMARY

The salient features of this naturally occurring model of persistent MuLV infection can be summarized as follows:

(1) Congenitally acquired, lifelong persistent infection with MuLV.

(2) Two classes of indigenous MuLV: (i) mouse-tropic; (ii) amphotropic.

(3) Immune tolerance specifically to indigenous MuLV. Absence of detectable viral immune complexes. General immunity intact. Cellular immunity important in controlling virus expression.

(4) Virus is essential determinant of lymphoma (both classes of MuLV) and paralysis (mouse-tropic class only).

(5) Neuronal damage due to a direct neurotropic effect of MuLV.

(6) Lymphoma of B or null (non-T cell) origin.

(7) Virus and associated diseases controllable by genetic means. Virus suppressible by passive immunization in newborn period.

The LC colony of wild mice is characterized by a congenitally acquired lifelong persistent infection with indigenous MuLV, a relative humoral immune tolerance specifically to this virus, and an increased incidence of lymphoma, carcinoma, and a neurogenic hind-leg paralysis. The indigenous MuLV is the essential determinant of the lymphoma and paralysis, the latter apparently by means of a direct viral neurotropism. The MuLV population in wild mice consists of two distinct classes with different antigenic and pathogenic properties. Virus replication and associated diseases are preventable by genetic cross-breeding, and virus is suppressed by passive immunization of LC newborns with heterologous anti-virus immunoglobulin.

ACKNOWLEDGMENTS

The work described in this paper was conducted under Public Health Service contract NO1 CP 53500 with the Virus Cancer Program of the National Cancer Institute.

LITERATURE CITED

1. **Andrews, J. M., and M. B. Gardner.** 1974. Lower motor neuron degeneration associated with type C RNA virus infection in mice: neuropathological features. J. Neuropathol. Exp. Neurol. **33:**285–307.

2. **Blankenhorn, E. P., M. B. Gardner, and J. D. Estes.** 1975. Immunogenetics of a thymus antigen in lymphoma-prone and lymphoma-resistant colonies of wild mice. J. Natl. Cancer Inst. **54:**665–672.

3. **Bryant, M. L., and V. Klement.** 1976. Clonal heterogeneity of wild mouse leukemia viruses: host range and antigenicity. Virology **73:**532–536.

4. **Gardner, M. B., B. E. Henderson, J. D. Estes, H. Menck, J. C. Parker, and R. J. Huebner.** 1973. Unusually high incidence of spontaneous lymphomas in wild house mice. J. Natl. Cancer Inst. **50:**1571–1579.

5. **Gardner, M. B., B. E. Henderson, J. D. Estes, R. W. Rongey, J. Casagrande, M. Pike, and R. J. Huebner.** 1976. The epidemiology and virology of C-type virus-associated hematological cancers and related diseases in wild mice. Cancer Res. **36:**574–581.

6. **Gardner, M. B., B. E. Henderson, J. E. Officer, R. W. Rongey, J. C. Parker, C. Oliver, J. D. Estes, and R. J. Huebner.** 1973. A spontaneous lower motor neuron disease apparently caused by indigenous typeC RNA virus in wild mice. J. Natl. Cancer Inst. **51:** 1243–1254.

7. **Gardner, M. B., B. E. Henderson, R. W. Rongey, J. D. Estes, and R. J. Huebner.** 1973. Spontaneous tumors of aging wild house mice. Incidence, pathology, and C-type virus expression. J. Natl. Cancer Inst. **50:** 719–734.

8. **Gardner, M. B., V. Klement, B. E. Henderson, J. D. Estes, M. Dougherty, J. Casagrande, and R. J. Huebner.** 1976. Efforts to control type C virus expression in wild mice, p. 391–407. In M. A. Chirigos (ed.), Control of neoplasia by modulation of the immune system. Raven Press, New York.

9. **Gardner, M. B., V. Klement, B. E. Henderson, H. Meier, J. D. Estes, and R. J. Huebner.** 1976. Genetic control of type C virus of wild mice. Nature (London) **259:**143–145.

10. **Gardner, M. B., V. Klement, R. W. Rongey, P. McConahey, J. D. Estes, and R. J. Huebner.** 1976. Type C virus expression in lymphoma-paralysis prone LC wild mice. J. Natl. Cancer Inst. **57:**585–590.

11. **Gardner, M. B., J. E. Officer, J. Parker, J. D. Estes, and R. J. Huebner.** 1974. Induction of disseminated virulent cytomegalovirus infection by immunosuppression of naturally chronically infected wild mice. Infect. Immun. **10:**966–969.

12. **Hartley, J. W., and W. P. Rowe.** 1976. Naturally occurring murine leukemia viruses in wild mice: characterization of a new "amphotropic" class. J. Virol. **19:**19–25.

13. **Henderson, B. E., M. B. Gardner, R. V. Gilden, J. D. Estes, and R. J. Huebner.** 1974. Prevention of lower limb paralysis by neutralization of type-C RNA virus in wild mice. J. Natl. Cancer Inst. **53:**1091–1092.

14. **Klein, J., M. Hauptfeld, C. F. Merryman, P. H. Maurer, and M. B. Gardner.** 1976. Histocompatibility-2 system of wild mice. IV. Ia and Ir typing of two wild mouse populations. Cold Spring Harbor Symp. Quant. Biol., in press.

15. **Klement, V., M. B. Gardner, B. E. Henderson, J. N. Ihle, J. D. Estes, A. G. Stanley, and R. V. Gilden.** 1976.

Inefficient humoral immune response of lymphoma-prone wild mice to persistent leukemia virus infection. J. Natl. Cancer Inst. **57**:1169–1173.

16. **Officer, J. E., N. Tecson, J. D. Estes, E. Fontanilla, R. W. Rongey, and M. B. Gardner.** 1973. Isolation of a neurotropic type C virus. Science **181**:945–947.

17. **Rasheed, S., M. B. Gardner, and E. Chan.** 1976. Amphotropic host range of naturally occurring wild mouse leukemia viruses. J. Virol. **19**:13–18.

18. **Rongey, R. W., A. H. Abtin, J. D. Estes, and M. B. Gardner.** 1975. Mammary tumor virus particles in the submaxillary gland, seminal vesicle, and nonmammary tumors of wild mice. J. Natl. Cancer Inst. **54**:1149–1156.

19. **Rongey, R. W., A. Hlavackova, S. Lara, J. D. Estes, and M. B. Gardner.** 1973. Types B and C RNA virus in breast tissue and milk of wild mice. J. Natl. Cancer Inst. **50**:1581–1589.

Aleutian Disease of Mink: a Persistent Viral Infection

DAVID D. PORTER AND AUSTIN E. LARSEN

*Department of Pathology, University of California School of Medicine, Los Angeles, California 90024, and
Department of Microbiology, University of Utah College of Medicine, Salt Lake City, Utah 84112*

Aleutian disease (AD) is the most important disease of ranch-raised mink from an economic standpoint. Aleutian disease virus (ADV) initially replicates as rapidly in vivo as viruses causing acute infections, but it produces a persistent infection in most mink. The disease does not appear to result from ADV replication, but rather is caused by deposition of immune complexes in tissues with subsequent inflammation. ADV appears to be an autonomous parvovirus, and it is temperature sensitive for in vitro replication as initially isolated from persistently infected mink. Although the mechanism by which ADV produces persistent infection is unclear, we propose testable hypotheses.

THE VIRUS AND VIRAL REPLICATION

ADV has an icosahedral 23- to 25-nm structure, but its nucleic acid type and structure have not been determined by chemical methods. It initially replicates in cell nuclei, has a density of 1.405 to 1.430 g/ml in CsCl, and is relatively stable to many chemicals, low pH, and high temperatures. These properties suggest that ADV is likely to be a member of the parvovirus group. ADV has recently been reviewed (3). In vivo, initial viral replication is rapid, and maximal titers of 10^8 to 10^9 ID_{50}/g are found in the spleen, liver, and lymph nodes 10 days after intraperitoneal infection (14). Virus titers then slowly fall to 10^5 ID_{50}/g in tissues and 10^4 ID_{50}/ml in serum 2 or more months after infection. Unlike some other persistent viral infections, the ability of ADV to establish a persistent infection is not dependent upon the age of the host. Immunofluorescence studies show ADV antigens principally in the cytoplasm of macrophages in many organs of infected mink. It has not been established whether ADV replicates in these cells or is phagocytized as an immune complex. Although all the tested strains of ADV behave in a similar fashion in mink of the Aleutian genotype, there are marked variations in viral titers and disease production by various ADV strains in non-Aleutian mink (1, 4).

In vitro, ADV can be isolated in feline kidney cells only if the cells are maintained at a reduced temperature of 31.8°C (D. D. Porter et al., Fed. Proc. **34**:947, 1975; Porter et al., Intervirology, in press). After serial passage at the reduced temperature, three of five ADV strains tested replicated well at 37 or 39°C. We have found four additional ADV strains which induce viral antigen but produce no infectious virus even at 31.8°C. Koch's postulates have been fulfilled with the three isolates which grow at 37°C. When the 37°C-adapted virus is returned to mink there appears to be a tendency for the mink to reselect ADV which will grow only at reduced temperatures. Our ADV isolates produce infectious virus only in feline cells, although they will induce viral antigen in mink cells. It should be noted that our isolates have properties significantly different from ADV studied by Yoon et al. (18). We have found no immunological relationship of ADV to a number of other parvoviruses.

PATHOLOGY AND PATHOGENESIS

The host responses to ADV infection have been studied extensively, and three recent reviews are available (6, 7, 13). The characteristic lesion of ADV is a marked systemic proliferation of plasma cells which is associated with elevated immunoglobulin levels. Mink with severe AD typically have an immunoglobulin level of 4 to 6 g/100 ml of serum, and in extreme cases 11 g/100 ml is observed. The majority of the increased immunoglobulin is IgG (11), but increases in IgM and IgA are found (Porter, unpublished data). Persistently infected mink develop extremely high levels of ADV-specific antibody (1, 14), but the proportion of the increased immunoglobulin which is virus-specific antibody remains unknown. Although mink antibody can be shown to combine with the virion surface by electron microscopy, no viral neutralization can be demonstrated in vivo or in vitro. The best ADV antibody test for routine use is counterelectrophoresis (Crawford et al., J. Immunol., in press). Various sizes of antigen-antibody complexes smaller than complete virions are present in the serum of chronically infected mink (11), and ADV in the circulation of such mink is in the form of infectious virion-antibody complexes (12). Glomerulonephritis and arteritis are produced by tissue deposition of ADV-antibody-complement complexes, and the majority of deaths of mink with AD are caused by these two lesions (8, 14, 16).

The tissue lesions of AD can be prevented by continuous immunosuppression (2), and the drug treatment does not alter ADV titers. Passive transfer of specific antibody to ADV into mink with early infection causes lesions characteristic of late AD, and immunization of mink with a killed ADV vaccine causes accelerated lesions and enhanced infectivity of the virus when the mink are subsequently challenged with live ADV (15).

Although it is clear that mink of all genetic types may develop persistent ADV infection and get severe AD, some mink of non-Aleutian genotypes may have nonpersistent infections. About one-fourth of non-Aleutian mink inoculated with 10^5 ID_{50} of the most virulent strain of AD clear their viremia and fail to develop tissue lesions or elevated immunoglobulin or ADV antibody levels. Offspring of such mink have a similar response to ADV challenge, indicating that such resistance is not due to one or two host genes (9). Less virulent ADV strains fail to induce progressive disease in non-Aleutian mink, but at least some such mink retain low levels of ADV in their lymphoid tissue (4).

HOST RANGE AND TRANSMISSION

The epizootiology of Aleutian disease has been thoroughly reviewed (5). Wild and domesticated mink in all areas of the world have an appreciable incidence of AD which is probably near 20%. The closely related ferret often becomes persistently infected by the virus and develops hyperglobulinemia, but usually fails to develop other tissue lesions. Several wild carnivores, especially skunks, have antibody to ADV (7) and might serve as reservoirs of this virus.

Chronically infected mink excrete ADV in the urine, feces, and saliva, and transmission by these materials is probable. In addition, the virus can cross the placenta and infect the offspring (10). The relative importance of vertical and horizontal transmission of the virus has not been established.

CONCLUSIONS

Although AD was not recognized until the coat-color mutant mink of Aleutian genotype were raised in commercial numbers, the nature of the host-virus interaction suggests that an extensive mutual adaptation has occurred. ADV replication in mink is relatively or completely innocuous. The severe disease observed during persistent infection by this agent results from the host immune response and ensuing ADV-antibody complexes which are deposited in tissue. Inadequate information exists on viral characterization and the mechanism of viral persistence in the face of an apparently maximal host immune response. The temperature-sensitive replication of the wild-type virus may well be responsible for viral persistence in vivo (17). We are currently attempting to assess this point. Alternatively, the mink antibody response to the virus may be qualitatively deficient, and this may aid persistence by encouraging phagocytosis of virion-antibody complexes which may replicate in the phagocytic cells (14). We believe that the chances are good for defining the mechanism by which ADV can persistently infect mink.

ACKNOWLEDGMENTS

This work was supported by Public Health Service grant AI-09476 from the National Institute of Allergy and Infectious Diseases and by the Mink Farmers' Research Foundation.

LITERATURE CITED

1. **Bloom, M. E., R. E. Race, W. J. Hadlow, and B. Chesebro.** 1975. Aleutian disease of mink: the antibody response of sapphire and pastel mink to Aleutian disease virus. J. Immunol. **115:**1034–1037.
2. **Cheema, A., J. B. Henson, and J. R. Gorham.** 1972. Aleutian disease of mink. Prevention of lesions by immunosuppression. Am. J. Pathol. **66:**543–556.
3. **Cho, H. J.** 1976. Purification and structure of Aleutian disease virus, p. 159–174. *In* R. H. Kimberlin (ed.), Slow virus diseases of animals and man. North-Holland Publishing Co., Amsterdam.
4. **Eklund, C. M., W. J. Hadlow, R. C. Kennedy, C. C. Boyle, and T. A. Jackson.** 1968. Aleutian disease of mink: properties of the etiologic agent and the host responses. J. Infect. Dis. **118:**510–526.
5. **Gorham, J. R., J. B. Henson, T. B. Crawford, and G. A. Padgett.** 1976. The epizootiology of Aleutian disease, p. 135–158. *In* R. H. Kimberlin (ed.), Slow virus diseases of animals and man. North-Holland Publishing Co., Amsterdam.
6. **Henson, J. B., J. R. Gorham, T. C. McGuire, and T. B. Crawford.** 1976. Pathology and pathogenesis of Aleutian disease, p. 175–205. *In* R. H. Kimberlin (ed.), Slow virus diseases of animals and man. North-Holland Publishing Co., Amsterdam.
7. **Ingram, D. G., and H. J. Cho.** 1974. Aleutian disease in mink: virology, immunology and pathogenesis. J. Rheumatol. **1:**74–92.
8. **Johnson, M. I., J. B. Henson, and J. R. Gorham.**

1975. The influence of genotype on the development of glomerular lesions in mink with Aleutian disease virus. Am. J. Pathol. **81:**321–336.

9. **Larsen, A. E., and D. D. Porter.** 1975. Pathogenesis of Aleutian disease of mink: identification of non-persistent infections. Infect. Immun. **11:**92–94.

10. **Padgett, G. A., J. R. Gorham, and J. B. Henson.** 1967. Epizootiologic studies of Aleutian disease. I. Transplacental transmission of the virus. J. Infect. Dis. **117:**35–38.

11. **Porter, D. D., F. J. Dixon, and A. E. Larsen.** 1965. Metabolism and function of gamma globulin in Aleutian disease of mink. J. Exp. Med. **121:**889–900.

12. **Porter, D. D., and A. E. Larsen.** 1967. Aleutian disease of mink: infectious virus-antibody complexes in the serum. Proc. Soc. Exp. Biol. Med. **126:**680–682.

13. **Porter, D. D., and A. E. Larsen.** 1974. Aleutian disease of mink. Prog. Med. Virol. **18:**32–47.

14. **Porter, D. D., A. E. Larsen, and H. G. Porter.** 1969. The pathogenesis of Aleutian disease of mink. I. In vivo viral replication and the host antibody response to viral antigen. J. Exp. Med. **130:**575–593.

15. **Porter, D. D., A. E. Larsen, and H. G. Porter.** 1972. The pathogenesis of Aleutian disease of mink. II. Enhancement of tissue lesions following the administration of a killed virus vaccine or passive antibody. J. Immunol. **109:**1–7.

16. **Porter, D. D., A. E. Larsen, and H. G. Porter.** 1973. The pathogenesis of Aleutian disease of mink. III. Immune complex arteritis. Am. J. Pathol. **71:**331–334.

17. **Preble, O. T., and J. S. Youngner.** 1975. Temperature-sensitive viruses and the etiology of chronic and inapparent infections. J. Infect. Dis. **131:**467–473.

18. **Yoon, J-W., A. K. Dunker, and A. J. Kenyon.** 1975. Characterization of Aleutian mink disease virus. Virology **64:**575–580.

Chronic Theiler's Virus Infection in Mice

HOWARD L. LIPTON, MAURO C. DAL CANTO, AND STANLEY G. RABINOWITZ

Departments of Neurology, Pathology, and Internal Medicine, Northwestern University-McGaw Medical
Center and Veterans Administration Lakeside Hospital, Chicago, Illinois 60611

HISTORICAL PERSPECTIVE

In 1934, Theiler reported that he had recovered several isolates from the central nervous systems (CNS) of spontaneously paralyzed mice (11). Experimental transmission of these isolates to other mice by intracerebral and intranasal inoculation produced a similar paralytic disease, and the histopathology of CNS lesions closely resembled human poliomyelitis. Theiler showed by membrane filtration that these agents were indeed viruses, in the range of 20 nm in diameter, and by cross-neutralization tests he showed that they were serologically related (12). In addition, he also demonstrated that surviving paralyzed mice had chronic CNS infection. This was one of the first reports of a chronic virus infection of an animal host. Several years later, similar isolates were recovered from the intestinal contents of normal weanling mice, and it then became clear that Theiler's viruses are enteric pathogens that usually cause asymptomatic intestinal infections (9, 13). On rare occasion, viremia with spread of virus to the CNS probably occurs and results in spontaneous paralysis.

In 1952, Daniels and co-workers (2) described extensive myelin destruction in the spinal cords of four mice sacrificed several months after infection with the DA strain of Theiler's virus. This was the first recognition that this persistent infection was associated with a more chronic CNS pathology. Aside from the identification of Theiler's virus nucleic acid as RNA (3), very little is known about the molecular biology of these viruses.

It is now possible to separate Theiler's viruses into two groups on the basis of their biological behavior (Table 1). All isolates from brains of spontaneously paralyzed mice and stools of asymptomatic mice resemble Theiler's original virus isolates and are referred to as TO strains. In contrast, more neurovirulent strains of Theiler's viruses also exist and are a documented cause of epizootics of encephalitis in mice (8, 14). However, only the TO strains are known to produce persistent CNS infections.

PATHOGENESIS OF THEILER'S VIRUS INFECTION

We have found that experimental Theiler's virus infection of weanling mice produces a biphasic disease process—an initial phase of flaccid paralysis and a later phase of generalized spasticity (4). Although there are differences in susceptibility among various strains of mice, SJL/J mice are particularly prone to develop the late manifestations of this infection (6). After intracerebral inoculation of approximately 1,000 50% suckling mouse mean lethal doses of the DA strain of Theiler's virus, two-thirds of mice develop flaccid paralysis between 9 and 20 days (early disease), but only a small percentage die (Fig. 1). The majority of animals then recover from paralysis within a few weeks of its onset, and subsequently almost all infected mice develop spastic paralysis between 1 and 3 months (late disease). We have also found that the Yale strain produces both phases of disease. These mice have a distinctive waddling and spastic gait, and minimal stimulation results in loss of balance and prolonged extensor spasms. Although the clinical manifestations of late disease are progressive, most affected mice can be kept alive for many months.

Although there may be brief viremia after intracerebral inoculation, limited virus growth occurs in extraneural organs. However, during the first 3 weeks there is logarithmic virus growth in the CNS (Fig. 1), and virus antigen is found in the cytoplasm of neurons and possibly other cell types in the gray matter of the spinal cord, brainstem, and thalamus by fluorescent-antibody staining. Between 1 and 12 months, low levels of infectious virus are still detectable in the spinal cords of most mice, but the titer declines over this period of time. Virus antigen has not been observed in the CNS after 1 month.

The histopathology of this infection is limited to the nervous system. Initially, gray-matter involvement predominates and principally consists of patchy areas of neuronal necrosis, neuronophagia, and microglial cell proliferation

TABLE 1. *Biology of Theiler's virus isolates*

Characteristic	TO strains[a]	GDVII and FA
Incubation period	7–30 days	2–8 days
CNS syndrome..........	Paralysis	Encephalitis
CNS virus content ($\log_{10}$/g)...............	$<10^6$	$>10^6$
Cytopathic effect (brain-derived virus) ...	–	+
Hemagglutination[b]	±	+

[a] Those strains resembling Theiler's original isolates.
[b] Type O human erythrocytes.

in the spinal cord, brainstem, and thalamus. Some mononuclear and plasma cells are present in the neuropil and in perivascular sites of the gray matter. As illustrated in Fig. 1, the activity of this lesion ceases by about 1 month. Spinal cord leptomeningeal and white-matter involvement commences later (third week of infection), gradually increases in severity, and is still present 8 to 12 months after infection (Fig. 1). Focal collections of mononuclear and some plasma cells are found in the leptomeninges, in perivascular sites, and extending into the white matter. Epon-embedded, toluidine blue-stained sections have shown that myelin is the primary structure damaged in the white matter (1). Single demyelinated axons as well as clusters are found scattered amidst the inflammatory cells, and numerous macrophages containing myelin debris are located in these lesions. Remyelinating axons and astrocytic gliosis become more prominent with the passage of time. Ultrastructurally, stripping of myelin lamellae by mononuclear cell processes and vesiculation of myelin independent of mononuclear cells are the morphological events accompanying myelin destruction. In addition, oligodendrocytes, the myelin-maintaining cells, do not appear to be infected since normal oligodendrocytes are frequently identified in the vicinity of naked axons whereas degenerating oligodendrocytes have not been observed. As yet, picornavirus particles have not been seen in the CNS at any stage of the infection, but this is not unexpected considering the relatively low virus titers and the small size of these virions.

The temporal development of humoral and cellular immunity in this experimental infection is shown in Fig. 1. Although serum neutralizing antibodies are present by 1 week, there is an unusually gradual rise of antibody titers during the first 2 months of infection. In addition, the kinetics of the cellular immune response to virus as determined by in vitro incorporation of [³H]thymidine into DNA of spleen cells in response to UV-inactivated Theiler's virus antigen

is also unusual (10). Spleen cell reactivity is not detectable until 2 months, but once established it is present throughout the first year after intracerebral inoculation in parallel with CNS virus replication. In contrast to this pattern of response, after intraperitoneal infection spleen cell reactivity reaches a maximum by 1 week and declines by 2 weeks.

Since Theiler's virus does not appear to be an inherently poor antigen, the delay in these host immune responses may in part be due to limited exposure of the immune system to virus. Without significant extraneural virus replication, systemic immune responses would depend in large measure on the continuous leakage of virus across the blood-brain barrier. Because spleen cells from infected mice respond to the T cell mitogens concanavalin A and phytohemagglutinin as well as cells from control animals, the absence of spleen cell reactivity to virus antigen until 2 months does not appear to be due to an immunosuppressive effect of this infection (10). Since the clearance of viruses is dependent on host immune responses, it is possible that the lack of brisk immune responses somehow may promote the establishment of persistent Theiler's virus infection.

EFFECT OF IMMUNOSUPPRESSION ON THEILER'S VIRUS INFECTION

The involvement of two populations of cells in the CNS at different times after infection suggested to us that there may be more than a single mechanism of virus-induced cellular injury responsible for tissue damage in Theiler's virus infection. The earlier gray-matter lesion could be due to direct cytolytic infection of neurons, a mechanism consistent with the known effects of picornavirus replication in permissive cell cultures. Although the chronic white-matter lesion may also be the result of a direct cytocidal effect of virus, the following indirect evidence suggested an immune-mediated pathology: (i) the mononuclear inflammatory cell infiltrates in white matter are characteristic of delayed hypersensitivity reactions and clearly differ from the predominantly microglial cell response in gray matter, (ii) white-matter involvement is extensive and the amount of tissue injury seems disproportionate to the relatively low virus titers present in the spinal cord, (iii) normal oligodendrocytes, the myelin-maintaining cells, are found in the vicinity of demyelinating axons by electron microscopy and degenerating oligodendrocytes have not been seen, and (iv) the occurrence of spasticity 2 months after infection when there is maximal pathological involvement suggests that the in-

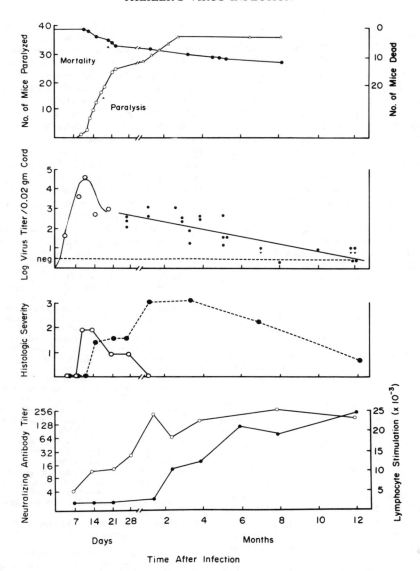

FIG. 1. *Theiler's virus infection following intracerebral inoculation of 3-week-old SJL/J mice. Top frame: Clinical course; (O) flaccid paralysis; (△) spastic paralysis. Second frame: Log$_{10}$ CNS virus titers; (O) pools of three mice; (●) individual mice. Third frame: Histological changes graded as severe (3+), moderate (2+), and mild (1+); (O) gray matter; (●) white matter. Bottom frame: Temporal course of immune responses; (O) neutralizing antibody titers determined by plaque reduction; (●) spleen cell reactivity to virus antigen determined in vitro by incorporation of [³H]thymidine into DNA.*

flammation seen in the CNS not only functions in host defense but may in fact play a role in disease production.

Because immunosuppression of experimental viral infections is now a recognized method for characterizing the role of the immune response in host defense and determining the mechanisms of cellular injury, the effect of immunosuppressive drug treatment on Theiler's virus infection was studied. In these experiments SJL/J mice were inoculated intracerebrally with Theiler's virus and then given cyclophosphamide, rabbit anti-mouse thymocyte serum, or no treatment until sacrificed on days 17 to 22. The details of the immunosuppressive regimens and the control groups are reported elsewhere (5; H. L. Lipton and M. C. Del Canto, in preparation). Both immunosuppressive agents had a similar effect on the outcome and pathology of this infection. The net result of both modalities of immunosuppression was potentiation of the infection since a significant increase in mortality and a shorter time to death were observed. There was a substantial increase in microglial proliferation and neuronal necrosis in brains and spinal cords of immunosuppressed Theiler's virus-infected mice. In the diencephalon this resulted in some focal areas of parenchymal necrosis. The distribution of virus antigen was restricted to gray matter, but there was spread of antigen to CNS areas not involved in the untreated infection, i.e., the neocortex and hippocampal complex. Virus replication was enhanced because of slower virus clearance, and this resulted in longer maintenance of higher virus levels in the CNS. Taken together, these findings indicate that Theiler's virus causes a cytolytic infection of neurons and possibly other cells in gray matter. Thus, it is reasonable to think that potentiation of a cytolytic infection in gray matter of infected, immunosuppressed mice was responsible for the increase in mortality.

In contrast to the augmented gray-matter involvement, immunosuppression caused a dramatic reduction in mononuclear inflammatory cells in the spinal cord leptomeninges and white matter. Since the induction of the inflammatory response in CNS virus infections appears to be immunologically specific (7), the lack of parenchymal inflammation would be expected if such treatment sufficiently suppressed host immunity. More important, treatment with cyclophosphamide and anti-mouse thymocyte serum prevented actual parenchymal damage, i.e., demyelination, from occurring, which suggests that this white-matter lesion is immune mediated. Adoptive immunization experiments of immunosuppressed Theiler's virus-infected mice are being conducted to further document the immunological nature of this lesion and to determine whether demyelination is due to a host immune response to virus antigen.

At present, the mechanisms involved in the establishment and maintenance of persistent picornavirus infections, including the Theiler's viruses, are unknown. However, stable carrier culture systems have been described for a number of different picornaviruses (reviewed in 15). These persistent viral cultures are in part distinguished by the fact that the virus replicates in only a fraction of the cells at a given time. The stability of these cultures has been attributed to genetic resistance of the majority of the cell population which may develop in vitro from selective pressures of the virus. It has been further hypothesized that the continued appearance of some permissive cells which become infected allows for perpetuation of the infection without total destruction of the cell monolayer. In some systems antiviral antibody or other interfering factors in addition to cellular resistance modulate the infection by preventing cell-to-cell spread of these highly cytolytic viruses. This paradigm of the persistent picornavirus state mainly describes the virus-cell relationships. The properties of the carried virus, which may be equally important in understanding the mechanisms involved in the establishment and maintenance of persistent infection, remain to be elucidated.

LITERATURE CITED

1. **Dal Canto, M. C., and H. L. Lipton.** 1975. Primary demyelination in Theiler's virus infection. An ultrastructural study. Lab. Invest. **33:**626–637.
2. **Daniels, J. B., A. M. Pappenheimer, and S. Richardson.** 1952. Observations on encephalomyelitis of mice (DA strain). J. Exp. Med. **96:**517–530.
3. **Franklin, R. M., E. Wecker, and C. Henry.** 1959. Some properties of an infectious ribonucleic acid from mouse encephalomyelitis virus. Virology **7:**220–235.
4. **Lipton, H. L.** 1975. Theiler's virus infection in mice: an unusual biphasic disease process leading to demyelination. Infect. Immun. **11:**1147–1155.
5. **Lipton, H. L., and M. C. Dal Canto.** 1976. Theiler's virus-induced demyelination: prevention by immunosuppression. Science **192:**62–64.
6. **Lipton, H. L., and M. C. Dal Canto.** 1976. Chronic neurologic disease in Theiler's virus infection of SJL/J mice. J. Neurol. Sci., in press.
7. **McFarland, H. F., D. E. Griffin, and R. T. Johnson.** 1972. Specificity of the inflammatory response in viral encephalitis. I. Adoptive immunization of immunosuppressed mice infected with Sindbis virus. J. Exp. Med. **136:**216–226.
8. **Melnick, J. L., and J. T. Riordan.** 1947. Latent mouse encephalomyelitis. J. Immunol. **57:** 331–342.
9. **Olitsky, P. K.** 1939. Viral effect produced by intestinal contents of normal mice and those having spontaneous encephalomyelitis. Proc. Soc. Exp. Biol. Med. **41:**434–437.
10. **Rabinowitz, S. G., and H. L. Lipton.** 1976. Cellular immunity in chronic Theiler's virus central nervous system infection. J. Immunol. **117:**357–363.
11. **Theiler, M.** 1934. Spontaneous encephalomyelitis of mice—a new virus disease. Science **80:**122.
12. **Theiler, M.** 1937. Spontaneous encephalomyelitis of mice, a new virus disease. J. Exp. Med. **65:** 705–719.
13. **Theiler, M., and S. Gard.** 1940. Encephalomyelitis of mice. III. Epidemiology. J. Exp. Med. **72:**79–90.
14. **Thompson, R., V. M. Harrison, and F. P. Myers.** 1951. A spontaneous epizootic of mouse encephalomyelitis. Proc. Soc. Exp. Biol. Med. **77:**262–266.
15. **Walker, D. L.** 1964. The viral carrier state in animal cell cultures. Prog. Med. Virol. **6:**111–148.

Herpes Simplex Infections as Models of Latency

JACK G. STEVENS

*Department of Microbiology and Immunology, University of California School of Medicine,
Los Angeles, California 90024*

INTRODUCTION

As I have detailed elsewhere (5), an attractive hypothesis explaining the natural history of herpetic disease involves reactivation of virus from a reservoir in latently infected sensory ganglia. In general terms, the infection is postulated to follow a circuit from skin, mucous membrane, or eye (the primary infection) to the corresponding sensory ganglia via associated nerves. The virus would then become latent in the ganglia and later, as a result of one of the many provocations known to be associated with recurrence of herpetic lesions, would be reactivated, travel via the nerve to the surface, and again produce lesions. Our earlier work, coupled with subsequent findings made both here and in other laboratories, has given this hypothesis firm experimental support (reviewed in 5).

First, and most importantly, we showed that the virus was *selectively* harbored in the sensory ganglia after cutaneous or corneal inoculation of experimental animals. The technique used to demonstrate this phenomenon was one of explantation and maintenance of the ganglia as organ cultures in vitro. Here, although virus could not be isolated directly from the tissues at the time of explant, after a few days of culture infectious herpes simplex virus (HSV) could be detected in supernatant fluids bathing the ganglia. This work was quickly confirmed and extended by others to human tissues where, using the same methods, they found that HSV can be efficiently recovered from trigeminal ganglia explanted and processed at autopsy (reviewed in reference 1).

As to the route taken to ganglia, experiments conducted in several laboratories over the past 15 years make it certain that the virus travels centripetally in sensory nerve trunks. Evidence has also been presented indicating that centrifugal passage in these nerves follows reactivation from sensory ganglia. In addition, several types of experiments suggest that the intraneural route taken is an axonal one (5).

From these considerations then, it is clear that HSV travels in nerves from cutaneous areas to the corresponding sensory ganglia where latent infections are established. As will be discussed in greater detail below, the virus can be experimentally reactivated from latently infected ganglia and subsequently travels centrifugally in associated nerves. However, the clinical and virological consequences of experimental reactivation have not been striking. Although in some latently infected animals virus spontaneously appears at the surface (2–4), clinically apparent lesions attributable to the virus have never been shown to follow a defined manipulation of the experimental animal. If a system could be developed in which an "induced" reactivation was followed by cutaneous lesions, and if the development of lesions could be prevented by section of the appropriate nerve, the entire hypothesis presented above would be experimentally satisfied.

CHARACTERISTICS OF THE LATENT INFECTION IN SENSORY GANGLIA

Since it has been shown that HSV is selectively harbored in sensory ganglia, a definition of this tissue-virus interaction is central to understanding the natural history of herpetic disease. Therefore, the remainder of this communication will deal with (i) a definition of the cell type harboring the latent infection, (ii) studies concerning the state in which the viral genome is maintained in these cells, (iii) the mechanism by which the viral genome is maintained, (iv) phenomena associated with reactivation, and (v) initial studies concerning the "biochemistry" of latency.

To establish unequivocally which cells harbor virus, the various cell types in ganglia must be separated and incubated, and the cultures that produce virus must be assessed. In our hands, such a separation has not been achieved, and we have therefore relied on several indirect experiments to indicate the cell type harboring virus. As has been discussed in detail elsewhere (1, 5), these experiments were of several designs, and they are all consistent with a neuronal site. The most convincing study was one in which virus-specific radioactive complementary RNA was used as a probe to search for viral DNA in frozen sections of ganglia taken directly from the latently infected animals (in situ hybridization). There, autoradiographs made of the sections demonstrated that silver grains referable to hybridized radioactive RNA could be detected only over neuronal nuclei.

The state of the virus in latently infected neurons is as yet unknown, but the evidence now available from several indirect experiments is most consistent with maintenance of the agent in some nonreplicating state (1, 5). To summarize, viral products (except for the viral DNA discussed above) cannot be detected in ganglia processed immediately after removal from the animal. However, after a few days in culture, many widely scattered neurons containing morphologically complete virus, antigens, and viral DNA can be found. If the virus is indeed maintained in a nonreplicating state, it is obvious that a definition of the precise nature of this state is central to understanding the phenomenon of latency. Although integration of the genome into cellular DNA is certainly a possibility, there is no necessity to invoke integration as a means of efficient perpetuation of the latent state, since neurons do not divide.

Our studies of the mechanism by which the viral genome is maintained have suggested that antiviral immunoglobulin G (IgG) plays an important role in this phenomenon (6). Here, latently infected ganglia were transplanted into mice previously injected with HSV-immune or -nonimmune IgG, and the induction of viral DNA synthesis was scored. Significantly fewer neurons were induced to replicate viral DNA in those ganglia maintained in mice passively immunized than in those animals given nonimmune IgG. Possible mechanisms explaining this "modulation" of infection have been discussed (6).

A predictable reactivation of infection has been accomplished following two types of manipulation, both in murine systems. In one, latent infections were established in the lumbosacral spinal ganglia, and branches of the sciatic nerve were sectioned at the intervertebral foramina. Three days later, infectious virus could be recovered in the corresponding ganglia, but not in ganglia from control animals (6). More recently, we showed that a superimposed pneumococcal pneumonitis resulted in reactivation of active infection from the ganglia and subsequent passage of virus to associated nerves (7). It is important to emphasize that in neither of these systems did neurologic signs or cutaneous lesions develop after viral reactivation from the ganglia. In addition, the biochemical basis for these reactivations is not at all understood.

From these considerations, it is quite clear that we have a somewhat superficial understanding of the latent state. The principal reason for this state of affairs relates to the current lack of additional incisive methods to characterize the infection in ganglia and to the lack of an in vitro system in which latency can be established and then studied by quantitative biochemical methods. We are now trying to develop both areas, the former by employing temperature-sensitive mutants of defined phenotypes in vivo and the latter by attempting to establish latent infections in various clones of the mouse C-1300 neuroblastoma line maintained in vitro. We have recently shown that temperature-sensitive mutants differ in their capacity to establish latent infections in the mouse (K. W. Lofgren et al., in preparation) and are now attempting to relate these differences to morphogenic and biochemical differences expressed at the restrictive temperature. Additionally, these mutants and the wild-type agent are being used in the neuroblastoma lines manipulated by various physical and chemical means in the hope that latent infections can be established in this more readily studied in vitro stystem.

LITERATURE CITED

1. **Baringer, J. R.** 1975. Herpes simplex virus infection of nervous tissue in animals and man. Prog. Med. Virol. **20:**1–29.
2. **Hill, T. J., H. J. Field, and W. A. Blyth.** 1975. Acute and recurrent infection with herpes simplex virus in the mouse; a model for studying latency and recurrent disease. J. Gen. Virol. **28:**341–353.
3. **Nesburn, A. B., J. H. Elliott, and H. M. Leibowitz.** 1967. Spontaneous reactivation of experimental Herpes keratitis in rabbits. Arch. Ophthalmol. **79:** 523–529.
4. **Scriba, M.** 1975. Herpes simplex virus infection in guinea pigs: an animal model for studying latent and recurrent herpes simplex virus infection. Infect. Immun. **12:**162–165.
5. **Stevens, J. G.** 1975. Latent Herpes simplex virus and the nervous system. Curr. Top. Microbiol. Immunol. **70:**31–50.
6. **Stevens, J. G., and M. L. Cook.** 1975. Maintenance of latent herpetic infection: an apparent role for antiviral IgG. J. Immunol. **113:**1685–1693.
7. **Stevens, J. G., M. L. Cook, and M. C. Jordan.** 1975. Reactivation of latent herpes simplex virus following pneumococcal pneumonia in mice. Infect. Immun. **11:**635–639.
8. **Walz, M. A., R. W. Price, and A. L. Notkins.** 1975. Latent infection with Herpes simplex virus types 1 and 2: viral reactivation in vivo after neurectomy. Science **184:**1185–1187.

Subacute Sclerosing Panencephalitis: Animal Models

KENNETH P. JOHNSON AND DONALD P. BYINGTON

*Department of Neurology, Veterans Administration Hospital and University of
California School of Medicine, San Francisco, California 94121*

INTRODUCTION

Animal models of subacute sclerosing panencephalitis (SSPE) must be assessed in the light of what is known about the human disease (15), in which there is an initial exposure to measles virus between 1 and 3 years of life, followed by a latent period of 4 to 12 years before the onset of progressive central nervous system (CNS) disease. No acute predisposing event has been recognized that regularly triggers the appearance of clinical SSPE. Elevated levels of antibody to measles antigens, most prominently to the nucleocapsid (20), are noted in both serum and cerebrospinal fluid (CSF). Evidence of viral persistence in the CNS observed by one of the following methods is universally present: (i) typical inflammatory and inclusion cell pathology, (ii) immunofluorescent staining of viral antigen, (iii) ultrastructural demonstration of paramyxovirus nucleocapsid, or (iv) isolation of virus. Attempts at virus isolation often fail but where successful have always required cocultivation of brain cells with permissive cells, except in two cases where virus was rescued from lymphocytes (12), or in another unique case of inoculation of biopsy material into suckling mice (7). These procedures have yielded complete extracellular virus within one passage in some cases; in other more common experiences, multiple passages and cocultivations were necessary to demonstrate even the presence of viral antigens (23). These studies suggest that, although the persistent virus in SSPE is always cell associated or defective, the characteristics of the agent in the host may not be uniform. No consistent immunological defect has been documented in human SSPE (19).

Numerous animal species have been exposed to standard SSPE measles strains in an effort to produce an adequate SSPE model (Table 1). It is evident that "slow" clinical disease has been associated with viral persistence in the CNS. Also, in studies which considered it, a clear relationship was observed between the age of the animal when inoculated and subsequent disease or even infection.

Numerous studies have shown marked biological and morphological differences in strains of standard measles or SSPE viruses in either tissue culture or animals, and further alteration in behavior has occurred with repeated passage or change in passage history (9, 13). Thus, it is difficult to generalize findings in various models when species, age at inoculation, source of virus, dose, and passage history are inconsistent. Therefore, this paper will concentrate on studies of the SSPE-like disease in weanling hamsters (5), with other findings noted where appropriate.

HISTORY AND CHARACTERISTICS OF THE HAMSTER MODEL

The hamster-adapted HBS virus strain (4) was derived by Byington from the Mantooth strain, isolated from an SSPE brain biopsy (11). Intracerebral inoculation of HBS virus into newborn hamsters always produces (i) an acute giant-cell encephalitis, (ii) massive growth of cell-free virus in brain, and (iii) death within 5 days (14). In contrast, adult hamsters occasionally exhibit clinical disease but produce mainly cell-associated virus in brain and will clear all evidence of virus by 12 days. Of most interest, HBS virus in 21-day-old weanling animals produces a fatal, subacute inclusion cell encephalitis in one-third of the animals; however, in those surviving over 21 days, there is evidence of persistent CNS measles virus (5). This can be documented by histological, immunofluorescent, and ultrastructural methods (24). Serum measles antibody levels develop, sometimes to excessive levels, and consist of antibodies to all the well-characterized antigens of measles virus (17). Most animals appear well and grow normally; however, occasional ones spontaneously develop myoclonic seizures and subacute clinical disease leading to death at unpredictable times. Virus can occasionally be recovered by cocultivating trypsin-treated brain cells with permissive cell lines, but this is uncommon and unpredictable. This model provides not only a method of achieving persistent CNS infection but also an animal—the adult hamster—which is able to eradicate virus rapidly. Most studies have

TABLE 1. *Animal studies with laboratory and SSPE strains of measles virus*

Species	Virus strain	Disease type	Viral persistence	Relation to age	Reference
Hamster	Measles	Acute and slow	+	+	30
	SSPE	Acute and slow	+	+	5, 17
Ferret	SSPE	Acute and slow	+		18, 21, 29
Monkey	Measles	Acute and slow	+		1
	SSPE	Acute	0		25
Dog	Measles	0	0		21
	SSPE	Acute and slow	+		
Mouse	Measles	Acute	0	+	8, 10
	SSPE	Acute	0		7
Rat	Measles	Acute	0	+	3
Lamb	Measles	0	0		28
	SSPE	Acute	0		
Calf	Measles	0	0		28
	SSPE	Acute	0		
Guinea pig	SSPE	0	0		—[a]

[a] K. P. Johnson and D. P. Byington, unpublished data.

manipulated the infected adult to determine factors which may lead to viral persistence and slow disease.

CNS MATURATION VERSUS IMMUNE COMPETENCE AND VIRAL PERSISTENCE

The progressive resistance to disease, death, and viral persistence noted in the growing hamster could be explained in several ways, such as by an age-related insusceptibility of certain CNS cells to infection, or by increasing maturity and competence of the immune system. Adult hamsters were deprived of immune responsiveness by thymectomy within 24 h of birth (16). When such animals were infected, some developed severe encephalitis between 8 and 17 days while others remained well. The sick animals, killed when moribund, had no ability to raise antibodies, whereas the well animals, taken later, all had serum antibodies to measles. The sick ones contained no thymus, grew large amounts of cell-free virus, and developed severe necrotic and inclusion cell pathology. All animals which remained well contained thymic remnants. These studies show that in the hamster the host immune system plays a major role in viral clearance, even in adults.

Maturation of immune competence may not be the sole age-related factor operative in measles infection, however. Griffin et al. (8), studying mice infected with the HNT measles strain (2), showed that suckling animals grew large amounts of virus and died of acute encephalitis. Weanling mice often remained well even though widespread foci of viral antigen developed in the brain. No cell-free virus formed, and virus could not be recovered by any method beyond 16 days. Immunosuppressive treatment of weanling mice with cyclophosphamide failed to alter the course of infection. These authors suggested that increasing resistance of CNS cells to infection or to production of infectious virus was the significant factor in aborting the infection.

BIOLOGICAL MODIFICATION OF VIRUS

In weanling hamsters, viral behavior changed from a complete cell-free infectious state to a cell-associated defective state coincident with the appearance of serum antibodies (4, 17). Thus, antibody may modify CNS virus characteristics or may eradicate any virus capable of producing cell-free progeny while selecting out substrains within the initial inoculum with defective, cell-associated features. To study this conversion from a cell-free to a cell-associated state, various schedules of treatment with hamster antilymphocyte serum (ALS) were employed in adult hamsters (6). Appearance of serum antibodies was abolished by continuous ALS therapy, and then large amounts of cell-free CNS infectious virus developed and animals died. With transient ALS therapy, antibody appearance was delayed and growth of cell-free virus occurred prior to antibody, but only cell-associated virus developed later. Adult hamsters could also be persistently infected with this method.

Once persistent, cell-associated virus growth had been achieved, it tended to remain defective (17). Primary brain cell cultures were grown from animals before they raised serum antibodies and after antibodies were present. Cultures were maintained in medium free from measles antibody and were assayed for extracellular virus production. Cultures derived from animals without antibody produced more virus and were destroyed by measles cytopathic effects, whereas cultures derived later produced little virus and survived longer.

Thus, in hamsters the host humoral immune response seems capable of altering virus growth characteristics, or of selecting viral subpopulations capable of cell-associated behavior and enhanced persistent survival. Other studies indicate similar mechanisms of antibody-induced virus modification. Wear and Rapp (30) inoculated the Schwartz strain of measles virus into suckling hamsters with maternal antibodies derived from preimmunized mothers and showed that CNS measles virus persistence could also be achieved. These studies also suggest that antibody may alter viral behavior in vivo in suckling hamsters.

CHARACTERISTICS OF PERSISTENT CNS VIRUS

What is the state in which the persistent virus survives within the CNS? Does the virus disappear or does morphological evidence of virus remain? Nothing is known of the latent phase of SSPE in humans; however, in each animal system studied, there is morphological and antigenic evidence of virus, suggesting a focal steady-state infection where viral and host factors are in equilibrium. Persistently infected hamsters between 21 and 120 days after inoculation contain CNS nucleocapsid material (Fig. 1), even if clinically well. Virus is in focal groups of neurons, astrocytes, oligodendroglia, and ependymal cells, usually in the brain stem at the floor of the fourth ventricle or in the hippocampal formation (24). Inclusion cells occur associated with inflammatory cells, including plasma cells. Increased hamster immunoglobulin G is also present within the focus. Measles antigen can be demonstrated in both nucleus and cytoplasm of such cells. The cerebellum is always spared in the hamster, as it is in human SSPE (22), indicating the variable susceptibility of CNS cell types to virus infection.

Other investigators have demonstrated somewhat similar pathology in other animal models.

Albrecht et al. (1), studying monkeys inoculated with the HNT strain (2), showed that virus persisted for over 5 weeks in animals which often appeared well and that it raised antibodies to measles. Measles antigen, focal inflammation, and inclusion cells were observed. Cyclophosphamide treatment increased the severity of clinical disease in such animals. The Edmonston or Schwartz strain failed to produce either disease or CNS pathology even with immunosuppression. Katz et al. (18) and Thormar et al. (29), investigating various SSPE isolates in ferrets, also found evidence of chronic focal inflammation and some inclusion cell pathology in occasional animals. Notermans et al. (21) showed inclusion cell pathology in dogs surviving up to 36 days after inoculation.

Different pathological reactions developed in weanling mice infected with HNT virus and studied 16 days later by Herndon et al. (10). There was little inflammation and no nucleocapsid formation. However, analysis by immunofluorescence or by electron microscopy immunoperoxidase techniques showed focal collections of cells bearing measles antigens which were distributed diffusely throughout the cytoplasm. They interpreted these studies to show that in mice, measles virus assembly was defective prior to the stage of nucleocapsid formation, even though virus antigens were produced.

HOST IMMUNE RESPONSE TO PERSISTENT CNS INFECTION

The measles antibody response in most animals is adequate or excessive, as it is in human SSPE (15, 20). Persistently infected hamsters raise antibodies to measles nucleocapsid antigens as well as the hemagglutinin and hemolysin antigens of the envelope (17). No adequate analysis of cellular immune reactivity has been reported in any animal system, and results of human studies are conflicting (19). Studies of children with SSPE show that a soluble blocking factor which inhibits lymphocyte cytotoxicity of measles-bearing cells is present both in serum and in greater concentration in CSF (26, 27). Very indirect evidence suggests that such a factor may be present in infected hamsters as well. Immunoperoxidase studies show that measles antigens can be labeled in nucleus and in cytoplasm (Fig. 2). Analysis of cytoplasmic membranes of infected cells shows that viral antigens may be present in the membrane without direct relationship to nucleocapsid material. Thus, a soluble blocking factor may shelter such cell surface antigens from immune surveillance. Alternatively, the extracellular space within the

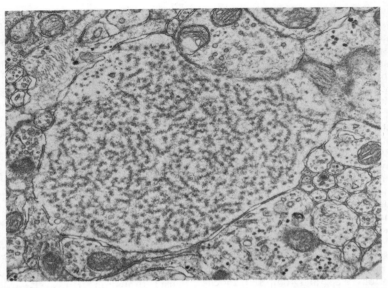

FIG. 1. *Section of hamster brain stem taken 16 days after intracerebral inoculation of HBS virus showing "fuzzy" measles nucleocapsid filling a neuronal dendrite. Uranyl acetate and lead citrate stain, ×31,000.*

mature CNS is sparse, and lymphocyte access may be limited.

CONCLUSIONS

Several studies show that species differences are significant when attempting to establish measles virus persistence, and hamsters, monkeys, dogs, and ferrets are more readily infected than most common laboratory species. Age seems an important variable in initially infecting the CNS and establishing viral persistence. This probably is due to at least two factors: (i) increasing maturation and resistance of the CNS to infection and virus assembly, and (ii) increasing competence of the immune sys-

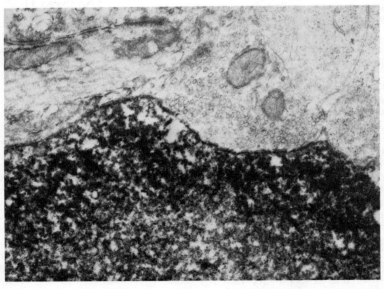

FIG. 2. *Section of hamster brain stem taken 16 days after inoculation with HBS virus showing dense labeling of measles nucleocapsid with immunoperoxidase. Note presence of labeled antigen in the cytoplasmic membrane of cells. Immunoperoxidase stain, ×35,000.*

tem. The importance of each of these factors may vary in different species.

Studies in hamsters suggest that the antibody response plays a role in segregating defective subpopulations within the inoculum better able to persist in protected intracellular sites or that the biological characteristics of virus growth, assembly, and antigen expression are, in fact, altered on exposure to antibody.

Once CNS infection is established, a focal steady-state infection develops with continuous focal pathology and presence of virus structure. This may produce no clinical disease and may be analogous to the prolonged latent phase characteristic of human SSPE when viral and host factors seem to be in balance. Increasing evidence suggests that a soluble "blocking factor" protects cell surface antigens from immune detection and eradication.

ACKNOWLEDGMENTS

This work was supported by Public Health Service grant NS 12064 and by the Veterans Administration Hospital, San Francisco, Calif.

The excellent assistance of Peggy Swoveland is gratefully acknowledged.

LITERATURE CITED

1. **Albrecht, P., A. L. Shabo, G. R. Burns, and N. M. Tauraso.** 1972. Experimental measles encephalitis in normal and cyclophosphamide-treated rhesus monkeys. J. Infect. Dis. **126**:154–161.

2. **Burnstein, T., J. H. Jensen, and B. H. Waksman.** 1964. The development of a neurotropic strain of measles virus in hamsters and mice. J. Infect. Dis. **114**:265–272.

3. **Byington, D. P., and T. Burnstein.** 1973. Measles encephalitis produced in suckling rats. Exp. Mol. Pathol. **19**:36–43.

4. **Byington, D. P., A. E. Castro, and T. Burnstein.** 1970. Adaptation to hamsters of neurotropic measles virus from subacute sclerosing panencephalitis. Nature (London) **225**:554.

5. **Byington, D. P., and K. P. Johnson.** 1972. Experimental subacute sclerosing panencephalitis in the hamster: correlation of age with chronic inclusion-cell encephalitis. J. Infect. Dis. **126**:18–26.

6. **Byington, D. P., and K. P. Johnson.** 1975. Subacute sclerosing panencephalitis virus in immunosuppressed adult hamsters. Lab. Invest. **32**:91–97.

7. **Greenham, L. W., D. B. Peacock, T. J. Hill, B. Brownell, and W. H. Schutt.** 1974. The isolation of S.S.P.E. measles virus in newborn mice. Arch. Gesamte Virusforsch. **44**:109–120.

8. **Griffin, D. E., Janice Mullinix, O. Narayan, and R. T. Johnson.** 1974. Age dependence of viral expression: comparative pathogenesis of two rodent-adapted strains of measles virus in mice. Infect. Immun. **9**:690–695.

9. **Hamilton, R., L. Barbosa, and M. Dubois.** 1973. Subacute sclerosing panencephalitis measles virus: study of biological markers. J. Virol. **12**:632–642.

10. **Herndon, R. M., L. Rena-Descalzi, D. E. Griffin, and P. K. Coyle.** 1975. Age dependence of viral expression. Electron microscopic and immunoperoxidase studies of measles virus replication in mice. Lab. Invest. **33**:544–553.

11. **Horta-Barbosa, L., D. A. Fuccillo, and J. L. Sever.** 1969. Subacute sclerosing panencephalitis: isolation of measles virus from a brain biopsy. Nature (London) **221**:974.

12. **Horta-Barbosa, L., R. Hamilton, B. Wittig, D. A. Fuccillo, and J. L. Sever.** 1971. Subacute sclerosing panencephalitis: isolation of suppressed measles virus from lymph node biopsies. Science **173**:840–841.

13. **Janda, Z., E. Norrby, and H. Marusyk.** 1971. Neurotropism of measles virus variants in hamsters. J. Infect. Dis. **124**:553–564.

14. **Johnson, K. P., and D. P. Byington.** 1971. Subacute sclerosing panencephalitis (SSPE) agent in hamsters. I. Acute giant cell encephalitis in newborn animals. Exp. Mol. Pathol. **15**:373–379.

15. **Johnson, K. P., D. P. Byington, and L. Gaddis.** 1974. Subacute sclerosing panencephalitis. Adv. Neurol. **6**:77–86.

16. **Johnson, K. P., E. G. Feldman, and D. P. Byington.** 1975. Effect of neonatal thymectomy on experimental subacute sclerosing panencephalitis in adult hamsters. Infect. Immun. **12**:1464–1469.

17. **Johnson, K. P., and E. Norrby.** 1974. Subacute sclerosing panencephalitis (SSPE) agent in hamsters. III. Induction of defective measles infection in hamster brain. Exp. Mol. Pathol. **21**:166–178.

18. **Katz, M., L. B. Rorke, W. S. Masland, H. Koprowski, and S. H. Tucker.** 1968. Transmission of an encephalitogenic agent from brains of patients with subacute sclerosing panencephalitis to ferrets. Preliminary report. N. Engl. J. Med. **279**:793–798.

19. **Lennette, E. H.** 1975. Cellular immunity and SSPE. (Summary of the Conference.) Arch. Neurol. **32**:489–493.

20. **Link, H., M. Panelius, and A. A. Salmi.** 1973. Immunoglobulins and measles antibodies in subacute sclerosing panencephalitis. Arch. Neurol. **28**:23–30.

21. **Notermans, S. L. H., W. F. J. Tijl, F. T. C. Willems, and J. L. Slooff.** 1973. Experimentally induced subacute sclerosing panencephalitis in young dogs. Neurology **23**:543–553.

22. **Ohya, T., A. J. Martinez, J. T. Jabbour, H. Lemmi, and D. A. Duenas.** 1974. Subacute sclerosing panencephalitis. Neurology **3**:211–218.

23. **Payne, F. E., and J. V. Baublis.** 1971. Measles virus and subacute sclerosing panencephalitis. Perspect. Virol. **7**:179–195.

24. **Raine, C. S., D. P. Byington, and K. P. Johnson.** 1974. Experimental subacute sclerosing panencephalitis in the hamster. Ultrastructure of the chronic disease. Lab. Invest. **31**:355–368.

25. **Schumacher, H. P., P. Albrecht, R. G. Clark, R. L. Kirschstein, and N. M. Tauraso.** 1971. Intracerebral inoculation of rhesus monkeys with a strain of measles virus isolated from a case of subacute sclerosing panencephalitis. Infect. Immun. **4**:419–424.

26. **Sell, K. W., G. B. Thurman, and A. Ahmed.** 1973. Plasma and spinal fluid blocking factor in SSPE. N. Engl. J. Med. **228**:215.

27. **Steele, R. W., D. A. Fuccillo, S. A. Hensen, M. M. Vincent, and J. A. Bellanti.** 1976. Specific inhibitory factors of cellular immunity in children with subacute sclerosing panencephalitis. J. Pediatr. **88**:56–62.

28. **Thein, P., A. Mayr, V. terMeulen, H. Koprowski, M. Y. Kackell, D. Muller, and R. Meyermann.** 1972. Subacute sclerosing panencephalitis. Transmission of the virus to calves and lambs. Arch. Neurol. **27**:540–548.

29. **Thormar, H., G. A. Jervis, S. C. Karl, and H. R. Brown.** 1973. Passage in ferrets of encephalitogenic cell-associated measles virus isolated from brain of a patient with subacute sclerosing panencephalitis. J. Infect. Dis. **127**:678–685.

30. **Wear, D. J., and F. Rapp.** 1971. Latent measles infection of the hamster central nervous system. J. Immunol. **107**:1593–1598.

Live Virus Vaccines for Use in Humans: Strategies and Problems

Rationale for Development of Live Virus Vaccines by Use of Temperature-Sensitive Mutants

ROBERT M. CHANOCK, BRIAN R. MURPHY, SUSAN B. SPRING, AND DOUGLAS D. RICHMAN[1]

Laboratory of Infectious Diseases, National Institute of Allergy and Infectious Diseases, Bethesda, Maryland 20014

Viruses that produce acute infections are rather economical organisms and usually do not carry genes that are not involved in viral replication. Thus, in most instances a mutational change that decreases the amount or functional activity of the affected gene product would be expected to produce a decrease in virulence. In other words, any mutation that partially restricts viral replication should lead to some degree of attenuation. Conditional lethal, temperature-sensitive (*ts*) mutation is of interest in this regard since such genetic change can occur or be induced in essentially every cistron of the viral genome and thus a large array of genetic defects can be assessed for their effect upon virulence.

Conditional lethal, temperature-sensitive mutants have been derived from virtually every major virus group, and in almost every instance this type of mutation has led to a reduction in virulence for the natural or experimental host (16). This is not surprising since virulence is a composite property which reflects the activity of most viral genes. Evidence from a number of sources suggests that it is the *ts* lesion which is responsible for the attenuation exhibited by *ts* mutants. Specification of attenuation by a defined genetic lesion or set of lesions that can be assayed for in the laboratory offers an advantage to the use of *ts* mutants for vaccination in that such mutants can be evaluated for their relevant genetic lesions during the process of vaccine production and later during infection of humans. In this manner, the genetic basis for attenuation and genetic stability can be monitored directly during all phases of vaccine development, manufacture, and usage. During the past few years, we have evaluated *ts* mutants of influenza A virus and respiratory syncytial virus (RSV) for their attenuation in humans and for their suitability for use in a live virus vaccine. Mutants that are restricted in their replication in vitro at 37 to 38°C should also be limited in their growth in the lower respiratory tract, which has a temperature of 37°C and is the major site of significant pathology. However, such mutants should grow with reasonable efficiency in the cooler passages of the upper respiratory tract (32 to 34°C) and thereby stimulate local and systemic immunological defense mechanisms.

Discussion will be limited to the *ts* mutants of influenza A virus since its genetic properties are well understood and its genes can be manipulated with facility and transferred with ease from one type A virus to another (4, 5, 18). Thus far, we have not been able to demonstrate such genetic reassortment with RSV, but the general principles that have emerged from the study of the influenza A virus mutants appear to apply also to the RSV mutants (20).

In current work, *ts* mutants of influenza A virus are being developed for use in live attenuated respiratory vaccines with the expectation that their *ts* lesions are responsible for suppression of growth in the lower respiratory tract. This approach is especially applicable to the influenza A virus, which periodically undergoes variation in one or both of its surface antigens. When this occurs, there is an urgent need to develop a new vaccine strain that contains the new surface antigen or antigens. The method we favor consists of the transfer of *ts* lesions from an older, suitably attenuated strain to the new antigenic variant. Transfer of *ts* genes from one influenza A virus to another is easily accomplished since the virus possesses a segmented RNA genome and reassortment of genes occurs with high frequency during mixed infection (18). It is implicit in this approach that the *ts* lesions are responsible for attenuation, that they are not on the cistrons that determine the structure of the surface antigens, and that they can be monitored by in vitro techniques during all phases of vaccine development, manufacture, and usage.

The *ts* mutants were derived by growing

[1] Present address: Department of Pathology and Medicine, Veterans Administration Hospital, San Diego, Calif. 92161.

influenza A virus in the presence of a chemical mutagen, 5-fluorouracil (5FU), and a series of *ts* recombinants was derived from such mutants (6, 13, 18). The mutants and recombinants were analyzed genetically by the method of complementation-recombination on the assay plate (6, 18). In brief, this technique involves dual infection of primary monkey kidney cell monolayers at the restrictive temperature of 39°C. At this temperature, neither virus of the pair under test produces a significant number of plaques, whereas a pair of mutants which undergoes genetic interaction produces plaques with high efficiency.

By means of the complementation-recombination technique, our mutants and recombinants were ordered into seven non-overlapping complementation-recombination groups (18, 19). The single mutants that emerged from this classification should prove useful as genetic probes for characterization of the lesion or lesions transferred from an older *ts* vaccine strain to a newly emerged strain possessing new surface glycoprotein antigens (13, 14). In this manner, one can verify that the new *ts* recombinant vaccine strain possesses only the desired *ts* lesions of its attenuated, parental strain.

The mutagens that are used to produce *ts* mutants are also capable of inducing non-*ts* lesions (17, 22). Thus, it is possible that induced genetic lesions that do not contribute to the *ts* phenotype may be responsible for some or all of the restriction of growth exhibited by certain *ts* mutants. The following observations from studies in hamsters and in humans argue that it is the *ts* lesion(s) itself that specifies attenuation.

First, mutants or recombinants with a *ts* lesion localized to one cistron were compared with the wild-type virus with respect to growth in the lower respiratory tract of the hamster. The introduction of a *ts* lesion into any one of six cistrons resulted in a significant decrease in the capacity of the virus to grow in the lungs of the hamster (16, 19). In these studies restriction of growth in this region was considered to be equivalent to attenuation. Thus, among the six complementation groups studied, the induction of a *ts* lesion resulted in attenuation regardless of the gene affected.

Second, restriction of growth of each of the six single lesion mutants was greater in the lungs, which have a temperature of 37°C, than in the nasal turbinates, where the temperature is 32°C (16, 19). This temperature-dependent restriction of virus replication suggests that *ts* lesions play a major role in attenuation of these *ts* mutants for the hamster. If non-*ts* genetic

lesions were primarily responsible for restriction of virus replication, then one would expect the decrease in virus growth to be equivalent in the lungs and nasal turbinates.

Third, the extent to which *ts* recombinants were restricted in growth in the lower respiratory tract was a function of their temperature sensitivity as measured by shutoff temperature of plaque formation in tissue culture (6, 12, 16): the lower the shutoff temperature of the *ts* recombinants studied, the lower the level of virus replication in the hamster's lungs. The gradient of attenuation seen in the hamster was also observed when certain of the *ts* recombinants were evaluated in adult volunteers who lacked serum hemagglutination-inhibiting (HI) antibody for the virus under study. The *ts*-1[A] recombinant, the most temperature sensitive of the Hong Kong/1968 virus recombinants, was overattenuated and failed to infect volunteers (8). At the other end of the spectrum, the Hong Kong/1968 *ts*-1[H], Hong Kong/1968 *ts*-2[C], and Udorn/1972 *ts*-1[E] clone 13 recombinants, which were the least temperature sensitive, infected volunteers and induced mild influenzal illness (8, 10, 12, 15). The Hong Kong/1968 *ts*-1[E], Udorn/1972 *ts*-1[E], and Georgia/1974 *ts*-1[E] recombinants, which were of intermediate temperature sensitivity, were suitably attenuated and produced an immunizing infection without unacceptable signs or symptoms of illness.

Fourth, wild-type revertants (*ts*⁺) of the influenza A/Hong Kong/1968 (H3N2) *ts*-1[E] mutant grew as well as wild-type virus in the hamster's lungs (12).

Fifth, elimination of *ts* lesions by recombination led to restoration of a normal virus growth pattern in the lungs of hamsters (12). The *ts*⁺ recombinant viruses were produced by mating two genetically distinct, complementing *ts* mutants, Hong Kong/1968 *ts*-1[E] and Hong Kong/1968 *ts*-2[C]. The *ts*⁺ recombinants grew as well in the lungs as the wild-type virus. In these two mutants, *ts*-1[E] and *ts*-2[C], it appeared that the *ts* lesions were the sole determinants of growth restriction in the lower respiratory tract.

Sixth, after transfer of a defined set of *ts* lesions into three successive antigenic variants of the H3N2 influenza A virus subtype, each of the viruses exhibited a similar and satisfactory degree of attenuation for humans (12). Initially, *ts* lesions from the *ts*-1 mutant of an H2N2 1965 influenza A virus were transferred into the 1968 Hong Kong H3N2 virus (8, 18). One of the recombinants, Hong Kong *ts*-1[E] virus, appeared to exhibit the proper balance between attenuation and immunogenicity desired of a strain to be used for vaccination (8, 9). This virus had the following properties: (i) capacity to stimulate moderate levels of serum HI and neuraminidase-inhibiting (NI) antibodies and local respiratory tract neutralizing antibodies (8, 9), (ii) capacity to induce resistance to natural or experimental challenge (8), (iii) genetic stability after replication in seronegative adults and older children (3, 8), (iv) genetic stability after growth in leucosis virus-free eggs (9), (v) lack of communicability (8, 21), (vi) failure to induce alterations in pulmonary function in humans (2), and (vii) safety and antigenicity in the elderly and chronically ill (1). These characteristics suggest that the Hong Kong/1968-ts-1[E] virus might serve as a satisfactory donor of its ts lesions to new antigenic variants of influenza A virus.

The genetic defects present in the influenza A/Hong Kong/1968-ts-1[E] (H3N2) candidate vaccine virus were analyzed by transferring them by genetic reassortment into a 1943 H0N1 wild-type virus (13). Three classes of ts viruses bearing the H0 hemagglutinin were identified. One class consisted of two clones of virus, R1 and R8, which underwent complementation-recombination with each other but not with the Hong Kong/1968 (H3N2)-ts-1[E] parent virus. The second class consisted of clones of virus, such as R4 and R11, that failed to undergo complementation-recombination with each other or with R1, R8, or the ts-1[E] parent. This indicated that the parent Hong Kong ts-1[E] virus possessed two ts lesions that segregated independently of each other, and these lesions were presumably on different segments of the influenza A virus genome. In addition, the two ts lesions of the ts-1[E] virus segregated independently of the genes that coded for the neuraminidase and the hemagglutinin glycoproteins. This property of the Hong Kong/68-ts-1[E] virus made it possible to produce recombinants possessing the ts-1[E] genetic lesions and both surface antigens of new, wild-type influenza A viruses that emerged after prevalence of the Hong Kong virus. Thus, the ts lesions from the Hong Kong/1968-ts-1[E] virus have been transferred to the wild-type influenza A/Udorn/1972 (H3N2) virus (16; antigenically indistinguishable from the A/England/1972 prototype virus) and later to the A/Georgia/1974 (H3N2) virus (Richman et al., unpublished data) and most recently to the A/Victoria/1975 (H3N2) virus (Murphy et al., unpublished data).

Each time the ts-1[E] lesions were transferred into a new wild-type virus, the resultant recombinant grew poorly in the hamster's lungs,

and infection in seronegative adults was attenuated (12). The Hong Kong ts-1[E] and the double-lesion ts-1[E] recombinants derived from the Udorn/1972, Georgia/1974, and Victoria/1975 viruses exhibited a significant restriction of growth in the hamster's lungs (12, 16; Murphy et al., unpublished data). It is of interest that a single-lesion Udorn ts-1[E] recombinant, which contained only the complementation group 1 or R1 lesion, was less restricted in the hamster's lungs than the double-lesion Udorn recombinants or their Hong Kong ts-1[E] parent (16).

Three successive ts-1[E] recombinants (Hong Kong/1968, Udorn/1972, and Georgia/1974) that contain both ts-1[E] lesions have been evaluated in adults who lacked serum HI antibody, and each recombinant was found to be satisfactorily attenuated (12). Symptoms were minimal or did not occur. The duration and extent of infection was significantly less than with wild-type, virulent virus. These findings provide support for the view that the ts-1[E] lesions conferred attenuation and that recombinants that have a specified set of ts lesions will behave predictably in humans.

Because of the need to develop effective immunoprophylaxis against influenza A virus disease in children, the Hong Kong ts-1[E] recombinant was evaluated in this age group. In prior studies, each of the adult vaccinees lacked serum HI antibody but did possess measurable serum NI antibody. In contrast, many young children lack both serum HI and NI antibodies for viruses of the H3N2 subtype. Since neuraminidase immunity is effective in reducing the clinical response to infection with wild-type virus, it might also do so for the attenuated ts recombinant viruses (7, 11). Indeed, the full expression of residual virulence of an attenuated influenza A virus vaccine may be manifest only in serum HI- and NI-negative individuals, i.e., doubly seronegative persons.

In a collaborative study at Children's Hospital of D.C., the Hong Kong ts-1[E] recombinant was found to be fully attenuated for serum HI antibody-negative children who possessed detectable NI antibody. Infection occurred, but symptoms were minimal (mild rhinitis) or absent (3). In contrast, each of the six vaccinees who lacked serum antibody for both surface antigens of the virus shed a relatively larger quantity of virus over a longer interval than the first group; in addition, four children developed a transient febrile response during infection and three had mild rhinitis. Two children who lacked serum antibody to both surface antigens of influenza virus were given the influenza A/Udorn/1972-*ts*-1[E] recombinant virus, which had the same genetic lesions as the Hong Kong/1968-*ts*-1[E] recombinant virus. Both of the children were infected, and one developed a transient fever. None of the 23 vaccinees given the Hong Kong/1968-*ts*-1[E] or Udorn/1972-*ts*-1[E] recombinant at Children's Hospital of D.C. developed signs or symptoms of lower respiratory tract involvement.

These findings suggest that anti-neuraminidase immunity, naturally acquired from previous infection, provided some protection against the low level of residual virulence of the candidate vaccine virus. Only when doubly seronegative children were evaluated did it become apparent that the *ts*-1[E] recombinant viruses retained some virulence. This observation supports the view that a complete assessment of the virulence of candidate live influenza A vaccine viruses can only be made in individuals who lack immunity to both surface antigens of the influenza A virus. It is important to achieve attenuation for such persons, especially if one plans to use live attenuated vaccines to control pandemic disease caused by new antigenic variants of influenza A virus. If the next pandemic shift involves the hemagglutinin and neuraminidase antigens, every member of the population would resemble the doubly seronegative child in lacking immunity to both surface antigens. In this circumstance, viruses that were acceptably attenuated for individuals with neuraminidase immunity might produce a febrile response similar to that induced by the *ts*-1[E] recombinants in doubly seronegative children.

As mentioned earlier, the *ts*-1[E] recombinants were shown recently to contain discrete *ts* lesions that were located on two different RNA pieces of the segmented genome (13). Despite the existence of *ts* lesions on separate RNA segments, the *ts*-1[E] recombinants exhibited evidence of genetic instability during infection of two of eight doubly seronegative young children (3). Although *ts*+ revertants could not be detected in original nasopharyngeal swab specimens, such genetically altered virus was demonstrated as a minority component (10^{-2} to 10^{-3}) in several tissue culture isolates recovered from doubly seronegative vaccinees. Significantly, the emergence of revertant virus under these conditions was not associated with lower respiratory tract disease. Four of the 18 children who received 10^4 TCID$_{50}$ of the Hong Kong/1968 *ts*-1[E] recombinant during studies at Vanderbilt University shed revertant virus in their original nasopharyngeal wash specimens, but infection was not transmitted to other doubly seronegative children who were in close contact (21). In contrast, the *ts*-1[E] recombinants were stable genetically when isolated from a considerably larger group of 100 adults and 6 older children who lacked serum HI antibody but possessed NI antibody (8, 9, 12, 15). It appears that emergence of *ts*+ revertants occurred only in the absence of immunity to both hemagglutinin and neuraminidase antigens; presumably only in this circumstance did vaccine virus infection occur without immunological restriction.

The observations just described suggest that two different master strains of influenza A virus may be required as donors of attenuating genes for vaccine viruses. One master strain would contain *ts* lesions which render influenza A virus suitably attenuated and immunogenic for persons with some neuraminidase immunity. This type of donor virus would be used during interpandemic intervals or after a pandemic shift which involved only the hemagglutinin. In both instances adults and older children would possess some neuraminidase immunity from prior experience with preceding influenza A viruses. The *ts*-1[E] lesions appear to be satisfactory for this purpose.

The other master strain would contain *ts* lesions which render influenza A virus more defective and restricted than the *ts*-1[E] recombinants. These *ts* lesions would render influenza A virus sufficiently defective that infection of doubly seronegative individuals would not lead to disease. On the other hand, the defect imposed by the *ts* lesions could not be too great; otherwise infection and induction of resistance would not occur. Thus, a fine balance between attenuation and immunogenicity would be required. Recombinants which meet these requirements could be used at the time of a pandemic shift involving both surface antigens of influenza A virus when all members of the population were susceptible to infection and disease. In addition, there would be a need at all times for the same type of vaccine virus for use in doubly seronegative infants and children. Candidate *ts* recombinants that contain lesions in regions of the genome that do not code for the hemagglutinin or neuraminidase antigen and are more restricted in growth and more stable genetically than *ts*-1[E] recombinants are currently under study. Several of these candidate viruses will be evaluated in volunteers shortly.

LITERATURE CITED

1. **Douglas, R. G., D. W. Bentley, R. F. Bells, D. A. Zaky, F. K. Roth, and B. R. Murphy.** 1976. Evaluation of a temperature sensitive influenza virus in elderly and

chronically ill subjects. Am. Rev. Respir. Dis. **113:** 293–299.

2. **Hall, W. J., R. G. Douglas, Jr., D. A. Zaky, R. W. Hyde, D. D. Richman, and B. R. Murphy.** 1976. Evaluation of an attenuated influenza virus in normal adults: role of pulmonary function studies in vaccine trials. J. Infect. Dis. **133:**145–152.

3. **Kim, H. W., J. O. Arrobio, C. D. Brandt, R. H. Parrott, B. R. Murphy, D. D. Richman, and R. M. Chanock.** 1976. Temperature-sensitive mutants of influenza A virus: response of children to the influenza A/ Hong Kong/68-ts-1[E] (H3N2) and influenza A/Udorn/ 72-ts-1[E] (H3N2) candidate vaccine viruses and the significance of immunity to neuraminidase antigen. Pediatr. Res. **10:**238–242.

4. **Maassab, H. F., A. P. Kendal, and F. M. Davenport.** 1972. Hybrid formation of influenza A virus at 25°. Proc. Soc. Exp. Biol. Med. **139:**768–773.

5. **McCahon, D., G. G. Schild, A. S. Beare, and T. S. Hall.** 1973. Use of recombination in the production of influenza vaccine strains. Postgrad. Med. J. **49:** 195–199.

6. **Mills, J. V., and R. M. Chanock.** 1971. Temperature-sensitive mutants of influenza virus. I. Behavior in tissue culture and in experimental animals. J. Infect. Dis. **123:**145–157.

7. **Monto, A. S., and A. P. Kendal.** 1973. Effect of neur-aminidase antibody on Hong Kong influenza. Lancet **i:**623–625.

8. **Murphy, B. R., E. G. Chalhub, S. R. Nusinoff, and R. M. Chanock.** 1972. Temperature-sensitive mutants of influenza virus. II. Attenuation of ts recombinants for man. J. Infect. Dis. **126:**170–178.

9. **Murphy, B. R., E. G. Chalhub, S. R. Nusinoff, J. A. Kasel, and R. M. Chanock.** 1973. Temperature-sensitive mutants of influenza virus. III. Further characterization of the ts-1[E] influenza A recombinant (H3N2) virus in man. J. Infect. Dis. **128:**479–487.

10. **Murphy, B. R., D. S. Hodes, S. R. Nusinoff, S. Spring-Stewart, E. L. Tierney, and R. M. Chanock.** 1974. Temperature sensitive mutants of influenza virus. V. Evaluation in man of an additional ts recombinant virus with a 39°C shutoff temperature. J. Infect. Dis. **130:**144–149.

11. **Murphy, B. R., J. A. Kasel, and R. M. Chanock.** 1972. Association of serum anti-neuraminidase antibody with resistance to influenza in man. N. Engl. J. Med. **286:**1329–1332.

12. **Murphy, B. R., D. D. Richman, S. B. Spring, and R. M. Chanock.** 1976. Use of temperature-sensitive mutants of influenza A virus as live virus vaccine strainsevaluation in laboratory animals, adults, and children. Postgrad. Med. J. **52:**381–388.

13. **Murphy, B. R., S. B. Spring, D. D. Richman, E. L. Tierney, J. A. Kasel, and R. M. Chanock.** 1975. Temperature-sensitive mutants of influenza virus. VII. Transfer of the ts-1[E] lesions to a wild type influenza A virus with the H0N1 surface antigens. Virology **66:**533–541.

14. **Murphy, B. R., E. L. Tierney, S. B. Spring, and R. M. Chanock.** 1976. Temperature-sensitive mutants of influenza A virus. XI. Transfer of the ts lesions in the Hong Kong/68-ts-1[A] virus to the A/Udorn/72 wild type. J. Infect. Dis., in press.

15. **Richman, D. D., B. R. Murphy, R. M. Chanock, J. M. Gwaltney, R. G. Douglas, R. F. Betts, N. R. Blacklow, F. B. Rose, T. A. Parrino, M. M. Levine, and E. S. Caplan.** 1976. Temperature-sensitive mutants of influenza A virus. XII. Safety, antigenicity, transmissibility, and efficacy of influenze A/Udorn/72-ts-1[E] recombinant temperature sensitive viruses in adult volunteers. J. Infect. Dis., in press.

16. **Richman, D. D., B. R. Murphy, S. B. Spring, M. T. Coleman, and R. M. Chanock.** 1975. Temperature-sensitive mutants of influenza virus. IX. Genetic and biological characterization of ts-1[E] lesions when transferred to a 1972 (H3N2) influenza A virus. Virology **66:**533–541.

17. **Schuerch, A. R., and N. K. Joklik,** 1973. Temperature-sensitive mutants of reovirus. IV. Evidence that anomalous electrophoretic migration behavior of certain double-stranded RNA hybrid species is mutant group-specific. Virology **56:**218–229.

18. **Spring, S. B., S. R. Nusinoff, J. Mills, D. D. Richman, E. L. Tierney, B. R. Murphy, and R. M. Chanock.** 1975. Temperature-sensitive mutants of influenza virus. VI. Transfer of ts lesions from the Asian subtype of influenza A virus (H2N2) to the Hong Kong subtype (H3N2). Virology **66:**522–532.

19. **Spring, S. B., S. R. Nusinoff, E. L. Tierney, D. D. Richman, B. R. Murphy, and R. M. Chanock.** 1975. Temperature-sensitive mutants of influenza virus. VIII. Genetic and biological characterization of ts mutants of influenza virus A (H3N2) and their assignment to complementation groups. Virology **66:**542–550.

20. **Wright, P. F., M. A. Gharpure, D. S. Hodes, and R. M. Chanock.** 1973. Genetic studies of respiratory syncytial virus temperature sensitive mutants. Arch. Gesamte Virusforsch. **41:**238–247.

21. **Wright, P. F., S. H. Sell, T. Shinozaki, J. Thompson, and D. T. Karzon.** 1975. Safety and antigenicity of influenza A/Hong Kong/68-ts-1[E] (H3N2) vaccine in young seronegative children. J. Pediatr. **87:**1109–1116.

22. **Wunner, W. H., and C. R. Pringle.** 1974. A temperature-sensitive mutant of vesicular stomatitis virus with two abnormal virus proteins. J. Gen. Virol. **23:**97–106.

Problems in Development of Safe and Effective Live Virus Vaccines for Use in Humans

PAUL D. PARKMAN AND PAUL ALBRECHT

Bureau of Biologics, Bethesda, Maryland 20014

One of the major challenges to a national control authority such as the Bureau of Biologics is to be able to translate new information into guidelines and standards for vaccine development and vaccine control. This challenge must be met in order to continue to provide improvements in the levels of safety, purity, and effectiveness for the regulated product.

The Food and Drug Administration has established regulations for vaccines under development which allow the assessment of risk for humans in a stepwise fashion. This is commonly referred to as the "phase" concept in the evaluation of experimental biological materials in human subjects. Base-line data are, of course, first developed in animals and in vitro systems before any tests are undertaken in humans. Once such preliminary studies have been completed and the experimental vaccine appears to be safe, protocols for the initial trials in humans can be developed. The parameters that help in defining the three phases of clinical investigation of a new vaccine are presented in Table 1. This represents the Bureau of Biologics' current interpretation of the Food and Drug Administration's regulations relating to the investigational use of biologicals (15). The studies begin with phase 1, when the material is first introduced into humans. The human subjects are evaluated to provide data concerning the reactogenicity of the vaccine and transmissibility to uninoculated persons, as well as for evidence for the potency and efficacy of the new product. First, a small group of about 10 individuals is tested along with a similar number of uninoculated susceptible contact subjects. These study participants are inoculated under conditions suitable to restricting spread of the live virus. Because of the small numbers, only those events that are likely to occur at high frequency will be detected. The most important type of information gained at this stage of the evaluation relates to measurement of gross safety, reactogenicity, and antigenicity. Such studies would be expected to provide data on the level of attenuation of the vaccine virus as compared with that causing the natural disease, i.e., its propensity to revert to a virulent form and cause disease in contacts or, on the other hand, to have become overattenuated in its development and be nonimmunogenic. Results of these trials in a small group of persons provide an important guide to the investigator in making decisions on whether to proceed with large numbers of vaccinees or to attempt further modification of the virus. If the initial trial has gone well, the next step would be to increase the number of subjects by an increment of about 0.5 $\log_{10}$ (i.e., a factor of 3) to 30 persons. The phase concept, then, is simply a controlled incremental increase in the number of humans participating as subjects in the evaluation of a new biological product. The inoculation of larger and larger numbers of people is based on the evaluation of the data at each preceding stage and the conclusion that the new product continues to be acceptable. It is only during phase 2, after several hundred people have been inoculated, that significant information can be obtained to assess safety and efficacy under conditions approximating "normal" use. With some new products, at this point it may be possible to evaluate effectiveness by artificial challenge. Phase 3 studies correspond to large clinical trials conducted by several groups using a similar protocol. It is only at this stage that one can assess adverse reactions or other events which occur at low frequency. The efficacy of the product under field conditions often can be evaluated only at this stage. At this point, potency data developed in the studies up to and including those of phase 3 are linked to the efficacy observations.

A major problem in the development and use of live viral vaccines relates to the safety of the vaccine virus itself. Past examples have shown that unless carefully handled, such viruses may show a spectrum of changes ranging from increased virulence, with the production of disease, to overattenuation, with the loss of immunogenicity. The experience of the mid-1940s with yellow fever vaccines of increased neuro-

TABLE 1. *Phases of clinical investigation of new vaccines*

Phase	No. of subjects	Rate of increase	Safety: reactogenicity and transmissibility	Potency	Efficacy
I	10–100	$0.5 \log_{10}$	Reveals only high-frequency events	Broad confidence limits	Minimal data
II	100–300	$0.5 \log_{10}$	Reveals events of moderate frequency	Narrow confidence limits	Majority of critical data
III	300–30,000	$0.5 \log_{10}$	Reveals low-frequency events	Potency-efficacy correlations	

virulence (3) and the more recent experience with an overattenuated rubella virus vaccine produced in canine renal cell cultures are pertinent examples. With the rubella virus, duplicate attempts to produce vaccine by identical passage series led in one instance to a preparation of satisfactory immunogenicity and in another to marked overattenuation (10).

A more complex problem related to monitoring the use of live virus vaccines is that posed by the possibility of long-term effects which do not become apparent during the first three phases of the trials. Problems of this sort may arise only after more extensive general use of the product. An example of this is the rare occurrence of vaccine-associated paralytic disease following the use of live oral poliovirus vaccines. Another example is the discovery of the relationship of natural measles virus and subacute sclerosing panencephalitis (SSPE). Could measles vaccine also be involved in the pathogenesis of the disease? Both epidemiological and laboratory approaches have been used to examine this problem. There are several reports in the literature indicating that strains of measles virus developed neurotropism for laboratory rodents on passage in continuous lines of primate cell cultures (1, 7, 16). Using this lead, a study in our laboratory has shown that neurotropism for hamsters could readily be induced in wild measles virus strains by several passages in Vero cell cultures, a line of African green monkey kidney cells. In contrast, neurotropism for hamsters developed rarely when attenuated strains of measles virus were passaged in the same way. It appeared that Vero cells could select for a neurotropic variant in measles virus progeny and that this selection occurred much more readily with natural than with attenuated strains. The finding, although encouraging, left unanswered the question about the significance of this phenomenon in relation to human disease.

Epidemiological investigations concerning the SSPE problem are being supported by the Bureau of Biologics in collaboration with the Center for Disease Control (CDC) and J. T. Jabbour of the University of Tennessee. Both retrospective and prospective analyses have been initiated. The results of these studies are incomplete, but initial findings in the retrospective study indicate that the incidence of SSPE following natural measles is approximately 5- to 10-fold higher than the incidence of the disease in children who have been vaccinated. Thus, if measles vaccination bears any causal relationship with SSPE, it appears to be less of a threat than experiencing natural disease (J. Modlin, unpublished data). Continued use of the vaccine is indicated since in the evaluation of benefit/risk ratio the morbidity and mortality produced by natural measles in the absence of protective immunization clearly would be substantial. Problems such as these make it imperative that the scientific community be alert to disease manifestations that might be attributable to consequences of immunizations. They have also led to suggestions that a more formal system of monitoring the behavior of vaccines in widespread use be developed. The scope and high cost of this type of program have thus far prevented a resolution of the issue, but continued debate about the feasibility and design of such a program are continuing.

No less important than considerations related to the vaccine virus itself is the problem of contaminating microbial agents. Such contamination can result from endogenous contamination of the cell cultures used for vaccine production or from exogenous contamination introduced during manufacture. In the past, both types of contamination have occurred.

The first significant experience with endogenous contamination was that of simian virus 40-contaminated poliomyelitis vaccine grown in rhesus monkey kidney cells. A second major incident was the discovery in 1960 by Rubin that chicken flocks and the embryonated eggs derived from them were contaminated with avian leucosis viruses. Both of these viruses have been shown to be oncogenic in animals. Prior to recognition of these agents, simian virus 40-contaminated poliovirus vaccine (9) and leucosis virus-containing measles vaccines (14) were administered to thousands of individuals. This experience has been well documented in the literature (4, 8). As a result of these experiences, many new systems have been applied to the testing of experimental vaccines for the detection of overt or latent viruses. Techniques used have included cocultivation of the production culture with other species and types of cells, examination by electron microscopy, immunofluorescence staining, examination by use of enzyme detection for reverse transcriptase of oncogenic RNA (oncorna) viruses, and attempted induction of latent viruses by use of halogenated deoxyuridines. It is important to stress that, to date, no vaccine viruses or contaminants of vaccines have been found to be oncogenic for humans.

A serum-related contaminant of live virus vaccines was discovered in 1973. Batches of bovine sera purchased for laboratory use were found to be contaminated with bacteriophages. This observation was applied to live virus vaccines by use of standard phage isolation techniques as well as electron microscopy (12); these vaccines were found to be contaminated with phage. The bacteriophages appear to have been introduced initially from the bacterial contaminants present in the sera used as a medium component to nourish the cell cultures used for vaccine production. Phages pass readily through the "sterilizing" filters used to retain the bacteria. Although there is no evidence to suggest that the presence of phages in vaccines is harmful to humans, their discovery in vaccines has provided the impetus for the development of systems for aseptic serum collection that will result in a product free from bacteria and, thus, bacteriophages. These several examples from the past illustrate clearly that advances in knowledge and technology have provided means for improvement in the live vaccine products.

Finally, mention should be made of problems that may be encountered in the development of new live virus vaccines. Any of several new vaccine candidates could be used as examples; however, the herpesviruses illustrate the complex problems that may arise.

Varicella and its recrudescent form, herpes zoster, frequently produce significant morbidity. Consideration of a varicella virus vaccine raises the unanswered question concerned with virus latency. What assurance is there that a vaccine strain might not emerge from the latent state and produce zoster? Currently we have no clear understanding of the factors that control the change from the latent to the recrudescent state.

The cytomegaloviruses, a relatively common cause of congenital defects (17), have also shown a significant cause of morbidity in patients treated with immunosuppressive agents (11). The immunological diversity of this group of viruses raises special problems for cytomegalovirus vaccine development. A major problem concerns the relationship between the herpesviruses and oncogenicity (5). Herpesvirus types 1 and 2 have been linked with human cancers (6, 13); however, the Epstein-Barr virus has the most solid credentials as a human tumor virus. It has been closely associated with Burkitt's lymphoma and nasopharyngeal carcinoma. Further evidence of its association with human disease is its production of infectious mononucleosis. Epstein-Barr virus transforms human leukocytes into continuously propagating lymphoblastoid carrier cell lines and has produced lymphomas in marmosets similar to those in Burkitt's lymphoma patients (2).

Such problems as latency, immunological diversity, and relationship to oncogenic effects make it clear that a great deal more must be learned about these viruses before a serious commitment can be made to develop vaccines against them. These considerations are representative of many of the new problems to be resolved if additional live virus vaccines are to be developed. Progress in each instance will, in good part, depend on the acquisition of new information that will allow an assessment of these questions.

Ideally, the regulatory agency can work creatively as a catalyst to bring the best scientific information to bear on the problems of vaccine development and to foster the intelligent appreciation of this information in vaccine manufacture and testing.

LITERATURE CITED

1. **Albrecht, P., and H. Schumacher.** 1971. Neurotropic properties of measles virus in hamsters and mice. J. Infect. Dis. **124**:86–93.

2. **Epstein, M. A.** 1976. Implications of a vaccine for the prevention of Epstein-Barr virus infection: ethical and logistic considerations. Cancer Res. **36**:711–714.

3. **Fox, J. P., and H. A. Penna.** 1943. Behavior of 17D yellow fever virus in rhesus monkeys. Relation to substrain, dose, and neural or extraneural inoculation. Am. J. Hyg. **38**:152–172.

4. **Fraumeni, J. J., Jr., F. Ederer, and R. W. Miller.** 1963. An evaluation of the carcinogenicity of simian virus 40 in man. J. Am. Med. Assoc. **185**:713.

5. **Geder, L., R. Lausch, F. O'Neill, and F. Rapp.** 1976. Oncogenic transformation of human embryo lung cells by human cytomegalovirus. Science **192**:1134–1137.

6. **Hollinshead, A. C., P. B. Chretien, L. O'Bong, J. L. Tarpley, S. E. Kerney, N. A. Silverman, and J. C. Alexander.** 1976. *In vivo* and *in vitro* measurements of the relationship of human squamous carcinomas to herpes simplex virus tumor-associated antigens. Cancer Res. **36:**821–828.

7. **Matumoto, M., Y. Saburi, Y. Aoyama, and M. Mutai.** 1959. A neurotropic variant of measles virus in suckling mice. Arch. Gesamte Virusforsch. **14:**683–696.

8. **Miller, R. W.** 1968. Monitoring vaccines for human oncogenicity, p. 453–457. Proceedings of the Conference on Cell Cultures for Virus Vaccine Production, 6–8 November 1967. Natl. Cancer Inst. Monogr. no. 29, National Cancer Institute, Bethesda, Md.

9. **Murray, R.** 1967. Contemporary problems in regulating the potency and safety of virus vaccines, p. 577. First International Conference on Vaccines Against Viral and Rickettsial Diseases of Man, Sci. Publ. no. 147, May 1967. Pan American Health Organization, WHO, Washington, D.C.

10. **Musser, S. J., and L. J. Hilsabeck.** 1969. Production of rubella virus vaccine. Am. J. Dis. Child. **118:** 355–361.

11. **Pagano, J. S.** 1975. Infections with cytomegalovirus in bone marrow transplantation: report of a workshop. J. Infect. Dis. **132:**209–223.

12. **Petricciani, J. C., F. C. Chu, and J. B. Johnson.** 1973. Bacteriophages in live virus vaccines. Proc. Soc. Exp. Biol. Med. **144:**789–792.

13. **Rawls, W. E., C. H. Garfield, P. Seth, and E. Adam.** 1976. Serological and epidemiological considerations of the role of herpes simplex virus type 2 in cervical cancer. Cancer Res. **36:**829–835.

14. **Rubin, H.** 1960. A virus in chick embryos which induces resistance *in vitro* to infection with Rous sarcoma virus. Proc. Natl. Acad. Sci. U.S.A. **46:** 1105.

15. **United States Code of Federal Regulations.** 1974. March 29. Title 21, part 312.1(a)(2). Food and Drug Administration, Department of Health, Education and Welfare, Washington, D.C.

16. **Wear, D. J., and F. Rapp.** 1970. Encephalitis in newborn hamsters after intracerebral injection of attenuated human measles virus. Nature (London) **227:**1347–1348.

17. **Weller, T. H.** 1971. The cytomegaloviruses; ubiquitous agents with protean clinical manifestations. N. Engl. J. Med. **285:**203–214.

Dissemination and Monitoring of Live Virus Vaccines Licensed for Use in Humans

JOHN J. WITTE

Center for Disease Control, Atlanta, Georgia 30333

There are currently four licensed live virus vaccines recommended for general use in the United States: (i) live attenuated measles virus vaccine, (ii) live mumps virus vaccine, (iii) trivalent live oral poliovirus vaccines, and (iv) live rubella virus vaccines. Other live virus vaccines are licensed and recommended for special circumstances, such as yellow fever and smallpox vaccines for international travel; however, these products, because of their limited distribution, will not be included in the present report.

The Center for Disease Control (CDC) maintains continuing surveillance of morbidity and mortality for these diseases through established reporting systems from state health departments. These data are published weekly in the Morbidity and Mortality Weekly Report. In addition, adverse reactions occurring after administration of these antigens are reported to the CDC. Reports of complications following vaccination, as well as detailed analyses of epidemiological trends of the diseases, are regularly included in the Surveillance Reports issued for measles, rubella, polio, and mumps. Furthermore, the CDC also maintains a surveillance of licensed biologics in general use. The net distribution of each vaccine is reported by the manufacturers to the CDC, and these data are published quarterly in a Biologics Surveillance Report. These sources of data comprise the material contained in this report. For each of the vaccines, poliomyelitis, measles, rubella, and mumps, I will present data on disease trends, emphasizing impact of vaccine use and vaccine distribution. In addition, I will focus on three related problems: (i) paralytic illness associated with oral polio virus vaccine, (ii) encephalitis and encephalopathy following measles vaccines, and (iii) the temporal association between measles vaccines and subacute sclerosing panencephalitis (SSPE).

Prior to the introduction of poliomyelitis vaccines, tens of thousands of cases of paralytic polio occurred each year. Large epidemics were common, and the disease caused considerable national concern each year. Figure 1 shows the annual poliomyelitis incidence rates in the United States from 1941 to 1975. The inactivated vaccine was introduced in 1955. In 1961 and 1962, the three monovalent live oral poliovirus vaccines (OPV) were licensed. In 1963, the trivalent OPV became available. To date, more than 285.0 million doses of oral poliovirus vaccine, monovalent and trivalent, have been distributed. The impact on polio morbidity has been striking. Epidemic polio, in its classic sense, has been absent from the United States for more than a decade. Now, reported cases are few and, generally, scattered.

The net doses of trivalent polio vaccine distributed in the United States are shown in Fig. 2. In recent years, the distribution has been rather constant, between 20 and 25 million doses per year.

Shortly after OPV was licensed, it was noted that paralytic illness occurred in a small number of persons who received OPV, who had no documented exposure to wild poliovirus, and for whom no diagnosis other than polio could be attributed (1). The risk appeared to be higher in persons over 18 years of age, and recommendations for use were changed in 1964 to exclude OPV from adults except under circumstances of increased risk (5).

Cases of vaccine-associated polio among recipients of vaccine and their contacts continue to occur, although the rate is *very* low. During the period 1969–1974, for example, the risk was one case per 15 million doses distributed in vaccinees, or one case in contacts of vaccinees per 9 million doses distributed (Center for Disease Control, unpublished data). Although these risks are very low, the so-called vaccine-associated cases comprise a substantial proportion of the handful of reported cases each year. In fact, some adherents of inactivated polio vaccine (IPV), in particular Jonas Salk, have implied that this number is more than we should tolerate and that we should give

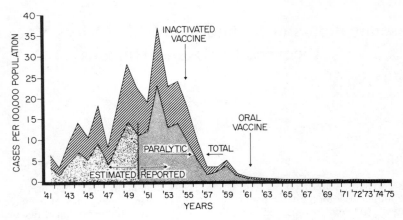

FIG. 1. *Annual poliomyelitis incidence rates in the United States from 1941–1975.*

IPV exclusively and thereby eliminate vaccine-associated cases. He has presented his arguments to the Public Health Service Advisory Committee on Immunization Practices and the American Academy of Pediatrics "Redbook" Committee; however, it is unlikely that major changes in recommendations for the use of polio vaccine will occur in the near future.

The incidence of reported rubella from 1928 to 1975 is shown in Fig. 3. The striking periodicity for this disease shows years of high incidence in 1935, 1943, and 1964. Lesser peaks were noted in 1952 and 1958. Vaccine was introduced for general use in 1969, and a total of 69.1 million doses have been distributed. A substantial decline in the occurrence of rubella and congenital rubella has resulted. Further, the pandemic that many epidemiologists predicted for the early 1970s has not materialized.

The net doses of rubella vaccine distributed by year are shown in Fig. 4. The peak of more than 22 million doses in 1970 reflects extensive school immunization campaigns conducted during that period. The vaccine is very well tolerated. Reactions in children are uncommon and appear to be self-limited.

The CDC is following a population of several thousand persons with vaccine-induced immunity, residing in the Hawaiian Islands Kauai and Hawaii. More than 5,000 susceptible subjects were vaccinated in 1969 with one of the three licensed vaccines. Of these, 99% seroconverted. These populations are quite stable, and a substantial proportion are still under surveillance. In 1975, 99% of persons seroconverting after vaccine still had antibodies, despite the fact there have been very few natural infections introduced in these populations (2).

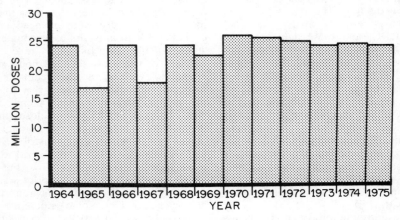

FIG. 2. *Net doses of trivalent polio vaccine distributed in the United States from 1964 to 1975. Source: Biologics Surveillance Program.*

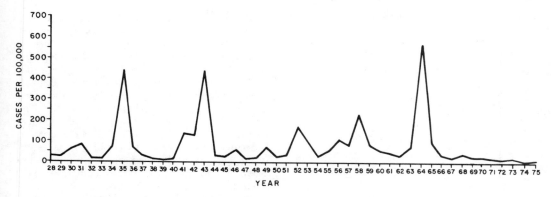

FIG. 3. *Rubella incidence in 10 selected areas of the United States (Maine, Rhode Island, Connecticut, New York City, Ohio, Illinois, Wisconsin, Maryland, Washington, and Massachusetts) from 1928 to 1975.*

The reported incidence of mumps, mumps encephalitis, and mumps deaths is shown in Fig. 5. Mumps vaccine was introduced as a monovalent product in 1968 and was combined with measles and rubella in 1973. Use of vaccine was quite limited until the combined products became available. Use in children is largely in the private practice of medicine. Because the cost of a dose of mumps vaccine is two or three times that of measles vaccine, public health use has been limited. Nevertheless, a modest decline in cases, complications, and deaths is apparent. Since licensure, 26.6 million doses have been distributed. Vaccine is well tolerated, and no substantive untoward effects have been documented to date.

Shown in Fig. 6 is the reported incidence of measles from 1960 to 1975. Prior to the introduction of live attenuated measles virus vaccines, there were 400,000 to 500,000 cases of measles reported each year. Serological surveys for measles antibodies showed the true incidence to be approximately 4 million cases per year on the average (with some year-to-year variability). Live virus vaccines were introduced in 1963, and Federal monies for vaccine purchases became available in 1965. Since licensure, 81.0 million doses have been distributed. It is obvious that vaccine has had a substantive impact on the occurrence of the disease. In 1975 there were 25,000 reported cases—a decrease of 95% compared with the prevaccine era. The further control of measles is becoming exasperatingly elusive. There continue to be 25 to 30 measles deaths per year, and this is more than we should be willing to accept. The reduction in deaths parallels the reduction in morbidity, as shown in Fig. 7. Essentially all of the deaths occurred in unimmunized

children, so that any deaths resulting from measles are inexcusable.

The net doses of live measles vaccine distributed between 1963 and 1975 in the United States are shown in Fig. 8. For the past 5 years, a relatively constant 7 to 8 million doses were distributed. The annual birth rate is between 3 and 3.5 million, so we should be reaching an increasing proportion of susceptible children each year.

Measles virus vaccines appear to be among

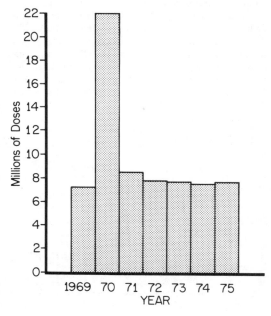

FIG. 4. *Net doses of rubella vaccine distributed in the United States from 1969 to 1975.*

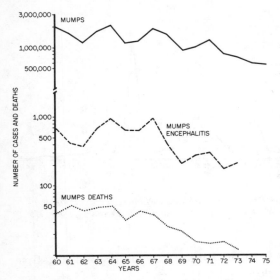

FIG. 5. *Reported cases of mumps, mumps encephalitis, and mumps-associated deaths in the United States from 1960 to 1975 (mumps encephalitis data and mumps deaths data through 1973).*

the safest of biological agents. Because of the neurological sequelae of naturally occurring measles, we have been concerned with the possibility of rare neurological sequelae following vaccine, even though prelicensure field trials involving several thousand children provided evidence that the encephalotogenic properties of wild measles virus had apparently been excluded from the vaccine. Surveillance for central nervous system (CNS) events occurring within 30 days after vaccine administration has been maintained by the CDC. From 1963 through 1971, a total of 84 cases

of neurological disorders with onset less than 30 days after live measles virus vaccination was reported in the United States. Thirteen of these were documented as caused by something other than the vaccines' virus, and another 11 cases were uncomplicated febrile convulsions probably related to vaccination. One case met diagnostic criteria for SSPE. The remaining 59 reported cases showed clinical features of encephalitis or encephalopathy. The causes of these cases could not be established, but 45 (76%) had onset of illness between 6 and 15 days after vaccination. This clustering at the time of expected virus replication suggests that some of these cases may have been caused by the vaccine. Between 1963 and 1971, 51 million doses of measles vaccine were distributed. Therefore, the incidence of the reported neurological disorders was 1.16 cases per million doses of vaccine administered.

Cases of encephalitis may be expected to occur in any large childhood population in a defined period of time, even when no vaccines are given. A 1965 New Jersey survey showed that 2.86 cases of encephalitis occurred per million children 1 to 9 years old per 28-day period (4). A 1968 survey in Tampa, Fla., showed that the incidence of encephalitis of unknown cause was 2.28 cases per million children in the same age group per 4-week period. Both surveys showed a rate twice that found in the vaccinated population. Thus, encephalitis and encephalopathy following vaccine, if indeed they do occur, are a very small problem. On the other hand, the risk of encephalitis following measles infection is one per thousand reported cases of measles (3).

SSPE is a rare degenerative disease of the

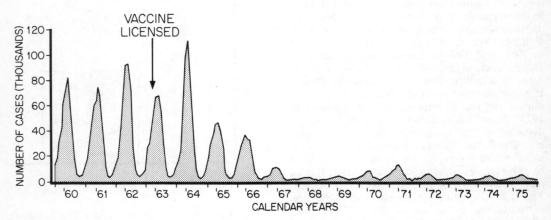

FIG. 6. *Reported cases of measles by 4-week periods in the United States from 1960 to 1975.*

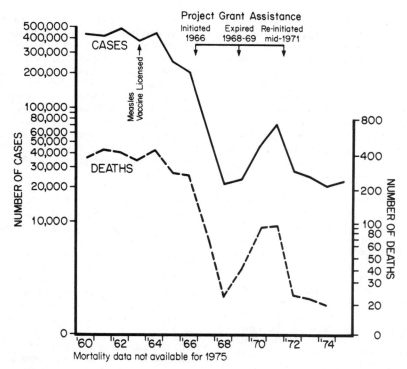

FIG. 7. *Reported measles cases and deaths in the United States from 1960 to 1975.*

CNS of children and adolescents. The disease is characterized by insidious onset of mental deterioration, motor dysfunction, and inevitable progression to convulsions, coma, emaciation, and death. Although the duration of illness may vary widely, most patients succumb within 3 years after onset of symptoms. Spontaneous temporary remissions can occur. No specific therapy is effective.

Although the causes of SSPE remain poorly understood, there is convincing evidence that the measles virus plays a role in the pathogenesis. It is therefore conceivable that the live, attenuated measles virus vaccine may also contribute

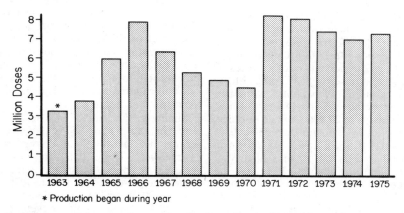

FIG. 8. *Net doses of live measles vaccine distributed in the United States from 1963 to 1975.*

to the pathogenesis of SSPE. The literature contains brief references to children with a history of measles vaccine who later developed SSPE. However, the possible association of SSPE, if any, with measles vaccine virus has not been examined in a systematic fashion.

We have reviewed a total of 375 cases of SSPE in the United States that occurred between 1960 and 1974. Data from these cases were compared with estimated measles morbidity and measles vaccine distribution data from the same time period. This information was obtained as part of an epidemiological study of SSPE in the United States, conducted in collaboration with the University of Tennessee and the Bureau of Biologics, Food and Drug Administration. I am particularly indebted to John Modlin, formerly of the CDC and now at the Children's Hospital in Boston, who collected and analyzed most of these data.

The National Registry for Subacute Sclerosing Panencephalitis has been maintained at the University of Tennessee Center for the Health Sciences since 1969. The information sought for each reported case includes the patient's past medical history and a detailed clinical history, including rash illnesses and immunizing agents received. When possible, each medical record was reviewed by an epidemiologist from the CDC, and additional information was obtained from interviews with parents and primary physicians, and by examination of school or clinic immunization records.

By July 1975, a total of 432 patients with onset of SSPE between 1960 and 1974 was reported to the registry. The diagnosis of SSPE was confirmed in 375 or 87% of the cases, either by characteristic electroencephalograph (EEG) tracings, by elevated cerebrospinal fluid (CSF) measles antibody titers, or by characteristic histology of CNS specimens.

Of these 375 confirmed SSPE cases, 265 were male and 110 were female, which is a male-to-female ratio of 2.4:1. There were 342 cases in United States-born whites, 16 in United States-born blacks, and 17 in persons of other races or nationalities. Age at onset of SSPE ranged from 2 to 32 years, with 85% of patients having had initial symptoms between 5 and 14 years of age. Only four patients were 20 years of age or older.

Measles histories were obtained for 350 or 93% of the 375 confirmed SSPE cases. As shown in Table 1, a total of 292, 83%, had a history of prior measles illness. Only 58, 17%, had no history of measles illness.

A total of 207 SSPE patients had histories of measles illness but did not receive live measles vaccine prior to onset of SSPE. Age at the time of measles infection was known in 261 of the 292 cases and ranged from 5 months to 12 years. However, 46% of these patients had had measles before the second birthday, which is substantively lower than expected. The mean time from measles to onset of SSPE was 7.0 years (ranging from 1 month to 27 years). The mean interval from measles illness to onset of SSPE symptoms for those persons who subsequently received live measles vaccine was not significantly different from the mean interval for those who never received vaccine.

There were 58 patients, 17% of the total group studied, with no history of measles illness (Table 1). Of these 58 patients, 40 had a history of receiving live, attenuated measles vaccine. For the 35 of these 40 patients for whom the date of vaccination was known, the interval from vaccination to onset of SSPE symptoms ranged from 1 month to 9 years, with a mean of 3.3 years. The age at vaccination ranged from 12 months to 10 years, and there was no apparent association of SSPE with vaccination at any particular age.

In 13 cases, parents of patients denied that their children had had either measles illness or measles vaccine; however, measles antibodies were present in the serum of each of the four patients in this group for whom measles serologies were done.

The year of measles illness is listed in Table 2 for the 196 SSPE patients who had measles in 1960 or later, and these data are compared with the estimated annual number of measles cases since 1960. As expected, the yearly occurrence of measles in the SSPE patients parallels national measles trends. Between 5.2 and 9.7 cases of SSPE ultimately developed for each million cases of measles estimated to have occurred each year from 1960 to 1968. Because of the lengthy interval between measles and onset of SSPE, the annual ratios of SSPE cases to estimated measles incidence since 1968 are smaller than observed earlier, but would be expected to increase as future cases of SSPE occur in children who have had measles in recent years.

Similarly, the year of measles vaccination is listed in Table 3 for SSPE patients vaccinated against measles who did not have a prior history of measles. These data are compared with measles vaccine distribution data during the same time period. From 1964 to 1970, there were between 0.48 and 1.13 recipients of measles vaccine who subsequently developed SSPE per

TABLE 1. *Measles and measles vaccination status of 350 patients with subacute sclerosing panencephalitis*

History	No. of patients (%)		
History of having had measles			292 (83.4)
Also received live measles vaccine	44	(15.1)	
Did not receive live measles vaccine	207	(70.9)	
Vaccine history unknown	41	(14.0)	
Total	292	(100.0)	
History of not having had measles			58 (16.6)
Received live measles vaccine	40	(69.0)	
Did not receive live measles vaccine	13	(22.4)	
Vaccine history unknown	5	(8.6)	
Totals..	58	(100.0)	350 (100.0)

million doses of measles vaccine distributed each year.

Since 1967, however, there has been a downward trend in the annual number of cases reported. This decline has resulted primarily from a decline in cases who have a prior history of measles. By contrast, the small number of cases in persons who have received live measles vaccine but have not had measles has remained relatively constant at three to seven cases per year since 1967.

These data neither prove nor disprove an etiological relationship between live, attenuated measles vaccine and SSPE, but they do indicate that if there is a risk associated with the vaccine it is exceedingly low. In fact, the exact relationship between natural measles infection and SSPE

remains unclear, and other factors may play a role in the pathogenesis of the disease.

Since this retrospective survey has not given definitive information about the role, if any, of vaccine virus, we have begun a prospective case-controlled study of SSPE. This will examine a number of epidemiological parameters, including measles vaccine.

In summary, a number of live virus vaccines have been extensively used in the United States, which has resulted in dramatic reductions in morbidity and mortality. These appear to be very safe biological products, and the minute risks associated with inoculation are far outweighed by the overwhelming benefits resulting from their use.

TABLE 2. *Ratio of SSPE cases (by year of measles illness) to estimated annual number of measles cases, 1960–1974*

Year	Estimated measles cases (in millions)	No. of SSPE patients who had had measles	Cases of SSPE per million estimated measles cases
1960	4.41	28	6.3
1961	4.23	31	7.3
1962	4.81	25	5.2
1963	3.85	32	8.3
1964	4.58	36	7.9
1965	2.61	16	6.1
1966	2.04	14	6.9
1967	0.62	6	9.7
1968	0.22	2	9.1
1969	0.25	1	4.0
1970	0.47	2	4.2
1971	0.75	2	2.6
1972	0.32	1	3.1
1973	0.26	—	—
1974	0.22	—	—

TABLE 3. *Ratio of reported SSPE cases historically associated with measles vaccine (by year of measles vaccination) to annual number of doses of measles vaccine distributed, United States, 1963–1974*

Year	No. of doses of measles vaccine distributed (in millions)	No. of SSPE patients[a] who received vaccine	Cases of SSPE[a] per million doses of measles vaccine distributed
1963	3.2	0	0
1964	4.2	2	0.48
1965	5.7	5	0.88
1966	7.9	9	1.13
1967	6.5	7	1.08
1968	5.3	3	0.57
1969	5.0	3	0.60
1970	4.7	3	0.64
1971	8.6	1	0.12
1972	8.5	1	0.12
1973	7.4	1	0.13
1974	7.0	1	0.14

[a] SSPE patients with a history of measles vaccination but no history of measles illness.

LITERATURE CITED

1. **Henderson, D. A., J. J. Witte, L. Morris, and A. D. Langmuir.** 1964. Paralytic disease associated with oral polio vaccines. J. Am. Med. Assoc. **190:**41–48.
2. **Herrmann, K. L., S. B. Halstead, A. D. Brandling-Bennet, J. J. Witte, N. H. Wiebenga, and D. L. Eddins.** 1976. Persistence of antibody four years after a large-scale field trial. J. Am. Med. Assoc. **235:**2201–2204.
3. **Landrigan, P. J., and J. J. Witte.** 1973. Neurologic disorders following live measles-virus vaccination. J. Am. Med. Assoc. **223:**1459–1462.
4. **Miller, D. L.** 1964. Frequency of complications of measles 1963. Br. Med. J. **2:**75–78.
5. **Special Advisory Committee on Oral Poliomyelitis Vaccine.** 1964. Report to the Surgeon General of the Public Health Service, 17–18 July 1974. J. Am. Med. Assoc. **190:**49.

Persistent Viral Infections of Man

Persistent Viral Infections of Humans: an Overview

NEAL NATHANSON

Department of Epidemiology, School of Hygiene and Public Health, The Johns Hopkins University, Baltimore, Maryland 21205

Persistent infection is produced by a number of human viruses. This brief review is designed to indicate the frequency of the phenomenon and the variety of associated diseases, to sketch the mechanisms of persistence as illustrated by two examples, hepatitis B virus (HBV) and Epstein-Barr virus (EBV), and to consider some chronic illnesses of unknown etiology which may be associated with persistent viruses. Persistent infections of animals and humans are treated in greater detail in several recent volumes (6, 8, 17).

OVERVIEW

Well-documented persistent viruses are listed in Table 1 according to virus group. A wide variety of RNA and DNA viruses may persist, and the infections are associated with a multiplicity of disease states, although each virus usually causes a stereotyped, sometimes pathognomonic, syndrome.

The biology of persistence may be classified according to the expression of the viral genome and the antiviral immune response (Table 2). Since there are several potent host defenses (antibody, cellular immunity, interferon, phagocytosis) which usually terminate and clear infection, persistence implies a subversion of clearance processes.

One mechanism is latency, in which a viral genome is not expressed. Under these circumstances, lytic viruses, such as herpes, do not destroy parasitized cells, and they escape immune surveillance since virus-coded neoantigens are not produced. At the other extreme are the spongiform encephalopathy agents, which are apparently nonimmunogenic and therefore can persist at high titer over a long time.

Agents such as rubella virus and JC virus (JCV) persist under circumstances that suggest a partially defective immune response. In some instances, there is probably an unstable balance between the immune response and the infectious process. Thus, human papilloma virus (HPV) is probably held in rein and often eliminated by immune surveillance, as suggested by flamboyant warts sometimes seen in immunode-pressed subjects. Subacute sclerosing panencephalitis (SSPE) virus in vivo is an abortive infection with little if any maturation at the plasma membrane so that the supranormal antibody response may be ineffective in dealing with an essentially intracellular infection.

As with acute viral infections, persistent viruses cause disease in several ways (Table 3). Agents that are latent frequently produce cytocidal lesions when activated, with manifestations determined by localization and extent of the overt phase of infection. Relatively noncytocidal viruses, such as rubella, may prevent development by retarding cell division. Conversely, transforming agents, such as EBV and HPV (possibly JCV and cytomegalovirus) stimulate proliferation of selected cells, with production of tumors ranging from innocuous warts to malignant lymphomas. The ability of viruses to initiate immunopathological lesions has been well documented in many animal models (13, 18; Lipton et al., this volume, p. 505), but is less well established for persistent human viral infection. Evidence is accumulating that HB may be such a disease, and other immunopathologies of unknown etiology may in part be associated with persistent viruses.

CONTRASTING MECHANISMS OF VIRAL PERSISTENCE: HBV AND EBV INFECTION

Two examples will serve to illustrate some of the foregoing overly concise generalizations. Like a landscape seen through clearing fog, the biology of HB is gradually emerging (1). The complete virion is probably the 42-nm Dane particle that carries the surface antigen (HBsAg) on its outer coat. HBsAg is also released into the plasma in the form of 22-nm spheres and filaments. The inner core of the virion containing the viral DNA and a polymerase also carries antigenic activity (HBcAg), although free cores are usually not seen in plasma. Lastly, another antigen (HBeAg), associated with a protein of about 300,000 daltons, is found in a few sera.

TABLE 1. *Persistent viral infections of humans: virus class and associated disease* [a]

Class		Agent	Disease	Reference
RNA	?Toga	Rubella	Fetal anomalies Panencephalitis	22
	Paramyxo	Measles	Panencephalitis (SSPE)	Johnson and Byington, this volume, p. 511
DNA	Papova	JCV	Leucoencephalopathy (PML)	19, 28
		BKV	?	19
	Papilloma	HPV	Warts	20
	?	HB	Hepatitis	1
	??	Non A/B	Hepatitis	1
	Adeno	Adeno	?	21
	Herpes	HSV-1,2	Herpes	24; Stevens, this volume, p. 509
		VZV	Zoster	25
		CMV	Mononucleosis CID	4
		EBV	Mononucleosis Burkitt's lymphoma	3,9
	Spongiform	Kuru	Kuru	8
	Encephalopathy	CJ	Creutzfeldt-Jacob D	8

[a] Abbreviations: JCV, JC virus; BKV, BK virus; HPV, human papilloma virus; HB, hepatitis B; HSV, herpes simplex virus; VZV, varicella-zoster virus; CMV, cytomegalovirus; CID, cytomegalic inclusion disease; EBV, Epstein-Barr virus; PML, progressive multifocal leucoencephelopathy.

A reanalysis of serial bleedings from susceptible human volunteers who were infected parenterally with HBV has been most instructive (5). Infections may be divided into three major patterns: (i) acute hepatitis with transient antigenemia (HBsAg) followed by appearance first of anti-HBc and then anti-HBs (70%); (ii) a similar acute infection that is subclinical and where HBsAg appears fleetingly if at all (25%); and (iii) a silent infection in which HBsAg persists with appearance of anti-HBc but not anti-HBs (5%). This latter group represents the silent carriers whose blood is the classical source of transfusion-associated HB. It has more recently been observed that there is a relatively rare subgroup (perhaps 10%) of carriers who have HBeAg in their serum. These individuals seem prone to chronic liver disease and may be particularly infectious by direct contact as well as through their blood.

Major inferences which may be drawn are that the carrier state is associated with release into the circulation of large amounts of HBsAg (which may attain levels as high as 10^{13} particulates per ml) and with absence of free anti-HBs. It can be postulated that the ability of HBV to produce overwhelming levels of surface antigen which can bind large amounts of antibody provides the biological basis of HB persistence. Conversely, anti-HBs is associated both with clearance of virus and development of hepatitis. Anti-HBc does not seem to play a major role either in viral clearance or disease production.

A further inference is that HBV is not cytocidal (since many carriers have normal liver function and histology) and that hepatitis is an immunopathology. The widespread impression that immunodeficient subjects are at reduced risk of overt hepatitis and at enhanced risk of becoming HBV carriers is consistent with this hypothesis.

Epidemiological observations on naturally occurring HB enlarge our understanding of HBV persistence which was initially associated with parenterally transmitted infection. Data on populations living under relatively primitive condi-

TABLE 2. *Persistent viral infections of humans: expression of viral genome and immune response*

Expression of viral genome	Virus[a]	Immune response	Expression: immuno-depression	Activation
Latent	HS	Normal	?	+
	VZ	Normal	?	+
	CM	Normal	+	
	EB	Normal		
	Adeno	Normal		
	BK	Normal	+	
Partial/minimal	SSPE	High		
	JC/PML	Low	+	
Overt	Papilloma	Normal	±	
	HB	Low	±	
	Rubella	Low		
	Kuru/CJ	None		

[a] Abbreviations as in Table 1.

tions throw some key issues into clearer profile, as illustrated by a recent study (23) of Greenland eskimos (Table 4). HBV is highly prevalent in this population, more so (81%) in isolated rural areas where infection is frequently acquired at an early age, presumably by direct person-to-person spread under conditions of limited personal hygiene and intimate contact. These circumstances are associated with a high frequency of the carrier state (about 25%) and a low case-to-infection ratio (estimated 1:100). In "urban" villages infection is delayed, overall prevalence is somewhat lower (46%), the carrier state is less frequent (7%), and disease is more common (estimated case-and-infection ratio of 25:100).

These data indicate that host factors such as age of infection play a critical role in the frequency with which HBV initiates the carrier state. Immunological immaturity (mother-infant transmission in Greenland) and perhaps the amount of HBsAg production in infants favor persistence, whereas at an older age a brisk immune response favors a transient infection associated with clinical disease.

The biology of EBV (3,9) persistence differs strikingly from that of HBV. Primary EBV infections are often silent but can be detected retrospectively by serum antibody. From normal subjects with prior EBV infection, lines of immortalized lymphoblastoid cells can be isolated, in close to 100% of instances if lymph node cells are used. These lines exhibit B cell markers and they always carry the EBV genome, but they fall into two major classes, producer and nonproducer lines. Nonproducer lines usually are positive for a nuclear antigen (EBNA) but fail to express other virus-coded antigens. Producer lines consist of a majority of nonproducer cells and a minority of cells which produce a variety of viral antigens (membrane-associated, MA; early, EA) and virions plus virion capsid antigen (VCA), although they rarely release infectious virions. Cloning studies have shown that producer cells represent the occasional activation of EBV genome in nonproducer cells. Since producer cells undergo a cytocidal infection, their constant presence implies that they are continually generated from the nonproducer subpopulation.

Prospective studies of primary EBV infection suggest the following sequence: after initiation of infection (perhaps by the oral route), B cell producer lines appear in peripheral blood and persist for several months, when they are replaced by nonproducer lines. Antibodies to VCA, EA, and MA tend to appear fairly early (several weeks), and titers gradually decrease over a period of months. Antibody against

TABLE 3. *Persistent viral infections of humans: mechanisms of associated disease*

Disease mechanism	Agent[a]	Disease entity
Cytolysis	HSV	Herpes
	VZV	Zoster
	CMV	CID
	JCV(PML)	Oligodendroglia Leucoencephalopathy
	Kuru/CJ	Spongiform encephalopathy
	Measles	SSPE[b]
Inhibition of cell division	Rubella	Fetal anomalies
Transformation	EBV	Mononucleosis Lymphoma
	CMV	Mononucleosis
	Papilloma	Warts
	JCV(PML)	Astrogliosis
Immunopathology	HB	Hepatitis[b]
None	Adeno	?
	BK	?

[a] Abbreviations as in Table 1.
[b] Provisional classification.

EBNA appears late (several months) but is then maintained at a plateau level. It is thought that this antibody sequence reflects the sequential changes in infection of B lymphocytes.

The mechanism of EBV persistence can be reconstructed as a consequence of several phenomena: viral infection immortalizes clones of lymphocytes, and, in the case of nonproducer cells, the infection is noncidal and does not

TABLE 4. *Hepatitis B in Greenland eskimos (after Skinhoj, 23)*

	East	Southwest
Residence	Rural	Urban
1965 Population	2,356	16,869
Viral hepatitis 1960–1696	5	398
Annual incidence per 10,000	2	25
HBsAg......................	25%	7%
Anti-HBs	56%	39%
Total	81%	46%
HBeAg	2%	0.2%
Anti-HBe	6%	2%
Anti-HBc[a]	47%	23%
Case/infection[a]	1.1/100	25/100

[a] Extrapolations from the data.

involve the expression of MA, so the transformed cells may escape immune surveillance. Meanwhile, the conversion of occasional cells to producers offers the opportunity for transmission of infection to susceptible human hosts, a critical requirement for long-term perpetuation of the viral genome.

EBV disease is obviously a consequence of its ability to transform lymphoid cells. Furthermore, observations on the other lymphotropic herpesviruses (Marek's virus, herpesviruses ateles, saimiri, and sylvaligus) help to substantiate the oncogenic potential of these agents. However, it is far from clear why infectious mononucleosis is a fairly frequent consequence of primary infection between the ages of 10 and 30 years but is infrequent when infection occurs in early childhood. Burkitt's lymphoma, which apparently has onset about 6 to 12 months after some infections of children in East Africa, has been attributed to a state of immunodepression perhaps associated with holoendemic malaria. This is consistent with the view that a critical component in the malignant aspect of Marek's disease is a virus-induced destruction of lymphoid tissue which permits transformed cells (also lymphocytes) to multiply unchecked.

POORLY UNDERSTOOD CHRONIC DISEASES POSSIBLY ASSOCIATED WITH PERSISTENT VIRUSES

One of the sources of interest in persistent viruses is the suspicion that they may play a role in the induction of several chronic human diseases where etiology is a partial or total enigma. Some of the more prominent syndromes under suspicion are set forth in Table 5.

Immune complexes, deposited in or around blood vessels, undoubtedly are important in the genesis of a proportion of cases of chronic glomerulonephritis, systemic lupus erythematosis, and polyarteritis nodosa (18). Animal models suggest that persistent viral infection could provide antigens that contribute to these complexes. Although it has been possible to demonstrate immunoglobulin and complement (C3) deposits in many instances, the identification of specific antigens is still in its infancy. Recently, HBsAg has been incriminated in some cases developing in chronic carriers (1), and EBV and SSPE virus have been implicated in a few patients.

Amyotrophic lateral sclerosis (ALS) is a well-defined fatal neurological disease of middle age. Although frequently postulated to have a viral etiology, there is little direct evidence other than a possible increased frequency of prior paralytic poliomyelitis. Two animal models, Theiler's murine encephalomyelitis virus (Lipton et al.,

p. 505) and neurotropic murine leukemia virus (Gardner, p. 498), produce diseases reminiscent of certain aspects of the pathology of ALS. These observations can only be regarded as provocative, and ALS awaits a critical breakthrough.

Multiple sclerosis (MS) must be regarded as one of the major medical enigmas among affections of relatively high prevalence (100,000 cases in the United States). To date, in spite of an extensive effort, the etiology of MS has defied search for a definitive solution.

Epidemiological studies (12) have provided a body of data which presents certain features compatible with an infectious etiology: (i) onset at 15 to 50 years with a peak in the early thirties; (ii) increase in prevalence with latitude which is striking (fourfold or greater spread from low- to high-prevalence areas); (iii) studies of migrants between low- and high-incidence areas which indicate that risk is determined by residence prior to the age of 15 years; (iv) increase (twofold) of prevalence with increasing social class. All of these observations are reminiscent of the epidemiology of poliomyelitis if one postulates that a delay in infection beyond childhood enhances risk of a disease with an incubation period of 10 to 15 years.

The pathology of MS (12) has certain striking characteristics, including focal lesions, demyelination, and round-cell infiltration. Some viral infections of animals (canine distemper, hamster SSPE, and ovine visna) have selected features quite similar to MS.

In the search for a viral etiology, the most intriguing leads relate to measles (15), a virus that already has been proven to cause one other progressive fatal neurological disease (SSPE). MS patients have consistently been shown to have higher serum measles antibody titers in a large number of independent studies, although the quantitative differences are small (about twofold). More suggestive are studies (16) of cerebrospinal fluid which indicate local central nervous system anti-measles antibody production in 50% of MS cases. Also, MS cerebrospinal fluid immunoglobulins often migrate as a few discrete oligoclonal bands in electrophoresis. Excitement over these findings has been somewhat blunted by the failure to adsorb these bands with measles antigen. Furthermore, an intense search has failed to reveal evidence of measles antigens, nucleocapsids, or virions in MS brains, and recent vigorous efforts to isolate a viral agent have so far been unsuccessful. Reports by Carp and others (11) of a transmissible agent have yet to be confirmed in blind tests.

Measles virus exhibits interesting interactions with T lymphocytes. T cells bind the virus,

TABLE 5. *Human diseases of poorly defined etiology possibly associated with persistent virus infection* [a]

Disease	Candidate human viruses	Animal models		Reference
		Example	Mechanism	
GN	HB, EB, SSPE	LCM, MuL, AD	Immune complex	1, 18
SLE, PAN	HB	NZB/W, AD Canine lupus	Immune complex	1, 18
ALS	?	?TME	Immunopathology	7; Lipton et al., this volume, p. 505
		?NMuL	Cytocidal	Garder, this volume, p. 498
MS	??Measles	?CD	?Immunopathology	7, 10
		?Visna	Immunopathology	14

[a] Abbreviations: GN, glomerulonephritis; SLE, systemic lupus erythematosis; ALS, amyotrophic lateral sclerosis; MS, multiple sclerosis; HB, hepatitis B; EB, Epstein-Barr; LCM, lymphocytic choriomeningitis; MuL, murine leukemia; NZB/W, New Zealand black/white; AD, Aleutian disease; TME, Theiler's murine encephalomyelitis; NMuL, neurotropic murine leukemia; CD, canine distemper.

and primary measles infection causes an acute but transient depression of cellular immunity which probably is due to interference with T cell function. In this perspective, several reports of apparent aberrations in the cellular responses of MS patients to measles virus are of interest: (i) reduction of migration inhibition factor (MIF) response to measles antigens (28), and (ii) quantitative alterations in the binding of lymphocytes to measles antigens or measles-infected cells (27, 30). If these observations constitute valid signposts linking MS and measles, the nature of the association remains elusive.

AFTERWORD: PROOF OF VIRAL ETIOLOGY FOR CHRONIC OR OBSCURE HUMAN DISEASES

In closing, it is appropriate to comment upon the evidence required to relate persistent viruses to obscure human diseases, a subject considered more fully by Evans (2). The classical statement by Koch (Henle-Koch postulates) suggested three major criteria: (i) the agent occurs in every case; (ii) the agent is found in no other disease; and (iii) the agent will induce disease after growth in pure culture.

Clearly, these postulates have become outmoded by recognition of several aspects of viral ecology: (i) certain syndromes can be produced by a variety of agents; (ii) certain viruses can produce a variety of diseases; (iii) risk factors can markedly influence the probability that infection with a given virus results in disease.

The following guidelines are suggested as a substitute for the Henle-Koch postulates for use in testing the relationship of persistent viruses to obscure human disease. (i) Disease prevalence is higher in infected than uninfected persons. Conversely, in retrospective studies infection is more common in cases than in controls. (ii) In prospective studies infection precedes the onset of disease. Incubation periods may show a log-normal distribution. (iii) The candidate virus can be transmitted to humans or animals with production of disease. Alternatively, there are animal models in which agents related to the candidate virus produce a syndrome(s) resembling the human disease. (iv) Intervention, by either immunization or hygienic measures, reduces the incidence of infection with a subsequent reduction in disease incidence.

LITERATURE CITED

1. **Committee on Viral Hepatitis.** 1975. Symposium on viral hepatitis. Am. J. Med. Sci. **270:**2–412.
2. **Evans, A. S.** 1976. Causation and disease: the Henle-Koch postulates revisited. Yale J. Biol. Med. **49:**179–195.
3. **Henle, W., and G. Henle.** 1975. Immune responses to Epstein-Barr virus, p. 261–272. *In* A. L. Notkins (ed.), Viral immunology and immunopathology. Academic Press Inc., New York.
4. **Henshaw, J. B.** 1972. Cytomegalovirus infections, p. 175–181. *In* F. H. Top, Sr., and P. F. Wehrle (ed.), Communicable and infectious diseases. Mosby, St. Louis.
5. **Hoofnagle, J. H., R. J. Gerety, and L. F. Barker.** 1975. Antibody to hepatitis B core antigen. Am. J. Med. Sci. **270:**179–187.
6. **Hotchin, J. (ed.).** 1974. Slow virus diseases. Prog. Med. Virol. **18:**1–371.
7. **Johnson, R. T., and R. M. Herndon.** 1974. Virologic studies of multiple sclerosis and other chronic and relapsing neurological diseases. Prog. Med. Virol. **18:**214–228.
8. **Kimberlin, R. H. (ed.).** 1976. Slow virus diseases of animals and man. Frontiers in Biology. North-Holland Publishing Co., Amsterdam.
9. **Klein, G.** 1973. The Epstein-Barr virus, p. 521–557. *In* A. S. Kaplan (ed.), The herpesviruses. Academic Press Inc., New York.
10. **Koestner, A.** 1975. Animal model of human disease:

subacute sclerosing panencephalitis, multiple sclerosis; animal model: distemper-associated demyelinating encephalomyelitis. Am. J. Pathol. **78:**361–364.

11. **Koldovsky, U., P. Koldovsky, G. Henle, W. Henle, R. Ackermann, and G. Haase.** 1975. Multiple sclerosis-associated agent: transmission to animals and some properties of the agent. Infect. Immun. **12:**1355–1366.

12. **McAlpine, D., C. E. Lumsden, and E. D. Acheson.** 1972. Multiple sclerosis. Churchill-Livingstone, Edinburgh.

13. **Nathanson, N., A. A. Monjan, H. S. Panitch, E. D. Johnson, G. Petursson, and G. A. Cole.** 1975. Virus-induced cell-mediated immunopathological disease, p. 357–392. *In* A. L. Notkins (ed.), Viral immunology and immunopathology. Academic Press Inc., New York.

14. **Nathanson, N., H. Panitch, P. A. Palsson, G. Georgsson, and G. Petursson.** 1976. Pathogenesis of visna. II. Influence of immunosuppression upon lesions developing within one month. Lab. Invest. **35:**444–460.

15. **Norrby, E.** 1974. Measles and multiple sclerosis. Proc. R. Soc. Med. **67:**1129–1133.

16. **Norrby, E., and B. Vandvik.** 1975. Relationship between measles virus-specific antibody activities and oligoclonal IgG in the central nervous system of patients with subacute sclerosing encephalitis and multiple sclerosis. Med. Microbiol. Immunol. **162:**63–72.

17. **Notkins, A. L. (ed.).** 1975. Viral immunology and immunopathology. Academic Press Inc., New York.

18. **Oldstone, M. B. A.** 1975. Virus neutralization and virus-induced immune complex disease. Prog. Med. Virol. **19:**85–120.

19. **Padgett, B. L., and D. L. Walker.** 1976. New human papovaviruses. Prog. Med. Virol. **22:**1–35.

20. **Pass, F.** 1974. Warts. Minn. Med. **57:**844–852.

21. **Pereira, H. G.** 1972. Persistent infection by adenoviruses. J. Clin. Pathol. Suppl. **6:**39–42.

22. **Rawls, W. E.** 1974. Viral persistence in congenital rubella. Prog. Med. Virol. **18:**273–288.

23. **Skinhoj, P.** 1977. Hepatitis and hepatitis B antigen in Greenland. II. Occurrence and interrelation of hepatitis B associated surface, core, and "e" antigen-antibody systems in a highly endemic area. Am. J. Epidemiol., in press.

24. **Stevens, J.** 1975. Latent herpes simplex virus and the nervous system. Curr. Top. Microbiol. Immunol. **70:** 31–50.

25. **Taylor-Robinson, D., and A. E. Caunt.** 1972. Varicella virus. Virol. Monogr. **12:**1–88.

26. **Utermohlen, V., J. Levine, M. Ginsparg.** 1975. Lymphocyte agglutination in multiple sclerosis. Lancet **2:**772.

27. **Utermohlen, V., and J. B. Zabriskie.** 1973. A suppression of cell-mediated immunity in patients with multiple sclerosis. J. Exp. Med. **138:**1591–1596.

28. **Weiner, L. P., and O. Narayan.** 1974. Virologic studies of progressive multifocal leucoencephalopathy. Prog. Med. Virol. **18:**229–240.

29. **Levy, N. L., P. S. Auerbach, and E. C. Hayes.** 1976. A blood test for multiple sclerosis based on the adherence of lymphocytes to measles-infected cells. N. Engl. J. Med. **294:**1423–1427.

VI. THE ENDOGENOUS TUMOR VIRUSES

Introduction

PATTON T. ALLEN

National Cancer Institute, Frederick Cancer Research Center, Frederick, Maryland 21701

During recent years, considerable research effort has been expended in the study of the RNA tumor viruses or retraviruses. One outcome of this effort has been the development of better concepts for the classification of retraviruses into related groups. This has come about largely through the use of nucleic acid sequence homology techniques, serological procedures, and through the development of simplified methods for detecting and quantitating the infectious activity of these viruses.

As our knowledge of the retraviruses has increased, it has become increasingly clear that unexpressed viral genetic sequences may be present in the DNA of normal cells of some mammalian species. Under appropriate conditions this genetic information is expressed, resulting in the production of viral components. Viral genetic sequences may be transmitted from parental cell to daughter cells during cell division or they may be passed from parent to offspring through the germ cells. This process is known as vertical transmission. Viruses which may be passed in this manner are commonly referred to as endogenous viruses. Some endogenous viruses have oncogenic potential in the species of origin, whereas others apparently do not. Some of these agents, the xenotropic viruses, cannot be readily transmitted to members of the species of origin, although they will replicate in the cells of animals of a foreign species.

The following papers represent the proceedings of a seminar on endogenous RNA tumor viruses, held at the 1976 Annual Meeting of the American Society for Microbiology. The participants pursued a variety of approaches in studying the functions and characteristics of endogenous viruses, and the reader will observe that, in certain aspects, these agents are now well characterized. There is one area, however, in which our knowledge is still incomplete. The possibility has been raised that endogenous viruses can perform a useful function for the host. As will be seen, this question was addressed by several of the speakers and will undoubtedly receive continued attention.

Differential Regulation of Endogenous Type C Viruses of Mouse Cells

JOHN R. STEPHENSON AND STUART A. AARONSON

Laboratory of RNA Tumor Viruses, National Cancer Institute, Bethesda, Maryland 20014

The etiological involvement of type C RNA viruses in mouse leukemia was established by the development of high-leukemia-incidence inbred strains and the transmission of disease to low-incidence strains by cell-free filtrates (13, 19, 38). Several lines of evidence later led to the demonstration that these viruses were genetically transmitted. Early immunological studies indicated subviral expression in mouse strains which did not yield infectious virus (23, 24). Further, it was shown that, after growth for many generations in the absence of virus production, mouse cells could begin to release type C virus either spontaneously (2) or following treatment with halogenated pyrimidines (6, 37). The fact that virus could be activated from clonal mouse cells established that virus was present in an unexpressed form in every cell (6, 37). Independent evidence for the genetic transmission of mouse type C viral information was derived from the demonstration of nucleotide sequence homology between normal mouse cell DNA and type C viral DNA probes prepared by reverse transcription of viral RNA (9, 14, 15, 48). Similar techniques have subsequently been used to establish that endogenous viruses are present in an increasing number of vertebrate species (5, 33).

In the mouse, increasing evidence indicates that there exist several biologically distinguishable endogenous viruses. The present report reviews evidence concerning the mechanisms involved in regulation of these naturally integrated type C viral genes.

EVIDENCE FOR AT LEAST THREE CLASSES OF BIOLOGICALLY DISTINGUISHABLE ENDOGENOUS MOUSE TYPE C VIRUSES

In studies initially involving several prototype mouse strains, BALB/c, NIH Swiss, C58, and NZB, evidence was obtained for the existence of at least three biologically distinguishable endogenous mouse type C viruses (Table 1). These viruses can be partially differentiated on the basis of standard host range and serological tests and by more recently developed, highly specific competition radioimmunoassays for their structural polypeptides (20, 58). Moreover, the three prototype viruses can be differentiated by the manner in which the cell regulates their expression. One class of endogenous virus, inducible from BALB/c cells, preferentially replicates in NIH Swiss mouse cells and, hence, is termed N-tropic. This virus can be spontaneously activated (2) or induced by halogenated pyrimidines (6, 37). Whereas only one locus for activation of class I virus exists in BALB/c cells (51), multiple loci for its induction have been demonstrated in C58 cells (52). Many other strains have also been shown to contain one or more loci for this class of endogenous virus (32, 45, 58, 60).

A second prototype endogenous virus, initially shown to be inducible from BALB/c cells, was designated BALB:virus-2. This virus is non-infectious for cells of most inbred strains, but replicates well in cells of several other species (3). BALB:virus-2 can be efficiently activated by exposure of cells to halogenated pyrimidines (3, 55) or to inhibitors of protein synthesis (1). This class of virus has also been shown to be present in embryo cells of many strains (58). Information for a third class of endogenous virus has been shown to be present in each of the inbred strains tested to date. Although class III viruses cannot be activated by known inducers from embryo cells in culture (50), this virus has been isolated from certain strains in vivo (54, 61) and from their spleen cells in culture (29). Like class II virus, class III endogenous virus is xenotropic in host range. Antigens coded for by this endogenous virus are expressed by embryo cells of many strains in the absence of virus release (58, 59). Table 2 summarizes some of the inbred strains that have been studied and their known endogenous type C viruses.

Radioimmunological assays have provided powerful tools for distinguishing otherwise closely related type C viruses (58, 62, 63). In

TABLE 1. *Classification of endogenous type C viruses of mouse cells*

Characteristic	Class I (BALB: virus-1)	Class II (BALB: virus-2)	Class III (NIH Swiss: virus)
Host range	N-tropic	X-tropic	X-tropic
Inducible by:			
Halogenated pyrimidines ..	+	+	−
Inhibitors of protein synthesis	−	+	−
Neutralized by normal mouse sera	−	+	+
Influenced by Fv-1 regulatory locus	+	−	−
Antigen expression in the absence of complete virus ..	−	−	+

competition immunoassays in which antisera prepared against prototype class I, II, and III viruses are used at limiting concentration to precipitate the ^{125}I-labeled 12,000-molecular-weight polypeptide (p12) of the homologous virus, the pattern of immunological reactivity of an unknown virus can be compared with that of prototype viruses of each class. As shown in Fig. 1A, a representative class I virus reacts most efficiently in the homologous BALB:virus-1 p12 assay and to a lesser extent in either BALB:virus-2 or NIH Swiss virus p12 assays. Similarly, class II (Fig. 1B) and class III (Fig. 1C) viruses in each case react most efficiently in immunoassays for their homologous viral p12. The prototype viruses of each class can also be distinguished in immunoassays for their respective 70,000-dalton envelope glycoproteins (20).

DIFFERENTIAL ACTIVATION OF ENDOGENOUS VIRUSES

Two groups of chemicals, halogenated pyrimidines and inhibitors of protein synthesis, are highly efficient inducers of endogenous mouse type C viruses (1, 6, 37). Evidence that their mechanisms of action differ comes both from knowledge of their dissimilar biochemical effects and from observed differences in the virus induction response to these agents. This can be demonstrated by differences in the kinetics of induction of a prototype class II virus, BALB:virus-2, from BALB/c fibroblasts in response to iododeoxyuridine (IUdR) and cycloheximide. Following exposure to IUdR, virus release reaches a peak at around 3 to 4 days, persists at this level for several days, and subsequently declines. The kinetics of virus induction after exposure to cycloheximide are strikingly different (1). Virus release is maximal within the first 12 h after drug treatment and declines rapidly thereafter. By

72 h, virus-positive cells are no longer detectable. The fact that retreatment of the cells with cycloheximide at 72 h results in a return in the level of virus activation argues that differences in the actions of the two chemicals, rather than cell toxicity from drug treatment, are responsible for the much more transient virus activation observed with cycloheximide (1).

These two chemical inducers also differ in the efficiency with which they activate different classes of endogenous viruses. Class II virus can be efficiently activated by both inducers. In contrast, class I viruses are activated at high efficiency by IUdR, but very poorly by cycloheximide (1, 10). In general, class III endogenous viruses appear to be completely resistant to induction from embryo cells in culture by either inducer (10). However, with cells of one strain, NZB, that spontaneously generate class III virus, virus release can be enhanced by treatment with IUdR (53).

ENHANCEMENT OF ENDOGENOUS TYPE C VIRUS RELEASE BY STEROID HORMONES

Glucocorticoids have been shown to enhance type C virus release in response to both halogenated pyrimidines (10, 16, 41) and inhibitors of protein synthesis (10). Unlike virus inducers that impair chronic virus release at concentrations at which they are potent activators of endogenous virus (10), steroid hormones also enhance type C virus release by chronically producing cells. This suggests that steroids act to enhance rather than to initiate virus synthesis (10, 27). Recently, Wu et al. (64) reported that these drugs affect type C virus production post-transcriptionally since no increase was detected in the level of virus-

TABLE 2. *Distribution of endogenous type C viruses among inbred strains of mice*

Geographic origin	Inbred strain	Endogenous virus class		
		I	II	III
Boston, Mass., 1907	DBA	+	+	+
	CBA	+	+	+
	C3H/He	+	+	+
Ohio, 1913	BALB/c	+	+	+
	A/He	+	+	+
Cold Spring Harbor, N.Y.	C58	+	+	NT[a]
Granly, Mass., 1921	C57BL/6	+	+	+
	C57BL/10	+	+	+
Philadelphia, 1928	AKR	+	+	NT
Switzerland, 1920	NIH Swiss	−	−	+
Rockefeller Institute, 1926	SWR	−	−	+
Imperial Cancer Laboratories, England	NZB	−	−	+
	NZW	+	+	NT

[a] NT, Not tested.

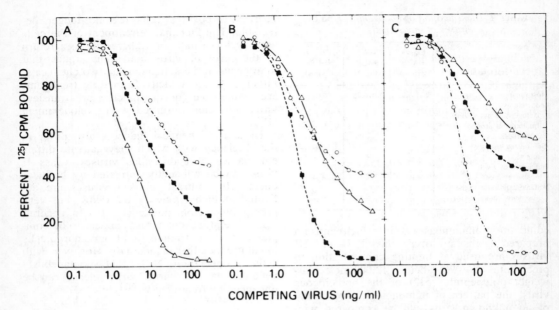

FIG. 1. *Comparison of immunological reactivities of endogenous type C viruses of BALB/c and NIH Swiss mouse cells in type-specific immunoassays for the p12 virion structural polypeptide. Detergent-disrupted viruses were assayed at twofold serial dilutions by measuring their capacity to compete with ^{125}I-labeled p12 polypeptide for limiting antibody as previously described (58). The results are expressed as the percentage of the total ^{125}I counts per minute in the antigen-antibody precipitate standarized to 100% in the absence of competing antigen. Reactivity was tested in the anti-BALB:virus-1:^{125}I-labeled BALB:virus-1 p12 ($\triangle$), anti-BALB:virus-2:^{125}I-BALB:virus-2 p12 ($\blacksquare$), and anti-NIH Swiss virus:^{125}I-NIH Swiss virus p12 ($\bigcirc$) type-specific competition immunoassays. Viruses tested included: (A) BALB:virus-1, (B) BALB:virus-2, (C) NIH Swiss virus.*

specific RNA in steroid-treated cells. In contrast, with mouse mammary tumor virus, another virus whose release can be enhanced by steroids (42), treatment with dexamethasone is associated with an increase in the cellular level of type B virus-specific RNA (42). These findings suggest an effect at the level of transcription in this system. Thus, the mechanism of the enhancement of RNA tumor virus release by steroids remains to be further clarified.

A GENE AFFECTING EXPRESSION OF CLASS I VIRUS

Fv-1 is a gene known to affect cell susceptibility to exogenous infection by many strains of murine leukemia virus (7, 44). The effect of this regulatory locus appears to be mediated at a step in virus replication beyond adsorption or penetration (11, 22, 28). Induction of cells containing class I virus and permissive at Fv-1 for infection by N-tropic virus results in the reproducible establishment of chronic virus production. In contrast, persistence of this virus in Fv-1 nonpermissive cells is much less likely (46, 51, 55). Whether this restriction pertains only to virus

spread or also involves the activation process remains to be resolved. There appears to be no effect of the known alleles at Fv-1 on the activation and persistence of class II virus (55).

GENETIC CONTROL OF CLASS III ENDOGENOUS VIRUS EXPRESSION

Investigations of the genetic basis for the high spontaneous levels of class III endogenous virus release from cells of the NZB strain (31, 53) have led to findings that in crosses with strains such as NIH Swiss, which express high levels of class III viral antigens in the absence of detectable virus, type C virus is released at an intermediate level (53). Analysis of virus expression in backcross and F$_2$ generations involving NZB and NIH Swiss strains indicates a pattern of virus release consistent with that expected for segregation of a partially dominant gene restricting spontaneous release of this virus (53).

A GENE CONFERRING SUSCEPTIBILITY TO EXOGENOUS INFECTION OF MOUSE CELLS BY XENOTROPIC VIRUS

An effective restriction to virus infection can occur at the cell surface through a block to virus adsorption and/or penetration. Findings that murine sarcoma virus pseudotypes, which possess the xenotropic virus envelope, are absolutely restricted in their ability to induce focus formation in cells of most inbred mouse strains (1, 55) strongly suggest that restriction to xenotropic virus infection occurs at an early step involving virus adsorption/penetration or integration within the cellular genome.

In contrast to results obtained with inbred strains of mice tested to date, embryo cells from certain wild mice have been found to be susceptible to focus formation by murine sarcoma virus pseudotypes of xenotropic virus. The pattern of segregation of susceptibility to xenotropic virus infection in backcross and F_2 generations argues for segregation of a dominant gene conferring susceptibility at an early step in xenotropic virus infection. The absence of this allele in most, if not all, inbred strains appears to be a major factor responsible for the "xenotropic" host range of class II and II xenotropic viruses.

RELEASE OF TYPE C VIRUSES FROM LYMPHOID CELLS AFTER ANTIGENIC STIMULATION

Immune stimulation as in the graft-versus-host reaction and in mixed lymphocyte cultures can lead to release of either mouse cell-tropic (21) or xenotropic (49) virus. Further, recent studies have established that exposure of lymphoid cells to a B-cell mitogen, lipopolysaccharide (LPS), is associated with a specific and very marked stimulation of xenotropic virus production (17, 39). Immunological analysis of this virus indicates that it is indistinguishable from BALB:virus-2 (43). A number of other mitogens, including concanavalin A and phytohemagglutinin, which are at least as active in causing blastogenesis, are much less effective or completely inactive in causing virus release (43). By use of purified subpopulations of spleen cells, the major target of LPS-stimulated virus release has been shown to be the B cell (43, 37). T cells, macrophages, and BALB/c embryo fibroblasts are poorly, if at all, inducible by LPS. These findings suggest that the differentiated state of the cell plays an important role in endogenous virus regulation.

SYSTEMIC REGULATION OF ENDOGENOUS TYPE C VIRUS EXPRESSION

It has been established that leukemogenesis associated with class I type C virus is influenced by one or more genes within the H-2 region of chromosome 17 of the mouse (34). Accumulating evidence indicates that this may involve H-2-linked immune response genes (34, 36). By measurement of immunoprecipitation of radioactively labeled intact virus, antibodies to several type C viral structural polypeptides have been detected in sera of many inbred strains of mice (25, 26, 40). In addition, mice of several strains have been shown to develop antibody to the major 70,000-molecular-weight envelope glycoprotein of class I virus following spontaneous activation of this virus in older animals (57). Sera of many mouse strains have also been shown to possess high-titered neutralizing activities directed against xenotropic class II and III endogenous viruses (4), and recent evidence indicates that this activity differs from known immunoglobulins (12, 30).

BIOLOGICAL SIGNIFICANCE OF ENDOGENOUS TYPE C VIRUSES

The above studies summarize some of the current investigations concerning endogenous mouse type C viruses and their differential cellular regulation. A major biological question regarding these viruses concerns their actions in the host. In this regard, it is now established that class I endogenous viruses are oncogenic. Both C58-murine leukemia virus and BALB:virus-1 induced from virus-negative cells in culture have been shown to cause lymphoid leukemia following inoculation in newborn NIH Swiss mice (18, 56). Further, measurement of endogenous virus expression in genetic crosses involving the high leukemia incidence of AKR strain has indicated a positive correlation between the magnitude of class I virus release in the young animal and the subsequent development of leukemia (35). The pathogenicity of class II and III endogenous viruses has been more difficult to study because these viruses lack infectivity for inbred mouse strains.

Current evidence indicates that endogenous type C viruses have existed in vertebrate species over a long period of evolution (8, 33). Therefore, some selective advantage for their presence would be expected. In this regard, roles for endogenous viruses in processes including cellular differentiation and information transfer have been postulated (5, 33). In the process of studies aimed at investigating the biological functions of endogenous viruses, it is hoped that systematic study of the mechanisms by which the host affects their expression may aid in understanding the molecular processes involved in gene regulation.

LITERATURE CITED

1. **Aaronson, S. A., and C. Y. Dunn.** 1974. High frequency C-type virus induction by inhibitors of protein synthesis. Science **183**:422–424.

2. **Aaronson, S. A., J. W. Hartley, and G. J. Todaro.** 1969. Mouse leukemia virus: spontaneous release by mouse embryo cells after long-term *in vitro* cultivation. Proc. Natl. Acad. Sci. U.S.A. **64**:87–93.

3. **Aaronson, S. A., and J. R. Stephenson.** 1973. Independent segregation of loci for activation of biologically distinguishable RNA C-type viruses in mouse cells. Proc. Natl. Acad. Sci. U.S.A. **70**:2055–2058.

4. **Aaronson, S. A., and J. R. Stephenson.** 1974. Widespread natural occurrence of high-titered neutralizing antibodies to a specific class of endogenous mouse C-type virus. Proc. Natl. Acad. Sci. U.S.A. **71**: 1957–1961.

5. **Aaronson, S. A., and J. R. Stephenson.** 1976. Endogenous type-C RNA viruses of mammalian cells. Biochimica et Biophysica Acta: Reviews on Cancer **458**:323–354.

6. **Aaronson, S. A., G. J. Todaro, and E. M. Scolnick.** 1971. Induction of C-type viruses from clonal lines of virus-free BALB/3T3 cells. Science **174**:157–159.

7. **Axelrad, A.** 1966. Genetic control of susceptibility to Friend leukemia virus in mice: studies with the spleen focus assay method. Natl. Cancer Inst. Monogr. **22**: 619–629.

8. **Benveniste, R. E., and G. J. Todaro.** 1976. Evolution of type-C viral genes: evidence for an Asian origin of man. Nature (London) **261**:101–108.

9. **Chattopadhyay, S. K., D. R. Lowy, N. M. Teich, A. S. Levine, and W. P. Rowe.** 1974. Evidence that the AKR murine-leukemia-virus genome is complete in DNA of the high-virus AKR mouse and incomplete in the DNA of the "virus-negative" NIH mouse. Proc. Natl. Acad. Sci. U.S.A. **71**:161–171.

10. **Dunn, C. Y., S. A. Aaronson, and J. R. Stephenson.** 1975. Interactions of chemical inducers and steroid enhancers of endogenous mouse type-C RNA viruses. Virology **66**:579–588.

11. **Eckner, R. J.** 1973. Helper-dependent properties of Friend spleen focus-forming virus: effect of the Fv-1 gene on late stages of virus synthesis. J. Virol. **12**:523–533.

12. **Fischinger, P. J., J. N. Ihle, D. P. Bolognesi, and W. Schäfer.** 1976. Inactivation of murine xenotropic oncornavirus by normal mouse sera is not immunoglobulin-mediated. Virology **71**:346–351.

13. **Furth, J., H. R. Seibold, and R. R. Rathbone.** 1933. Experimental studies on lymphomatosis of mice. Am. J. Cancer **19**:521–604.

14. **Gelb, L. D., S. A. Aaronson, and M. A. Martin.** 1971. Heterogeneity of murine leukemia virus *in vitro* DNA; detection of viral DNA in mammalian cells. Science **172**:1353–1355.

15. **Gelb, L. D., J. B. Milstien, M. A. Martin, and S. A. Aaronson.** 1973. Characterization of murine leukemia virus-specific DNA present in normal mouse cells. Nature (London) New Biol. **244**:76–79.

16. **Greenberger, J. S., and S. A. Aaronson.** 1975. Cycloheximide induction of xenotropic type C virus from synchronized mouse cells: metabolic requirements for virus activation. J. Virol. **15**:64–70.

17. **Greenberger, J. S., S. M. Phillips, J. R. Stephenson, and S. A. Aaronson.** 1975. Induction of mouse type-C RNA virus by lipopolysaccharide. J. Immunol. **115**: 317–320.

18. **Greenberger, J. S., J. R. Stephenson, W. C. Moloney, and S. A. Aaronson.** 1975. Different hematologic diseases induced by type-C viruses chemically activated from embryo cells of different mouse strains. Cancer Res. **35**:245–252.

19. **Gross, L.** 1951. Pathogenic properties, and "vertical" transmission of the mouse leukemia agent. Proc. Soc. Exp. Biol. Med. **78**:342–348.

20. **Hino, S., J. R. Stephenson, and S. A. Aaronson.** 1976. Radioimmunoassays for the 70,000-molecular-weight glycoproteins of endogenous type C viruses: viral antigen expression in normal mouse tissues and sera. J. Virol. **18**:933–941.

21. **Hirsch, M. S., S. M. Phillips, C. Solnik, P. H. Black, R. S. Schwartz, and C. B. Carpenter.** 1972. Activation of leukemia viruses by graft-versus-host and mixed lymphocyte reactions *in vitro*. Proc. Natl. Acad. Sci. U.S.A. **69**:1069–1072.

22. **Huang, A. S., P. Besmer, L. Chu, and D. Baltimore.** 1973. Growth of pseudotypes of vesicular stomatitis virus with N-tropic murine leukamia virus coats in cells resistant to N-tropic viruses. J. Virol. **12**:659–662.

23. **Huebner, R. J., G. J. Kelloff, P. S. Sarma, W. T. Lane, H. C. Turner, R. V. Gilden, S. Oroszlan, H. Meier, D. D. Myers, and R. L. Peters.** 1970. Group-specific antigenic expression during embryogenesis of the genome of the C-type RNA virus: implications for ontogenesis and oncogenesis. Proc. Natl. Acad. Sci. U.S.A. **67**:366–376.

24. **Huebner, R. J., P. S. Sarma, G. J. Kelloff, R. V. Gilden, H. Meier, D. D. Myers, and R. L. Peters.** 1971. Immunological tolerance to RNA tumor virus genome expressions: significance of tolerance and prenatal expressions in embryogenesis and tumorigenesis. Ann. N.Y. Acad. Sci. **181**:246–271.

25. **Ihle, J. N., J. J. Domotor, and K. M. Bengali.** 1976. Characterization of the type and group specificities of the immune response in mice to murine leukemia viruses. J. Virol. **18**:124–131.

26. **Ihle, J. N., M. N. Hanna, Jr., L. E. Roberson, and F. T. Kenney.** 1974. Autogenous immunity to endogenous RNA tumor virus. Identification of antibody reactivity to select viral antigens. J. Exp. Med. **139**:1568–1581.

27. **Ihle, J. N., S. E. Lane, F. T. Kenney, and J. G. Farcelly.** 1975. Effect of glucocorticoids on activation of leukemia virus in AKR mouse embryo cells. Cancer Res. **35**:442–446.

28. **Krontiris, T., R. Soeiro, and B. N. Fields.** 1973. Host range restriction of Friend leukemia virus. Role of the viral outer coat. Proc. Natl. Acad. Sci. U.S.A. **70**:2549–2553.

29. **Levy, J. A.** 1973. Xenotropic viruses: murine leukemia viruses associated with NIH Swiss, NZB, and other mouse strains. Science **182**:1151–1153.

30. **Levy, J. A., J. N. Ihle, Oleszko, and R. D. Barnes.** 1975. Virus-specific neutralization by a soluble non-immunoglobulin factor found naturally in normal mouse sera. Proc. Natl. Acad. Sci. U.S.A. **72**:5071–5075.

31. **Levy, J. A., and T. Pincus.** 1970. Demonstration of biological activity of a murine leukemia virus of New Zealand Black mice. Science **170**:326–327.

32. **Lieber, M. M., C. J. Sherr, and G. J. Todaro.** 1974. S-tropic murine type-C viruses: frequency of isolation from continuous cell lines, leukemia virus preparations and normal spleens. Int. J. Cancer **13**:587–598.

33. **Lieber, M. M., and G. J. Todaro.** 1975. Mammalian type-C RNA viruses, p. 91–130. *In* F. F. Becker (ed.), Cancer: a comprehensive treatise, vol. 2. Plenum Press, New York.

34. **Lilly, F., E. A. Boyse, and L. J. Old.** 1964. Genetic basis of susceptibility to viral leukaemogenesis. Lancet **2**:1207–1209.

35. **Lilly, F., M. L. Duran-Reynals, and W. P. Rowe.** 1975. Correlation of early murine leukemia virus titer and H-2 type with spontaneous leukemia in mice of the BALB/c X AKR cross: a genetic analysis. J. Exp. Med. **141**:882–889.

36. **Lilly, F., and T. Pincus.** 1973. Genetic control of murine viral leukemogenesis. Adv. Cancer Res. **17**:231.

37. **Lowry, D. R., W. P. Rowe, N. Teich, and J. W. Hartley.** 1971. Murine leukemia virus: high-frequency activation *in vitro* by 5-iododeoxyuridine and 5-bromodeoxyuridine. Science **174**:155–156.

38. **MacDowell, E. C., and M. N. Richter.** 1935. Mouse leukemia. IX. The role of heredity in spontaneous cases. Arch. Pathol. **20**:709–724.

39. **Moroni, C., G. Schumann, M. Robert-Guroff, E. R. Suter, and D. Martin.** 1975. Induction of endogenous murine C-type virus in spleen cell cultures treated with mitogens and 5-bromo-2'-deoxyuridine. Proc. Natl. Acad. Sci. U.S.A. **72**:535–538.

40. **Nowinski, R. C., and S. L. Kaehler.** 1974. Antibody to leukemia virus: widespread occurrence in inbred mice. Science **185**:869–871.

41. **Paran, M., R. C. Gallo, L. S. Richardson, and A. M. Wu.** 1973. Adrenal corticosteroids enhance production of type-C virus induced by 5-iodo-2'-deoxyuridine from cultured mouse fibroblasts. Proc. Natl. Acad. Sci. U.S.A. **70**:2391–2395.

42. **Parks, W. P., E. M. Scolnick, and E. H. Kozikowski.** 1974. Dexamethasone stimulation of murine mammary tumor virus expression: a tissue culture source of virus. Science **184**:158–160.

43. **Phillips, S. M., J. R. Stephenson, J. S. Greenberger, P. E. Lane, and S. A. Aaronson.** 1975. Release of xenotropic type-C RNA virus in response to lipopolysaccharide: activity of lipid-A portion upon B lymphocytes. J. Immunol. **116**:1123–1128.

44. **Pincus, T., W. P. Rowe, and F. Lilly.** 1971. A major genetic locus affecting resistance to infection with murine leukemia viruses. II. Apparent identity to a major locus described for resistance to Friend murine leukemia virus. J. Exp. Med. **133**:1234–1241.

45. **Rowe, W. P.** 1972. Studies of genetic transmission of murine leukemia virus by AKR mice. I. Crosses with Fv-1 strains of mice. J. Exp. Med. **136**:1272–1301.

46. **Rowe, W. P., and J. W. Hartley.** 1972. Studies of genetic transmission of murine leukemia virus by AKR mice. II. Crosses with Fv-1^b strains of mice. J. Exp. Med. **136**:1286–1301.

47. **Schumann, G., and C. Moroni.** 1976. Mitogen induction of murine C-type viruses. I. Analysis of lymphoid cell subpopulations. J. Immunol. **116**:1145–1150.

48. **Scolnick, E. M., W. Parks, T. Kawakami, D. Kohne, H. Okabe, R. Gilden, and M. Hatanaka.** 1974. Primate and murine type-C viral nucleic acid association kinetics: analysis of model systems and natural tissues. J. Virol. **13**:363–369.

49. **Sherr, C. J., M. M. Lieber, and G. J. Todaro.** 1974. Mixed splenocyte cultures in graft versus host reactions selectively induce an "S-tropic" murine type-C virus. Cell **1**:55–58.

50. **Stephenson, J. R., and S. A. Aaronson.** 1972. Genetic factors influencing C-type RNA virus induction. J. Exp. Med. **136**:175–184.

51. **Stephenson, J. R., and S. A. Aaronson.** 1972. A genetic locus for inducibility of C-type virus in BALB/c cells: the effect of a nonlinked regulatory gene on detection of virus after chemical activation. Proc. Natl. Acad. Sci. U.S.A. **69**:2798–2801.

52. **Stephenson, J. R., and S. A. Aaronson.** 1973. Segregation of genetic loci for virus inducibility in high and low leukemia incidence strains of mice. Science **180**:865–866.

53. **Stephenson, J. R., and S. A. Aaronson.** 1974. Demonstration of a genetic factor influencing spontaneous release of a xenotropic virus of mouse cells. Proc. Natl. Acad. Sci. U.S.A. **71**:4925–4929.

54. **Stephenson, J. R., S. A. Aaronson, P. Arnstein, R. J. Huebner, and S. R. Tronick.** 1974. Demonstration of two immunologically distinct xenotropic RNA type-C viruses of mouse cells. Virology **61**:244–248.

55. **Stephenson, J. R., J. D. Crow, and S. A. Aaronson.** 1974. Differential activation of biologically distinguishable endogenous mouse type-C RNA viruses: interaction with host cell regulatory factors. Virology **61**:411–419.

56. **Stephenson, J. R., J. S. Greenberger, and S. A. Aaronson.** 1974. Oncogenicity of an endogenous C-type virus chemically activated from mouse cells in culture. J. Virol. **13**:237–240.

57. **Stephenson, J. R., S. Hino, R. L. Peters, R. M. Donahoe, L. K. Long, S. A. Aaronson, and G. J. Kelloff.** Natural immunity in mice to structural polypeptides of endogenous type C RNA viruses. J. Virol. **19**:890–898.

58. **Stephenson, J. R., R. K. Reynolds, S. R. Tronick, and S. A. Aaronson.** 1975. Distribution of three classes of endogenous type-C RNA viruses among inbred strains of mice. Virology **67**:404–414.

59. **Stephenson, J. R., S. R. Tronick, R. K. Reynolds, and S. A. Aaronson.** 1974. Isolation and characterization of C-type viral gene products of virus negative mouse cells. J. Exp. Med. **139**:427–438.

60. **Taylor, B. A., H. Meier, and D. D. Myers.** 1971. Host-gene control of C-type RNA tumor virus: inheritance of the group specific antigen of murine leukemia virus. Proc. Natl. Acad. Sci. U.S.A. **68**:3190–3194.

61. **Todaro, G. J., P. Arnstein, W. P. Parks, E. H. Lennette, and R. J. Huebner.** 1973. A type-C virus in human rhabdomyosarcoma cells after innoculation into NIH Swiss mice treated with antithymocyte serum. Proc. Natl. Acad. Sci. U.S.A. **70**:859–862.

62. **Tronick, S. R., J. R. Stephenson, and S. A. Aaronson.** 1973. Immunological characterization of a low molecular weight polypeptide of murine leukemia virus. Virology **54**:199–206.

63. **Tronick, S. R., J. R. Stephenson, and S. A. Aaronson.** 1974. Comparative immunological studies of RNA C-type viruses: radioimmunoassay for a low molecular weight polypeptide of woolly monkey leukemia virus. Virology **57**:347–356.

64. **Wu, A. M., M. S. Reitz, M. Paran, and R. C. Gallo.** 1974. Mechanism of stimulation of murine type-C RNA tumor virus production by glucocorticoids: post-transcriptional effects. J. Virol. **14**:802–812.

Propagation and Analysis of Mouse Mammary Tumor Viruses from Different Mouse Strains

J. SCHLOM, D. COLCHER, W. DROHAN, P. KIMBALL, R. MICHALIDES,
G. SCHOCHETMAN, AND G. VLAHAKIS

National Cancer Institute, Bethesda, Maryland 20014, and Meloy Laboratories,
Springfield, Virginia 22151

Various strains of mice have been shown to harbor viral agents capable of causing mammary carcinoma. These agents may differ, however, in a variety of biological parameters (1, 13; Table 1). Until recently, the primary sources of mouse mammary tumor viruses (MMTVs) have been milk and tumor homogenates, both of which are biochemically complex media. Cell cultures producing MMTV would eliminate major problems of cellular contamination and allow more precise comparative studies of MMTVs from various mouse strains. Recently, the MMTV from primary cultures of mammary tumors from BALB/cfC3H mice has been well characterized (4, 11). We have found this technique of culturing primary tumors (4, 11) useful for producing MMTV from all mouse strains tested. Primary mammary tumors have been successfully cultivated from RIII, GR, C3H, C3HfC57BL, BALB/c, and BALB/cfC3H mice, and significant levels of MMTVs are produced by all of these cultures (9, 10). Furthermore, production of type C virus is sufficiently low that these tumor cell cultures can serve as a source of viral antigens, enzymes, and nucleic acids for studies concerning the relatedness among MMTVs from different mouse strains.

ESTABLISHMENT OF TUMOR CELL CULTURES

Mammary tumors from RIII, GR, DD, BALB/c, and BALB/cfC3H mice were minced, and the cells were dissociated and seeded at 10^6 cells/cm^2 of culture surface area in medium containing insulin and hydrocortisone (4, 11). A typical tumor, 2.5 cm in diameter, yielded from 6×10^7 to 25×10^7 viable cells, depending on the mouse strain. By 3 to 5 days in culture, confluent monolayers were highlighted by acinar-like "domes" (11). In general, primary cultures were successfully maintained for 5 to 8 weeks with media harvested daily. Electron microscopic examination of cultures revealed typical intra-cytoplasmic A particles, and budding and mature type B particles.

ASSAYS FOR MMTV ANTIGENS

Radioimmunoassays (RIAs) have provided sensitive quantitative assays for antigens of murine type C viruses and MMTVs. Therefore, we utilized such assays to quantitate and characterize the MMTVs being produced from RIII, GR, DD, BALB/cfC3H, and BALB/c mammary tumor cell cultures. The primary antisera for MMTV antigens used in these studies was prepared against undisrupted BALB/cfC3H MMTV. Precipitation of MMTV by this antiserum has been shown (3) not to be inhibited by murine leukemia virus (MuLV), homogenates of BALB/c lactating mammary glands, defatted BALB/c milk, and fetal calf serum, and to be inhibited by at least 70% with purified gp52 of MMTV from RIII mouse milk. Binding of the labeled RIII culture virus could be inhibited substantially (up to 90%) by MMTV purified from RIII milk (Fig. 1, open circles). Samples of purified virus from primary tumor cell cultures of RIII, GR, DD, BALB/cfC3H, and BALB/c mice all inhibited precipitation of the labeled RIII MMTV with similar efficiencies within the range of protein tested (0.1 to 10.0 μg). The inhibition curves shown in Fig. 1 were plotted in logit form (5), which is used to linearize inhibition curves, so that slopes may be compared accurately. It should be noted that the slopes of the inhibition curves for all the five MMTVs are essentially the same, indicating that in this particular inhibition assay, which is set up to measure group-specific determinants (i.e., RIII virus antigen and anti-BALB/cfC3H virus antibody), the surface antigens of the MMTVs from these five different mouse strains are immunologically indistinguishable (10).

548

TABLE 1. *Biological properties of MMTV variants*[a]

MMTV variant	Reference mouse strain	Mode of transmission	Virulence	Tumor type
S	C3H-A^{vy}	Horizontal	++++	Hormone independent; fast-growing carcinomas
P	GR	Horizontal and vertical	+++	Hormone dependent; P (plaque)-type
PS	RIII	Horizontal	++++	Hormone independent; fast-growing carcinomas
L	C3H-A^{vy}fb	Vertical	+	Hormone independent; slow-growing carcinomas

[a] From references 1, 2, and 12.

The MMTV RIA was also used to quantitate the amount of MMTV being produced by the various cultures. Between 0.8 and 2.1 μg of density gradient-purified MMTV protein was produced per ml of supernatant fluid per 24 h in cultures from all five mouse strains. The viruses purified from supernatant fluids of primary cell cultures of mammary tumors contained only limited amounts of MuLV. This was measured by a radioimmunoprecipitation assay for the p30 protein of MuLV (6). The percentage of particles determined to be MuLV by this method was less than 0.4% of the total virus produced by the various mammary tumor cell cultures. Only the BALB/c cultures produced virus that contained as much as 1 to 3% MuLV particles. Virus purified from RIII mouse milk contained approximately 0.2%

MuLV particles. Therefore, the immunological evidence suggests that primary cell cultures of mouse mammary tumors from several strains of mice produce virus and antigens which are sufficiently low in, or free from, MuLV to be used in comparative biochemical and immunological investigations of MMTVs.

CHARACTERIZATION OF RNAs OF MMTVs

To further characterize the MMTVs from primary mouse mammary tumor cultures, radioactively labeled RNA was extracted from concentrated virions and analyzed by velocity sedimentation. Distinct peaks of trichloroacetic acid-precipitable radioactivity with a sedimentation coefficient of 60 to 70S were readily observed. The molecular weight of the 60 to 70S [^{3}H]RNAs was estimated to be 8 $\times$ 10^6 by analysis by electrophoresis on polyacrylamide gels (Fig. 2). These ^{3}H-labeled MMTV 60 to 70S RNAs were extremely useful in the molecular hybridization experiments described below.

RELATIONSHIPS AMONG RNA GENOMES OF MMTVs

MMTV proviral sequences have been claimed to be uniformly present in the cellular genome of high and low mammary tumor incidence mouse strains (14), and to be expressed in tissues of mouse strains irrespective of their mammary tumor history (15). Those studies, however, were conducted with complementary DNA probes that did not represent the entire viral genome (15), and they did not consider a possible difference in nucleic acid sequences be-

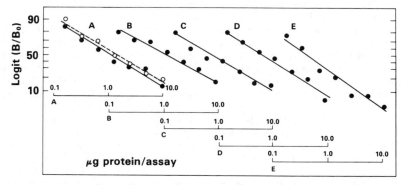

FIG. 1. *Radioimmunoprecipitation assay for MMTV antigens in purified virus preparations. All viruses were purified on two successive isopycnic sucrose gradients. The open circles in curve A represent MMTV from RIII milk; all curves of closed circles are for viruses from mammary tumor cell cultures, as follows: A, RIII; B, GR; C, BALB/cfC3H; D, DD; and E, BALB/c. In the ratio (B/B$_0$), B is the amount of labeled antigen bound in the presence of competing antigen, and B$_0$ is the amount bound with no competing antigen added. These ratios, expressed as percentages, are plotted in logit form for comparison of slopes. Each point represents average values for several experiments with different samples of each virus (10).*

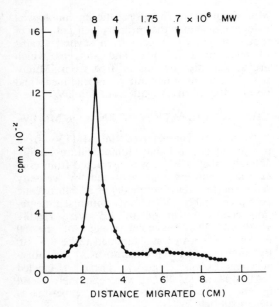

FIG. 2. *Characterization of ^{3}H-labeled 60 to 70 S RNA from RIII tumor cell culture virus. Virus was labeled with a mixture of ^{3}H-labeled ribonucleic acids and purified as described (9, 10). The RNA was extracted and layered on an isokinetic glycerol gradient for analysis. The RNA in the 60 to 70 S region of the gradient was pooled and precipitated with ethanol. The RNA was then subjected to electrophoresis on a gel of 2% acrylamide and 0.5% agarose as described (10). The arrows indicate positions in parallel gels of the 60 to 70 S RNA (8 × 10⁶) ^{3}H]RNA from vesicular stomatitis virus (4 × 10⁶), and 28 S (1.75 × 10⁶) and 18 S (0.7 × 10⁶ daltons) ribosomal ^{3}H]RNA.*

tween vertically and horizontally transmitted MMTVs. We have conducted studies in which the entire 60 to 70S RNA genomes of various MMTVs were employed, and the technique of competitive molecular hybridization was used. We have found (12) that the nucleic acid sequences of the horizontally transmitted MMTV variants from four mouse strains (RIII, C3H-A^{vy}, GR, and A) are at least 95% homologous to one another and are approximately 25% different from the vertically transmitted MMTV variant from the mouse strain C3H-A^{vy}fB. This C3H-A^{vy}fB strain was developed (7) by removing one male and one female C3H-A^{vy} by Cesarean section and foster nursing them on a female of strain C57BL, a strain without overt MMTV in its milk.

The RIII, GR, C3H, and C3Hf virus preparations which were the source of viral RNA, and which were subsequently used in competitive molecular hybridizations, did not contain contaminating murine type C virus, as assayed by RIA for MuLV p30 and by magnesium cation preference of viral DNA poly-

merase. In competitive molecular hybridization experiments, addition of MuLV RNA to the hybrid formations between radioactively labeled MMTV RNAs and mammary tumor DNAs had no effect on the final extent of hybrid formation. No common nucleic acid sequences were detected, furthermore, between the RNAs of MMTVs and the RNAs of the bromodeoxyuridine-induced guinea pig virus or Mason-Pfizer virus.

The addition of increasing amounts (0.6 to 1,200 ng) of unlabeled RNAs from GR, RIII, and C3H MMTVs to the hybridization reaction between the radioactively labeled 60 to 70S RNA of MMTV(RIII) and the DNA from RIII mammary tumors all resulted in equal displacements of the radioactive MMTV(RIII) 60 to 70S RNA from the hybrid formations. The nucleic acid sequence of MMTV released in the mammary tumor cell cultures of the RIII mouse strain also appeared to be identical to that of the MMTV released into RIII milk.

The addition of increasing amounts of RNA from GR, RIII, and C3H MMTVs to the hybridization reaction between the radioactively labeled 60 to 70S RNA from MMTV(GR) and the DNA from GR mammary tumors also resulted in the same equal displacement of the radioactive MMTV(GR) 60 to 70S RNA from hybrid formations. Finally, the addition of increasing amounts of unlabeled RNA from GR, RIII, and C3H MMTVs to the hybridization reaction between radioactive MMTV(C3H) 60 to 70S RNA and DNA from C3H mammary tumors resulted in a similar equal inhibition of hybrid formations (12). These data indicate that the viral genomes of these three MMTVs from different mouse strains (MMTV-P, -PS, and -S; see Table 1) are very similar in nucleic acid sequences.

The relationship in nucleic acid sequences between the C3H milk-transmitted MMTV-S and the vertically transmitted MMTV-L of C3H mice was studied by saturation hybridization and molecular competitive hybridization. In saturation hybridization experiments, a constant amount (2,000 cpm) of ^{32}P-labeled 60 to 70S RNA from C3H MMTV-S (produced by C3H mammary tumors in culture) was hybridized to increasing amounts of cellular DNA fragments from mammary tumors and livers of the same tumor-bearing C3H mice. Livers were chosen because they have been reported negative for MMTV antigens (8). Fifty-two percent of the ^{32}P-labeled 60 to 70S RNA of MMTV-S (from C3H) hybridized to the DNA from "early" (at approximately 8 months) mammary tumors; under identical conditions, the hybridization value to the DNA from livers of these same animals reached saturation at approximately 42%. This implies a nucleic acid sequence homology of approximately 80% between the horizontally transmitted (milk) transmitted MMTV-S and the vertically transmitted MMTV-L. A similar nucleic acid sequence relationship between the horizontally and vertically transmitted MMTV variants of the C3H mouse was obtained by competitive hybridization experiments. Increasing amounts of the RNA of MMTV(C3H) and of MMTV-(C3Hf) were added to the hybridization reaction between ^{3}H-labeled MMTV(C3H) 60 to 70S RNA and C3H mammary tumor DNA. The hybrid formation was almost completely (94%) inhibited by the addition of MMTV(C3H) RNA, whereas addition of the same amount of MMTV-(C3Hf) RNA inhibited the hybrid formation by only 67%.

GENERAL COMMENTS

The viral genomes of the horizontally transmitted variants of the mouse mammary tumor virus of the mouse strains GR, RIII, C3H, and A appear to be at least 95% homologous, as analyzed by molecular competitive hybridization. Minor differences may exist, however, that were not detected because of the limitations in the sensitivity of the assays employed. The technique of competitive hybridization as used here considers the total genome of the RNA tumor virus and avoids inconclusive results that may arise as a result of the use of incomplete or preferential complementary DNA transcripts.

The similarity in nucleic acid sequences of the horizontally transmitted MMTVs is reflected in the similarity of their virulence and antigenic composition (1, 13). The similarity in nucleic acid sequence of the MMTV(GR), which is transmitted both by milk and vertically via gametes (2), to the horizontally transmitted MMTVs of the other mouse strains studied is particularly interesting. The difference in nucleic acid sequences between the horizontally and vertically transmitted MMTV variants of the C3H mouse is approximately 25%, as measured both by saturation hybridization and competition hybridization. The nucleic acid sequence differences of the RNAs of the C3H MMTV transmitted as a germinal provirus and the C3H MMTV transmitted via an alternate mechanism, such as nursing, are also in accord

with the differences in virulence of these variants (1, 13).

ACKNOWLEDGMENT

These studies were supported by National Cancer Institute Contract No1CP43223.

LITERATURE CITED

1. **Bentvelzen, P.** 1972. The biology of the mouse mammary tumor virus. Int. Rev. Exp. Pathol. **11**:259–297.
2. **Bentvelzen, P.** 1974. Host-virus interactions in murine mammary carcinogenesis. Biochim. Biophys. Acta **355**:236–259.
3. **Cardiff, R. D.** 1973. Quantitation of mouse mammary tumor virus (MTV) virions by radioimmunoassay. J. Immunol. **111**:1722–1729.
4. **Cardiff, R. D., P. B. Blair, and K. B. DeOme.** 1968. In vitro cultivation of the mouse mammary tumor virus; replication of MTV in tissue culture. Virology **36**:313–317.
5. **Feldman, H., and D. Rodbard.** 1971. Chapter 7, p. 158–199. *In* W. Odell and W. Daughaday (ed.), Principles of competitive protein-binding assays. J. B. Lippincott Co., Philadelphia.
6. **Green, R. W., D. P. Bolognesi, W. Schafer, L. Pister, G. Hunsmann, and F. Noronha.** 1973. Polypeptides of mammalian oncornaviruses I. Isolation and serological analysis of polypeptides from murine and feline C-type viruses. Virology **56**:565–579.
7. **Heston, W. E., and G. Vlahakis.** 1968. C3H-A^{vy}—a high hepatoma and mammary tumor strain of mice. J. Natl. Cancer Inst. **40**:1161–1166.
8. **Hilgers, J. H. M., G. J. Theuns, and R. Van Nie.** 1973. Mammary tumor virus (MMTV) antigens in normal and mammary tumor-bearing mice. Int. J. Cancer **12**:568–576.
9. **Kimball, P. C., R. Michalides, D. Colcher, and J. Schlom.** 1976. Characterization of mouse mammary tumor viruses from primary tumor cell cultures. II. Biochemical and biophysical studies. J. Natl. Cancer Inst. **56**:119–124.
10. **Kimball, P., M. B. Truitt, G. Schochetman, and J. Schlom.** 1976. Characterization of mouse mammary tumor viruses from primary cell cultures. I. Immunological and structural studies. J. Natl. Cancer Inst. **56**:111–117.
11. **McGrath, C. M.** 1971. Replication of mammary tumor virus in tumor cell cultures: dependence on hormone-induced cellular organization. J. Natl. Cancer Inst. **47**:455–467.
12. **Michalides, R., and J. Schlom.** 1975. Relationship in nucleic acid sequences between mouse mammary tumor virus variants. Proc. Natl. Acad. Sci. U.S.A. **72**:4635–4639.
13. **Nandi, S., and C. M. McGrath.** 1973. Mammary neoplasia in mice. Adv. Cancer Res. **17**:353–414.
14. **Varmus, H. E., J. M. Bishop, R. C. Nowinski, and N. Sarkar.** 1972. Mammary tumor virus specific nucleotide sequences in mouse DNA. Nature (London) New Biol. **238**:189–191.
15. **Varmus, H., N. Quintrell, E. Medeiros, J. M. Bishop, R. C. Nowinski, and N. H. Sarkar.** 1973. Transcription of mouse mammary tumor virus genes in tissues from high and low tumor incidence mouse strains. J. Mol. Biol. **79**:663–679.

Type C RNA Virus Expression in Reproductive Tissue: Possible Biological Significance

A. HELLMAN and A. K. FOWLER

National Cancer Institute, Bethesda, Maryland 20014

Our laboratory has been interested for a number of years in steroid viral enhancement and possible cocarcinogenic function (2). Estrogens have been known to enhance and/or activate expression of genetic information. They specifically act on target tissue such as the uterus by accelerating RNA and DNA synthesis and ensuing cell division. It is not inconceivable that, in the proper physiological milieu, estrogen specifically and steroids in general may act as cocarcinogens, particularly by modifying cells of the target organ. In this process, if viral information is being repressed, steroids may act as derepressors for such latent information.

Evidence leading to the following conclusions will be presented:

1. Hormones, in particular estrogen, activate or enhance endogenous type C RNA viral information.

2. Type C RNA viral information is expressed during stages of fetal development.

3. Most, if not all, species thus far examined express viral information in reproductive tissue.

4. Expression of type C RNA viral information most likely does not lead to malignancy directly but may be associated with normal physiological functions and possible cocarcinogenic function.

Utilizing the random-bred NIH/Swiss mouse, a strain recognized as having a low level of expression of type C RNA viruses, we first examined the uterus for the presence of one of the major virion core proteins, p30. All uteri of sexually mature female NIH mice were found to express p30 (2). To obliterate this estrogen influence, and thereby gain the capacity to control such viral expression, we ovariectomized mice prior to their developing the capacity to produce estrogen, namely, at 18 to 21 days after birth.

To provide evidence that one can control RNA tumor viral expression in a target tissue by hormone therapy, we initially determined the influence of near-physiological levels of various estrogen and estrogen-like compounds on p30

and RNA-directed DNA polymerase activity.

The uterine response to estradiol-17β showed a threefold increase over controls based on radioimmunoassay. Similarly, RNA-directed DNA polymerase activity increased approximately eightfold after the administration of 1 μg of estradiol-17β in peanut oil. Comparison of the natural estrogen metabolites (Table 1) estradiol-17β, estrone, estriol, and estradiol-17α revealed, in general, a decrease in response, indicative of their decreasing biological potency in vivo. In the case of diethylstilbesterol (DES), as well as the oral contraceptives Mestranol, Enovid (norethynodrel and mestranol), and Provest, there was substantially higher viral expression. Although the majority of these contraceptives are now off the market, it is of interest that DES has been implicated in vaginal carcinoma of young women whose mothers were receiving DES therapy during that pregnancy. DDT, a chemical known to interfere with normal hormonal balance, has a structure similar to that of DES and gives a similar viral activation response.

The rate of viral response to estrogen is very rapid, as one might suspect in a target tissue, and suggests an enhancement phenomenon. A p30 response occurs after a single administration of estradiol-17β. Within 8 h, viral protein is detected in the uterus, reaching a maximal level at approximately 48 h but declining during the next 28 days. The organ is responsive to subsequent stimuli. In mouse uteri, the site of p30 localization is the cells forming the secretory lumen of the uterus, as can be seen in a cross-section preparation (Fig. 1) stained with fluorescein-labeled anti-RLV p30 goat serum.

Our second point concerns type C RNA viral information expression during stages of fetal development. After copulation, a rapid viral response is noted in relation to the luteal phase; this reaches its maximum 8 days after conception, levels off during the next 5 days, and rises again near term. When one looks at NIH uterine tissue during gestation, one also notes the expression of whole type C viruses during the first 8 days of gestation. Budding and mature particles are readily observed. This is rather unusual since the adult NIH mouse normally does not readily express whole xenotropic virus in adult tissue.

An effort to confirm this viral-gestational relationship in cats was made in collaboration with R. G. Olsen and his group at Ohio State University. The uterus, fetus, and placenta of specific pathogen-free, pregnant cats were assayed for RD114 (p28 antigen). In most cases several cat uteri, placentae, and fetal tissues were sampled from 28 through 56 days of gestation. At 56 days all uteri were negative for RD114 (a cat xenotropic virus), and going back to 42 and 28 days uterine tissues either were negative or had relatively low levels of viral expression. In contrast, the placenta at 28 days had very high RD114 activity which gradually decreased over gestation. In general, the fetus followed a pattern similar to that of the placenta, but at a lower level of expression.

Our third point is that all species thus far examined exhibit such viral expression in normal reproductive tissue, to some degree and by one means or another (6). The various degrees of expression observed, i.e., by electron microscopy, virus isolation, etc., appear to be due to the degree of control that the animal has over such expression, and this is probably related to the genetics of the animal. This can be demonstrated by returning to our observations in mice. In all of the mouse strains studied (Table 2), we observed the typical uterotropic response to estrogen, that is, increase in uterine weight, fluid accumulation, and increased cellular synthesis. However, some strains, such as the C57 Leighton mouse, are highly repressed and do not readily express RNA-directed DNA polymerase activity or p30, whereas others, such as the AKR mouse, show a much stronger response.

Interestingly, the C57L mouse has a low leukemia incidence, whereas the AKR mouse has a very high and early leukemia incidence. The only time we have observed whole virus in the C57L mouse is during the first 7 days of gestation. We therefore suggest that viral expression as influenced by hormones may take the form of whole virus that is able to replicate in a heterologous host, or there may be merely partial viral expression or perhaps no viral expression, depending on the degree of repression and the genetics of the host. We are not saying, therefore, that the viruses we see have any function in oncogenesis, nor are we saying that they do not. This, then, leads to our last point: what possible functional relation-

TABLE 1. *MuLV p30 in pooled uterine extracts from ovariectomized NIH Swiss mice*

Treatment	Level	p30 per uterus[a] (ng)	Uterus wt[a] (mg)
Control	Sham	2.7 ± 0.8	7.6 ± 0.7
Estradiol-17β	1 × 1.0 μg	24.7 ± 2.0	23.0 ± 2.5
Estrone	1 × 1.0 μg	28.5 ± 2.1	27.0 ± 2.0
Estriol	1 × 1.0 μg	16.4 ± 1.1	20.0 ± 0.0
Estradiol-17α	1 × 1.0 μg	6.2 ± 0.2	14.0 ± 1.5
DES	1 × 1.0 μg	60.4 ± 7.9	25.0 ± 4.0
o,p-DDT	5 × 10.0 mg	8.1 ± 2.0	12.6 ± 1.0
Mestranol	3 × 1.0 μg	66.9 ± 6.7	45.2 ± 3.0
Enovid E, Searle ...	3 × 1.0 μg	83.7 ± 13.2	49.4 ± 2.0
Provest, Upjohn ...	3 × 1.0 μg	38.7 ± 2.9	31.5 ± 4.0

[a] Mean ± SE.

ship exists between type C RNA viruses, estrogen, and the host?

We have treated mice with estrogen over a 2-year period and have not seen any higher incidence of malignancy. However, when mice with increased estrogen levels due to either pregnancy or estrogen therapy are challenged with transformed cells, the rate of tumor growth is greatly accelerated. This may be an indirect phenomenon brought about by immunological suppression.

Evidence that cellular controls associated with repression of tumor growth are compromised is provided by the adrenal glands of NIH mice that were ovariectomized approximately 2.5 years ago and left to age. Two interesting observations were made from this study. First of all, the adrenal gland may be decontrolled by the pituitary hormone functional changes brought about by ovariectomy, and the mouse then develops adrenal carcinomas. Second, control of reverse transcriptase expression and p30 expression seem to be independent genetic functions. In these aged animals, p30 expression in the uterus is readily evident and responsive to estrogen, whereas reverse transcriptase expression is not detected.

Where might the virus fit? In the case of type C virus, it is clear that actively metabolizing and replicating cells are necessary for viral expression. Steroids may act as cocarcinogens by permitting tumor viral expression or bringing about immunosuppression, or perhaps they act as carcinogens directly. The similarity in structure and function between well-documented experimental carcinogens and estradiol-17β is noteworthy.

We believe that type C viruses by themselves are probably not oncogenic except in very genetically selective cases. They may become oncogenic by interacting with other environmental cocarcinogens, such as radiation and

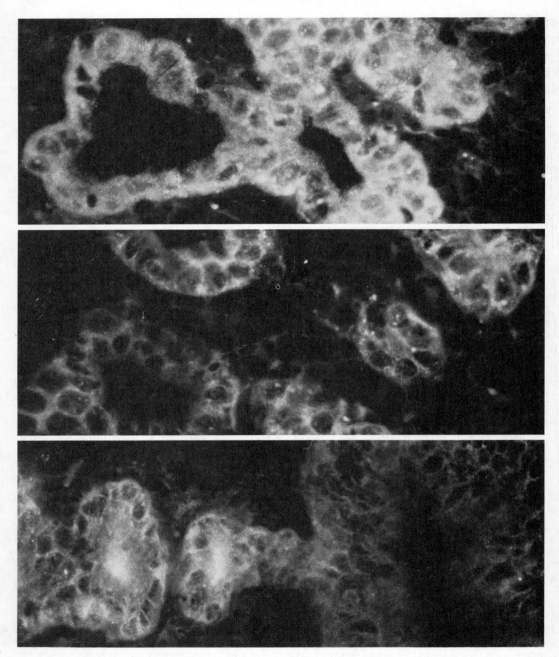

FIG. 1. *Location of fluorescence for type C viral group-specific antigen sites in the estrogen-stimulated NIH/Swiss mouse uterus.*

other immunosuppressants, or certain chemical carcinogens, and possibly by modification of the internal hormonal balance of the host (3).

There is, however, a much more interesting possibility existing between estrogen action and type C viral expression in reproductive tissue. Perhaps the viruses serve normal physiological functions. We have been trying very hard to obtain data for such normal functions. Obviously this is very difficult, and progress is slow. Direct experiments to prove a cause-effect relationship are difficult to devise. However, the following indirect evidence suggests such physiological functions as: (i) graft accept-

TABLE 2. *RNA-directed DNA polymerase activity in uterine tissue from ovariectomized mice*

Strain	Treatment	No.[a]	Uterine wt (mg)	[³H]thymidine triphosphate incorporated per reaction (cpm)	
				Poly(rA)·oligo(dT)	Poly(dA)·oligo(dT)
C57L	Control	3	4.6 ± 0.37	417.3 ± 70.73	2,641.2 ± 376.92
	Estrogen	9	58.1 ± 1.73	455.6 ± 91.37	11,372.7 ± 738.76
NIH/Swiss	Control	6	5.5 ± 0.16	354.2 ± 78.41	1,729.8 ± 54.09
	Estrogen	6	47.1 ± 2.32	1,292.0 ± 182.80	10,473.4 ± 1,527.55
BALB/cAnN	Control	2	7.6 ± 0.15	339.5 ± 5.51	5,806.0 ± 2,344.50
	Estrogen	2	107.4 ± 10.65	1,035.5 ± 242.00	14,737.2 ± 4,757.75
AKR/N	Control	6	9.6 ± 1.07	2,939.3 ± 1,222.58	3,773.7 ± 497.16
	Estrogen	5	64.1 ± 4.67	1,936.8 ± 175.69	18,325.0 ± 1,999.51

[a] Number of pooled samples tested.

ance as in the case of the maternal-fetal interaction (4); (ii) tissue differentiation (5); and (iii) species differentiation and evolution.

Of course, there may be no function for these viruses, and their expression may merely represent a loss of cellular control during rapid cell proliferation.

In the case of species evolution, few data can be offered. However, the data obtained by Benveniste and Todaro, who used these viruses to trace evolution (1), might implicate them in more than mere fingerprints to permit dating the evolutionary process of the species. As far as tissue differentiation is concerned, the only evidence for a possible viral involvement that I am aware of is the potential for these viruses to carry hemoglobin messenger RNA, as shown by Ikawa et al. (5).

In the case of acceptance of the fetus as an allograft, at least some indirect evidence is available. First of all, type C viruses seen in the placenta are associated with the syncytiotrophoblast cells that are fetally derived but are carried throughout the maternal circulation (7). In some quarters these cells have been implicated in the phenomenon of fetal acceptance. It is also recognized that type C viruses participate in immunosuppression.

In our own laboratory, Kouttab et al. have observed that extracts from the uterus and placenta of pregnant mice contain an inhibitor to mixed lymphocyte reactions. This globulin is found at maximal concentrations after 15 days of gestation and is absent or present at very low concentration in nongravid mice (8). It shows some cross-reactivity with certain proteins of the type C viruses and is inhibitory to mixed lymphocyte reactions. More recently, A. K. Fowler in our laboratory, using protein fractions from type C viruses, has found evidence for the presence of inhibitors to mixed lymphocyte and phytohemagglutinin-stimulated lymphocyte transformation in these proteins. The presence of the virus during fetal development has been clearly demonstrated by us in mice and cats, and if the viruses serve a function our findings might suggest a role in modifying a graft-versus-host reaction.

LITERATURE CITED

1. **Benveniste, R. E., and G. J. Todaro.** 1974. Evolution of type-C viral genes. I. Nucleic acid from baboon type-C virus as a measure of divergence among primate species. Proc. Natl. Acad. Sci. U.S.A. **71:**4513–4518.

2. **Hellman, A., and A. K. Fowler.** 1971. Hormone activated expression of the C-type RNA tumor virus genome. Nature (London) New Biol. **233:**142–144.

3. **Hellman, A., A. K. Fowler, J. E. Strickland, and N. M. Kouttab.** 1976. Type-C virus modulation: its possible biological function, p. 206–216. *In* E. Deutsch, K. Moser, H. Rainer, and A. Stacher. (ed.), Molecular base of malignancy. Georg Thieme Verlag, Stuttgart.

4. **Hirsch, M. S., A. P. Kelly, M. R. Proffitt, D. A. Ellis, P. N. Black, A. P. Moriaco, and M. L. Wood.** 1975. Activation of C-type viruses, during skin graft rejection of the mouse. Interrelationship between immunostimulation and immunosuppression. Int. J. Cancer **15:**493–502.

5. **Ikawa, Y. J., J. Ross, and P. Teder.** 1974. An association between globin messenger RNA and 60S RNA derived from Friend leukemia virus. Proc. Natl. Acad. Sci. U.S.A. **71:**1154–1163.

6. **Kalter, S. S., R. L. Heberling, R. J. Helmke, M. Panigel, G. E. Smith, D. C. Kraemer, A. Hellman, A. K. Fowler, and J. E. Strickland.** 1975. A comparative study on the presence of C-type viral particles in placentas from primates and other animals, p. 391–401. *In* Y. Ito and R. M. Dutcher (ed.), Comparative leukemia research, Bibl. Haematol., vol. 40. University of Tokyo Press, Tokyo.

7. **Kalter, S. S., R. J. Helmke, R. L. Heberling, M. Panigel, A. K. Fowler, J. E. Strickland, and A. Hellman.** 1973. C-type particles in normal human placentas. J. Natl. Cancer Inst. **50:**1081–1084.

8. **Kouttab, N. M., A. K. Fowler, J. E. Strickland, and A. Hellman.** 1976. Suppression of *in vitro* lymphocyte stimulation in mice by uterine extract. J. Immunol. **117:**1644–1650.

RD-114 Virus: Studies of RNA of Virus and DNA of Provirus

R. M. McALLISTER AND M. O. NICOLSON

University of Southern California School of Medicine, Children's Hospital of Los Angeles,
Los Angeles, California 90054

INTRODUCTION

RD-114 virus was recovered from human rhabdomyosarcoma (RD) cells that formed a tumor in a kitten (12, 14). The virus was a typical type C virus in morphological, biological, and biophysical properties (13, 14, 17, 19). Identification of the virus as an endogenous virus of domestic cats was established by several groups (6, 11, 18). Surprisingly, when Todaro and associates discovered the first baboon type C virus, M-28, they noted that it closely resembled RD-114 virus (20). In fact, they considered M-28 to be either an RD-114 virus contaminant or an endogenous baboon virus that was related to RD-114 virus.

Thereafter, Benveniste and Todaro suggested that RD-114 virus is derived from primate type C viral genes that entered the germ line of domestic cats and several closely related species of the genus Felis 5 to 10 million years ago (4). On the basis of these and additional biochemical observations, RD-114 virus illustrates three new concepts introduced into virology by type C viruses in general. First, it exists in two forms, as extracellular infectious virus with an RNA genome (13, 14) and as intracellular proviral DNA (1, 5, 7, 15) containing all the information for production of the extracellular virus (11, 18). Second, the infectious virus contains an RNA-directed DNA polymerase (14, 19). Third, viral genes may be transmitted from one species to another with subsequent incorporation of the viral genes into the germ line of the newly infected species (4). This brief review presents more data about the two forms of RD-114 virus.

RD-114 VIRAL RNA

The structure, subunit composition, and molecular weight of RD-114 RNA have been studied (8–10). The high-molecular-weight RNA extracted from the virus has a sedimentation coefficient of 52S and a molecular length measured by electron microscopy of 16 to 20 kb. This RNA molecule is an inverted dimer containing monomer subunits 8 to 10 kb in length (3×10^6 molecular weight). The two

TABLE 1. *Transfection efficiency of RD-114 whole-cell DNA for RD cells*

RD-114 DNA/ culture (μg)[a]	Percentage of cultures positive for RT[b] and RD-114 p30 at 12 weeks	
	RD-114 DNA alone	RD-114 DNA plus salmon sperm DNA (10 μg/ml)
1.0	100	67
0.5	100	67
0.2	67	33
0.1	0	0
0.05	0	0
0.02	0	0

[a] All cultures treated with calcium phosphate. Transfection technique described in reference 16.

[b] Cultures were considered positive for reverse transcriptase (RT) if 1 ml of culture fluid incorporated $\geqq 1,000$ cpm of [*methyl*-^{3}H]TMP per 60 min of incubation (background of 50 to 200 cpm subtracted).

[c] All cultures positive for p30 antigen had titers of $\geqq 8$, the reciprocal of the highest dilution giving a 3 to 4+ complement fixation with antibody to RD-114 p30. Correlation between RT positivity and detection of p30 antigen was 100%.

monomers are joined at their non-polyadenylic acid [poly(A)] ends in a Y- or T-shaped dimer linkage structure. Each monomer has a large loop of similar size and position with respect to the dimer linkage structure. Poly(A) mapping by electron microscopy shows that the 52S molecule contains two poly(A) segments, one at each free end (2).

RD-114 PROVIRAL DNA

Infectivity of Proviral DNA in RD Cells Exogenously Infected with RD-114 Virus

Highly purified DNA extracted from RD-114 cells induces the production of progeny virus in human RD cells and D-17 dog cells that are treated with calcium phosphate or DEAE-dextran (16). The progeny virus was characterized biophysically (density banding, RNA sedimentation, RNA structure by electron microscopy), immunologically (identity of p30 antigen, neutralization of virus and of reverse transcriptase), and biologically (interference with focus formation by pseudotypes, non-transforming, rescue of transforming virus, syncytia induction, host range). In all assessed properties, the progeny virus was identical to RD-114 virus.

The minimal quantity of DNA required to induce progeny virus is 0.1 to 0.2 μg per 2×10^6 cells, giving a specific infectivity of one infectious event per 5×10^4 or 5×10^5 gene copies if there are 2 or 20 copies per cell, respectively (Table 1). The infectious DNA was largely associated with chromosomal DNA as determined by its nuclear location, co-sedimentation with high-molecular-weight DNA, and separation by Hirt fractionation (16).

Fractions of sheared DNA were separated by velocity sedimentation and measured by electron microscopy. The minimal size that infected indicator cells was 4.2×10^6 to 5.5×10^6 daltons (Table 2).

Infectivity of Endogenous RD-114 Virus-Related Genes in the DNA of CCC Cells but Not Other Cat Cells

In view of the above findings and because the cells of domestic cats have been reported to contain 2 to 200 copies of RD-114 virus-related genes (5, 7), we tested the DNAs of domestic cat cells and tissues for infectivity on RD cells and dog cells.

Although only one (CCC-B) of the four sublines of CCC cells was releasing virus detectable as polymerase activity in the supernatant fluids, assays of cell culture fluids from all four CCC sublines on RD or D-17 cells detected infectious RD-114 virus by the presence of both polymerase activity and specific p30 antigen (Table 3).

On the other hand, none of the four strains of cat embryo fibroblasts released virus into the

TABLE 2. *Infectivity of RD-114 DNA related to size*

Approx mol wt range	Cultures positive for RT[a]/ cultures treated (12 weeks)	
	10 μg/culture	1 μg/culture
$6.6 \times 10^6 - 8.8 \times 10^6$	2/2	2/2
$6.2 \times 10^6 - 6.9 \times 10^6$	2/2	1/2
$5.5 \times 10^6 - 6.2 \times 10^6$	2/2	1/2
$4.2 \times 10^6 - 5.5 \times 10^6$	2/2	2/2
$2.3 \times 10^6 - 4.2 \times 10^6$	2/2	0/2
$1.3 \times 10^6 - 2.0 \times 10^6$	0/2	0/2
$0.75 \times 10^6 - 1.3 \times 10^6$	0/2	0/2
$0.33 \times 10^6 - 0.75 \times 10^6$	0/2	0/2

[a] See footnote *b* of Table 1.

TABLE 3. *Virus release by feline cells in culture*

Cells	RT feline cells (cpm/ml)	Assay of feline culture fluids		Weeks post-inoculation
		RT (cpm/ml) assayed on:		
		RD	D-17	
CCC subline				
CCC-3A	125	5,793	ND[a]	5
CCC-B	540	16,789	2,246	4
CRFK	19	1,180	ND	5
C-C	94	6,188	514	3
Other feline fibroblasts				
FEF	12	10	ND	6
AG581[b]	0	118	46	12
AG581 + BUdR[c]	0	32	0	12
AH927[b]	0	57	206	12
AH927 + BUdR	0	0	0	12
AG601[b]	0	0	135	12
AG601 + BUdR	0	45	407	12

[a] Not done.

[b] Cells also co-cultivated with RD cells. Assays at 3 weeks for RT and RD-114 p30 antigen were all negative.

[c] Bromodeoxyuridine.

culture fluids as measured by polymerase activity, and no released virus was detected even after treatment of the cells with bromodeoxyuridine and co-cultivation with the sensitive indicator cells.

Neither infectious virus nor p30 antigen was detected in sensitive indicator cells treated with DNAs of the four cat fibroblast strains or the three cat tissues, but the DNAs of all four sublines of CCC cells induced the release of RD-114 virus from the indicator cells (data not shown). The virus released from a transfected culture was the same as RD-114 virus as determined by virus neutralization, interference, and polymerase neutralization assays (16).

LITERATURE CITED

1. **Baluda, M. A., and P. Roy-Burman.** 1973. Partial characterization of RD-114 virus by DNA-RNA hybridization studies. Nature (London) New Biol. **244:**59–62.
2. **Bender, W., and N. Davidson.** 1976. Mapping of poly (A) sequences with the electron microscope reveals unusual structure of type-C oncornavirus RNA molecules. Cell **7:**595–607.
3. **Bender, W., S. Hu, Y. H. Chien, P. Chandler, S. Dube, N. Davidson, and J. Maisel.** 1976. A common structure for the high molecular weight RNA's of all type-C viruses? Cold Spring Harbor Symp., in press.
4. **Benveniste, R. E., and G. J. Todaro.** 1974. Evolution of type-C viral genes. Inheritance of exogenously acquired viral genes. Nature (London) **252:**456–459.
5. **Benveniste, R. W., and G. J. Todaro.** 1974. Multiple divergent copies of endogenous C-type virogenes in mammalian cells. Nature (London) **252:**170–173.
6. **Fischinger, P., P. T. Peebles, S. Nomura, and D. Haapala.**

1973. Isolation of an RD-114-like oncornavirus from a cat cell line. J. Virol. **11:**978–985.

7. **Fujinaga, K., A. Rankin, H. Yamazaki, K. Sekikawa, J. Bragdon, and M. Green.** 1973. RD-114 virus: analysis of viral gene sequences in feline and human cells by DNA-DNA reassociation kinetics and RNA-DNA hybridization. Virology **56:**484–495.

8. **Kung, H., J. M. Bailey, N. Davidson, M. O. Nicolson, and R. M. McAllister.** 1975. Structure, subunit composition, and molecular weight of RD-114 RNA. J. Virol. **16:**397–411.

9. **Kung, H. J., J. M. Bailey, M. O. Nicolson, and R. M. McAllister.** 1975. Structure and molecular length of the large subunits of RD-114 viral RNA. J. Virol. **14:**170–173.

10. **Kung, H., S. Hu, W. Bender, J. M. Bailey, N. Davidson, M. O. Nicolson, and R. M. McAllister.** 1976. RD-114 baboon and wooly monkey viral RNA's compared in size and structure. Cell **7:**609–620.

11. **Livingston, D. M., and G. J. Todaro.** 1973. Endogenous type C virus from a cat cell clone with properties distinct from previously described feline type C virus. Virology **53:**142–151.

12. **McAllister, R. M., W. A. Nelson-Rees, E. Y. Johnson, R. W. Rongey, and M. B. Gardner.** 1971. Disseminated rhabdomyosarcomas formed in kittens by cultured human rhabdomyosarcoma cells. J. Natl. Cancer Inst. **47:**603–611.

13. **McAllister, R. M., M. Nicolson, M. B. Gardner, S. Rasheed, R. W. Rongey, W. D. Hardy, Jr., and R. V. Gilden.** 1973. RD-114 virus compared with feline and murine type-C viruses released from RD cells. Nature (London) New Biol. **242:**75–78.

14. **McAllister, R. M., M. Nicolson, M. B. Gardner, R. W. Rongey, S. Rasheed, P. S. Sarma, R. J. Huebner, M. Hatanaka, S. Oroszlan, R. V. Gilden, A. Kabigting, and L. Vernon.** 1972. C-type virus released from cultured human rhabdomyosarcoma cells. Nature (London) New Biol. **235:**3–6.

15. **Neiman, P. E.** 1973. Measurement of RD-114 nucleotide sequences in feline cellular DNA. Nature (London) New Biol. **244:**62–64.

16. **Nicolson, M. O., F. Hariri, H. M. Krempin, R. M. McAllister, and R. V. Gilden.** 1976. Infectious proviral DNA in human cells infected with transformation-defective type C viruses. Virology **70:**301–312.

17. **Oroszlan, S., D. Bova, M. H. M. White, R. Toni, C. Foreman, and R. V. Gilden.** 1972. Purification and immunological characterization of the major internal protein of the RD-114 virus. Proc. Natl. Acad. Sci. U.S.A. **69:**1211–1215.

18. **Sarma, P. S., J. Tseng, Y. K. Lee, and R. V. Gilden.** 1973. Virus similar to RD-114 in cat cells. Nature (London) New Biol. **244:**56–58.

19. **Scolnick, E. M., W. P. Parks, G. J. Todaro, and S. A. Aaronson.** 1972. Immunological characterization of primate C-type virus reverse transcriptase. Nature (London) New Biol. **235:**35–40.

20. **Todaro, G. J., S. S. Tevethia, and J. L. Melnick.** 1973. Isolation of an RD-114 related type-C virus from feline sarcoma virus-transformed baboon cells. Intervirology **1:**399.

Endogenous C-Type Viruses in Normal Development, Autoimmunity, and Cancer

JAY A. LEVY

Department of Medicine and Cancer Research Institute, University of California School of Medicine, San Francisco, California 94143

INTRODUCTION

C-type RNA viruses have been observed by electron microscopy in 18 different mammalian species, including humans, several avian species, snakes, and fish (21a). Their presence as integrated genomes (endogenous viruses) in vertebrates suggests that, by natural selection, evolution has preserved them as necessary regulators of natural life processes. To understand their role in nature, I have concentrated on studies of the endogenous C-type viruses of mice.

THE MOUSE AS A MODEL FOR HUMAN DEVELOPMENT AND DISEASE

The study of New Zealand Black (NZB) mice, probably the most well-studied strain in history, has provided a great deal of information in immunology and virology. Developed by Bielschowsky in the 1950s (6), this strain has a disease complex that resembles autoimmune disease in man—particularly lupus erythematosus. Its syndrome includes a large number of humoral and cellular immune disorders including hypergammaglobulinemia, depressed thymocyte (T cell) activity, and antibodies to red blood cells, thymus, and nucleic acids. Most mice succumb to immune complex glomerulonephritis; 20% develop reticulum cell sarcomas or immunoblastic lymphomas (6, 13, 32).

In the 1960s, several laboratories reported the finding of C-type viruses budding from tissue of this mouse strain and suggested that this virus might be responsible for their disease complex (10, 27, 37). Cultivation of the virus in pure culture in mouse cells, however, was not possible, and studies aimed at finding the pathogenic potential of this presumed "defective" (i.e., noninfectious) virus were therefore limited. We discovered in 1970 that this NZB C-type virus represented the prototype of a new class of endogenous C-type viruses of mice (24). Although inherited in the genes of the mouse, this virus could not reinfect other mouse cells. It was infectious, however, for a wide variety of cells from heterologous species, including those from a different animal class, the avian species (Table 1; 18–20). For this reason, it was defined descriptively as xenotropic (X-tropic), from the Greek *xenos*—foreign—and *tropos*—turning (18). Counterparts of this class of endogenous virus have since been described in cats (26) and baboons (4) and may be present in humans (16). These murine C-type viruses could be distinguished serologically (e.g., virus neutralization) and by host range from the previously described endogenous murine leukemia virus (MuLV) Gross-AKR (12), which can productively infect mouse cells, i.e., the *ecotropic* class, from the Greek *oikos*—home, one's environment (19). Recently, a third class of endogenous viruses has been discovered in wild mice captured in the canyons around Los Angeles. Since these viruses can infect and replicate in both mouse cells and cells from heterologous species, they have been called *amphotropic* viruses, from the Greek *amphos*—both (12a, 27a). They may represent the progenitor of the xenotropic and ecotropic viruses or a recombinant. The ecotropic viruses are found in many but not all house mice and can give rise to leukemia and lymphomas. Thus far, the amphotropic type have been found only in wild mice and may produce the neurological disease and/or lymphoma associated with some of these mice. The role of the X-tropic virus, which is probably present in all house mice, is still unknown.

EXPRESSION OF THE X-TROPIC VIRUS

We and others have recovered the xenotropic virus from many strains of laboratory mice, including the nude as well as wild house mice from Japan and San Francisco (1, 5, 18, 19, 21). Some 11- to 15-day embryos and placentas from other laboratory strains, such as NIH/Swiss, SJL/J, nude (Swiss), and C57 Leaden, have also yielded the virus (21). Identification of X-tropic virus in nude mice is important since this strain is used for cultiva-

559

TABLE 1. *Animal cell lines susceptible to infection by mouse xenotropic virus*

MAMMALIAN

Anteater	Lion
Bear	Marmoset
Cat	Mink
Chimpanzee	Miopithicus
Cow	Mongoose (African water)
Deer (black-footed)	Mongoose (black-footed)
Dog	Muntjac
Gazelle	Orangutan
Gorilla	Rabbit
Guinea pig	Raccoon
Horse	Rat
Human	Rhesus monkey

AVIAN

Duck	Pheasant
Quail	Pigeon
Parakeet	Turkey

tion of heterologous cells. Infection of these cells by the X-tropic virus would be the most likely reason for C-type viruses observed in transplanted heterologous cells.

An important qualification to X-tropic virus recovery has been the extent of virus production by mice from different strains, individual mice from the same strain, and cells from the same mouse (23). The virus was first recovered from NZB mice since every cell in this mouse, throughout its lifetime, spontaneously produces the virus. Clones of NZB adult and embryo cells all yield X-tropic virus (23). With individual NZB mice, however, titers of infectious virus produced range between 100 and 10,000 infectious particles/ml, depending on the mouse and tissue tested. Moreover, individual cells from a single NZB embryo can differ 100-fold in the quantity of X-tropic virus spontaneously produced (23). With other mice, X-tropic virus is produced with less frequency and titer. In 129/J and SWR/J, for instance, no virus or only 1 to 10 infectious particles/ml can be recovered. Cells from (NZB × 129)F_1 and (NZB × SWR)-F_1 hybrids, however, produce large quantities of the virus and demonstrate that the intracellular regulation for spontaneous production of X-tropic virus is dominant in the NZB mice. These studies suggest that cells of mice are programmed to release X-tropic virus at certain times in the life of the mouse and in specific quantities. The variation in virus production must be determined by an intracellular mechanism since the number of X-tropic viral genomes in each cell of all house mice appears to be the same (8). In NZB mice, this regulation is completely "turned on" to virus production.

Because of the recognition by electron microscopy of C-type viruses in blastocysts (7), we have looked for X-tropic virus in embryos at the two-, four-, and eight-cell stages and in morulae and in blastocysts of ICR mice. In 20% of the cases, infectious virus in low but detectable titer has been cultivated from late-stage morulae and blastocysts (Levy, Kazan, and Golbus, unpublished data). It is interesting that these stages in embryonic development correspond to the onset of differentiation.

NEUTRALIZING FACTOR

Since X-tropic virus can be recovered from early embryos and fetuses, it was surprising to find that normal mouse sera neutralize this class of endogenous C-type viruses (2, 19, 21; J. A. Levy, Abstr. Annu. Meet. Am. Soc. Microbiol. 1973, V164, p. 222). We expected that the host would be tolerant to these "embryonic" antigens. The neutralization was specific for X-tropic virus, not ecotropic virus, and was considered a classic immunological response. It did not correlate, however, with the presence of naturally occurring antibodies detected by radioimmune precipitation (15, 17). These immunoglobulins (IgG and IgM) bind to both xenotropic and ecotropic viruses (17). Experiments performed in our laboratory have now demonstrated that this X-tropic virus neutralization is not due to a conventional immunoglobulin (21, 22). A soluble circulating serum factor which is resistant to proteases, lipases, amylases, acid, and even boiling temperatures has been identified (Table 2). Recent work in collaboration with Joanne Leong and John Kane

TABLE 2. *Sensitivity of the neutralizing factor found naturally in mouse sera to various physicochemical treatments*

RESISTANT

Dialysis
Heat: 56 and 70°C for 30 min; 100°C for 20 min
pH 2.0
Trichloroacetic acid (activity recoverable in precipitate)
Pronase, protease K, pepsin, trypsin
RNase, DNase
Amylase, hyaluronidase, neuraminidase
Phospholipase A, ether extraction, 0.1% sodium dodecyl sulfate

SENSITIVE

pH 12.0
Ethanol-ether extraction (3:1, vol/vol)
Freezing and thawing three times

has shown that the neutralization is associated with circulating lipoproteins (17a). This result is exciting since it represents the first time a specific humoral antiviral effect is associated with lipoproteins and not immunoglobulins.

VIRUS-CELL INTERACTION

Cells infected by viruses or expressing an endogenous virus can be altered antigenically. The cell membrane either carries viral proteins which represent "new antigens" on the cell surface, or the normal structural antigens of the cell are modified by the virus so that they are now immunogenic. These cell surface alterations caused by virus infection could induce an immunological response leading to cell destruction by autoantibody production or T-cell cytotoxicity. Lindenmann demonstrated, for instance, that Ehrlich ascites cells became immunogenic only after infection by influenza virus. This virus, by budding from the cell membrane, acted as a carrier for cell surface proteins which were not recognized by the host as antigenic, e.g., a carrier-hapten effect (25).

Besides the modification in the cell, the virus itself can be altered after infection. If the recipient cell contains a C-type virus which does not prevent superinfection by another virus, the two viruses may exchange their outside envelope coats during replication. This kind of mixing has been called *phenotypic* because the viruses maintain their own genomes. No interference to virus superinfection of cells occurs with the endogenous ecotropic and xenotropic viruses (23). An ecotropic C-type virus can infect a mouse cell making xenotropic virus and emerge with its genome enveloped in a xenotropic coat. This phenotypic mixing leads to hybrid or pseudotype viruses which can now transfer known oncogenic genomes to heterologous cells. After passing the AKR virus through NZB embryo cells, we demonstrated that infection of mongoose, gazelle, human, and duck cells with the progeny virus leads to ecotropic virus production by these cells (Levy, Virology, in press). Since AKR viruses cannot enter these heterologous cells, a xenotropic pseudotype AKR virus was obviously responsible for this infection.

Similarly, we have found that a xenotropic virus can infect a rat cell chronically infected with ecotropic virus and emerge in an ecotropic coat. This pseudotype virus can now infect and replicate in mouse cells. The resistance of mouse cells to X-tropic virus therefore appears to be more at the penetration than at the intracellular level. This mixing of C-type viruses occurs among mouse and rat and even C-type viruses of birds (Levy, Virology, in press). We

have, for instance, made a chicken virus in a xenotropic and ecotropic coat and both classes of mouse C-type viruses in an avian C-type virus coat (Levy and Vogt, Abstr. Annu. Meet. Am. Soc. Microbiol. 1976, S109, p. 222). The potential for spread of these animal genomes among the different species is great and may be responsible for variances in differentiation, characteristics of evolution, or somatic changes, characteristic of malignancy.

ROLE OF X-TROPIC VIRUSES

We have reviewed briefly the incidence and frequency of X-tropic virus expression in mice from embryo to adulthood. We have discussed its interaction with normal factors in the blood which specifically inactivate it, and its possible interplay with other endogenous or exogenous viruses in recipient cells. All these factors may be important in the ultimate function of this virus.

In examining its role more directly, we have inoculated X-tropic virus into newborn mice, rats, and ducks. No pathology has been noted

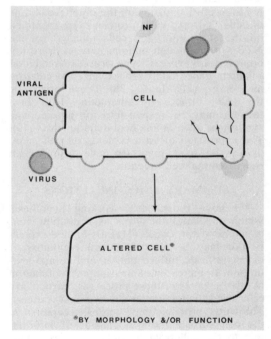

FIG. 1. *Possible role of neutralizing factor (NF) in regulating cell function. A mechanism is proposed by which NF reacts with xenotropic virus antigens present on the surface of cells. The viral proteins, when expressed, act as receptors for the transfer of information to the cell from its outside environment. This interaction leads to changes in the cell morphology and/or function.*

in any animal after 2 years. In ducks inoculated with an X-tropic pseudotype of the murine sarcoma virus (MSV), multiple fibrosarcomas developed which contained high-titered X-tropic MSV. This observation in vivo confirmed the ability of the X-tropic virus envelope to transfer oncogenic genes to formerly resistant host cells.

The X-tropic virus has also been recovered selectively from mice undergoing graft-versus-host reaction (GVHR; 30; J. A. levy, S. Datta, and R. S. Schwartz, Clin. Immunol. Immunopathol., in press). In these experiments, spleens of CAF_1 mice inoculated with BALB/c spleen cells were completely "turned on" to production of X-tropic virus, whereas only one-third of control CAF spleens yielded the virus. Since NZB mice have a GVHR-like syndrome, this immunological disorder in itself may enhance the already increased X-tropic virus expression in this strain.

We have discussed the antigenic changes that occur in cells following C-type virus infection or expression of endogenous virus. In collaboration with L. Oshiro, we have demonstrated that a budding C-type virus is not needed for expression of its antigens on the outer membrane of cells. X-tropic virus proteins were identified on the surface of dog cells infected by the NZB virus although budding viruses were not observed. Likewise, C-type viruses on red blood cell membranes have been visualized by electron microscopy (21, 21a, 28, 36). These viruses on the cell surface, by interacting with host factors, may be responsible for autoimmune syndromes such as the hemolytic anemias (19). The expression of viral proteins on cell membranes, however, may also have an important role in normal cell function.

SUMMARY AND CONCLUSIONS

We have proposed a working hypothesis which implicates the virus as a double agent in natural life processes (21a). By limited expression it may be one of several regulators of embryogenesis, differentiation, and normal maturation. In increased expression it may function in other aspects of these processes, particularly cell aging (autoimmune disease and cancer). The virus proteins may act as receptors on the cell surface for the transfer of information to the cell from its outside environment. The control of cell function would then be mediated by substances such as the neutralizing factor which interact with these viral antigens on the cell membrane when they are expressed and thereby effect a change in the cells (Fig. 1). A similar explanation has been given for the regulatory role of protein hormones (29) and of lipoproteins which affect cholesterol synthesis and T-cell function by interacting with cell surface receptors (9, 11). Use of purified neutralizing factor in cultures of mouse embryos and differentiating tissue may help elucidate this possibility.

By this hypothesis, production of endogenous virus is not needed and evolution should select for viral expression without virus replication. Such a phenomenon would explain the inability to cultivate human C-type viruses which we and others have seen in limited number in human placentas (16, 21, 35). These probably represent human X-tropic viruses which need not be infectious to have a function, and may only be infectious for a very select group of heterologous cells. The latter property of X-tropic viruses and viruses in general has been cited as a means of transferring information among the species, and affecting evolution (3). It may have been the phenomenon that brought endogenous viruses into some mammalian hosts (34).

Embryogenesis, differentiation, and normal maturation would therefore depend on a limited cellular expression of endogenous C-tropic viruses and the interaction of their antigens with factors like neutralizing factor (Fig. 1). In the process of aging, the intracellular regulation of C-type virus expression would change, leading to autoimmunity and malignancy. Autoimmunity would result from an excess of virus or factor production. Cancer would develop from chronic production, interaction, and exchange of endogenous C-type viruses (14, 33; Levy, Virology, in press). These processes associated with aging might also occur from exogenous infection by other C-type viruses which place new antigens on the cell surface, or transfer oncogenic genomes to the host. Transduction of genetic material from normal duck cells has been demonstrated with the Rous C-type virus (31), and ecotropic viruses may represent xenotropic or recombinant viruses from other species. The answer to these possibilities and their relevance to human development and disease should become more apparent with further studies of the endogenous C-type viruses of mice.

ACKNOWLEDGMENTS

My research cited in this paper was supported by Public Health Service grant CA 13086 from the National Cancer Institute, by National Cancer Institute contract N01 CP 43381, and by a grant from the Council for Tobacco Research. I am recipient of Research Career Development Award 5 K04 CA 70990 from the National Cancer Institute.

LITERATURE CITED

1. **Aaronson, S. A., and J. R. Stephenson.** 1973. Independent segregation of loci for activation of biologically distinguishable RNA C-type viruses in mouse cells. Proc. Natl. Acad. Sci. U.S.A. **70:**2055-2058.

2. **Aaronson, S. A., and J. R. Stephenson.** 1974. Widespread natural occurrence of high titers of neutralizing antibodies to a specific class of endogenous mouse type-C virus. Proc. Natl. Acad. Sci. U.S.A. **71:** 1957–1961.

3. **Anderson, N. G.** 1970. Evolutionary significance of virus infection. Nature (London) **227:** 1346–1347.

4. **Benveniste, R. E., M. M. Lieber, D. M. Livingston, C. J. Sherr, G. J. Todaro, and S. S. Kalter.** 1974. Infectious C-type virus isolated from a baboon placenta. Nature (London) **248:** 17–20.

5. **Benveniste, R. E., M. M. Lieber, and G. J. Todaro.** 1974. A distinct class of inducible murine type C viruses which replicate in the rabbit SIRC cell line. Proc. Natl. Acad. Sci. U.S.A. **71:** 602–606.

6. **Bielschowsky, M., B. J. Helyer, and J. B. Howie.** 1959. Spontaneous haemolytic anaemia in mice of the NZB/B1 strain. Proc. Univ. Otago Med. Sch. **37:** 9–11.

7. **Chase, D. G., and L. Piko.** 1973. Expression of A- and C-type particles in early mouse embryos. J. Natl. Cancer Inst. **51:** 1971–1975.

8. **Chattopadhyay, S. K., D. R. Lowy, N. M. Teich, A. S. Levine, and W. P. Rowe.** 1974. Evidence that the AKR murine leukemia virus genome is complete in DNA of the high-virus AKR mouse and incomplete in the DNA of the virus-negative NIH mouse. Proc. Natl. Acad. Sci. U.S.A. **71:** 167–171.

9. **Chisari, F. V., and T. S. Edgington.** 1975. Lymphocyte E rosette inhibitory factor: a regulatory serum lipoprotein. J. Exp. Med. **142:** 1092–1107.

10. **East, J., P. R. Prosser, E. J. Holborrow, and H. Jaquet.** 1967. Autoimmune reactions and virus-like particles in germ-free NZB mice. Lancet **i:** 755–757.

11. **Goldstein, J. L., and M. S. Brown.** 1974. Binding and degradation of low density lipoproteins by cultured human fibroblasts. J. Biol. Chem. **249:** 51–53.

12. **Gross, L.** 1951. "Spontaneous" leukemia developing in C3H mice following inoculation, in infancy, with AK-leukemic extracts, or AK-embryos. Proc. Soc. Exp. Biol. Med. **76:** 27–32.

12a. **Hartley, J., and W. P. Rowe.** 1976. Naturally occurring murine leukemia viruses in wild mice: characterization of a new "amphotropic" class. J. Virol. **19:** 19–25.

13. **Helyer, B. J., and J. B. Howie.** 1963. Spontaneous autoimmune disease in NZB/B1 mice. Br. J. Haematol. **9:** 119.

14. **Huebner, R. J., and G. J. Todaro.** 1969. Oncogenes of RNA tumor viruses as determinants of cancer. Proc. Natl. Acad. Sci. U.S.A. **64:** 1087–1095.

15. **Ihle, J. N., M. Yurconic, Jr., and M. G. Hanna, Jr.** 1973. Autogenous immunity to endogenous RNA tumor virus. Radioimmune precipitation assay of mouse serum antibody levels. J. Exp. Med. **138:** 194–208.

16. **Kalter, S. S., R. J. Helmke, R. L. Heberling, M. Panigel, A. K. Fowler, J. E. Strickland, and A. Hellman.** 1973. C-type particles in normal human placentas. J. Natl. Cancer Inst. **50:** 1081–1084.

17. **Lee, J. C., M. G. Hanna, Jr., J. N. Ihle, and S. A. Aaronson.** 1974. Autogenous immunity to endogenous RNA tumor virus: differential reactivities of immunoglobulins M and G to virus envelope antigens. J. Virol. **14:** 773–781.

17a. **Leong, J. C., J. P. Kane, O. Oleszko, and J. A. Levy.** 1977. Antigen-specific, non-immunoglobulin factor that neutralizes xenotropic virus is associated with mouse lipoproteins. Proc. Natl. Acad. Sci. U.S.A. **74:** 276–280.

18. **Levy, J. A.** 1973. Xenotropic viruses: murine leukemia viruses associated with NIH Swiss, NZB, and other mouse strains. Science **182:** 1151–1153.

19. **Levy, J. A.** 1974. Autoimmunity and neoplasia: the possible role of C-type viruses. Am. J. Clin. Pathol. **62:** 258–280.

20. **Levy, J. A.** 1975. Host range of murine xenotropic virus: replication in avian cells. Nature (London) **253:** 140–142.

21. **Levy, J. A.** 1975. Xenotropic C-type viruses and autoimmune disease. J. Rheumatol. **2:** 135–148.

21a. **Levy, J. A.** 1976. Endogenous C-type viruses: double agents in natural life processes. Biomedicine **24:** 84–93.

22. **Levy, J. A., J. N. Ihle, O. Oleszko, and R. D. Barnes.** 1975. Virus-specific neutralization by a soluble non-immunoglobulin factor found naturally in normal mouse sera. Proc. Natl. Acad. Sci. U.S.A. **72:** 5071–5075.

23. **Levy, J. A., P. Kazan, O. Varnier, and H. Kleiman.** 1975. Murine xenotropic C-type viruses. I. Distribution and further characterization of the virus in NZB mice. J. Virol. **16:** 844–853.

24. **Levy, J. A., and T. Pincus.** 1970. Demonstration of biological activity of a murine leukemia virus of New Zealand black mice. Science **170:** 326–327.

25. **Lindenmann, J.** 1974. Viruses as immunological adjuvants in cancer. Biochim. Biophys. Acta **49:** 355.

26. **McAllister, R. M., M. Nicolson, M. B. Gardner, R. W. Rongey, S. Rasheed, P. S. Sarma, R. J. Huebner, M. Hatanaka, S. Oroszlan, R. V. Gilden, A. Kabigting, and L. Vernon.** 1972. C-type virus released from cultured human rhabdomyosarcoma cells. Nature (London) New Biol. **235:** 3.

27. **Mellors, R. C., and C. Y. Huang.** 1966. Immunopathology of NZB/B1 mice. V. Virus-like (filtrable) agent separable from lymphoma cells and identifiable by electron microscopy. J. Exp. Med. **124:** 1031–1038.

27a. **Rasheed, S., M. B. Gardner, and E. Chan.** 1976. Amphotropic host range of naturally occurring wild mouse leukemia viruses. J. Virol. **19:** 13–18.

28. **Reilly, C. A., and G. T. Schloss.** 1971. The erythrocyte as virus carrier in Friend and Rauscher virus leukemias. Cancer Res. **34:** 841–846.

29. **Robinson, G. A., R. W. Butcher, and E. W. Sutherland.** 1971. Cyclic AMP. Academic Press Inc., New York.

30. **Sherr, C. J., M. M. Lieber, and G. J. Todaro.** 1974. Mixed splenocyte cultures and graft versus host reactions selectively induce an "S-tropic" murine type C virus. Cell **1:** 55–58.

31. **Shoyab, M., P. D. Markham, and M. A. Baluda.** 1975. Host induced alteration of avian sarcoma virus B-77 genome. Proc. Natl. Acad. Sci. U.S.A. **72:** 1031–1035.

32. **Talal, N., and A. D. Steinberg.** 1974. The pathogenesis of autoimmunity in New Zealand Black mice. Curr. Top. Microbiol. Immunol. **64:** 79–103.

33. **Temin, H. M.** 1971. The protovirus hypothesis: speculations on the significance of RNA-directed synthesis for normal development and for carcinogenesis. J. Natl. Cancer Inst. **46:** III.

34. **Todaro, G. J.** 1975. Evolution and modes of transmission of RNA tumor viruses. Am. J. Pathol. **81:** 590–606.

35. **Vernon, M. L., M. J. McMahon, and J. J. Hackett.** 1974. Additional evidence of type-C particles in human placentas. J. Natl. Cancer Inst. **52:** 987–989.

36. **Wollmann, R. L., E. J. Pang, A. E. Evans, and W. H. Kirsten.** 1970. Virus-induced hemolytic anemia in mice. Cancer Res. **30:** 1003–1010.

37. **Yumoto, T., and L. Dmochowski.** 1967. Studies on the relationship of murine leukemia virus to autoimmune disease of mice prone to leukemia. Med. Rec. Ann. **60:** 133–139.

VII. VIRUSES AND PLASMIDS IN FUNGI AND PROTOZOA

Introduction

PAUL A. LEMKE

Mellon Institute, Carnegie-Mellon University, Pittsburgh, Pennsylvania 15213

Viruses have infiltrated all microbial life forms. Evidence for the presence of viruses in eukaryotic microbes has emerged slowly, partly as a result of the fact that viruses in these life forms are often latent or nonsymptomatic and have not been amenable to analysis through rapid tests for infectivity. To date, relatively few viruses from fungi and protozoa have been characterized as to nucleoprotein composition, and none has really satisfied all criteria expected of a virus. Those studied most extensively have proven to be infectious by heredity—a criterion normally attributed to a plasmid. The cytoplasmically inherited virus particles in the killer systems of *Saccharomyces cerevisiae* and *Paramecium aurelia* are examples discussed in this symposium. The adage which implies that "one man's virus is another man's plasmid" is especially descriptive of genetic determinants for killer phenotypes in these two organisms. This adage applies equally well to a series of double-stranded RNA viruses recognized as cytoplasmic inclusions in a variety of fungi.

Double-Stranded RNA Viruses Among Filamentous Fungi

PAUL A. LEMKE

Mellon Institute, Carnegie-Mellon University, Pittsburgh, Pennsylvania 15213

Early evidence for double-stranded RNA (dsRNA) and dsRNA viruses in fungi developed through interest in antiviral activity associated with two *Penicillium* molds (30, 33). This interest was concurrent with the search for antiviral compounds to combat poliovirus and predated the first report of dsRNA in a virus (17). It is now known that the antiviral component associated with *P. stoloniferum* (2, 19) and *P. funiculosum* (2, 22) is dsRNA of viral origin.

In 1967, Ellis and Kleinschmidt (16) demonstrated that an antiviral preparation derived from *P. stoloniferum* contained virus-like particles (VLP) about 30 nm in diameter. These particles, although isometric, are now known to represent two serologically distinct and electrophoretically separable viruses, and both viruses contain dsRNA (6, 9, 10). The electrophoretically slow virus of *P. stoloniferum* is the most thoroughly characterized of fungal viruses. Purified particles have been shown to possess RNA-dependent RNA polymerase activity (23). The product of this activity has proven to be dsRNA, which indicates that the polymerase of this virus is a replicase rather than a transcriptase for synthesis of mRNA (7). Based on this result, Buck and Ratti (12) have proposed a model for replication of dsRNA fungal viruses. Simply stated, the model involves a particle-associated duplication of dsRNA. The two dsRNA molecules per product particle are released and separately encapsidated, resulting in two virus particles, each containing one dsRNA molecule. Thus, for every particle originally present, a duplicate particle is ultimately produced. Presumably, in this model the plus strand of dsRNA can serve as mRNA. Such replication by duplication is quite different from that of dsRNA viruses in nonfungal hosts (35) or from that generally expected of a virus, since in a typical viral system a unit of infectivity is expected to multiply and not simply to duplicate.

Since the first reports of VLP and dsRNA in *P. stoloniferum* (16, 19), the list of fungi containing similar particles has grown steadily (Table 1). Thus far, all of the dsRNA-containing

TABLE 1. *Representative virus particles and molecular weight forms of dsRNA among fungi[a]*

Host species	Particle size (nm)	dsRNA ($\times 10^6$)	Key references
Agaricus bisporus	25, 34	0.67, 1.60, 170, 1.76, 1.89, 2.17	26, 28, 32[b]
Aspergillus foetidus[c]	40[d]	1.24, 1.44, 170, 1.87, 2.31	11, 31
	40[e]	2.24, 2.76	11, 31
Helminthosporium maydis	48	6.3	5
Penicillium brevicompactum	40	1.89, 1.99, 2.18	38
P. chrysogenum	35–40	0.14, 1.89, 1.99, 2.18	8, 13, 29, 36
P. stoloniferum[c]	35[c]	0.46, 0.89, 0.99	6, 10
	35[d]	0.94, 1.11	6, 9, 10
Periconia circinata	32	0.42, 0.48, 1.10, 1.25, 1.40, 1.75	15
Saccharomyces cerevisiae	34	0.25, 0.50, 1.19, 1.29, 1.40, 2.50	1, 3, 18, 34
Thielaviopsis basicola[c]	40	2.7, 3.8, 3.9, 4.2, 4.5	4
Ustilago maydis	40	0.06, 0.44, 0.49, 0.56, 0.70, 0.93, 1.80, 2.10, 2.52, 2.87, 4.70	20, 28, 37

[a] Only the more extensively characterized viruses and dsRNA's are listed in the table. Readers interested generally in this subject should consult recent and more comprehensive review papers on fungal viruses (14, 24; K. N. Saksena and P. A. Lemke, *in* H. Fraenkel-Conrat and R. R. Wagner [ed.], *Comprehensive virology*, vol. 11, in press).

[b] See also R. J. Barton, Abstr. 3rd Int. Congr. Virol., Madrid, 1975, p.147.

[c] Serologically distinct, isometric particles recognized in this host.

[d] Electrophoretically fast virus.

[e] Electrophoretically slow virus.

viruses from fungi have proven to be spherical in shape with simple capsid structure and to be relatively small in size, ranging in diameter from 25 to 48 nm. These viruses are often multicomponent; that is, the dsRNA genome is represented in a population of particles rather than in a single particle. Molecular weight forms of dsRNA identified from fungal viruses range from 60,000 to 6,300,000. This range embraces the smallest and the largest known species of dsRNA.

Four molecular weight forms of dsRNA have been described from the mold *P. chrysogenum* (8, 13, 25, 29, 36), and at least three of these are derived from particles as separately encapsidated components of a single virus (36). In other fungi, especially *Saccharomyces cerevisiae* (1, 18, 34) and *Ustilago maydis* (20, 21, 37), differences in spectra of dsRNA molecules have been identified from specific strains, and certain of these dsRNA molecules appear to be accessory to those represented in particles. From still other fungi, serological evidence for dsRNA has been obtained without corresponding evidence for the presence of VLP (27). Collectively, these data suggest that dsRNA genomes represented in fungi not only may be multicomponent for distribution of dsRNA segments into particles but may involve extraparticulate components (dsRNA plasmids) as well.

CONCLUSIONS

Although relatively few fungal viruses have been studied in detail, certain impressions regarding the nature of these viruses have developed.

First among these is an apparent prevalence of dsRNA viruses among fungi. Although all of the known dsRNA fungal viruses are structurally simple and relatively small, they are serologically heterogeneous and have genomes that exhibit diversity in both size and segmentation. Such heterogeneity implies that these viruses may be unrelated and simple by reduction.

Second, the majority of dsRNA fungal viruses appear to be latent or cryptic and to persist indefinitely in infected cell lines. In this regard, they appear to be adapted for transmission by cytoplasmic exchange and can be manipulated experimentally as plasmids. None has been shown to be infectious as free particles. Many are multicomponent, and in some instances satellite segments of dsRNA may be involved.

Third, although the dsRNA fungal viruses appear generally to be latent, examples of alteration in host phenotype related to their presence can be cited. Specific examples include the killer systems of *S. cerevisiae* and *U. maydis* and a degenerative disease of the cultivated mushroom, *Agaricus bisporus*. Studies with the killer system of yeast (discussed below) have indicated that cytoplasmic dsRNA and nuclear genes may act in concert. By studying viruses in fungal systems that are genetically well characterized, we should gain considerable insight into nucleo-cytoplasmic interactions in the eukaryotic cell.

Fourth, evidence for replication by duplication has been obtained for at least one fungal virus. Replication by this method is consistent with adaptation for persistent infection and indeed implies that viral titer is determined by a doubling time of the virus relative to doubling time of the host cell. In experiments designed to demonstrate infectivity by these viruses, early levels of infection might remain at low titer and be difficult to demonstrate. One might also expect to find incremental differences in viral titer among cell lines infected by such viruses.

Finally, those of us who study fungal viruses refer to them as "viruses" with some reservation, since thus far these particles have proven to be infectious only through cytoplasmic exchange. Fungal viruses may prove to be commonly defective for infectivity as free particles and to be dependent upon cell-mediated transfer, in which case a new set of postulates should be devised to accommodate endogenous or plasmid-like viruses. Fungal viruses are called viruses mainly because of their morphology and nucleoprotein composition and because purified particles have been shown to contain polymerase activity and dsRNA.

LITERATURE CITED

1. **Adler, J., H. A. Wood, and R. F. Bozarth.** 1976. Virus-like particles from killer, neutral, and sensitive strains of *Saccharomyces cerevisiae*. J. Virol. **17**:472–476.
2. **Banks, G. T., K. W. Buck, E. B. Chain, F. Himmelweit, J. E. Marks, J. M. Tyler, M. Hollings, F. T. Last, and O. M. Stone.** 1968. Viruses in fungi and interferon stimulation. Nature (London) **218**:542–545.
3. **Berry, E. A., and E. A. Bevan.** 1972. A new species of double stranded RNA from yeast. Nature (London) **239**:279–280.
4. **Bozarth, R. F., and A. Goenaga.** 1976. A complex of virus-like particles from *Thielaviopsis basicola*. Proc. Am. Phytopathol. Soc. **3**:240.
5. **Bozarth, R. F., and E. H. Harley.** 1976. The electrophoretic mobility of double-stranded RNA in polyacrylamide gels as a function of molecular weight. Biochim. Biophys. Acta **432**:329–335.
6. **Bozarth, R. F., H. A. Wood, and A. Mandelbrot.** 1971. The *Penicillium stoloniferum* virus complex: two similar double-stranded RNA virus-like particles in a single cell. Virology **45**:516–523.
7. **Buck, K. W.** 1975. Replication of double-stranded RNA in particles of *Penicillium stoloniferum* S. Nucleic Acids Res. **2**:1889–1902.
8. **Buck, K. W., E. B. Chain, and F. Himmelweit.** 1971. Comparison of interferon induction in mice by purified *Penicillium chrysogenum* virus and derived double-stranded RNA. J. Gen. Virol. **12**:131–139.
9. **Buck, K. W., and G. F. Kempson-Jones.** 1973. Biophysical properties of *Penicillium stoloniferum* virus S. J. Gen. Virol. **18**:223–235.
10. **Buck, K. W., and G. F. Kempson-Jones.** 1974. Capsid polypeptides of two viruses isolated from *Penicillium stoloniferum*. J. Gen. Virol. **22**:441–445.
11. **Buck, K. W., and G. Ratti.** 1975. Biophysical and biochemical properties of two viruses isolated from *Aspergillus foetidus*. J. Gen. Virol. **27**:211–224.
12. **Buck, K. W., and G. Ratti.** 1975. A model for the

replication of double-stranded ribonucleic acid mycoviruses. Biochem. Soc. Trans. **3**:542–544.

13. **Cox, R. A., K. Kanagalingham, and E. S. Sutherland.** 1970. Double-helical character of ribonucleic acid from virus-like particles found in *Penicillium chrysogenum*. Biochem. J. **120**:549–558.

14. **Detroy, R. W.** 1976. Mycoviruses: significance in industrially and agriculturally important fungi, p. 563–564. *In* D. Schlessinger (ed.), Microbiology—1976. American Society for Microbiology, Washington, D.C.

15. **Dunkle, L. G.** 1974. Double-stranded RNA mycovirus in *Periconia circinata*. Physiol. Plant Pathol. **4**:107–116.

16. **Ellis, L. F., and W. J. Kleinschmidt.** 1967. Virus-like particles of a fraction of statolon, a mould product. Nature (London) **215**:649–650.

17. **Gomatos, P. J., and I. Tamm.** 1963. The secondary structure of reovirus RNA. Proc. Natl. Acad. Sci. U.S.A. **49**:707–714.

18. **Herring, A. J., and E. A. Bevan.** 1974. Virus-like particles associated with double-stranded RNA species found in killer and sensitive strains of yeast *Saccharomyces cerevisiae*. J. Gen. Virol. **22**:387–394.

19. **Kleinschmidt, W. J., L. F. Ellis, R. M. Van Frank, and E. B. Murphy.** 1968. Interferon stimulation by a double-stranded RNA of a mycophage in statolon preparations. Nature (London) **220**:167–168.

20. **Koltin, Y., and P. R. Day.** 1976. Inheritance of killer phenotypes and double-stranded RNA in *Ustilago maydis*. Proc. Natl. Acad. Sci. U.S.A. **73**:594–598.

21. **Koltin, Y., and P. R. Day.** 1976. Suppression of the killer phenotype in *Ustilago maydis*. Genetics **82**:629–637.

22. **Lampson, G. P., A. A. Tytell, A. K. Field, M. M. Nemes, and M. R. Hilleman.** 1967. Inducers of interferon and host resistance. I. Double-stranded RNA from extracts of *Penicillium funiculosum*. Proc. Natl. Acad. Sci. U.S.A. **58**:782–789.

23. **Lapierre, H., S. Astier-Mainfacier, and P. Cornuet.** 1971. Activité RNA polymerase associtée aux preparations purifées de virus du *Penicillium stoloniferum*. C.R. Acad. Sci. Ser. D **273**:992–994.

24. **Lemke, P. A.** 1976. Viruses of eucaryotic microorganisms. Annu. Rev. Microbiol. **30**:105–145.

25. **Lemke, P. A., and T. M. Ness.** 1970. Isolation and characterization of a double-stranded ribonucleic acid from *Penicillium chrysogenum*. J. Virol. **6**:813–819.

26. **Marino, R., K. N. Saksena, M. Schuler, J. E. Mayfield, and P. A. Lemke.** 1976. Double-stranded ribonucleic acid in *Agaricus bisporus*. Appl. Environ. Microbiol. **31**:433–438.

27. **Moffitt, E. M., and R. M. Lister.** 1975. Application of a serological screening test for detecting double-stranded RNA mycoviruses. Phytopathology **65**:851–859.

28. **Molin, G., and H. Lapierre.** 1973. L'acide nucleique des virus de champignons: cas de virus de l'*Agaricus bisporus*. Ann. Phytopathol. **5**:233–240.

29. **Nash, C. H., R. J. Douthart, L. F. Ellis, M. M. Van Frank, J. B. Burnett, and P. A. Lemke.** 1973. On the mycophage of *Penicillium chrysogenum*. Can. J. Microbiol. **19**:97–103.

30. **Powell, H. M., C. G. Culbertson, J. M. McGuire, M. M. Hoehn, and L. A. Baker.** 1962. A filtrate with chemoprophylactic and chemotherapeutic action against MM and Semliki Forest Virus in mice. Antibiot. Chemother. **2**:432–434.

31. **Ratti, G., and K. W. Buck.** 1972. Virus particles in *Aspergillus foetidus*: a multicomponent system. J. Gen. Virol. **14**:165–175.

32. **Saksena, K. N.** 1975. Isolation and large-scale purification of mushroom viruses. Dev. Ind. Microbiol. **16**:134–144.

33. **Shope, R. E.** 1953. An antiviral substance from *Penicillium funiculosum*. I. Effect upon infection in mice with swine influenza virus and Columbia SK encephalomyelitis virus. J. Exp. Med. **97**:601–625.

34. **Vodkin, M., F. Katterman, and G. R. Fink.** 1974. yeast killer mutants with altered double-stranded ribonucleic acid. J. Bacteriol. **117**:681–686.

35. **Wood, H. A.** 1973. Viruses with double-stranded RNA genomes. J. Gen. Virol. **20**:61–85.

36. **Wood, H. A., and R. F. Bozarth.** 1972. Properties of virus-like particles of *Penicillium chrysogenum*: one double-stranded RNA molecule per particle. Virology **47**:604–609.

37. **Wood, H. A., and R. F. Bozarth.** 1973. Heterokaryon transfer of virus-like particles and a cytoplasmically inherited determinant in *Ustilago maydis*. Phytopathology **63**:1019–1021.

38. **Wood, H. A., R. F. Bozarth, and P. B. Mislivec.** 1971. Virus-like particles associated with an isolate of *Penicillium brevi-compactum*. Virology **44**:592–598.

Genetics of a Double-Stranded RNA Plasmid: the Killer Character of *Saccharomyces cerevisiae*

REED B. WICKNER AND MICHAEL J. LEIBOWITZ

Laboratory of Biochemical Pharmacology, National Institute of Arthritis, Metabolism and Digestive Diseases, Bethesda, Maryland 20014

KILLER YEAST

Killer strains of yeast secrete a toxin which is lethal to sensitive strains, but to which the killers themselves are immune (4, 5, 12, 22; M. Makower and E. A. Bevan, Proc. Int. Congr. Genet., 11th, **1**:202, 1963; R. G. E. Palfree and H. Bussey, in preparation). Figure 1 shows colonies of a killer strain preventing growth of a lawn of a sensitive strain on a plate containing methylene blue for contrast.

We denote phenotypes as K^+ or K^- for ability or inability to kill and R^+ or R^- for resistance or sensitivity to the toxin. Wild-type killers are K^+R^+, and wild-type nonkillers (sensitives) are K^-R^-.

When wild-type killers and wild-type nonkillers are mated, the diploids formed are killers (killing is dominant), and all meiotic segregants are killers (14). Since a single chromosomal gene difference between the haploid parents should segregate 2:2 in meiosis, Somers and Bevan (14) proposed that a nonchromosomal genome (killer plasmid) is responsible for the killer phenotype. This was confirmed when strains carrying differently marked killer plasmids were mated and the diploids formed showed mitotic segregation of the parental phenotypes (2). Furthermore, killers may be efficiently converted to nonkillers by such nonmutagenic treatments as growth in low concentrations of cycloheximide (8) or at 37°C (16). These cured strains behave like wild-type nonkillers in crosses with wild-type killers.

dsRNA AND VIRUS-LIKE PARTICLES

Figure 2 shows slab gel electrophoresis of double-stranded RNA (dsRNA) isolated from various strains. Bevan and co-workers (1) and Vodkin et al. (15) first correlated the species called M with the presence of the killer plasmid. This 1.4×10^6-dalton dsRNA is present in all wild-type killers and absent in wild-type nonkillers. The larger L and XL species are present in almost all strains examined so far, regardless of killer phenotype (1, 15, 19, 20).

No strains have been reported to carry the M species but not the L or XL species. Thus, the role, if any, of L or XL in the killer character remains unknown.

The L and M dsRNA's are found encapsulated in virus-like particles about 40 nm in diameter (3, 9). However, infection with the isolated virus has not been reported; the virus is transmitted only by mating. The identity of the genetically defined killer plasmid and the M dsRNA has not been proven beyond doubt, but seems likely.

CHROMOSOMAL GENES ESSENTIAL FOR MAINTENANCE AND EXPRESSION OF THE KILLER PLASMID

If the M dsRNA is indeed the killer plasmid, it is only large enough to code for 100,000 daltons of protein. It is reasonable to expect that such a plasmid may utilize host (chromosomal) genes in its replication and expression. We have already identified 14 such genes (see below). It is also reasonable to assume that such chromosomal genes may have host functions, unrelated to the killer plasmid. This expectation has also been realized in several cases.

There are two classes of chromosomal genes which the killer plasmid uses: one class is termed *mak* (for *ma*intenance of *k*iller); the other comprises the *kex* and *rex* genes (for *k*iller *ex*pression and *r*esistance *ex*pression).

We have isolated mutants in nine chromosomal genes (called *mak1* through *mak9*) which are needed for maintenance or replication of the cytoplasmic killer genome (17, 20; Leibowitz and Wickner, unpublished data). Mutants in two other such genes have been described by others (8, 14; E. A. Bevan, J. Somers, and K. Theivendirarajah, Abstr. 11th Int. Bot. Congr., Seattle, Wash., 1969, p. 14). A *mak* mutant has the K^-R^- phenotype and yields only K^-R^- progeny in crosses with wild-type nonkillers. In crosses with killers, *mak* mutations segregate as single recessive chromosomal gene defects. The *mak* mutants invariably lose the M

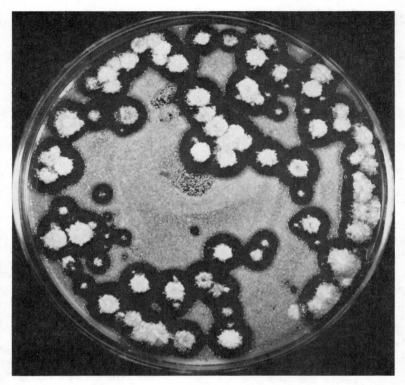

FIG. 1. *Killer phenomenon. An agar plate buffered at pH 4.7 and containing methylene blue to stain dead cells is seeded with a lawn of a sensitive strain. Colonies of a killer strain growing on another plate were replica-plated onto the lawn, and the plate shown was incubated for 3 days at 20°C. A clear zone can be seen around each killer colony.*

dsRNA, but retain the L and XL species (e.g., dsRNA of a *mak1* strain in Fig. 2; 1, 15, 20).

Most of the *mak* genes have been located on the genetic map of yeast (Fig. 3; 20). Note that *m* and *pets* are genes of the *mak* type first described by others (8, 14; Bevan et al., Abstr. 11th Int. Bot. Congr., 1969, p. 14).

Mutations in the *pets* gene result in three phenotypes: (i) loss of the killer plasmid (Bevan et al., see above) and the M dsRNA (15); (ii) inability to grow on a nonfermentable carbon source (Bevan et al., see above) and loss of mitochondrial DNA (M. J. Leibowitz and R. B. Wickner, in preparation); and (iii) temperature sensitivity for growth (20). The *mak1–3* mutation also results in temperature sensitivity for growth (20).

Two chromosomal genes called *kex* (for *k*iller *ex*pression) are needed for secretion of an active toxin, but not for resistance to the toxin or for maintenance of the killer plasmid (17, 19). Mutants in either gene are recessive to wild type and segregate 2 K⁻R⁺:2 K⁺R⁺ in crosses with wild-type killers or nonkillers. The *kex1* and *kex2* strains carry the M dsRNA (Fig. 2; 19), consistent with the notion that this is the cytoplasmic killer genome. The *kex1* gene is on chromosome VII, and *kex2* is located on chromosome XIV (Fig. 3).

Mutants in *kex2* always show two defects in the sexual cycle of yeast: (i) an α-mating type-specific mating defect and (ii) an inability of homozygous *kex2* diploids to complete meiosis and spore formation (10). In the mating reaction, yeast of each mating type secrete pheromones which arrest cells of the other mating type in the G_1 phase of the cell cycle and make them elongate in preparation for mating (6). The *kex2* strains of the α mating type (which cannot mate) do not secrete α factor or respond to *a* factor I, but respond normally to *a* factor II (11). The biochemical lesion in *kex2* mutants is not yet known.

At least one gene, called *rex*, is needed for resistance *ex*pression, but not for toxin production or for plasmid replication (17).

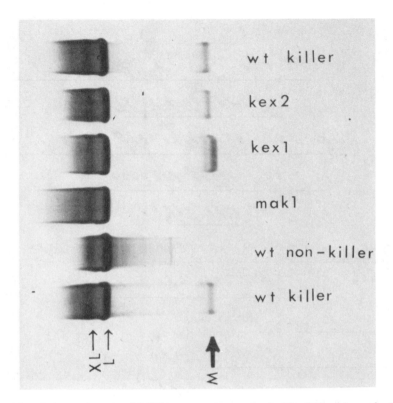

FIG. 2. *Acrylamide gel electrophoresis of dsRNA preparations stained with ethidium bromide. Electrophoresis was from top to bottom.* $M \rightarrow 1.7 \times 10^6$; $L \rightarrow 3.0 \times 10^6$; $XL \rightarrow 3.8 \times 10^6$.

KILLER PLASMID MUTANTS

Several types of killer plasmid (virus) mutants are known. Two types are of special interest.

"Suppressive" killer mutants first described by Somers (13) and named after the analogous mutants of the mitochondrial genome (7) are K^-R^- plasmid mutants which, on mating with wild-type K^+R^+ strains, yield only K^-R^- diploids. All meiotic progeny are also K^-R^- and have the same "suppressive" character as the original mutant. Vodkin et al. (15) found that these mutants lack M dsRNA and have a new, smaller dsRNA species (called S) which is presumably a deletion mutant of M. These mutants are analogous to the defective interfering particles described in many animal viruses. They provide the strongest evidence to date that the M dsRNA is the killer plasmid.

A second kind of plasmid (or virus) mutant is called "diploid dependent" because it has a normal phenotype in diploid strains and a defective phenotype as a haploid (18). These unusual mutants are restored to normalcy by mating with any other strain, even one carrying the same defective plasmid. Meiosis and sporulation, however, yield an apparently random assortment of defective phenotypes in the haploid progeny of a single diploid K^+R^+ clone. The molecular basis of this phenomenon is unknown.

KILLER REPLICATION BYPASS

Often, on crossing a *mak7* strain with a wild-type killer, a predominantly K^-R^- haploid segregant has a stable K^+R^+ sector (R. B. Wickner and M. J. Leibowitz, Fed. Proc. **35**:1737, 1976). These killer sectors carry the *mak7* mutation as do the rest of the colony, but are killers nonetheless and carry the M dsRNA. These strains have acquired a dominant change (*KRB*, for *k*iller *r*eplication *b*ypass) which segregates as if it were a chromosomal change. This change results in the bypass of three different mutations in distant plasmid replication genes (*mak7-1*, *pets-1*, and *pets-2*). *KRB* changes are all tightly centromere linked and are not translational suppressors.

KRB changes have two unusual properties. First, growth of *mak7-1 KRB* (K^+R^+) strains at 37°C or in low cycloheximide (treatments

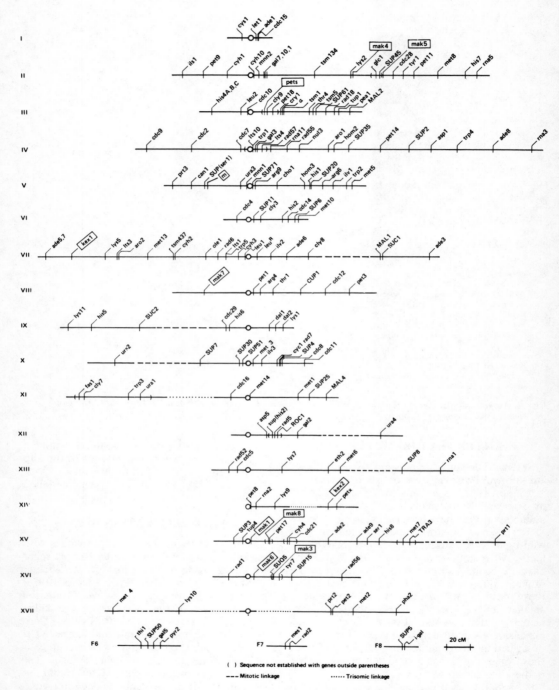

FIG. 3. *Genetic map of* Saccharomyces cerevisiae *(emphasizing the genes involved in maintenance of the killer plasmid (*m, pets, *and* mak1 *through* mak8*) and in expression of killing ability (* kex1 *and* kex2*). Most of the remainder of the genetic map is from Mortimer and Hawthorne (11).*

which cure the wild-type killer plasmid) results in K⁻R⁻ strains which have lost the *KRB* change as well. Second, mating two strains with opposite mating types but both *mak7-1 KRB* (K⁺R⁺; same killer plasmid) yields mostly 2 K⁺R⁺:2 K⁻R⁻ segregation instead of the expected 4 K⁺R⁺:0 segregation (Wickner and Leibowitz, Fed. Proc. **35**:1737, 1976). The explanation for these phenomena is unclear, but conceivably *KRB* could be the association of the killer dsRNA plasmid with a centromere (Wickner and Leibowitz, submitted for publication).

In summary, the study of the killer character of yeast should reveal some general properties of dsRNA genomes (reviewed in 21), such as their replication and expression and their relation to the host in these processes.

LITERATURE CITED

1. **Bevan, E. A., A. J. Herring, and D. J. Mitchell.** 1973. Preliminary characterization of two species of *ds* RNA in yeast and their relationship to the "killer" character. Nature (London) **245**:81–86.
2. **Bevan, E. A., and J. M. Somers.** 1969. Somatic segregation of the killer (k) and neutral (n) cytoplasmic genetic determinants in yeast. Genet. Res. **14**:71–77.
3. **Buck, K. W., P. Lhoas, and B. K. Street.** 1973. Virus particles in yeast. Biochem. Soc. Trans. **1**:1141–1142.
4. **Bussey, H.** 1972. Effects of yeast killer factor on sensitive cells. Nature (London) New Biol. **235**:73–75.
5. **Bussey, H., D. Sherman, and J. M. Somers.** 1973. Action of yeast killer factor: a resistant mutant with sensitive spheroplasts. J. Bacteriol. **113**:1193–1197.
6. **Duntze, W., D. Stötzler, E. Bücking-Throm, and S. Kalbitzer.** 1973. Purification and partial characterization of α-factor, a mating-type specific inhibitor of cell reproduction in *Saccharomyces cerevisiae*. Eur. J. Biochem. **35**:357–365.
7. **Ephrussi, B., H. de Margerie-Hottinguer, and H. Roman.** 1955. Suppressiveness: a new factor in the genetic determinism of the synthesis of respiratory enzymes in yeast. Proc. Natl. Acad. Sci. U.S.A. **41**:1065–1071.
8. **Fink, G. R., and C. A. Styles.** 1972. Curing of a killer factor in *Saccharomyces cerevisiae*. Proc. Natl. Acad. Sci. U.S.A. **69**:2846–2849.
9. **Herring, A. J., and E. A. Bevan.** 1974. Virus-like particles associated with the double-stranded RNA species found in killer and sensitive strains of the yeast *Saccharomyces cerevisiae*. J. Gen. Virol. **22**:387–394.
10. **Leibowitz, M. J., and R. B. Wickner.** 1976. A chromosomal gene required for killer plasmid expression, mating, and spore maturation in *Saccharomyces cerevisiae*. Proc. Natl. Acad. Sci. U.S.A. **73**:2061–2065.
11. **Mortimer, R. K., and D. C. Hawthorne.** 1975. Genetic mapping in yeast. Methods Cell Biol. **11**:221–233.
12. **Philliskirk, G., and T. W. Young.** 1975. The occurrence of killer character in yeasts of various genera. Antonie van Leeuwenhoek J. Microbiol. Serol. **41**:147–151.
13. **Somers, J. M.** 1973. Isolation of suppressive mutants from killer and neutral strains of *Saccharomyces cerevisiae*. Genetics **74**:571–579.
14. **Somers, J. M., and E. A. Bevan.** 1968. The inheritance of the killer character in yeast. Genet. Res. **13**:71–83.
15. **Vodkin, M., F. Katterman, and G. R. Fink.** 1974. Yeast killer mutants with altered double-stranded ribonucleic acid. J. Bacteriol. **117**:681–686.
16. **Wickner, R. B.** 1974. "Killer character" of *Saccharomyces cerevisiae*: curing by growth at elevated temperatures. J. Bacteriol. **117**:1356–1357.
17. **Wickner, R. B.** 1974. Chromosomal and nonchromosomal mutations affecting the "killer character" of *Saccharomyces cerevisiae*. Genetics **76**:423–432.
18. **Wickner, R. B.** 1976. Mutants of the killer plasmid of *Saccharomyces cerevisiae* dependent on chromosomal diploidy for expression and maintenance. Genetics **82**:273–285.
19. **Wickner, R. B., and M. J. Leibowitz.** 1976. Two chromosomal genes required for killing expression in killer strains of *Saccharomyces cerevisiae*. Genetics **82**:429–444.
20. **Wickner, R. B., and M. J. Leibowitz.** 1976. Chromosomal genes essential for replication of a double-stranded RNA plasmid of *Saccharomyces cerevisiae*: the killer character of yeast. J. Mol. Biol. **105**:427–443.
21. **Wood, H. A.** 1973. Viruses with double-stranded RNA genomes. J. Gen. Virol. **20**:61–85.
22. **Woods, D. R., and E. A. Bevan.** 1968. Studies on the nature of the killer factor produced by *Saccharomyces cerevisiae*. J. Gen. Microbiol. **51**:115–126.

The Killer System in Paramecium—Kappa and Its Viruses[1]

JOHN R. PREER, JR.

Department of Zoology, Indiana University, Bloomington, Indiana 47401

BACTERIAL ENDOSYMBIONTS OF PARAMECIUM

Much of the work covered in this paper has been recently reviewed by me and my co-workers (5). Only papers not included in or subsequent to that review will be cited here.

Bacterial intracellular symbionts are common in the eukaryotes. In the ciliated protozoa they are especially numerous. For example, in many localities endosymbionts are found in most freshly collected specimens of the *Paramecium aurelia* complex of species. Most have lost all capacity for infection and are transmitted strictly by heredity. Many confer the killer character upon their hosts, which become resistant killers, liberating a toxin (usually the symbiont itself) that is capable of killing ciliates free from the symbionts. Many others produce no toxin, and their hosts are sensitive non-killers. Effects on viability of the host are usually not observed. An exception is the bacterial endosymbiont omikron, found in *Euplotes aediculatus*, which is essential for the survival of its host (3). Degenerate changes in the bacteria are common: most are slow growing and have lost their capacity to grow outside their hosts. One has been shown to respire. Flagella may be retained, but usually do not result in motility. Nucleoids are found in some strains (3), but are not observed in most. Genome size is small, a bit less than 10^9 daltons, and it is reported that multiple genomes are found (8). Great diversity of forms exists. The commonest bacteria in the 14 species of paramecia which make up the *P. aurelia* complex belong to the genus *Caedobacter*. Strains of kappa (*Caedobacter taeniospiralis*) have refractile inclusions (R bodies), are killers, and are found in species 2 and 4 of the *P. aurelia* complex. Many rather different strains of kappa have been found, and work on DNA hybridization by Quackenbush (6) indicates that *C. taeniospiralis* (kappa) actually consists of more than one species. Table 1 lists the endosymbionts described in the *P. aurelia* complex.

DEFECTIVE PHAGES AND R BODIES

Phages have been found only in kappa. All observations are consistent with the view that each strain of kappa bears a defective phage carried in a prophage form. Infection has not been demonstrated for any of the phages, and their identification is based on their structure as seen by electron microscopy and on their chemical composition. Spontaneous induction in a small fraction of the kappas leads to a great increase in phage genomes and death of the kappas, but not their immediate lysis. The production of R bodies, usually one in each individual kappa, also accompanies induction. The R body is a ribbon of protein wound into a tight roll. Induced kappas bearing R bodies are the toxic particles liberated into the medium by killer paramecia. When induced kappas find their way into the food vacuoles of sensitive paramecia lacking kappa (4), the kappas lyse, and the R bodies suddenly unroll into long (10 to 15 μm) ribbons that penetrate the food vacuole membrane and extend into the cytoplasm. This process is thought to play a role in the killing of sensitive paramecia. The chemistry of the toxin is unknown, but it is thought to be a protein associated with the R bodies. Singler (7) has produced data indicating that the R-body protein and the phage coats are serologically related. It is likely that the R-body protein is coded by the phage DNA.

The phage DNA in some strains, such as stocks 7 and 562, is found in icosahedral phage particles. The phages of 562 have been isolated and found to contain protein and about 10^8 daltons of DNA. In strain 1039 the DNA is never enclosed in protein coats, and empty capsids are produced. In stock 51 capsids are not seen, although helical structures thought to be unassembled capsid protein are found. Here, the DNA takes the form of covalently closed circles (CCC DNA) about 14 μm in length (1), approximately one-fourth the amount of the DNA in a single 562 phage. The forms con-

[1] Contribution no. 1049 from the Department of Zoology, Indiana University, Bloomington.

stitute an interesting series because they vary from well-formed but apparently defective phages (stock 562) to forms which seem very similar to typical bacterial plasmids (stock 51). Since all produce R bodies, and since the R bodies of 562 and 51 appear to be serologically related (Singler, personal communication), there seems to be little doubt that the phages of 562 and the plasmids of 51 are phylogenetically related.

A mutant of 51 kappa, designated 51m43, was isolated after X irradiation by Widmayer (9). Although up to 40% of strain 51 kappa particles may bear R bodies, 51m43 produces R bodies with great rarity. Hence, 51m43 does not kill sensitive paramecia. It does, however, retain its capacity to render its host paramecia resistant to 51 toxin. Dilts (2) has shown that the densities of the chromosomal DNA of 51 and 51m43 kappa are indistinguishable (1.700 g/cm^3), and that the plasmid DNAs of the two strains are also alike (1.698 g/cm^3). Quackenbush (6) has found that the chromosomal DNAs of 51 and 51m43 kappas hybridize with high efficiency. Dilts has also found that, unlike 51, which has plasmids of about 2.8×10^7 daltons, 51m43 has plasmid DNA consisting of CCC DNA of about 2.9×10^7, 5.9×10^7, 9.7×10^7, and 11.8×10^7 daltons, and thus appears to be concatenated. Whether the 51m43 mutation is in the genome of kappa or in the plasmid is unknown.

Stock 51 causes sensitive paramecia to acquire prelethal cytoplasmic blebs or humps. Mutant 51m1, which was derived from 51, was originally thought to be a mutant of 51 kappa. It causes sensitive paramecia to spin before death. The R bodies of 51m1, however, are rather different in morphology from the R bodies of 51, and the kappas show serological and morphological differences as well. More recently, Dilts (2) has found that the buoyant density of the DNA from 51 kappa (1.700 g/cm^3) is distinguishable from that of 51m1 kappa (1.703 g/cm^3). Furthermore, 51 kappa DNA does not hybridize well with 51m1 kappa DNA (6). Therefore, it is likely that 51m1 is not a mutant of 51 kappa but was present as a second related, but rather different, symbiont in the original isolation of stock 51 paramecia.

Many years ago, sublines of stock 51 were derived that produced no toxin and were sensitive to killers. They were shown to contain symbionts, which were designated pi; pi-like particles were also found in stock 139, a stock which once killed like 51. The origin of pi has only recently become clear. Dilts (2) showed that the buoyant density of the DNA of pi in stock 51 (1.694 g/cm^3) is quite different from that of kappa in 51 (1.700 g/cm^3). Furthermore, she

TABLE 1. *Bacterial symbionts in the* Paramecium aurelia *complex*

Common name	Bionomial name	*P. aurelia* species	Characteristic
Kappa	*Caedobacter taeniospiralis*	2, 4	R-body killers
Mu	*C. conjugatus*	1, 2, 8	Mate killers
Nu	*C. falsus*	2, 5	Nonkillers
Gamma	*C. minuta*	8	Killers; no R
Lambda	*Lyticus flagellatum*	4, 8	Rapid-lysis killers
Sigma	*L. sinuosum*	2	Rapid-lysis killers
Alpha	*Cytophaga caryophila*	2	Macro-nuclear
Delta	*Tectobacter vulgaris*	1, 2, 4, 6, 8	Nonkillers

showed that, whereas the plasmids of stock 51 kappa have a molecular weight of 2.8×10^7, the plasmids from pi of stock 51 have molecular weights of 0.3×10^7, 2.3×10^7, and 4.5×10^7 (2). Quackenbush (6) confirmed these differences in density and found that they apply to pi from stock 139 as well. Quackenbush also found that the DNA of stock 51 kappa does not hybridize well with the DNA from pi. Thus, the original stock 51 isolate most likely contained a large number of typical hump-killing kappas and a small number of spinner kappas and pis. The individual particles have been segregated at later times in the laboratory. Of 51m43, 51m1, and pi, only 51m43 appears to be a true mutant.

EVOLUTIONARY SIGNIFICANCE

Symbionts are often lost from their hosts in the laboratory. Rapid multiplication of the paramecia, presence of antibiotics, unfavorable media, and extremes of temperature can easily cause elimination of the symbionts. It is likely that similar losses occur in nature. If so, then what principles of population genetics act to maintain the symbionts in such high frequency in natural habitats? The possibility that the losses are balanced by new infections is unlikely for most of the symbionts. Alpha is an exception, for it is highly infectious through the medium. Infection of the other symbionts has been brought about in the laboratory in but a few cases and only by very high concentrations of symbionts extracted from cells, a situation surely not encountered in nature. No new infections by free-living bacteria have ever been found in the laboratory, although there has been ample opportunity to detect new infections during many years of routine stock maintenance. The possibility that transfer at conjugation plays a significant role in spread has been shown to be unlikely by Landis (personal communication). Therefore, we are led to the conclusion that loss is most probably balanced by natural selection; i.e., symbiont-bearing cells contribute more progeny to each succeeding generation than do symbiont-free cells. We know little about the factors responsible for such selection, but in the case of the killer trait it is likely that killing itself plays a role, the occasional death of a sensitive paramecium balancing the occasional loss of symbionts. Since only a single toxic particle can kill a sensitive paramecium, no threshold concentration for killing exists. Furthermore, Landis (personal communication) found paramecia in nature in sufficient concentrations to produce killing, judged by their behavior in the laboratory. In the case of symbionts which do not kill, such as nu, pi, and delta, it is assumed that they bestow unknown advantages upon their hosts. So we are presented with a picture of endosymbionts which are normally transmitted by heredity, are rarely established anew, and which very likely benefit their hosts.

How long have the symbionts inhabited their hosts? If new infections occur only rarely, it follows that the symbiotic relations may well be very old. A further clue to the answer to the question comes from a consideration of the geographical distribution of the symbionts. Spinner killers with characteristic kappa, R bodies, and phages are known from North America, Scotland, and eastern and western continental Europe. Hump-type killers (like stock 51) with characteristic R bodies have been collected in Indiana, Florida, Panama, Japan, and Australia. Gamma endosymbionts are indistinguishable in collections from Florida and Uganda. Numerous other cases illustrate the cosmopolitan distribution of specific kinds of killers. It is not likely that the similar forms in diverse localities represent separate and new infections from free-living progenitors, for the reasons stated above and also because no similar free-living forms are known. It appears more likely that the distributions are to be explained by single origins, followed by wide dispersal of the endosymbiont-bearing paramecia themselves. Paramecia do not form cysts, cannot withstand drying, and

cannot survive seawater. It is not possible to rule out with certainty transfer by humans on ships, by waterfowl, or by aquatic flying insects. However, such means of transfer appear dubious to me. If these explanations of widespread distribution are rejected, one is left only with the possibility that the endosymbionts are of very ancient origin and that they were transported to their present locations during geological times when the continental land masses were adjacent, or at least connected by land bridges. Such times must have been as far back as the early Cenozoic or late Mesozoic era. If so, then the seemingly delicate balance between the 51-type plasmid, 51 kappa, and 51 paramecia must be older than man himself and was well established when evolution of the mammals was taking place. It is unfortunate that evolutionary hypotheses can rarely be proved, but the picture just presented seems to me more likely than others. If, indeed, it is true, then Sonneborn's original view that kappa is an intrinsic organelle of paramecium may be more nearly accurate than the view that it is merely a parasite.

ACKNOWLEDGMENT

This work was supported by Public Health Service grant GM 20038 from the National Institute of General Medical Sciences.

LITERATURE CITED

1. **Dilts, J. A.** 1976. Covalently closed, circular DNA in kappa endosymbionts of Paramecium. Genet. Res. **27**:161–170.
2. **Dilts, J. A.** 1977. Studies on chromosomal and extrachromosomal DNA from four bacterial endosymbionts derived from stock 51 of *Paramecium tetraurelia*. J. Bacteriol. **129**:888–894.
3. **Heckman, K.** 1975. Omikron, ein essentieler Endosymbiont von *Euplotes aediculatis*. J. Protozool. **22**:97–104.
4. **Preer, J. R., Jr.** 1976. The hereditary symbionts of *Paramecium aurelia*. Symp. Soc. Exp. Biol. **29**:125–144.
5. **Preer, J. R., Jr., L. B. Preer, and A. Jurand.** 1974. Kappa and other endosymbionts in *Paramecium aurelia*. Bacteriol. Rev. **38**:113–163.
6. **Quackenbush, R. L.** 1977. Phylogenetic relationships of bacterial endosymbionts of *Paramecium aurelia*: polynucleotide sequence relationships of 51 kappa and its mutants. J. Bacteriol. **129**:895–900.
7. **Singler, M. J.** 1974. Antigenic studies on the relationship of the viral capeid, R body, and toxin of kappa in stock 562, *Paramecium aurelia*. Genetics **77**:s60–61.
8. **Soldo, A. T.** 1974. Intracellular particles in *Paramecium aurelia*, p. 375–442. *In* W. van Wagtendonk (ed.), Paramecium: a current survey. Elsevier Press, Amsterdam.
9. **Widmayer, D. J.** 1965. A non-killer resistant kappa and its bearing on the interpretation of kappa in *Paramecium aurelia*. Genetics **51**:613–623.

Virus-Like Particles in the Amoeboflagellate
Naegleria gruberi EG$_S$

F. L. SCHUSTER AND T. H. DUNNEBACKE[1]

Department of Biology, Brooklyn College, Brooklyn, New York 11210, and Virus Laboratory,
University of California, Berkeley, California 94720

The study of viruses and virus-like elements among invertebrates has generally lagged behind the extensive research efforts directed toward virus infections of vertebrate cells. With the exception of insects, where a clear threat exists because of their role as vectors of viruses infecting plants and animals and where the search for viruses as a means of biological control of insect pests has been undertaken, the majority of studies dealing with "viruses" in invertebrate phyla have been restricted to sporadic and largely descriptive accounts based on preliminary observations. Indeed, because of the lack of evidence for infectivity in these accounts, the term "virus-like particles" (VLP) is to be preferred. Heightened interest in pollution of coastal waters with human fecal wastes and the chance that aquatic filter-feeders might concentrate potentially harmful viruses has provided some impetus for critical examination of invertebrate-virus associations in nature, especially among protozoans pathogenic or potentially pathogenic to humans and domestic animals.

In this review, we focus attention on a soil protozoan, a strain of the amoeboflagellate *Naegleria gruberi*, found to harbor VLP having an apparent intracellular developmental cycle coupled with a mode of VLP transmission by means of a unique packaging and release mechanism. A distinct advantage of this protozoan-virus system as an experimental model lies in the ability to induce VLP in the amoebae with all the attendent opportunities for experimentation (use of inhibitors of nucleic acid and protein syntheses, application of labeled precursor compounds, manipulation of culture conditions, etc.) to dissect VLP development in *N. gruberi*.

[1] Present address: Viral and Rickettsial Disease Laboratory, State of California Department of Health, Berkeley, Calif. 94704.

THE AMOEBA

N. gruberi is an amoeboflagellate whose life cycle includes a trophic (feeding) amoeboid stage, a flagellated swimming (dispersive) stage, and a thick-walled (resistant) cyst stage, related to one another as follows:

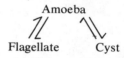

Feeding and mitosis are restricted to the amoeboid stage; the flagellate stage is transitory and occurs, or can be induced, through dilution of the growth substrate. Cysts develop upon depletion of the food supply, or under conditions of desiccation. The VLP work has been done on one particular strain of *N. gruberi*, designated EG$_S$, isolated from a California soil sample.

VLP INDUCTION

EG$_S$ amoebae can be grown axenically in a rich medium containing yeast extract-peptone-liver supplemented with fetal calf serum. Under the conditions of axenic cultivation, amoebae exhibit no evidence of VLP when examined microscopically. Transfer of amoebae to a mono-bacterial culture medium (dilute medium containing peptone-yeast extract-glucose plus an edible bacterium) results in the appearance, over a period of 2 to 6 days, of VLP, first in the nuclear compartment of the cells and later in the cytoplasm. With depletion of the bacterial food supply, extensive evidence of VLP presence is seen in the amoebae, with many of the cells exhibiting obvious degenerative changes. Encystment, normal at this stage in bacteria-fed populations of *Naegleria* amoebae, is virtually nonexistent (<1%). Flagellate formation, induced by washing of VLP-containing cultures, is also considerably reduced below

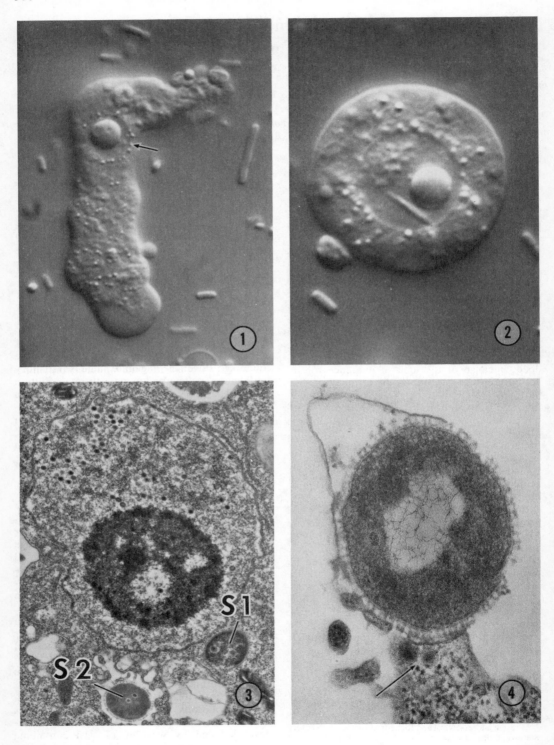

normal levels. Agar plates of such bacteria-fed EG$_S$ cultures contain extensive debris which, when stained with phosphotungstic acid and examined in an electron microscope, can be seen to contain spheres resembling VLP in size and morphology.

VLP DEVELOPMENT

Our initial studies of development were based on examination of sectioned material in a transmission electron microscope (4–8). It is possible, however, to recognize certain features of VLP development with a light microscope. After about 2 days of feeding on bacteria, some cells (approximately 5%) exhibit a granular region in the nucleoplasm (arrow in Fig. 1) between the large, central nucleolus and the nuclear envelope. In older cultures (3 to 6 days), cells show enlarged nuclei and assume a rounded shape (Fig. 2). The granular nucleoplasmic region is more obvious, and there are often splinter-shaped rods in the nucleoplasm. These cells ultimately swell, causing rupture of the plasma membrane and, in most instances, releasing intact a nucleus filled with VLP.

Electron microscopy permits a more critical analysis of these developments. Nuclei exhibit VLP (ca. 100 nm in diameter) in the nucleoplasm (Fig. 3) and, in early stages of development, a densely granular generative region. This complex of particles and generative material is what is visible at the light-microscopic level. VLP pass out from the nucleus through tubes on the nuclear envelope and, once in the cytoplasm, are difficult to resolve until such time as a membranous complex forms de novo about the VLP (S1 in Fig. 3). This membrane is different from any of the amoeba cytoplasmic membranes and comes to enclose not only the VLP but also a region of granularity. Ultimately, these membranous bodies condense into spheres having a characteristic outer fringe (S2 in Fig. 3) and come to lie in vacuoles from which they are ejected into the extracellular space. Once released from the amoebae, the spheres appear to attach themselves to the plasma membranes of other amoebae (Fig. 4), a process that may involve the peripheral fringe. Dense masses approximately the diameter of VLP have been observed in the amoeba cytoplasm at the point of contact with the sphere, suggesting passage of VLP from the sphere into the amoeba (arrow in Fig. 4). We have reported elsewhere (5; Schuster and Dunnebacke, submitted for publication) the presence of papillae in the wall of the sphere through which VLP passage might conceivably occur.

As already noted, in VLP-containing cultures few cysts form and the cysts that have been examined in an electron microscope never exhibit VLP. Similarly, flagellation of amoebae, which can be in excess of 90% in normal *N. gruberi* strains, is much reduced in VLP-containing populations; no amoeba containing VLP has been observed to undergo this morphogenetic change.

SOURCE OF VLP

Because of the apparent association of substrate bacteria with induction of VLP in amoebae, our initial assumption was that VLP were derived from the bacterial food organisms.

FIG. 1. *Light micrograph of typical trophic EG$_S$ amoeba. The nucleus contains a large central nucleolus; the nuclear envelope is outlined by refractile (lipid) particles. An arrow points to a small granular region in the nucleoplasm, representing incipient VLP material. Bacteria can be seen in the vicinity of the amoeba. Living cell photographed with microflash and interference-contrast optics. ×4,800.*

FIG. 2. *Light micrograph of rounded EG$_S$ amoeba with clear evidence of VLP material in the nucleoplasm. The nucleolus is still obvious but the granular region has expanded, as has nuclear volume. Note presence of a rodlet, typical of VLP-containing cells, within the nucleoplasm. Optics as in Fig. 1. ×7,800.*

FIG. 3. *Electron micrograph of VLP-containing nucleus, roughly comparable in stage of development to nucleus of cell in Fig. 1. VLP measuring ca. 100 nm are scattered in nucleoplasm. At S1 is a VLP surrounded by granular material and almost completely enclosed by a forming membrane. At S2, a VLP-containing sphere with typical fringe is seen lying within a vacuole. ×17,500.*

FIG. 4. *Electron micrograph showing an ejected sphere (similar to S2 in Fig. 3). Note its apparent attachment at the amoeba plasma membrane and the presence (arrow) of dense concentrations (VLP) on the cytoplasmic side of the membrane. The nature of the fringe can be seen clearly. ×57,000.*

The use, however, of a wide variety of bacterial species suitable as food organisms (various strains of *Aerobacter aerogenes* and *Escherichia coli*) also led to VLP induction, which suggests that the bacteria were not the source of the VLP. More recently, we have found that treatment of axenic cultures of EG$_S$ with 5-bromodeoxyuridine results in the appearance of VLP, lending support to the view that VLP are latent in the amoebae and that their development and the subsequent lysing of amoebae is initiated by some modification of growth conditions. Of interest is the apparent similarity in induction of the EG$_S$-VLP system and various vertebrate cell lines that harbor latent viruses inducible through the use of 5-bromodeoxyuridine (1, 3).

ECOLOGICAL IMPLICATIONS

Species of *Naegleria* and other soil amoebae are an important component of soil fauna (2, 9). Depending upon soil conditions, amoebae may exist in the trophic stage, when bacterial food organisms are abundant, or in the cystic stage, when scarcity of food or moisture serves to limit the population. In attempting to make some ecological generalizations from the EG$_S$-VLP system, it might be suggested that temperate viral infections in soil protozoans (and other soil protists) may serve as a density-dependent mechanism for limitation of the predator (amoeba) population since, as the numbers of amoebae increase because of excess bacterial food, two consequences might be expected: (i) activation of a latent infection, and (ii) transmission of VLP through the high-density amoeba population. This, in turn, would permit the bacterial population to increase. It would appear that some critical density of amoebae is needed for spread of VLP; we have found that, when amoebae are cultivated in sparse populations, induction of particles is delayed, and relatively few cells exhibit the characteristic VLP cycle typical of dense populations. Thus, virus infections similar to the EG$_S$-VLP system reviewed here may, in conjunction with purely physical factors, have a role in the fluctuation of populations of soil protozoans and, perhaps, other soil protists.

ACKNOWLEDGMENTS

This research was supported by Public Health Service grants AI 12058 and AI 10845 from the National Institute of Allergy and Infectious Diseases.

LITERATURE CITED

1. **Aaronson, S. A., G. J. Todaro, and E. M. Scolnick.** 1971. Induction of murine C-type viruses from clonal lines of virus-free BALB/3T3 cells. Science **174**:157–159.
2. **Danso, S. K. A., and M. Alexander.** 1975. Regulation of predation by prey density: the protozoan-*Rhizobium* relationship. Appl. Microbiol. **29**:515–521.
3. **Lowy, D. R., W. P. Rowe, N. Teich, and J. W. Hartley.** 1971. Murine leukemia virus: high-frequency activation *in vitro* by 5-iododeoxyuridine and 5-bromodeoxyuridine. Science **174**:155–156.
4. **Schuster, F. L.** 1969. Intranuclear virus-like bodies in the amoeboflagellate *Naegleria gruberi*. J. Protozool. **16**:724–727.
5. **Schuster, F. L., and T. H. Dunnebacke.** 1971. Formation of bodies associated with virus-like particles in the amoeboflagellate *Naegleria gruberi*. J. Ultrastruct. Res. **36**:659–668.
6. **Schuster, F. L., and T. H. Dunnebacke.** 1974. Growth at 37°C of the EG$_S$ strain of the amoeboflagellate *Naegleria gruberi* containing virus-like particles. I. Nuclear changes. J. Invertebr. Pathol. **23**:172–181.
7. **Schuster, F. L., and T. H. Dunnebacke.** 1974. Growth at 37°C of the EG$_S$ strain of the amoeboflagellate *Naegleria gruberi* containing virus-like particles. II. Cytoplasmic changes. J. Invertebr. Pathol. **23**:182–189.
8. **Schuster, F. L., and T. H. Dunnebacke.** 1974. Virus-like particles and an unassociated infectious agent in amoebae of the genus *Naegleria*. Ann. Soc. Belge Med. Trop. **54**:359–370.
9. **Singh, B. N.** 1975. Pathogenic and non-pathogenic amoebae. John Wiley & Sons, Inc., New York.

Cytopathogenic Material from Amoebae of the Genus *Naegleria*

T. H. DUNNEBACKE[1] AND F. L. SCHUSTER

Virus Laboratory, University of California, Berkeley, California 94720, and Department of Biology, Brooklyn College, Brooklyn, New York 11210

Amoebae of the genus *Naegleria* are distinguished from other soil amoebae by morphological and physiological features including: (i) ability to flagellate in response to changes in environmental conditions, (ii) a role as the causative agent for a human disorder, primary amoebic meningoencephalitis (PAM), (iii) the presence in some amoebae of virus-like particles (VLP) and related structures (5–8), and (iv) the presence of a cytopathogen in cell-free lysate, which is capable of destroying avian and mammalian cells in tissue culture (2; T. H. Dunnebacke, Am. J. Trop. Med. Hyg., in press). The cytopathogen is unrelated to the VLP and has been designated *Naegleria* amoeba cytopathogenic material (NACM). The preceding paper presents a discussion of VLP in the amoebae, whereas this paper deals mainly with NACM: what it is, how it responds to various treatments, and its relationship with the amoebae and the cultured cells. Characterization of this material has been difficult, but it is apparent that we are dealing with an infectious inducer of cytopathogenicity that may be quite different from known pathogenic agents.

THE CYTOPATHOGEN AND THE AMOEBA

The cytopathogen (NACM) was found during the search for a biological activity that might be associated with or used to assay VLP observed in the EG$_S$ strain of *N. gruberi* (5). Cell-free lysates of the VLP-containing amoebae destroyed cultures of chick embryo cells. It was soon discovered, however, that this capacity extended to strains and species of *Naegleria* amoebae regardless of the presence or absence of the VLP (2, 9); thus, the cytopathogen became an additional characteristic of the amoebae. Screening for NACM activity has in-

cluded at least five strains of *N. gruberi*, *N. jadini* (0400), 10 strains of *N. fowleri*, 2 free-living *Acanthamoeba* species (*A. astronyxis* and *A. castellanii*), 3 strains of *Acanthamoeba* pathogenic for mice (*A. culbertsoni* and the Australian isolates HOV-6 and RUS-22), and cultures of the slime molds *Polysphondylium pallidum*, *Didymium nigripes*, and *Dictyostelium discoideum*. These organisms represent amoebae isolated as free living from the soil as well as pathogens from human PAM victims. Some are recognized as pathogenic for mice; some grow preferentially at room temperature, whereas others grow preferentially at 37°C. The cell-free, filtered NACM has been found in each of the amoeba cultures tested from the genus *Naegleria*, regardless of temperature preference, geographical location, or pathogenicity. NACM has not been found in any of the amoebae of the other genera (3; unpublished data).

The relationship between NACM and the EG$_S$ amoebae was studied by determining the quantity of the biologically active material present within the cells and free in the medium measured at daily intervals during the growth phase of the amoebae. The NACM was found in the intracellular fraction and increased in quantity as the amoebae increased in numbers. It also appeared free in the medium, and its appearance in medium accompanied normal lysis of amoebae in older cultures. The amount of NACM present in an amoeba ranged from 3 to 20 units (1 unit = number of amoebae/titer of activity × number of cells in the cytopathic culture).

It thus appears that NACM is a component of normal *Naegleria* amoebae, as opposed to the notion that it is a product, such as a toxin, or a virus released into the medium from infected amoebae. Experiments designed to test for the possible transfer of NACM from the *Naegleria* amoebae to amoebae of other genera are, however, under investigation.

[1] Present address: Viral and Rickettsial Disease Laboratory, State of California Department of Health, Berkeley, Calif. 94704.

THE CYTOPATHOGEN AND CULTURED CELLS

The effects of NACM were first observed in cultures of chick embryo fibroblasts. Other cell lines such as human embryonic brain, rat glioma cells, and HeLa cells also respond to NACM (F. L. Schuster and T. H. Dunnebacke, J. Protozool. 23:7A, 1976). The cells inoculated with NACM do not appear to differ from the uninoculated controls for the first 4 days after inoculation when observed by light microscopy. Within an additional 12-h period, however, the NACM effect is evident and involves shrinkage and lysis of cells throughout the culture. This uniform response of several million cells in the culture supports the idea that, at the time of inoculation, each of the cells must have been affected in a like manner by the NACM. This morphological reaction of cells is the basis of the assay for NACM (2, 3; Schuster and Dunnebacke, J. Protozool. 23:7A, 1976). The assay differs from viral assays in tissue culture in the long delay (4 days) before the cellular response, and this delay is not shortened by higher concentrations of NACM. These characteristics also vary from what would be expected if NACM were a toxin. In addition, the NACM assay is typified by a sharp end point. The end-point dilution destroys completely the cells in the cultures; yet as little as an additional 2-fold to 10-fold dilution will leave the cells morphologically unaffected and indistinguishable from the uninoculated control cultures.

The fluids from cytopathogenic cultures exposed to NACM have been passed to other cultures at dilutions of 1:5 or 1:10, where they, in turn, elicit a cytopathology. NACM from different amoebae (*N. gruberi*, *N. jadini*, *N. fowleri*) have the same assay characteristics.

SOME PHYSICAL CHARACTERISTICS OF NACM

Preparations of NACM were obtained from filtered lysates of axenically grown amoebae that had been frozen and thawed four to six times. This material was used for the characterization of NACM by comparing the titers of the biological activity of treated and untreated samples.

It was found that NACM did not sediment when subjected to 100,000 × g for a period of 4 h, a condition known to sediment viruses and cellular particulates. The activity of NACM was unchanged after extractions (vol/vol) with ether 10 times, nor was it changed by treatment with 1% Triton X or Genesolv-D, or by pH variations between 4.5 and 8.2. It survived dialysis against distilled water and storage for 6 weeks in 33% cesium chloride. It could be lyophilized and rehydrated. It could be stored for months at −20 and 2°C or for several days at room temperature. It did become inactivated at 37°C at a rate of about 50% per 24-h period. This rate increased with higher temperatures to 90% inactivation at 44°C for 24 h, 90% inactivation at 56°C for 5 min, and complete inactivation at 100°C for 5 min. Sodium dodecyl sulfate (SDS) at concentrations of 0.05% or greater completely inactivated NACM. Urea at 6 M also inactivated NACM, whereas concentrations of 3 M or less did not affect the biological activity. No activity was recovered in the aqueous phase after phenol extraction at 2 or 37°C. Ultraviolet light reduced the activity of NACM only after exposures of more than 10^5 ergs/mm^2 had been attained. In comparison with the known infectious agents, NACM was extremely resistant to UV irradiation. It fell into the same order of magnitude for resistance as the scrapie agent (4). Treatment of NACM in the filtered amoeba lysates with the enzymes trypsin, chymotrypsin, papain, Pronase, DNase, and RNase did not reduce the biological activity. Papain and Pronase, however, when reacted with material that had been partially purified from the lysates by column chromatography, did inactivate the cytopathogen.

Column chromatography has been found to be a reliable step in the separation of NACM from the gross materials in the amoeba lysates. The increase in relative amounts of NACM to total protein was on the order of 1,000-fold. A comparison of the elution profiles from a Sephadex gel (G-200) column of NACM and of marker proteins indicated that NACM was somewhat more retarded by the gel than hemoglobin, and estimates of its molecular weight were on the order of 50,000. It was the column-eluted material (c-NACM) that was inactivated by papain and Pronase.

A comparative investigation of NACM prepared from the free-living *N. gruberi* with that prepared from the pathogenic *N. jadini* and *N. fowleri* showed that NACM from each responded similarly to the treatments described above and eluted in the same position from the Sephadex gel chromatographs.

SOME BIOLOGICAL CHARACTERISTICS OF NACM

Comparisons of the biological activities of the NACM and c-NACM from the different amoebae showed that they elicited identical cytopathogenic response of the tissue-cultured cells, including the time of onset of cytopathogenicity and the ability of the fluids from the cytopathic cells to be passed to other cultured cells.

Only one distinction among NACM derived from the various strains has been made, and that is the amount of NACM extracted per amoeba. Preliminary investigations have indicated that higher yields in the order of 20 units of NACM per cell were obtained from the *N. fowleri* strains and, in particular, the Belgian strain 0360. Some of the *N. fowleri* strains seemed to be composed of cells of somewhat larger volume than the *N. gruberi* cells, and a study is being continued to relate amoeba strain, amoeba volume, and yield of NACM on a per cell basis.

NATURE OF NACM

In summary, NACM is a small molecule, smaller than known viruses or viroids (1). It is a protein or at least has a protein component. The NACM molecule increases in number in conjunction with an increase of amoebae, and it increases in tissue-cultured cells, again in proportion with the increase in the number of cultured cells during the interim between inoculation and onset of cytopathogenicity. This material opens up many questions which we are not able to answer, and it raises the distinct possibility that NACM may represent a new kind of cytopathogenic material. Most important is a possible role of NACM from *Naegleria* amoebae in the human disease PAM.

ACKNOWLEDGMENTS

This research was supported by Public Health Service grants AI 10845, and AI 12058, and AI 13345 from the National Institute of Allergy and Infectious Diseases. T.H.D. is deeply indebted to Robley C. Williams for his continued support and many helpful suggestions.

LITERATURE CITED

1. **Diener, T. O.** 1976. Towards an understanding of viroid nature and replication. Ann. Microbiol. (Paris) **127:** 7–17.
2. **Dunnebacke, T. H., and F. L. Schuster.** 1971. Infectious agent from a free-living soil amoeba, *Naegleria gruberi*. Science **174:**516–518.
3. **Dunnebacke, T. H., and F. L. Schuster.** 1974. An infectious agent associated with amebas of the genus *Naegleria*. J. Protozool. **21:**327–329.
4. **Haig, D. A., M. C. Clarke, E. Blum, and T. Alper.** 1969. Further studies on the inactivation of the scrapie agent by ultraviolet light. J. Gen. Virol. **5:**455–457.
5. **Schuster, F. L.** 1969. Intranuclear virus-like bodies in the amoeboflagellate *Naegleria gruberi*. J. Protozool. **16:**724–727.
6. **Schuster, F. L., and T. H. Dunnebacke.** 1971. Formation of bodies associated with virus-like particles in the amoeboflagellate *Naegleria gruberi*. J. Ultrastruct. Res. **36:**659–668.
7. **Schuster, F. L., and T. H. Dunnebacke.** 1974. Growth at 37°C of the EG$_S$ strain of the amoeboflagellate *Naegleria gruberi* containing viruslike particles. I. Nuclear changes. J. Invertebr. Pathol. **23:**172–181.
8. **Schuster, F. L., and T. H. Dunnebacke.** 1974. Growth at 37°C of the EG$_S$ strain of the amoeboflagellate *Naegleria gruberi* containing viruslike particles. II. Cytoplasmic changes. J. Invertebr. Pathol. **23:**182–189.
9. **Schuster, F. L., and T. H. Dunnebacke.** 1974. Viruslike particles and an unassociated infectious agent in amoebae of the genus *Naegleria*. Ann. Soc. Belge Med. Trop. **54:**359–370.

Author Index

Subject Index